Dear

The present vol
of the
Great Britain and Ireland.

The unbiased and independent selection
of hotels and restaurants
is the result of local visits and enquiries
by our inspectors.
In addition we receive considerable help
from our readers' invaluable letters
and comments.

Full colour has been introduced this year
throughout the guide in order to
make the presentation of the information
much clearer and more attractive.

It is our purpose
to provide up-to-date information
and thus render a service to our readers.
The next edition is already in preparation.

Therefore, only the guide of the year
merits your complete confidence,
so please remember to use the latest edition

Bon voyage

Contents

Choosing
a hotel or restaurant

This guide offers a selection of hotels and restaurants to help the motorist on his travels. In each category establishments are listed in order of preference according to the degree of comfort they offer.

CATEGORIES

	Luxury in the traditional style	XXXXX
	Top class comfort	XXXX
	Very comfortable	XXX
	Comfortable	XX
	Quite comfortable	X
	Simple comfort	
	Other recommended accommodation, at moderate prices	
without rest.	The hotel has no restaurant	
	The restaurant also offers accommodation	with rm

PEACEFUL ATMOSPHERE AND SETTING

Certain establishments are distinguished in the guide by the red symbols shown below.
Your stay in such hotels will be particularly pleasant or restful, owing to the character of the building, its decor, the setting, the welcome and services offered, or simply the peace and quiet to be enjoyed there.

to	Pleasant hotels
XXXXX to X	Pleasant restaurants
« Park »	Particularly attractive feature
	Very quiet or quiet, secluded hotel
	Quiet hotel
< sea	Exceptional view
<	Interesting or extensive view

The maps located at the beginning of each regional section in the guide indicate places with such peaceful, pleasant hotels and restaurants.
By consulting them before setting out and sending us your comments on your return you can help us with our enquiries.

Hotel facilities

In general the hotels we recommend have full bathroom and toilet facilities in each room. However, this may not be the case for certain rooms in categories , , and .

30 rm	Number of rooms
	Lift (elevator)
	Air conditioning
	Television in room
	Establishment either partly or wholly reserved for non-smokers
	Telephone in room: outside calls connected by the operator
	Telephone in room: direct dialling for outside calls
	Rooms accessible to disabled people
	Outdoor or indoor swimming pool
	Exercise room – Sauna
	Garden
	Hotel tennis court – Golf course and number of holes
	Fishing available to hotel guests. A charge may be made
150	Equipped conference hall: maximum capacity
	Hotel garage (additional charge in most cases)
	Car park for customers only
	Dogs are not allowed in all or part of the hotel
Fax	Telephone document transmission
May-October	Dates when open, as indicated by the hotelier
season	Probably open for the season – precise dates not available Where no date or season is shown, establishments are open all year round
LL35 OSB	Postal code
(T.H.F.)	Hotel Group (See list at end of the Guide)

Animals

It is forbidden to bring domestic animals (dogs, cats...) into Great Britain and Ireland.

Cuisine

STARS

Certain establishments deserve to be brought to your attention for the particularly fine quality of their cooking. **Michelin stars** are awarded for the standard of meals served. For each of these restaurants we indicate three culinary specialities typical of their style of cooking to assist you in your choice.

❀❀❀	**Exceptional cuisine, worth a special journey** Superb food, fine wines, faultless service, elegant surroundings. One will pay accordingly!
❀❀	**Excellent cooking, worth a detour** Specialities and wines of first class quality. This will be reflected in the price.
❀	**A very good restaurant in its category** The star indicates a good place to stop on your journey. But beware of comparing the star given to an expensive « de luxe » establishment to that of a simple restaurant where you can appreciate fine cuisine at a reasonable price.

THE RED « M »

Whilst appreciating the quality of the cooking in restaurants with a star, you may, however, wish to find some serving a perhaps less elaborate but nonetheless always carefully prepared meal.
Certain restaurants seem to us to answer this requirement. We bring them to your attention by marking them with a red « M » in the text of the Guide.

Please refer to the map of ❀ and M rated restaurants located at the beginning of each regional section in the guide.

Alcoholic beverages-conditions of sale

The sale of alcoholic drinks is governed in Great Britain and Ireland by licensing laws which vary greatly from country to country.
Allowing for local variations, restaurants may stay open and serve alcohol with a bona fide meal during the afternoon. Hotel bars and public houses are generally open between 11am and 11pm at the discretion of the licensee. Hotel residents, however, may buy drinks outside the permitted hours at the discretion of the hotelier.
Children under the age of 14 are not allowed in bars.

Prices

Prices quoted are valid for autumn 1990. Changes may arise if goods and service costs are revised.

Your recommendation is self-evident if you always walk into a hotel guide in hand.

Hotels and restaurants in bold type have supplied details of all their rates and have assumed responsibility for maintaining them for all travellers in possession of this guide.

Prices are given in £ sterling, except for the Republic of Ireland (Punts)

Where no mentoin **s., t.,** or **st.** is shown, prices are subject to the addition of service charge, V.A.T., or both (V.A.T. does not apply in the Channel Islands).

MEALS

M 13.00/19.00	**Set meals** – Lunch 13.00, dinner 19.00 – including cover charge, where applicable
M 15.00/20.00	See page 7
s. t.	Service only included – V.A.T. included
st.	Service and V.A.T. included
🍷 6.00	Price of 1/2 bottle or carafe of house wine
M a la carte 20.00/25.00	**A la carte meals** – The prices represent the range of charges from a simple to an elaborate 3 course meal and include a cover charge where applicable
☕ 8.50	Charge for full cooked breakfast (i.e. not included in the room rate) Continental breakfast may be available at a lower rate

⌂: Dinner in this category of establishment will generally be offered from a fixed price menu of limited choice, served at a set time to residents only. Lunch is rarely offered. Many will not be licensed to sell alcohol.

ROOMS

rm 50.00/70.00	Lowest price 50.00 for a comfortable single and highest price 70.00 for the best double room
rm ☕ 55.00/75.00	Full cooked breakfast (whether taken or not) is included in the price of the room
suites 100.00/200.00	Lowest and highest prices for a suite comprising bedroom, bathroom and sitting room

SHORT BREAKS

Many hotels now offer a special rate for a stay of two nights which comprises dinner, room and breakfast usually for a minimum of two people.

SB 65.00/85.00	Prices indicated are lowest and highest per person for two nights.

DEPOSITS – CREDIT CARDS

Some hotels will require a deposit, which confirms the commitment of customer and hotelier alike. Make sure the terms of the agreement are clear.

Access AE Diners VISA	Credit cards accepted by the establishment: Access – American Express – Diners Club – Visa

Towns

✉ York	Postal address
☎ 0225 Bath	STD dialling code (name of exchange indicated only when different from name of the town). Omit 0 when dialling from abroad
401 M 27, ⑩	Michelin map and co-ordinates or fold
West Country G.	See the Michelin Green Guide England : The West Country
pop. 1057	Population
ECD: Wednesday	Early closing day (shops close at midday)
BX **A**	Letters giving the location of a place on the town map
18	Golf course and number of holes (handicap usually required, telephone reservation strongly advised)
✳, ⋞	Panoramic view, viewpoint
✈	Airport
☎ 218	Place with a motorail connection; further information from telephone number listed
⛴	Shipping line
⛴	Passenger transport only *see list of companies at the end of the Guide*
ℹ	Tourist Information Centre

Standard Time

In winter standard time throughout the British Isles is Greenwich Mean Time (G.M.T.). In summer British clocks are advanced by one hour to give British Summer Time (B.S.T.). The actual dates are announced annually but always occur over weekends in March and October.

Sights

STAR-RATING

★★★	Worth a journey
★★	Worth a detour
★	Interesting
AC	Admission charge

LOCATION

See	Sights in town
Envir.	On the outskirts
Exc.	In the surrounding area
N, S, E, W	The sight lies north, south, east or west of the town
A 22	Take road A 22, indicated by the same symbol on the Guide map
2 m.	Mileage

Town plans

Hotels – Restaurants

Sights

Place of interest and its main entrance
Interesting place of worship

Roads

Motorway
Interchanges : complete, limited
Dual carriageway with motorway characteristics
Main traffic artery
Primary route
(network currently being reclassified)
One-way street – Unsuitable for traffic
Pedestrian street
Piccadilly — Shopping street – Car park
Gateway – Street passing under arch – Tunnel
Low headroom (16′6″ max.) on major through routes
Station and railway
Funicular – Cable-car
Lever bridge – Car ferry

Various signs

Tourist information Centre
Mosque – Synagogue
Communications tower or mast – Ruins
Garden, park, wood – Cemetery
Stadium – Racecourse – Golf course
Golf course (with restrictions for visitors)
View – Panorama
Monument – Fountain – Hospital
Pleasure boat harbour – Lighthouse
Airport – Underground station
Ferry services :
passengers and cars
Main post office with poste restante, telephone
Public buildings located by letter :
C — Country Council Offices
H M T — Town Hall – Museum – Theatre
U — University, College
POL. — Police (in large towns police headquarters)

London

BRENT SOHO — Borough – Area
Borough boundary – Area boundary

Car, tyres

The wearing of seat belts in Great Britain is obligatory for drivers, front seat passengers and children under 14 in the rear where seat belts are fitted. It is illegal for front seat passengers to carry children on their lap.

In the Republic of Ireland seat belts are compulsory, if fitted, for drivers and front seat passengers. Children under 12 are not allowed in front seats unless in a suitable safety restraint.

CAR DEALERS, GARAGES AND MICHELIN TYRE SUPPLIERS

In the text of many towns are to be found the names of car dealers, garages and tyre dealers many of which offer a breakdown service.

ATS Tyre dealers

The address of the nearest ATS tyre dealer can be obtained by contacting the address below between 9am and 5pm.

ATS HOUSE
180-188 Northolt Rd.
Harrow,
Middlesex HA2 OED
(081) 423 2000

MOTORING ORGANISATIONS

The major motoring organisations in Great Britain are the Automobile Association and the Royal Automobile Club. Each provides services in varying degrees for non-resident members of affiliated clubs.

AUTOMOBILE ASSOCIATION
Fanum House
BASINGSTOKE, Hants., RG21 2EA
(0256) 20123

ROYAL AUTOMOBILE CLUB
RAC House, Lansdowne Rd.
CROYDON, Surrey CR9 2JA
(081) 686 2525

Ami lecteur

Le présent volume représente la 18e édition du Guide Michelin Great Britain and Ireland.

Réalisée en toute indépendance, sa sélection d'hôtels et de restaurants est le fruit des recherches de ses inspecteurs, que complètent vos précieux courriers et commentaires.

La couleur, introduite cette année dans l'ensemble de l'ouvrage, est un nouveau pas vers la clarté et l'agrément de son information.

Soucieux d'actualité et de service, le Guide prépare déjà sa prochaine édition.

Seul le Guide de l'année mérite ainsi votre confiance.

Pensez à le renouveler...

Bon voyage avec Michelin

Sommaire

Le choix
d'un hôtel, d'un restaurant

Ce guide vous propose une sélection d'hôtels et restaurants établie à l'usage de l'automobiliste de passage. Les établissements, classés selon leur confort, sont cités par ordre de préférence dans chaque catégorie.

CATÉGORIES

🏨🏨🏨🏨🏨	Grand luxe et tradition	XXXXX
🏨🏨🏨🏨	Grand confort	XXXX
🏨🏨🏨	Très confortable	XXX
🏨🏨	De bon confort	XX
🏨	Assez confortable	X
	Simple mais convenable	
	Autre ressource hôtelière conseillée, à prix modérés	
Without rest.	L'hôtel n'a pas de restaurant	
	Le restaurant possède des chambres	with rm

AGRÉMENT ET TRANQUILLITÉ

Certains établissements se distinguent dans le guide par les symboles rouges indiqués ci-après. Le séjour dans ces hôtels se révèle particulièrement agréable ou reposant.
Cela peut tenir d'une part au caractère de l'édifice, au décor original, au site, à l'accueil et aux services qui sont proposés, d'autre part à la tranquillité des lieux.

🏨🏨🏨🏨🏨 à	Hôtels agréables
XXXXX à X	Restaurants agréables
« Park »	Élément particulièrement agréable
	Hôtel très tranquille ou isolé et tranquille
	Hôtel tranquille
⩽ sea	Vue exceptionnelle
⩽	Vue intéressante ou étendue.

Les localités possédant des établissements agréables ou tranquilles sont repérées sur les cartes placées au début de chacune des régions traitées dans ce guide.
Consultez-les pour la préparation de vos voyages et donnez-nous vos appréciations à votre retour, vous faciliterez ainsi nos enquêtes.

L'installation

Les chambres des hôtels que nous recommandons possèdent, en général, des installations sanitaires complètes. Il est toutefois possible que dans les catégories 🏘, 🏠, ⛱ et ⌂, certaines chambres en soient dépourvues.

30 ch	Nombre de chambres
	Ascenseur
	Air conditionné
TV	Télévision dans la chambre
	Établissement entièrement ou en partie réservé aux non-fumeurs
	Téléphone dans la chambre relié par standard
	Téléphone dans la chambre, direct avec l'extérieur
	Chambres accessibles aux handicapés physiques
	Piscine : de plein air ou couverte
	Salle de remise en forme - Sauna
	Jardin de repos
9	Tennis à l'hôtel - Golf et nombre de trous
	Pêche ouverte aux clients de l'hôtel (éventuellement payant)
150	Salles de conférences : capacité maximum
	Garage dans l'hôtel (généralement payant)
P	Parking réservé à la clientèle
	Accès interdit aux chiens (dans tout ou partie de l'établissement)
Fax	Transmission de documents par télécopie
May-October	Période d'ouverture, communiquée par l'hôtelier
season	Ouverture probable en saison mais dates non précisées. En l'absence de mention, l'établissement est ouvert toute l'année.
LL35 OSB	Code postal de l'établissement
(T.H.F.)	Chaîne hôtelière (voir liste en fin de guide)

Animaux

L'introduction d'animaux domestiques (chiens, chats...) est interdite en Grande-Bretagne et en Irlande.

La table

LES ÉTOILES

Certains établissements méritent d'être signalés à votre attention pour la qualité de leur cuisine. Nous les distinguons par **les étoiles de bonne table**.
Nous indiquons, pour ces établissements, trois spécialités culinaires qui pourront orienter votre choix.

✿✿✿ **Une des meilleures tables, vaut le voyage**
Table merveilleuse, grands vins, service impeccable, cadre élégant... Prix en conséquence.

✿✿ **Table excellente, mérite un détour**
Spécialités et vins de choix... Attendez-vous à une dépense en rapport.

✿ **Une très bonne table dans sa catégorie**
L'étoile marque une bonne étape sur votre itinéraire.
Mais ne comparez pas l'étoile d'un établissement de luxe à prix élevés avec celle d'une petite maison où à prix raisonnables, on sert également une cuisine de qualité.

LE « M » ROUGE

Tout en appréciant les tables à « étoiles », on peut souhaiter trouver sur sa route un repas plus simple mais toujours de préparation soignée. Certaines maisons nous ont paru répondre à cette préoccupation.
Un « M » rouge les signale à votre attention dans le texte de ce guide.
Consultez les cartes des localités (étoiles de bonne table et M) *placées au début de chacune des régions traitées dans ce guide.*

La vente de boissons alcoolisées

En Grande-Bretagne et en Irlande, la vente de boissons alcoolisées est soumise à des lois pouvant varier d'une région à l'autre.
D'une façon générale, les hôtels, les restaurants et les pubs peuvent demeurer ouverts l'après-midi et servir des boissons alcoolisées dans la mesure où elles accompagnent un repas suffisamment consistant. Les bars ferment après 23 heures.
Néanmoins, l'hôtelier a toujours la possibilité de servir, à sa clientèle, des boissons alcoolisées en dehors des heures légales.
Les enfants au-dessous de 14 ans n'ont pas accès aux bars.

Les prix

Les prix que nous indiquons dans ce guide ont été établis en automne 1990. Ils sont susceptibles de modifications, notamment en cas de variations des prix des biens et services.

Entrez à l'hôtel le guide à la main, vous montrerez ainsi qu'il vous conduit là en confiance.

Les prix sont indiqués en livres sterling (1 L = 100 pence), sauf en République d'Irlande (Punts).

Lorsque les mentions **s., t.**, ou **st.** ne figurent pas, les prix indiqués peuvent être majorés d'un pourcentage pour le service, la T.V.A., ou les deux. (La T.V.A. n'est pas appliquée dans les Channel Islands.)

Les hôtels et restaurants figurent en gros caractères lorsque les hôteliers nous ont donné tous leurs prix et se sont engagés, sous leur propre responsabilité, à les appliquer aux touristes de passage porteurs de notre guide.

REPAS

M 13.00/19.00	**Repas à prix fixe** – Déjeuner 13.00, diner 19.00. Ces prix s'entendent couvert compris
M 15.00/20.00	Voir page 17
s. t.	Service compris – T.V.A comprise
st.	Service et T.V.A. compris (prix nets)
6.00	Prix de la 1/2 bouteille ou carafe de vin ordinaire
M à la carte 20.00/25.00	**Repas à la carte** – Le 1er prix correspond à un repas simple mais soigné, comprenant : petite entrée, plat du jour garni, dessert. Le 2e prix concerne un repas plus complet, comprenant : hors-d'œuvre, plat principal, fromage ou dessert. Ces prix s'entendent couvert compris
8.50	Prix du petit déjeuner à l'anglaise, s'il n'est pas compris dans celui de la chambre Un petit déjeuner continental peut être obtenu à moindre prix

: Dans les établissements de cette catégorie, le dîner est servi à heure fixe exclusivement aux personnes ayant une chambre. Le menu, à prix unique, offre un choix limité de plats. Le déjeuner est rarement proposé. Beaucoup de ces établissements ne sont pas autorisés à vendre des boissons alcoolisées.

CHAMBRES

rm 50.00/70.00	Prix minimum 50.00 d'une chambre pour une personne et prix maximum 70.00 de la plus belle chambre occupée par deux personnes
rm 55.00/75.00	Le prix du petit déjeuner à l'anglaise est inclus dans le prix de la chambre, même s'il n'est pas consommé
suites 100.00/200.00	Prix minimum et maximum d'un appartement comprenant chambre, salle de bains et salon

« SHORT BREAKS »

SB 65.00/85.00	Prix minimum et maximum par personne pour un séjour de deux nuits en conditions avantageuses ou « Short Break ». Ce forfait comprend la chambre, le dîner et le petit déjeuner, en général pour un minimum de deux personnes.

LES ARRHES – CARTES DE CRÉDIT

Certains hôteliers demandent le versement d'arrhes. Il s'agit d'un dépôt-garantie qui engage l'hôtelier comme le client. Bien faire préciser les dispositions de cette garantie.

AE VISA	Cartes de crédit acceptées par l'établissement : Access (Eurocard) – American Express – Diners Club – Visa

Les villes

York	Bureau de poste desservant la localité
0225 Bath	Indicatif téléphonique interurbain suivi, si nécessaire, de la localité de rattachement (De l'étranger, ne pas composer le 0)
401 M 27, ⑩	Numéro des cartes Michelin et carroyage ou numéro du pli
West Country G.	Voir le guide vert Michelin England : The West Country
pop. 1057	Population
ECD : Wednesday	Jour de fermeture des magasins (après-midi seulement)
BX **A**	Lettres repérant un emplacement sur le plan
18	Golf et nombre de trous (Handicap généralement demandé, réservation par téléphone vivement recommandée)
✻, ⋞	Panorama, point de vue
	Aéroport
218	Localité desservie par train-auto. Renseignements au numéro de téléphone indiqué
	Transports maritimes
	Transports maritimes (pour passagers seulement) *Voir liste des compagnies en fin de guide*
	Information touristique

Heure légale

Les visiteurs devront tenir compte de l'heure officielle en Grande Bretagne : une heure de retard sur l'heure française.

Les curiosités

INTÉRÊT

★★★	Vaut le voyage
★★	Mérite un détour
★	Intéressant
AC	Entrée payante

SITUATION

See	Dans la ville
Envir.	Aux environs de la ville
Exc.	Excursions dans la région
N, S, E, W	La curiosité est située : au Nord, au Sud, à l'Est, à l'Ouest
A 22	On s'y rend par la route A 22, repérée par le même signe sur le plan du Guide
2 m.	Distance en miles

Les plans

Hôtels – Restaurants

Curiosités

Bâtiment intéressant et entrée principale
Édifice religieux intéressant

Voirie

M 1 Autoroute
échangeurs : complet, partiel
Route à chaussées séparées de type autoroutier
Grand axe de circulation
A 2 Itinéraire principal (Primary route)
réseau en cours de révision
Sens unique – Rue impraticable
Rue piétonne
Piccadilly P Rue commerçante – Parc de stationnement
Porte – Passage sous voûte – Tunnel
15'5 Passage bas (inférieur à 16'6") sur les grandes voies de circulation
Gare et voie ferrée
Funiculaire – Téléphérique, télécabine
B Pont mobile – Bac pour autos

Signes divers

Information touristique
Mosquée – Synagogue
Tour ou pylône de télécommunication – Ruines
Jardin, parc, bois – Cimetière
Stade – Hippodrome – Golf
Golf (réservé)
Vue – Panorama
Monument – Fontaine – Hôpital
Port de plaisance – Phare
Aéroport – Station de métro
Transport par bateau :
passagers et voitures
Bureau principal de poste restante, téléphone
Bâtiment public repéré par une lettre :
C Bureau de l'Administration du Comté
H M T Hôtel de ville – Musée – Théâtre
U Université, grande école
POL. Police (commissariat central)

Londres

BRENT SOHO Nom d'arrondissement (borough) – de quartier (area)
Limite de « borough » – d'« area »

La voiture, les pneus

En Grande-Bretagne, le port de la ceinture de sécurité est obligatoire pour le conducteur et le passager avant ainsi qu'à l'arrière, si le véhicule en est équipé, pour les enfants de moins de 14 ans. La loi interdit au passager avant de prendre un enfant sur ses genoux.

En République d'Irlande, le port de la ceinture de sécurité est obligatoire pour le conducteur et le passager avant, si le véhicule en est équipé. Les enfants de moins de 12 ans ne sont pas autorisés à s'asseoir à l'avant, sauf si le véhicule est muni d'un système d'attache approprié.

GARAGISTES, RÉPARATEURS FOURNISSEURS DE PNEUS MICHELIN

Au texte de la plupart des localités figure une liste des garagistes ou concessionnaires automobiles pouvant, éventuellement, vous aider en cas de panne.

ATS Spécialistes du pneu

Des renseignements sur le plus proche point de vente de pneus ATS pourront être obtenus en s'informant entre 9 h et 17 h à l'adresse indiquée ci-dessous.

ATS HOUSE
180-188 Northolt Rd.
Harrow,
Middlesex HA2 OED
(081) 423 2000

Dans nos agences, nous nous faisons un plaisir de donner à nos clients tous conseils pour la meilleure utilisation de leurs pneus.

AUTOMOBILE CLUBS

Les principales organisations de secours automobile dans le pays sont l'Automobile Association et le Royal Automobile Club, toutes deux offrant certains de leurs services aux membres de clubs affilés.

AUTOMOBILE ASSOCIATION
Fanum House
BASINGSTOKE, Hants., RG21 2EA
✆ (0256) 20123

ROYAL AUTOMOBILE CLUB
RAC House, Lansdowne Rd,
CROYDON, Surrey CR9 2JA
✆ (081) 686 2525

Amico Lettore

Questo volume rappresenta
la 18esima edizione
della Guida Michelin
Great Britain and Ireland.

La sua selezione di alberghi e ristoranti,
realizzata in assoluta indipendenza,
è il risultato
delle indagini dei suoi ispettori,
che completano
le vostre preziose informazioni e giudizi.

I colori, introdotti quest'anno nella Guida,
costituiscono un nuovo passo avanti
verso la chiarezza e una gradevole
presentazione delle informazioni.

Desiderosa di mantenersi sempre aggiornata
per fornire un buon servizio,
la Guida sta già preparando
la sua prossima edizione.

Soltanto la Guida dell'anno merita perciò
la vostra fiducia. Pensate a rinnovarla...

Buon viaggio con Michelin

Sommario

La scelta
di un albergo, di un ristorante

Questa guida Vi propone una selezione di alberghi e ristoranti stabilita ad uso dell'automobilista di passaggio. Gli esercizi, classificati in base al confort che offrono, vengono citati in ordine di preferenza per ogni categoria.

CATEGORIE

	Gran lusso e tradizione	
	Gran confort	
	Molto confortevole	
	Di buon confort	
	Abbastanza confortevole	
	Semplice, ma conveniente	
	Altra risorsa, consigliata per prezzi contenuti	
without rest.	L'albergo non ha ristorante	
	Il ristorante dispone di camere	with rm

AMENITÀ E TRANQUILLITÀ

Alcuni esercizi sono evidenziati nella guida dai simboli rossi indicati qui di seguito. Il soggiorno in questi alberghi dovrebbe rivelarsi particolarmente ameno o riposante.
Ciò può dipendere sia dalle caratteristiche dell'edifico, dalle decorazioni non comuni, dalla sua posizione e dal servizio offerto, sia dalla tranquillità dei luoghi.

a	Alberghi ameni
a	Ristoranti ameni
« Park »	Un particolare piacevole
	Albergo molto tranquillo o isolato e tranquillo
	Albergo tranquillo
sea	Vista eccezionale
	Vista interessante o estesa

Le località che possiedono degli esercizi ameni o tranquilli sono riportate sulle carte che precedono ciascuna delle regioni trattate nella guida.

Consultatele per la preparazione dei Vostri viaggi e, al ritorno, inviateci i Vostri pareri ; in tal modo agevolerete le nostre inchieste.

Installazioni

Le camere degli alberghi che raccomandiamo possiedono, generalmente, delle installazioni sanitarie complete. È possibile tuttavia che nelle categorie , , e alcune camere ne siano sprovviste.

30 rm	Numero di camere
	Ascensore
	Aria condizionata
	Televisione in camera
	Esercizio riservato completamente o in parte ai non fumatori
	Telefono in camera collegato con il centralino
	Telefono in camera comunicante direttamente con l'esterno
	Camere di agevole accesso per i minorati fisici
	Piscina : all'aperto, coperta
	Palestra – Sauna
	Giardino da riposo
	Tennis appartenente all'albergo – Golf e numero di buche
	Pesca aperta ai clienti dell' albergo (eventualmente a pagamento)
150	Sale per conferenze : capienza massima
	Garage nell'albergo (generalmente a pagamento)
	Parcheggio riservato alla clientela
	Accesso vietato ai cani (in tutto o in parte dell'esercizio)
Fax	Trasmissione telefonica di documenti
May-October	Periodo di apertura, comunicato dall'albergatore
season	Probabile apertura in stagione, ma periodo non precisato. Gli esercizi senza tali menzioni sono aperti tutto l'anno.
LL35 OSB	Codice postale dell' esercizio
(T.H.F.)	Catena alberghiera (Vedere la lista alla fine della Guida)

Animali

L'introduzione di animali domestici (cani, gatti...), in Gran Bretagna e in Irlanda, è vietata.

La tavola

LE STELLE

Alcuni esercizi meritano di essere segnalati alla Vostra attenzione per la qualità tutta particolare della loro cucina. Noi li evidenziamo con le « **stelle di ottima tavola** ».
Per questi ristoranti indichiamo tre specialità culinarie e alcuni vini locali che potranno aiutarVi nella scelta.

✿✿✿ **Una delle migliori tavole, vale il viaggio**
Tavola meravigliosa, grandi vini, servizio impeccabile, ambientazione accurata... Prezzi conformi.

✿✿ **Tavola eccellente, merita una deviazione**
Specialità e vini scelti... AspettateVi una spesa in proporzione.

✿ **Un'ottima tavola nella sua categoria**
La stella indica una tappa gastronomica sul Vostro itinerario.
Non mettete però a confronto la stella di un esercizio di lusso, dai prezzi elevati, con quella di un piccolo esercizio dove, a prezzi ragionevoli, viene offerta una cucina di qualità.

LA « M » ROSSA

Pur apprezzando le tavole a « stella », si desidera alle volte consumare un pasto più semplice ma sempre accuratamente preparato.
Alcuni esercizi ci son parsi rispondenti a tale esigenza e sono contraddistinti nella guida da una « **M** » in rosso.
Consultate le carte delle località con stelle e con **M** *che precedono ciascuna delle regioni trattate nella guida.*

La vendita di bevande alcoliche

In Gran Bretagna e Irlanda la vendita di bevande alcoliche è soggetta a leggi che possono variare da una regione all'altra.
In generale gli alberghi, i ristoranti e i pubs possono restare aperti il pomeriggio e servire bevande alcoliche nella misura in cui queste accompagnano un pasto abbastanza consistente.
I bars chiudono dopo le ore 23.00.
L'albergatore ha tuttavia la possobilità di servire alla clientela bevande alcoliche anche oltre le ore legali.
Ai ragazzi inferiori ai 14 anni è vietato l'accesso ai bar.

I prezzi

I prezzi che indichiamo in questa guida sono stati stabiliti nel l'autunno 1990. Potranno pertanto subire delle variazioni in relazione ai cambiamenti dei prezzi di beni e servizi.

Entrate nell'albergo o nel ristorante con la guida alla mano, dimostrando in tal modo la fiducia in chi vi ha indirizzato.

Gli alberghi e i ristoranti vengono menzionati in carattere grassetto quando gli albergatori ci hanno comunicato tutti i loro prezzi e si sono impegnati, sotto la propria responsabilità, ad applicarli ai turisti di passaggio, in possesso della nostra guida.

I prezzi sono indicati in lire sterline (1 £ = 100 pence) ad eccezione per la Repubblica d'Irlanda (Punts).

Quando non figurano le lettere **s.**, **t.**, o **st.** i prezzi indicati possono essere maggiorati per il servizio o per l'I.V.A. o per entrambi. (L'I.V.A. non viene applicata nelle Channel Islands).

PASTI

M 13.00/19.00	**Prezzo fisso** – Pranzo 13.00, cena 19.00. Questi prezzi comprendono il coperto
M 15.00/20.00	Vedere p. 27
s. t.	Servizio compreso. – I.V.A. compresa
st.	Servizio ed I.V.A. compresi (prezzi netti)
🍶 6.00	Prezzo della mezza bottiglia o di una caraffa di vino
M a la carte 20.00/25.00	**Alla carta** – Il 1° prezzo corrisponde ad un pasto semplice comprendente : primo piatto, piatto del giorno con contorno, dessert. Il 2° prezzo corrisponde ad un pasto più completo comprendente : antipasto, piatto principale, formaggio e dessert Questi prezzi comprendono il coperto
☕ 8.50	Prezzo della prima colazione inglese se non è compreso nel prezzo della camera Una prima colazione continentale può essere ottenuta a minor prezzo

⌂ : Negli alberghi di questa categoria, la cena viene servita, ad un'ora stabilita, esclusivamente a chi vi allogia. Il menu, a prezzo fisso, offre una scelta limitata di piatti. Raramente viene servito anche il pranzo. Molti di questi esercizi non hanno l'autorizzazione a vendere alcolici.

CAMERE

rm 50.00/70.00	Prezzo minimo 50.00 per una camera singola e prezzo massimo 70.00 per la camera più bella per due persone
rm ☕ 55.00/75.00	Il prezzo della prima colazione inglese è compreso nel prezzo della camera anche se non viene consumata
suites 100.00/200.00	Prezzo minimo e massimo per un appartamento comprendente camera, bagno e salone

« SHORT BREAKS »

SB 65.00/85.00	Prezzo minimo e massimo per persona per un soggiorno di due notti a condizioni vantaggiose o « Short Break ». Questo forfait comprende la camera, la cena e la colazione del mattino generalmente per un minimo di due persone.

LA CAPARRA – CARTE DI CREDITO

Alcuni albergatori chiedono il versamento di una caparra. Si tratta di un deposito-garanzia che impegna tanto l'albergatore che il cliente. Vi raccomandiamo di farVi precisare le norme riguardanti la reciproca garanzia di tale caparra.

AE VISA	Carte di credito accettate dall'esercizio Access (Eurocard) – American Express – Diners Club – Visa

Le città

✉ York	Sede dell'ufficio postale
0225 Bath	Prefisso telefonico interurbano (nome del centralino indicato solo quando differisce dal nome della località). Dall'estero non formare lo 0
401 M 27, ⑩	Numero della carta Michelin e del riquadro o numero della piega
West Country G.	Vedere la Guida Verde Michelin England : The West Country
pop. 1057	Popolazione
ECD : Wednesday	Giorno di chiusura settimanale dei negozi (solo pomeriggio)
BX **A**	Lettere indicanti l'ubicazione sulla pianta
18	Golf e numero di buche (handicap generalmente richiesto, prenotazione telefonica vivamente consigliata)
✻, <	Panorama, punto di vista
	Aeroporto
218	Località con servizio auto su treno. Informarsi al numero di telefono indicato
	Trasporti marittimi
	Trasporti marittimi (solo passeggeri) *Vedere la lista delle compagnie alla fine della Guida*
	Ufficio informazioni turistiche

Ora legale

I visitatori dovranno tenere in considerazione l'ora ufficiale in Gran Bretagna : un'ora di ritardo sull'ora italiana.

Le curiosità

GRADO DI INTERESSE

★★★	Vale il viaggio
★★	Merita una deviazione
★	Interessante
AC	Entrata a pagamento

UBICAZIONE

See	Nella città
Envir.	Nei dintorni della città
Exc.	Nella regione
N, S, E, W	La curiosità è situata : a Nord, a Sud, a Est, a Ovest
A 22	Ci si va per la strada A 22 indicata con lo stesso segno sulla pianta
2 m.	Distanza in miglia

Le piante

a Alberghi – Ristoranti

Curiosità

Edificio interessante ed entrata principale

Costruzione religiosa interessante

Viabilità

M 1 Autostrada
svincoli : completo, parziale,

Strada a carregiate separate di tipo autostradale

Asse principale di circolazione

A 2 Itinerario principale
(« Primary route », rete stradale in corso di revisione)

Senso unico – Via impraticabile

Via pedonale

Piccadilly P Via commerciale – Parcheggio

Porta – Sottopassaggio – Galleria

15'5 Sottopassaggio (altezza inferiore a 16'6") sulle grandi vie di circolazione

Stazione e ferrovia

Funicolare – Funivia, Cabinovia

B Ponte mobile – Battello per auto

Simboli vari

Ufficio informazioni turistiche

Moschea – Sinagoga

Torre o pilone per telecomunicazione – Ruderi

Giardino, parco, bosco – Cimitero

Stadio – Ippodromo – Golf

Golf riservato

Vista – Panorama

Monumento – Fontana – Ospedale

Porto per imbarcazioni da diporto – Faro

Aeroporto – Stazione della Metropolitana

Trasporto con traghetto :
passeggeri ed autovetture

Ufficio centrale di fermo posta, telefono

Edificio pubblico indicato con lettera :

C Sede dell'Amministrazione di Contea

H M T Municipio – Museo – Teatro

U Università, grande scuola

POL. Polizia (Questura, nelle grandi città)

Londra

BRENT SOHO Nome del distretto amministrativo (borough) – del quartiere (area)

Limite del « borough » – di « area »

L'automobile, I pneumatici

In Gran Bretagna, l'uso delle cinture di sicurezza è obbligatorio per il conducente e il passeggero del sedile anteriore, nonchè per i sedili posteriori, se ne sono equipaggiati e se occupati da bambini di meno di 14 anni. La legge non consente al passaggero d'avanti di tenere un bambino sulle ginocchia.

Nella Repubblica d'Irlanda, l'uso delle cinture di sicurezza è obligatorio per il conducente e il passeggero d'avanti, se il veicolo ne è equipaggiato. I bambini di meno di 12 anni non sono autorizzati a viaggiare sul sedile anteriore, a meno che questo non sia fornito di un sistema di ritenuta espressamente concepito per loro.

GARAGISTI RIPARATORI RIVENDITORI DI PNEUMATICI MICHELIN

Nel testo di molte località abbiamo elencato gli indirizzi di garage o concessionari in grado di effettuare, eventualmente, il traino o le riparazioni.

ATS Specialista in pneumatici

Potrete avere delle informazioni sul più vicino punto vendita di pneumatici ATS, rivolgendovi, tra le 9 e le 17, all'indirizzo indicato qui di seguito :

ATS HOUSE
180-188 Northolt Rd.
Harrow,
Middlesex HA2 OED
(081) 423 2000

Le nostre Succursali sono in grado di dare ai nostri clienti tutti i consigli relativi alla migliore utilizzazione dei pneumatici.

AUTOMOBILE CLUBS

Le principali organizzazioni di soccorso automobilistico sono l'Automobile Association ed il Royal Automobile Club : entrambe offrono alcuni loro servizi ai membri dei club affiliati.

AUTOMOBILE ASSOCIATION
Fanum House
BASINGSTOKE, Hants., RG21 2EA
✆ (0256) 20123

ROYAL AUTOMOBILE CLUB
RAC House, Lansdowne Rd,
CROYDON, Surrey CR9 2JA
✆ (081) 686 2525

Lieber Leser

Der Rote Michelin-Führer
Great Britain and Ireland
liegt nun schon in der 18. Ausgabe vor.

Er bringt eine
in voller Unabhängigkeit getroffene,
bewußt begrenzte Auswahl
an Hotels und Restaurants.
Sie basiert auf den regelmäßigen
Überprüfungen durch unsere Inspektoren,
komplettiert durch die zahlreichen
Zuschriften und Erfahrungsberichte
unserer Leser.

Die in diesem Jahr eingeführte
farbige Gestaltung des Führers
ist ein weiterer Schritt
in unserem Bemühen um
Modernisierung und Aktualisierung.

Wir sind stets um die Aktualität
unserer Informationen bemüht
und bereiten schon jetzt
den Führer des nächsten Jahres vor.
Nur die neueste Ausgabe
ist wirklich zuverlässig —
denken Sie bitte daran,
wenn der nächste
Rote Michelin-Führer erscheint.

Gute Reise mit Michelin !

Inhaltsverzeichnis

Wahl
eines Hotels, eines Restaurants

Die Auswahl der in diesem Führer aufgeführten Hotels und Restaurants ist für Durchreisende gedacht. In jeder Kategorie drückt die Reihenfolge der Betriebe (sie sind nach ihrem Komfort klassifiziert) eine weitere Rangordnung aus.

KATEGORIEN

Großer Luxus und Tradition

Großer Komfort

Sehr komfortabel

Mit gutem Komfort

Mit ausreichendem Komfort

Bürgerlich

Preiswerte, empfehlenswerte Gasthäuser und Pensionen

without rest. — Hotel ohne Restaurant

Restaurant vermietet auch Zimmer — with rm

ANNEHMLICHKEITEN

Manche Häuser sind im Führer durch rote Symbole gekennzeichnet (s. unten). Der Aufenthalt in diesen Hotels ist wegen der schönen, ruhigen Lage, der nicht alltäglichen Einrichtung und Atmosphäre und dem gebotenen Service besonders angenehm und erholsam.

bis	Angenehme Hotels
bis	Angenehme Restaurants
« Park »	Besondere Annehmlichkeit
	Sehr ruhiges, oder abgelegenes und ruhiges Hotel
	Ruhiges Hotel
sea	Reizvolle Aussicht
	Interessante oder weite Sicht

Die den einzelnen Regionen vorangestellten Übersichtskarten, auf denen die Orte mit besonders angenehmen oder ruhigen Häusern eingezeichnet sind, helfen Ihnen bei der Reisevorbereitung. Teilen Sie uns bitte nach der Reise Ihre Erfahrungen und Meinungen mit. Sie helfen uns damit, den Führer weiter zu verbessern.

Einrichtung

Die meisten der empfohlenen Hotels verfügen über Zimmer, die alle oder doch zum größten Teil mit einer Naßzelle ausgestattet sind. In den Häusern der Kategorien 🏨, 🏠, ♆ und ⌂ kann diese jedoch in einigen Zimmern fehlen.

30 rm	Anzahl der Zimmer
	Fahrstuhl
	Klimaanlage
TV	Fernsehen im Zimmer
	Hotel ganz oder teilweise reserviert für Nichtraucher
	Zimmertelefon mit Außenverbindung über Telefonzentrale
☎	Zimmertelefon mit direkter Außenverbindung
♿	Für Körperbehinderte leicht zugängliche Zimmer
	Freibad, Hallenbad
	Fitneßcenter – Sauna
	Liegewiese, Garten
	Hoteleigener Tennisplatz – Golfplatz und Lochzahl
	Angelmöglichkeit für Hotelgäste, evtl. gegen Gebühr
150	Konferenzräume : Höchstkapazität
	Hotelgarage (wird gewöhnlich berechnet)
P	Parkplatz reserviert für Gäste
	Hunde sind unerwünscht (im ganzen Haus bzw. in den Zimmern oder im Restaurant)
Fax	Telefonische Dokumentenübermittlung
May-October	Öffnungszeit, vom Hotelier mitgeteilt
season	Unbestimmte Öffnungszeit eines Saisonhotels. Die Häuser, für die wir keine Schließungszeiten angeben, sind im allgemeinen ganzjährig geöffnet
LL35 OSB	Angabe des Postbezirks (hinter der Hoteladresse)
(T.H.F.)	Hotelkette (Liste am Ende des Führers)

Tiere

Das Mitführen von Haustieren (Hunde, Katzen u. dgl.) bei der Einreise in Großbritannien und Irland ist untersagt.

Küche

DIE STERNE

Einige Häuser verdienen wegen ihrer überdurchschnittlich guten Küche Ihre besondere Beachtung. Auf diese Häuser weisen die Sterne hin.

Bei den mit « **Stern** » ausgezeichneten Betrieben nennen wir drei kulinarische Spezialitäten, die Sie probieren sollten.

✿✿✿ **Eine der besten Küchen : eine Reise wert**

Ein denkwürdiges Essen, edle Weine, tadelloser Service, gepflegte Atmosphäre ... entsprechende Preise.

✿✿ **Eine hervorragende Küche : verdient einen Umweg**

Ausgesuchte Menus und Weine ... angemessene Preise.

✿ **Eine sehr gute Küche : verdient Ihre besondere Beachtung**

Der Stern bedeutet eine angenehme Unterbrechung Ihrer Reise.

Vergleichen Sie aber bitte nicht den Stern eines sehr teuren Luxusrestaurants mit dem Stern eines kleineren oder mittleren Hauses, wo man Ihnen zu einem annehmbaren Preis eine ebenfalls vorzügliche Mahlzeit reicht.

DAS ROTE « M »

Wir glauben, daß Sie neben den Häusen mit « Stern » auch solche Adressen interessieren werden, die einfache, aber sorgfältig zubereitete Mahlzeiten anbieten.

Auf solche Häuser weisen wir im Text durch das rote « **M** » hin.

*Siehe Karten der Orte mit « Stern » und « **M** », die den einzelnen im Führer behandelten Regionen vorangestellt sind.*

Ausschank alkoholischer Getränke

In Großbritannien und Irland unterliegt der Ausschank alkoholischer Getränke gesetzlichen Bestimmungen, die in den einzelnen Gegenden verschieden sind.

Generell können Hotels, Restaurants und Pubs nachmittags geöffnet sein und alkoholische Getränke ausschenken, wenn diese zu einer entsprechend gehaltvollen Mahlzeit genossen werden. Die Bars schließen nach 23 Uhr.

Hotelgästen können alkoholische Getränke jedoch auch außerhalb der Ausschankzeiten serviert werden.

Kindern unter 14 Jahren ist der Zutritt zu den Bars untersagt.

Preise

Die in diesem Führer genannten Preise wurden uns im Herbst 1990 angegeben. Sie können sich mit den Preisen von Waren und Dienstleistungen ändern.
Halten Sie beim Betreten des Hotels den Führer in der Hand. Sie zeigen damit, daß Sie aufgrund dieser Empfehlung gekommen sind.
Die Preise sind in Pfund Sterling angegeben (1 £ = 100 pence) mit Ausnahme der Republik Irland (Punts).
Wenn die Buchstaben **s.**, **t.**, oder **st.** nicht hinter den angegebenen Preisen aufgeführt sind, können sich diese um den Zuschlag für Bedienung und/oder MWSt erhöhen (keine MWSt auf den Channel Islands).
Die Namen der Hotels und Restaurants, die ihre Preise genannt haben, sind fett gedruckt. Gleichzeitig haben sich diese Häuser verpflichtet, die von den Hoteliers selbst angegebenen Preise den Benutzern des Michelin-Führers zu berechnen.

MAHLZEITEN

M 13.00/19.00	**Feste Menupreise** – Mittagessen 13.00, Abendessen 19.00 (inkl. Couvert)
M 15.00/20.00	Siehe Seite 37
s. t.	Bedienung inkl. – MWSt inkl.
st.	Bedienung und MWSt inkl.
🍶 6.00	Preis für 1/2 Flasche oder eine Karaffe Tafelwein
M a la carte 20.00/25.00	**Mahlzeiten « à la carte »** – Der erste Preis entspricht einer einfachen aber sorgfältig zubereiteten Mahlzeit, bestehend aus kleiner Vorspeise, Tagesgericht mit Beilage und Nachtisch. Der zweite Preis entspricht einer reichlicheren Mahlzeit mit Vorspeise, Hauptgericht, Käse oder Nachtisch (inkl. Couvert)
☕ 8.50	Preis des englischen Frühstücks, wenn dieser nicht im Übernachtungspreis enthalten ist Einfaches, billigeres Frühstück (Continental breakfast) erhältlich

⌂ : In dieser Hotelkategorie wird ein Abendessen normalerweise nur zu bestimmten Zeiten für Hotelgäste angeboten. Es besteht aus einem Menu mit begrenzter Auswahl zu festgesetztem Preis. Mittagessen wird selten angeboten. Viele dieser Hotels sind nicht berechtigt, alkoholische Getränke auszuschenken.

ZIMMER

rm 50.00/70.00	Mindestpreis 50.00 für ein Einzelzimmer und Höchstpreis 70.00 für das schönste Doppelzimmer
rm ☕ 55.00/75.00	Übernachtung mit englischem Frühstück, selbst wenn dieses nicht eingenommen wird
suites 100.00/200.00	Mindest- und Höchstpreis für ein Appartement bestehend aus Wohnzimmer, Schlafzimmer und Bad

« SHORT BREAKS »

SB 65.00/85.00	Mindest- und Höchstpreis pro Person bei einem Aufenthalt von 2 Nächten (« Short Break »). Diese Pauschalpreise (für mindestens 2 Personen) umfassen Zimmer, Abendessen und Frühstück.

ANZAHLUNG – KREDITKARTEN

Einige Hoteliers verlangen eine Anzahlung. Diese ist als Garantie sowohl für den Hotelier als auch für den Gast anzusehen.

AE VISA	Vom Haus akzeptierte Kreditkarten : Access (Eurocard) – American Express – Diners Club – Visa (Carte Bleue)

Städte

York	Zuständiges Postamt
0225 Bath	Vorwahlnummer und evtl. zuständiges Fernsprechamt (bei Gesprächen vom Ausland aus wird die erste Null weggelassen)
401 M 27, ⑩	Nummer der Michelin-Karte und Koordinaten des Planfeldes oder Faltseite
West Country G.	Siehe auch den grünen Michelinführer « England : The West Country »
pop. 1057	Einwohnerzahl
ECD : Wednesday	Tag, an dem die Läden nachmittags geschlossen sind
BX **A**	Markierung auf dem Stadtplan
18	Öffentlicher Golfplatz und Lochzahl (Handicap erforderlich, telefonische Reservierung empfehlenswert)
	Rundblick, Aussichtspunkt
	Flughafen
218	Ladestelle für Autoreisezüge – Nähere Auskünfte unter der angegebenen Telefonnummer
	Autofähre
	Personenfähre *Liste der Schiffahrtsgesellschaften am Ende des Führers*
	Informationsstelle

Uhrzeit

In Großbritannien ist eine Zeitverschiebung zu beachten und die Uhr gegenüber der deutschen Zeit um 1 Stunde zurückzustellen.

Sehenswürdigkeiten

BEWERTUNG

★★★	Eine Reise wert
★★	Verdient einen Umweg
★	Sehenswert
AC	Eintritt (gegen Gebühr)

LAGE

See	In der Stadt
Envir.	In der Umgebung der Stadt
Exc.	Ausflugsziele
N, S, E, W	Im Norden (N), Süden (S), Osten (E), Westen (W) der Stadt
A 22	Zu erreichen über die Straße A 22
2 m.	Entfernung in Meilen

Stadtpläne

Hotels – Restaurants

Sehenswürdigkeiten

Sehenswertes Gebäude mit Haupteingang
Sehenswerter Sakralbau

Straßen

M 1 Autobahn
Anschlußstellen : Autobahneinfahrt und/oder-ausfahrt,
Schnellstraße mit getrennten Fahrbahnen
Hauptverkehrsstraße
A 2 Fernverkehrsstraße (Primary route)
Netz wird z.Z. neu eingestuft
Einbahnstraße – nicht befahrbare Straße
Fußgängerzone
Piccadilly Einkaufsstraße – Parkplatz
Tor – Passage – Tunnel
15'5 Unterführung (Höhe angegeben bis 16'6") auf Hauptverkehrsstraßen
Bahnhof und Bahnlinie
Standseilbahn – Seilschwebebahn
B Bewegliche Brücke – Autofähre

Sonstige Zeichen

Informationsstelle
Moschee – Synagoge
Funk-, Fernsehturm – Ruine
Garten, Park, Wäldchen – Friedhof
Stadion – Pferderennbahn – Golfplatz
Golfplatz (Zutritt bedingt erlaubt)
Aussicht – Rundblick
Denkmal – Brunnen – Krankenhaus
Jachthafen – Leuchtturm
Flughafen – U-Bahnstation
Schiffsverbindungen :
Autofähre
Hauptpostamt (postlagernde Sendungen), Telefon
Öffentliches Gebäude, durch einen Buchstaben gekennzeichnet :
C Sitz der Grafschaftsverwaltung
H M T Rathaus – Museum – Theater
U Universität, Hochschule
POL. Polizei (in größeren Städten Polizeipräsidium)

London

BRENT SOHO Name des Verwaltungsbezirks (borough) – des Stadtteils (area)
Grenze des « borough » – des « area »

Das Auto, die Reifen

In Großbritannien herrscht Anschnallpflicht für Fahrer, Beifahrer und Kinder unter 14 Jahren auf dem Rücksitz, wenn Gurte vorhanden sind. Es ist verboten, Kinder auf den Vordersitzen auf dem Schoß zu befördern. In Irland besteht für den Fahrer und den Beifahrer Anschnallpflicht, wenn Gurte vorhanden sind. Kinder unter 12 Jahren dürfen allerdings nicht auf den Vordersitzen befördert werden, es sei denn es existiert ein entsprechender Kindersitz.

REPARATURWERKSTÄTTEN LIEFERANTEN VON MICHELIN-REIFEN

Bei den meisten Orten geben wir Adressen von Kfz-Vertragswerkstätten an ; viele davon haben einen Abschlepp- bzw. Reparaturdienst.

ATS Reifenhändler

Die Anschrift der nächstgelegenen ATS-Verkaufsstelle erhalten Sie auf Anfrage (9-17 Uhr) bei

ATS HOUSE
180-188 Northolt Rd.
Harrow,
Middlesex HA2 OED
(081) 423 2000

AUTOMOBILCLUBS

Die wichtigsten Automobilclubs des Landes sind die Automobile Association und der Royal Automobile Club, die den Mitgliedern der der FIA angeschlossenen Automobilclubs Pannenhilfe leisten und einige ihrer Dienstleistungen anbieten.

AUTOMOBILE ASSOCIATION
Fanum House
BASINGSTOKE, Hants., RG21 2EA
✆ (0256) 20123

ROYAL AUTOMOBILE CLUB
RAC House, Lansdowne Rd
CROYDON, Surrey CR9 2JA
✆ (081) 686 2525

Starred establishments

Les établissements à étoiles

Gli esercizi con stelle

Die Stern-Restaurants

✿✿✿

England and Wales

Bray-on-Thames	Waterside Inn
London	Le Gavroche

✿✿

England and Wales

London	La Tante Claire
–	Harvey's
–	Chez Nico
Oxford	Le Manoir aux Quat'Saisons
Reading	L'Ortolan

✿

England and Wales

Aylesbury	Hartwell House
Chester	Arkle
Esher	Les Alouettes
Great Malvern	Croque-en-Bouche
Haslemere	Morels
Ilkley	Box-Tree
London	L'Arlequin
–	Capital
–	Cavaliers'
–	Connaught
–	Four Seasons
–	Oak Room
–	Suntory
–	Sutherlands
New Milton	Chewton Glen
Norwich	Adlard's
Oakham	Hambleton Hall
Plymouth	Chez Nous
Pwllheli	Plas Bodegroes
Royal Leamington Spa	Mallory Court
South Molton	Whitechapel Manor
Stroud	Oakes
Tetbury	Calcot Manor

Scotland

Aberfoyle	Braeval Old Mill
Gullane	La Potinière
Peat Inn	Peat Inn
Port Appin	Airds
Portpatrick	Knockinaam Lodge
Ullapool	Altnaharrie Inn

Northern Ireland

Belfast	Roscoff

Republic of Ireland

Dublin	Patrick Guilbaud

Further establishments which merit your attention

Autres tables qui méritent votre attention
Altre tavole particolarmente interessanti
Weitere empfehlenswerte Häuser

M

England and Wales

Amersham	King's Arms
Baslow	Fisher's at Baslow Hall
Bath	Homewood Park
Bath	The Priory
Blackpool	River House
Bradford	Restaurant 19
Brimfield	Poppies
Bristol	Lettonie
Broadway	Buckland Manor
Brockenhurst	Le Poussin
Cheltenham	Redmond's
Clun	Old Post Office
Dartmouth	Mansion House
Dorking	Partners
Earl Stonham	Mr Underhill's
Eastbourne	Hungry Monk
Fowey	Food for Thought
Glemsford	Barretts
Grantham	Harry's Place
Grasmere	Michael's Nook
–	Country House
Grasmere	White Moss House
Hastings	Röser's
Henley-on-Thames	Stonor Arms
King's Lynn	Congham Hall
Knowl Hill	Warrener
London	Al San Vincenzo
–	Bibendum
–	Le Caprice
–	Chinon
–	Dynasty 2
–	Hilaire
–	Keats
–	Kensington Place
–	Red Fort
–	Turner's
–	Vijay
–	Zen Central
Melton Mowbray	Stapleford Park
Old Burghclere	Dew Pond
Padstow	Seafood
Pool-in-Wharfedale	Pool Court
Royal Tunbridge Wells	Cheevers
South Brent	Brookdale House
Storrington	Manley's
Torquay	Table
Truro	Long's
Ullswater	Sharrow Bay Country House
Ware	Fabden's Park
Waterhouses	Old Beams
Williton	White House
Windermere	Miller Howe
Wiveliscombe	Langley House
Worcester	Brown's
Wrightington Bar	Highmoor

Scotland

Edinburgh	Vintners Room
Kingussie	The Cross
Mull (isle of)	Tiroran House
Newtonmore	Ard-na-Coille

Northern Ireland

Portrush	Ramore

Channel Islands

Jersey : Rozel Bay	Granite Corner

Republic of Ireland

Adare	Mustard Seed
Ahakista	Shiro
Bunratty	McCloskey's
Cork	Cliffords
Dingle	Doyle's Seafood Bar
Dublin	Park
Gorey	Marlfield House
Kenmare	Lime Tree
Kinsale	Skippers
Mallow	Longueville House
Moycullen	Drimcong House
Shanagarry	Ballymaloe House

England and Wales

County abbreviations

Abbréviations des comtés

Abbreviazioni delle contee

Abkürzungen der Grafschaften

England

Avon	Avon
Bedfordshire	Beds.
Berkshire	Berks.
Buckinghamshire	Bucks.
Cambridgeshire	Cambs.
Cheshire	Cheshire
Cleveland	Cleveland
Cornwall	Cornwall
Cumbria	Cumbria
Derbyshire	Derbs.
Devon	Devon
Dorset	Dorset
Durham	Durham
East Sussex	East Sussex
Essex	Essex
Gloucestershire	Glos.
Greater Manchester	Greater Manchester
Hampshire	Hants.
Hereford and Worcester	Heref. and Worc.
Hertfordshire	Herts.
Humberside	Humberside
Isle of Wight	I.O.W.
Kent	Kent
Lancashire	Lancs.
Leicestershire	Leics.
Lincolnshire	Lincs.
Merseyside	Merseyside
Norfolk	Norfolk
Northamptonshire	Northants.
Northumberland	Northumb.
North Yorkshire	North Yorks.
Nottinghamshire	Notts.
Oxfordshire	Oxon.
Shropshire	Shropshire
Somerset	Somerset
South Yorkshire	South Yorks.
Staffordshire	Staffs.
Suffolk	Suffolk
Surrey	Surrey
Tyne and Wear	Tyne and Wear
Warwickshire	Warw.
West Midlands	West Midlands
West Sussex	West Sussex
West Yorkshire	West Yorks.
Wiltshire	Wilts.

Wales

Clwyd	Clwyd
Dyfed	Dyfed
Gwent	Gwent
Gwynedd	Gwynedd
Mid Glamorgan	Mid Glam.
Powys	Powys
South Glamorgan	South Glam.
West Glamorgan	West Glam.

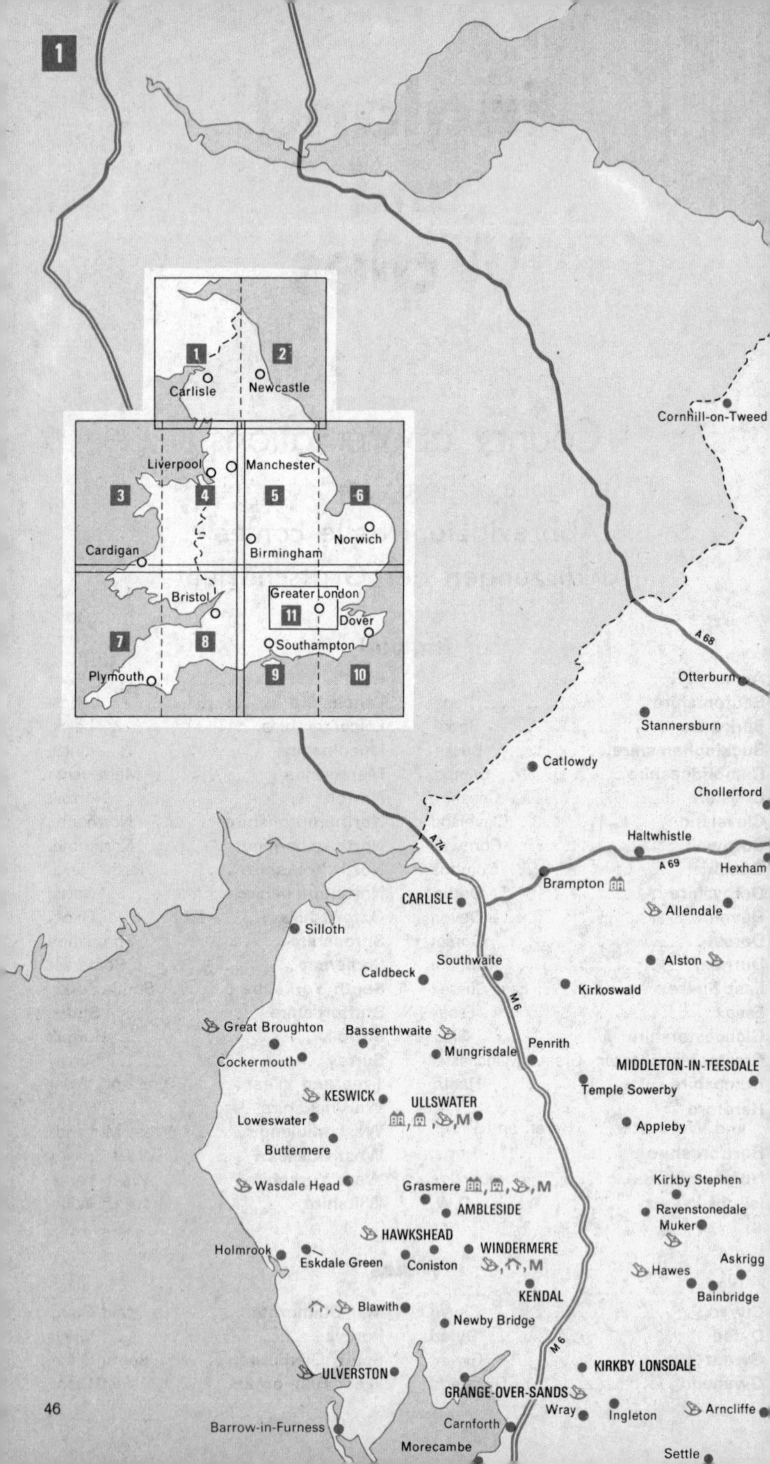
1
2
Carlisle
Newcastle
Liverpool
Manchester
3
4
5
6
Norwich
Cardigan
Birmingham
Bristol
Greater London
11
Dover
7
8
Southampton
9
10
Plymouth
Cornhill-on-Tweed
A 68
Otterburn
Stannersburn
Catlowdy
Chollerford
A 74
Haltwhistle
A 69
Hexham
Brampton
CARLISLE
Allendale
Silloth
Southwaite
Alston
Caldbeck
Kirkoswald
M 6
Great Broughton
Bassenthwaite
Mungrisdale
Penrith
Cockermouth
MIDDLETON-IN-TEESDALE
Temple Sowerby
KESWICK
ULLSWATER
M
Loweswater
Appleby
Buttermere
Wasdale Head
Grasmere
M
Kirkby Stephen
AMBLESIDE
Ravenstonedale
Muker
HAWKSHEAD
Holmrook
WINDERMERE
Askrigg
Eskdale Green
Coniston
M
Hawes
KENDAL
Bainbridge
Blawith
Newby Bridge
M 6
KIRKBY LONSDALE
ULVERSTON
GRANGE-OVER-SANDS
Wray
Ingleton
Arncliffe
Barrow-in-Furness
Carnforth
Morecambe
Settle

Place with at least :

one hotel or restaurant .... ● Ripon
one pleasant hotel .... 🏨, ⌂, ✗ with rm
one quiet, secluded hotel .... 🐎
one restaurant with .... ✿, ✿✿, ✿✿✿, M
See this town for establishments
located in its vicinity .... LEICESTER

Localité offrant au moins :

une ressource hôtelière .... ● Ripon
un hôtel agréable .... 🏨, ⌂, ✗ with rm
un hôtel très tranquille, isolé .... 🐎
une bonne table à .... ✿, ✿✿, ✿✿✿, M
Localité groupant dans le texte
les ressources de ses environs .... LEICESTER

La località possiede come minimo :

una risorsa alberghiera .... ● Ripon
un albergo ameno .... 🏨, ⌂, ✗ with rm
un albergo molto tranquillo, isolato .... 🐎
un'ottima tavola con .... ✿, ✿✿, ✿✿✿, M
La località raggruppa nel suo testo
le risorse dei dintorni .... LEICESTER

Ort mit mindestens :

einem Hotel oder Restaurant .... ● Ripon
einem angenehmen Hotel .... 🏨, ⌂, ✗ with rm
einem sehr ruhigen und abgelegenen Hotel .... 🐎
einem Restaurant mit .... ✿, ✿✿, ✿✿✿, M
Ort mit Angaben über Hotels und Restaurants
in seiner Umgebung .... LEICESTER

Berwick-upon-Tweed
Bamburgh
Belford
Seahouses
Wooler
Powburn
Alnwick
Alnmouth
Rothbury
Longframlington
Morpeth
Whitley Bay
A 696
Tynemouth
Corbridge
NEWCASTLE UPON-TYNE
Gateshead
South Shields
Washington
Sunderland
Blanchland
Chester-le-Street
DURHAM
Crook
Bowburn
Hamsterley
A1
HARTLEPOOL
Bishop Auckland
Billingham
Redcar
Barnard Castle
STOCKTON-ON-TEES
Saltburn-by-the-Sea
Thornaby-on-Tees
Middlesbrough
Greta Bridge
Loftus
DARLINGTON
Yarm
Great Ayton
WHITBY
Scotch Corner
Sleights
Castleton
Moulton
GREAT BROUGTON
RICHMOND
GOATHLAND
Kirkby Fleetham
Rosedale Abbey
Hartoft End
Patrick Brompton
NORTHALLERTON
Leeming Bar
LASTINGHAM
SCARBOROUGH
Kirkbymoorside
W. Witton
MIDDLEHAM
Bedale
Pickhill
MASHAM
THIRSK
HELMSLEY
PICKERING
Brompton
Kirklington
Hunmanby
KETTLEWELL
Hovingham
Ripon
EASINGWOLD
MALTON
PATELEY BRIDGE
Sherrif Hutton
Whitwell-on-the-Hill
Bridlington
Boroughbridge

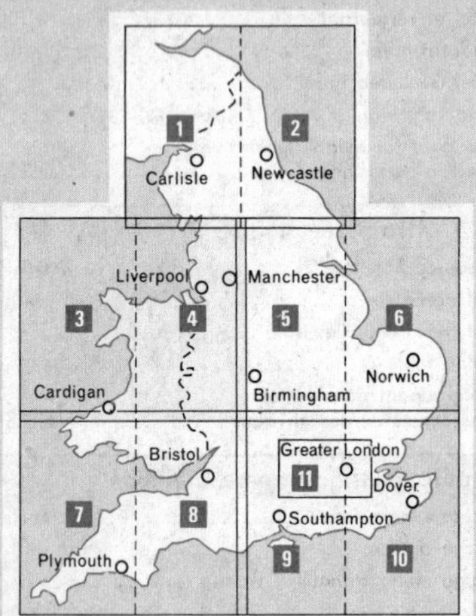
1
2
Carlisle
Newcastle
Liverpool
Manchester
3
4
5
6
Norwich
Cardigan
Birmingham
Bristol
Greater London
11
Dover
7
8
Southampton
Plymouth
9
10

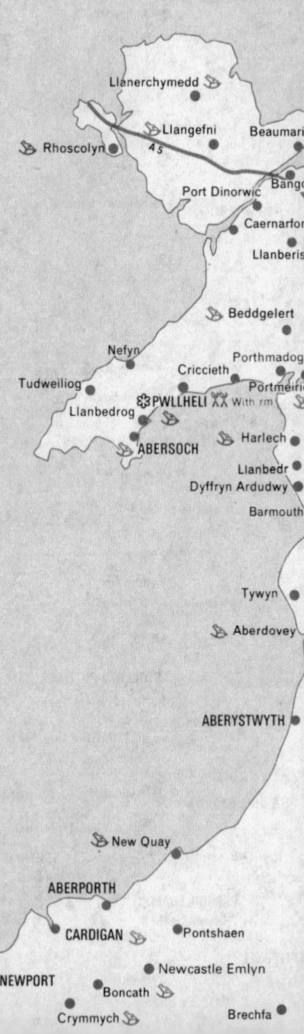
Llanerchymedd
Llangefni
Beaumaris
Rhoscolyn
A5
Port Dinorwic
Caernarfon
Llanberis
Beddgelert
Nefyn
Porthmadog
Criccieth
Tudweiliog
PWLLHELI
With rm
Llanbedrog
ABERSOCH
Harlech
Llanbedr
Dyffryn Ardudwy
Tywyn
Aberdovey
ABERYSTWYTH
New Quay
ABERPORTH
CARDIGAN
Pontshaen
Newcastle Emlyn
NEWPORT
FISHGUARD
Boncath
Crymmych
Brechfa

4
Barrow-in-Furness
Carnforth
Wray
Ingleton
Arncliffe
Morecambe
Heysham
LANCASTER
Settle
Hetton
M 6
Slaidburn
Fleetwood
Grindleton
Gisburn
Chipping
Sawley
Thornton Cleveleys
St-Michaels-on-Wyre
M, BLACKPOOL
Hurst Green
Colne
Kirkham
Whalley
PRESTON
Burnley
LYTHAM ST. ANNE'S
BLACKBURN
Clayton-le-Moors
Leyland
Clayton le Woods
Mere Brow
CHORLEY
Ramsbottom
Southport
Wrightington Bar
M
Adlington
Bury
M 61
Standish
BOLTON
Birch
Ormskirk
Wigan
Salford
Kirkby
Eccles
Haydock
MANCHESTER
Sale
Birkenhead
LIVERPOOL
M 62
ALTRINCHAM
Greasby
WARRINGTON
Stockport
Rock Ferry
Lymm
Llandudno
Bromborough
Widnes
Daresbury
Runcorn
KNUTSFORD
WILMSLOW
CONWY
COLWYN-BAY
Parkgate
Eastham
Frodsham
Alderley Edge
Holywell
Puddington
Hartford
Llansantffraid Glan Conwy
St.Asaph
M 56
MACCLESFIELD
Llannefydd
Mold
CHESTER
HOLMES CHAPEL
M 6
LLANRWST
Tattenhall
Congleton
Beeston
Sandbach
Rossett
Ruthin
Broxton
Crewe
Alsager
BETWS-Y-COED
Wrexham
Nantwich
A 5
Dolwyddelan
Malpas
STOKE-ON-TRENT
A 483
Newcastle-under-Lyme
Llangollen
Hanmer
Whitchurch
Stone
Bala
Llandrillo
Glyn Ceiriog
Market Drayton
Llanarmon Dyffryn Ceiriog
Oswestry
Hodnet
Lake Vyrnwy
Stafford
NEWPORT
LLANFYLLIN
DOLGELLAU
SHREWSBURY
TELFORD
Tal-y-Llyn
Welshpool
A 5
M 54
Abergynolwyn
Shifnal
Berriew
MACHYNLLETH
R. Severn
WOLVERHAMPTON
Montgomery
Church Stretton
BRIDGNORTH
NEWTOWN
Ditton Priors
STOURBRIDGE
Craven Arms
Diddlebury
Hopton Wafers
Pant Mawr
Clun M
KIDDERMINSTER
Llangurig
Ludlow
Bucknell
Stourport-on-Severn
Knighton
M Brimfield
Abberley
Rhayader
A 483
Presteigne
Shrawley
Crossgates
Droitwich
LLANDRINDOD WELLS
Penybont
LEOMINSTER
Kington
M, WORCESTER
Lyonshall
Ullingswick
Knightwick
Weobley
Llanwrtyd Wells
Llangammarch Wells
Bredwardine
GREAT MALVERN
M 5
HEREFORD
Upton upon Severn
Hay-on-Wye
49
Three Cocks
Vowchurch
LEDBURY
A 40
Llyswen
Talgarth
Fownhope
Woolhope
Brecon
TEWKESBURY

5
Ripon
EASINGWOLD
MALTON
PATELEY BRIDGE
Boroughbridge
Sherrif Hutton
Whitwell-on-the Hill
Bridlington
GRASSINGTON
Burnsall
Bolton Abbey
Knaresborough
GREAT DRIFFIELD
Skipton
HARROGATE
YORK
Ilkley
Wetherby
POCKLINGTON
Pool in Wharfedale
Otley
With rm., M
Boston Spa
Tadcaster
Haworth
Bingley
Harewood
BEVERLEY
Shipley
A1
LEEDS
Selby
BRADFORD
Howden
M 62
KINGSTON-UPON-HULL
Hedo
Hebden Bridge
Brighouse
Monk Fryston
M 62
A 63
HALIFAX
Wakefield
Winteringham
M 62
HUDDERSFIELD
Wentbridge
Barnsdale Bar
Meltham
Scunthorpe
HOLMFIRTH
Oldham
BARNSLEY
DONCASTER
Ashton-under-Lyne
Glossop
Rotherham
M 18
Marple
Bawtry
Aston
Clayworth
SHEFFIELD
Castleton
Blyth
Barnby Moor
Dinnington
Disley
Hathersage
Todwick
Ingham
Grindleford
Renishaw
Prestbury
Dronfield
Clowne
Markham Moor
Sturton-by-Stow
A1
Buxton
Eyam
Baslow
With rm. M
Tuxford
LINCOLN
Chesterfield
R. Trent
BAKEWELL
PEL
Longnor
Rowsley
Ollerton
Woodhall Spa
Hartington
MATLOCK
South Normanton
Leek
Alfreton
M1
Beckingham
Southwell
NEWARK-ON-TRENT
Thorpe
Waterhouses
with rm., M
A 17
Sleaford
Ashbourne
NOTTINGHAM
Bottesford
DERBY
GRANTHAM M
Uttoxeter
CASTLE DONINGTON
Colsterworth
Tutbury
BURTON-UPON-TRENT
LOUGHBOROUGH
Melton Mowbray
, M
Bourne
Rugeley
Ashby de la Zouch
Cannock
Armitage
Lichfield
Markfield
Tamworth
STAMFORD
OAKHAM
Dordon
LEICESTER
WALSALL
Aldridge
EARL SHILTON
PETERBOROUGH
Countesthorpe
UPPINGHAM
Sutton Coldfield
Hinckley
Coleshill
NUNEATON
Corby
Stilton
Bedworth
MARKET HARBOROUGH
Oundle
BIRMINGHAM
M 69
Lutterworth
M 6
Husbands Bosworth
Sawtry
Knowle
Aldwincle
SOLIHULL
COVENTRY
RUGBY
Old
Keyston
Hopwood
Hockley-Heath
Kenilworth
Huntingdon
Bromsgrove
Dunchurch
M1
WELLINGBOROUGH
REDDITCH
Royal Leamington Spa
With rm.
Buckden
Daventry
Studley
Henley in-Arden
WARWICK
Weedon-Bec
NORTHAMPTON
ST. NEOTS
Alcester
Badby
Castle Ashby
Charlecote
Wellesbourne
A1
Abbot's Salford
Priors Hardwick
Horton
STRATFORD-UPON-AVON
A 428
Roade
SANDY
Olney
Pershore
Harvington
Stoke Bruerne
BEDFORD
Evesham
Towcester
Newport Pagnell
SHIPSTON-ON-STOUR
STONY STRATFORD
Milton Keynes
CHIPPING CAMPDEN
BANBURY
Flitwick
Aspley Guise
Blockley
Brackley
Woburn
BROADWAY
MORETON-IN-MARSH
Letchworth

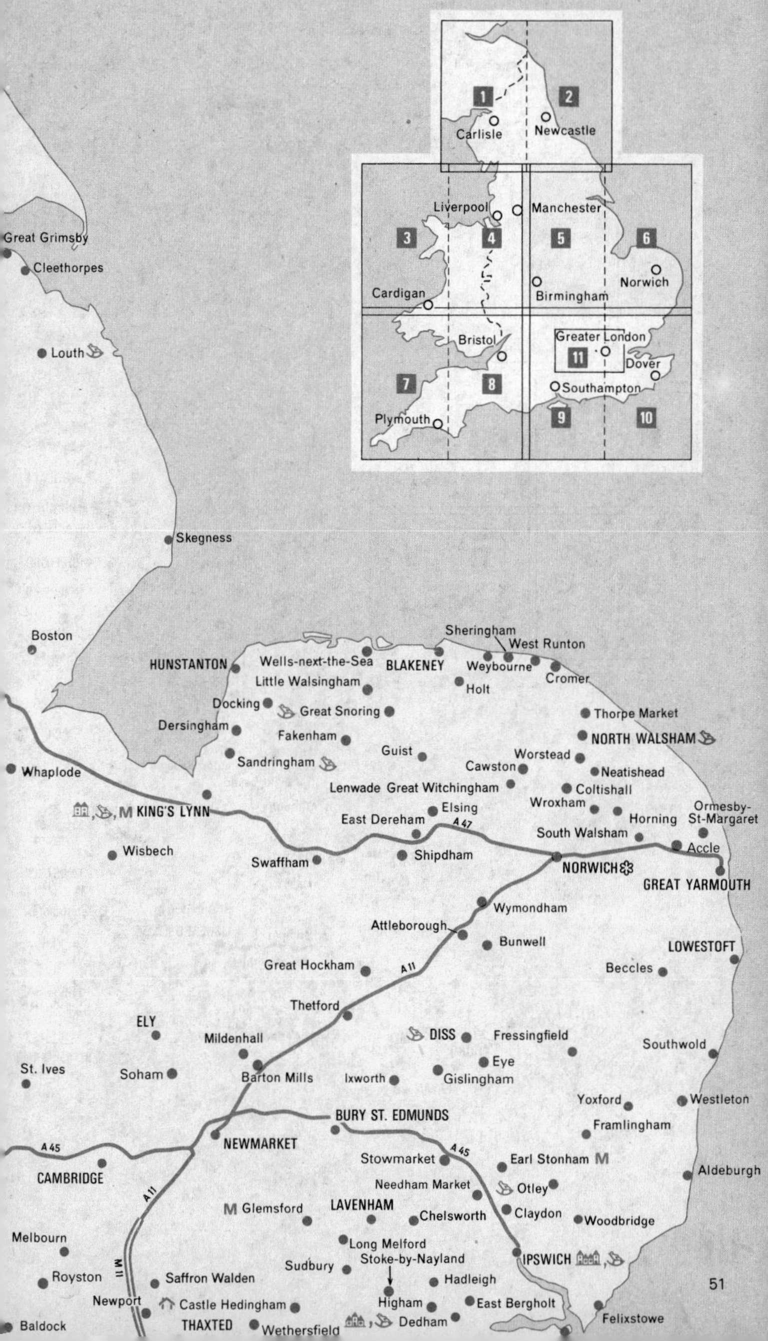
1
2
Carlisle
Newcastle
Liverpool
Manchester
3
4
5
6
Norwich
Cardigan
Birmingham
Bristol
Greater London
11
Dover
7
8
Southampton
Plymouth
9
10
Great Grimsby
Cleethorpes
Louth
Skegness
Boston
HUNSTANTON
Wells-next-the-Sea
BLAKENEY
Sheringham
West Runton
Weybourne
Cromer
Little Walsingham
Holt
Docking
Great Snoring
Thorpe Market
Dersingham
Fakenham
NORTH WALSHAM
Guist
Worstead
Sandringham
Cawston
Neatishead
Whaplode
Lenwade Great Witchingham
Coltishall
Wroxham
KING'S LYNN
Elsing
Horning
Ormesby-St-Margaret
East Dereham
A 47
South Walsham
Wisbech
Swaffham
Shipdham
Accle
NORWICH
GREAT YARMOUTH
Wymondham
Attleborough
Bunwell
LOWESTOFT
Great Hockham
A 11
Beccles
Thetford
ELY
DISS
Fressingfield
Mildenhall
Southwold
Eye
St. Ives
Soham
Barton Mills
Ixworth
Gislingham
Yoxford
Westleton
BURY ST. EDMUNDS
Framlingham
NEWMARKET
A 45
Stowmarket
Earl Stonham
CAMBRIDGE
Aldeburgh
Needham Market
Otley
A 11
M Glemsford
LAVENHAM
Claydon
Chelsworth
Woodbridge
Melbourn
Long Melford
Stoke-by-Nayland
IPSWICH
M 11
Sudbury
Royston
Saffron Walden
Hadleigh
Higham
Newport
Castle Hedingham
East Bergholt
Felixstowe
Baldock
THAXTED
Wethersfield
Dedham

7

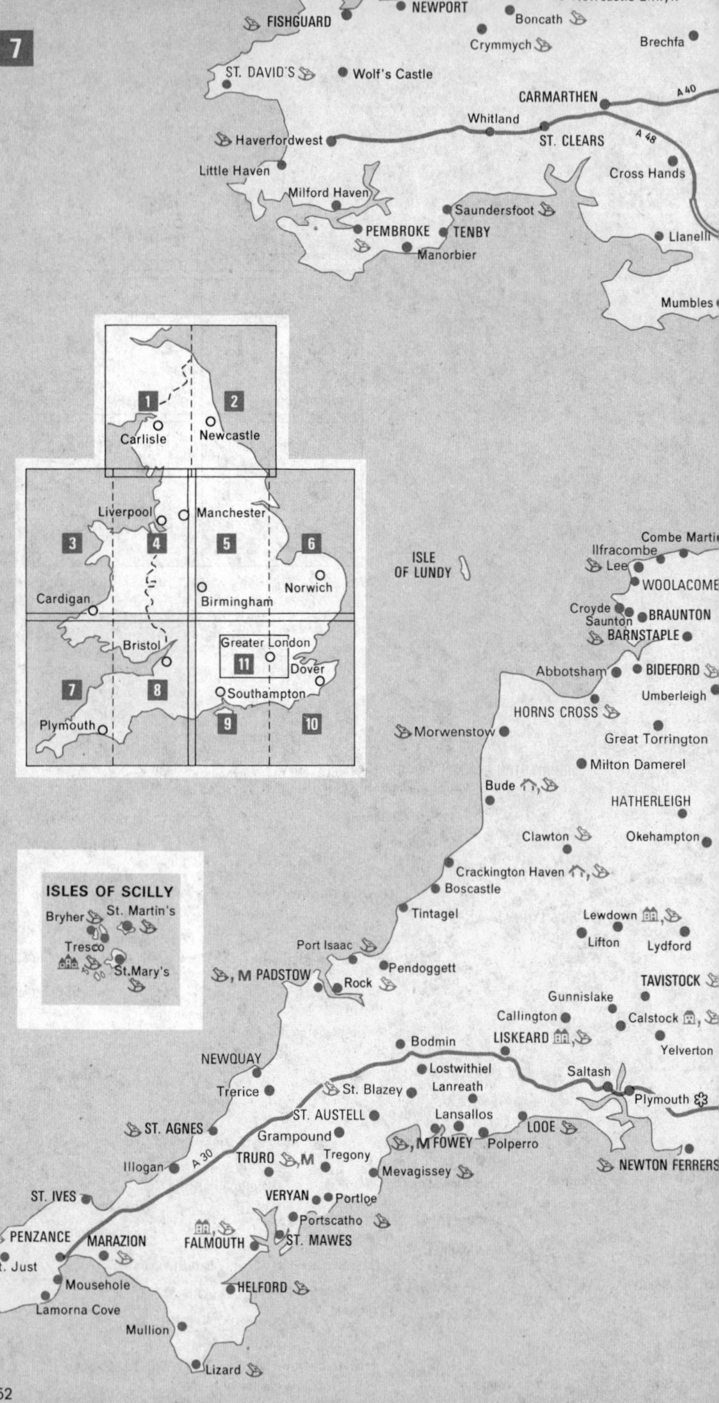

FISHGUARD
NEWPORT
Newcastle Emlyn
Boncath
Crymmych
Brechfa
ST. DAVID'S
Wolf's Castle
CARMARTHEN
A 40
Whitland
ST. CLEARS
A 48
Haverfordwest
Little Haven
Cross Hands
Milford Haven
Saundersfoot
PEMBROKE
TENBY
Manorbier
Llanelli
Mumbles
1
2
Carlisle
Newcastle
Liverpool
Manchester
3
4
5
6
Cardigan
Birmingham
Norwich
Bristol
Greater London
11
Dover
7
8
Southampton
9
10
Plymouth
ISLE OF LUNDY
Combe Martin
Ilfracombe
Lee
WOOLACOMBE
Croyde
Saunton
BRAUNTON
BARNSTAPLE
Abbotsham
BIDEFORD
Umberleigh
HORNS CROSS
Morwenstow
Great Torrington
Milton Damerel
Bude
HATHERLEIGH
Clawton
Okehampton
Crackington Haven
Boscastle
Tintagel
Lewdown
Lifton
Lydford
ISLES OF SCILLY
Bryher
St. Martin's
Tresco
St. Mary's
Port Isaac
Pendoggett
M PADSTOW
Rock
TAVISTOCK
Gunnislake
Callington
Calstock
Bodmin
LISKEARD
Yelverton
NEWQUAY
Lostwithiel
Saltash
Trerice
St. Blazey
Lanreath
Plymouth
ST. AUSTELL
Lansallos
ST. AGNES
Grampound
LOOE
M FOWEY
Polperro
TRURO
M
Tregony
Illogan
A 30
Mevagissey
NEWTON FERRERS
ST. IVES
VERYAN
Portloe
Portscatho
PENZANCE
MARAZION
FALMOUTH
ST. MAWES
St. Just
Mousehole
HELFORD
Lamorna Cove
Mullion
Lizard

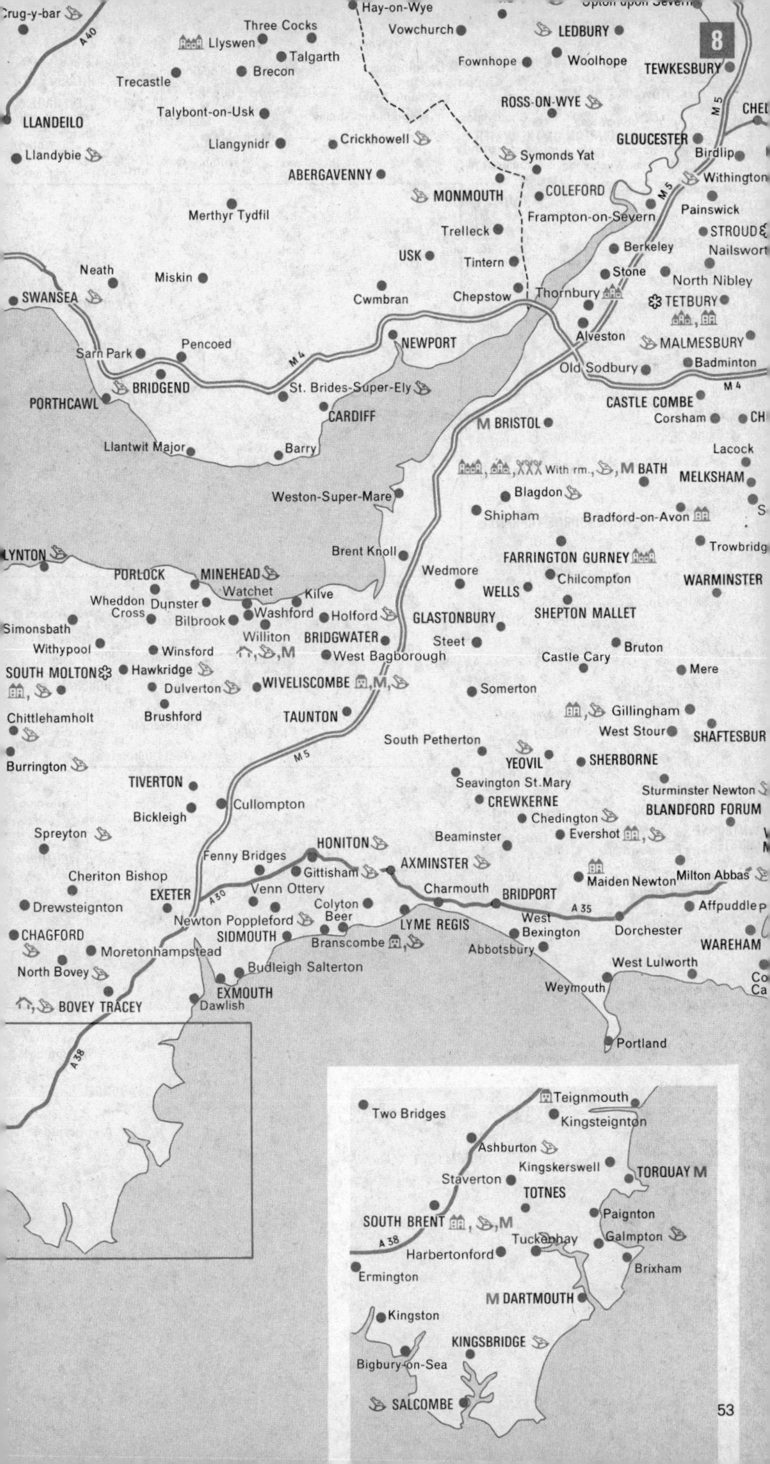

8
A40
Hay-on-Wye
Three Cocks
Llyswen
Talgarth
Brecon
Trecastle
Vowchurch
LEDBURY
Fownhope
Woolhope
TEWKESBURY
LLANDEILO
Talybont-on-Usk
ROSS-ON-WYE
M 5
GLOUCESTER
Llandybie
Llangynidr
Crickhowell
Symonds Yat
Birdlip
ABERGAVENNY
MONMOUTH
COLEFORD
Withington
Painswick
Merthyr Tydfil
Frampton-on-Severn
Trelleck
STROUD
USK
Berkeley
Tintern
Neath
Miskin
Stone
North Nibley
SWANSEA
Cwmbran
Chepstow
Thornbury
TETBURY
NEWPORT
Alveston
Pencoed
MALMESBURY
Sarn Park
M 4
Old Sodbury
Badminton
BRIDGEND
St. Brides-Super-Ely
PORTHCAWL
CARDIFF
CASTLE COMBE
Corsham
M BRISTOL
Llantwit Major
Barry
Lacock
With rm.,
M BATH
MELKSHAM
Weston-Super-Mare
Blagdon
Shipham
Bradford-on-Avon
Brent Knoll
LYNTON
FARRINGTON GURNEY
PORLOCK
MINEHEAD
Wedmore
Chilcompton
WARMINSTER
Watchet
Kilve
WELLS
Wheddon Cross
Dunster
SHEPTON MALLET
Washford
Holford
GLASTONBURY
Bilbrook
Simonsbath
Williton
BRIDGWATER
Steet
Bruton
Withypool
Winsford
M
West Bagborough
Castle Cary
Mere
SOUTH MOLTON
Hawkridge
Somerton
WIVELISCOMBE
M,
Dulverton
Gillingham
Chittlehamholt
Brushford
TAUNTON
West Stour
South Petherton
M 5
YEOVIL
SHERBORNE
Burrington
Seavington St.Mary
TIVERTON
Sturminster Newton
CREWKERNE
Cullompton
Bickleigh
Chedington
BLANDFORD FORUM
Spreyton
Beaminster
Evershot
HONITON
Fenny Bridges
AXMINSTER
Gittisham
Cheriton Bishop
Maiden Newton
Milton Abbas
Venn Ottery
Charmouth
EXETER
BRIDPORT
A 30
Drewsteignton
Colyton
A 35
Affpuddle
Newton Poppleford
Beer
LYME REGIS
West Bexington
Dorchester
CHAGFORD
SIDMOUTH
Branscombe
Abbotsbury
WAREHAM
Moretonhampstead
North Bovey
Budleigh Salterton
West Lulworth
EXMOUTH
Weymouth
BOVEY TRACEY
Dawlish
A 38
Portland
Teignmouth
Two Bridges
Kingsteignton
Ashburton
Kingskerswell
TORQUAY M
Staverton
TOTNES
Paignton
SOUTH BRENT
M
A 38
Tuckenhay
Galmpton
Harbertonford
Brixham
Ermington
M DARTMOUTH
Kingston
KINGSBRIDGE
Bigbury-on-Sea
SALCOMBE

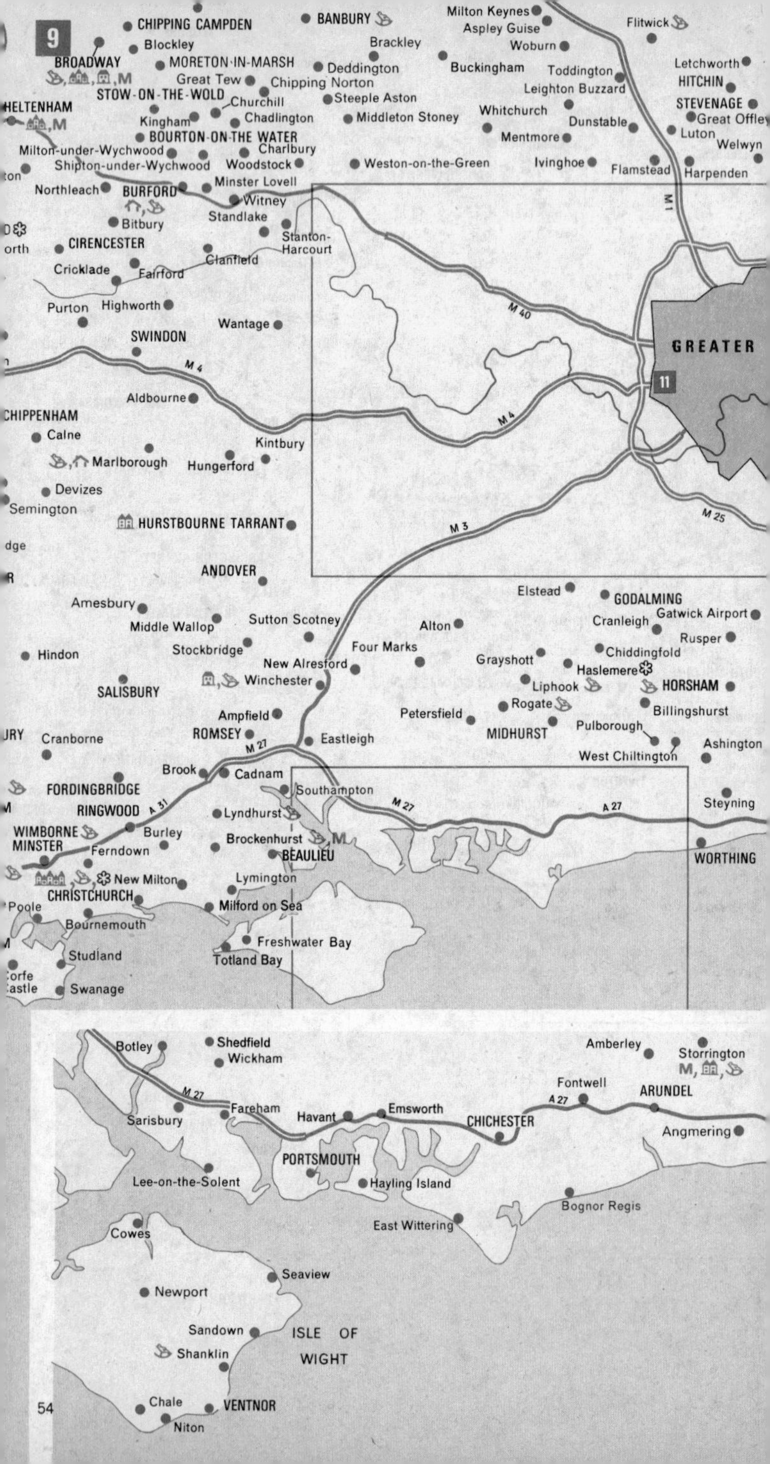
9
CHIPPING CAMPDEN
BANBURY
Milton Keynes
Aspley Guise
Flitwick
Blockley
Brackley
Woburn
BROADWAY
MORETON-IN-MARSH
Deddington
Buckingham
Toddington
Letchworth
HITCHIN
Great Tew
Chipping Norton
Leighton Buzzard
STOW-ON-THE-WOLD
Churchill
Steeple Aston
STEVENAGE
HELTENHAM
Whitchurch
Great Offley
Kingham
Chadlington
Middleton Stoney
Dunstable
Luton
BOURTON-ON-THE WATER
Mentmore
Welwyn
Milton-under-Wychwood
Charlbury
Shipton-under-Wychwood
Woodstock
Weston-on-the-Green
Ivinghoe
Flamstead
Harpenden
Northleach
BURFORD
Minster Lovell
Witney
M 1
Standlake
Bitbury
Stanton-Harcourt
CIRENCESTER
Clanfield
Cricklade
Fairford
Purton
Highworth
M 40
Wantage
GREATER
SWINDON
M 4
11
Aldbourne
M 4
CHIPPENHAM
Calne
Kintbury
Marlborough
Hungerford
Devizes
Semington
M 25
HURSTBOURNE TARRANT
M 3
ANDOVER
Elstead
GODALMING
Amesbury
Cranleigh
Gatwick Airport
Middle Wallop
Sutton Scotney
Alton
Rusper
Hindon
Stockbridge
Four Marks
Grayshott
Chiddingfold
New Alresford
Haslemere
Winchester
Liphook
HORSHAM
SALISBURY
Rogate
Billingshurst
Ampfield
Petersfield
Pulborough
ROMSEY
MIDHURST
Cranborne
Eastleigh
Ashington
M 27
West Chiltington
Brook
Cadnam
Southampton
Steyning
FORDINGBRIDGE
M 27
A 27
RINGWOOD
A 31
Lyndhurst
WIMBORNE MINSTER
Burley
Brockenhurst
Ferndown
BEAULIEU
WORTHING
New Milton
Lymington
CHRISTCHURCH
Poole
Milford on Sea
Bournemouth
Freshwater Bay
Studland
Totland Bay
Swanage
Botley
Shedfield
Amberley
Storrington
Wickham
Fontwell
ARUNDEL
M 27
A 27
Sarisbury
Fareham
Havant
Emsworth
CHICHESTER
Angmering
PORTSMOUTH
Lee-on-the-Solent
Hayling Island
Bognor Regis
East Wittering
Cowes
Seaview
Newport
Sandown
ISLE OF WIGHT
Shanklin
Chale
VENTNOR
Niton

10
Royston
Saffron Walden
Sudbury
Hadleigh
Newport
Castle Hedingham
Higham
East Bergholt
Baldock
THAXTED
Wethersfield
Dedham
Felixstowe
Clavering
Harwich and Dovercourt
Stanstead Airport
Coggeshall
Colchester
BISHOP'S STORTFORD
Braintree
Great Dunmow
Frinton-on-Sea
WARE With rm. M
Rivenhall End
Witham
Clacton-on-Sea
West Mersea
CHELMSFORD
M 11
Maldon
South Woodham Ferrers
M 25
Burnham-on-Crouch
Rochford
Basildon
Southend-on-Sea
LONDON
Horndon on the Hill
North Stifford
Gravesend
A 2
Rochester
Shorne
Cobham
Farthing Corner
Herne Bay
Broadstairs
Whitstable
Hoath
RAMSGATE
Sittingbourne
M 2
FAVERSHAM
Selling
Sandwich
Sheldwich
CANTERBURY
Wingham
M 25
MAIDSTONE
Warren Street
DEAL
M 23
Edenbridge
Tonbridge
Wye
Horley
Penhurst
Pluckley
Ashford
Turners Hill
M
ROYAL TUNBRIDGE WELLS
Bethersden
DOVER
Goudhurst
Biddenden
EAST GRINSTEAD
Frant
CRAWLEY
Wadhurst
CRANBROOK
Folkestone
FOREST ROW
Hythe
Hawkhurst
TENTERDEN
Crowborough
Northiam
Robertsbridge
A 259
Cuckfield
Mayfield
New Romney
Dallington
SEDLESCOMBE
Uckfield
RYE
Heathfield
Rushlake Green
Halland
Battle
A 23
Lewes
A 27
Herstmonceux
Bexhill
BRIGHTON AND HOVE
HAILSHAM
Hastings and St. Leonards M
Alfriston
Rottingdean
EASTBOURNE M
Seaford
1
2
Carlisle
Newcastle
Liverpool
Manchester
3
4
5
6
Norwich
Cardigan
Birmingham
Greater London
11
Bristol
Dover
7
8
Southampton
Plymouth
9
10

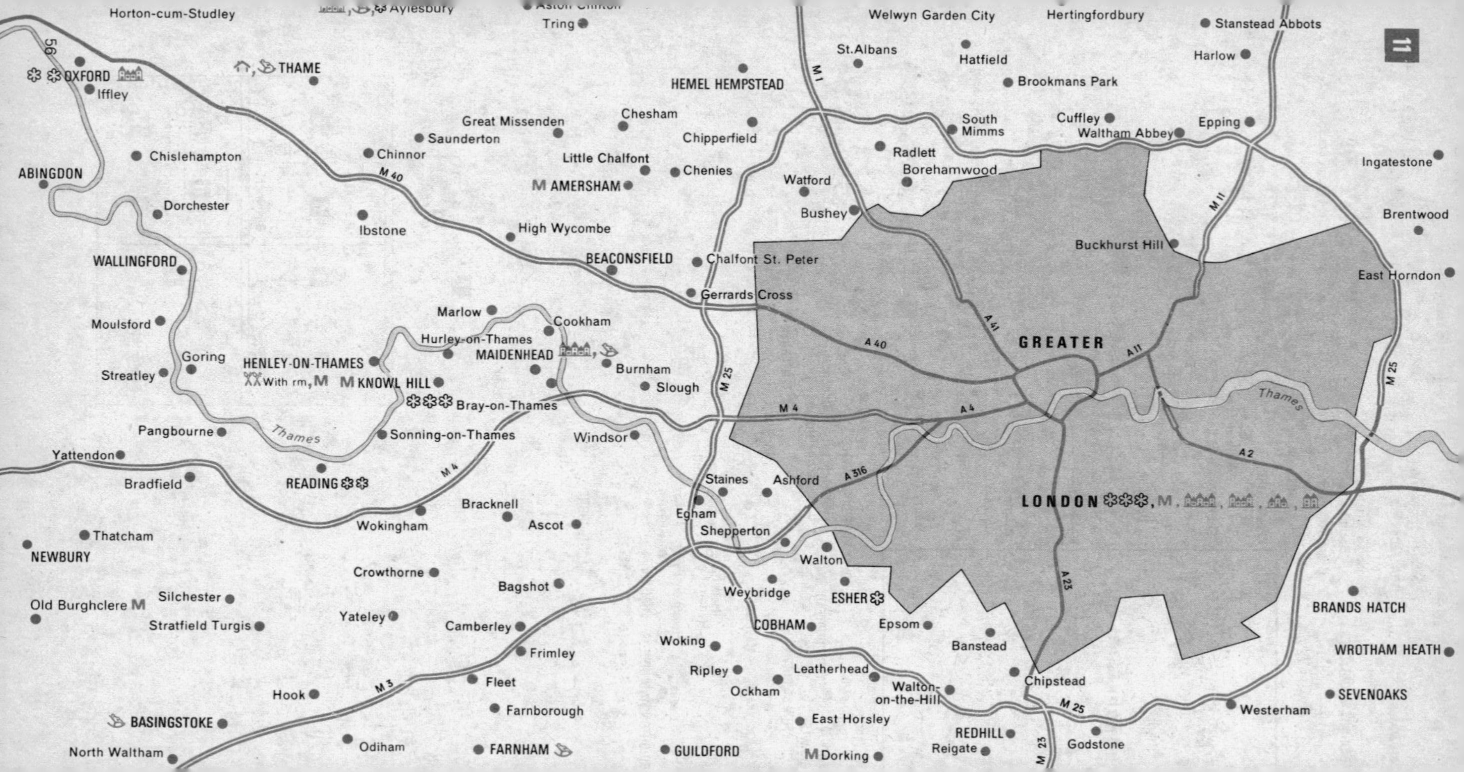
Horton-cum-Studley
Aylesbury
Tring
Welwyn Garden City
Hertingfordbury
Stanstead Abbots
St.Albans
Hatfield
Harlow
OXFORD
Iffley
THAME
HEMEL HEMPSTEAD
Brookmans Park
Great Missenden
Chesham
South Mimms
Cuffley
Epping
Saunderton
Chipperfield
Waltham Abbey
Chislehampton
Chinnor
Radlett
Ingatestone
Little Chalfont
Chenies
Borehamwood
ABINGDON
M 40
AMERSHAM
Watford
M 1
M 11
Dorchester
Bushey
Brentwood
Ibstone
High Wycombe
Buckhurst Hill
WALLINGFORD
BEACONSFIELD
Chalfont St. Peter
East Horndon
Gerrards Cross
Marlow
Cookham
Moulsford
Hurley-on-Thames
A 41
GREATER
A 40
MAIDENHEAD
A 11
Goring
HENLEY-ON-THAMES
Burnham
M 25
Streatley
With rm, M
KNOWL HILL
Slough
Bray-on-Thames
M 4
A 4
Thames
Pangbourne
Sonning-on-Thames
Windsor
Yattendon
A 2
Bradfield
READING
M 4
Staines
Ashford
A 316
Bracknell
LONDON
Egham
Wokingham
Ascot
Thatcham
Shepperton
NEWBURY
Walton
Crowthorne
A 23
Bagshot
Weybridge
ESHER
BRANDS HATCH
Silchester
Old Burghclere
Yateley
Camberley
COBHAM
Epsom
Stratfield Turgis
Woking
Banstead
WROTHAM HEATH
Frimley
Ripley
Leatherhead
Chipstead
Walton-on-the-Hill
Fleet
Ockham
M 25
Westerham
SEVENOAKS
Hook
M 3
Farnborough
East Horsley
BASINGSTOKE
REDHILL
Godstone
Reigate
M 23
North Waltham
Odiham
FARNHAM
GUILDFORD
Dorking

ABBERLEY Heref. and Worc. 403 404 M 27 – pop. 604 – ECD : Wednesday – ✉ Worcester – ☎ 0299 Great Witley.

♦ London 137 – ♦Birmingham 27 – Worcester 13.

- **The Elms** (Q.M.H.) ⚲, WR6 6AT, W : 2 m. on A 443 ✆ 896666, Telex 337105, Fax 896804, ←, « Queen Anne Mansion », ⛱, park, 🎾 – TV ☎ P – 🏛 30. AE VISA. ✻
  M 13.95/20.00 **st.** and a la carte 20.95/26.95 **st.** – **24 rm** ▭ 85.00/120.00 **st.**, **1 suite** 145.00/165.00 **st.** – SB 130.00/150.00 **st.**
- **Manor Arms** ⚲, Abberley Village, WR6 6BN, ✆ 896507, ⛱ – TV ☎ P. VISA
  closed 25 and 26 December – **M** *(closed Sunday dinner)* 9.50/12.50 **t.** and a la carte 🍷 4.00 – **10 rm** ▭ 40.00/50.00 **t.** – SB 63.00 **st.**

ABBOTSBURY Dorset 403 404 M 32 **The West Country G.** – pop. 401 – ☎ 0305.

See : Site★★.

♦London 146 – Exeter 50 – Bournemouth 44 – Weymouth 10.

- **Ilchester Arms,** 9 Market St., DT3 4JR, ✆ 871243 – ⊭ rest TV ☎ ♿ P. VISA
  M 7.50 **t.** (lunch) and a la carte 6.70/10.45 **t.** 🍷 3.00 – **10 rm** ▭ 45.00/55.00 **t.** – SB (November-March) (except Christmas-New Year) 55.00 **st.**

FORD, VOLVO Alban Sq. ✆ 570312

ABBOTSHAM Devon 403 H 30 – see Bideford.

ABBOT'S SALFORD Heref Worc. 403 404 O 27 – see Evesham.

Prices — For full details of the prices quoted in the guide, consult the introduction.

ABERDAUGLEDDAU = Milford Haven.

ABERDOVEY (ABERDYFI) Gwynedd 403 H 26 – pop. 778 – ECD : Wednesday – ☎ 065 472 (4 fig.) and 0654 (6 fig.).

See : Afon Dovey's mouth (site★★).

Envir. : Llanegryn (church★) N : 8 m. – Dolgoch Falls★, NE : 10 m.

⛳18 Aberdovey ✆ 210.

ℹ The Wharf ✆ 72321 (summer only).

♦ London 230 – Dolgellau 25 – Shrewsbury 66.

- **Plas Penhelig** ⚲, LL35 0NA, E : 1 m. by A 493 ✆ 767676, Fax 7783, ←, « Terraced gardens », park, 🎾 – TV ☎ P. AE VISA. ✻
  closed 24 December-February – **M** (bar lunch Monday to Saturday)/dinner 15.50 **t.** – **11 rm** ▭ 55.00/85.00 **t.**
- **Trefeddian,** Tywyn Rd, LL35 0SB, W : 1 m. on A 493 ✆ 767213, ← golf course and sea, 🏊, ⛱, park, 🎾 – 🛗 ⊭ rest TV ☎ 🚗 P. VISA
  17 March-December – **M** 7.50/13.00 **t.** – **46 rm** ▭ (dinner included) 35.00/96.00 **t.** – SB 72.00/96.00 **st.**
- **Penhelig Arms,** Terrace Rd, LL35 0LT, ✆ 767215, Fax 7761, ← – TV P. VISA
  M (bar lunch Monday to Saturday)/dinner 14.50 **t.** – **11 rm** ▭ 29.00/67.00 **t.** – SB 74.00/90.00 **st.**
- **Harbour,** LL35 0EB, ✆ 767250, ← – TV. AE VISA
  M *(April-October)* 17.50 **st.** (dinner) and a la carte 🍷 3.25 – **12 rm** ▭ 40.00/80.00 **st.**
- **Maybank,** LL35 0PT, E : 1 m. on A 493 ✆ 767500, ← – TV. VISA
  closed 9 January-10 February and last week November – **M** (booking essential) (dinner only) 25.00 **t.** and a la carte 🍷 4.95 – **5 rm** ▭ 25.00/47.90 **t.**
- **Morlan,** Tywyn Rd, LL35 0SE, W : 1½ m. on A 493 ✆ 7706, ←, ⛱ – ⊭ rm TV P. ✻
  M 12.00 **st.** 🍷 3.00 – **4 rm** ▭ 24.00/36.00 **st.**

ABERGAVENNY (Y-FENNI) Gwent 403 L 28 – pop. 9 427 – ECD : Thursday – ☎ 0873.

Envir. : Llanthony Priory★, N : 10 m. – Bwlch (←★ of the Usk Valley), NW : 9½ m.

⛳18 Monmouthshire, Gypsy Lane, Llanfoist ✆ 3171, S : 2 m. off B 4269.

ℹ Swan Meadow, Cross St. ✆ 3254/77588 (summer only).

♦ London 163 – Gloucester 43 – Newport 19 – ♦Swansea 49.

- **Angel** (T.H.F.), 15 Cross St., NP7 5EW, ✆ 7121, Fax 78059 – TV ☎ P – 🏛 60. AE VISA. ✻
  M *(closed Monday lunch)* 12.00 **st.** (lunch) and a la carte approx. 18.70 **st.** 🍷 4.35 – ▭ 7.00 – **29 rm** 55.00/65.00 **st.** – SB 82.00 **st.**
- **Halidon House** without rest., 63 Monmouth Rd, NP7 5HR, ✆ 77855, ←, 🏊, ⛱ – P. ✻
  April-October – **5 rm** ▭ 15.00/30.00 **s.**
- **Bagan Tandoori,** 35 Frogmore St., NP7 5AN, ✆ 77389, Indian rest. – AE VISA
  closed 25 and 26 December – **M** 9.90 **t.** and a la carte.

at Llanwenarth NW : 3 m. on A 40 – ✉ Abergavenny – ☎ 0873 Crickhowell :

Llanwenarth Arms, Brecon Rd, NP8 1EP, ☎ 810550, Fax 811880, ←, – TV ☎ P. AE VISA.
M a la carte 11.70/19.90 **st.** – **18 rm** 48.00/58.00 **st.**

RENAULT 9 Monmouth Rd ☎ 2323
ROVER, FORD Brecon Rd ☎ 2126
ATS 11 Monmouth Rd ☎ 4348

ABERGWAUN = Fishguard.

ABERGYNOLWYN Gwynedd 402 403 I 26 – ✉ Twywn – ☎ 0654.
London 228 – Dolgellau 12 – Shrewsbury 63.

Dolgoch Falls, LL36 9UW, SW : 2½ m. on B 4405 ☎ 782258, ←, – P. VISA
March-October – **M** 12.50 **t.** 3.25 – **6 rm** 17.95/41.90 **t.** – SB 45.50/53.90 **st.**

ABERHONDDU = Brecon.

ABERLLYNFI = Three Cocks.

ABERMAW = Barmouth.

ABERMULE **(ABER-MIWL)** Powys 403 K 26 – see Newtown.

ABERPORTH Dyfed 403 G 27 – pop. 1 614 – ECD : Wednesday – ☎ 0239.
See : Site★.
Envir. : Llangranog (cliffs★) NE : 4 m.
London 249 – Carmarthen 29 – Fishguard 26.

Penrallt, SA43 2BS, SW : 1 m. by B 4333 ☎ 810227, Fax 811375, ←, , heated, , – TV ☎ P. AE VISA.
closed 25 to 27 December – **M** (bar lunch Monday to Saturday)/dinner 12.00 **t.** and a la carte 3.95 – **16 rm** 40.00/64.00 **t.** – SB (winter only) 70.00 **st.**

at Tresaith NE : 1¾ m. – ✉ ☎ 0239 Aberporth :

Glandwr Manor, SA43 2JH, ☎ 810197, – rest P.
March-October – **M** *(closed Sunday to non-residents)* (dinner only) 8.00 **t.** and a la carte – **7 rm** 19.00/38.00 **t.**

ABERRIW = Berriew.

ABERSOCH Gwynedd 402 403 G 25 – ECD : Wednesday – ✉ Pwllheli – ☎ 075 881.
Envir. : Llanengan (church★ : twin aisles rood screen) W : 2 m. – Hell's Mouth★, W : 3 m. – Aberdaron (site★) W : 10 m. – Braich y Pwll (←★★ from 2nd car park) W : 12 m.
18 Golf Rd, Pwllheli, ☎ 0758 (Pwllheli) 612520, NE : 7 m – 9 Abersoch ☎ 2622, S : ½ m.
Village Hall ☎ 2929.
London 265 – Caernarfon 28 – Shrewsbury 101.

Riverside, LL53 7HW, ☎ 2419, – TV ☎ P. VISA.
March-November – **M** (bar lunch)/dinner 17.50 **t.** 4.00 – **12 rm** 32.50/77.00 **t.** – SB 93.00 **st.**

Abersoch Harbour, Lon Engan, LL53 7HR, ☎ 2406, ← – TV ☎ P. AE VISA
closed January and February – **M** 12.00 **t.** and a la carte 3.50 – **14 rm** 33.00/100.00 **t.** – SB (September-November) (weekdays only) 69.00 **st.**

Tudor Court, Lon Sarr Bach, LL53 7EB, ☎ 3354 – TV P. VISA
M 10.50/18.50 **t.** and a la carte 3.75 – **6 rm** 27.50/53.00 **t.** – SB 60.00/120.00 **st.**

Llwyn Du, Sarn Bach Rd, LL53 7EL, ☎ 2186, – rm P.
M approx. 7.00 – **3 rm** 28.00 **s.**

at Bwlchtocyn S : 2 m. – ✉ Pwllheli – ☎ 075 881 Abersoch :

Porth Tocyn, LL53 7BU, ☎ 3303, Fax 3538, ← Cardigan Bay and mountains, « Country house atmosphere », heated, , – TV ☎ P.
25 March-mid November – **M** (bar lunch)/dinner 22.00 **t.** 4.50 – **17 rm** 37.00/86.00 **t.**

ABERTAWE = Swansea.

ABERTEIFI = Cardigan.

Bitte beachten Sie die Geschwindigkeitsbeschränkungen in Großbritannien
– 60 mph (= 96 km/h) außerhalb geschlossener Ortschaften
– 70 mph (= 112 km/h) auf Straßen mit getrennten Fahrbahnen und Autobahnen.

ABERYSTWYTH Dyfed 403 H 26 – pop. 8 636 – ECD : Wednesday – 0970.
See : Site★ – ≤★ from the National Library.
Envir. : Elan Valley★★ – Strata Florida★, SE : 15 m – Devil's Bridge★.
18 Bryn-y-mor, ℘ 615104, N : ½ m.
Terrace Rd ℘ 612125 and 611955.
◆ London 238 – Chester 98 – Fishguard 58 – Shrewsbury 74.

Belle Vue Royal, The Promenade, SY23 2BA, ℘ 617558, Fax 612190, ≤ – TV ☎. AE VISA.
accommodation closed 23 to 27 December – **M** 7.95/12.50 **t.** and a la carte 3.75 – **42 rm** 25.00/65.00 **t.** – SB (except Bank Holidays) 67.00/74.00 **st.**

The Groves, 44-46 North Par., SY23 2NF, ℘ 617623 – TV ☎ P. AE VISA.
closed Christmas and New Year – **M** (bar lunch)/dinner a la carte 9.95/15.30 **st.** 3.25 – **11 rm** 28.50/48.50 **st.** – SB 58.00 **st.**

Four Seasons, 50-54 Portland St., SY23 2DX, ℘ 612120 – TV ☎ P. VISA.
closed 23 December-3 January – **M** (bar lunch Monday to Saturday)/dinner 13.50 **st.** 4.00 – **14 rm** 44.00/54.00 **st.** – SB 63.75/72.50 **st.**

Glyn-Garth, South Rd, SY23 1JS, ℘ 615050 – TV.
M (by arrangement) – **10 rm** 13.50/38.00 **st.**

at Chancery (Rhydgaled) S : 4 m. on A 487 – ✉ 0970 Aberystwyth :

Conrah Country, SY23 4DF, ℘ 617941, Telex 35892, Fax 624546, ≤, « 18C country house », park – rest TV ☎ P – 40. AE VISA.
closed 22 to 30 December – **M** 12.50/18.50 **t.** and a la carte 3.60 – **22 rm** 46.50/83.00 **t.** – SB (October-June) 90.00/108.00 **st.**

FIAT Llanfarian ℘ 612311
HONDA North Parade ℘ 617607
ROVER, LAND-ROVER, RANGE-ROVER, JAGUAR-DAIMLER Park Av. ℘ 624841
ATS Glanyrafon Ind Est., Llandabarn ℘ 611166

We suggest :
For a successful tour, that you prepare it in advance.
Michelin maps and guides will give you much useful information on route planning, places of interest, accommodation, prices etc.

ABINGDON Oxon. 403 404 Q 28 – pop. 29130 – ECD : Thursday – 0235.
See : Site★.
18, 18 Frilford Heath ℘ 390864.
The Old Gaol, Bridge St. ℘ 22711.
◆ London 64 – ◆Oxford 6 – Reading 25.

Upper Reaches (T.H.F.), Thames St., OX14 3JA, ℘ 522311, Fax 555182 – TV ☎ P – 30. AE VISA
M 15.00 **st.** (dinner) and a la carte 4.35 – 7.00 – **26 rm** 70.00/115.00 **st.** – SB (weekends only) 50.00/60.00 **st.**

Crown and Thistle (B.C.B.), Bridge St., OX14 3HS, ℘ 522556, Fax 553281 – rm TV ☎ P – 30. AE VISA.
M 8.00/15.00 **st.** – **21 rm** 43.00/75.00 **st.**

at Clifton Hampden SE : 3 ¾ m. on A 415 – ✉ Abingdon – 086 730 Clifton Hampden :

Barley Mow (B.C.B.), OX14 3EH, on Long Wittenham Rd ℘ 7847, – TV ☎ P. AE VISA.
M 8.00/15.00 **st.** – **4 rm** 34.50/54.00 **st.**

at Frilford W : 3 ¾ m. on A 415 – ✉ 0865 Abingdon :

Dog House, Frilford Heath, OX13 6QY, NE : 1 ¼ m. by A 338 on Cothill rd ℘ 390830, Fax 390860, – TV ☎ P. AE VISA
M 10.00/15.50 **t.** and a la carte 3.35 – **19 rm** 49.50/59.50 **t.**

RENAULT Drayton Rd ℘ 528828
ROVER Drayton Rd ℘ 522822

ACLE Norfolk 404 Y 26 – 0493.

Travelodge without rest., Acle by Pass, NR1 3BE, ℘ 751970 Reservations (Toll free) 0800 850950 – TV ☎ P. AE VISA.
40 rm 24.00/29.50 **st.**

ACOCKS GREEN West Midlands 403 404 ⑳ – see Birmingham.

ADLINGTON Lancs. 402 404 M 23 – ECD : Wednesday – 0257.
◆London 217 – ◆Liverpool 35 – ◆Manchester 21 – Preston 16.

Gladmar, Railway Rd, PR6 9RG, ℘ 480398, Fax 482681, – TV ☎ P. VISA.
closed Christmas Day – **M** (bar lunch)/dinner 12.50 **st.** and a la carte 3.20 – **20 rm** 35.00/54.00 **st.**

AFFPUDDLE Dorset 403 404 N 31 – pop. 425 – ✉ Dorchester – ☎ 030 584 (3 and 4 fig.) and 0305 (6 fig.) Puddletown.

♦London 121 – Bournemouth 19 – Exeter 60 – ♦Southampton 47 – Weymouth 14.

- **Old Vicarage** without rest., DT2 7HH, ☎ 848315, « Tastefully furnished », – TV P.
  closed Christmas-New Year – **3 rm** 20.00/36.00 **st.**

AIGBURTH Merseyside – see Liverpool.

AISLABY North Yorks. – see Pickering.

ALBRIGHTON Shropshire 402 403 L 25 – see Shrewsbury.

ALCESTER Warw. 403 404 O 27 – pop. 5 207 – ECD : Thursday – ☎ 0789.

Envir. : Ragley Hall★★ (17C) *AC*, SW : 2 m.

♦London 104 – ♦Birmingham 20 – ♦Coventry 28 – Gloucester 34.

Hotels and restaurants see : **Stratford-upon-Avon** E : 9 m.

FORD Priory Rd ☎ 762408
RENAULT Stratford Rd ☎ 762191
ROVER Station Rd ☎ 764146

ALDBOURNE Wilts. 403 404 P 29 – pop. 1 479 – ☎ 0672 Marlborough.

♦London 77 – ♦Oxford 36 – ♦Southampton 53 – Swindon 9.

- XX **Raffles,** 1 The Green, SN8 2BW, ☎ 40700 – AE VISA
  closed lunch Monday and Saturday, Sunday, last 2 weeks August, 25 to 30 December and Bank Holidays – **M** a la carte 13.50/18.95 **st.** 3.00.

ALDEBURGH Suffolk 404 Y 27 – pop. 2 711 – ECD : Wednesday – ☎ 072 885 (4 fig.) and 0728 (6 fig.).

18 at Thorpeness ☎ 452176, N : 2½ m – 18, 9 Aldeburgh ☎ 452408.

The Cinema, High St. ☎ 453637 (summer only).

♦ London 97 – ♦Ipswich 24 – ♦Norwich 41.

- **Wentworth,** Wentworth Rd, IP15 5BD, ☎ 452312, ← – TV ☎ P. AE VISA
  closed 27 December-11 January – **M** 12.50/15.50 **t.** and a la carte – **31 rm** 34.65/95.00 **t.**
- **White Lion** (Best Western), Sea Front, IP15 5BJ, ☎ 452720, Telex 94017152, Fax 452986, ← – TV ☎ P – 100. AE VISA
  M (bar lunch)/dinner 14.95/30.00 **st.** – **38 rm** 50.00/90.00 **st.** – SB 80.00/110.00 **st.**
- **Brudenell** (T.H.F.), The Parade, IP15 5BU, ☎ 452071, Fax 454082, ← – TV ☎ P – 50. AE VISA
  M 7.50/11.95 **st.** and a la carte 4.35 – **47 rm** 45.00/70.00 **st.** – SB 84.00/92.00 **st.**
- **Uplands,** Victoria Rd, IP15 5DX, ☎ 452420, – TV ☎ P. AE VISA.
  closed 21 December-3 January – **M** (dinner only) a la carte approx 15.00 **t.** – **20 rm** 25.00/60.00 **t.** – SB (October-May) 70.00/100.00 **st.**
- **Cotmandene,** 6 Park Lane, IP15 5HL, ☎ 453775 – TV. VISA.
  M 7.95 **st.** – **7 rm** 15.00/35.00 **st.**

ALDERLEY EDGE Cheshire 402 403 404 N 24 – pop. 4 272 – ECD : Wednesday – ☎ 0625.

Envir. : Capesthorne Hall★ (18C) *AC*, S : 4½ m.

9 Brook Lane ☎ 585583.

♦ London 187 – Chester 34 – ♦Manchester 14 – ♦Stoke-on-Trent 25.

- **Alderley Edge,** Macclesfield Rd, SK9 7BJ, ☎ 583033, Fax 586343 – TV ☎ P. AE VISA
  M 25.00 **t.** and a la carte 4.95 – 7.95 – **32 rm** 79.00/120.00 – SB (weekends only) 122.00 **st.**
- **De Trafford Arms,** London Rd, SK9 7AA, ☎ 583881, Telex 666741, Fax 586625 – TV ☎ P. AE VISA
  M (dinner only and Sunday lunch)/dinner 11.00 **st.** and a la carte 4.00 – **37 rm** 45.00/60.00 **st.** – SB (weekends only) 99.00/114.00 **st.**
- X **Octobers,** 47 London Rd, SK9 7JT, ☎ 583942, Bistro – VISA
  closed Sunday – **M** (dinner only) 12.50 **t.** and a la carte 4.00.

ROVER London Rd ☎ 582218
VAUXHALL-OPEL 34 Knutsford Rd ☎ 585411
VOLVO 77 London Rd ☎ 583912

When in a hurry use the Michelin Main Road Maps:
970 *Europe,* 980 *Greece,* 984 *Germany,* 985 *Scandinavia-Finland,*
986 *Great Britain and Ireland,* 987 *Germany-Austria-Benelux,* 988 *Italy,*
989 *France,* 990 *Spain-Portugal and* 991 *Yugoslavia.*

ALDRIDGE West Midlands 402 403 404 O 26 – pop. 17 549 – ECD : Thursday – ✉ Walsall – ☎ 0922.

Druids Heath, Stonnall Rd ☎ 55595.

London 130 – Birmingham 12 – Derby 32 – Leicester 40 – Stoke-on-Trent 38.

Fairlawns, 178 Little Aston Rd, WS9 0NU, E : 1 m. on A 454 ☎ 55122, Telex 339873, Fax 743210 – rest TV ☎ P – 70. AE VISA
M *(closed Saturday lunch, Sunday dinner and 24 December-2 January)* 16.50 **st.** and a la carte 4.25 – **36 rm** 39.50/79.50 **st.** – SB (weekends only) 65.00 **st.**

ATS 106 Leighswood Rd ☎ 51968/53970

ALDWINCLE Northants. 402 404 S 26 – pop. 302 – ✉ Kettering – ☎ 08015.

London 84 – Cambridge 40 – Leicester 40 – Northampton 26 – Peterborough 18.

The Maltings without rest., NN14 3EP, ☎ 233, Fax 326, – P. VISA.
3 rm 19.00/38.00 **st.**

ALFRETON Derbs 402 403 404 P 24 – ☎ 0773.

London 134 – Derby 13 – Nottingham 19 – Sheffield 27.

Granada, DE55 1HJ, S : ¾ m. by A 61 at juntion A 38 ☎ 520040, Fax 521087 – rm TV ☎ P – 30. AE VISA.
M (Grill Rest.) a la carte approx. 12.00 **t.** – **61 rm** 35.00/39.00 **t.**

ALFRISTON East Sussex 404 U 31 – pop. 811 – ECD : Wednesday – ✉ Polegate – ☎ 0323.

London 66 – Eastbourne 9 – Lewes 10 – Newhaven 8.

Star (T.H.F.), High St., BN26 5TA, ☎ 870495, Fax 870922 – rm TV ☎ P. AE VISA
M 11.50/13.25 **st.** and a la carte 4.35 – 7.00 – **34 rm** 65.00/90.00 **st.** – SB 94.00/110.00 **st.**

Moonrakers, High St., BN26 5TD, ☎ 870472
closed Sunday, Monday and 13 January-13 February – **M** (dinner only) 18.90 **t.** 3.40.

ALLENDALE Northumb. 401 402 N 19 – ✉ Hexham – ☎ 0434.

Thornley Gate ☎ 091 (Tyneside) 267 5875, W : ¾ m.

London 314 – Carlisle 39 – Newcastle 33.

Bishop Field Country House, NE47 9EJ, W : 1 m. on Whitfield rd ☎ 683248, Fax 683830, , park – TV ☎ P. VISA
closed 1 week Christmas – **M** (lunch residents only)/dinner 15.00 **st.** 3.50 – **11 rm** 32.00/54.00 **st.**

ALLESLEY West Midlands 403 404 P 26 – see Coventry.

ALMONDSBURY Avon 403 404 M 29 – see Bristol.

ALNE North Yorks. – see Easingwold.

ALNMOUTH Northumb. 401 402 P 17 – pop. 605 – ECD : Wednesday – ☎ 0665.

Foxton Hall ☎ 830368, NE : 1 m. – Alnmouth Village, Marine Rd ☎ 830370.

London 314 – Edinburgh 90 – Newcastle-upon-Tyne 37.

Marine House, 1 Marine Rd, NE66 2RW, ☎ 830349, <, – P
8 rm (dinner included) 46.00 **t.** – SB (October-April) 57.00 **st.**

ALNWICK Northumb. 401 402 O 17 – pop. 6 972 – ECD : Wednesday – ☎ 0665.

See : Site★ – Castle★★ (Norman) *AC*.

Envir. : Dunstanburgh Castle★ (14C-15C) (ruins, coastal setting★) *AC*, 1 ¼ m. walk from Craster, no cars, NE : 7 ½ m. – Warkworth castle★ (12C) *AC*, SE : 7 m. – Rothbury (Cragside gardens★ : rhododendrons) *AC*, SW : 12 m.

Swansfield Park ☎ 602632.

The Shambles ☎ 510665.

London 320 – Edinburgh 86 – Newcastle-upon-Tyne 34.

White Swan, Bondgate Within, NE66 1TD, ☎ 602109, Fax 510400 – rm TV ☎ P – 60. AE VISA
M 11.00/15.00 **t.** – **41 rm** 60.00/85.00 **t.** – SB 78.00/95.00 **st.**

Hotspur, Bondgate Without, NE66 1PR, ☎ 510101, Fax 605033 – TV ☎ P. AE VISA
M (bar lunch)/dinner 10.75 **t.** and a la carte 2.65 – **26 rm** 25.00/55.00 **t.** – SB 34.00/36.00 **st.**

Bondgate House, 20 Bondgate Without, NE66 1PN, ☎ 602025, Fax 602554 – TV.
M (by arrangement) 7.50 **st.** 2.80 – **8 rm** 28.00/32.00 **st.**

FORD Lagny St. ☎ 602294
TOYOTA Pottergate ☎ 604909
VAUXHALL Station Rd ☎ 604737

ALPORT Derbs. – see Bakewell.

ALSAGER Cheshire 402 403 404 N 24 – pop. 12 944 – ✉ Stoke-on-Trent – ☎ 093 63 (4 and 5 fig.) or 0270 (Crewe) (6 fig.).

◆ London 180 – Chester 36 – ◆ Liverpool 49 – ◆ Manchester 32 – ◆ Stoke-on-Trent 11.

Manor House, Audley Rd, ST7 2QQ, SE : ½ m. ☎ 878013, Fax 882483 – TV ☎ P
27 rm.

FORD 52 Sandbach Rd South ☎ 873241 ROVER Lawton Rd ☎ 882146

ALSTON Cumbria 401 402 M 19 – pop. 1 968 – ECD : Tuesday – ☎ 0434.

Alston Moor, The Hermitage ☎ 81675, SE : 2 m. on B 6277.

Railway Station ☎ 381696.

◆ London 309 – ◆Carlisle 28 – ◆Newcastle-upon-Tyne 45.

Lovelady Shield Country House, Nenthead Rd, CA9 3LF, E : 2 ½ m. on A 689 ☎ 381203, Fax 381515, ≤, – rest TV ☎ P. VISA
closed 5 January-27 February – **M** (bar lunch)/dinner 24.00 **t.** – **12 rm** 29.50/82.00 **t.** – SB (November-May) (except Bank Holidays) 75.00/100.00 **st.**

ALSTON CROSS Devon – see Newton Ferrers.

ALTON Hants. 404 R 30 – pop. 14 163 – ECD : Wednesday – ☎ 0420.

Old Odiham Rd ☎ 82042, N : 2 m by A 32.

◆ London 53 – Reading 24 – ◆Southampton 29 – Winchester 18.

Swan (T.H.F.), High St., GU34 1AT, ☎ 83777, Telex 859916, Fax 87975 – rm TV ☎ P – 45. VISA
M 10.20/16.00 **st.** and a la carte 4.35 – 7.00 – **38 rm** 60.00/75.00 **st.** – SB (weekends only) 66.00/80.00 **st.**

Alton House, Normandy St., GU34 1DW, ☎ 80033, Fax 89222, heated, – TV ☎ P – 180. VISA.
M 8.50/11.25 **t.** and a la carte – **38 rm** 45.00/75.00 **t.** – SB (weekends only) 66.50/78.50 **st.**

Grange, London Rd, GU34 4EG, NE : 1 m. on A 339 ☎ 86565, Fax 541346, – TV ☎ P. VISA.
closed Christmas-New Year – **M** (bar lunch Saturday) 8.95/9.95 **t.** and a la carte 3.95 – **33 rm** 45.00/120.00 **t.**, **1 suite.**

FORD Ackender Rd ☎ 83993 ROVER, VAUXHALL Butts Rd ☎ 84141
PEUGEOT-TALBOT Four Marks ☎ 62354

ALTRINCHAM Greater Manchester 402 403 404 N 23 – pop. 39 528 – ECD : Wednesday – ☎ 061 Manchester.

Stockport Rd, Timperley ☎ 928 0761, E : 1 m. – Dunham Forest, Oldfield Lane ☎ 928 2605, SW : 1 m. – Ringway, Hale Mount, Hale Barns ☎ 904 9609 – Hale, Rappax Rd ☎ 980 4225.

Stamford New Rd. ☎ 941 7337.

◆ London 191 – Chester 30 – ◆Liverpool 30 – ◆Manchester 8.

Cresta Court (Best Western), Church St., WA14 4DP, on A 56 ☎ 927 7272, Telex 667242, Fax 926 9194 – TV ☎ P – 300. VISA
M a la carte 6.85/11.60 **st.** – **139 rm** 55.00/74.00 **st.**

George and Dragon, 22 Manchester Rd, WA14 4PH, on A 56 ☎ 928 9933, Fax 929 8060 – rm TV ☎ P. VISA
M (bar lunch)/dinner 17.00 **st.** and a la carte 4.25 – **47 rm** 52.00/65.00 **st.** – SB (weekends only) 56.00/84.00 **st.**

Pelican Inn (De Vere), Manchester Rd, West Timperley, WA14 5NH, N : 2 m. on A 56 ☎ 962 7414, Telex 668014 – TV ☎ P
50 rm.

Bollin without rest., 58 Manchester Rd, WA14 4PJ, on A 56 ☎ 928 2390 – TV P
10 rm 21.70/32.00 **st.**

at Hale SE : 1 m. on B 5163 – ✉ Altrincham – ☎ 061 Manchester :

Ashley (De Vere), Ashley Rd, WA15 9SF, ☎ 928 3794, Group Telex 669406, Fax 926 9046 – rm TV ☎ – 250. VISA
M (closed Saturday lunch) 11.00/18.00 **st.** and a la carte – **48 rm** 57.00/68.00 **st.** – SB 60.00/70.00 **st.**

at Halebarns SE : 3 m. on A 538 – ✉ Altrincham – ☎ 061 Manchester :

Four Seasons, Manchester Airport, Hale Rd, WA15 8XW, ☎ 904 0301, Telex 665492, Fax 980 1787 – TV ☎ P – 160. VISA
M 15.95/26.95 **t.** and a la carte 3.95 – 8.95 – **94 rm** 85.50/155.50 **st.**

at Bowdon SW : 1 m. – ✉ Altrincham – ☎ 061 Manchester :

Bowdon, Langham Rd, WA14 2HT, ☎ 928 7121, Telex 668208, Fax 927 7560 – TV ☎ P – 140. AE VISA
M 12.75 **t.** and a la carte 3.00 – **82 rm** 60.00/75.00 **t.** – SB (weekends only) 66.00 **st.**

Bowdon Croft, Green Walk, WA14 2SN, ☎ 928 1718, Fax 928 1718, ≤, « Tastefully furnished 19C house », – TV ☎ P. AE VISA
M (booking essential) 16.50 (lunch) and a la carte 3.50 – **8 rm** 49.00/80.00.

ALFA-ROMEO Money Ash Rd, Hale Bridge ☎ 928 5980
RENAULT, HYUNDAI Manchester Rd ☎ 973 3021
ROVER Victoria Rd ☎ 928 7124
SAAB Bancroft Rd, Hale ☎ 980 8004
TOYOTA Mobberley Rd, Ashley ☎ 928 3112
VAUXHALL-OPEL 276-280 Stockport Rd, Timperley ☎ 980 3212
VOLVO Manchester Rd ☎ 928 2384

ATS 74 Oakfield Rd ☎ 928 7024

ALVELEY Shropshire – see Bridgnorth.

ALVESTON Avon 403 404 M 29 – pop. 3 154 – ECD : Wednesday – ✉ Bristol – ☎ 0454 Thornbury.

London 127 – Bristol 11 – Gloucester 23 – Swindon 42.

Alveston House, BS12 2LJ, on A 38 ☎ 415050, Telex 449212, Fax 415425, – TV ☎ P – 80. AE VISA
M 15.25 **st.** and a la carte 4.75 – **30 rm** 67.50/85.50 **st.** – SB (weekends only) 81.00/89.00 **st.**

Post House (T.H.F.), Thornbury Rd, BS12 2LL, on A 38 ☎ 412521, Telex 444753, Fax 413920, heated, – rm TV ☎ P – 80. AE VISA
M a la carte approx. 20.75 **st.** 4.35 – 7.50 – **75 rm** 65.00/85.00 **st.** – SB (weekends only) 76.00 **st.**

Die Preise — Einzelheiten über die in diesem Führer angegebenen Preise finden Sie in der Einleitung.

ALWALTON Cambs. 402 404 T 26 – see Peterborough.

AMBERLEY West Sussex 404 S 31 – pop. 516 – ✉ Arundel – ☎ 0798 Bury.

London 56 – Brighton 24 – Portsmouth 31.

Amberley Castle, BN18 9ND, SW : ½ m. on B 2139 ☎ 831992, Fax 831998, « 14C castle of 12C origin », – TV ☎ P. AE VISA
M 17.50/23.50 **t.** and a la carte – **12 rm** 100.00/175.00 **t.** – SB 175.00 **st.**

AMBLESIDE Cumbria 402 L 20 – pop. 2 689 – ECD : Thursday – ☎ 05394.

Envir. : Tarn Hows★★, (lake) SW : 6 m. by A 593 AY – Langdale Valley★★, W : 7 m. by B 5343 AY – Brantwood★, SW : 6½ m. – Helvellyn★, NW : 8 m.

Old Courthouse, Church St. ☎ 32582 (summer only).

London 278 – Carlisle 47 – Kendal 14.

Plan on next page

Kirkstone Foot Country House, Kirkstone Pass Rd, LA22 9EH, NE : ¼ m. ☎ 32232, – rest TV ☎ P. AE VISA AZ **c**
closed 3 January-1 February – **M** (dinner only) 17.25 **t.** 3.75 – **15 rm** (dinner included) 44.50/95.00 **t.** – SB 70.00/78.00 **st.**

Rothay Garth, Rothay Rd, LA22 0EE, ☎ 32217, Fax 34400, – TV ☎ P. AE VISA AZ **e**
M 10.50/15.50 **t.** 4.00 – **15 rm** 39.00/78.00 **t.**, **1 suite** 98.00 **t.** – SB (except September) 64.00/89.00 **st.**

Elder Grove, Lake Rd, LA22 0DB, ☎ 32504 – rest TV P. VISA AZ **a**
Mid February-mid November – **M** 12.50 **t.** 3.75 – **12 rm** 23.50/47.00 **t.** – SB 67.00/71.50 **st.**

Crow How, Rydal Rd, LA22 9PN, NW : ½ m. on A 591 ☎ 32193, ≤, – TV P
closed 10 December-25 January – **M** 10.00 **st.** 3.25 – **9 rm** 21.00/55.00 **st.** – SB (winter only) (weekends only) 47.50/61.00 **st.** BY **x**

Chapel House, Kirkstone Rd, LA22 9DZ, ☎ 33143 – rest. AZ **n**
closed January-February and restricted service November-December – **M** 12.50 **t.** – **10 rm** (dinner included) 24.00/63.00 **t.** – SB 48.00/59.50 **st.**

at Rothay Bridge S : ½ m. on A 593 – ✉ ☎ 05394 Ambleside :

Rothay Manor, LA22 0EH, ☎ 33605, Fax 33607, ≤, « Elegant Regency interior », – rest TV ☎ P. AE VISA BY **r**
closed 3 January-11 February – **M** (buffet lunch Monday to Saturday)/dinner 22.50 **t.** 3.50 – **15 rm** 63.00/100.00 **t.**, **3 suites** 120.00/130.00 **t.** – SB (November-Easter except Christmas and New Year) (weekdays only) 114.00/130.00 **st.**

AMBLESIDE
GRASMERE

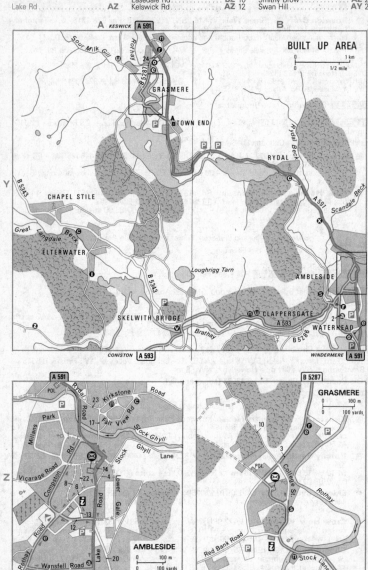

Borrans Rd. .... BY 2
Broadgate .... BZ 3
Cheapside .... AZ 4
Church St. .... AZ 6
Compston St .... AZ 8
Easedale Rd .... BZ 10
Kelswick Rd .... AZ 12
King St .... AZ 1
Market Pl .... AZ 1
North Rd .... AZ 1
Old Lake Rd. .... AZ 2
St. Mary's Lane .... AZ 2
Smithy Brow .... AZ 2
Swan Hill .... AY 2
Lake Rd .... AZ

BUILT UP AREA

0 1 km
0 1/2 mile

A KESWICK A 591 B
Sour Milk Gill
Rothay
24
B 5287
GRASMERE
A TOWN END
RYDAL
Rydal Beck
Y
B 5343
CHAPEL STILE
A 591
Scandale Beck
Great Langdale Beck
ELTERWATER
Loughrigg Tarn
AMBLESIDE
B 5343
SKELWITH BRIDGE
CLAPPERSGATE
A 593
2
WATERHEAD
Brathay
B 5286
CONISTON A 593
WINDERMERE A 591

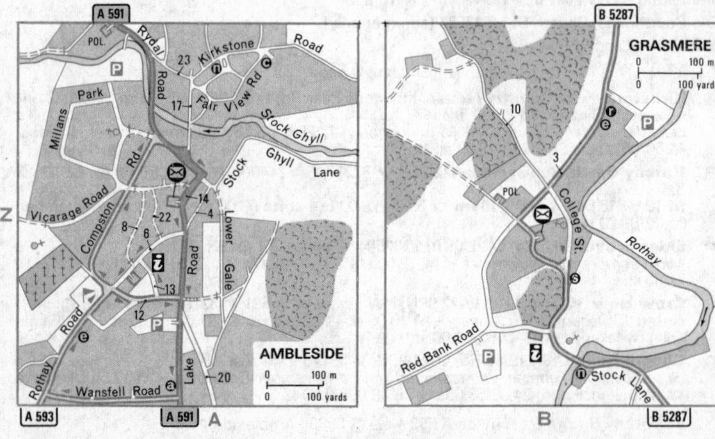

Town plans: *roads most used by traffic and those on which guide listed hotels and restaurants stand are fully drawn; the beginning only of lesser roads is indicated.*

Borrans Park, Borrans Rd, LA22 0EN, ✆ 33454, – TV ☎ ♿ P. BY a
closed 20 to 28 December – **M** (dinner only) 13.00 **st.** 4.00 – **13 rm** 36.00/62.00 **st.** – SB (4 November-12 April except Christmas and New Year) 70.00/80.00 **st.**

Riverside, Under Loughrigg, LA22 9LJ, ✆ 32395, – rest TV ☎ P. VISA
mid February-mid November – **M** (bar lunch)/dinner 22.00 **t.** and a la carte 3.70 – **10 rm** 50.00/76.00 **t.** – SB 68.00/76.00 **st.** BY s

at Waterhead S : 1 m. on A 591 – ✉ 05394 Ambleside :

Wateredge, Borrans Rd, LA22 0EP, ✆ 32332, Fax 32332, ≤, « Part 17C Fishermans cottages, lakeside setting », – TV ☎ P. AE VISA. BY o
closed mid December-early February – **M** (bar lunch)/dinner 21.90 **t.** 3.90 – **23 rm** (dinner included) 59.50/140.00 **t.**

Regent, Borrans Rd, LA22 0ES, ✆ 32254, – rest TV ☎ P. VISA BY e
M 8.00/20.00 **t.** 3.50 – **21 rm** 42.00/90.00 **t.** – SB (except September and October) 79.00/91.00 **st.**

Low Wood, LA23 1LP, SE : ½ m. on A 591 ✆ 33338, Fax 34072, ≤, , , squash – rest TV ☎ P – 350
99 rm.

at Clappersgate W : 1 m. on A 593 – ✉ 05394 Ambleside :

Nanny Brow Country House, LA22 9NF, ✆ 32036, Fax 32036 (ext : 231), ≤, « Landscaped gardens », – rm TV ☎ P. AE VISA BY u
M 12.50/25.00 **st.** 4.25 – **16 rm** 60.00/85.00 **st.**, **3 suites** 65.00/85.00 **st.** – SB (weekends only) (November-May) 89.00/141.00 **st.**

Grey Friar Lodge, LA22 9NE, ✆ 33158, ≤, – TV. BY n
March-October – **M** (dinner only) 13.75 **st.** 2.90 – **8 rm** (dinner included) 30.25/86.90.

at Skelwith Bridge W : 2 ½ m. on A 593 – ✉ 05394 Ambleside :

Skelwith Bridge, LA22 9NJ, ✆ 32115, Fax 34254, ≤, – rest TV P. VISA
closed January and February – **M** (bar lunch Monday to Saturday)/dinner 15.95 **t.** 4.10 – **24 rm** 35.00/70.00 **t.** – SB (except September and October) 60.00/95.00 **st.** AY v

at Little Langdale W : 4 ½ m. by A 593 – ✉ 096 67 Langdale :

Three Shires Inn, LA22 9NZ, ✆ 215, ≤, – rest P. AY z
11 rm.

at Elterwater W : 4 ½ m. by A 593 off B 5343 – ✉ Ambleside – 096 67 Langdale :

Langdale H & Country Club, Great Langdale, LA22 9JD, NW : 1 ¼ m. on B 5343 ✆ 302, Fax 694, , , park, squash – rest TV ☎ P – 100. AY c
41 rm, 12 suites.

Eltermere Country House, LA22 9HY, ✆ 207, ≤, – rest TV P. AY i
closed 20 to 27 December – **M** (dinner only) 14.95 **st.** 3.70 – **15 rm** 28.00/56.00 **st.**

at Rydal NW : 1 ½ m. on A 591 – ✉ 05394 Ambleside :

Rydal Lodge, LA22 9LR, ✆ 33208, – rest P. VISA BY c
closed January – **M** 11.00 **t.** 2.50 – **8 rm** 20.00/50.00 **t.**

AMERSHAM (Old Town) Bucks. 404 S 28 – pop. 21 326 – ECD : Thursday – 0494.
♦London 29 – Aylesbury 16 – ♦Oxford 33.

Crown (T.H.F.), High St., HP7 0DH, ✆ 721541, Fax 431383, – TV ☎ P. AE VISA
M 10.50/16.95 **st.** and a la carte 4.50 – 7.00 – **22 rm** 74.00/84.00 **st.**, **1 suite** 140.00 **st.** – SB (weekends only) 80.00/90.00 **st.**

King's Arms, High St., HP7 0DJ, ✆ 726333 – AE VISA
closed Sunday dinner and Monday – **M** 11.50 **t.** (lunch) and a la carte 19.50/26.50 **t.** 3.50.

Romna, 20-22 The Broadway, HP7 0HP, ✆ 433732, Indian rest. – AE VISA
M (buffet lunch Sunday) 12.00/18.00 **t.** and a la carte.

at Penn Street SW : 2 m. by A 404 – ✉ 0494 Amersham :

Hit or Miss Inn, HP7 0PX, ✆ 713109 – P. AE VISA
closed Saturday lunch, Sunday dinner and Monday – **M** 11.95/18.50 **t.** and a la carte 3.80.

DAIMLER-JAGUAR London Rd ✆ 28013
JAGUAR London Rd ✆ 725911
PEUGEOT-TALBOT 4-8 White Lion Rd ✆ 024 04 (Little Chalfont) 4666
RENAULT The Broadway ✆ 729411

AMESBURY Wilts. 403 404 O 30 – 0980 Stonehenge

Travelodge without rest., SP4 7AS, N : ¼ m. at junction of A 303 and A 345, ✆ 624966 Reservations (Toll free) 0800 850950 TV ♿ P. AE VISA.
32 rm 24.00/29.50 **t.**

AMPFIELD Hants. 403 404 P 30 – pop. 1 675 – ECD : Wednesday – ✉ Romsey – ☎ 0794 Braishfield.

Ampfield Par Three, Winchester Rd ☎ 68480.

◆London 79 – Bournemouth 31 – Salisbury 19 – ◆Southampton 11 – Winchester 7.

Potters Heron (Lansbury), Winchester Rd, SO51 9ZF, on A 31 ☎ 0703 (Southampton) 266611, Telex 47459, Fax 251359, – rm – 120. VISA.
M 14.95 **t.** (dinner) and a la carte – **60 rm** 72.00/140.00 **t.** – SB (weekends only) 76.00 **st.**

Keats, Winchester Rd, SO51 9BQ, on A 31 ☎ 68252, Italian rest. – . VISA
closed Sunday and Monday – **M** 8.90 **t.** (lunch) and a la carte 15.55/20.35 **t.** 4.75.

ANDOVER Hants. 403 404 P 30 – pop. 30 632 – ECD : Wednesday – ☎ 0264.

51 Winchester Rd ☎ 23980, S : 1 m. on A 3057.

Town Mill car park, Bridge St. ☎ 24320.

◆London 74 – Bath 53 – Salisbury 17 – Winchester 11.

Danebury (Lansbury), High St., SP10 1NX, ☎ 323332, Telex 47587, Fax 334021 – – 60. VISA.
M a la carte 10.15/17.75 **t.** 3.95 – **24 rm** 59.00/71.00 **t.** – SB (weekends only) 60.00 **st.**

Ashley Court, Micheldever Rd, via London Rd, SP11 6LA, ☎ 57344, Fax 56755, – rm – 150. VISA
M 10.00/15.00 **st.** and a la carte 3.50 – 5.00 – **35 rm** 64.00/80.00 **st.** – SB (weekends only) 78.00/84.00 **st.**

White Hart (T.H.F.), Bridge St., SP10 1BH, ☎ 52266 – – 50
20 rm.

at Barton Stacey SE : 5 ½ m. by A 303 – ✉ ☎ 0264 Andover :

Travelodge without rest., SO21 3NP, on A 303 ☎ 72260, Reservations (Toll free) 0800 850950 – . VISA.
20 rm 24.00/29.50 **t.**

AUDI-VW Colebrook Way, Weyhill Rd ☎ 55200
FORD West St. ☎ 332144
MERCEDES-BENZ, FIAT Salisbury Rd ☎ 61166
ROVER 278 Weyhill Rd ☎ 23781
VAUXHALL Newbury Rd ☎ 24233
ATS 51a New St. ☎ 23606/7

ANGMERING West Sussex 404 S 31 – see Worthing.

ANSTY Warw. – see Coventry (West Midlands).

APPLEBY-IN-WESTMORELAND Cumbria 402 M 20 – pop. 2 344 – ECD : Thursday – ☎ 07683.

Appleby ☎ 51432, SE : 2 m. by A 66.

Moot Hall, Boroughgate ☎ 51177.

◆London 285 – ◆Carlisle 33 – Kendal 24 – ◆Middlesbrough 58.

Tufton Arms, Market Square, CA16 6XA, ☎ 51593, Fax 52761, – . VISA
M 12.50 **t.** (dinner) and a la carte 3.40 – **17 rm** 35.00/75.00 **t.**, **2 suites** 96.00/100.00 **t.** – SB (except Bank Holidays) 61.00/111.00 **st.**

Appleby Manor (Best Western), Roman Rd, CA16 6JD, E : 1 m. by B 6542 via Station Rd ☎ 51571, Fax 52888, ←, – rest . VISA.
M 14.50 **st.** and a la carte 4.45 – **30 rm** 53.00/84.00 **st.** – SB 84.00/98.00 **st.**

Royal Oak Inn, Bongate, CA16 6UN, SE : ½ m. on B 6542 ☎ 51463 –
7 rm.

FORD The Sands ☎ 51133

ARBERTH = Narberth.

ARDSLEY South Yorks. – see Barnsley.

ARMITAGE Staffs. 402 403 404 O 25 – ✉ Rugeley – ☎ 0543.

◆London 135 – ◆Birmingham 25 – Derby 26 – ◆Stoke-on-Trent 25.

Old Farmhouse, Armitage Rd, WS15 4AT, on A 513 ☎ 490353 – . VISA
closed Saturday lunch, Sunday dinner, Monday, 13 to 26 August and 26 to 31 December – **M** 19.00/23.00 **t.** and a la carte 4.00.

ARNCLIFFE North Yorks. 402 N 21 – pop. 67 – ✉ Skipton – ☎ 075 677.

◆London 232 – Kendal 41 – ◆Leeds 41 – Preston 50 – York 52.

Amerdale House, BD23 5QE, ☎ 250, ←, – rest . VISA.
Mid March-mid November – **M** (dinner only) 17.00 **st.** 3.50 – **11 rm** (dinner included) 57.00/98.00 **t.**

The Guide changes,
so renew your Guide every year.

ARUNDEL West Sussex 404 S 31 – pop. 2 595 – ECD : Wednesday – ☏ 0903.

See : Castle★ (keep 12C, ≤★ 119 steps, State apartments★) *AC* – St. Nicholas' Church (chancel or Fitzalan chapel★ 14C).

Envir. : Bignor (Roman Villa : mosaics★★ *AC*) NW : 7 m.

🅸 61 High St. ℘ 882268.

◆London 58 – ◆Brighton 21 – ◆Southampton 41 – Worthing 9.

- **Norfolk Arms,** 22 High St., BN18 9AD, ℘ 882101, Telex 878436, Fax 884275 – ⇔ rm TV ☎ P. AE VISA
  M 9.85 **t.** (lunch) and a la carte 5.45 – **34 rm** 49.00/82.50 **t.** – SB 90.00/100.00 **st.**
- **Arundel Resort,** Chichester Rd, BN18 0AD, W : 1 m. on A 27 ℘ 882677, Fax 884154 – TV ☎ P. AE VISA
  M 8.75/12.00 **st.** and dinner a la carte – 6.50 – **16 rm** 44.00/54.00 **t.** – SB (weekends only) 76.00 **st.**
- **Swan,** 29 High St., BN18 9AG, ℘ 882314 – ⇔ rest TV ☎. AE VISA.
  M (bar lunch Monday to Saturday)/dinner 10.00 **t.** and a la carte 3.50 – **13 rm** 47.00/60.00 **t.**
- **Portreeves Acre** without rest., The Causeway, BN18 9JJ, ℘ 883277, – TV P
  3 rm 30.00/37.00 **st.**

at Burpham NE : 3 m. by A 27 – ✉ ☏ 0903 Arundel :

- **Burpham Country** ⑤, Old Down, BN18 9RJ, ℘ 882160, ≤, – ⇔ rest TV P. VISA.
  M (dinner only) 11.50 **t.** 3.50 – **10 rm** 36.00/64.00 **t.** – SB 69.00/79.00 **st.**

at Walberton W : 3 m. by A 27 on B 2132 – ✉ Arundel – ☏ 0243 Yapton :

- **Avisford Park,** Yapton Lane, BN18 0LS, ℘ 551215, Telex 86137, Fax 552485, ≤, heated, , 9, , park, , squash – TV ☎ P – 200. AE VISA.
  M *(closed Saturday lunch)* (buffet lunch Monday to Friday)/dinner 25.00 **st.** and a la carte – **97 rm** 70.00/120.00 **st.**, **3 suites** 128.00/192.00 **st.** – SB (weekends only) 114.00/120.00 **st.**

ASCOT Berks. 404 R 29 – pop. 17 930 (inc Sunningdale) – ECD : Wednesday – ☏ 0990 (during 1990 will change to 0344).

18 Royal Ascot, Winkfield Rd ℘ 25175 – 18, 18, 18 Wentworth, Virginia Water ℘ 099 04 (Wentworth) 2201 – 18, 18 Sunningdale ℘ 21681 – 9 Lavender Park, Swinley Rd ℘ 0344 (Bracknell) 884074, SW : 3½ m.

◆London 36 – Reading 15.

- **Royal Berkshire** (Hilton) ⑤, London Rd, Sunninghill, SL5 0PP, E : 2 m. on A 329 ℘ 23322, Telex 847280, Fax 27100, « Queen Anne mansion in garden », , , park, , squash – TV ☎ P – 75. AE VISA
  M (see **Stateroom rest.** below) – 10.50 – **79 rm** 85.00/175.00 **t.**, **3 suites** 250.00/350.00 **t.** – SB (weekends only) 150.00 **st.**
- **Berystede** (T.H.F.), Bagshot Rd, Sunninghill, SL5 9JH, S : 1¼ m. on A 330 ℘ 23311, Telex 847707, Fax 872301, heated, – ⇔ rm TV ☎ P – 120. AE VISA
  M 16.50/19.50 **st.** and a la carte 4.95 – 7.60 – **90 rm** 84.00/105.00 **st.**, **1 suite** 160.00/185.00 **st.** – SB (weekends only) 94.00/110.00 **st.**
- Royal Foresters, London Rd, SL5 8DR, W : 1 ½ m. on A 329 ℘ 0344 (Winkfield Row) 884747, Fax 884115 – TV ☎ P
  34 rm.
- XXX **Stateroom** (at Royal Berkshire H.), London Rd, Sunninghill, SL5 0PP, E : 2 m. on A 329 ℘ 23322, Telex 847280, Fax 27100 – P. AE VISA
  M 21.50/28.50 **t.** and a la carte 7.50.
- XXX Ascot Guinea, Mill Ride Estate, Mill Ride, North Ascot, SL5 8LT, ℘ 0344 (Bracknell) 886737 – P.
- XX Hyns Beijing, 4 Brockenhurst Rd, South Ascot, SL5 9DL, S : ½ m. on A 330 ℘ 872583, Chinese rest. – P.

CITROEN Lyndhurst Rd, South Ascot ℘ 22257 ROVER Ascot Motor Works ℘ 20324

ASHBOURNE Derbs. 402 403 404 O 24 – pop. 5 909 – ☏ 0335.

9 Clifton ℘ 42078, SW : 2 m. on A 515.

🅸 13 The Market Pl. ℘ 43666.

◆London 146 – Derby 14 – ◆Manchester 48 – ◆Nottingham 33 – ◆Sheffield 44.

Callow Hall , Mappleton Rd, DE6 2AA, W : ¾ m. (via Union St.) 43403, Fax 43624, , , park – . .
closed 2 weeks February – **M** *(closed Sunday dinner to non-residents)* (dinner only and lunch Sunday and Tuesday) 11.00/21.50 **t.** and a la carte 4.50 – **12 rm** 60.00/110.00 **t.** – SB 110.00/140.00 **st.**

Ashbourne Lodge (Best Western), Derby Rd, DE6 1XH, SE : 1 m. on A 52 46666, Telex 378560, Fax 46549 – rm – 170. .
M (carving lunch)/dinner 15.00 **st.** and a la carte 3.75 – **49 rm** 70.00/95.00 **st.**, **2 suites** 120.00/130.00 **st.** – SB 68.00/86.00 **st.**

ATS Blenheim Rd 44644

ASHBURTON Devon 403 I 32 The West Country G. – pop. 3 610 – ECD : Wednesday – 0364.

London 220 – Exeter 20 – Plymouth 23.

Holne Chase , TQ13 7NS, NW : 3 m. on Two Bridges rd 036 43 (Poundsgate) 471, Fax 453, , « Country house atmosphere », , , park – rest .
M 16.00/25.00 **t.** 3.75 – **14 rm** 60.00/120.00 **t.** – SB 60.00/100.00 **st.**

Dartmoor Lodge, Peartree Cross, TQ13 7JW, SW : ½ m. 52232 – .
M (bar lunch)/dinner a la carte 10.40/14.70 **st.** – 4.50 – **32 rm** 26.50/45.00 **st.**

Gages Mill, Buckfastleigh Rd, TQ13 7JW, SW : 1 m. on old A 38 52391, – rest .
Mid March-October – **M** (dinner only) 9.00 **st.** 3.80 – **8 rm** -/39.00 **st.**

MITSUBISHI 6 East St. 52215

Jährlich eine neue Ausgabe
Aktuellste Informationen,
jährlich für Sie!

ASHBY DE LA ZOUCH Leics. 402 403 404 P 25 – pop. 9 987 – ECD : Wednesday – 0530.

Willesley Park, Measham Rd 411532.

North St. 411767.

London 119 – Birmingham 29 – Leicester 18 – Nottingham 22.

Royal Osprey, Station Rd, LE6 5GP, 412833, Telex 341629, Fax 416304, – rm – 100.
M *(closed Saturday lunch)* a la carte 8.15/13.90 **st.** – **31 rm** 52.50/62.50 **st.** – SB (weekends only) 45.15/50.90 **st.**

Fallen Knight, Kilwardby St., LE6 5FQ, 412230, Fax 417596 – . .
M 14.00 **t.** and a la carte 4.00 – 7.50 – **16 rm** 55.00/100.00 **t.**

Mews, Mill Lane (off Market St.), LE6, 416683.
closed Sunday and Bank Holidays – **M** 5.75/11.95 **t.** and dinner a la carte 4.45.

ATS Kilwardby St. 412791

ASHFORD Kent 404 W 30 – pop. 45 198 – ECD : Wednesday – 0233.

Envir. : Hothfield (St. Margaret's Church : memorial tomb★ 17C) NW : 3 m. – Lenham (St. Mary's Church : woodwork★) NW : 9 ½ m.

Sandyhurst Lane 620180, NW : 1 ½ m. by A 20.

Lower High St. 37311 ext 316.

London 56 – Canterbury 14 – Dover 24 – Hastings 30 – Maidstone 19.

Eastwell Manor (Q.M.H.) , Eastwell Park, Boughton Lees, TN25 4HR, N : 3 m. by A 28 on A 251 635751, Telex 966281, Fax 635530, , « Reconstructed period mansion in formal gardens », park, – – 70.
M 25.00/35.00 **t.** and a la carte 7.50 – **20 rm** 85.00/195.00 **t.**, **3 suites** 225.00 **t.** – SB 87.50 **st.**

Ashford International, Simone Weil Av., TN24 8UX, 611444, Fax 627708, , , – rm rest – 400.
closed 25 to 27 December – **M** 15.00 **st.** and a la carte – **197 rm** 89.00/105.00 **st.**, **2 suites** 115.00/275.00 **st.** – SB (weekends only) 104.00/124.00 **st.**

Post House (T.H.F.), Canterbury Rd, TN24 8QQ, 625790, Telex 966685, Fax 643176, – rm – 120. .
M 10.25/16.95 **st.** and a la carte 4.35 – 7.50 – **60 rm** 65.00/75.00 **st.** – SB (weekends only) 70.00/90.00 **st.**

Master Spearpoint (Best Western), Canterbury Rd, Kennington, TN24 9QR, NE : 2 m. on A 28 636863, Telex 965978, Fax 610119, – – 50
36 rm.

NISSAN Maidstone Rd 634177
ROVER Concept House, Hewood Industrial Estate 620334
VOLVO Chart Rd 635661
ATS Hythe Rd 622450/624891

ASHFORD Surrey 404 S 29 – ECD : Wednesday – ☎ 078 42.

♦London 21 – Reading 27.

XX **Terrazza,** 45 Church Rd, TW15 2TY, ☎ 244887, Italian rest. – ▤. AE ⓓ VISA
closed Saturday lunch, Sunday and Bank Holidays – **M** 18.50 **st.** and a la carte 22.30/32.90 **st.**

CITROEN 594 London Rd ☎ 52125
VAUXHALL Staines Rd ☎ 41901
VW-AUDI 554 London Rd ☎ 50051

ASHINGTON West Sussex 404 S 31 – pop. 1 728 – ECD : Wednesday – ✉ Pulborough – ☎ 0903.

♦London 50 – ♦Brighton 20 – Worthing 9.

Mill House ⑤, Mill Lane, RH20 3BZ, ☎ 892426, Fax 892855, ⛲ – TV ☎ P. AE ⓓ VISA
M 9.95/12.50 **t.** and a la carte 3.15 – **10 rm** ☐ 38.50/80.00 **t.** – SB (except Christmas) (weekends only) 85.00 **st.**

ATS Lintonville Terr. ☎ 817013/817038

ASHTON-UNDER-LYNE Greater Manchester 402 403 404 N 23 – pop. 43 605 – ECD : Tuesday – ☎ 061 Manchester.

18 Gorsey Way, Hurst ☎ 330 1537 – 9 Yew Tree Lane, Dunkinfield ☎ 338 2340.

♦London 209 – ♦Leeds 40 – ♦Manchester 7 – ♦Sheffield 34.

York House, York Pl., off Richmond St., OL6 7TT, ☎ 330 5899, Fax 343 1613 – TV ☎ P. AE ⓓ VISA
M *(closed Sunday dinner)* 8.50/12.00 **st.** and a la carte 3.50 – **34 rm** ☐ 45.00/62.00 **st.** – SB (weekends only) 70.00 **st.**

XX **Woodlands,** 33 Shepley Rd, Audenshaw, M34 5DJ, S : 2 m. by A 635, Audenshaw Rd and Guide Lane (A 6017) on B 6169 ☎ 336 4241 – P. VISA
closed Saturday lunch, Sunday, Monday, 1 week Easter, 2 weeks August and first week January – **M** 11.95/13.95 **t.** and a la carte.

FORD Manchester Rd ☎ 330 0121
LADA Dukinfield Rd ☎ 368 3632
PEUGEOT-TALBOT Oldham Rd ☎ 343 1333
VAUXHALL 185 Katherine St. ☎ 330 2222

ASKRIGG North Yorks. 402 N 21 – pop. 404 – ✉ Leyburn – ☎ 0969 Wensleydale.

♦London 251 – Kendal 32 – ♦Leeds 70 – York 63.

King's Arms, Market Sq., DL8 3HQ, ☎ 50258, Fax 50635 – TV ☎. VISA. ✱
M *(closed Sunday dinner)* (bar lunch Monday to Saturday)/dinner 20.00 **t.** and a la carte 2.95 – **10 rm** ☐ 30.00/60.00 **t.** – SB 75.00/80.00 **st.**

Winville, Main St., DL8 3HG, ☎ 50515, ⛲ – ⇸ rest TV P. AE ⓓ VISA
M 7.50/14.75 **st.** 2.95 – **6 rm** ☐ 31.00/46.00 **st.** – SB 66.00/72.00 **st.**

ASPLEY GUISE Beds. 404 S 27 – pop. 2 314 – ✉ Woburn – ☎ 0908 Milton Keynes.

18 Woburn Sands, West Hill ☎ 582264, W : 2 m. by M 1 (junction 13).

♦London 52 – Bedford 13 – Luton 16 – ♦Northampton 22.

Moore Place, The Square, MK17 8DW, ☎ 282000, Fax 281888, ⛲ – TV ☎ P – 50. AE ⓓ VISA. ✱
closed 25 to 29 December – **M** *(closed Saturday lunch)* 15.00/19.50 **t.** and a la carte – **53 rm** ☐ 75.00/90.00 **t.**, **1 suite** 140.00 **t.** – SB (weekends only) 85.00 **t.**

ASTON South Yorks. 402 403 404 Q 23 – pop. 13 864 – ✉ ☎ 0742 Sheffield.

♦London 161 – Lincoln 39 – ♦Sheffield 8.

Aston Hall ⑤, Worksop Rd, S31 0EE, ☎ 872309, Fax 873228, ⛲ – TV ☎ P – 200. VISA. ✱
closed 25 December and 1 January – **M** *(closed Saturday lunch and Sunday dinner)* 9.95/17.95 **st.** and a la carte 3.50 – **21 rm** ☐ 61.00/125.00 **st.**

ASTON CLINTON Bucks. 404 R 28 – pop. 3 671 – ECD : Wednesday – ✉ ☎ 0296 Aylesbury.

♦London 42 – Aylesbury 4 – ♦Oxford 26.

Bell Inn, HP22 5HP, ☎ 630252, Telex 83252, Fax 631250, « Courtyard and gardens » – ⇸ rest TV ☎ P – 300. VISA
M 15.50/19.50 **t.** and a la carte 31.00/47.00 **t.** 5.00 – ☐ approx. 6.00 – **15 rm** 86.00/175.00 **t.**, **6 suites** 125.00/175.00 **t.**

ATTLEBOROUGH Norfolk 404 X 26 – pop. 6 322 – ECD : Wednesday – ☎ 0953.

♦London 94 – ♦Cambridge 47 – ♦Norwich 15.

Sherbourne, Norwich Rd, NR17 2JX, NE : ½ m. ☎ 454363, Fax 454363, ⛲ – ⇸ rest TV ☎ P. AE VISA. ✱
M (bar lunch)/dinner 21.00 **t.** and a la carte 3.55 – **8 rm** ☐ 20.00/75.00 **t.** – SB 70.00/85.00 **st.**

Griffin, Church St., NR17 2AH, ℘ 452149 – TV P.
M *(closed Sunday dinner and Bank Holiday Mondays)* (bar lunch)/dinner a la carte 9.55/16.05 **st.** 2.90 – **8 rm** 18.00/35.00 **st.**

FORD High St. ℘ 452274
RENAULT Station Rd ℘ 452223
ATS London Rd ℘ 453883

AUST SERVICE AREA Avon – ✉ Bristol – 045 45 Aust

Rank Motor Lodge without rest., BS12 3BJ, M 4 juntion 21 ℘ 3313, Fax 3819 – rm TV P. VISA
51 rm 27.50/34.50 **st.**

AVON Hants. – see Ringwood.

AXBRIDGE Somerset 403 L 30 **The West Country G.** – pop. 1 724 – ECD : Wednesday – 0934.

See : Site★★ – King John's Hunting Lodge★ *AC* – St. John the Baptist Church★.

Envir. : The Cheddar Gorge★★ (The Gorge★★ - Jacob's Ladder ★ *AC* - The Caves★★ *AC*) – St. Andrews Church★, SE : 1½ m.

♦London 142 – ♦Bristol 17 – Taunton 31 – Weston-Super-Mare 10.

Hotels and restaurants see : Weston-Super-Mare NW : 7½ m.

AXMINSTER Devon 403 L 31 – pop. 4 457 – ECD : Wednesday – 0297.

Old Court House, Church St. ℘ 34386 (summer only).

♦London 156 – Exeter 27 – Lyme Regis 5.5 – Taunton 22 – Yeovil 24.

at Hawkchurch NE : 4½ m. by A 35 off B 3165 – ✉ Axminster – 029 77 Hawkchurch :

Fairwater Head, EX13 5TX, S : ¾ m. ℘ 349, Axe Vale, – rest TV P. VISA.
closed 21 December-21 February – **M** (bar lunch)/dinner 20.00 **st.** and a la carte 3.50 – **20 rm** 50.00/110.00 **st.**

AYLESBURY Bucks. 404 R 28 – pop. 51 999 – ECD : Thursday – 0296.

Envir. : Waddesdon Manor★★ (Rothschild Collection★★★) *AC*, NW : 5½ m. – Ascott House★★ (Rothschild Collection★★) and gardens★ *AC*, NE : 8½ m. – Stewkley (St. Michael's Church★ 12C) NE : 12 m.

18 Weston Turville, New Rd ℘ 24084, SE : 2½ m – 18 Butlers Cross ℘ 622375, S : 7½ m. – 9 Aston Hill, Halton ℘ 630899, SE : 5 m. – 9 Whiteleaf, Princes Rinborough ℘ 084 44 (Princes Rinborough) 3097, S : 8½ m. by A 4010.

County Hall, Walton St. ℘ 382308.

♦London 46 – ♦Birmingham 72 – Northampton 37 – ♦Oxford 22.

⊛ **Hartwell House**, Oxford Rd, HP17 8NL, SW : 2 m. on A 418 ℘ 747444, Telex 837108, Fax 747450, « Part Jacobean, part Georgian house, former residence of Louis XVIII », park – TV P. VISA.
M 19.00/38.00 **st.** and a la carte 35.00/44.00 **st.** 6.00 – 10.00 – **29 rm** 88.00/132.00 **st.** **3 suites** 195.00/295.00 **st.** – SB 190.00/242.00 **st.**
Spec. Vegetable summer pudding, Poached breast of guinea fowl, herb mousse and vegetable tagliatelle, Butterscotch and poppy seed parfait.

Forte (T.H.F.), Aston Clinton Rd, HP22 5AA, SE : 2 m. on A 41 ℘ 393388, Telex 838820 Fax 392211, – rm TV P – 100. VISA
M *(closed Saturday lunch)* 25.00 **st.** and a la carte 4.75 – 8.65 – **94 rm** 90.00/100.00 **st.** **2 suites** 120.00/130.00 **st.** – SB (weekends only) 80.00/90.00 **st.**

Horse and Jockey Motel without rest, Buckingham Rd, HP19 3QL, ℘ 23803, Fax 395142 – TV P. VISA.
24 rm 40.00/50.00 **t.**

XX **Pebbles,** 1 Pebble Lane, HP20 2JH, ℘ 86622 – VISA
closed Sunday dinner and Monday – **M** 12.50/30.00 **t.** and a la carte 6.75.

CITROEN Park St. ℘ 435331
FORD Griffin Lane ℘ 26162
LAND-ROVER, RANGE-ROVER Buckingham Rd ℘ 84071
MERCEDES-BENZ Bicester Rd ℘ 81641
RENAULT Little Kimble ℘ 029 661 (Stoke Mandeville) 2239
VAUXHALL-OPEL 143 Cambridge St. ℘ 82321
ATS Gatehouse Way ℘ 433177

BABBACOMBE Devon 403 J 32 – see Torquay.

BACKFORD CROSS Cheshire 402 403 L 24 – see Chester.

BADBY Northants. – ✉ Daventry – 0327.

♦London 67 – ♦Cambridge 55 – ♦Coventry 36 – Northampton 2 – ♦Oxford 39.

Windmill Inn, Main St., NN11 6AN, ℘ 702363 – TV P
5 rm.

BADMINTON Avon 403 404 N 29 The West Country G. – pop. 283 – ☎ 045 423 Didmarton.

See : Badminton House★ *AC*.

◆London 114 – ◆Bristol 19 – Gloucester 26 – Swindon 33.

Petty France, Dunkirk, GL9 1AF, NW : 3 m. on A 46 ℘ 361, Fax 768, – rest – 25. AE VISA
M 13.50 **t.** (lunch) and a la carte 4.50 – **20 rm** 54.00/110.00 **t.**

BAE COLWYN = Colwyn Bay.

BAGSHOT Surrey 404 R 29 – pop. 4 239 – ECD : Wednesday – ☎ 0276.

◆London 37 – Reading 17 – ◆Southampton 49.

Pennyhill Park, College Ride, GU19 5ET, off A 30 ℘ 71774, Telex 858841, Fax 73217, ←, heated, 9, park, – rm – 25. AE VISA.
M 35.00/50.00 **t.** and a la carte – 12.00 – **63 rm** 115.00/200.00 **t.**, **2 suites** 250.00/300.00 **t.** – SB (weekends only) 175.00 **st.**

FORD 577 London Rd, Blackwater ℘ 33033

ROVER London Rd, Windlesham, Nr Bagshot ℘ 73561

BAINBRIDGE North Yorks. 402 N 21 – pop. 474 – ECD : Wednesday – ✉ Leyburn – ☎ 0969 Wensleydale.

◆London 249 – Kendal 31 – ◆Leeds 68 – York 61.

Rose and Crown, DL8 3EE, ℘ 50225 – . VISA
M a la carte 14.00/17.50 **t.** – **12 rm** 33.00/58.00 **t.** – SB (October-April) 72.00 **st.**

BAKEWELL Derbs. 402 403 404 O 24 – pop. 3 839 – ECD : Thursday – ☎ 062 981 (4 fig.) or 0629 (6 fig.).

Envir. : Chatsworth★★★ : site★★, house★★★ (Renaissance) garden★★★ *AC*, NE : 2½ m. – Haddon Hall★★ (14C-16C) *AC*, SE : 3 m.

9 Station Rd ℘ 812307.

Old Market Hall, Bridge St. ℘ 813227.

◆London 160 – Derby 26 – ◆Manchester 37 – ◆Nottingham 33 – ◆Sheffield 17.

Rutland Arms (Best Western), The Square, DE4 1BT, ℘ 812812, Fax 814600 – – 35. AE VISA
M 9.95/15.95 **t.** and a la carte 4.25 – **36 rm** 49.00/69.00 **t.** – SB 84.00/90.00 **st.**

Milford House, Mill St., DE4 1DA, ℘ 812130, – .
April-October – **M** *(closed Sunday dinner)* (dinner only and Sunday lunch)/dinner 13.50 **t.** 3.50 – **12 rm** 36.00/66.00 **t.**

at Hassop N : 3½ m. by A 619 on B 6001 – ✉ Bakewell – ☎ 062 987 Great Longstone :

Hassop Hall, DE4 1NS, ℘ 488, Telex 378485, Fax 577, ←, « Part 16C hall », park, – . AE VISA.
accommodation closed 3 days at Christmas – **M** *(closed Monday lunch and Sunday dinner)* 15.00/25.00 **t.** 5.50 – 9.80 – **12 rm** 60.00/100.00 **t.** – SB (November-March) 180.00/230.00 **st.**

at Great Longstone N : 4 m. by A 619 off B 6001 – ✉ Bakewell – ☎ 062 987 Great Longstone :

Croft, DE4 1TF, ℘ 278, – . VISA.
closed January, February and 22 to 31 December – **M** *(closed Monday to Wednesday to non-residents)* (dinner only) 16.00 **t.** – **9 rm** 48.00/72.00 **t.** – SB 77.00/95.00 **st.**

at Alport S : 4 m. by A 6 off B 5056 – ✉ Bakewell – ☎ 0629 Youlgreave :

Rock House without rest., DE4 1LG, ℘ 636736, – .
3 rm 17.00/30.00 **s.**

BALA Gwynedd 402 403 J 25 – pop. 1 852 – ECD : Wednesday – ☎ 0678.

See : Site★.

Envir. : SW : Road ★ from Pandy to Dinas Mawddwy.

9 Penlan ℘ 520359, SW : ¾ m. off A 494 – 9 Bala Lake ℘ 520344, 1½ m. on B 4403.

High St. ℘ 520367 (summer only).

◆London 216 – Chester 46 – Dolgellau 18 – Shrewsbury 52.

Palé Hall, Llandderfel, LL23 7PS, E : 4¾ m. by A 494 on B 4401 ℘ 067 83 (Llandderfel) 285, ←, « Ornate decor », park – rest . AE VISA.
M (closed lunch Monday to Friday to non-residents) 12.50/21.00 **st.** and a la carte 4.25 – **15 rm** 96.00/130.00 **st.**, **2 suites** 130.00 **st.** – SB (except summer and Christmas-new Year) 100.00/135.00 **st.**

White Lion Royal, 61 High St., LL23 7AE, ℘ 520314 – . AE VISA
closed Christmas Day – **M** 7.25/11.75 **st.** 3.25 – **22 rm** 32.50/54.50 **st.** – SB 59.50/65.50 **st.**

Plas Coch, High St., LL23 7AB, ✆ 520309 – ⇆ rest TV ☎ P. VISA
M (bar lunch)/dinner 11.75 and a la carte 2.50 – **10 rm** 29.70/47.00 **st.**

Fron Feuno Hall, LL23 7YF, SW : 1 m. on A 494 ✆ 521115, ← Bala Lake, , park – P.
closed 10 December-10 January – **M** (communal dining) 16.50 **st.** – **3 rm** 28.50/50.00 **st.**

Dewis Cyfarfod, Llandderfel, LL23 7DR, E : 3 ¼ m. by A 494 on B 4401 ✆ 067 83 (Llandderfel) 243, ←, , park – TV P.
M (by arrangement) 14.50 **st.** 4.00 – **5 rm** 22.00/44.00 **st.**

Llidiardau Mawr , Llidiardau, LL23 7SG, NW : 4 ¼ m. by A 4212 ✆ 520555, « 17C Stone-built mill house », – P.
Easter-October – **M** approx. 9.50 – **3 rm** 18.00/32.00 **s.**

VOLVO High St. ✆ 520210

BALDOCK Herts. 404 T 28 – pop. 6 703 – ECD : Thursday – ✆ 0462.

Envir. : Ashwell (St. Mary's Church★ (14C) : Medieval graffiti) NE : 4 ½ m.

◆London 42 – Bedford 20 – ◆Cambridge 21 – Luton 15.

Travelodge without rest., A 1 Great North Road, Hinxworth (southbound carriageway), SG7 5EX, NW : 3 m. by A 507 on A 1 ✆ 835329, Reservations (Toll free) 0800 850950 – TV P. AE VISA.
40 rm 24.00/29.50 **t.**

BALSALL COMMON West Midlands – see Coventry.

BAMBER BRIDGE Lancs. 402 M 22 – see Preston.

BAMBURGH Northumb. 401 402 O 17 – pop. 567 – ECD : Wednesday – ✆ 066 84.

See : Castle★ (12C-18C) *AC.*

Bamburgh Castle ✆ 378, N : 1 m.

◆London 337 – ◆Edinburgh 77 – ◆Newcastle-upon-Tyne 51.

Lord Crewe Arms, Front St., NE69 7BL, ✆ 243 – TV P. VISA
March-November – **M** (bar lunch)/dinner 17.00 **t.** 3.65 – **25 rm** 32.00/57.00 **t.** – SB 74.00/82.00 **st.**

BANBURY Oxon. 403 404 P 27 – pop. 37 463 – ECD : Tuesday – ✆ 0295.

Envir. : Upton House★ (pictures★★★, porcelain★★) *AC,* NW : 7 m. – East Adderbury (St. Mary's Church : corbels★) SE : 3 ½ m. – Broughton Castle (great hall★, white room : 1599 plaster ceiling★★) and St. Mary's Church (memorial tombs★) *AC,* SW : 3 ½ m. – Wroxton (thatched cottages★) NW : 3 m. – Farnborough Hall (interior plasterwork★) *AC,* NW : 6 m.

Cherwell Edge, Chacombe ✆ 711591, NE : 4 m – Wigginton ✆ 737649, W : 5m. by B 4035.

Banbury Museum, 8 Horsefair ✆ 259855.

◆London 76 – ◆Birmingham 40 – ◆Coventry 25 – ◆Oxford 23.

Whately Hall (T.H.F.), Horsefair, by Banbury Cross, OX16 0AN, ✆ 263451, Telex 837149, Fax 271736, « Part 17C hall », – ⇆ rm TV ☎ P – 80. AE VISA
M 9.50/13.50 **st.** and a la carte 5.50 – 7.60 – **70 rm** 75.00/100.00 **st.**, **2 suites** 125.00/150.00 **st.** – SB (weekends only) 84.00/110.00 **st.**

Banbury Moat House (Q.M.H) 27-29 Oxford Rd, OX16 9AH, ✆ 259361, Telex 838967, Fax 270954 – TV ☎ P – 60. AE VISA
M *(closed Saturday lunch)* 10.50/11.50 **st.** and a la carte 3.50 – **48 rm** 69.00/89.00 **st.**

Easington House, 50 Oxford Rd, OX16 9AN, ✆ 259395, – TV ☎ P. AE VISA
closed Christmas-1 January – **M** (by arrangement) 8.50 **st.** 3.00 – **13 rm** 28.00/70.00 **st.**

at Bloxham SW : 3 ½ m. on A 361 – ✉ ✆ 0295 Banbury :

Olde School, Church St., OX15 4ET, ✆ 720369, Fax 721748 – TV ☎ P – 80. AE VISA.
M 10.50/20.00 **t.** and a la carte 5.50 – **40 rm** 55.00/95.00 **t.** – SB (weekends only) 78.00/90.00 **st.**

at North Newington W : 2 ¼ m. by B 4035 – ✉ Banbury – ✆ 0295 Banbury :

La Madonette Country without rest., OX15 6AA, ✆ 730212, heated, – TV ☎ P. VISA.
closed 20 December-4 January – **6 rm** 35.00/48.50 **st.**

at Swalcliffe W : 6 m. on B 4035 – ✉ Banbury – ✆ 029 578 Swalcliffe :

Swalcliffe Manor, OX15 5EH, on B 4035 ✆ 348, « Part 13C manor house », , – P.
March-November – **M** 15.00 **s.** – **4 rm** 45.00/50.00 **s.**

at Wroxton NW : 3 m. by A 41 on A 422 – ✉ Banbury – ✆ 0295 Banbury :

Wroxton House (Best Western), Silver St., OX15 6QB, ✆ 730777, Telex 83409, Fax 730800, – TV ☎ P – 25. AE VISA
M 16.50/24.50 **st.** and a la carte 4.50 – **32 rm** 75.00/120.00 **st.** – SB 106.00/120.00 **st.**

at Shenington NW : 6 m. by A 41 off A 422 – ✉ Banbury – ☎ 029 588 Tysoe :

Sugarswell Farm ⑤, OX15 6HW, NW : 2¼ m. on Edge Hill rd ℘ 512, ≤, – – P.
M 16.00 **st.** – **3 rm** ⊐ 27.00/40.00 **st.**

DAIHATSU Hook Norton ℘ 0608 (Hook Norton) 737641
FIAT 21-27 Broad St. ℘ 50733
FORD 98 Warwick Rd ℘ 67711
MITSUBISHI Thorpe Rd, Middleton Cheney ℘ 710325
PEUGEOT-TALBOT Southam Rd ℘ 53511
ROVER Southam Rd ℘ 51551
VAUXHALL-OPEL 8 Middleton Rd ℘ 3551
VW-AUDI 9-16 Southam Rd ℘ 50141

ATS Beaumont Industrial Est., Beaumont Close ℘ 253525

BANGOR Gwynedd 402 403 H 24 – pop. 12 126 – ECD : Wednesday – ☎ 0248.
Envir. : Bethesda (slate quarries★) SE : 5 m. – Nant Francon Pass★★, SE : 9 m.
St. Deiniol ℘ 353098, E : 1 m. on A 5022.
Theatr Gwynedd, Deiniol Rd ℘ 352786 (summer only).
◆London 247 – Birkenhead 68 – Holyhead 23 – Shrewsbury 83.

Menai Court, Craig-Y-Don Rd, LL57 2BG, ℘ 354200 – TV ☎ P – 60. VISA
closed 1 to 14 January – **M** 11.50/20.50 **t.** and a la carte 3.75 – **12 rm** ⊐ 43.00/72.00 **t.** – SB 72.00/83.00 **st.**

Telford, Holyhead Rd, LL57 2HX, ℘ 352543, ≤ Menai Bridge and Isle of Anglesey, – rm TV P. AE VISA.
M (bar lunch)/dinner 15.00 **t.** 3.50 – **9 rm** ⊐ 28.95/85.00.

Ty-Uchaf, Tal-y-Bont, LL57 3UR, SE : 2 m. by A 5122 ℘ 352219 – TV P. VISA.
closed 24 December-2 January – **M** *(closed Sunday lunch and Sunday dinner to non-residents)* (bar lunch)/dinner 12.00 **t.** 3.50 – **9 rm** ⊐ 22.00/39.00 **t.**

DAIHATSU High St. ℘ 362444
FORD 49 High St. ℘ 355107

BANSTEAD Surrey 404 T 30 – pop. 35 360 (inc. Tadworth) – ECD : Wednesday – ✉ Tadworth – ☎ 0737 Burgh Heath.
◆London 17 – ◆Brighton 39.

Heathside, Brighton Rd, Burgh Heath, KT20 6BW, S : 1½ m. on A 217 ℘ 353355, Telex 929908, Fax 370857, , – TV ☎ P – 200. AE VISA
M 7.00/10.00 **t.** and a la carte – ⊐ 5.00 – **73 rm** 55.00/75.00 **t.** – SB (weekends only) 80.00 **st.**

BANTHAM Devon – see Kingsbridge.

BARFORD Warw. 403 404 P 27 – see Warwick.

BAR HILL Cambs. 404 U 27 – see Cambridge.

BARKSTON Lincs. 402 404 S 25 – see Grantham.

BARMBY MOOR Humberside 402 R 22 – see Pocklington.

BARMOUTH **(ABERMAW)** Gwynedd 402 403 H 25 – pop. 2 142 – ECD : Wednesday – ☎ 0341.
See : Site★★ – Panorama walk★★.
The Old Library ℘ 280787 (summer only).
◆London 231 – Chester 74 – Dolgellau 10 – Shrewsbury 67.

Ty'r Craig Castle, Llanaber Rd, LL42 1YN, on A 496 ℘ 280470, ≤ – TV ☎ P. VISA
closed January-mid March – **M** (bar lunch Monday to Saturday)/dinner 20.00 **t.** and a la carte 5.00 – **12 rm** ⊐ 35.00/50.00 **t.** – SB 70.00 **st.**

Cranbourne, 9 Marine Par., LL42 1NA, ℘ 280202 – TV. VISA.
M 7.50 **st.** – **10 rm** ⊐ 17.50/40.00 **st.** – SB (March and October) 49.50 **st.**

Bryn Melyn ⑤, Panorama Rd, LL42 1DQ, ℘ 280556, Fax 280990, ≤ Mawddach estuary and mountains – TV P. VISA
March-October – **M** 10.95 **t.** 4.00 – **8 rm** ⊐ 15.00/45.00 **t.** – SB 57.00 **st.**

COLT Smithy Garage ℘ 034 17 (Dyffryn) 279
ROVER, DAIMLER-JAGUAR Rover Park Rd ℘ 280449

BARNARD CASTLE Durham 402 O 20 – pop. 6 075 – ECD : Thursday – ☎ 0833 Teesdale.

See : Bowes Museum★ *AC*.

Envir. : High force★★ (waterfalls) *AC*, NW : 14 m. – Raby Castle★ (14C) *AC*, NE : 6 m.

18 Harmire Rd ☎ 37237, N : ¾ m. on B 6278.

ℹ 43 Galgate ☎ 690909.

◆London 258 – ◆Carlisle 63 – ◆Leeds 68 – ◆Middlesbrough 31 – ◆Newcastle-upon-Tyne 39.

Jersey Farm 🐎, Darlington Rd, DL12 8TA, E : 1 ½ m. on A 67 ☎ 38223, Fax 31988, ≤, « Working farm » – TV ☎ P. VISA
M (dinner only and Sunday lunch)/dinner 11.50 **t.** 3.60 – **16 rm** 35.00/44.00 **t.**, **4 suites** 55.00 **t.** – SB (except Bank Holidays) (weekends only) 55.00/65.00 **st.**

at Romaldkirk NW : 6 m. by A 67 on B 6277 – ✉ Barnard Castle – ☎ 0833 Teesdale :

Rose and Crown, DL12 9EB, ☎ 50213, Fax 50828 – TV ☎ P. VISA
M *(closed Sunday dinner)* (bar lunch Monday to Saturday)/dinner 16.50 **st.** 3.50 – **9 rm** 44.00/60.00 **st.**, **2 suites** 70.00 **st.** – SB (mid October-mid May) (weekends only) 75.00/85.00 **st.**

VAUXHALL Newgate ☎ 38352

BARNBY MOOR Notts. 402 403 404 Q 23 – pop. 268 – ECD : Wednesday – ✉ ☎ 0777 Retford.

◆London 151 – ◆Leeds 44 – Lincoln 27 – ◆Nottingham 31.

Ye Olde Bell, DN22 8QS, ☎ 705121, Fax 860424, – rm TV ☎ P – 200. AE VISA
M 7.50/13.50 **st.** and a la carte 3.95 – **55 rm** 60.00/85.00 **st.** – SB (except Christmas) 60.00/70.00 **st.**

BARNSDALE BAR West Yorks. 402 404 Q 23 – ✉ ☎ 0977 Pontefract.

◆London 181 – ◆Leeds 22 – ◆Nottingham 53 – ◆Sheffield 26.

Travelodge without rest., WF8 3JB, on A 1 ☎ 620711, Reservations (Toll free) 0800 850950 – TV ☎ P. AE VISA.
56 rm 24.00/29.50 **t.**

BARNSLEY Glos. 403 404 O28 – see Cirencester.

BARNSLEY South Yorks. 402 404 P 23 – pop. 76 783 – ECD : Thursday – ☎ 0226.

18 Wakefield Rd, Staincross ☎ 382856, N : 4 m. on A 61.

ℹ 56 Eldon St. ☎ 206757.

◆London 177 – ◆Leeds 21 – ◆Manchester 36 – ◆Sheffield 15.

at Ardsley E : 2 ½ m. on A 635 – ✉ ☎ 0226 Barnsley :

Ardsley Moat House (Q.M.H.), Doncaster Rd, S71 5EH, ☎ 289401, Telex 547762, Fax 205374, – TV ☎ P – 250. AE VISA
closed 25 December – **M** (bar lunch Saturday) 12.00/16.00 **t.** and a la carte 5.00 – 8.00 – **73 rm** 61.00/77.00 **t.** – SB (weekends only) 80.00 **st.**

CITROEN The Cross, Silkstone ☎ 790636
FIAT, PEUGEOT-TALBOT, VOLVO Stairfoot ☎ 206675
FORD Dodworth Rd ☎ 732732
HONDA Doncaster Rd ☎ 287417
RENAULT Doncaster Rd ☎ 291554
ROVER Claycliff Rd, Barkgreen ☎ 299891
VAUXHALL New St. ☎ 733833
VW-AUDI Huddersfield Rd ☎ 299494

ATS Huddersfield rd. ☎ 281888/287406

BARNSTAPLE Devon 403 H 30 **The West Country G.** – pop. 24 490 – ECD : Wednesday – ☎ 0271.

See : Site★ – The Long Bridge★.

Envir. : Arlington Court★★ *AC* The Carriage Collection★, NE : 8 m. on A 39.

ℹ North Devon Library, Tuly St., ☎ 47177.

◆London 222 – Exeter 40 – Taunton 51.

Imperial (T.H.F.), Taw Vale Par., EX32 8NB, ☎ 45861, Fax 24448 – rm TV ☎ P. AE VISA
M (buffet lunch)/dinner 20.00 **st.** 3.95 – 7.00 – **56 rm** 55.00/70.00 **st.**

Park, Taw Vale, EX32 8NJ, ☎ 72166, Group Telex 42551, Fax 78558 – TV ☎ P. AE VISA
M 7.00/13.50 **t.** and a la carte 3.55 – **42 rm** 44.00/69.00 **t.** – SB (except Christmas) 77.00/100.00 **st.**

XX **Lynwood House** with rm, Bishops Tawton Rd, EX32 9DZ, on A 377 ☎ 43695, Fax 79340, Seafood – rest TV ☎ P. VISA
M *(closed Sunday lunch)* a la carte 12.65/28.60 **t.** 4.05 – **5 rm** 47.50/67.50 **t.** – SB (except Bank Holidays) 97.50 **st.**

at Bishop's Tawton S : 2 m. on A 377 – ✉ ☎ 0271 Barnstaple :

Downrew House ⛰, EX32 0DY, SE : 1½ m. on Chittlehampton rd ☎ 42497, Fax 23947, ←, « Country house atmosphere », heated, park, – rest TV ☎ P. VISA
M (bar lunch Monday to Saturday)/dinner 24.50 **t.** and a la carte 5.50 – **12 rm** (dinner included) 84.00/143.20 **t.** – SB (except April-October) 104.00/114.00 **st.**

Halmpstone Manor ⛰, EX32 0EA, SE : 3 m. by Chittlehampton rd ☎ 830321, Fax 830826, ←, « Working farm », park – TV ☎ P. AE VISA
M *(closed Sunday dinner to non-residents)* (lunch by arrangement)/dinner 20.00 **t.** and a la carte – **5 rm** 60.00/100.00 **t.**

DAIHATSU Newport Rd ☎ 45363
FIAT, TOYOTA, VOLVO Pottington Industrial Estate, Pillandway ☎ 76551
FORD New Rd ☎ 74173
ROVER Hollowtree Rd ☎ 73232
VAUXHALL-OPEL 42 Boutport St. ☎ 74366
ATS Pottington Ind. Est., Braunton Rd ☎ 42294/5

BARROW-IN-FURNESS Cumbria 402 K 21 – pop. 50 174 – ☎ 0229.

Rakesmoore Lane, Hawcoat ☎ 25444, N : 2 m. by A 590 – Furness, Walney Island ☎ 41232, E : 1¾ m. by A 590.

Town Hall, Duke St. ☎ 870156.

London 295 – Kendal 34 – Lancaster 47.

Abbey House, Abbey Rd, LA13 0PA, NE : 2 m. on A 590 ☎ 838282, Telex 65357, Fax 820403, « Lutyens house », park – TV ☎ P – 100. AE VISA
M 12.50/19.50 **st.** and a la carte 4.50 – **28 rm** 64.50/85.50 **st.** – SB (weekends only) 80.50/161.00 **st.**

ATS 149-151 Ainslie St. ☎ 28513/28663
ATS Walney Rd ☎ 39034

BARRY (BARRI) South Glam. 403 K 29 – pop. 44 443 – ECD : Wednesday – ☎ 0446.

Port Rd ☎ 735061 – RAF, St Atham ☎ 751043.

The Promenade, Barry Island ☎ 747171 (summer only).

London 167 – Cardiff 10 – Swansea 39.

Egerton Grey, CF6 9BZ, SW : 4½ m. by A 4226 and Porthkerry rd via Cardiff Airport ☎ 711666, Fax 711690, ←, « Country house atmosphere », park, – rest TV ☎ P. AE VISA.
M 15.00/24.50 **st.** 4.50 – 4.00 – **10 rm** 55.00/110.00 **st.** – SB 95.00/125.00 **st.**

Mount Sorrel, Porthkerry Rd, CF6 8AY, ☎ 740069, Telex 497819, Fax 746600, – TV ☎ P – 200. AE VISA
M *(closed Sunday dinner)* 10.00/11.95 **t.** and a la carte 4.15 – **50 rm** 42.00/69.50 **t.** – SB (weekends only) 79.00/85.00 **st.**

Aberthaw House, 28 Porthkerry Rd, CF6 8AX, ☎ 737314 – TV ☎
9 rm.

Cwm Ciddy Toby, Airport Rd, CF6 9BA, NW : 1½ m. by B 4266 ☎ 700075 – TV ☎ P
14 rm.

BARTON MILLS Suffolk. 404 V 26 – pop. 866 – ☎ 0638 Newmarket.

London 72 – Cambridge 21 – Ipswich 37 – Norwich 40.

Travelodge without rest., Fiveways Roundabout, IP28 6AE, on A 11 ☎ 717675, Reservations (Toll free) 0800 850950 – TV P. AE VISA.
32 rm 24.00/29.50 **t.**

FORD A 11, Barton Mills ☎ 712118

BARTON STACEY Hants. 403 404 P 30 – see Andover.

BARTON UNDER NEEDWOOD Staffs. – see Burton-upon-Trent.

BARWICK Somerset 403 404 M 31 – see Yeovil.

BASFORD Staffs. – see Stoke-on-Trent.

BASILDON Essex 404 V 29 – pop. 94 800 – ECD : Wednesday – ☎ 0268.

See : Basildon Park★.

Clayhill Lane, Kingswood ☎ 533297, S : 1 m. by A 176 – Pipps Hill Country Club, Cranes Farm Rd ☎ 23456, N : by A 127.

London 30 – Chelmsford 17 – Southend-on-Sea 13.

Crest (T.H.F.), Cranes Farm Rd, SS14 3DG, NW : 2¼ m. by A 176 off A 1235 ☎ 533955, Telex 995141, Fax 530119, – rm TV ☎ P – 200. AE VISA.
M *(closed Saturday lunch)* 10.75/15.00 **st.** and a la carte 2.75 – 8.50 – **110 rm** 78.00/125.00 **st.** – SB (weekends only) 76.00 **st.**

Travel Inn, Felmores, East Mayne, SS13 1BW, N : 1 ½ m. on A 132 ℘ 522227, Fax 530092 – TV ♿ P. AE VISA.
closed 25 and 26 December – **M** (Beefeater grill) a la carte approx. 12.25 **t.** – 4.50 – **32 rm** -/27.50 **t.**

Campanile, A 127 Southend Arterial Rd, Pipp's Hill, SS14 3AE, NW : 1 m. on A 176 ℘ 530810, Telex 995068, Fax 286710 – TV ☎ ♿ P – 25. VISA
M 9.40 **st.** and a la carte 2.60 – 3.95 – **97 rm** 33.00 **st.**

FIAT Nethermayne ℘ 522261
FORD Cherrydown East Basildon ℘ 522744
RENAULT South Hill, Langdon Hills ℘ 42234
ROVER Southern Hay ℘ 522661
VW-AUDI Great Oaks ℘ 288541
ATS Archers Field ℘ 525177/8

Dieser Führer ist kein vollständiges Hotel- und Restaurantverzeichnis.
Um den Ansprüchen aller Touristen gerecht zu werden,
haben wir uns auf eine Auswahl in jeder Kategorie beschränkt.

BASINGSTOKE

London Street	Y 19
Upper Church Street	Y 24
Winchester Street	Y 27
Aldermaston Road	Z 2
Beaconsfield Road	Y 3
Buckland Avenue	Z 5
Chequers Road	Y 6
Church Street	Y 7
Churchill Way East	Z 9
Churchill Way West	Z 10
Council Road	Y 12
Cross Street	Y 13
Fairfields Road	Y 14
Houndmills Road	Z 17
New Road	Y 20
Reading Road	Z 22
Southern Ringway	Z 23
Victoria Street	Y 25
Wote Street	Y 28

North is at the top on all town plans.

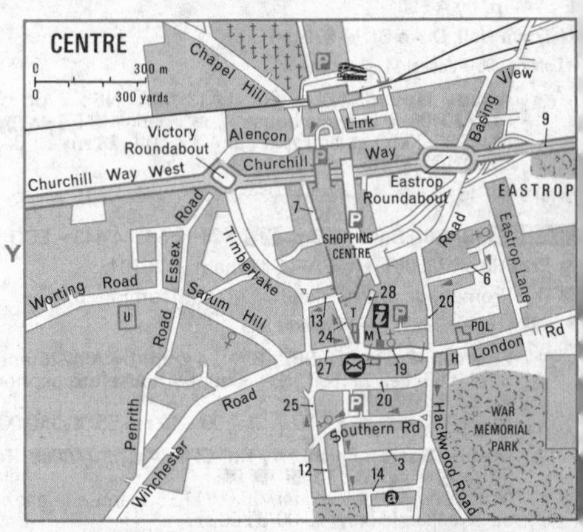

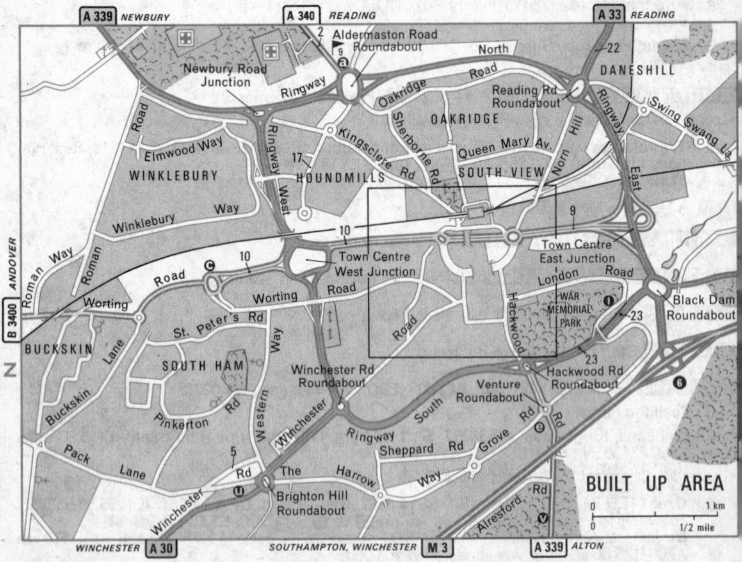

A 339 NEWBURY · A 340 READING · A 33 READING
Aldermaston Road Roundabout
Newbury Road Junction
Ringway North
Oakridge Road
Reading Rd Roundabout
DANESHILL
Swing Swang La
OAKRIDGE
Kingsclere Rd
Sherborne Rd
Queen Mary Av.
Norn Hill
Ringway East
SOUTH VIEW
HOUNDMILLS
WINKLEBURY
Elmwood Way
Winklebury Way
Ringway West
Roman Way
Roman Road
Worting Road
Town Centre West Junction
Town Centre East Junction
London Road
WAR MEMORIAL PARK
Black Dam Roundabout
B 3400 ANDOVER
BUCKSKIN
Buckskin Lane
St. Peter's Rd
SOUTH HAM
Western Way
Winchester Rd Roundabout
Hackwood Rd Roundabout
Venture Roundabout
Pinkerton Rd
Ringway South
Sheppard Rd
Grove Rd
Pack Lane
The Harrow Way
Brighton Hill Roundabout
Winchester Rd
Alresford Rd
BUILT UP AREA
0 1 km
0 1/2 mile
WINCHESTER A 30 · SOUTHAMPTON, WINCHESTER M 3 · A 339 ALTON

BASINGSTOKE Hants. 403 404 Q 30 – pop. 73 027 – ☎ 0256.

18 Kempshott Park ☎ 465990, SW : 3 m. by A 30 Z – 18 Sandford Springs, Wolverton ☎ 0635 (Newbury) 297881, NW : 8½m. by A 339 Z – 18 Tylney Park, Rotherwick ☎ 762079, E : 5 m. Z – 9 Bishopwood Lane, Tadley ☎ 0734 (Silchester) 815213, N : 6 m. by A 340 Z – 9 Basingstoke Hospitals, Aldermaston Rd ☎ 20347 Z.

Willis Museum, Old Town Hall, Market Sq ☎ 817618.

London 55 – Reading 17 – Southampton 31 – Winchester 18.

Plan opposite

Audley's wood (Mt. Charlotte Thistle), Alton Rd, RG25 2JT, S : 1 ½ m. on A 339 ☎ 817555, Telex 858273, Fax 817500, « Gothic renaissance mansion », park – rm – 40. AE VISA Z v
M *(closed Saturday lunch)* 16.50/27.00 **t.** and a la carte 5.00 – 8.00 – **69 rm** 80.00/100.00 **t.**, **2 suites** 150.00/170.00 **t.** – SB (weekends only) 127.00 **st.**

Centrecourt H. & Tennis Centre, Centre Drive, Chineham, RG24 0FY, NE : 2½ m. by A 33 and Great Binfield Rd. Z – ☎ 816664, Fax 816727, – rm – 45. AE VISA.
M 13.50/17.00 **t.** and a la carte 4.75 – **50 rm** 89.00/160.00 **st.**

Hilton Lodge, Old Common Rd, Black Dam, RG21 3PR, ☎ 460460, Telex 859038, Fax 840441, – rm rest – 150. AE VISA Z i
M *(closed lunch Saturday and Bank Holidays)* (carving rest.) 13.00/16.50 **t.** and a la carte 4.50 – 8.50 – **144 rm** 86.00/116.00 **st.** – SB (weekends only) 98.00/130.00 **st.**

Hilton National, Poplar Way, Aldermaston Roundabout, Ringway North, RG24 9NV, N : 2 m. junction A 339 and A 340 ☎ 20212, Telex 858223, Fax 842835, – rm – 160. AE VISA Z a
M *(closed Saturday lunch)* (carving rest.) 11.50/13.50 **t.** and a la carte 5.25 – 7.95 – **138 rm** 79.00/109.00 **st.**

Crest (T.H.F.), Grove Rd, RG21 3EE, S : 1 m. junction A 339 and A 30 ☎ 468181, Telex 858501, Fax 840081 – rm – 200. AE VISA Z e
M *(closed Saturday lunch)* 8.50/15.95 **st.** and a la carte 3.95 – 7.95 – **85 rm** 85.00/98.00 **st.** – SB (weekends only) 80.00 **st.**

Travelodge without rest., Winchester Rd, RG22 6HN, ☎ 843566, Reservations (Toll free) 0800 850950 – . AE VISA. Z u
32 rm 24.00/29.50 **t.**

Travel Inn, Worthing Rd, RG22 6PG, ☎ 811477, Fax 819329 – rm . AE VISA. Z c
M (Beefeater grill) a la carte approx. 12.95 **t.** – 4.50 – **49 rm** -/27.50 **t.**

Fernbank without rest., 4 Fairfields Rd, RG21 3DR, ☎ 21191, Fax 21191 – . VISA. Y a
closed Christmas – **18 rm** 22.00/44.00 **st.**

at Rotherwick E : 6¾ m. by Black Dam roundabout, A 30 – Z – and Rotherwick Rd – ✉ – ☎ 0256 Basingstoke :

Tylney Hall, RG27 9AJ, W : 1 m. ☎ 764881, Telex 859864, Fax 768141, « 19C mansion in extensive gardens », heated, , park, – – 100. AE VISA.
M 17.00/40.00 **st.** and a la carte 7.00 – **80 rm** 85.00/99.00 **st.**, **11 suites** 190.00/220.00 **st.** – SB (weekends only) 130.00/420.00 **st.**

at Oakley W : 4¾ m. on B 3400 Z – ✉ Oakley – ☎ 0256 Basingstoke :

Beach Arms, RG23 7EP, on B 3400 ☎ 780210, Fax 780557, – – 30
32 rm.

AUDI-VW London Rd ☎ 24444
FIAT, LANCIA, MASERATI London Rd ☎ 55221
FORD Lower Wote St. ☎ 473561
PEUGEOT-TALBOT, CITROEN Houndmills ☎ 465991
RANGE-ROVER, JAGUAR, HONDA New Rd ☎ 24561
VAUXHALL-OPEL West Ham ☎ 840540
VOLVO London Rd ☎ 466111

ATS Moniton Trading Estate ☎ 51431
ATS Armstrong Rd, Daneshill East ☎ 462448

BASLOW Derbs. 402 403 404 P 24 – pop. 1 205 – ECD : Wednesday – ✉ Bakewell – ☎ 0246.

London 161 – Derby 27 – Manchester 35 – Sheffield 13.

Cavandish, DE4 1SP, on A 619 ☎ 582311, Telex 547150, Fax 582312, ≤ Chatsworth Park, – rest . AE VISA.
M 25.00 **t.** and a la carte 5.35 – 7.50 – **23 rm**, **1 suite.**

XX **Fischer's at Baslow Hall** with rm, Calver Rd, DE4 1RR, ☎ 583259, – rest . AE VISA.
M *(closed Monday lunch and Sunday dinner)* 22.00/27.50 **t.** and a la carte 4.75 – **5 rm** 60.00/95.00 **t.**, **1 suite** 95.00 **t.** – SB (October-Easter) (weekends only) 115.00/132.50 **st.**

When in a hurry use the ***Michelin Main Road Maps*** *:*
970 *Europe,* 980 *Greece,* 984 *Germany,* 985 *Scandinavia-Finland,*
986 *Great Britain and Ireland,* 987 *Germany-Austria-Benelux,* 988 *Italy,*
989 *France,* 990 *Spain-Portugal and* 991 *Yugoslavia.*

BASSENTHWAITE Cumbria 401 402 K 19 – pop. 533 – ✉ – ☎ 07687 Keswick.

◆London 300 – ◆Carlisle 24 – Keswick 7.

Armathwaite Hall 🐦, CA12 4RE, W : 1 ½ m. on B 5291 ✉ Keswick ☎ 76551, Telex 64319, Fax 76220, ≤ Bassenthwaite Lake, « Part 18C mansion in extensive grounds », ⛶, ⌂s, ⛶, ⛶, ⛶, park, ⛶ – ⛶ TV ☎ P – ⛶ 100. ⛶ AE ⓞ VISA
M 12.00/25.00 **t.** and a la carte – **42 rm** ⛶ 45.00/175.00 **t.**

Overwater Hall 🐦, CA5 1HH, NE : 2 ¼ m. on Uldale Rd ✉ Ireby ☎ 566, ≤, ⛶, park – TV ☎ P. ⛶ VISA
closed 24 December-22 February – **M** (dinner only) 14.50 **t.** 🍷 3.50 – **13 rm** ⛶ 26.00/52.00 **t.** – SB (February-June) 66.00/70.00 **st.**

Pheasant Inn, CA13 9YE, SW : 3 ¼ m. by B 5291 off A 66 ✉ Cockermouth ☎ 76234, « 16C inn », ⛶ – ⛶ rest P. ⛶
closed 25 December – **M** 8.50/18.00 **st.** 🍷 3.00 – **20 rm** ⛶ 42.00/72.00 **st.** – SB (4 November-March) 84.00/94.00 **st.**

Si vous écrivez à un hôtel à l'étranger,
joignez à votre lettre un coupon-réponse international.
(disponible dans les bureaux de poste).

BATH Avon 403 404 M 29 **The West Country G.** – pop. 84 283 – ECD : Monday and Thursday – ☎ 0225.

See : Site★★★ : Royal Crescent★★★ (Nº 1 Royal Crescent) AV **D** – The Circus★★★ AV – Roman Baths★★ BX **B** – Pump Room★*AC* BX **A** – Bath Abbey★ BX – Assembly Rooms★*AC* (Museum of costume★★★*AC*) AV – Pulteney Bridge★ BV.

Envir. : Dyrham Park★ *AC* N : 9 m. – at Claverton, E : 2 m. by A 36 American Museum★ *AC*.

⛳, ⛳ Tracy Park, Bath Rd, Wick ☎ 027 582 (Abson) 2251, N : 5 m. by Lansdown Rd Y – ⛳ Lansdown ☎ 425007, NW : 3 m. by Lansdown Rd Y – ⛳ Sham Castle, North Rd ☎ 425182, SE : 1 ½ m. by A 36 Y – ⛳, ⛳ Entry Hill ☎ 834248, S : 1 m. by A 367 Z – ⛳ Saltford, Golf Club Lane ☎ 873220, SW : 6 m. Z.

ℹ 8 Abbey Church Yard ☎ 462831.

◆London 119 – ◆Bristol 13 – ◆Southampton 63 – Taunton 49.

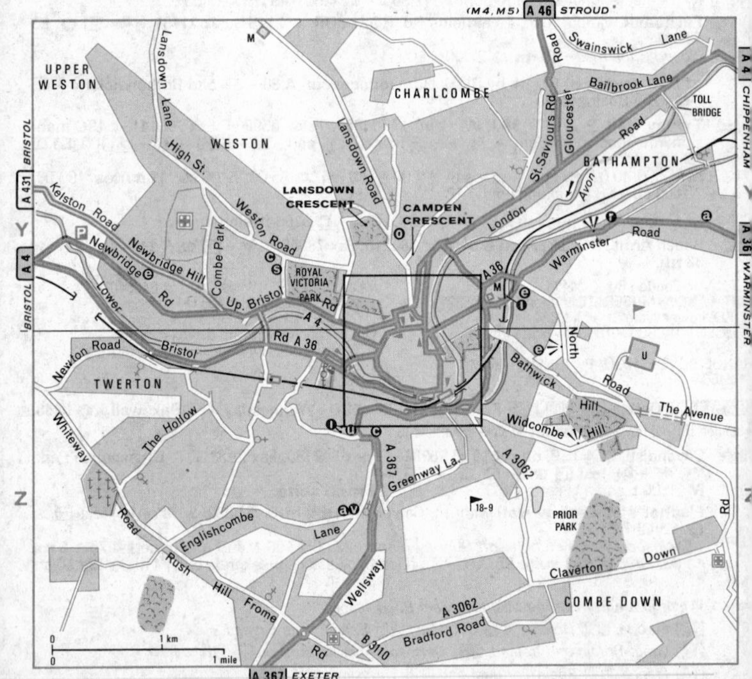

Bath Spa (T.H.F.) Sydney Rd, BA2 6JF, ☏ 444424, Telex 449729, Fax 444006, « Part 19C mansion, in landscape gardens », Ⅎ5, ⌖, ⊞, ✂ – |✈| ⟨⟩ rm ▤ rest TV ☎ ♿ P – ⛭ 150. ⎕ AE ⊕ VISA Y e
M 22.00/33.00 **st.** and a la carte – ⊏ 11.50 – **96 rm** 115.00/150.00 **st.**, **7 suites** 225.00/395.00 **st.** – SB 190.00/220.00 **st.**

Royal Crescent (Q.M.H.), 16 Royal Cres., BA1 2LS, ☏ 319090, Telex 444251, Fax 339401, ≤, « Tastefully restored Georgian town houses », ⊞ – |✈| ▤ rest TV ☎ ⇔ – ⛭ 30. ⎕ AE ⊕ VISA. ✂ AV a
M 21.00/50.00 **t.** and a la carte 33.00/40.00 **t.** 🌢 8.00 – ⊏ 10.00 – **35 rm** 90.00/175.00 **t.**, **9 suites** 240.00/330.00 **t.**

The Priory, Weston Rd, BA1 2XT, ☏ 331922, Telex 44612, Fax 448276, ≤, ⌖ heated, ⊞ – ⟨⟩ rest TV ☎ P. ⎕ AE ⊕ VISA. ✂ Y c
M 22.00/29.50 **t.** and a la carte 27.00/32.50 **t.** 🌢 6.50 – **21 rm** ⊏ 85.00/154.00 **t.** – SB (November-April) 135.00/170.00 **st.**

P.T.O. →

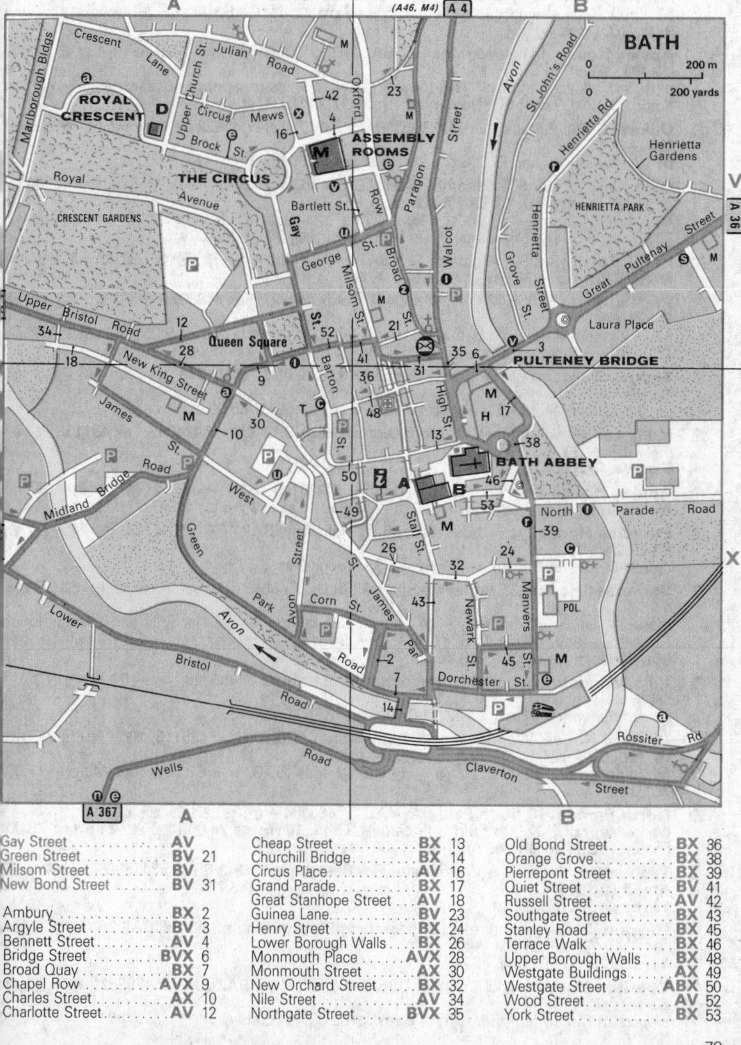

Gay Street AV
Green Street BV 21
Milsom Street BV
New Bond Street BV 31

Ambury BX 2
Argyle Street BV 3
Bennett Street AV 4
Bridge Street BVX 6
Broad Quay BX 7
Chapel Row AVX 9
Charles Street AX 10
Charlotte Street AV 12

Cheap Street BX 13
Churchill Bridge BX 14
Circus Place AV 16
Grand Parade BX 17
Great Stanhope Street AV 18
Guinea Lane BV 23
Henry Street BX 24
Lower Borough Walls BX 26
Monmouth Place AVX 28
Monmouth Street AX 30
New Orchard Street BX 32
Nile Street AV 34
Northgate Street BVX 35

Old Bond Street BX 36
Orange Grove BX 38
Pierrepont Street BX 39
Quiet Street BV 41
Russell Street AV 42
Southgate Street BX 43
Stanley Road BX 45
Terrace Walk BX 46
Upper Borough Walls BX 48
Westgate Buildings AX 49
Westgate Street ABX 50
Wood Street AV 52
York Street BX 53

Queensberry without rest., Russell St., BA1 2QF, ✆ 447928, Telex 445628, Fax 446065 – AV x
closed 23 December-4 January – **24 rm** 75.00/135.00 **st.**

Fountain House without rest., 9-11 Fountain Buildings, Lansdown Rd, BA1 5DV, ✆ 338622, Telex 444905, Fax 445855 – BV e
14 suites 92.00/152.00 **st.**

Francis (T.H.F.), Queen Sq., BA1 2HH, ✆ 424257, Telex 449162, Fax 319715 – rm – 60. AV i
M 12.95/15.50 **st.** and a la carte 3.95 – 7.50 – **93 rm** 70.00/100.00 **st.**, **1 suite** 170.00 **st.** – SB (weekends only) 116.00/128.00 **st.**

Hilton National, Walcot St., BA1 5BJ, ✆ 463411, Telex 449519, Fax 464393, – rm – 200. BV i
M 9.50/14.75 **t.** and a la carte 7.50 – 7.95 – **150 rm** 75.00/150.00 **t.** – SB (weekends only) 114.00 **st.**

Lansdown Grove (Best Western), Lansdown Rd, BA1 5EH, ✆ 315891, Telex 444850, Fax 448092, – – 100. Y o
M 11.00/20.00 **st.** and a la carte 3.75 – **45 rm** 62.00/180.00 **st.** – SB (weekends only) 92.00/100.00 **st.**

Apsley House, 141 Newbridge Hill, BA1 3PT, ✆ 336966, ←, – rest Y e
closed 1 to 15 January – **M** (dinner only) a la carte approx. 18.50 **st.** 4.45 – **7 rm** 65.00/120.00 **st.** – SB (November-April) 90.00/120.00 **st.**

Dukes, Great Pulteney St., BA2 4DN, ✆ 463512, Telex 449227 – rest BV s
M (bar lunch)/dinner 15.00 **st.** 5.00 – **21 rm** 55.00/95.00 **st.** – SB 90.00 **st.**

Bath (Best Western), Widcombe Basin, BA2 4JP, ✆ 338855, Telex 445876, Fax 428941 – – 80. BX a
M *(closed Saturday)* 14.00 **st.** (dinner) and a la carte 3.75 – 7.00 – **93 rm** 68.00/133.00 **st.** – SB (weekends only) (except Christmas) 90.00/110.00 **st.**

Berni Royal (B.C.B.), Manvers St., BA1 1JP, ✆ 463134 – BX e
M 8.00/15.00 **st.** – **30 rm** 54.50/70.00 **st.**

Pratt's, South Par., BA2 4AB, ✆ 460441, Telex 444827, Fax 448807 – – 50. BX c
M (bar lunch Monday to Saturday)/dinner 20.00 **st.** and a la carte 5.25 – **46 rm** 60.00/75.00 **st.** – SB (except Christmas) 95.00 **st.**

Sydney Gardens without rest., Sydney Rd, BA2 6NT, ✆ 464818, ←, – Y i
closed Christmas and 3 weeks January – **6 rm** 60.00/65.00 **st.**

Holly Lodge without rest., 8 Upper Oldfield Park, BA2 3JZ, ✆ 424042, Fax 481138, ←, – Z i
6 rm 40.00/65.00 **st.**

Audley House, Park Gdns, BA1 2XP, ✆ 333110, – Y s
M (unlicensed) (dinner only, residents only) 16.00 **st.** – **3 rm** 40.00/60.00 **st.**

Paradise House without rest., 86-88 Holloway, BA2 4PX, ✆ 317723, ←, – Z c
closed 6 days at Christmas – **9 rm** 33.00/60.00 **st.**

Somerset House, 35 Bathwick Hill, BA2 6LD, ✆ 466451, ←, –
closed 4 January-4 February – **M** *(closed Sunday dinner)* (dinner only and Sunday lunch November-May)/dinner 16.50 **st.** 3.00 – **9 rm** 27.50/55.00 **st.** – SB (November-mid May) (weekdays only) 73.10 **st.** Z e

Villa Magdala without rest., Henrietta Rd, BA2 6LX, ✆ 466329, – BV r
closed January – **17 rm** 42.00/67.00 **st.**

Orchard House, Warminster Rd, Bathampton, BA2 6XG, ✆ 466115, – rest Y a
M (dinner only) 12.00 **t.** 2.75 – **14 rm** 45.00/59.00 **t.** – SB (October-March) 71.00/75.00 **st.**

North Parade, 10 North Par., BA2 4AL, ✆ 463384 – BX i
M (dinner only) 12.50 **t.** and a la carte 3.80 – **16 rm** 24.00/62.00 **t.**, **2 suites** 78.00/85.00 **t.** – SB (November-April) 58.00/84.00 **st.**

Tasburgh without rest., Warminster Rd, Bathampton, BA2 6SH, ✆ 425096, ←, – Y r
13 rm 30.00/56.00 **st.**

Haydon House without rest., 9 Bloomfield Park off Bloomfield Rd, BA2 2BY, ✆ 427351, – Z a
4 rm 38.00/55.00 **st.**

Cheriton House without rest., 9 Upper Oldfield Park, BA2 3JX, ✆ 429862, – Z u
closed 24 December-1 January – **8 rm** 32.00/48.00 **st.**

Oldfields without rest., 102 Wells Rd, BA2 3AL, 317984, – . VISA. AX **n**
14 rm 30.00/51.00 **st.**

Oakleigh without rest., 19 Upper Oldfield Park, BA2 3JX, 315698 – . VISA. Z **i**
4 rm 30.00/50.00 **s.**

Leighton House, 139 Wells Rd, BA2 3AL, 314769 – . VISA AX **e**
M (by arrangement) 14.00 **st.** – **7 rm** 38.00/56.00 **st.** – SB (November-April) 67.50/75.00 **st.**

Wentworth House, 106 Bloomfield Rd, BA2 2AP, 339193, , – . VISA. Z **v**
closed mid December-mid January – **M** *(by arrangement)* 11.00 **st.** – **20 rm** 30.00/48.00 **st.**

Popjoys, Beau Nash House, Sawclose, BA1 1EU, 460494, « Former residence of Beau Nash » – AE VISA AX **c**
closed Saturday lunch, Sunday and Monday – **M** 17.00/25.00 **t.** 6.00.

Pino's Hole in the Wall, 16 George St., BA1 2EH, 425242, Italian rest. – AE VISA AV **u**
closed Sunday, Christmas and New Year – **M** a la carte 14.60/26.95 **t.**

Rajpoot, 4 Argyle St., BA2 4BA, 466833, Indian rest. – AE VISA BV **v**
closed 25 and 26 December – **M** 14.00/25.00 **st.** and a la carte.

Woods, 9-13 Alfred St., BA1 2QX, 314812 – VISA AV **v**
closed Sunday and 23 to 28 December – **M** 9.50/16.95 **t.** and a la carte 3.50.

The Circus, 34 Brock St., BA1 2LN, 330208 – VISA AV **e**
closed Sunday dinner, 25-26 December and 1-2 January – **M** 16.00/19.00 **t.** and a la carte 3.50.

Tarts, 8 Pierrepont Pl., BA1 1JX, 330280 – VISA BX **r**
closed Sunday, 3 days at Christmas and 1 January – **M** a la carte 14.95/19.15 **t.** 4.80.

Moon and Sixpence, 6a Broad St., BA1 5LJ, 460962 – AE VISA BV **z**
closed 25-26 December and 1 January – **M** 10.95/20.80 **t.** and a la carte 4.50.

Peking, 1-2 New St., BA1 2AF, 466377, Chinese rest. – . AE VISA AX **u**
M 14.95 **t.** and a la carte 3.95.

Xian, 28 Charles St., BA1 1HU, 424917, Chinese rest. – . AE VISA AX **a**
M 12.00/18.00 **t.** and a la carte 3.50.

at Box (Wilts.) NE : 5½ m. on A 4 – Y – Box – 0225 Bath :

Clos du Roy at Box House with rm, SN14 9NR, on A 4 744447, Fax 743971, French rest., « Converted Georgian rectory », heated, – . AE VISA
M (booking essential) 14.95/36.00 **st.** and a la carte 7.50 – **7 rm** 70.00/95.00 **st.**, **1 suite** 110.00/130.00 **st.**

at Colerne (Wilts.) NE : 6½ m. by A 4 – Y – and Bannerdown rd – 0225 Bath :

Lucknam Park , SN14 8AZ, N : ½ m. on Marshfield rd 742777, Telex 445648, Fax 743536, <, « Early 18C country house in park », , , , , – – 25. VISA.
M 16.50/31.50 **t.** and a la carte – 5.00 – **39 rm** 90.00/155.00 **t.**, **4 suites** 200.00/275.00 **t.** – SB 180.00 **st.**

at Bathford E : 3½ m. by A 4 – Y – off A 363 – 0225 Bath :

Eagle House without rest., Church St., BA1 7RS, 859946, <, « Georgian house », –
closed 20 December-4 January – 2.50 – **6 rm** 26.00/80.00 **st.**

Orchard without rest., 80 High St., BA1 7TG, 858765, « Georgian house », – .
March-October – **4 rm** 55.00 **st.**

at Winsley (Wilts) SE : 6½ m. by A 36 – Y – on B 3108 – Bradford-on-Avon – 0225 Bath :

Burghope Manor , on B 3108, BA15 2LA, 723557, Fax 723113, « 13C manor house, country house atmosphere », – . AE VISA.
M (booking essential) (lunch by arrangement)/dinner 35.00 **st.** – **6 rm** 45.00/70.00 **st.**

at Hinton Charterhouse S : 5¾ m. by A 367 –Z– on B 3110 – 0225 Bath :

Homewood Park , BA3 6BB, E : 1¼ m. on A 36 (North) 723731, Telex 444937, Fax 723820, <, « Tastefully converted country house », , park, – rest – 25. AE VISA.
M 17.50/29.50 **st.** – 7.50 – **15 rm** 85.00/135.00 **st.** – SB (November-March) (weekdays only) 135.00 **st.**

Green Lane House without rest., Green Lane, BA3 6BL, 723631 – VISA.
closed December and January – **4 rm** 23.00/52.00 **st.**

at Monkton Combe S : 6 m. by A 36 – Y – Bath – 0225 Bath :

Wheelwrights Arms, BA2 7HD, 722287 – . VISA.
M (bar lunch)/dinner a la carte approx. 10.45 **t.** 3.30 – **8 rm** 40.00/46.00 **t.** – SB (October-March) 66.00/72.00 **st.**

at Norton St. Philip (Somerset) S : 7 ¼ m. by A 367 – Z – on B 3110 – ✉ Bath (Avon) – ☎ 0225 Limpley Stoke :

Bath Lodge, BA3 6NH, E : 1 ¼ m. by A 366 on A 36 ☎ 723737, Fax 723193, « Early 19C gatehouse », – ⇆ TV ☎ P. VISA.
M a la carte 15.50/20.85 **t.** – **4 rm** 65.00/95.00 **t.**

at Hunstrete W : 8 ½ m. by A 4 – Y – and A 39 off A 368 – ✉ Bristol – ☎ 0761 Compton Dando :

Hunstrete House, BS18 4NS, ☎ 490490, Telex 449540, Fax 490732, ≤, « 18C Country house, gardens and deer park », heated, – ⇆ rest TV ☎ P. VISA.
M 15.00/32.00 **t.** – **23 rm** 95.00/200.00 **t.**, **1 suite** 225.00 **t.** – SB (October-April except Christmas) 175.00/220.00 **st.**

BMW Wellsway ☎ 29187
CITROEN, DAIHATSU Prior Park Rd ☎ 319463
FIAT, ALFA-ROMEO Margarets Buildings, Circus Pl. ☎ 428000
FORD 5-10 James St. West ☎ 444000
MAZDA Upper Bristol Rd ☎ 24240
NISSAN Lower Bristol Rd ☎ 25864
PEUGEOT-TALBOT Upper Bristol Rd ☎ 20391
RENAULT 130 Wells Rd ☎ 334202
ROVER Newbridge Rd ☎ 312774
SEAT Walcot St. ☎ 66752
TOYOTA 50-52 Wellsway ☎ 27408
VAUXHALL Rush Hill ☎ 833338
VAUXHALL-OPEL Upper Bristol Rd ☎ 22131
VOLVO Lower Bristol Rd ☎ 446082
VW Cheltenham St. ☎ 315021

ATS London Rd ☎ 338899/338924

BATTLE East Sussex 404 V 31 – pop. 4 662 – ☎ 042 46.

See : Abbey★ (11C-14C) *AC* (site of the Battle of Hastings 1066).

88 High St. ☎ 3721.

♦London 55 – ♦Brighton 34 – Folkestone 43 – Maidstone 30.

Netherfield Place, TN33 9PP, NW : 2 m. by A 2100 on Netherfield Rd ☎ 4455, Telex 95284, Fax 4024, ≤, « Georgian style country house », park, – TV ☎ P – 50. AE VISA.
closed last week December and first two weeks January – **M** 13.50/22.00 **t.** and a la carte 20.45/21.25 **t.** 4.50 – **14 rm** 45.00/80.00 **t.** – SB (October-March) 145.00/165.00 **st.**

Burnt Wood H. & Country Club, Powdermill Lane, TN33 0SU, S : 2 m. on B 2095 ☎ 5151, Fax 2459, ≤, heated, park, – ⇆ rm TV ☎ P. AE VISA
M 12.50/16.25 **t.** and a la carte 4.00 – **10 rm** 50.00/75.00 **t.** – SB (except Easter, Christmas and New Year) 70.00/90.00 **st.**

George, 23 High St., TN33 0EA, ☎ 4466, Fax 4853 – TV ☎ P. AE VISA
M 11.95/12.95 **t.** and a la carte 3.95 – **21 rm** 41.00/56.00 **st.** – SB (weekend only) 65.00/75.50 **st.**

Little Hemingfold Farmhouse, Telham, TN33 0TT, SE : 1 ¾ m. on A 2100 ☎ 4338, ≤, « Lakeside setting », park, – ⇆ rest TV ☎ P. VISA
M 18.00 **st.** 3.50 – **12 rm** 30.00/60.00 **st.** – SB 68.00/84.00 **st.**

La Vieille Auberge with rm, 27 High St., TN33 0EA, ☎ 5171, Fax 4015 – TV ☎. AE VISA
closed Monday lunch – **M** 14.50/21.95 **st.** and a la carte 6.00 – **7 rm** 29.50/55.00 **st.** – SB (October-May) 80.00/90.00 **st.**

CITROEN Whatlington ☎ 042 487 (Sedlescombe) 307
FORD Upper Lake ☎ 3155
ROVER High St. ☎ 2425

BAWTRY South Yorks. 402 403 404 Q 23 – pop. 2 677 – ✉ ☎ 0302 Doncaster.

Austerfield Park, Cross Lane ☎ 710841, NE : 2 m. by A 614.

♦London 158 – ♦Leeds 39 – Lincoln 32 – ♦Nottingham 36 – ♦Sheffield 22.

Crown (T.H.F.), Market Place, DN10 6JW, ☎ 710341, Telex 547089, Fax 711798, – ⇆ rm TV ☎ & P – 150. AE VISA
M *(closed Saturday lunch)* 8.95/16.95 **st.** and a la carte – 7.00 – **57 rm** 68.00/80.00 **st.** – SB (weekends only) 74.00/82.00 **st.**

FORD Market Pl. ☎ 710212
RENAULT Bawtry Rd ☎ 710595

BEACONSFIELD Bucks. 404 S 29 – pop. 13 397 – ECD : Wednesday and Saturday – ☎ 049 46 (4 and 5 fig.) or 0494 (6 fig.).

Beaconsfield ☎ 676545.

♦London 26 – Aylesbury 19 – ♦Oxford 32.

Bellhouse (De Vere), Oxford Rd, HP9 2XE, E : 1 ¾ m. on A 40 ☎ 0753 (Gerrard's Cross) 887211, Telex 848719, Fax 888231, squash – ⇆ rm TV ☎ P – 350. AE VISA
M 18.00/20.00 **st.** and a la carte 7.50 – **133 rm** 100.00/130.00 **st.**, **3 suites** 150.00/170.00 **st.**.

XX **Leigh House,** 53 Wycombe End, HP9 1LX, ✆ 676348, Chinese (Peking) rest. – ▤. AE VISA
M approx. 17.00 **t.** and a la carte.

XX China Diner, 7 The Highway, Station Rd, Beaconsfield New Town, HP9 1LG, ✆ 678346, Chinese rest.

XX **La Lanterna,** 57 Wycombe End, HP9 1LX, ✆ 675210, Italian rest. – AE VISA
closed Sunday, 25 to 26 December and 1 January – **M** 10.50 **t.** and a la carte.

XX **Wheeler's,** 14 London End, HP9 2JH, ✆ 677077, Seafood – AE VISA
closed Sunday dinner and 25-26 December – **M** a la carte approx. 20.00 **t.** 4.50.

at Wooburn Common SW : 3 ½ m. by A 40 – ✉ Beaconsfield – ☎ 062 85 (5 fig.) or 0628 (6 fig.) Bourne End :

Chequers Inn, Kiln Lane, HP10 0JQ, ✆ 29575, Telex 850124 – TV ☎ P – 30. AE VISA.
M 16.95 **t.** and a la carte – **17 rm** 70.00/75.00 **t.** – SB (weekends only) 82.00 **st.**

MERCEDES-BENZ 55 Station Rd ✆ 672141
VAUXHALL Penn Rd, Knotty Green ✆ 673730

BEAMINSTER Dorset 403 L 31 – pop. 2 338 – ☎ 0308.

♦London 149 – Dorchester 19 – Exeter 40 – Taunton 31.

Hams Plot without rest., DT8 3LU, ✆ 862979, heated, – P
April-October – **5 rm** 30.00/46.00 **st.**

BEARSTED Kent 404 V 30 – see Maidstone.

BEAULIEU Hants. 403 404 P 31 – pop. 1 027 – ECD : Tuesday and Saturday – ✉ Brockenhurst – ☎ 0590.

See : Site★★ – National Motor Museum★ Buckler's Hard Maritime Museum *AC*.

John Montagu Building ✆ 612345.

♦London 102 – Bournemouth 24 – ♦Southampton 13 – Winchester 23.

Montagu Arms, Palace Lane, SO42 7ZL, ✆ 612324, Fax 612188, « Part 18C inn, gardens » – rest TV ☎ P. AE VISA.
M 18.50/29.50 **st.** and a la carte 5.90 – 6.50 – **22 rm** 75.00/140.00 **st.**, **2 suites** 175.00 **st.** – SB 112.00/145.00 **st.**

at Bucklers Hard S : 2 ½ m. – ✉ Brockenhurst – ☎ 0590 Bucklers Hard :

Master Builder's House, SO4 7XB, ✆ 616253, – TV ☎ P – 40. AE VISA
M 11.95/30.00 **st.** and a la carte 3.45 – **23 rm** 55.00/95.00 **st.**

BEAUMARIS Gwynedd 402 403 H 24 – pop. 1 413 – ECD : Wednesday – ☎ 0248.

See : Castle★★ (13C) *AC*.

Envir. : Anglesey★★ – Menai Strait★ (Channel), Menai Suspension Bridge ★ SW : 4 ½ m. – Bryn Celli Du (burial chamber★) SW : 8 m.

Baron Hill ✆ 810231, SW : 1 m. on A 545.

♦London 253 – Birkenhead 74 – Holyhead 25.

Bishopsgate House, 54 Castle St., LL58 8AB, ✆ 810302 – TV ☎ P. VISA
closed 23 December-12 February – **M** (dinner only and Sunday lunch)/dinner 11.95 **t.** and a la carte 3.95 – **10 rm** 25.00/48.00 **t.**

Liverpool Arms without rest., Castle St., LL58 8BA, ✆ 810362 – TV ☎ P. AE VISA.
10 rm 28.50/56.00 **t.**

XX **Ye Olde Bull's Head** with rm, Castle St., LL58 8AP, ✆ 810329, Fax 811294 – TV ☎ P. VISA.
M *(closed 24-25 December and 1 January)* (dinner only and Sunday lunch)/dinner a la carte 15.95/19.25 **t.** 4.25 – **11 rm** 36.50/62.00 **t.** – SB (except summer) 95.00/100.00 **st.**

BECCLES Suffolk 404 Y 26 – pop. 10 677 – ECD : Wednesday – ☎ 0502.

The Common ✆ 712244.

The Quay, Fen Lane ✆ 713196 (summer only).

♦London 113 – Great Yarmouth 15 – ♦Ipswich 40 – ♦Norwich 18.

King's Head (B.C.B.), New Market Sq., NR34 9HA, ✆ 712147 – rest TV ☎ P – 100.
12 rm.

Riverview House without rest., 29 Ballygate, NR34 9ND, ✆ 713519 – TV
closed 21 December-4 January – **10 rm** 14.50/35.00 **st.**

FORD Station Rd ✆ 717023
LAND ROVER, RANGE-ROVER Beccles Rd, Barnby ✆ 050 276 (Barnby) 204
ATS Waveney Garage, Ravensmere ✆ 713222/715570

BECKINGHAM Lincs. 402 404 R 24 – pop. 255 – ✉ ☎ 0636 Fenton Claypole.
♦London 124 – Leicester 43 – Lincoln 20 – ♦Nottingham 28 – ♦Sheffield 46.

XX **Black Swan,** Hillside, LN5 0RF, ℘ 626474, – Ⓟ. VISA
closed Sunday, Monday and 2 weeks September – **M** (booking essential) (lunch by arrangement)/dinner 23.00 **t.**

BECKWITHSHAW North Yorks. 402 P 22 – see Harrogate.

BEDALE North Yorks. 402 P 21 – pop. 2 158 – ECD : Thursday – ✉ Darlington – ☎ 0677.
18 Leyburn Rd ℘ 22568.
Bedale Hall ℘ 24604 (summer only).
♦London 225 – ♦Leeds 45 – ♦Newcastle 30 – York 38.

XX **Plummer's,** North End, DL8 1AF, ℘ 23432 – VISA
closed Monday lunch and Sunday dinner – **M** a la carte 8.95/16.00 **t.** 3.80.

BEDDGELERT Gwynedd 402 403 H 24 – pop. 646 – ECD : Wednesday – ☎ 076 686.
Envir. : NE : Llyn Dinas valley★★ – Llyn Gwynant valley★.
Exc. : Blaenau Ffestiniog (site : slate quarries★) E : 14 m. by Penrhyndeudraeth.
Llewelyn Cottage ℘ 293.
♦London 249 – Caernarfon 13 – Chester 73.

Royal Goat, LL55 4YE, ℘ 224, Fax 422, – rm Ⓟ. AE VISA
M 12.00/22.00 **st.** and a la carte 5.50 – **34 rm** 38.00/75.00 **st.** – SB (October-April) 82.00/120.00 **st.**

Tanronen, LL55 4YB, ℘ 347 – Ⓟ. VISA.
M 6.00/11.50 **t.** 3.50 – **8 rm** 17.00/34.00 **t.** – SB 50.00 **st.**

Sygun Fawr Country House , LL55 4NE, NE : ¾ m. by A 498 ℘ 258, ≤ mountain and valley, « Part 16C stone built house », , park – Ⓟ
M 9.00 **t.** 3.60 – **7 rm** 22.50/38.00 **t.** – SB (winter only) 52.00 **st.**

I prezzi — Per ogni chiarimento sui prezzi qui riportati, consultate le spiegazioni alle pagine dell'introduzione.

BEDFORD Beds. 404 S 27 – pop. 75 632 – ECD : Thursday – ☎ 0234.
See : Embankment★ – Cecil Higgins Art Gallery (porcelain★ 18C).
Envir. : Elstow (Abbey Church★ (11C), Moot Hall : John Bunyan Museum *AC*) S : 1 ¼ m. – Ampthill (Houghton House : site★, ≤★) S : 5 m. – Old Warden (St. Leonard's Church : woodwork★ – Aeroplane Museum, near Biggleswade Aerodrome : the Shuttleworth collection★ *AC*) SE : 7 ½ m.
18 Bedford and County, Green Lane, Clapham ℘ 52617, NW : 2 m. by A 6 – 18 Bedfordshire, Bromham Rd, Biddenham ℘ 53241, NE : 1 m. on A 428 – 18 Mowsbury, Cleat Hill, Kimbolton Rd ℘ 771042, N : 3 m. on B 660.
10 St. Paul's Sq. ℘ 215226.
♦London 59 – ♦Cambridge 31 – Colchester 70 – ♦Leicester 51 – Lincoln 95 – Luton 20 – ♦Oxford 52 – Southend-on-Sea 85.

Barns (Lansbury), Cardington Rd, MK44 3SA, E : 2 m. on A 603 ℘ 270044, Telex 827748, Fax 273102, « Extended 17C manor house with 13C tithe barn », , – rm Ⓟ – 90. AE VISA.
M *(closed Saturday lunch)* 11.50/17.00 **t.** and a la carte 4.50 – **49 rm** 70.00/82.00 **t.** – SB (weekends only) 76.00/84.00 **st.**

Bedford Swan, The Embankment, MK40 1RW, ℘ 46565, Telex 827779, – Ⓟ – 300
122 rm, 1 suite.

De Parys, 41-45 De Parys Av., MK40 2UA, ℘ 52121, – Ⓟ – 60. AE VISA
closed 1 week at Christmas – **M** 15.00 **st.** and a la carte 5.50 – **25 rm** 49.50/70.00 **st.** – SB (weekends only) 66.00/90.00 **st.**

Wayfarer, Goldington Rd, Goldington, MK41 0DS, E : 2 m. on A 428 ℘ 272707, Fax 272707, – Ⓟ – 35
29 rm.

Edwardian House, 15 Shakespeare Rd, MK40 2DZ, ℘ 211156 – Ⓟ. AE VISA.
M *(closed Saturday and Sunday)* (dinner only) a la carte 9.70/13.40 **st.** 3.25 – **19 rm** 30.00/38.00 **st.**

Hertford House without rest., 57 De Parys Av., MK40 2TR, ℘ 50007 – . AE VISA
closed 24 December-2 January – **16 rm** 30.00/50.00 **st.**

at Houghton Conquest S : 6 ½ m. by A 6 – ✉ ☎ 0234 Bedford :

XX **Knife and Cleaver** with rm, MK45 3LA, ℘ 740387, Fax 740900, – Ⓟ. AE VISA
closed dinner Sunday and Bank Holidays and 25 December-1 January – **M** (bar lunch Saturday) a la carte 11.85/22.75 **t.** 4.50 – **9 rm** 40.00/65.00 **t.**

at Marston Moretaine SW : 6 ¼ m. by A 6 off A 421 – ✉ ☎ 0234 Bedford :

Travelodge without rest., Beancroft Rd junction, MK43 0PZ, on A 421 ☎ 766755, Reservations (Toll free) 0800 850950 – TV ♿ P. AE VISA.
32 rm 24.00/29.50 **t.**

at Clapham NW : 2 m. on A 6 – ✉ ☎ 0234 Bedford :

Woodlands Manor, Green Lane, MK41 6EP, ☎ 363281, Telex 825007, Fax 272390, – TV ☎ P – 25. AE VISA.
closed 28 December-2 January – **M** 15.70/27.00 **st.** and a la carte 6.40 – **28 rm** 57.00/94.00 **st.**, **1 suite** 116.00/158.00 **st.** – SB (weekends only) 85.00/110.00 **st.**

MICHELIN Distribution Centre, Hammond Rd, Elms Farm Industrial Estate, MK41 0LG, ☎ 271100, Fax 269453

BMW, ROLLS-ROYCE, BENTLEY Shuttleworth Rd, Goldington ☎ 60411
CITROEN 89 Brickhill Drive ☎ 213381
FIAT, LANCIA 9 Kingsway ☎ 64491
FORD 8-12 The Broadway ☎ 58391
FORD Hudson Rd ☎ 40041
HONDA, VOLVO Windsor Rd ☎ 45454
JAGUAR Bedford Rd, Kempston ☎ 841444
MERCEDES-BENZ Ampthill Rd ☎ 272888
NISSAN 180 Goldington Rd ☎ 60121
RENAULT 87 High St., Clapham ☎ 54257
ROVER 120 Goldington Rd ☎ 55221
SAAB Station Rd, Oakley ☎ 023 02 (Oakley) 3118
VAUXHALL-OPEL Barker's Lane ☎ 270000

ATS 3 London Rd ☎ 58838/9

BEDWORTH Warw 403 404 P 26 – pop. 29 192 – ✉ – ☎ 0203 Nuneaton.

♦London 104 – ♦Birmingham 21 – ♦Coventry 4,5 – ♦Leicester 24.

Travel Inn, Coventry Rd, CV10 7PJ, N : 1 m. on B 4113 at junction with A 444 ☎ 343584, Fax 327156, – TV ♿ P. AE VISA.
M (Beefeater grill) a la carte approx. 12.25 **t.** – 4.50 – **38 rm** -/27.50 **t.**

Travelodge without rest., A 444 Southbound, CV12 0BN, N : 2 m. by B 4113 on A 444 ☎ 382541, Reservations (Toll free) 0800 850950 – TV ♿ P. AE VISA.
40 rm 24.00/29.50 **t.**

BEER Devon 403 K 31 – ✉ ☎ 0297 Seaton.

♦London 170 – Exeter 22 – Taunton 28.

Anchor Inn, Fore St., EX12 3ET, ☎ 20386, ← – TV. VISA.
closed 1 week Christmas – **M** a la carte 10.00/20.00 **t.** 4.50 – **9 rm** 30.00/55.00 **t.**

BEESTON Cheshire 402 403 404 L 24 – pop. 221 – ✉ Tarporley – ☎ 0829 Bunbury.

18 Gipsy Lane, Ring Rd ☎ 0532 (Leeds) 700479.

♦London 186 – Chester 15 – ♦Liverpool 40 – Shrewsbury 32.

Wild Boar, Bunbury, CW6 9NW, on A 49 ☎ 260309, Telex 61222, Fax 261081, – rest TV ☎ ♿ P – 50. AE VISA
M 10.95/15.95 **st.** and a la carte 4.75 – **37 rm** 65.00/95.00 **st.** – SB (weekends only) 86.00 **st.**

BEESTON Notts. 402 403 404 Q 25 – see Nottingham.

BELFORD Northumb. 401 402 O 17 – pop. 943 – ECD : Thursday – ☎ 0668.

Belford Craft Gallery, 2-3 Market Pl. ☎ 888.

♦London 335 – ♦Edinburgh 71 – ♦Newcastle-upon-Tyne 49.

Blue Bell, Market Sq., NE70 7NE, ☎ 213543, Fax 213878, – TV ☎ ♿ P. AE VISA.
M (bar lunch Monday to Saturday)/dinner 16.00 **t.** and a la carte 3.00 – **16 rm** 35.00/76.00 **t.**, **1 suite** – SB (October-mid April) 80.00/86.00 **st.**

BEPTON West Sussex – see Midhurst.

BEREA Dyfed – see St. Davids.

BERKELEY Glos. 403 404 M 28 – pop. 1 498 – ECD : Wednesday – ☎ 0453 Dursley.

♦London 129 – ♦Bristol 20 – ♦Cardiff 50 – Gloucester 18.

Old School House, Canonbury St., GL13 9BG, ☎ 811711 – TV ☎ P. VISA.
closed 25 December-7 January – **M** *(closed Monday)* a la carte lunch 9.30/13.50 dinner 14.50 **t.** 3.50 – **7 rm** 37.00/52.00 **t.**

BERKSWELL West Midlands 403 404 P 26 – see Coventry.

"Short Breaks"

Many hotels now offer a special rate for a stay of 2 nights which includes dinner, bed and breakfast.

BERRIEW (ABERRIW) Powys 402 403 K 26 – pop. 1167 – ✉ Welshpool – ☎ 0686.

♦London 190 – Chester 49 – Shrewsbury 26.

- **Lion**, SY21 8PQ, ✆ 640452 – TV ☎ P. VISA. ⁂
  M (bar lunch Monday to Saturday)/dinner 18.00 **t.** and a la carte 4.50 – **7 rm** 35.00/60.00 **t.**

BERWICK-UPON-TWEED Northumb. 401 402 O 16 – pop. 12 772 – ECD : Thursday – ☎ 0289.

See : City Walls★ (16C).

Envir. : Holy Island★ (Lindisfarne Castle★) : 6 m.

18 Goswick Beal ✆ 87256, S : 5 m. by A 1 – 18 Magdalene Fields ✆ 306384.

Castlegate Car Park ✆ 330733.

♦London 349 – ♦Edinburgh 57 – ♦Newcastle-upon-Tyne 63.

- **King's Arms** (Best Western), 43 Hide Hill, TD15 1EJ, ✆ 307454, Fax 308867, – TV ☎ 120. AE VISA
  M (carving lunch)/dinner 15.50 **st.** and a la carte 3.95 – **36 rm** 42.50/101.00 **st.** – SB (weekends only) 85.00 **st.**
- **Turret House**, Etal Rd, Tweedmouth, TD15 2EG, S : ¾ m. by A 1167 on B 6354 ✆ 330808, Fax 330467, – TV ☎ P. AE VISA
  closed January – **M** 7.50/15.50 **st.** 3.50 – **13 rm** 46.50/65.00 **st.** – SB 75.00/85.00 **st.**

ROVER Tweedside Trading Estate ✆ 330707
RENAULT Golden Sq. ✆ 307371
VAUXHALL 12 Silver St. ✆ 307436
VOLVO Tweed St. ✆ 307537
ATS 78-80 Church St. ✆ 305720/308222

BETHERSDEN Kent 404 W 30 – pop. 1 273 – ✉ ☎ 023 382.

♦London 63 – Folkestone 20 – Maidstone 27.

- **Little Hodgeham** , Smarden Rd ✉ Ashford, TN26 3HE, W : 2 m. ✆ 0233 (High Halden) 85023, « 15C cottage, antique furniture », , – rest P
  Mid March-September – 3.00 – **3 rm** (dinner included) 60.00/89.00 **s.**

BETWS-Y-COED Gwynedd 402 403 I 24 – pop. 654 – ECD : Thursday – ☎ 0690.

Envir. : Fairy Glen and Conway Falls★ *AC*, SE : 2 m. – Swallow Falls★ *AC*, NW : 2 m. – Nanty-Gwryd Valley★, W : by Capel Curig.

9 Betws-y-Coed ✆ 556, NE : ½ m. by A 5.

Royal Oak Stables ✆ 426 and 665 (summer only).

♦London 226 – Holyhead 44 – Shrewsbury 62.

- **Royal Oak**, Holyhead Rd, LL24 0AY, ✆ 710219, Fax 710433 – TV ☎ P. AE VISA. ⁂
  closed 25 and 26 December – **M** 8.50/20.00 **t.** and a la carte – **27 rm** 44.00/68.00 **t.** – SB 70.00/90.00 **st.**
- **Waterloo**, LL24 0AR, on A 5 ✆ 710411, , – TV ☎ P. AE VISA. ⁂
  closed 24 to 26 December – **M** (bar lunch Monday to Saturday)/dinner 14.50 **t.** and a la carte 3.45 – **39 rm** 32.50/51.50 **t.** – SB (except summer) 75.00/92.00 **st.**
- **Ty Gwyn**, LL24 0SG, SE : ½ m. on A 5 ✆ 710383, « 17C inn » – P. VISA
  M 11.95 **t.** and a la carte 3.25 – **13 rm** 16.50/60.00 **t.** – SB 56.90/83.90 **st.**
- **Park Hill**, Llanrwst Rd, LL24 0HD, NE : 1 m. by A 5 on A 470 ✆ 710540, ≤ Vale of Conwy, , , – rest TV P. AE VISA. ⁂
  M 13.00 **st.** 2.90 – **11 rm** 17.00/74.00 **st.** – SB (winter only) 60.00/70.00 **st.**

at Pont-y-Pant SW : 4½ m. on A 470 – ✉ ☎ 069 06 Dolwyddelan :

- **Plas Hall** , LL25 0PJ, ✆ 206, Fax 526, , – TV ☎ P. VISA. ⁂
  M 17.50/13.50 **st.** – **18 rm** 51.35/79.00 **st.** – SB 59.00/95.00 **st.**

BEVERLEY Humberside 402 S 22 – pop. 19 368 – ECD : Thursday – ✉ ☎ 0482 Kingston-upon-Hull.

See : Minster★★ (13C-15C) – St. Mary's Church★ (14C-15C).

18 The Westwood, Walkington Rd ✆ 867190, SW : 1 m. on B 1230.

Guildhall, Register Sq. ✆ 867430 – Museum of Army Transport ✆ 860445.

♦London 188 – ♦Kingston-upon-Hull 8 – ♦Leeds 52 – York 29.

- **Beverley Arms** (T.H.F.), North Bar Within, HU17 8DD, ✆ 869241, Telex 597568, Fax 870907 – rm TV ☎ P – 70. AE VISA
  M 16.95 **st.** and a la carte 4.35 – 7.25 – **57 rm** 65.00/80.00 **st.** – SB (weekends only) 84.00/90.00 **st.**
- Lairgate, 30 Lairgate, HU17 8EP, ✆ 882141, Fax 882141 – TV ☎ P
  24 rm.

at Tickton NE : 3½ m. by A 1035 – ✉ Kingston-upon-Hull – ☎ 0964 Hornsea :

- Tickton Grange, HU17 9SH, on A 1035 ✆ 543666, Telex 527254, – TV ☎ P – 100
  17 rm.

at Walkington SW : 3 ½ m. by A 164 – ✉ Beverley – ☎ 0482 Hull :

XXX **Manor House** 🐎 with rm, Northlands, Newbald Rd, HU17 8RT, NE : 1 m. via Northgate ✆ 881645, Fax 866501, « Late 19C country house, conservatory », 🌳 – TV ☎ P. AE VISA. ✂
M *(closed Sunday)* (dinner only) 24.50 **t.** 🌡 4.25 – ☕ 6.50 – **5 rm** 60.00/100.00 **t.**

at South Dalton NW : 6 ¼ m. by A 164 off B 1248 – ✉ ☎ 0430 Howden :

X **Pipe and Glass,** West End, HU17 7PN, ✆ 810246 – P. AE VISA
closed Sunday dinner and Monday – **M** (bar lunch)/dinner a la carte 12.25/22.95 **t.** 🌡 3.25.

FORD Wednesday Market ✆ 868311
ROVER Barmston Rd, Swinemoor Ind Est. ✆ 867922
VAUXHALL-OPEL Swinemoor Lane ✆ 882207
ATS 379 Grovehill Rd ✆ 868655/882644

BEXHILL East Sussex 404 V 31 – pop. 34 625 – ECD : Wednesday – ☎ 0424.

⛳18 Cooden Beach ✆ 042 43 (Cooden) 2040, W : 2 m. by A 259 – ⛳18 Ellerslie Lane ✆ 212625, N : 2 m.

ℹ De La Warr Pavilion, Marina ✆ 212023.

♦London 66 – ♦ Brighton 32 – Folkestone 42.

🏨 **Cooden Resort,** Cooden Sea Rd, Cooden Beach, TN39 4TT, W : 2 m. on B 2182 ✆ 32281, Fax 36142, ≘s, 🏊 heated, 🏊, 🌳 – TV ☎ P – 🎪 80. AE AE ⓓ VISA
M 11.50/16.50 **t.** and a la carte – **42 rm** ☕ 56.50/78.00 **t.** – SB (weekends only) 80.00/84.00 **st.**

X **Lychgates,** 5a Church St., Old Town, TN40 2HE, ✆ 212193 – AE VISA
closed Saturday lunch, Sunday, Monday and 2 weeks May-June – **M** 9.95/19.95 **t.** 🌡 4.95.

AUDI-VW King Offa Way ✆ 212255
FORD ✆ 212727
HONDA Beeching Rd ✆ 221330
RENAULT London Rd ✆ 210485
ROVER 57-69 London Rd ✆ 212000
TOYOTA London Rd ✆ 213577
YUGO Dorset Rd ✆ 211212

***En saison,** surtout dans les stations fréquentées, il est prudent de retenir à l'avance.*
Cependant, si vous ne pouvez pas occuper la chambre que vous avez retenue, prévenez immédiatement l'hôtelier.
Si vous écrivez à un hôtel à l'étranger, joignez à votre lettre un coupon-réponse international (disponible dans les bureaux de poste).

BIBURY Glos. 403 404 O 28 – pop. 603 – ECD : Wednesday – ✉ Cirencester – ☎ 028 574.

See : Arlington Row★ (17C).

♦London 86 – Gloucester 26 – ♦Oxford 30.

🏨 **Bibury Court** 🐎, GL7 5NT, ✆ 337, Fax 660, ≤, « Tudor mansion », 🎣, 🌳 – TV ☎ P. AE AE ⓓ VISA
closed 1 week Christmas – **M** (bar lunch Monday to Saturday)/dinner 17.00 **t.** 🌡 3.50 – ☕ 5.00 – **17 rm** 40.00/66.00 **t.**, **1 suite** 86.00 **t.**

BICKLEIGH Devon 403 J 31 – pop. 205 – ECD : Tuesday – ✉ Tiverton – ☎ 088 45.

See : Site★★ – Bickleigh Mill Craft Centre and Farms★★ *AC* – Bickleigh Castle★ *AC*.

♦London 195 – Exeter 9 – Taunton 31.

🏠 **Bickleigh Cottage Country,** Bickleigh Bridge, EX16 8RJ, on A 396 ✆ 230, « Part 17C thatched cottage, riverside setting », 🌳 – P. AE VISA. ✂
April-October – **M** (dinner only) (residents only) 8.50 **t.** – **9 rm** ☕ 17.50/39.00 **t.**

🏠 **Fisherman's Cot,** EX16 8RW, on A 396 ✆ 237, Fax 241, 🎣, 🌳 – ⇔ rm TV ☎ P. AE VISA
M a la carte 7.40/17.05 **t.** 🌡 4.10 – **23 rm** ☕ 39.50/59.50 **st.**

BIDDENDEN Kent 404 V 30 – pop. 2 229 – ✉ Ashford – ☎ 0580.

♦London 51 – Folkestone 29 – Hastings 23 – Maidstone 14.

XX **West House,** 28 High St., TN27 8AH, ✆ 291341, Italian rest. – P. AE VISA
closed Sunday, Monday, 1 week April and 2 weeks August-September – **M** 11.00/16.00 **t.** and a la carte 🌡 4.30.

BIDEFORD Devon 403 H 30 **The West Country G.** – pop. 13 826 – ECD : Wednesday – ☎ 023 72 (5 fig.) or 0237 (6 fig.).

See : The Bridge★★ – Burton Art Gallery★*AC*.

Envir. : Clovelly★★, W : 11 m. – Great Torrington : Dartington Glass★*AC*, SE : 7 m. – at Hartland (≤★★★) Church★ Quay★ (≤★★), W : 12 m. – at Thornbury, Devon Museum of Mechanical Music★*AC*, S : 15 m.

⛴ to the Isle of Lundy (Lundy Co.) 1-2 Weekly (2 h) (summer only).

ℹ The Quay ✆ 477676/474591 (summer only).

♦London 231 – Exeter 43 – ♦Plymouth 58 – Taunton 60.

Durrant House, Heywood Rd, Northam, EX39 3QB, N : 1 m. on A 386 ☎ 472361, Telex 46740, Fax 472361 (extn 326), ⇋, ⛱ – |‡| TV ☎ P – 🏛 350. AE VISA
M 7.00/14.00 **t.** and a la carte – **122 rm** 56.00/93.50 **t.**, **3 suites** 82.50/104.50 **t.** – SB (November-March) (weekends only) 65.00 **st.**

Yeoldon House, Durrant Lane, Northam, EX39 2RL, N : 1 ½ m. by A 386 ☎ 474400, Fax 476618, ≤ Torridge estuary, ⇋, – rest TV ☎ P. AE VISA
M 9.50/20.75 **st.** and a la carte 4.95 – **10 rm** 43.25/70.00 **st.** – SB (October-May) 71.00/75.00 **st.**

Orchard Hill, Orchard Hill, Northam, EX39 2QY, N : ¾ m. by A 386 ☎ 472872, – TV P. VISA.
M (dinner only) a la carte 12.00/20.00 **t.** 3.75 – **9 rm** 30.00/42.00 **t.**

at Instow N : 3 m. on A 39 – ✉ Bideford – ☎ 0271 Instow :

Commodore, Marine Par., EX39 4JN, ☎ 860347, Fax 861233, ≤ Taw and Torridge estuaries, – TV ☎ P. AE VISA.
M 12.00/18.00 **t.** and a la carte – **20 rm** 50.00/95.00 **t.** – SB (October-March) 74.00/78.00 **st.**

at Eastleigh NE : 2 ½ m. by A 386 (via Old Barnstaple Rd) – ✉ Bideford – ☎ 0271 Instow :

Pines, EX39 4PA, ☎ 860561, ≤, – rest P. VISA.
M 14.50 **st.** – **8 rm** 20.00/44.00 **st.** – SB 50.00/65.00 **st.**

at Abbotsham W : 2 ¾ m. by A 386 and Abbotsham rd – ✉ ☎ 0237 Bideford :

Tower House, EX39 5BH, N : 1 m. by Pump Lane ☎ 472418, ⛱, – TV P
M (by arrangement) (communal dining) 18.00 – **3 rm** 40.00/66.00 **t.**

ROVER 6 Queen St. ☎ 73304
VAUXHALL-OPEL Handy Cross ☎ 72282
ATS New Rd ☎ 72451

BIGBURY-ON-SEA Devon 403 I 33 – pop. 559 – ECD : Thursday – ✉ Kingsbridge – ☎ 0548.
♦London 196 – Exeter 42 – ♦Plymouth 17.

Burgh Island, TQ7 4AU, S : ½ m. by sea tractor ☎ 810514, Fax 810243, ≤ Bigbury Bay, « Idyllic island setting, Art Deco », ⇋, park, – |‡| TV ☎. AE VISA.
M (booking essential) 16.00/24.00 **t.** and dinner a la carte – **14 suites** (dinner included) 85.00/170.00 **t.**

Henley, Folly Hill, TQ7 4AR, ☎ 810240, ≤ Bigbury Bay and Bolt Head, – TV P. AE VISA
M 11.50 **t.** 3.00 – **8 rm** 18.50/43.00 **st.** – SB 60.00/64.00 **st.**

BILBROOK Somerset 403 J 30 – ✉ Minehead – ☎ 0984 Washford.
♦London 181 – Minehead 5 – Taunton 19.

Dragon House, TA24 6HQ, ☎ 40215, « Part 18C house with gardens » – rm TV ☎ P. AE VISA
M 14.50 **t.** (dinner) and a la carte 3.50 – **9 rm** 39.00/75.00 **t.**, **1 suite** 85.00 **t.**

BILBROUGH North Yorks. 402 Q 22 – see York.

BILLESLEY Warw. – see Stratford-upon-Avon.

BILLINGHAM Cleveland 402 Q 20 – pop. 36 855 – ✉ ☎ 0642 Stockton-on-Tees.
18 Sandy Lane ☎ 554494.
♦London 255 – ♦Middlesbrough 3 – Sunderland 26.

Billingham Arms, The Causeway, TS23 2HD, ☎ 553661, Telex 587746, Fax 552104 – rm TV ☎ P – 🏛 400. AE VISA
M *(closed Saturday lunch)* 6.95/10.95 **st.** and a la carte 3.40 – 3.50 – **69 rm** 20.00/90.00 **st.** – SB (weekends only) 65.00 **st.**

BILLINGSHURST West Sussex 404 S 30 – pop. 5 301 – ECD : Wednesday – ☎ 0403.
♦London 44 – ♦Brighton 24 – Guildford 25 – ♦Portsmouth 40.

Travelodge without rest., Five Oaks, Staines St., RH14 9AE, N : 1 m. on A 29 ☎ 812711, Reservations (Toll Free) 0800 850950 – TV ♿ P. AE VISA.
26 rm 24.00/29.50 **t.**

FORD The Green ☎ 550415
RENAULT Central Garage ☎ 553071
ROVER Wolviston Rd ☎ 553959

En saison, *surtout dans les stations fréquentées, il est prudent de retenir à l'avance.*
Cependant, si vous ne pouvez pas occuper la chambre que vous avez retenue, prévenez immédiatement l'hôtelier.

Si vous écrivez à un hôtel à l'étranger, joignez à vottre lettre un coupon-réponse international (disponible dans les bureaux de poste).

BINGLEY West Yorks. 402 O 22 – pop. 18 954 – ECD : Tuesday – ✉ ☎ 0274 Bradford.

18 St Ives Estate, Harden ✆ 562506, W : ¾ m. by B 6429 – 18 Shipley, Beckfoot Lane, Cottingley Bridge ✆ 563212, S : ½ m, by A 650 – 18 Moorgate, Baildon, Shipley ✆ 584266, NE : 3 m.

♦London 204 – Bradford 6 – Skipton 13.

- **Bankfield,** Bradford Rd, BD16 1TV, SE : 1½ m. on A 650 ✆ 567123, Fax 551331, – rm rest TV ☎ & P – 300. AE VISA
  M *(closed lunch Saturday and Bank Holidays)* (carving rest.) 13.00 **st.** and a la carte – ☐ 7.50 – **101 rm** 67.00/72.00 **st.** – SB (weekends only) 65.00/76.00 **st.**
- **Hallbank,** Beck Lane, BD16 4DD, ✆ 565296 – rest TV ☎ P.
  closed Christmas – **M** 8.50 **st.** 4.00 – **10 rm** ☐ 35.00/48.00 **st.** – SB (weekends only) 70.00/112.00 **st.**

BIRCH SERVICE AREA Greater Manchester 402 ㉒ 403 ③ 404 ⑩ – ✉ Heywood (Lancashire) – ☎ 061 Manchester

- **Granada Lodge** without rest., OL10 2QH, on M 62, between junctions 18 and 19 ✆ 655 3403 – TV & P. AE VISA.
  37 rm 27.50/29.50 **st.**

BIRDLIP Glos. 403 404 N 28 – ECD : Saturday – ✉ ☎ 0452 Gloucester.

♦London 107 – ♦Bristol 51 – Gloucester 9 – ♦Oxford 44 – Swindon 24.

- **Royal George** (Lansbury), GL4 8JH, ✆ 862506, Telex 437238, Fax 862277, – rm TV ☎ & P – 100. AE VISA
  M 8.95/14.00 **t.** and a la carte – **35 rm** ☐ 67.00/80.00 **t.**, **1 suite** – SB (weekends only) 76.00/92.00 **st.**

BIRKENHEAD Merseyside 402 403 K 23 – pop. 99 075 – ECD : Thursday – ☎ 051 Liverpool.

18 Arrowe Park, Woodchurch ✆ 677 1527 – 18 Prenton, Golf Links Rd ✆ 608 1461.

to Liverpool (Merseyside Transport) frequent services daily (7-8 mn).

Central Library, Borough Rd ✆ 652 6106 ext 36.

♦London 222 – ♦Liverpool 2.

Plan : see Liverpool p. 3

- **Bowler Hat,** 2 Talbot Rd, Oxton, L43 2HH, ✆ 652 4931, Telex 628761, – TV ☎ P – 100. AE VISA
  M 11.00/13.00 **t.** and a la carte 3.50 – ☐ 6.50 – **28 rm** 55.00/69.00 **t.**, **1 suite** 75.00 **t.** – SB (weekends only) 155.00/165.00 **st.**
- **Riverhill,** Talbot Rd, Oxton, L43 2HJ, ✆ 653 3773, Fax 653 7162, – TV ☎ P. AE VISA.
  M 8.95/9.90 **st.** and a la carte 3.95 – **16 rm** ☐ 39.95/59.95 **st.**
- **Beadles,** 15 Rose Mount, Oxton, L43 5SG, ✆ 653 9010
  closed Sunday, Monday and August – **M** (dinner only) a la carte approx 15.20 **t.** 2.75.

FIAT Claughton Firs ✆ 653 8555
MAZDA Albion St., Wallasey ✆ 638 2234
MITSUBISHI, COLT New Chester Rd ✆ 645 1025
NISSAN Hoylake Rd ✆ 678 1060
RENAULT Borough Rd ✆ 342 8471
VAUXHALL-OPEL 6 Woodchurch Rd ✆ 652 2366

BIRMINGHAM West Midlands 403 404 O 26 – pop. 1 013 995 – ECD : Wednesday – ☎ 021.

See : Museum and Art Gallery★★ JZ **M2** – Barber Institute of Fine Arts★★ (at Birmingham University) HX **U** – Aston Hall★★ HV **M1** – Museum of Science and Industry★ JY **M3** – Cathedral (stained glass windows★ 19C) KYZ.

18 Cocks Moor Woods, Alcester Rd, South King's Heath ✆ 444 3584, S : 6½ m. by A 435 FX – 18 Edgbaston, Church Rd ✆ 454 1736, S : 1 m. FX – 18 40 Tennal Rd, Harborne ✆ 427 1728 EX – 18 Hatchford Brook, Coventry Rd, Sheldon ✆ 743 9821 HX – 18 Chapel Lane ✆ 357 1232, NW : 6 m. CT – 9 Vicarage Rd, Harborne ✆ 427 1204, SW : 5 m. EX – 9 Warley, Lightwoods Hill ✆ 429 2440, W : 5 m. by A 456 BU.

Birmingham Airport : ✆ 767 7145, E : 6½ m. by A 45 DU.

2 City Arcade ✆ 643 2514 – The Piazza, National Exhibition Centre ✆ 780 4321 – Birmingham Airport ✆ 767 5511.

♦London 122 – ♦Bristol 91 – ♦Liverpool 103 – ♦Manchester 86 – ♦Nottingham 50.

Town plans : Birmingham pp. 2-7
Except where otherwise stated see pp. 6 and 7

- **Hyatt Regency,** 2 Bridge St., B1 2JZ, ✆ 643 1234, Telex 335097, Fax 616 2323, ←, , , – rm TV ☎ – 180.. AE VISA. JZ **a**
  M *a la carte* 22.40/27.00 **st.** 8.50 – ☐ 11.50 – **315 rm** 88.00/97.00 **s.** **4 suites** 150.00/500.00 **s.**
- **Swallow,** 12 Hagley Rd, B16 8SJ, ✆ 452 1144, Telex 333806, Fax 456 3442, , , – rm TV ☎ & P – 30. AE VISA FX **c**
  M Langtrys a la carte 12.00/16.00 **st.** 6.00 – (see also **Elgar's** below) – **94 rm** ☐ 97.50/120.00 **st.**, **4 suites** 175.00 **st.** – SB (weekends only) 150.00 **st.**

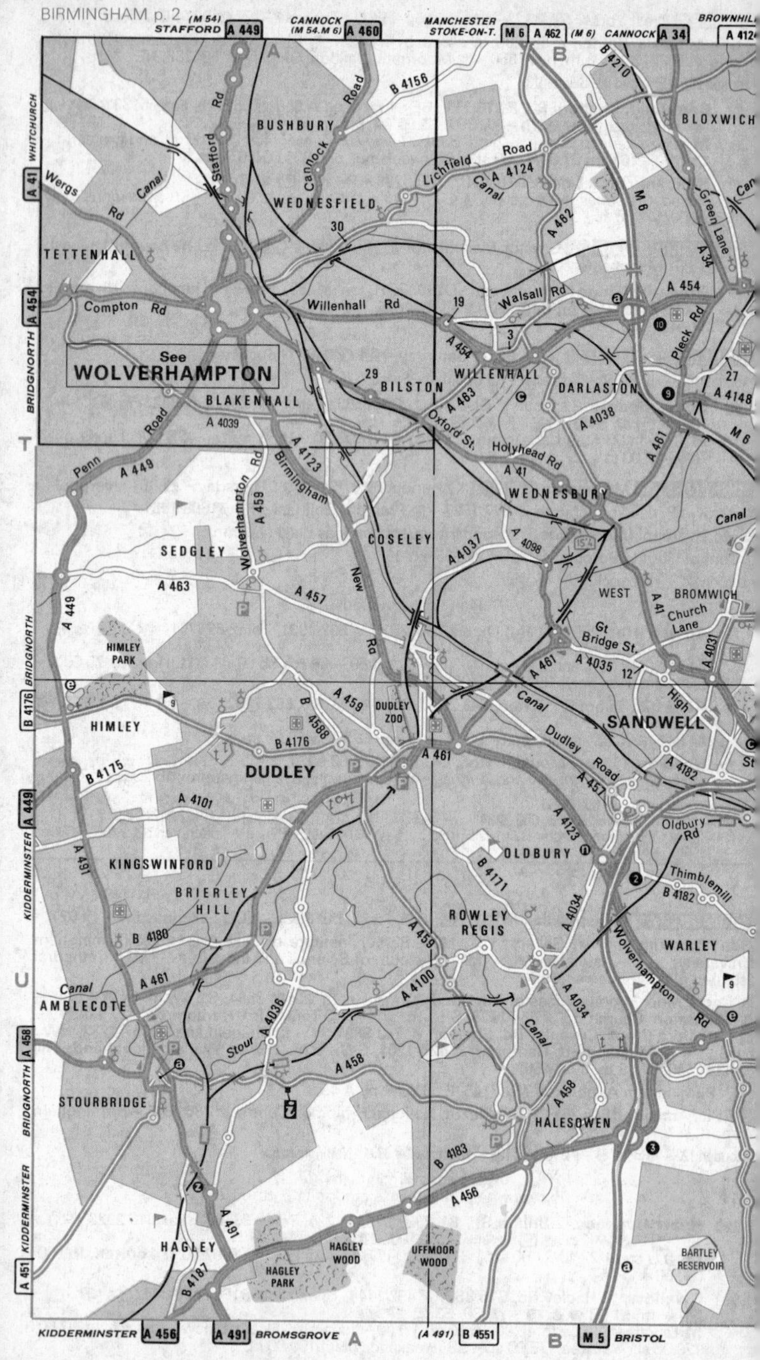

(M 54) STAFFORD A 449
CANNOCK (M 54.M 6) A 460
MANCHESTER STOKE-ON-T. M 6 A 462 (M 6) CANNOCK A 34
A 4124
BLOXWICH
BUSHBURY
WEDNESFIELD
TETTENHALL
See WOLVERHAMPTON
BLAKENHALL
BILSTON
WILLENHALL
DARLASTON
WEDNESBURY
COSELEY
SEDGLEY
HIMLEY PARK
HIMLEY
DUDLEY
DUDLEY ZOO
WEST BROMWICH
SANDWELL
OLDBURY
ROWLEY REGIS
WARLEY
KINGSWINFORD
BRIERLEY HILL
AMBLECOTE
STOURBRIDGE
HALESOWEN
HAGLEY
HAGLEY WOOD
HAGLEY PARK
UFFMOOR WOOD
BARTLEY RESERVOIR
WHITCHURCH A 41
BRIDGNORTH A 454
BRIDGNORTH B 4176
KIDDERMINSTER A 449
BRIDGNORTH A 458
KIDDERMINSTER A 451
KIDDERMINSTER A 456
A 491 BROMSGROVE
(A 491) B 4551
M 5 BRISTOL

BIRMINGHAM AND WOLVERHAMPTON

ENLARGED AREA

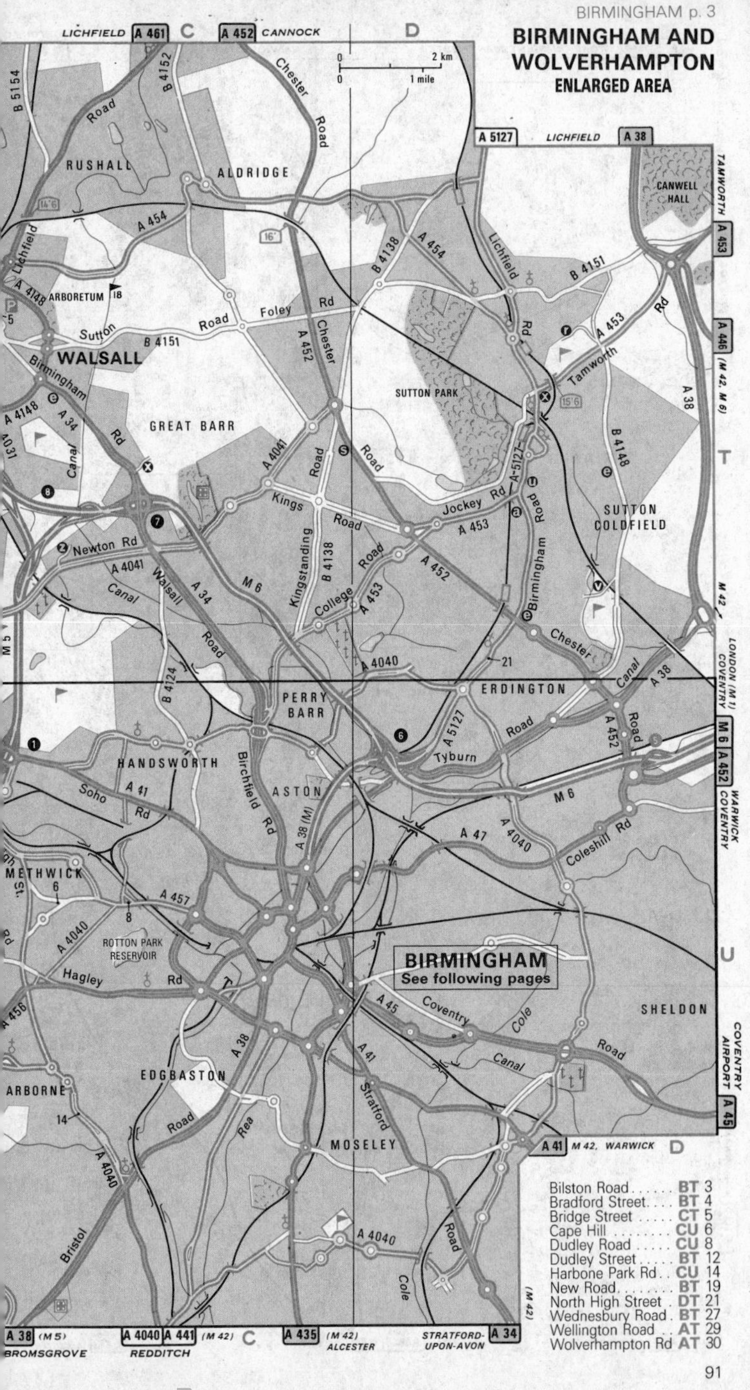

Bilston Road . . . . . . BT 3
Bradford Street. . . . BT 4
Bridge Street . . . . . CT 5
Cape Hill . . . . CU 6
Dudley Road . . . . . CU 8
Dudley Street . . . . . BT 12
Harbone Park Rd . . CU 14
New Road. . . . . BT 19
North High Street . DT 21
Wednesbury Road . BT 27
Wellington Road . . AT 29
Wolverhampton Rd AT 30

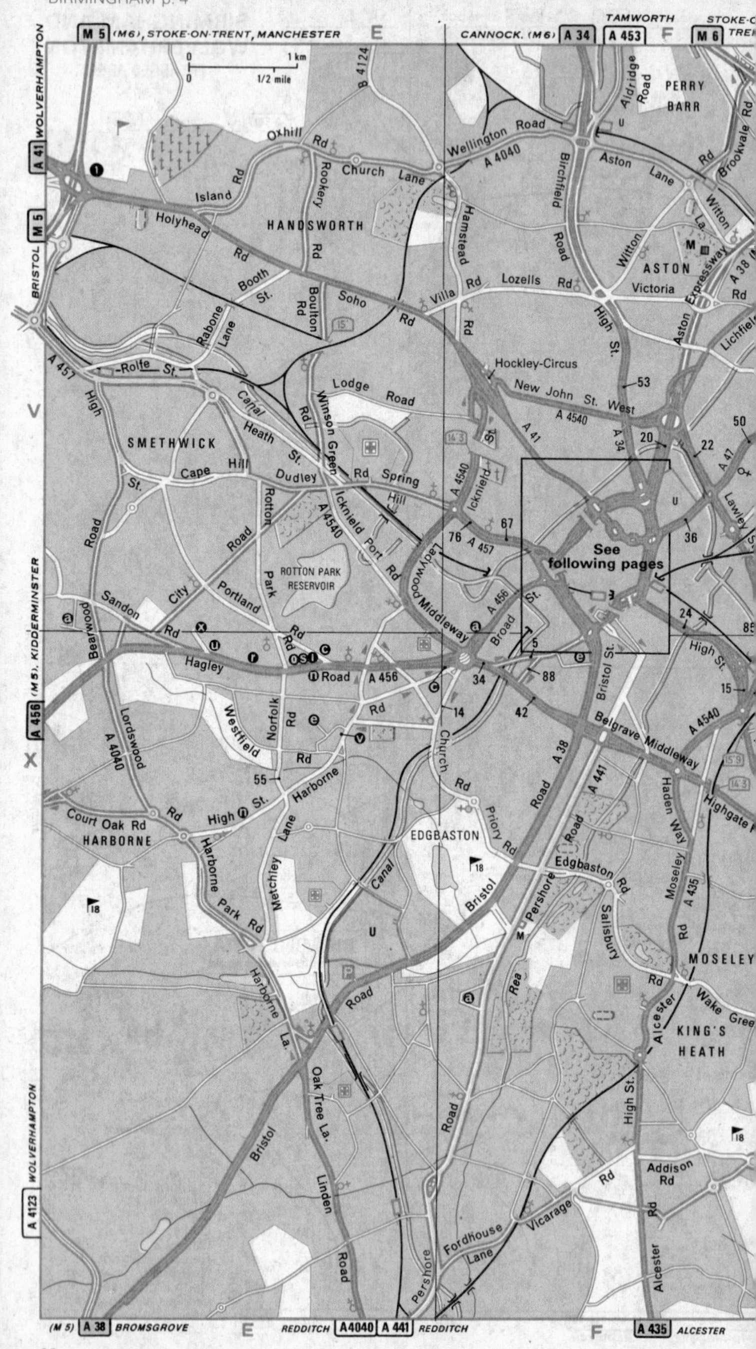
M 5 (M6), STOKE-ON-TRENT, MANCHESTER
CANNOCK. (M6) A 34
TAMWORTH A 453
M 6
WOLVERHAMPTON A 41
BRISTOL M 5
(M5). KIDDERMINSTER A 456
WOLVERHAMPTON A 4123
(M 5) A 38 BROMSGROVE
REDDITCH A4040 A 441 REDDITCH
A 435 ALCESTER
HANDSWORTH
PERRY BARR
ASTON
SMETHWICK
ROTTON PARK RESERVOIR
HARBORNE
EDGBASTON
MOSELEY
KING'S HEATH
Hockley-Circus
See following pages

BUILT UP AREA

For Street Index
see Birmingham p. 7

CENTRE

For Street Index
see Birmingham p. 7

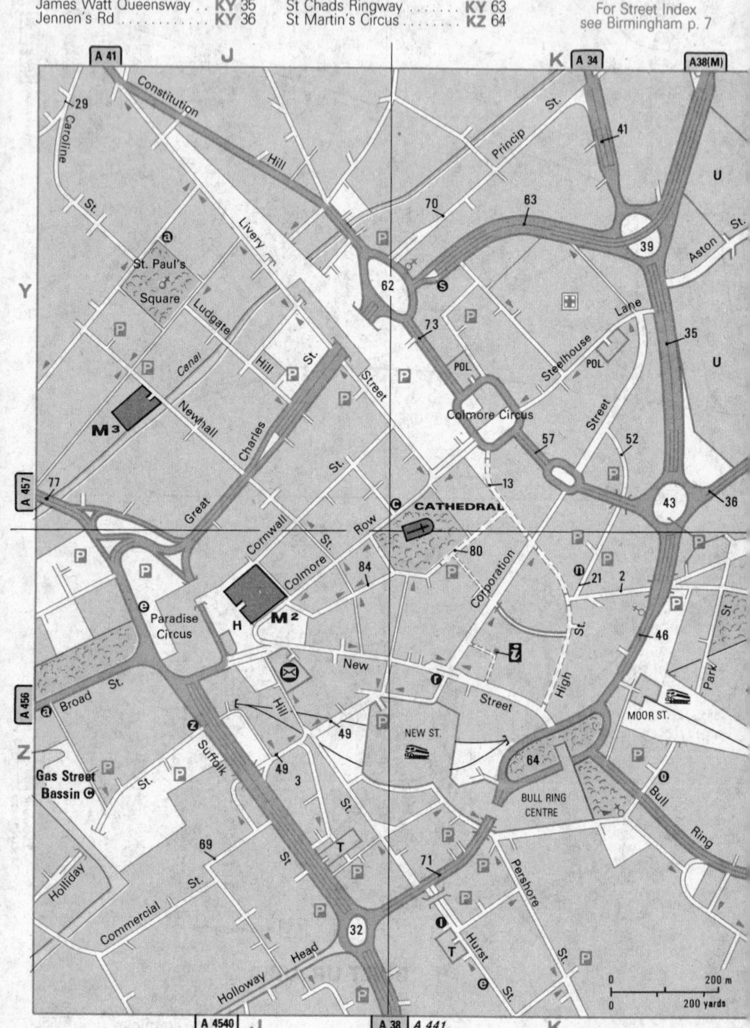

« Short Breaks »

Many hotels now offer a special rate for a stay of 2 nights which includes dinner, bed and breakfast.

STREET INDEX TO BIRMINGHAM TOWN PLANS

Street	Page	Grid	No.
Bull Ring Centre	p. 6	KZ	
Corporation St.	p. 6	KZ	
New St.	p. 6	JZ	
Addison Rd	p. 4	FX	
Albert St.	p. 6	KZ	2
Alcester Rd	p. 4	FX	
Aldridge Rd	p. 4	FV	
Alum Rock Rd	p. 5	GV	
Aston Expressway	p. 4	FV	
Aston Lane	p. 4	FV	
Aston St.	p. 6	KY	
Bath Row	p. 4	FX	5
Bearwood Rd	p. 4	EV	
Belgrave Middleway	p. 4	FX	
Birchfield Rd	p. 4	FV	
Booth St.	p. 4	EV	
Bordesley Green	p. 5	GV	
Bordesley Green Rd	p. 5	GV	
Bordesley Middleway	p. 4	FX	10
Boulton Rd	p. 4	EV	
Bowyer Rd	p. 5	GV	
Bradford Rd	p. 5	HV	
Bristol Rd	p. 4	EX	
Bristol St.	p. 4	FX	
Broad St.	p. 4	FV	
Bromford Lane	p. 5	GV	
Bromford Rd	p. 5	HV	
Brook Lane	p. 5	GX	
Brookvale Rd	p. 4	FV	
Bull Ring	p. 6	KZ	
Bull Ring Centre	p. 6	KZ	
Bull St.	p. 6	KY	13
Calthorpe Rd	p. 4	FX	14
Camp Hill	p. 4	FX	15
Cape Hill	p. 4	EV	
Caroline St.	p. 6	JY	
Cattell Rd	p. 5	GV	
Chester Rd	p. 5	HV	
Church Lane	p. 4	EV	
Church Rd EDGBASTON	p. 4	FX	
Church Rd SHELDON	p. 5	HX	
Church Rd YARDLEY	p. 5	HX	
City Rd	p. 4	EV	
Coleshill Rd	p. 5	HV	
College Rd	p. 5	GX	
Colmore Circus	p. 6	KY	
Colmore Row	p. 6	JZ	
Commercial St.	p. 6	JZ	
Constitution Hill	p. 6	JY	
Cornwall St.	p. 6	JY	
Corporation St.	p. 4	FV	20
Court Oak Rd	p. 4	EX	
Coventry Rd	p. 5	GX	
Dale End	p. 6	KZ	21
Darmouth Middleway	p. 4	FV	22
Digbeth	p. 4	FV	24
Dudley Park Rd	p. 5	GX	25
Dudley Rd	p. 4	EV	
Edgbaston Rd	p. 4	FX	
Fordhouse Lane	p. 4	FX	
Fox Hollies Rd	p. 5	GX	
Golden Hillock Rd	p. 5	GX	
Gravelly Hill	p. 5	GV	
Gravelly Hill Junction	p. 5	GV	
Great Charles St.	p. 6	JY	
Hadden Way	p. 4	FX	
Hagley Rd	p. 4	EX	
Hall St.	p. 6	JY	29
Hampstead Rd	p. 4	FV	
Harborne Lane	p. 4	EX	
Harborne Park Rd	p. 4	EX	
Harborne Rd	p. 4	EX	
Heath St.	p. 4	EV	
Highfield Rd	p. 5	GX	
Highfield Rd SALTLEY	p. 5	GV	
Highgate Rd	p. 4	FX	
High St.	p. 6	KZ	
High St. ASTON	p. 4	FV	
High St. BORDESLEY	p. 4	FX	
High St. HARBORNE	p. 4	EX	
High St. KING'S HEATH	p. 4	FX	
High St. SALTLEY	p. 5	GV	31
High St. SMETHWICK	p. 4	EV	
Hill St.	p. 6	JZ	
Hob's Moat Rd	p. 5	HX	
Hockley Circus	p. 4	FV	
Hockley Hill	p. 6	JY	
Holliday St.	p. 6	JZ	
Holloway Circus	p. 6	JZ	32
Holloway Head	p. 6	JZ	
Holyhead Rd	p. 4	EV	
Hurst St.	p. 6	KZ	
Icknield Port Rd	p. 4	EV	
Icknield St.	p. 4	FV	
Island Rd	p. 4	EV	
Islington Row Middleway	p. 4	FX	34
James Watt Queensway	p. 6	KY	35
Jennen's Rd	p. 4	FV	36
Kingsbury Rd	p. 5	HV	
Ladywood Middleway	p. 4	EV	
Lancaster Circus	p. 6	KY	39
Lancaster St.	p. 6	KY	41
Lawley St.	p. 4	FV	
Lee Bank Middleway	p. 4	FX	42
Lichfield Rd	p. 4	FV	
Linden Rd	p. 4	EX	
Livery St.	p. 6	JY	
Lodge Rd	p. 4	EV	
Lordswood Rd	p. 4	EX	
Lozells Rd	p. 4	FV	
Ludgate Hill	p. 6	JY	
Masshouse Circus	p. 6	KY	43
Metchley Lane	p. 4	EX	
Moor St. Queensway	p. 6	KZ	46
Moseley Rd	p. 4	FX	
Navigation St.	p. 6	JZ	49
Nechell's Parkway	p. 4	FV	50
Newhall St.	p. 6	JY	
New John St. West	p. 4	FV	
Newport Rd	p. 5	HV	
New St.	p. 6	JZ	
Newton St.	p. 6	KY	52
New Town Row	p. 4	FV	53
Norfolk Rd	p. 4	EX	
Nursery Rd	p. 4	EX	55
Oak Tree Lane	p. 4	EX	
Olton Bd East	p. 5	GX	
Oxhill Rd	p. 4	EV	
Paradise Circus	p. 6	JZ	
Park St.	p. 6	KZ	
Pershore Rd	p. 4	FX	
Pershore St.	p. 6	KZ	
Portland Rd	p. 4	EV	
Princip St.	p. 6	KY	
Priory Queensway	p. 6	KY	57
Priory Rd	p. 4	FX	
Rabone Lane	p. 4	EV	
Richmond Rd	p. 5	HX	
Robin Hood Lane	p. 5	GX	
Rolfe St.	p. 4	EV	
Rookery Rd	p. 4	EV	
Rotton Park Rd	p. 4	EV	
St Chads Circus	p. 6	JY	62
St Chads Ringway	p. 6	KY	63
St Martin's Circus	p. 6	KZ	64
St Paul's Square	p. 6	JY	
Salisbury Rd	p. 4	FX	
Saltley Rd	p. 5	GV	66
Sandon Rd	p. 4	EV	
Sand Pits Parade	p. 4	FV	67
Severn St.	p. 6	JZ	69
Shadwell St.	p. 6	KY	70
Shaftmoor Lane	p. 5	GX	
Sheaf Lane	p. 5	HX	
Sheldon Heath Rd	p. 5	HX	
Shirley Rd	p. 5	GX	
Smallbrook Queensway	p. 6	KZ	71
Small Heath Highway	p. 5	GX	
Snow Hill Queensway	p. 6	KY	73
Soho Rd	p. 4	EV	
Solihull Lane	p. 5	GX	74
Spring Hill	p. 4	EV	
Station Rd	p. 5	HV	
Stechford Lane	p. 5	HV	
Steelhouse Lane	p. 6	KY	
Stockfield Rd	p. 5	GX	
Stoney La. MOSELEY	p. 5	GX	
Stoney La. SHELDON	p. 5	HX	
Stratford Rd	p. 5	GX	
Suffolk St.	p. 6	JZ	
Summer Hill Rd	p. 4	FV	76
Summer Row	p. 6	JY	77
Temple Row	p. 6	KZ	80
Tyburn Rd	p. 5	GV	
Vicarage Rd	p. 4	FX	
Victoria Rd	p. 4	FV	
Villa Rd	p. 4	FV	
Wagon Lane	p. 5	HX	
Wake Green Rd	p. 4	FX	
Warwick Rd	p. 5	GX	
Washwood Heath Rd	p. 5	GV	
Waterloo St.	p. 6	JZ	84
Watery Lane	p. 4	FX	85
Wellington Rd	p. 4	FV	
Westfield Rd	p. 4	EX	
Westley Rd	p. 5	GX	87
Wheeley's Lane	p. 4	FX	88
Winson Green Rd	p. 4	EV	
Witton Lane	p. 4	FV	
Witton Rd	p. 4	FV	
Wood End Rd	p. 5	GV	
Yardley Rd	p. 5	HX	
Yardley Wood Rd	p. 5	GX	

« Short Breaks » (SB)

De nombreux hôtels proposent des conditions avantageuses
pour un séjour de deux nuits comprenant la chambre, le dîner et le petit déjeuner.

Plough and Harrow (T.H.F.), 135 Hagley Rd, Edgbaston, B16 8LS, ✆ 454 4111, Telex 338074, Fax 454 1868, – 30. AE VISA
M 19.00/28.00 **t.** and a la carte – 9.95 – **41 rm** 95.00/108.00 **st.**, **3 suites** 130.00/160.00 **st.** – SB (weekends only) 140.90/145.90 **st.** p. 4 EX **a**

Holiday Inn, Central Sq., Holliday St., B1 1HH, ✆ 631 2000, Telex 337272, Fax 643 9018, – rm – 150. AE VISA JZ **z**
M 11.95/14.25 **t.** and a la carte – 8.95 – **291 rm** 87.00/113.00 **st.**, **4 suites** 225.00/300.00 **st.** – SB 110.00/210.00 **st.**

Copthorne (Best Western), Paradise Circus, B3 3HJ, ✆ 200 2727, Telex 339026, Fax 200 1197, – rm rest – 150. AE VISA. JZ **e**
M 12.50/14.95 **t.** and a la carte 5.50 – 8.25 – **211 rm** 85.00/95.00 **t.**, **2 suites** 215.00 **t.**

Midland, 128 New St., B2 4JT, ✆ 643 2601, Telex 338419, Fax 643 5075 – – 220. AE VISA KZ **r**
M *(closed lunch Saturday and Sunday)* 12.50/15.00 **st.** and a la carte – 6.95 – **109 rm** 75.00/85.00 **st.**, **2 suites** 90.00/99.00 **st.**

Royal Angus Thistle (Mt. Charlotte Thistle), St. Chad's, Queensway, B4 6HY, ✆ 236 4211, Telex 336889, Fax 233 2195 – rm – 140. AE VISA KY **s**
M 14.00 **st.** and a la carte – 7.75 – **133 rm** 72.00/102.00 **st.**, **2 suites** – SB 88.00 **st.**

Strathallan Thistle (Mt. Charlotte Thistle), 225 Hagley Rd, Edgbaston, B16 9RY, ✆ 455 9777, Telex 336680, Fax 454 9432 – rm rest – 170. AE VISA p. 4 EX **i**
M a la carte 8.95/57.20 **st.** 4.00 – 7.25 – **163 rm** 72.00/90.00 **st.**, **4 suites** – SB 88.00 **st.**

Grand (Q.M.H.), Colmore Row, B3 2DA, ✆ 236 7951, Telex 338174, Fax 233 1465 – rest – 450. AE VISA JKY **c**
closed 4 days at Christmas – **M** 12.50 **st.** and a la carte 3.95 – **173 rm** 75.00/100.00 **st.**, **3 suites** 150.00 **st.** – SB (weekends only) 70.00 **st.**

Apollo (Mt. Charlotte Thistle), Hagley Rd, Edgbaston, B16 9RA, ✆ 455 0271, Telex 336759, Fax 456 2394 – rest – 120. AE VISA p. 4 EX **o**
M 11.75/13.75 **st.** and a la carte 4.00 – 7.25 – **126 rm** 69.50/85.00 **st.**, **2 suites** 76.50/99.00 **st.** – SB (weekends only) 59.00 **st.**

Novotel, 70 Broad St., B1 2HT, ✆ 643 2000, Telex 335556, Fax 643 9796, – rm rest – 300. AE VISA. p. 4 FV **a**
M 18.50 **st.** and a la carte 5.00 – 6.50 – **148 rm** 59.00/69.00 **st.**

Asquith House, 19 Portland Rd, off Hagley Rd, Edgbaston, B16 9HN, W : 2 m. by A 456 ✆ 454 5282, Fax 456 4668, « Attractive furnishings », – . AE VISA
closed Christmas – **M** (lunch by arrangement)/dinner 18.25 **st.** and a la carte 2.95 – **10 rm** 38.60/53.00 **st.** p. 4 EX **c**

Fountain Court, 339-343 Hagley Rd, Edgbaston, B17 8NH, ✆ 429 1754, Fax 429 1209, – . VISA p. 4 EX **u**
M (bar lunch)/dinner 12.50 **st.** 5.95 – **25 rm** 38.50/55.00 **st.**

Copperfield House, 60 Upland Rd, Selly Park, B29 7JS, ✆ 472 8344, – . VISA p. 4 FX **a**
closed 24 December-2 January – **M** *(closed Saturday and Sunday)* 10.95 **st.** – **14 rm** 32.50/47.50 **st.**

Westbourne Lodge, 27-29 Fountain Rd, Edgbaston, B17 8NJ, ✆ 429 1003, Fax 429 7436, – . VISA p. 4 EV **x**
M (bar lunch)/dinner 15.00 **st.** 4.40 – **19 rm** 36.00/53.00 **st.**

Portland, 313 Hagley Rd, Edgbaston, B16 9LQ, ✆ 455 0535, Telex 334200, Fax 456 1841 – rest – 100 p. 4 EX **r**
62 rm.

Hagley Court, 229 Hagley Rd, Edgbaston, B16 9RP, ✆ 454 6514, Fax 456 2722 – . AE VISA. p. 4 EX **s**
closed 24 December-3 January – **M** *(closed Friday to Sunday and Bank Holidays)* (bar lunch)/dinner 12.50 **st.** and a la carte 4.50 – **27 rm** 44.00/53.00.

New Cobden, 166-174 Hagley Rd, Edgbaston, B16 9NZ, ✆ 454 6621, Telex 333851, Fax 454 1910, – rm – 120. AE VISA.
M 11.75/16.00 **st.** and a la carte 4.00 – 5.00 – **230 rm** 49.00/66.00 **st.** – SB (weekends only) 70.00 **st.** p. 4 EX **n**

Travel Inn, 20-22 Bridge st., B1 2JH, ✆ 633 4820, Fax 633 4779 – rm . AE VISA. JZ **c**
M (Beefeater grill) a la carte approx. 12.25 **t.** – 4.50 – **54 rm** -/27.50 **t.**

Campanile, 55 Irving St., B1 1DH, ✆ 622 4925, Telex 333701, Fax 622 4195 – . VISA p. 4 FX **e**
M (grill rest.) 9.90 **st.** (dinner) and a la carte 5.10 – 4.15 – **48 rm** 32.50 **st.**

XXXX **Elgar's,** (at Swallow H.) 12 Hagley Rd, B16 8SJ, ☏ 452 1144, Telex 333806, Fax 456 3442 – ▤ Ⓟ. ▭ AE ◑ VISA p. 4 FX **c**
M 16.00/29.00 **st.** and a la carte 🍾 6.00.

XXX **Sloans,** Chad Sq., Hawthorne Rd, Edgbaston, B15 3TQ, ☏ 455 6697 – ▭ AE VISA
closed Saturday lunch, Sunday, 24 December-4 January and Bank Holidays – **M** 17.00 **t.** (lunch) and a la carte approx. 23.00 **t.** p. 4 EX **v**

XXX **Jonathans'** with rm, 16-24 Wolverhampton Rd, B68 0LH, W : 4 m. by A 456 ☏ 429 3757, Fax 434 3107, English rest., « Victoriana » – TV ☎ Ⓟ. ▭ AE VISA. ✗ p. 2 BU **e**
M 19.50 **st.** and a la carte 🍾 3.20 – ☐ 8.50 – **8 rm** 65.00/75.00 **t.**, **2 suites** 85.00/95.00 **t.** – SB (weekends only) 79.00 **st.**

XX **Days of the Raj,** 51 Dale End, B4 7LS, ☏ 236 0445, Indian rest. – ▤. ▭ AE ◑ VISA
closed lunch Saturday and Sunday, and 25-26 December – **M** (Buffet lunch)/dinner 14.00 **t.** and a la carte. KZ **n**

XX **Maharaja,** 23-25 Hurst St., B5 4AS, ☏ 622 2641, North Indian rest. – ▤. ▭ AE ◑ VISA
closed Sunday and last 2 weeks July – **M** 10.50/13.50 **t.** and a la carte. KZ **i**

XX **Henry's,** 27 St. Paul's Sq., B3 1RB, ☏ 200 1136, Chinese (Canton) rest. – ▭ AE ◑ VISA JY **a**
closed Sunday, last week August and Bank Holidays – **M** 13.50/15.00 **t.** and a la carte.

XX **Henry Wong,** 283 High St., Harborne, B17 9QH, W : 3 ¾ m. by A 456 ☏ 427 9799, Chinese (Canton) rest. – ▭ AE ◑ VISA p. 4 EX **n**
closed Sunday, last week August and Bank Holidays – **M** 12.50/13.50 **t.** and a la carte.

XX **Dynasty,** 93-103 Hurst St., B5 4TE, ☏ 622 1410, Chinese rest. – ▭ AE ◑ VISA
closed Bank Holidays – **M** 10.00/14.00 **st.** and a la carte. KZ **e**

XX Lorenzo, 3 Park St., Digbeth, B5 5JD, ☏ 643 0541, Italian rest. KZ **o**

X **Franzl's,** 151 Milcote Rd, Bearwood, Smethwick, B67 5BN, ☏ 429 7920, Austrian rest. – ▭ VISA p. 4 EV **a**
closed Sunday, Monday, first 3 weeks August and last week December – **M** (dinner only) 16.50 **t.** 🍾 3.85.

MICHELIN Distribution Centre, Valepits Rd, Garretts Green, B33 0YD, ☏ 789 7100, Fax 789 7323 p. 5 HX

CITROEN Barnes Hill, Weoley Castle ☏ 427 5231
FORD 156-182 Bristol St. ☏ 666 6000
FORD Long Acre, Nechells ☏ 322 2222
FORD Granby Av., Garretts Green ☏ 789 7000
JAGUAR Bristol St. ☏ 666 6999
MAZDA Rookery Rd, Handsworth ☏ 554 9333
MERCEDES-BENZ Charles Henry St. ☏ 622 3031
NISSAN Walkers Heath Rd, Kings Norton ☏ 451 1411
NISSAN 4 Birmingham Rd ☏ 358 7011
PEUGEOT-TALBOT Charlotte St. ☏ 236 4382
PEUGEOT-TALBOT 30 High St, Deritend ☏ 772 4388
ROLLS-ROYCE, BENTLEY, FERRARI Stratford Rd, Shirley ☏ 745 5566
ROVER Aston Hall Rd, Aston ☏ 328 0833
ROVER 71 Aston Rd North, Aston ☏ 359 3678
TOYOTA 138 Soho Hill, Handsworth ☏ 554 6311
VAUXHALL Queslett Rd,Great Barr ☏ 360 5445
VAUXHALL-OPEL 86 Orphanage Rd, Erdington ☏ 373 5241
VW-AUDI Digbeth ☏ 643 7341

Ⓜ ATS 1558 Pershore rd., Stirchley ☏ 458 2951

Except where otherwise stated see pp. 2 and 3

at Erdington NE : 5 m. by A 5127 – ✉ ☎ 021 Birmingham :

⌂ **Willow Tree,** 759 Chester Rd, B24 0BY, on A 452 ☏ 373 6388, 🚗 – TV ☎ Ⓟ. ▭ VISA. ✗
M 10.00 **st.** – **7 rm** ☐ 22.00/45.85 **st.** DT **e**

BMW Jockey Rd, Boldmere ☏ 354 8131
CITROEN Old Kingsbury Rd, Minworth ☏ 351 4367
FIAT 35 Sutton New Rd, Erdington ☏ 377 6533
HONDA Bromford Lane ☏ 328 4211
LADA Wood End Lane, Erdington ☏ 373 5805
MAZDA 29-33 Kings Rd, New Oscott ☏ 354 6781
PEUGEOT-TALBOT Newport Rd, Castle Bromwich ☏ 747 4712
ROVER Chester Rd ☏ 353 3231
SAAB Eachelhurst Rd, Erdington ☏ 351 1027
VAUXHALL 364 Chester Rd, Castle Bromwich ☏ 749 2222

Ⓜ ATS 158 Slade Rd, Erdington ☏ 327 2783/4
ATS 1189 Chester Rd ☏ 373 6104

at Acocks Green SE : 4 ½ m. on B 4146 – DU – ✉ ☎ 021 Birmingham :

⌂ **Atholl Lodge,** 16 Elmdon Rd, off Yardley Rd, B27 6LH, ☏ 707 4417, 🚗 – TV Ⓟ. ▭ VISA
M (by arrangement) 7.00 **st.** – **10 rm** ☐ 17.00/36.00 **st.** p. 5 HX **e**

ALFA-ROMEO 683 Stratford Rd, Sparkhill ☏ 778 1295
DAIHATSU, SKODA 266 Vicarage Rd, Kings Heath ☏ 444 3195
FIAT, LANCIA, LOTUS 979 Stratford Rd, Hall Green ☏ 778 2323
FSO 438 Stratford Rd, Sparkhill ☏ 773 8646
LADA, RELIANT 723-725 Stratford Rd, Sparkhill ☏ 777 6164
MAZDA 32-38 Coventry Rd, Bordesley ☏ 772 5916
ROVER 884 Warwick Rd ☏ 765 4488
VAUXHALL 291 Shaftmoor Lane, Hall Green ☏ 777 1074
VAUXHALL-OPEL 870 Stratford Rd, Sparkhill ☏ 702 2345

at Birmingham Airport SE : 7 m. on A 45 – DU – ✉ ☎ 021 Birmingham :

🏨 **Excelsior** (T.H.F.), Coventry Rd, Elmdon, B26 3QW, ☏ 782 8141, Telex 338005, Fax 782 2476 – ⇔ rm TV ☎ Ⓟ – 🎪 150. ▭ AE ◑ VISA
M 9.50/14.50 **st.** and a la carte 🍾 3.50 – ☐ 7.50 – **141 rm** 65.00/75.00 **st.**

at National Exhibition Centre SE : 9 ½ m. on A 45 – DU – ✉ ☎ 021 Birmingham :

Birmingham Metropole, Bickenhill, B40 1PP, ☎ 780 4242, Telex 336129, Fax 780 3923, ≘s, squash – |♦| ⇔ rm ▤ TV ☎ ♿ P – 🏛 1 800. AE ① VISA
M 15.95 **t.** and a la carte – ☕ 7.95 – **797 rm** 95.00/145.00 **t.**, **9 suites** 270.00/400.00 **t.** – SB (weekends only) 98.00/140.00 **st.**

Arden, Coventry Rd, B92 0EH, ☎ 067 55 (Hampton-in-Arden) 3221, Telex 334913, Fax 3225, Ɫ, ≘s, ▢ – |♦| TV ☎ ♿ P – 🏛 130. AE ① VISA
M (bar lunch Saturday) 12.00/22.00 **t.** and a la carte 🍷 4.65 – ☕ 7.00 – **76 rm** 65.00/72.50 **st.**

at Northfield SW : 6 m. by A 38 – CU – ✉ ☎ 021 Birmingham :

Norwood, 87-89 Bunbury Rd, B31 2ET, ☎ 411 2202, Fax 411 2202, 🌳 – TV ☎ P. VISA. ✗
closed 25-26 December – **M** *(closed Sunday)* (dinner only) 13.95 **st.** 🍷 3.75 – **17 rm** ☕ 25.00/65.00 **st.**

at King's Norton SW : 7 m. by A 441 – FX – ✉ ☎ 021 Birmingham :

Norton Place (at The Patrick Collection), 180 Lifford Lane, B30 3NT, ☎ 433 5656, Fax 433 3048, « Collection of classic motor cars », Ɫ, 🌳 – ⇔ rm TV ☎ ♿ P – 🏛 140. AE ① VISA. ✗
M (see **Lombard Room** below) – **9 rm** ☕ 120.00/150.00 **st.**, **1 suite** 180.00/210.00 **st.**.

XXX **Lombard Room** (at The Patrick Collection), 180 Lifford Lane, B30 3NT, ☎ 433 5656, Fax 433 3048, « Collection of classic motor cars », 🌳 – P. AE ① VISA
M 16.50/20.50 **st.** and a la carte 🍷 5.00.

CITROEN Hallam St., Balsall Heath, Kings Heath ☎ 440 4606/523 3421
FORD 82 St. Mary's Row, Moseley, Kings Heath ☎ 442 4000
NISSAN 57 Walkers Heath Rd ☎ 451 1411
SKODA 307 Northfield Rd, Harborne, Kings Heath ☎ 427 4050
VAUXHALL Ryland St., Edgbaston, Kings Heath ☎ 455 7171

at Frankley Service Area SW : 8 ¾ m. by A 456 on M 5 – ✉ ☎ 021 Birmingham :

Granada Lodge without rest., B32 4AR, ☎ 550 3261, Fax 501 2880 – ⇔ TV ♿ P. AE ① VISA. ✗ BU a
41 rm 29.00/32.00 **t.**

at Olbury W : 7 ¾ m. by A 456 on A 4123 – ✉ ☎ 021 Birmingham :

Travelodge without rest., Wolverhampton Rd, B69 2BH, on A 4123 ☎ 552 2967, Reservations (Toll free) 0800 850950 – TV ♿ P. AE VISA. ✗ p. 2 BU n
33 rm 24.00/29.50 **t.**

FIAT Birmingham Rd ☎ 525 9408
FORD 377 High St. ☎ 553 1881
ROVER High St. ☎ 553 0778
VAUXHALL-OPEL Ryland St. Edgbaston, Kings Heath ☎ 553 3777

at Great Barr NW : 6 m. on A 34 – ✉ ☎ 021 Birmingham :

Post House (T.H.F), Chapel Lane, B43 7BG, ☎ 357 7444, Telex 338497, Fax 357 7503, Ɫ, ≘s, ⛱ heated, ▢ – ⇔ rm TV ☎ P – 🏛 150. AE ① VISA CT x
M *(closed Saturday lunch and Sunday dinner)* 20.00/30.00 **st.** and a la carte 🍷 4.00 – ☕ 7.50 – **204 rm** 69.00/79.00 **st.** – SB (weekends only) 76.00 **st.**

Great Barr, Pear Tree Drive, Newton Rd, B43 6HS, W : 1 m. by A 4041 ☎ 357 1141, Telex 336406, Fax 357 7557, 🌳 – TV ☎ P – 🏛 100. AE ① VISA. ✗ CT z
M 10.00/13.00 **st.** and a la carte 🍷 5.00 – **114 rm** ☕ 62.00/72.00 **st.**

at West Bromwich NW : 6 m. on A 41 – ✉ ☎ 021 Birmingham :

West Bromich Moat House (Q.M.H.) Birmingham Rd, B70 6RS, ☎ 553 6111, Telex 336232, Fax 525 7403 – |♦| ⇔ rm ▤ rest TV ☎ P – 🏛 120. AE ① VISA BU c
M 11.00/13.00 **t.** – **180 rm** ☕ 72.50/85.00 **t.**

ATS 94 Aldrige Rd, Perry Barr ☎ 356 5925/6632

BISHOP AUCKLAND Durham 401 402 P 20 – pop. 23 560 – ECD : Wednesday – ☎ 0388.

⛳18 High Plains ☎ 602198.

◆London 253 – ◆Carlisle 73 – ◆Middlesbrough 24 – ◆Newcastle-upon-Tyne 28 – Sunderland 25.

Park Head, New Coundon, DL14 8QB, NE : 1 ¾ m. by A 689 on A 688 ☎ 661727, Fax 661727 – TV ☎ P. AE ① VISA. ✗
M 7.95/10.95 **t.** and a la carte 🍷 3.25 – **25 rm** 28.00/65.00 **t.** – SB (weekends only) 50.00/70.00 **st.**

ARG Tindale Cres. ☎ 604481
DAIHATSU Station Rd ☎ 832184
FORD St Helens ☎ 605184
RENAULT Holdforth Crest ☎ 602703

ATS Cockton Hill ☎ 603681

BISHOP'S HULL Somerset – see Taunton.

There is no paid publicity in this Guide.

BISHOP'S STORTFORD Herts. 404 U 28 – pop. 22 535 – ECD : Wednesday – ☎ 0279.

Dunmow Rd ☎ 654715, W : 1 m. on A 1250.

Stansted Airport : ☎ 502379, Telex 818708, NE : 3½ m.

Council Offices, 2 The Causeway ☎ 655261.

◆London 34 – ◆Cambridge 27 – Chelmsford 19 – Colchester 33.

at Hatfield Heath SE : 6 m. on A 1060 – ✉ ☎ 0279 Bishop's Stortford :

Down Hall Country House, CM22 7AS, S : 1 ½ m. ☎ 731441, Telex 81609, Fax 730416, ≤, « 19C Italianate mansion », park, – TV ☎ P – 200. AE VISA
M 14.50/18.00 **st.** and a la carte 5.50 – **103 rm** 80.50/130.00 **st.** – SB (weekends only) 105.00/125.00 **st.**

CITROEN Dunmow Rd ☎ 654335
FORD London Rd ☎ 652214
LANCIA London Rd ☎ 654181
PEUGEOT-TALBOT 26 Northgate End ☎ 653494
RENAULT,VAUXHALL Northgate End ☎ 653127
ROVER 123-129 South St. ☎ 757777
VAUXHALL-OPEL Stansted Rd ☎ 755100

ATS 14 Burnt Mill, Harlow ☎ 21965

BISHOP'S TAWTON Devon 403 H 30 – see Barnstaple.

BLACKBURN Lancs. 402 M 22 – pop. 109 564 – ECD : Thursday – ☎ 0254.

Beardwood Brow, ☎ 51122, NW : 1 ¼ m. by A 677 – Pleasington ☎ 201028, W : 3 m. – Wilpshire, 72 Valley Rd ☎ 248260.

Town Hall ☎ 55201/53277.

◆London 228 – ◆Leeds 47 – ◆Liverpool 39 – ◆Manchester 24 – Preston 11.

Blackburn Moat House (Q.M.H.), Yew Tree Drive, Preston New Rd, BB2 7BE, NW : 2 m. at junction A 677 and A 6119 ☎ 64441, Telex 63271, Fax 682435 – rm TV ☎ P – 350. AE VISA
M *(closed Saturday lunch)* (carving lunch) 8.45/12.95 **st.** and a la carte 3.85 – **96 rm** 64.00/76.00 **st.**, **2 suites** 86.00 **st.** – SB (weekends only) 69.00 **st.**

at Mellor NW : 4 m. by A 677 – ✉ Blackburn – ☎ 0254 Blackburn :

Millstone, Church Lane, BB2 7JR, ☎ 813333, Fax 812628 – rm TV ☎ P – 30. AE VISA
M *(closed Saturday lunch)* 8.45/17.75 **t.** and a la carte 4.50 – **18 rm** 47.00/70.00 **st.**, **1 suite** 70.00/95.00 **st.** – SB (weekends only) 64.00/84.00 **st.**

FIAT 52-56 King St. ☎ 52981
FORD Montague St. ☎ 57021
PEUGEOT, TALBOT Whalley New Rd ☎ 661616
RENAULT Gt. Harwood ☎ 886590
ROVER, DAIMLER-JAGUAR Park Rd ☎ 662721
TOYOTA Accrington Rd ☎ 57333
VAUXHALL Quarry St., Eanam ☎ 51191
VW, AUDI 854 Whalley New Rd ☎ 40621

ATS Pendle St., Copy Nook ☎ 55963/59272/665115

BLACKPOOL Lancs. 402 K 22 – pop. 146 297 – ECD : Wednesday – ☎ 0253.

See : Illuminations★★ (late September and early October) – Tower★ (★) *AC* AY A.

Blackpool North Shore, Devonshire Rd ☎ 51017, N : 1 ½ m. from main station BY – Blackpool Park, North Park Drive, ☎ 33960, E : 1 ½ m. BY – Poulton-le-Fylde, Myrtle Farm, Breck Rd ☎ 0253 (Poulton) 892444, E : 3 m. by A 586 BY.

Blackpool Airport : ☎ 43061, S : 3 m. by A 584.

1 Clifton St. ☎ 21623 and 25212 (weekdays only) – 87a Coronation St. ☎ 21891 – Blackpool Airport, Terminal Building, Squires Gate Lane ☎ 43061.

◆London 246 – ◆Leeds 88 – ◆Liverpool 56 – ◆Manchester 51 – ◆Middlesbrough 123.

Plan on next page

Imperial (T.H.F.), North Shore, North Promenade, FY1 2HB, ☎ 23971, Telex 677376, Fax 751784, ≤, – rm TV ☎ P – 400. AE VISA AY c
M 14.50/18.00 **st.** and a la carte 4.50 – 7.60 – **152 rm** 75.00/120.00 **st.**, **7 suites** 145.00/220.00 **s.** – SB 80.00/120.00 **st.**

Pembroke, North Promenade, FY1 2JQ, ☎ 23434, Telex 677469, Fax 27864, ≤, – rm TV ☎ P – 500. AE VISA AY x
(carving lunch) 13.50 **st.** and dinner a la carte 16.95/25.70 **st.** 7.25 – **194 rm** 85.00/107.00 **st.**, **6 suites** 210.00/330.00 **st.** – SB 92.00/106.00 **st.**

Savoy, Queens Promenade, FY2 9SJ, ☎ 52561, Telex 667570 – TV ☎ P – 150 AY a
145 rm, **5 suites.**

Warwick (Best Western), 603-609 New South Promenade, FY4 1NG, ☎ 42192, Fax 405776, – TV ☎ P – 50. AE VISA BZ u
closed first 2 weeks January – **M** (bar lunch)/dinner 11.95 **t.** 4.00 – **52 rm** 30.50/65.50 **t.** – SB 58.00/60.00 **st.**

Brabyns, 1-3 Shaftesbury Av., North Shore, FY2 9QQ, ☎ 54263 – TV ☎ P. VISA BY i
M 6.00/9.50 **t.** 3.75 – **25 rm** 30.00/58.00 **t.** – SB (November-Easter) 55.00 **st.**

BLACKPOOL

Central Drive	BZ 8
Church Street	AY
Hornby Road	BY
Queen's Promenade	BY
Abingdon Street	AY 2
Adelaide Street	AY 3
Ansdell Road	BZ 4
Blackpool Old Rd.	BY 5
Burlington Road West	AZ 6
Caunce Street	AY 7
Cherry Tree Rd.	BZ 9
Clifton Street	AY 12
Condor Grove	BZ 13
Cookson Street	AY 14
Deansgate	AY 15
Garstang Rd West	BY 16
George Street	AY 17
Grange Road	BY 19
Grasmere Road	BZ 20
Grosvenor Street	AY 21
High Street	AY 22
King Street	AY 23
Lark Hill Street	AY 24
New Bonny Street	AY 25
North Park Drive	BY 26
Pleasant Street	AY 27
Plymouth Road	BY 28
Poulton Road	BY 29
Preston Old Rd.	BZ 31
Reads Avenue	BZ 32
Rigby Road	BZ 33
South King St	AY 35
South Park Drive	BZ 36
Talbot Square	AY 37
Topping Street	AY 39
Westcliffe Drive	BY 40

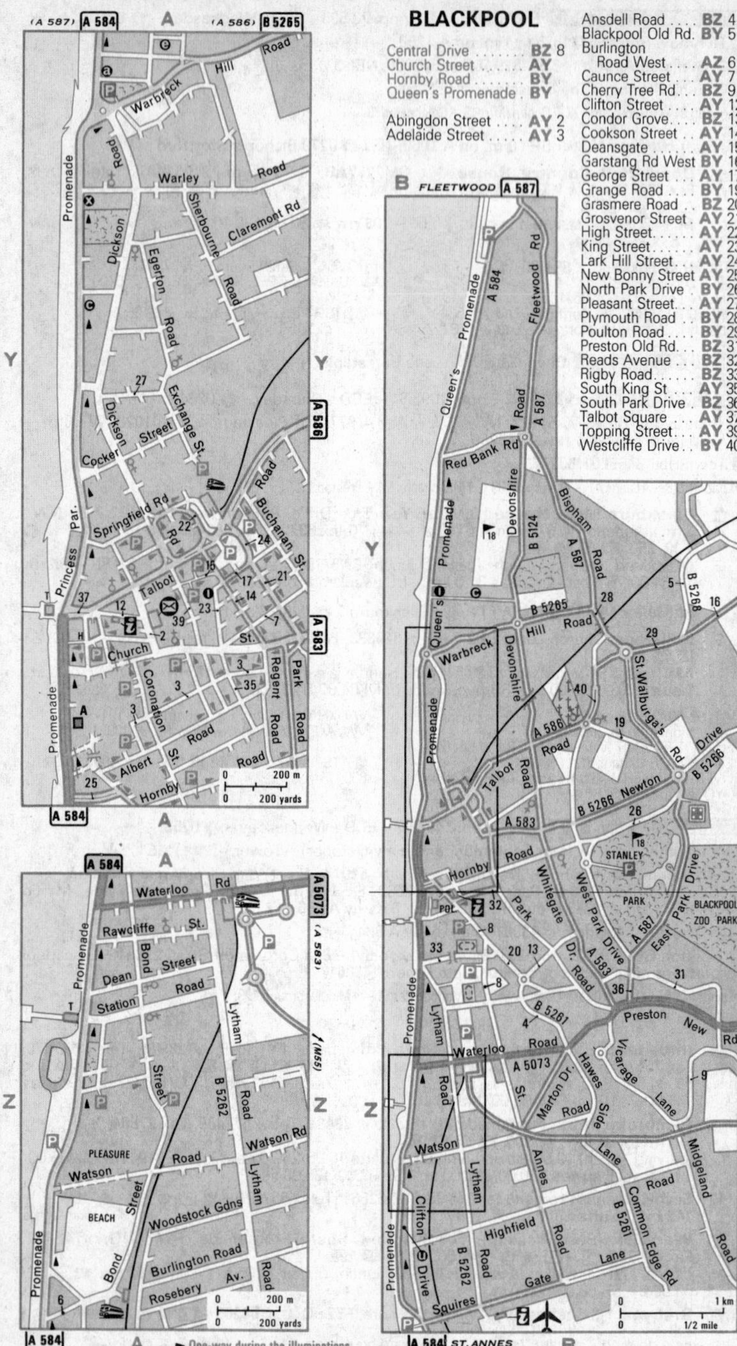

► One-way during the illuminations

Sunray, 42 Knowle Av., off Queens Promenade, FY2 9TQ, ✆ 51937 – TV ☎ P BY c
closed Christmas and New Year – **M** 10.00 **st.** – **9 rm** 20.00/50.00 **st.** – SB 53.00/73.00 **st.**

Denely, 15 King Edward Av., FY2 9TA, ✆ 52757 – P. AY ɜ
9 rm (dinner included) 18.00/40.00 **s.**

at Little Thornton NE : 5 m. by A 586 – BY – off A 588 – ✉ ☎ 0253 Blackpool :

River House with rm, Skippool Creek, Wyre Rd, FY5 5LF, ✆ 883497, ≤, – TV ☎ P. VISA
closed first 2 weeks August – **M** *(closed Sunday)* (booking essential) a la carte 23.50/37.00 **t.** 5.00 – **4 rm** 80.00/120.00 **t.** – SB (weekends only) 130.00 **st.**

at Little Singleton NE : 6 m. by A 586 – BY – on A 585 – ✉ ☎ 0253 Blackpool :

Mains Hall, 86 Mains Lane, FY6 7LE, ✆ 885130, Fax 894132, – rm TV ☎ P. VISA.
M *(closed Sunday)* (booking essential) (lunch by arrangement)/dinner 16.50/35.00 **st.** and a la carte 6.00 – **9 rm** 35.00/95.00 **st.** – SB (weekends only) (January-April) 80.00/115.00 **st.**

BMW Vicarage Lane ✆ 697101
FIAT 79/83 Breck Rd, Poulton-le-Fylde ✆ 882571
FORD Whitegate Drive ✆ 63333
HONDA Devonshire Rd ✆ 35816
LADA St. Annes Rd ✆ 405119
MERCEDES-BENZ Church St. ✆ 22257
MERCEDES-BENZ Church St. ✆ 28436
PEUGEOT-TALBOT Squires Gate Lane ✆ 45544
VW, AUDI Central Drive ✆ 401226
ROVER, DAIMLER-JAGUAR Vicarage Lane ✆ 67811
ROVER 159 Devonshire Rd ✆ 34301

ATS Clifton Rd, Marton ✆ 695033/4

BLACKWATER Cornwall 403 E 33 – see Truro.

BLAGDON Avon 403 L 30 – pop. 1 192 – ☎ 0761.
♦London 137 – ♦Bristol 16 – Taunton 34.

Butcombe Farm, Aldwick Lane, BS18 6UW, NE : 1 ½ m. via Station Rd ✆ 62380, ≤, « Farmhouse of 15C origin », heated, , park – TV ☎ P
M (by arrangement) 18.80 5.60 – **7 rm** 29.50/46.50.

BLAKENEY Norfolk 404 X 25 – pop. 1 559 – ECD : Wednesday – ✉ Holt – ☎ 0263 Cley.
♦London 127 – King's Lynn 37 – ♦Norwich 28.

Blakeney, The Quay, NR25 7NE, ✆ 740797, Fax 740795, ≤, , , – TV ☎ ♿ P – 100. AE VISA
M (bar lunch)/dinner 14.50 **t.** and a la carte 4.00 – **50 rm** 39.00/118.00 **t.**, **1 suite** 111.00/127.00 **t.** – SB 90.00/144.00 **st.**

Manor, The Quay, NR25 7ND, ✆ 740376, Fax 741116, – rest TV P
closed first 3 weeks December – **M** (bar lunch)/dinner 16.00 **st.** and a la carte 3.00 – **35 rm** 22.00/68.00 **st.**

at Cley next the Sea E : 1 ½ m. on A 149 – ✉ Holt – ☎ 0263 Cley :

George & Dragon, NR25 7RN, ✆ 740652 – P
M (bar lunch)/dinner a la carte 6.25/15.85 **t.** – **8 rm** 20.00/68.00 **t.**

Cley Mill, NR25 7NN, ✆ 740209, ≤, « 18C redbrick windmill on saltmarshes » – P
closed mid January-1 March – **M** 14.00 **t.** – **4 rm** 25.00/50.00 **t.**

at Morston W : 1 ½ m. on A 149 – ✉ Holt – ☎ 0263 Cley :

Morston Hall, NR25 7AA, ✆ 741041, Fax 741034, – rest TV ☎ P. AE VISA.
M *(closed Thursday)* 8.25/15.50 **t.** and a la carte 3.00 – **3 rm** 40.00/80.00 **st.** – SB (October-March) (weekdays only) 60.00/90.00 **st.**

BLANCHLAND Northumb. 401 402 N 19 – ECD : Monday and Tuesday – ✉ Consett (Durham) – ☎ 0434 Hexham.
♦London 298 – ♦Carlisle 47 – ♦Newcastle-upon-Tyne 24.

Lord Crewe Arms, DH8 9SP, ✆ 675251, Fax 675337, « Part 13C Abbey », – TV ☎. AE VISA
M (bar lunch Monday to Saturday)/dinner 20.50 **t.** and a la carte 5.50 – **15 rm** 60.00/84.00 **t.** – SB 102.00/126.00 **st.**

BLANDFORD FORUM Dorset 403 404 N 31 **The West Country G.** – pop. 7 249 – ECD : Wednesday – ☎ 0258 Blandford.
See : Site★.
Envir. : Royal Blandford Signals Museum★ *AC*, NE : 2 m. by B 3082.
18 Ashley Wood, Tarrant Rawston ✆ 452253, SW : 1 ½ m. on B 3082.
Marsh and Ham Car Park, West St. ✆ 451989/454770.
♦London 124 – Bournemouth 17 – Dorchester 17 – Salisbury 24.

Crown, West St., DT11 7AJ, ✆ 456626, Telex 418292, Fax 451084, ⛔, 🌳 – TV ☎ P. AE VISA
M *(closed Saturday lunch)* 10.00 **t.** and a la carte 4.00 – **28 rm** 54.00/64.00 **t.** – SB (weekends only) 70.00 **st.**

La Belle Alliance with rm, Portman Lodge, Whitecliff Mill St., DT11 7BP, ✆ 452842 – rest TV ☎ P. AE VISA.
closed January – **M** *(closed Sunday dinner except Bank Holidays and Monday)* (dinner only and Sunday lunch) 12.50/21.50 **st.** and a la carte 4.25 – **5 rm** 45.00/65.00 **st.** – SB 82.00/100.00 **st.**

at Pimperne NE : 2 ½ m. on A 354 – ✉ 0258 Blandford Forum :

Anvil, Salisbury Rd, DT11 8UQ, ✆ 453431 – TV ☎ P. AE VISA
M a la carte 10.75/19.75 **st.** 3.50 – **9 rm** 37.50/55.00 **st.**

FERRARI Pimperne ✆ 451211

BLAWITH Cumbria 402 K 21 – pop. 101 – ✉ Ulverston – 022 985 Lowick Bridge.

♦London 290 – ♦Carlisle 66 – Kendal 28 – Lancaster 43.

Highfield, LA12 8EG, on A 5084 ✆ 238, ←, 🌳 – TV P.
12 rm.

Appletree Holme ⛔, LA12 8EL, W : 1 m., taking unmarked rd opposite church and then the right hand fork ✆ 618, ←, 🌳 – TV ☎ P. AE.
M 19.00 **st.** 3.50 – **4 rm** (dinner included) 59.00/106.00 **st.**

BLEDINGTON Glos. 403 404 P 28 – see Stow-on-the-Wold.

Prices — For full details of the prices quoted in the guide, consult the introduction.

BLOCKLEY Glos. 403 404 O 27 – pop. 1 729 – ECD : Thursday – ✉ Moreton-in-Marsh – 0386.

♦London 89 – ♦Birmingham 40 – Gloucester 29 – ♦Oxford 33.

Crown Inn, High St., GL56 9EX, ✆ 700245, Fax 700247, « Converted 17C coach house and cottages » – TV ☎ P. AE VISA
M 16.95 (dinner) **t.** and a la carte – **21 rm** 52.00/116.00 **t.** – SB 88.00/122.00 **st.**

Lower Brook House ⛔, Lower St., GL56 9DS, ✆ 700286, « Converted 17C cottages », 🌳 – TV P. VISA
closed 3 January-3 February – **M** (bar lunch Monday to Saturday)/dinner 20.00 **st.** 4.25 – **8 rm** 35.00/70.00 **st.** – SB (November-March) (weekends only) 50.00 **st.**

BLOXHAM Oxon. 403 404 P 28 – see Banbury.

BLUNSDON Wilts. 403 404 O 29 – see Swindon.

BLYTH Notts. 402 403 404 Q 23 – pop. 1 179 – ✉ Worksop – 0909.

18 New Delaval ✆ 367728.

♦London 166 – Doncaster 13 – Lincoln 30 – ♦Nottingham 32 – ♦Sheffield 20.

Granada Lodge without rest., Hilltop roundabout, S81 8HG, N : ¾ m. by B 6045 at junction A 1 (M) and A 614 ✆ 591836, Fax 591831 – TV ♿ P. AE VISA. –
37 rm 27.50/29.50 **t.**

Fourways, High St., S81 8EW, ✆ 591235 – P
6 rm.

BODFUAN Gwynedd –see Pwllheli.

BODINNICK-BY-FOWEY Cornwall – see Fowey.

BODMIN Cornwall 403 F 32 **The West Country G.** – pop. 11 992 – ECD : Wednesday – 0208.

See : St. Petroc Church★.

Envir. : Lanhydrock★★*AC*, S : 3 m. – Bodmin Moor★★ – St. Endellion Church★★, NW : 12 m. – Pencarrow House★*AC*, NW : 4 m. – Cardinham Church★, NE : 5 m. – Blisland★ (Church★) NE : 6 m. – St. Mabyn Church★, N : 6 m. – St. Tudy★, N : 8 m.

Shire House, Mount Folly Sq. ✆ 76616.

♦London 273 – Exeter 63 – Penzance 47 – ♦Plymouth 30.

Hotels see : Liskeard E : 12 m.

BOGNOR REGIS West Sussex 404 R 31 – pop. 50 323 – ECD : Wednesday – 0243.

18 Downview Rd, felpham ✆ 865867.

Belmont St. ✆ 823140/820435.

♦London 65 – ♦Brighton 29 – ♦Portsmouth 24 – ♦Southampton 37.

Royal Norfolk (T.H.F), The Esplanade, PO21 2LH, ✆ 826222, Fax 826325, heated, – rm – 130.
M 10.80/12.50 **st.** 4.35 – **48 rm** 55.00/70.00 **st.**, **2 suites** 70.00/80.00 **st.** – SB (weekends only) 84.00/94.00 **st.**

ORD Lennox St. ✆ 864641
OVER 16 Durban Rd, South Bersted ✆ 864041
VW-AUDI 126 Felpham Way ✆ 583185

BOLHAM Devon 403 J 31 – see Tiverton.

BOLLINGTON Cheshire 402 403 404 N 24 – see Macclesfield.

BOLTON Greater Manchester 402 404 M 23 – pop. 143 960 – ECD : Wednesday – 0204.

Envir. : Hall I'Th'Wood★ (16C) *AC*, N : 1½ m.

18 Bolton Municipal, Links Rd, Chorley New Road ✆ 42336, W : 3 m. on A 673 – 18 Dunscar, Longworth Lane, Bromley Cross ✆ 53321, N : 3 m. by A 666 – 18 Lostock Park, ✆ 43278, W : 1½ m, W : 3½ m. – 18 Old Links, Chorley Old Rd ✆ 40050, NW: on B 6226 – 18 Great Lever & Farnworth, Lever Edge Lane ✆ 62582 – 9 Harwood, Springfield, Roading Brook Road ✆ 22878, NE : 4 m. – 9 Breightmet, Red Bridge, Ainsworth ✆ 27381, W : 3 m.

Town Hall, ✆ 36433.

♦London 214 – Burnley 19 – ♦Liverpool 32 – ♦Manchester 11 – Preston 23.

Crest (T.H.F.), Beaumont Rd, BL3 4TA, SW : 2½ m. on A 58 ✆ 651511, Telex 635527, Fax 61064 – rm – 80.
M *(closed Saturday lunch)* 25.00/30.00 **st.** and a la carte 5.60 – 7.95 – **100 rm** 72.00/84.00 **st.** – SB (weekends only) 74.00/126.50 **st.**

Pack Horse (De Vere), Nelson Sq., Bradshawgate, BL1 1DP, ✆ 27261, Telex 635168, Fax 364352 – rm – 200.
M *(closed Saturday lunch)* 9.85/12.50 **st.** and a la carte 4.75 – **73 rm** 65.00/95.00 **st.** – SB (weekends only, July and August) 74.00 **st.**

Broomfield, 33-35 Wigan Rd, Deane, BL3 5XP, SW : 1½ m. on A 6140 ✆ 61570 – rm
M *(closed Sunday)* (dinner only) 11.25 **t.** and a la carte 3.00 – 3.75 – **14 rm** 26.00/38.00 **t.**

at Egerton N : 3½ m. by A 666 – 0204 Bolton :

Egerton House, Blackburn Rd, BL7 9PL, ✆ 57171, Fax 593030, park –
closed 27 and 28 December – **M** *(closed Saturday lunch)* 10.85/16.95 **t.** and a la carte 5.50 – **29 rm** 48.00/80.00 **st.** – SB (weekends only) 82.00/90.00 **st.**

at Bromley Cross N : 4 m. by A 666 on B 6472 – 0204 Bolton :

Last Drop Village, Hospital Rd, BL7 9PZ, ✆ 591131, Telex 635322, Fax 54122, « Village created from restored farm buildings », squash – 200.
M *(closed Saturday lunch)* 11.50/14.00 **st.** and a la carte 8.00 – **80 rm** 50.00/80.00 **st.**, **3 suites** 89.00/110.00 **st.** – SB (weekends only) 84.00/92.00 **st.**

FORD 54-56 Higher Bridge St. ✆ 24474
ROVER Manchester Rd ✆ 32241
LANCIA Halliwell Rd ✆ 26566
PEUGEOT-TALBOT, RENAULT 157 Bradshawgate ✆ 31323
SEAT 154-160 Crook St. ✆ 24686
TOYOTA Radcliffe Rd ✆ 382234
VW, AUDI Morris St., Mill St. Ind Est., Bolton ✆ 31464
VW, AUDI St. Helens Rd ✆ 62131
YUGO Thynne St. ✆ 32511
ATS Foundry St. ✆ 22144/27841/388681
ATS Moss Bank Way, Astley Bridge, Bolton ✆ 50057

BOLTON ABBEY North Yorks. 402 O 22 – pop. 122 – Skipton – 075 671.

See : Bolton Priory★ (ruins) and woods (the Strid★ and nature trails in upper Wharfedale).

♦London 216 – Harrogate 18 – ♦Leeds 23 – Skipton 6.

Devonshire Arms (Best Western), BD23 6AJ, on A 59 at Bolton Bridge ✆ 441, Telex 51218, Fax 564, « Restored former coaching inn », park – 150.
M 15.00/23.50 **st.** and a la carte 5.50 – **40 rm** 75.00/110.00 **st.** – SB 115.00/125.00 **st.**

BONCATH Dyfed 403 G 27 – 0239.

Envir. : Cenarth Falls★, NE : 6 m.

♦London 247 – Carmarthen 27 – Fishguard 17.

Pantyderi Farm, SA37 0JB, W : 2¾ m. by B 4332 ✆ 841227, park –
M 8.00 **st.** 3.00 – **8 rm** 12.50/28.50 **st.**

BONCHURCH I.O.W. 403 404 Q 32 – see Wight (Isle of) : Ventnor.

BONTDDU Gwynedd 402 403 I 25 – see Dolgellau.

BOOTLE Merseyside 402 ㉜ 403 ② – see Liverpool.

BOREHAMWOOD Herts. 404 T 29 – 081.

- Oaklands Toby, Studio Way, WD6 5JY, off Elstree Way (A 5135) 905 1455, Fax 905 1370 – TV – 40
38 rm.

BOROUGHBRIDGE North Yorks. 402 P 21 – pop. 1 835 – ECD : Thursday – 0423 Harrogate

Fishergate 323373 (summer only).

London 216 – Leeds 26 – Middlesbrough 35 – York 17.

- Crown, Horsefair, YO5 9LB, 322328, Telex 57906 – TV – 120
41 rm, 1 suite.
- **Farndale,** Horsefair, YO5 9AH, 323463 – rest TV. AE VISA
M (by arrangement) 12.00 **t.** – **13 rm** 18.00/40.00 **t.** – SB (October-June) (weekend only) 50.00 **st.**

BORROWDALE Cumbria 402 K 20 – see Keswick.

BOSCASTLE Cornwall 403 F 31 **The West Country G.** – 084 05.

See : Site★.

London 260 – Bude 14 – Exeter 59 – Plymouth 43.

- **Bottreaux House,** PL35 0BG, on B 3266 231 – rest TV. VISA
March-November – **M** *(closed Monday lunch)* (bar lunch)/dinner 15.50 **st.** and a la carte 3.65 – **7 rm** 28.50/52.00 **st.** – SB (March-November) 65.00/73.00 **st.**
- **St. Christopher's Country House,** High St., PL35 0BD, S : ½ m. by B 3266 412 – rest. VISA
March-October – **M** 8.00 **st.** 2.80 – **9 rm** 17.00/34.00 **st.**

BOSHAM West Sussex 404 R 31 – see Chichester.

BOSTON Lincs. 402 404 T 25 – pop. 33 908 – ECD : Thursday – 0205.

See : St. Botolph's Church★ 14C.

Cowbridge, Horncastle Rd 62306, N : 2 m. by B 1183.

London 122 – Lincoln 35 – Nottingham 55.

- **White Hart,** Bridge Foot, PE21 8SH, 364877 – TV – 80. AE VISA.
M (grill rest.) 16.20 **t.** and a la carte – **23 rm** 39.00/55.00 **t.**
- **New England** (T.H.F.), Wide Bargate, PE21 6SH, 365255, Fax 310597 – rm TV. AE VISA
M 8.50/11.50 **st.** and a la carte 4.25 – **25 rm** 55.00/60.00 **st.** – SB (weekends only) 58.00 **st**

BMW Sleaford Rd 350000
FIAT 200 London Rd 355500
FORD 57 High St. 60404
NISSAN Main Ridge East 353737
PROTON, LADA, RELIANT Frith Bank 362230
ROVER, DAIMLER-JAGUAR Tawney St. 66677
TOYOTA Tawney St. 368626
VAUXHALL Butterwick 760421
VW, AUDI-NSU 363867
ATS London Rd 362854

BOSTON SPA West Yorks. 402 P 22 – pop. 6 022 – Wetherby – 0937 Boston Spa.

London 205 – Harrogate 11 – Leeds 12 – Middlesbrough 52 – York 14.

- **Royal** (B.C.B.), 182 High St., LS23 6HT, 842142 – TV. AE VISA.
M 8.00/15.00 **st.** – **9 rm** 38.00/50.00 **st.**

BOTLEY Hants. 403 404 Q 31 – pop. 2 156 – ECD : Thursday – Hedge End, Southampton – 0489.

London 83 – Portsmouth 17 – Southampton 6 – Winchester 11.

- **Botley Park,** Winchester Rd, Boorley Green, SO3 2UA, N : 1½ m. on B 3335 780888, Fax 789242, park, squash – rm rest TV – 200. AE VISA
M *(closed Saturday lunch)* 14.50/20.00 **t.** and a la carte 5.60 – **100 rm** 85.00/175.00 **st.** – SB (weekends only) 110.00/120.00 **st.**
- **Cobbett's,** 13-15 The Square, SO3 2EA, 782068, French rest. –. VISA
closed lunch Saturday and Monday, Sunday, 2 weeks in summer, 2 weeks in winter and Bank Holidays – **M** 15.50/16.50 **t.** and a la carte 4.95.

AUDI, VW Shamblehurst Lane 783434
ROVER Southampton Rd 785111

BOTTESFORD Leics. 402 404 R 25 – pop. 2 085 – ECD : Wednesday – 0949.

London 116 – Grantham 75 – Lincoln 26 – Leicester 32 – Nottingham 18.

- La Locanda, 26 High St., NG13 0AA, 42330, Italian rest. –.

BOUGHTON Kent – see Faversham.

BOUGHTON MONCHELSEA Kent – see Maidstone.

BOURNE Lincs. 402 404 S 25 – pop. 7 672 – ECD : Wednesday – ☎ 0778.

Envir. : Spalding Parish Church ★, E : 10 m. – Ayscoughfee Hall ★ 15C, E : 10 m.

♦London 101 – ♦Leicester 42 – Lincoln 35 – ♦Nottingham 42.

Bourne Eau House, 30 South St., PE10 9LY, on A 15 ✆ 423621, « Part Elizabethan and part Georgian house », – rm. *closed January and February* – **M** *(closed Sunday)* (residents only, communal dining) (dinner only) 15.00/18.00 **st.** – **3 rm** 35.00/65.00 **st.**

Toft House, Main Rd, Toft, PE10 0JT, SW : 3 m. by A 151 on A 6121 ✆ 077 833 (With-am-on-the-Hill) 614, 18, – – 70. VISA. **M** *(closed Sunday dinner)* 7.50/11.00 **t.** and a la carte 2.80 – **22 rm** 25.30/62.10 **t.**

FORD Spalding Rd ✆ 424464
ROVER Thurlby Rd ✆ 422892
ROVER North St. ✆ 422129
ATS 18 Abbey Rd ✆ 422811

BOURNE END Herts. 404 S 28 – see Hemel Hempstead.

BOURNEMOUTH Dorset 403 404 O 31 **The West Country G.** – pop. 142 829 – ECD : Wednesday and Saturday – ☎ 0202.

18 Meyrick Park ✆ 290871 CY – 18 Queen's Park, Queen's Park South Drive ✆ 36198, NE : 2 m. CV – 18 Knighton Heath, Francis Av., West Howe ✆ 572633, NW : 4 m. AV – 18 Parkstone, Links Road, Poole ✆ 708025, W : 3 m. AX.

Hurn Airport : ✆ 579751, Telex 41345, N : 5 m. by Hurn Rd DV.

Westover Rd ✆ 291715/290883.

♦London 114 – ♦Bristol 76 – ♦Southampton 34.

Plans on following pages

Royal Bath (De Vere), Bath Rd, BH1 2EW, ✆ 555555, Telex 41375, Fax 554158, ←, – – 300. AE VISA. DZ **a**
M (see **Oscars** below) – **124 rm** 85.00/190.00 **st.**, **7 suites** 175.00/240.00 **st.** – SB (weekends only, July and August) 260.00/470.00 **st.**

Carlton, Meyrick Rd, East Overcliff, BH1 3DN, ✆ 552011, Telex 41244, Fax 299573, ←, heated, – rest – 140. AE VISA. EZ **a**
M 17.00/26.00 **t.** and a la carte 6.50 – **61 rm** 100.00/145.00 **t.**, **4 suites** 195.00/480.00 **t.** – SB (except Bank Holidays) 155.00 **st.**

Norfolk Royale, Richmond Hill, BH2 6EN, ✆ 551251, Telex 418474, Fax 299729, – rm – 80. AE VISA. CY **u**
M 12.75/24.50 **t.** and a la carte 5.00 – **90 rm** 85.00/120.00 **t.**, **5 suites** 175.00/330.00 **t.** – SB (weekends only) 110.00 **st.**

Highcliff (Best Western), 105 St. Michael's Rd, West Cliff, BH2 5DU, ✆ 557702, Telex 417153, Fax 292734, ←, heated, – – 180. AE VISA.
M 12.00/15.00 **t.** and a la carte 4.50 – **107 rm** 70.00/120.00 **st.**, **3 suites** 95.00/135.00 **st.** – SB 110.00 **st.** CZ **z**

Marsham Court, Russell Cotes Rd, East Cliff, BH1 3AB, ✆ 552111, Telex 41420, Fax 294744, ←, heated – – 200. AE VISA. DZ **e**
M (buffet lunch)/dinner 13.50 **st.** and a la carte – **79 rm** 47.00/94.00 **st.**, **1 suite** 124.00/154.00 **st.** – SB 90.00/100.00 **st.**

Crest (T.H.F.), Meyrick Rd, The Lansdowne, BH1 2PR, ✆ 553262, Telex 41232, Fax 557698 – rm rest – 100. AE VISA DY **a**
M 6.95/14.45 **st.** and a la carte – 7.95 – **102 rm** 69.00/81.00 **st.**

Anglo-Swiss, 16 Gervis Rd, East Cliff, BH1 3EQ, ✆ 554794, Fax 299615, heated, – – 250. AE VISA EY **e**
M (bar lunch)/dinner 14.00 **t.** 4.50 – **68 rm** 60.00/96.00 **t.** – SB (except Christmas and New Year) 84.00/95.00 **st.**

Durley Hall, 7 Durley Chine Rd, Westcliff, BH2 5JS, ✆ 766886, Fax 762236, heated, – rest – 100. AE VISA CZ **s**
M (bar lunch Monday to Saturday)/dinner 15.50 **st.** and a la carte – **81 rm** 42.00/90.00 **st.** – SB 79.00/105.00 **t.**

Heathlands, 12 Grove Rd, East Cliff, BH1 3AY, ✆ 553336, Fax 555937, heated – – 250. AE VISA EZ **c**
M 10.50/15.00 **st.** – **114 rm** 55.00/90.00 **st.**, **2 suites** 100.00/120.00 **st.** – SB (weekends only) 80.00/90.00 **st.**

Burley Court, 29 Bath Rd, BH1 2NP, ✆ 552824, Fax 298514, heated – . VISA DY **i**
closed 1 to 7 January – **M** (bar lunch) (lunch weekends only in winter)/dinner 9.50 **t.** and a la carte – **39 rm** 36.00/73.00 **st.** – SB (November-May) (weekends only) 59.00/64.00 **st.**

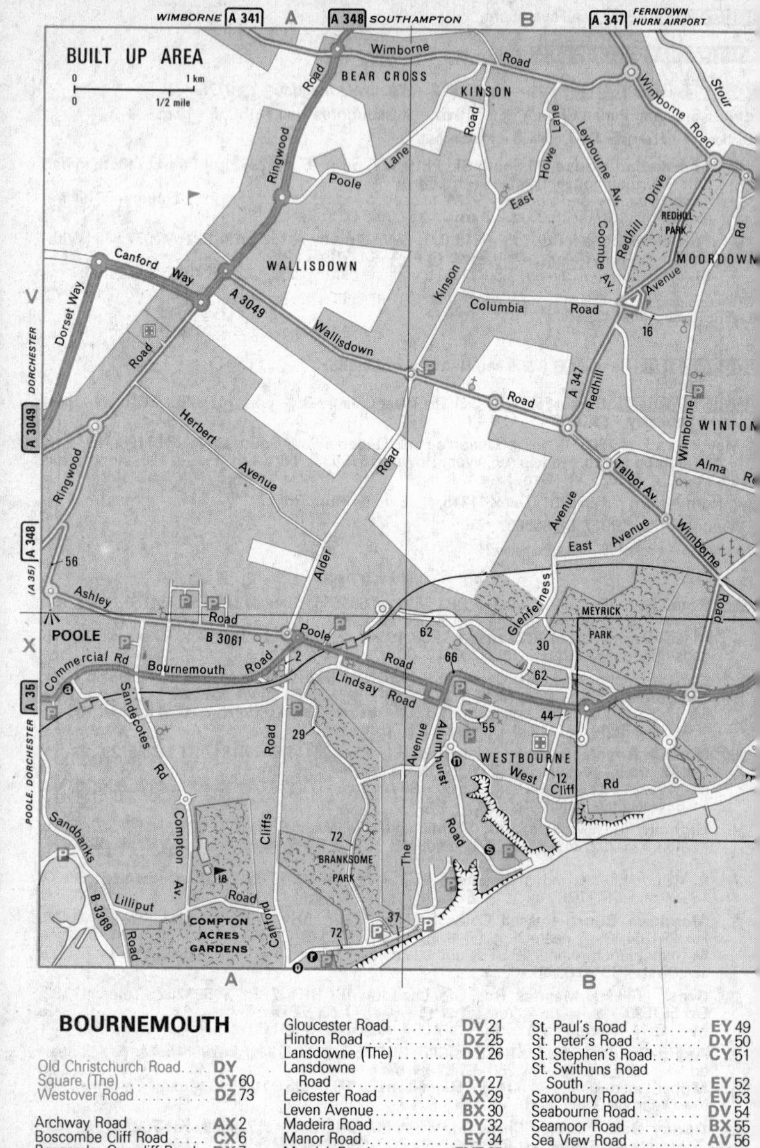

BOURNEMOUTH

Old Christchurch Road . . . . DY
Square (The) . . . . CY 60
Westover Road . . . . DZ 73

Archway Road . . . . AX 2
Boscombe Cliff Road . . . . . CX 6
Boscombe Overcliff Road . DX 7
Boscombe Spa Road . . . . . CX 8
Branksome Wood Road . . . CY 10
Clarendon Road . . . . BX 12
Commercial Road . . . . CY 13
Durley Road . . . . CZ 15
Ensbury Park Road . . . . . . BV 16
Exeter Road . . . . CDZ 17
Fir Vale Road . . . . DY 18
Gervis Place . . . . DY 20
Gloucester Road . . . . DV 21
Hinton Road . . . . DZ 25
Lansdowne (The) . . . . DY 26
Lansdowne Road . . . . DY 27
Leicester Road . . . . AX 29
Leven Avenue . . . . BX 30
Madeira Road . . . . DY 32
Manor Road . . . . EY 34
Meyrick Road . . . . EYZ 35
Owls Road . . . . CX 36
Pinecliff Road . . . . AX 37
Post Office Road . . . . CY 41
Priory Road . . . . CZ 43
Queen's Road . . . . BX 44
Richmond Hill . . . . CY 45
Richmond Park Road . . . . . CV 46
Russell Cotes Road . . . . . . DZ 47
St. Michael's Road . . . . . . CZ 48
St. Paul's Road . . . . EY 49
St. Peter's Road . . . . DY 50
St. Stephen's Road . . . . . . CY 51
St. Swithuns Road South . . . EY 52
Saxonbury Road . . . . EV 53
Seabourne Road . . . . DV 54
Seamoor Road . . . . BX 55
Sea View Road . . . . AV 56
Southbourne Grove . . . . . . DX 57
Southbourne Overcliff Drive . . DX 59
Suffolk Road . . . . CY 61
Surrey Road . . . . BX 62
Triangle (The) . . . . CY 63
Upper Hinton Road . . . . . . DZ 64
Wessex Way . . . . BX 66
West Cliff Promenade . . . . . CZ 67
Western Road . . . . AX 72

***Town plans:** the names of main shopping streets are indicated in red at the beginning of the list of streets.*

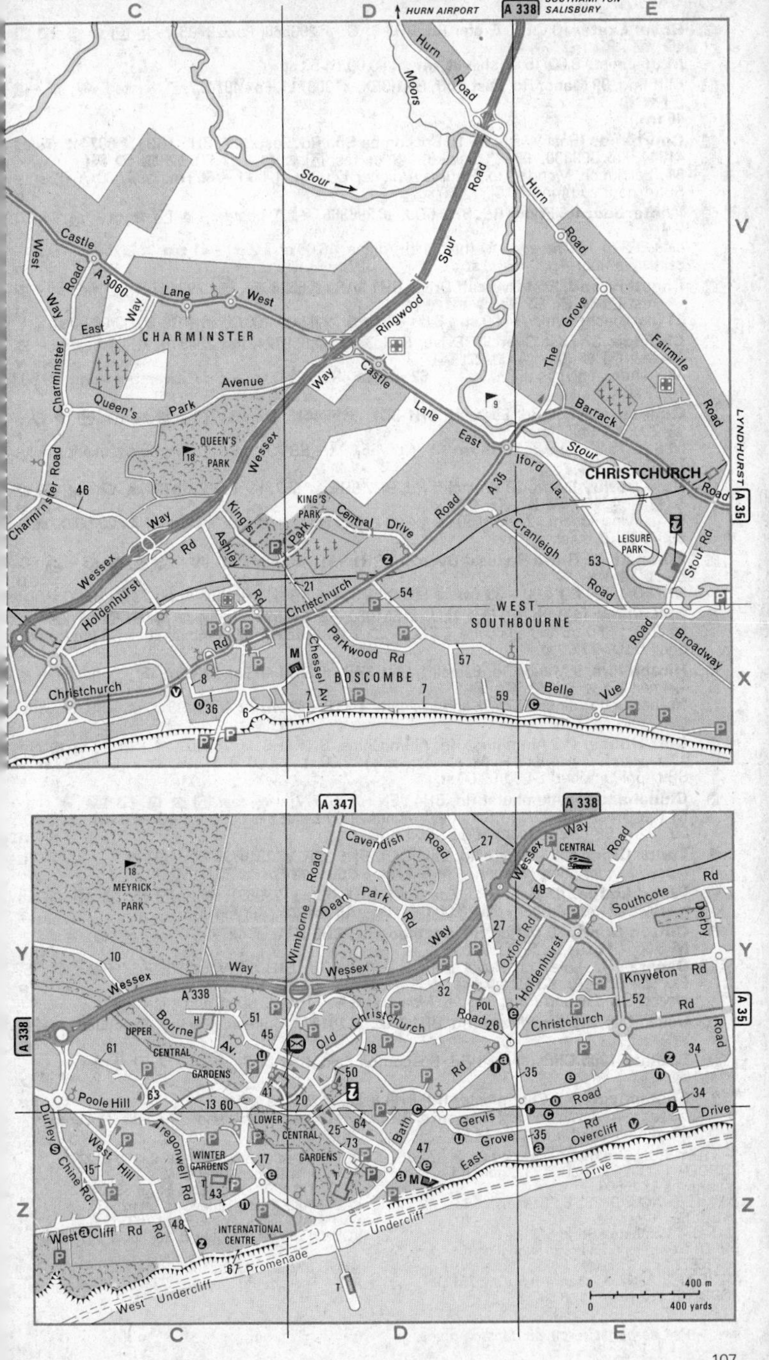

HURN AIRPORT
A 338
SOUTHAMPTON SALISBURY
C
D
E
V
X
Y
Z
Hurn Road
Moors
Stour
Spur Road
Hurn Road
Castle
West Way
Road
A 3060
Lane
West
East Way
CHARMINSTER
Ringwood
Way
Castle
Lane
East
Charminster
Avenue
Queen's Park
QUEEN'S PARK
Wessex
The Grove
Fairmile
Road
Barrack
Stour
CHRISTCHURCH
Road
LYNDHURST
A 35
Iford La.
A 35
Road
Cranleigh
Road
Charminster Road
46
Wessex Way
KING'S PARK
King's Park
Central Drive
Ashley Rd
LEISURE PARK
Stour Rd
53
Holdenhurst Rd
21
Christchurch
54
WEST SOUTHBOURNE
Road
Broadway
Parkwood Rd
57
M
Chessel Av.
BOSCOMBE
Christchurch
8
36
6
7
7
59
Belle Vue
A 347
A 338
Cavendish Road
27
Wessex Way
CENTRAL
Road
Rd
MEYRICK PARK
Wimborne Road
Dean Park Rd
49
Southcote
Derby
27
Way
Oxford Rd
Holdenhurst
10
Wessex
Way
Wessex
32
Knyveton Rd
A 338
POL.
52
Rd
A 338
Bourne
51
Christchurch
Road
26
Christchurch
Road
UPPER CENTRAL GARDENS
45
Av.
Old
18
61
35
34
50
Rd
Poole Hill
63
41
20
13
60
Road
34
Drive
Durley Chine Rd.
West Hill
Tregonwell Rd
LOWER CENTRAL GARDENS
64
25
73
Bath
Gervis
Grove
35
Rd
Overcliff
15
WINTER GARDENS
17
47
M
East
Drive
43
West Cliff Rd
Rd
48
INTERNATIONAL CENTRE
Undercliff
67
Promenade
West Undercliff
0
400 m
0
400 yards

Royal Exeter (B.C.B.), Exeter Rd, BH2 5AG, ✆ 290566, Fax 297968 – |♣| TV ☎ P. AE VISA. CZ e
M (grill rest.) 8.00/15.00 **st.** – **36 rm** 46.00/61.50 **st.**

Cliff End, 99 Manor Rd, East Cliff, BH1 3EX, ✆ 309711, Fax 491477, heated, – TV ☎ P CX v
40 rm.

Courtlands (Best Western), 16 Boscombe Spa Rd, East Cliff, BH5 1BB, ✆ 302442, Telex 41344, Fax 309880, heated – rest TV ☎ P – 50. AE VISA
M (bar lunch Monday to Saturday)/dinner 17.00 **st.** 4.00 – **60 rm** 37.00/76.00 **st.** – SB (except summer) 66.00/72.00 **st.** CX o

Winterbourne, Priory Rd, BH2 5DJ, ✆ 296366, ←, heated – TV ☎ P – 80. VISA
closed 2 to 14 January – **M** (bar lunch)/dinner 18.00 **st.** 2.90 – **41 rm** 36.50/71.00 **st.** – SB (November-April) 58.00 **st.** CZ n

Chesterwood, East Overcliff Drive, BH1 3AR, ✆ 5528057, Fax 293457, ←, heated – rest TV ☎ P. AE VISA EZ i
M (bar lunch)/dinner 14.00 **st.** 3.60 – **51 rm** 43.00/100.00 **st.** – SB 60.00/90.00 **st.**

Cliffside, 32 East Overcliff Drive, BH1 3AQ, ✆ 555724, Fax 294810, ←, heated – rest TV ☎ P – 60. VISA EZ v
M (dinner only) 14.95/20.20 **t.** – **62 rm** 43.50/87.00 **t.** – SB (November-April) 69.50/74.00 **st.**

Queens, Meyrick Rd, Eastcliff, BH1 3DL, ✆ 554415, Fax 294810 – rest TV ☎ P – 200. VISA EYZ r
M 9.25/15.95 **t.** 3.85 – **114 rm** 34.50/85.00 **t.** – SB (October-mid April) (weekends only) 73.50/78.50 **st.**

New Durley Dean, 28 Westcliff Rd, BH2 5HE, ✆ 557711, Fax 292815, – TV ☎ P – 150. AE VISA. CZ a
M (carving lunch) 12.50/19.50 **st.** 4.25 – **110 rm** (dinner included) 44.00/99.00 **st.** – SB 78.00/92.00 **st.**

Miramar, 19 Grove Rd, East Overcliff, BH1 3AL, ✆ 26581, ←, – TV ☎ P – 60. AE VISA. DZ u
M 7.50/12.50 **t.** 4.00 – **39 rm** 55.00/59.00 **t.** – SB (November-April) 73.00/87.00 **st.**

Belvedere, 14 Bath Rd, BH1 2EU, ✆ 551080, Fax 294699 – TV ☎ P. AE VISA.
M 7.95/11.50 **st.** and a la carte 2.95 – 5.00 – **62 rm** 32.00/45.00 **st.** – SB (weekends only) 68.00/77.00 **st.** DYZ c

Hinton Firs, 9 Manor Rd, Eastcliff, BH1 3HB, ✆ 555409, Fax 299607, heated – rest TV ☎ P. VISA. EY n
M (bar lunch)/dinner 9.75 **st.** and a la carte 3.90 – **52 rm** 46.00/96.00 **st.** – SB (November-April) 59.00/69.00 **st.**

Cliff House, 113 Alumhurst Rd, Alum Chine, BH4 8HS, ✆ 763003, ← – TV ☎ P.
Mid March-November – **M** (dinner only) 12.00 **st.** 2.50 – **11 rm** 21.00/50.00 **st.** – SB (April-October) 84.00/92.00 **st.** BX s

Chinehead, 31 Alumhurst Rd, BH4 8EN, ✆ 752777 – rest TV ☎ P. VISA.
M (bar lunch Monday to Saturday)/dinner 21.00 **t.** and a la carte 4.00 – **20 rm** 29.00/56.00 **t.** – SB (except summer) 53.00/58.00 **st.** BX n

Tudor Grange, 31 Gervis Rd, East Cliff, BH1 3EE, ✆ 291472, – TV P EY o
closed January and February – **M** 9.00 **st.** 4.00 – **12 rm** 26.00/52.00 **st.**

Wood Lodge, 10 Manor Rd, East Cliff, BH1 3EY, ✆ 290891, – TV P. VISA.
mid March-September – **M** 10.00 **t.** 4.00 – **15 rm** 27.00/54.00 **t.** EY z

Clifton Court, 30 Clifton Rd, Southbourne, BH6 3PA, ✆ 427753 – rest P.
M 6.00 – **11 rm** 18.00/40.00. EX c

XXX **Oscars** (De Vere) (at Royal Bath H.), Bath Rd, BH1 2EW, ✆ 555555, Telex 41375, Fax 554158 – P. AE VISA DZ a
closed Sunday and Bank Holiday Mondays – **M** 14.10/22.60 **st.** and a la carte.

XX Ocean City, 3-5 Lansdowne Rd, BH1 1RZ, ✆ 291277, Chinese (Peking, Szechuan) rest. – DY e

XX Salathai, 1066 Christchurch Rd, Boscombe East, BH1 6DS, ✆ 420772, Thai rest. – . DV z

X **Sophisticats,** 43 Charminster Rd, BH8 8UE, ✆ 291019 BV a
closed Sunday, Monday, 2 weeks February, 1 week June and 2 weeks November – **M** (dinner only) a la carte 14.65/17.95 **t.** 3.25.

BENTLEY, ROLLS-ROYCE Ringwood Rd ✆ 570575
CITROEN, PEUGEOT-TALBOT 3 Oxford Rd, Lansdowne ✆ 26566
DAIMLER-JAGUAR 382-6 Charminster Rd ✆ 510252
FIAT 674 Wimborne Rd ✆ 512121
FORD Tower Park, Canford Heath, Poole ✆ 715577
MERCEDES-BENZ Wallisdown Rd ✆ 525111
PORSCHE 282 New Rd ✆ 897688
ROVER Castle Lane West, Redhill ✆ 510201
ROVER 14 Carbery Row ✆ 423243
SEAT 318-320 Holdenhurst Rd ✆ 33304
VAUXHALL Castle Lane West ✆ 526434
VAUXHALL-OPEL Poole Rd ✆ 763361
VOLVO 582-600 Ringwood Rd, Poole ✆ 715733

ATS 892 Christchurch Rd, Boscombe ✆ 424457
ATS 1 Fernside Rd, Poole ✆ 733301/733326

Pas de publicité payée dans ce guide.

BOURTON-ON-THE-WATER Glos. 403 404 O 28 – pop. 2 538 – ECD : Saturday – 0451 Cotswold.
◆London 91 – ◆Birmingham 47 – Gloucester 24 – ◆Oxford 36.

Camalan House without rest., Station Rd, GL54 2ER, 21302 – P.
March-October – **3 rm** 15.00/30.00.

Triangle without rest., Station Rd, GL54 2ER, 21037 – rm P.
April-October – **3 rm** 15.00/28.00 **s.**

at Great Rissington SE : 3¼ m. – Cheltenham – 0451 Cotswold:

Lamb Inn, GL54 2LP, 20388, ≤, « Attractive part 17C Cotswolds stone inn », – P. VISA
closed 25 and 26 December – **M** a la carte 7.50/14.00 **st.** 4.25 – **11 rm** 28.00/48.00 **st.** – SB (winter only) 58.00/68.00 **st.**

at Lower Slaughter SW : 3 m. by A 429 – Bourton-on-the-Water – 0451 Cotswold :

Lower Slaughter Manor, GL54 2HP, 20456, Fax 22150, ≤, « 17C manor house, gardens », – P. AE VISA
M 16.50/28.50 **t.** – 8.50 – **19 rm** 79.00/175.00 **t.** – SB 150.00/230.00 **st.**

at Upper Slaughter NW : 2¾ m. by A 429 – Cheltenham – 0451 Bourton-on-the-Water :

Lords of the Manor, GL54 2JD, 20243, Telex 83147, Fax 20696, ≤, « Part 17C manor house », , park – P. AE VISA
M 18.00/29.75 **t.** and a la carte 5.25 – **29 rm** 70.00/95.00 **st.** – SB (October-April and August) 135.00/165.00 **st.**

FORD Station Rd 20366

"Short Breaks"

Many hotels now offer a special rate for a stay of 2 nights which includes dinner, bed and breakfast.

BOVEY TRACEY Devon 403 I 32 **The West Country G.** – pop. 3 434 – ECD : Wednesday – Newton Abbot – 0626.
See : St. Peter, St. Paul and St. Thomas of Canterbury Church★.
Lower Car Park, Station Rd 832047 (summer only).
◆London 214 – Exeter 14 – ◆Plymouth 32.

Edgemoor, Haytor Rd, TQ13 9LE, W : 1 m. on B 3387 832466, Fax 834760, – P. AE VISA
M (lunch by arrangement)/dinner 17.20 **t.** and a la carte 3.65 – **12 rm** 36.00/72.00 **t.** – SB 79.00/87.00 **st.**

Coombe Cross, Coombe Cross, TQ13 9EY, E : ½ m. on B 3344 832476, – rest P. AE VISA
M (bar lunch)/dinner 15.95 **st.** 4.20 – **26 rm** 34.00/54.00 **st.** – SB 70.00/74.00 **st.**

Willmead Farm without rest., TQ13 9NP, NW : 2¾ m. by A 382 064 77 (Lustleigh) 214, ≤, « Part 14C thatched farmhouse », , park – P.
closed Christmas and New Year – **3 rm** -/42.00 **s.**

Front House Lodge, East St., TQ13 9EL, 832202, – P. VISA
M (by arrangement) 12.00 **st.** – **8 rm** 22.00/38.00 **st.** – SB (November, January and February) (weekends only) 44.00/56.00 **st.**

at Haytor W : 2½ m. on B 3387 – Bovey Tracey – 0364 Haytor :

Bel Alp House, TQ13 9XX, on B 3387 661217, Fax 661292, ≤ countryside, « Country house atmosphere », – rest P. VISA
closed January and December – **M** (booking essential) 20.00/30.00 **t.** 4.50 – **9 rm** 66.00/132.00 **t.** – SB 168.00/216.00 **st.**

at Haytor Vale W : 3½ m. by B 3387 – Newton Abbot – 0364 Haytor :

Rock Inn, TQ13 9XP, 661305, Fax 661242, – P. AE VISA
M 16.95 **t.** (dinner) and a la carte 4.25 – **10 rm** 35.50/55.00 **t.**

BOWBURN Durham 401 402 P 19 – pop. 3 748 – 091 Tyneside.
◆London 265 – Durham 3 – ◆Middlesbrough 20.

Bowburn Hall, DH6 5NH, E : 1 m. 3770311, – rest P. AE VISA
M 10.95 **st.** (dinner) and a la carte 4.50 – **19 rm** 35.00/55.00 **st.** – SB (weekends only) 50.00 **st.**

BOWDON Greater Manchester 402 403 404 M 23 – see Altrincham.

BOWNESS-ON-WINDERMERE Cumbria 402 L 20 – see Windermere.

BOX Wilts. 403 404 N 29 – see Bath (Avon).

BRACKLEY Northants. 403 404 Q 27 – pop. 6 663 – ECD : Wednesday – ✉ ☎ 0280.

♦London 67 – ♦Birmingham 53 – Northampton 21 – ♦Oxford 21.

Crown (B.C.B.), 20-22 Market Sq., NN13 5DP, ☎ 702210, Fax 701840 – TV ☎ P
14 rm.

FORD Burwell Hill ☎ 702268

ATS Station Building, Northampton Rd ☎ 702000/703188

BRACKNELL Berks. 404 R 29 – pop. 52 257 – ECD : Wednesday – ☎ 0344.

18 Downshire Easthampstead Park, Wokingham ☎ 424066, SW : 3 m.

Central Library, Town Sq., ☎ 423149.

♦London 35 – Reading 11.

Hilton National, Bagshot Rd, RG12 3QJ, S : 2 m. on A 322 ☎ 424801, Telex 848058 Fax 487454 – lift rm rest TV ☎ P – 200
167 rm.

NISSAN Downshire Way ☎ 426500
RENAULT London Rd ☎ 54444
VAUXHALL Lovelace Rd ☎ 481925

BRADFIELD Berks. 403 404 Q 29 – ✉ ☎ 0734 Reading.

♦London 56 – ♦Oxford 28 – Reading 7.

Boot Farm without rest., Southend Rd., Southend Bradfield, RG7 6ES, SW : 2 m. ☎ 744298, – TV P.
4 rm 17.50/35.00 **st.**

BRADFIELD COMBUST Suffolk – see Bury St. Edmunds.

BRADFORD West Yorks. 402 O 22 – pop. 293 336 – ECD : Wednesday – ☎ 0274.

Envir. : Corsham Court ★★.

18 West Bowling, Newall Hall, Rooley Lane ☎ 724449, on A 6177 BY – 18 Hawksworth Lane, Guiseley ☎ 0943 (Guiseley) 75570, NE : 8½ m. BX – 9 Phoenix Park, Thornbury ☎ 667573, E : on A 647 BX – 9 Bradford Moor, Scarr Hall, Pollard Lane ☎ 638313 BX – 9 East Bierley, South View Rd ☎ 681023, SE : 4 m. BY – 9 Queensbury ☎ 882155, SW : 4 m. AY – 9 Pearson Road, Odsal ☎ 679195 BY.

Leeds and Bradford Airport : ☎ 0532 (Rawdon) 509696, Telex 557868 NE : 6 m. by A 658 BX.

City Hall, Channing Way ☎ 753678.

♦ London 212 – ♦Leeds 9 – ♦Manchester 39 – ♦Middlesbrough 75 – ♦Sheffield 45.

Plan of Enlarged Area : see Leeds
Plan opposite

Stakis Norfolk Gardens, Hall Ings, BD1 5SH, ☎ 734734, Telex 517573, Fax 306146 – lift TV ☎ & – 750. AE VISA — BZ e
M 8.50/16.50 **t.** and a la carte – 7.50 – **121 rm** 75.00/105.00 **t.**, **5 suites** 110.00 **t.** – SB 74.00/124.00 **st.**

Guide Post, Common Rd, Low Moor, BD12 0ST, S : 3 m. by A 641 off A 638 ☎ 607866, Telex 517635, Fax 671085 – TV ☎ P – 80. AE VISA.
M *(closed Saturday lunch and Sunday dinner)* 12.50/17.50 **t.** and a la carte 2.95 – **43 rm** 50.00/85.00 **t.** — on plan of Leeds AX c

Novotel Bradford, Euroway Trading Estate, Merrydale Rd, BD4 6SA, S : 3½ m. by A 641 and A 6117 off M 606 ☎ 683683, Telex 517312, Fax 651342, heated – lift TV ☎ & P – 300. AE VISA — on plan of Leeds AX a
M a la carte 11.15/17.75 **t.** – 6.50 – **132 rm** 54.00/58.00 **t.** – SB (weekends only) 75.00 **st.**

Victoria (T.H.F.), Bridge St., BD1 1JX, ☎ 728706, Telex 517456, Fax 736358 – lift rm TV ☎ P – 200. AE VISA — BZ c
M *(closed Saturday lunch)* (carving rest.) 11.00/11.95 **st.** 3.95 – 7.00 – **58 rm** 60.00/83.00 **st.**, **1 suite** 125.00 **st.**.

Cartwright, 308 Manningham Lane, BD8 7AX, ☎ 499908, Fax 481309 – TV ☎ P
14 rm. — BX a

Park Drive, 12 Park Drive, Heaton, BD9 4DR, ☎ 480194, – TV P. AE VISA.
M 10.50 **st.** – **7 rm** 43.00/53.00 **st.** — AX e

Norland House, 695 Great Horton Rd, BD7 4DU, ☎ 571698 – TV P
8 rm. — AY i

XXX **Restaurant Nineteen** with rm, North Park Rd, Heaton, BD9 4NT, ☎ 492559 – rest TV ☎. AE VISA — AX n
closed Sunday, Monday, 1 week January and 2 weeks August – **M** (dinner only) 27.00 **t.** 7.50 – **4 rm** **60.00/75.00 t.**

at Gomersal SE : 7 m. by A 650 on A 651 – ✉ Gomersal – ☎ 0274 Bradford :

Gomersal Park, Moor Lane, BD19 4LJ, NW : 1½ m. by A 651 off A 652 ☎ 869386, Fax 861042 – TV ☎ P – 100. AE VISA
M *(closed Saturday lunch)* 11.95/15.95 **t.** and a la carte 4.95 – 7.25 – **36 rm** 70.00/120.00 **t.**

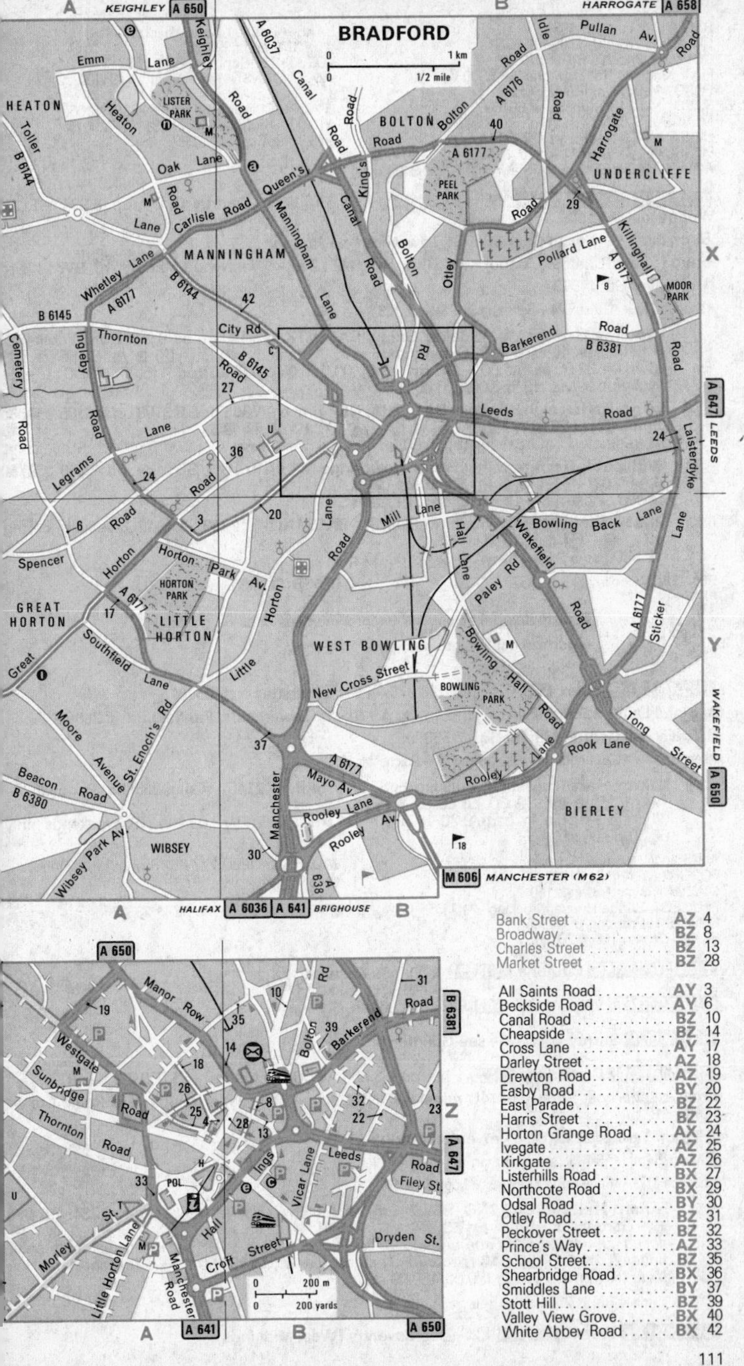

Bank Street .... AZ 4
Broadway .... BZ 8
Charles Street .... BZ 13
Market Street .... BZ 28

All Saints Road .... AY 3
Beckside Road .... AY 6
Canal Road .... BZ 10
Cheapside .... BZ 14
Cross Lane .... AY 17
Darley Street .... AZ 18
Drewton Road .... AZ 19
Easby Road .... BY 20
East Parade .... BZ 22
Harris Street .... BZ 23
Horton Grange Road .... AX 24
Ivegate .... AZ 25
Kirkgate .... AZ 26
Listerhills Road .... BX 27
Northcote Road .... BX 29
Odsal Road .... BY 30
Otley Road .... BZ 31
Peckover Street .... BZ 32
Prince's Way .... AZ 33
School Street .... BZ 35
Shearbridge Road .... BX 36
Smiddles Lane .... BY 37
Stott Hill .... BZ 39
Valley View Grove .... BX 40
White Abbey Road .... BX 42

BMW Oak Lane ✆ 495521
CITROEN Whetley Hill ✆ 495543
COLT St. Enoch's Rd ✆ 678272
FIAT Keighley Rd, Frizinghall ✆ 490031
FORD 44 Bowland St. ✆ 725131
FORD 146-148 Tong St. ✆ 681601
MERCEDES-BENZ Thornton Rd ✆ 494122
NISSAN 77 Otley Rd ✆ 727302
PORSCHE, VAUXHALL-OPEL Neville Rd ✆ 307600
ROVER, DAIMLER-JAGUAR Canal Rd ✆ 733488
SAAB Apperley Lane, Yeadon ✆ 0532 (Leeds) 502231
VOLVO 221 Sunbridge Rd ✆ 721720
VW, AUDI-NSU Ingleby Rd ✆ 494100

ATS 8 Cranmer Rd ✆ 632233/632106
ATS 177 Thornton Rd ✆ 731141/723015
ATS Tong St. ✆ 680155

BRADFORD-ON-AVON Wilts. 403 404 N 29 **The West Country G.** – **pop. 8 921** – **ECD Wednesday** – ✆ **022 16.**

See : Site★★ – Saxon Church of St. Lawrence★★ – Bridge★.

Envir. : Great Chalfield Manor★ *AC* (Church★) NE : 2 m. – Westwood Manor★ *AC*, SW : 1½ m.

34 Silver St. ✆ **5797.**

◆London 118 – ◆ Bristol 24 – Salisbury 35 – Swindon 33.

- **Woolley Grange**, Woolley Green, BA15 1TX, NE : ¾ m. by B 3107 on Woolley St ✆ 4705, Fax 4059, ←, « 17C manor house », heated, – ✆ P. AE VISA
  M 26.00/32.00 **st.** 5.50 – **18 rm** 80.00/155.00 **st.**, **2 suites** 115.00/160.00 **st.** – SB (November-March) 150.00/220.00 **st.**
- **Leigh Park,** Leigh Rd West, BA15 2RA, NE : 1 m. by A 363 and B 3109 on B 3105 ✆ 4885, Group Telex 2315, – ✆ P – 100. AE VISA
  M (restricted Saturday lunch) 15.50/20.50 **t.** 4.50 – **20 rm** 58.00/95.00 **t.** – SB 92.00 **st.**
- **Widbrook Grange** without rest., Trowbridge Rd, BA15 1UH, SE : 1 m. on A 363 ✆ 4750, ←, park – ✆ P. AE VISA.
  closed Christmas – **12 rm** 24.00/73.00 **st.**
- **Priory Steps,** Newtown, off Market St., BA15 1NQ, ✆ 2230, ←, « 17C weavers cottages », – P. VISA.
  M 14.00 **st.** 2.95 – **5 rm** 38.00/60.00 **st.**

RENAULT Woolley St. ✆ 2352
ROVER St Margarets ✆ 3215

Les prix	Pour toutes précisions sur les prix indiqués dans ce guide, reportez-vous à l'introduction.

BRAINTREE Essex 404 V 28 – **pop. 30 975** – **ECD : Thursday** – ✆ **0376.**

Kings Lane, Stisted ✆ **24117, E: 2 m. by A 120** – **Towerlands, Panfield Rd** ✆ **26802.**

Town Hall Centre, Market Sq. ✆ **550066.**

◆London 45 – ◆Cambridge 38 – Chelmsford 12 – Colchester 15.

- **White Hart** (Lansbury), Bocking End, CM7 6AB, ✆ 21401, Telex 988835, Fax 552628 – rm ✆ P – 30. AE VISA.
  M (grill rest.) a la carte 9.20/16.70 **t.** – **34 rm** 60.00/72.00 **t.** – SB (weekends only) 62.00/66.00 **st.**

AUDI, VW Dunmow Rd, Rayne ✆ 46335
FORD Rayne Rd ✆ 21202
MAZDA Rayne Rd ✆ 42159
PEUGEOT Bridge House, Brocking ✆ 41179
RENAULT Cressing ✆ 83345
ROVER Notley Rd ✆ 20690
VAUXHALL-OPEL 277-281 Rayne Rd ✆ 21456
VOLVO Skitts Hill ✆ 47797

ATS 271-275 Rayne Rd ✆ 23306

BRAITHWAITE Cumbria 401 402 K 20 – see Keswick.

BRAMHOPE West Yorks. 402 P 22 – see Leeds.

BRAMLEY Surrey 404 S 30 – see Guildford.

BRAMPTON Cumbria 401 402 L 19 – **pop. 3 686** – **ECD : Thursday** – ✆ **069 77.**

Envir. : Lanercost : Priory★ (14C ruins) *AC*, NE : 3 m. – Bewcastle (churchyard Runic Cross★ 8C) N : 12 m.

Talkin Tarn ✆ **2255, SE : 1 m. on B 6413.**

Moot Hall ✆ **3433 (summer only).**

◆ London 317 – ◆Carlisle 9 – ◆Newcastle-upon-Tyne 49.

- **Farlam Hall**, CA8 2NG, SE : 2¾ m. on A 689 ✆ 069 76 (Hallbankgate) 234, Fax 683, ←, « Gardens » – ✆ P. VISA.
  closed 27 January-29 February and 26 to 30 December – **M** (bar lunch residents only)/dinner 25.00 **t.** 4.50 – **13 rm** (dinner included) 80.00/190.00 **t.** – SB (except Bank Holidays) (November-April) 120.00/160.00 **st.**

ROVER Carlisle Rd ✆ 2508

BRANDON Warw. 403 404 P 26 – see Coventry (West Midlands).

BRANDS HATCH Kent – ✉ Dartford – ☎ 0474 Ash Green.

Corinthian, Gay Dawn Farm ☎ 047 47 (Fawkham) 7559.

London 22 – Maidstone 18.

Brands Hatch Thistle (Mt. Charlotte Thistle), on A 20, DA3 8PE, ☎ 854900, Telex 966449, Fax 853220 – rm rest – 300. VISA. **M** 13.00 **st.** and a la carte – 7.75 – **138 rm** 75.00/100.00 **st.**, **2 suites** 150.00/160.00 **st.** – SB 98.00 **st.**

at Fawkham E : 1½ m. by A 20 – ✉ Dartford – ☎ 0474 Ash Geen :

Brands Hatch Place, DA3 8NQ, ☎ 872239, Fax 879652, squash – 120. VISA. **M** 17.50 **st.** and a la carte – 7.00 – **29 rm** 75.00/105.00 **st.** – SB (weekend only) 115.00 **st.**

BRANSCOMBE Devon 403 K 32 The West Country G. – pop. 506 – ECD : Thursday – ✉ Seaton ☎ 029 780.

London 167 – Exeter 20 – Lyme Regis 11.

The Look Out, EX12 3DP, S : ¾ m. by Beach Rd ☎ 262, ≤ cliffs and Bear Head, « Tastefully converted coastguards cottages », – *closed 2 weeks Christmas* – **M** *(closed Monday)* (dinner only) 32.00 **t.** 5.25 – **6 rm** 45.00/85.00 **t.** – SB (November-April) 110.00/130.00 **st.**

Masons Arms, EX12 3DJ, ☎ 300, Fax 500, « 14C inn » – VISA **M** (bar lunch Monday to Saturday)/dinner 26.00 **st.** and a la carte 4.25 – **20 rm** 35.00/85.00 **st.** – SB (November-April) 85.00/109.00 **st.**

BRANSTON Lincs. 402 404 S 24 – see Lincoln.

BRANSTON Staffs. – see Burton-upon-Trent.

BRAUNSTONE Leics. 402 403 404 Q 26 – see Leicester.

BRAUNTON Devon 403 H 30 – pop. 9 004 – ECD : Wednesday – ☎ 0271.

Saunton ☎ 812436.

The Car Park ☎ 816400.

London 226 – Exeter 47 – Taunton 58.

XX **Otter's,** 30 Caen St., EX33 1AA, ☎ 813633 – VISA *closed Sunday, Monday, 2 weeks March and 2 weeks October-November* – **M** (dinner only) 13.75 and a la carte 13.30/20.50 **t.** 3.50.

at Wrafton SE : ½ m. on A 361 – ✉ ☎ 0271 Braunton :

Poyers, EX33 2DN, ☎ 812149, – rest VISA *closed 20 December-5 January* – **M** *(closed Sunday and Monday to non-residents)* (dinner only) a la carte 16.60/20.10 **st.** – **10 rm** 45.00/65.00 **st.** – SB 55.00 **st.**

at Knowle N : 1¼ m. on A 361 – ✉ ☎ 0271 Braunton:

XX **Grays Country,** EX33 2NA, ☎ 812809, – VISA *closed lunch Tuesday and Saturday, Sunday, Monday and 1 week November* – **M** 30.00 **t.** and a la carte.

BRAY-ON-THAMES Berks. 404 R 29 – pop. 9 427 – ✉ ☎ 0628 Maidenhead.

London 34 – Reading 13.

Plan : see Maidenhead

XXXX ✿✿✿ **Waterside Inn** (Roux), Ferry Rd, SL6 2AT, ☎ 20691, Fax 784710, French rest. « ≤ Thames-side setting », – VISA X a *closed Tuesday lunch, Sunday dinner 20 October-Easter, Monday and 26 December-8 February* – **M** 25.50/49.50 **st.** and a la carte 39.30/54.00 **st.** 10.00.
Spec. Blanc de poulet fermier en gelée aux champignons sauvages et pistaches, Caneton croisé Challandais aux clous de girofle et au miel (2 persons), Soufflé chaud aux framboises.

BREADSALL Derbs. – See Derby.

BRECHFA Dyfed 403 H 28 – ✉ Carmarthen – ☎ 0267.

London 223 – Carmarthen 11 – Swansea 30.

XX **Ty Mawr Country House** with rm, Abergorlech Rd, SA32 7RA, ☎ 202332, Fax 202437, – VISA *closed Sunday and Monday* – **M** (dinner only and Sunday lunch) (booking essential) 17.00 **t.** 4.50 – **5 rm** 28.00/48.00 **t.** – SB 77.00 **st.**

***En saison,** surtout dans les stations fréquentées, il est prudent de retenir à l'avance.*
Cependant, si vous ne pouvez pas occuper la chambre que vous avez retenue, prévenez immédiatement l'hôtelier.
Si vous écrivez à un hôtel à l'étranger, joignez à votre lettre un coupon-réponse international (disponible dans les bureaux de poste).

BRECON (ABERHONDDU) Powys 403 J 28 – pop. 7 166 – ECD : Wednesday – ☎ 0874.

See : Cathedral★ 13C.

Envir. : Craig-y-Nos (Dan-yr-Ogof Caves★★) SW : 18 m. – Road★ from Brecon to Hirwaun Road★ from Brecon to Merthyr Tydfil – Bwlch (<★ of the Usk Valley) SE : 8½ m.

18 Penoyre Park, Cradoc ℘ 3658, NW : 2 m. by B 4520 – 9 Llanfaes ℘ 2004, W : ¾ m. on A 40

Watton Mount ℘ 4437 – Market Car Park ℘ 2485 – Mountain Centre, Libanus ℘3366.

♦London 171 – ♦Cardiff 40 – Carmarthen 31 – Gloucester 65.

Wellington, The Bulwark, LD3 7AD, ℘ 5225 – TV ☎. AE VISA.
M 10.00/16.00 **st.** and a la carte – 5.50 – **21 rm** 35.00/56.00 **st.** – SB 50.00/70.00 **st.**

FORD ℘ 2401 — VAUXHALL County Garages ℘ 2266

BREDWARDINE Heref. and Worc. 403 L 27 – pop. 177 – ✉ Hereford – ☎ 098 17 Moccas.

♦London 150 – Hereford 12 – Newport 51.

Red Lion, HR3 6BU, ℘ 303, – TV ☎ P. AE VISA
M (bar lunch Monday to Saturday)/dinner a la carte 11.50/18.35 **t.** 4.15 – **9 rm** 20.00 48.00 **t.** – SB 30.00/40.00 **st.**

BRENT ELEIGH Suffolk – see Lavenham.

BRENT KNOLL Somerset 403 L 30 – pop. 1 092 – ECD : Wednesday and Saturday – ✉ Highbridge – ☎ 0278 Bridgwater.

♦London 151 – ♦Bristol 33 – Taunton 21.

Battleborough Grange, Bristol Rd, TA9 4HJ, on A 38 ℘ 760208, Fax 760208, – TV ☎ P – 80. AE VISA.
M 11.50 **t.** and a la carte 4.00 – **18 rm** 42.00/60.00 **t.** – SB (October-April) (weekend only) 52.00/70.00 **st.**

BRENTWOOD Essex 404 V 29 – pop. 51 212 – ECD : Thursday – ☎ 0277.

18 King George's playing fields, Ingrave Rd ℘ 218714 – 18 Bentley G & CC, Ongar Road ℘ 73179 – 9 Warley Park, Magpie Lane, Little Warley ℘ 231352.

♦London 22 – Chelmsford 11 – Southend-on-Sea 21.

Brentwood Moat House (Q.M.H.), London Rd, CM14 4NR, SW : 1 ¼ m. on A 102 ℘ 225252, Telex 995182, Fax 262809, – TV ☎ & P – 55. AE VISA.
M a la carte 12.10/28.75 **t.** 4.20 – 7.50 – **32 rm** 91.00/104.00 **st.**, **1 suite** 132.00 154.00 **st.** – SB (weekends only) 98.00 **st.**

Post House (T.H.F.), Brook St., CM14 5NF, SW : 1 ¾ m. on A 1023 ℘ 260260, Telex 995379, Fax 264264, – TV ☎ P – 100. AE VISA
M *(closed Saturday lunch)* 10.95/13.95 **st.** and a la carte 4.35 – 7.50 – **117 rm** 75.00 95.00 **st.** – SB (weekends only) 76.00 **st.**

AUDI-VW, DAIMLER-JAGUAR 2 Brook St. ℘ 216161
FORD 140 London Rd ℘ 261616
RENAULT 21 Hutton Rd, Shenfield ℘ 218686
ROVER Ingrave Rd ℘ 221401
VAUXHALL-OPEL Brook St. ℘ 263333
ATS Fairfield Rd ℘ 211079
ATS Unit 30, Wash Rd ℘ 262877

BRERETON Cheshire – see Holmes Chapel.

BRIDGEND (PEN-Y-BONT) Mid Glam. 403 J 29 – pop. 31008 – ECD : Wednesday – ☎ 0656.

18 Ewenny ℘ 880326.

♦London 177 – ♦Cardiff 20 – ♦Swansea 23.

Heronston, Ewenny, CF35 5AW, S : 2 m. on B 4265 ℘ 668811, Telex 498232, Fax 767391 heated, – TV ☎ P – 180. AE VISA
closed 25-26 December and 1 January – **M** 12.50 **st.** and a la carte 4.00 – **76 rm** 50.00/110.00 **st.** – SB (weekends only) 95.00/110.00 **st.**

at Coychurch (Llangrallo) E : 2¼ m. by A 473 – ✉ ☎ 0656 Bridgend :

Coed-y-Mwstwr , CF35 6AF, N : 1 m. ℘ 860621, Fax 863122, <, heated, , park – TV ☎ P. AE VISA.
M *(closed 26 December and 1 January)* 25.95/35.95 **st.** 4.95 – 7.25 – **27 rm** 79.50 150.00 **st.** – SB 100.00/140.00 **st.**

at Laleston W : 2 m. on A 473 – ✉ ☎ 0656 Bridgend :

Great House, CF32 OHP, on A 473 ℘ 657644 – P. VISA
closed Saturday lunch, Sunday dinner, Monday, 2 weeks July-August and 25-26 December – **M** 16.00/17.90 **t.** and a la carte 3.75.

MICHELIN Distribution Centre, Brackla Industrial Estate, CF31 2AG, ℘ 662343, Fax 645602

ROVER Brackla Ind. Est. ℘ 653376
VAUXHALL, OPEL Western Ave,. Ind. Est. ℘ 655007
VOLVO Ogmore Rd, Ewenny ℘ 769769
ATS Coity Rd ℘ 658775/6

BRIDGNORTH Shropshire 403 404 M 26 – pop. 10 332 – ECD : Thursday – ✆ 074 62 (4 and 5 fig.) or 0746 (6 fig).
Envir. : Claverley (Parish church : wall paintings★ 13C-15C) E : 5 m. – Much Wenlock : Wenlock priory★ (ruins 11C) AC, NW : 8½ m.
Stanley Lane ✆ 3315, N : 1 m.
Bridgnorth Library, Listley St. ✆ 763358.
London 146 – ♦Birmingham 26 – Shrewsbury 20 – Worcester 29.

Croft, St. Mary's St., WV16 4DW, ✆ 762416 – TV ☎. AE VISA
M 13.95 **st.** 3.25 – **12 rm** 30.00/47.00 **st.** – SB 58.00 **st.**

at Worfield NE : 4 m. by A 454 – ✉ Bridgnorth – ✆ 074 64 Worfield :

Old Vicarage, WV15 5JZ, ✆ 497, Fax 552, – TV ☎ P. AE VISA
closed 20 December-3 January – **M** *(closed Sunday dinner to non-residents)* 17.50/25.00 **t.** 4.95 – **15 rm** 60.00/82.50 **t.** – SB 85.00/97.50 **st.**

at Hampton Loade SE : 6¼ m. by A 442 – ✉ Bridgnorth – ✆ 0746 Quatt :

XX Haywain, WV15 6HD, ✆ 780404 – P.

at Alveley SE : 7 m. by A 442 – ✉ Bridgnorth – ✆ 0746 Quatt :

Mill, Birdsgreen, WV15 6HL, NE : ¾ m. ✆ 780437, Telex 337356, Fax 780850, park – rest TV ☎ P – 300. AE VISA.
M 7.00 **st.** (lunch) and a la carte 15.15/26.75 **st.** 3.50 – 5.50 – **21 rm** 49.50/140.00 **st.** – SB (weekends only) 96.00/111.00 **st.**

RENAULT Stanmore Ind. Est. ✆ 765315
ROVER Salop St. ✆ 2207
VW, AUDI Hollybush Rd ✆ 4343 (or after 5.30 ✆ 0836 502555)

Si vous cherchez un hôtel tranquille,
consultez d'abord les cartes de l'introduction
ou repérez dans le texte les établissements indiqués avec le signe ou

BRIDGWATER Somerset 403 L 30 **The West Country G.** – pop. 30 782 – ECD : Thursday – ✆ 0278.
See : Site★ – Castle St.★ – St. Mary's★ – Admiral Blake Museum★ AC.
Envir. : Stogursey Priory Church★★, NW : 14 m. by A 39 – Westonzoyland Church★★, SE : 3 m. – North Petherton Church Tower★★, S : 3 m.
Enmore Park ✆ 027 867 (Enmore) 244.
Town Hall, High St. ✆ 427652 (summer only).
London 160 – ♦Bristol 39 – Taunton 11.

Friarn Court, 37 St. Mary St., TA6 3LX, ✆ 452859, Fax 452988 – TV ☎ P. AE VISA.
M *(closed Sunday)* (dinner only) a la carte 11.80/17.30 **st.** 5.20 – 3.00 – **12 rm** 39.50/64.50 **st.** – SB (weekends only) 66.00/106.00 **st.**

Old Vicarage, 45-51 St. Mary's St., TA6 3LQ, ✆ 458891, Fax 445297, – TV ☎ P. VISA.
M a la carte 11.85/17.45 **t.** – **13 rm** 36.50/42.50 **t.**

Watergate, 10-11 West Quay, TA6 3DB, ✆ 423847 – TV ☎. AE VISA.
M *(closed Sunday)* 20.00 **t.** and a la carte 3.50 – **8 rm** 30.00/44.00 **t.**

at West Huntspill N : 6 m. on A 38 – ✉ Highbridge – ✆ 0278 Burnham-on-Sea :

Sundowner, 74 Main Rd, TA9 3QU, on A 38 ✆ 784766 – TV ☎ P. AE VISA
M *(closed Sunday dinner October-Easter)* 8.45/10.95 **t.** and a la carte 3.00 – **8 rm** 35.00/48.00 **t.** – SB (October-April) (weekends only) 66.00 **st.**

at North Petherton S : 3 m. on A 38 – ✉ ✆ 0278 Bridgwater :

Walnut Tree Inn (Best Western), TA6 6QA, ✆ 662255, Fax 663946 – TV ☎ P – 60. AE VISA.
M a la carte 12.50/14.90 **t.** – **27 rm** 42.00/72.00 **t.**, **1 suite** 92.00 **t.**

AUDI-VW Taunton Rd ✆ 428110
CITROEN Main Rd, Cannington ✆ 0278 (Combwich) 652228
FORD 37 Friar St. ✆ 451332
RENAULT 52 Eastover ✆ 422218
ROVER Market St. ✆ 422125
VOLVO Bristol Rd ✆ 455333

ATS Polden St ✆ 455795
ATS Friarn St. ✆ 450571/455795

BRIDLINGTON Humberside 402 T 21 – pop. 28 426 – ECD : Thursday – ✆ 0262.
See : Priory Church★ (12C-15C).
Envir. : Burton Agnes Hall★ (Elizabethan) AC, SW : 6 m.
Belvedere Rd ✆ 672092, S : 1½ m. on A 165 – Flamborough Head, Lighthouse Rd ✆ 850333, NE : 5 m.
25 Prince St. ✆ 673474/679626.
♦ London 236 – ♦Kingston-upon-Hull 29 – York 41.

Expanse, North Marine Drive, YO15 2LS, ℘ 675347, Fax 604928, ≤ – |$ TV ☎ P. AE VISA. ✱
M 7.50/13.00 **st.** and a la carte 4.40 – **48 rm** 38.50/89.00 **st.** – SB 73.00/82.50 **st.**

Monarch, South Marine Drive, YO15 3JJ, ℘ 674447, Fax 604928, ≤ – |$ TV ☎ P. AE VISA. ✱
closed 17 December-7 January – **M** (bar lunch Monday to Saturday)/dinner 30.00 and a la carte 4.00 – **40 rm** 38.00/60.00 **t.** – SB 75.00/85.00 **st.**

FIAT Quay Rd ℘ 670331
FORD Hamilton Rd ℘ 675336
TALBOT 74 Pessingby Rd ℘ 678141
VAUXHALL-OPEL 52-60 Quay Rd ℘ 672022
VOLVO Pinfold Lane ℘ 670351
ATS Springfield Av. ℘ 675571

BRIDPORT Dorset 403 L 31 **The West Country G.** – pop. 10 615 – ECD : Thursday – 0308.

Envir. : Parnham House★★ *AC*, N : 6 m. on A 3066.

Bridport and West Dorset, West Bay ℘ 22597, S : 1 ½ m.

32 South St. ℘ 24901.

London 150 – Exeter 38 – Taunton 33 – Weymouth 19.

Roundham House, Roundham Gdns, West Bay Rd, DT6 4BD, S : 1 m. by B 315 ℘ 22753, ≤, – TV ☎ P. AE VISA. ✱
mid January-mid November – **M** *(closed Sunday lunch)* (bar lunch)/dinner 13.95 **t.** 4.90 – **8 rm** 30.00/53.00 **t.** – SB (October-March) (except Bnak Holidays) 70.00/99.90 **st.**

Britmead House, 154 West Bay Rd, DT6 4EG, S : 1 ¼ m. on B 3157 ℘ 22941 – res TV P. AE VISA
M 10.00 **st.** 3.50 – **7 rm** 23.00/40.00 **st.**

at Powerstock NE : 4 m. by A 3066 – ✉ Bridport – 030 885 Powerstock :

XX **Three Horseshoes Inn** with rm, DT6 3TF, ℘ 328 – P. AE VISA
M *(closed dinner Sunday and Monday)* 10.50/25.00 **t.** and a la carte 3.75 – **4 rm** 20.00/50.00 **t.** – SB (September-April) (except Sunday and Monday) 65.00 **st.**

at Shipton Gorge SE : 3 m. by A 35 – ✉ 0308 Bridport :

XX **Innsacre Farmhouse** with rm, Shipton Lane, DT6 4LJ, N : 1 m. ℘ 56137, – TV P AE VISA
M 14.00/21.50 **st.** 5.00 – **7 rm** 35.00/60.00 **st.** – SB (November-March) 69.00 **st.**

at West Bay S : 1 ½ m. on B 3157 – ✉ 0308 Bridport :

Haddon House, DT6 4EL, ℘ 23626 – TV ☎ P. AE VISA
M 11.50/17.95 **t.** and a la carte 4.95 – **13 rm** 39.50/58.00 **t.** – SB 60.00/75.00 **st.**

at Chideock W : 3 m. on A 35 – ✉ Bridport – 0297 Chideock :

Betchworth House without rest., Main St., DT6 6JW, ℘ 89478, – P
March-November – **6 rm** 18.00/40.00 **st.**

ATS Victoria Grove ℘ 23661/2

BRIGHOUSE West Yorks. 402 O 22 – pop. 32 597 – 0484.

London 213 – Bradford 12 – Burnley 28 – Manchester 35 – Scheffield 39.

Forte (T.H.F.), Clifton Village, HD6 4HW, SE : 1 m. on A 644 ℘ 400400, Telex 518204, Fax 400068, , – rm TV ☎ & P – 200. AE VISA
M 15.50/22.50 **st.** and a la carte – 7.50 – **92 rm** 85.00/95.00, **2 suites** 145.00 **st.** – SB (weekends only) 100.00 **st.**

BRIGHTON AND HOVE East Sussex 404 T 31 – pop. 200 168 (inc. Hove) – ECD : Wednesday and Thursday – 0273.

See : Sea Front★★ – Royal Pavilion★ (interior★★) *AC* CZ – Booth Museum (bird collection)★ BV **M** – Preston Manor (Chinese collection★) BV **D** – The Lanes★ CZ – Aquarium★ *AC* CZ **A** – St. Bartholomews Church★ CX **B**.

Envir. : Stanmer Park (site★) N : 3 ½ m. by A 27 CV – Clayton (Church of St. John the Baptist frescoes★ 14C) N : 6 m. by A 23 BV.

East Brighton, Roedean ℘ 604838 CV – Dyke, Dyke Rd ℘ 079 156 (Poynings) 296, N : by Dyke Rd BV – Hollingbury Park, Ditching Rd ℘ 552010, NE : 1 m. CV – Waterhall, Devils Dyke Rd ℘ 508658, N : 3 m. AV – Dyke Rd ℘ 556482 BV.

Shoreham Airport : ℘ 452304, W : 8 m. by A 27 A.

Marlborough House, 54 Old Steine ℘ 23755/27560.

at Hove : Town Hall, Norton Rd ℘ 775400.

King Alfred Leisure Centre, Kingsway ℘ 720371.

London 53 – Portsmouth 48 – Southampton 61.

Plans on following pages

Grand (De Vere), King's Rd, BN1 2FW, ℘ 21188, Telex 877410, Fax 202694, ←, ≘, ⊡ – |♯| ▤ rest ⊡ ☎ – 🏛 300. ⊡ AE ⊙ VISA BZ **v**
M 15.50/21.00 **st.** and a la carte 6.00 – **157 rm** ⊐ 100.00/120.00 **st.**, **6 suites** 390.00/950.00 **st.** – SB 150.00/240.00 **st.**

Hospitality Inn (Mt. Charlotte Thistle), King's Rd, BN1 2GS, ℘ 206700, Telex 878555, Fax 820692, ←, ≘, ⊡ – |♯| ⇆ rm ▤ ⊡ ☎ ♿ ⇔ – 🏛 300. ⊡ AE ⊙ VISA CZ **n**
M 19.50/31.50 **st.** and a la carte – ⊐ 9.50 – **200 rm** 108.00/128.00 **t.**, **4 suites** 250.00/900.00 **t.** – SB (weekends only) 120.00/140.00 **st.**

Brighton Metropole, King's Rd, BN1 2FU, ℘ 775432, Telex 877245, Fax 207764, ←, ⊡ – |♯| ⊡ ☎ – 🏛 1200. ⊡ AE ⊙ VISA BZ **s**
M 19.50 **t.** and a la carte – **312 rm** ⊐ 110.00/147.00 **st.**, **16 suites** 250.00/390.00 **st.**

Royal Crescent, Marine Parade, BN2 1AX, ℘ 606311, Telex 87253, Fax 601042, ← – |♯| ⊡ ☎ – 🏛. ⊡ AE ⊙ VISA CV **e**
M 14.00/24.00 **t.** and a la carte 4.00 – **64 rm** ⊐ 60.00/95.00 **t.**, **2 suites** 140.00/180.00 **t.** – SB 125.00 **st.**

Granville, 123-125 King's Rd, BN1 2FA, ℘ 26302, Fax 202541, ← – |♯| ⊡ ☎ – 🏛 35
25 rm. BZ **a**

Kings, 139-141 King's Rd, BN1 2NA, ℘ 820854, Telex 878802, Fax 28120 – |♯| ⊡ ☎ Ⓟ – 🏛 80. ⊡ AE ⊙ VISA. ✻ BZ **r**
M *(closed Saturday lunch)* (buffet lunch)/dinner 14.50 **st.** 3.25 – **78 rm** ⊐ 58.00/75.00 **st.** – SB 79.00/85.00 **st.**

Twenty One, 21 Charlotte St., BN2 1AG, ℘ 686450 – ⊡ ☎. ⊡ AE VISA. ✻ CV **i**
closed first 2 weeks January – **M** *(closed Sunday and Monday)* (dinner only) 21.50 **t.** 4.15 – **6 rm** ⊐ 30.00/65.00 **st.**

Dove, 18 Regency Sq., BN1 2FG, ℘ 779222, Fax 746912 – ⇆ rest ⊡ ☎. ⊡ AE VISA. ✻
closed 1 week Christmas – **M** (dinner only) (by arrangement) 10.50 **st.** 2.50 – **8 rm** ⊐ 42.00/78.00 **st.** – SB (weekends only) (except Bank Holidays) 66.00/90.00 **st.** BZ **e**

Adelaide, 51 Regency Sq., BN1 2FF, ℘ 205286, Fax 220904 – ⇆ rest ⊡ ☎. ⊡ AE ⊙ VISA. ✻ BZ **z**
closed Christmas – **M** *(closed dinner Sunday and Wednesday)* (bar lunch)/dinner 12.50 **st.** – **12 rm** ⊐ 33.00/70.00 **st.** – SB (weekends only) (except Bank Holidays) 70.00/82.00 **st.**

Prince Regent without rest., 29 Regency Sq., BN1 2FH, ℘ 29962 – ⇆ rest ⊡ ☎. ⊡ ⊙ VISA. ✻ BZ **u**
19 rm ⊐ 28.00/48.00 **t.**

Dudley House without rest., 10 Madeira Pl., BN2 1TN, ℘ 676794 – ⇆ ⊡. ✻
6 rm ⊐ 30.00/65.00 **st.** CZ **a**

Harvey's without rest., 1 Broad St., BN2 1TJ, ℘ 699227 – ⇆ ⊡. ✻ CZ **x**
closed Christmas – **8 rm** ⊐ 30.00/55.00 **st.**

Hayward's, 51-52 North St., BN1 1RH, ℘ 24261 – ⊡ AE VISA CZ **e**
closed Sunday dinner – **M** 12.50 **t.** and a la carte 3.95.

Langan's Bistro, 1 Paston Pl., Kemp Town, BN2 1HA, ℘ 606933 – CV **a**

La Marinade, 77 St. Georges Rd, Kemp Town, BN2 1EF, ℘ 600992, French rest. – ▤ CV **c**

Whytes, 33 Western St., BN1 2PG, ℘ 776618 – ⊡ AE VISA
closed Sunday – **M** (dinner only) 15.75 **t.** 3.25. BZ **o**

Le Grandgousier, 15 Western St., BN1 2PG, ℘ 772005, French rest. – ⊡ AE VISA
closed Saturday lunch, Sunday and 24 December-3 January – **M** 25.00 **st.** 3.25. BY **x**

at Hove – ✉ Hove – ✆ 0273 Brighton :

Whitehaven, 34 Wilbury Rd, BN3 3JP, ℘ 778355, Fax 731177, ⚘ – ⊡ ☎. ⊡ AE ⊙ VISA. ✻ AX **c**
closed 24 December-2 January – **M** *(closed Saturday lunch and Sunday)* 18.50 **t.** 3.50 – **17 rm** ⊐ 48.00/70.00 **st.**

Claremont House, Second Av., BN3 2LL, ℘ 735161, Fax 24764, ⚘ – ⊡ ☎. ⊡ AE ⊙ VISA AY **c**
M 15.00 **st.** 4.00 – **12 rm** ⊐ 45.00/62.00 **st.** – SB (weekends only) 72.50/90.00 **st.**

Eaton Garden, 13 Eaton Gdns, BN3 3TN, ℘ 738921, Fax 779075, English rest. – Ⓟ. ⊡ AE ⊙ VISA AX **a**
M 15.00/18.00 **t.** and a la carte 4.25.

Le Classique, 37 Waterloo St., BN3 1AY, ℘ 734140, French rest. – ⊡ AE ⊙ VISA BY **i**
closed Sunday – **M** (dinner only) 13.95 **t.** and a la carte.

CITROEN, HYUNDAI, RENAULT Old Shoreham Rd, Portslade ℘ 411020
FIAT 100 Lewes Rd ℘ 508966
FORD 90-96 Preston Rd ℘ 550211
MAZDA Channel House, Fishergate Terr., Portslade ℘ 413833
MERCEDES-BENZ Victoria Rd ℘ 430787
PORSCHE Victoria Rd ℘ 414911
RENAULT Stephenson Rd ℘ 692111
ROVER 200 Dyke Rd ℘ 553061
VAUXHALL Old Shoreham Rd, Portslade ℘ 422552

ATS 40 Bristol Gdns ℘ 680150/686344

*Inclusion in the **Michelin Guide** cannot be achieved by pulling strings or by offering favours.*

BRIGHTON AND HOVE

- Churchill Square Shopping Centre ..... **BYZ**
- London Road .... **CX**
- North Street .... **CZ**
- Western Road .... **ABY**

- Adelaide Crescent ..... **AY** 2
- Brunswick Place .... **AY** 4
- Brunswick Square .... **AYZ** 5
- Carlton Terrace .... **AV** 6
- Chatham Place .... **BX** 7
- Denmark Road .... **BY** 8
- East Street .... **CZ** 9
- Eastern Road .... **CV** 10
- Gladstone Terrace .... **CX** 12
- Gloucester Place ..... **CY** 13
- Gloucester Road ..... **CY** 14
- Goldsmid Road ...... **BX** 15
- Grand Junction Road .. **CZ** 16
- Hollingbury Park Av. .. **BV** 17
- Hollingdean Road .... **CV** 18
- Hove Street .... **AV** 19
- Market Place .... **CX** 20
- Marlborough Place .... **CY** 21
- Montpelier Place ..... **BY** 22
- Old Steine .... **CZ** 23
- Pavillon Parade ...... **CZ** 26
- Richmond Place ...... **CY** 27
- Richmond Terrace .... **CX** 28
- St. George's Place .... **CY** 30
- St. Peter's Place ...... **CX** 31
- Terminus Road ..... **BCX** 32
- Upper Lewes Road ... **CX** 33
- Upper North Street ... **BY** 34
- Victoria Road .... **AV** 36
- Warren Road .... **CV** 37
- Waterloo Place .... **CX** 39
- Wellington Road ..... **AV** 40
- York Place .... **CY** 42

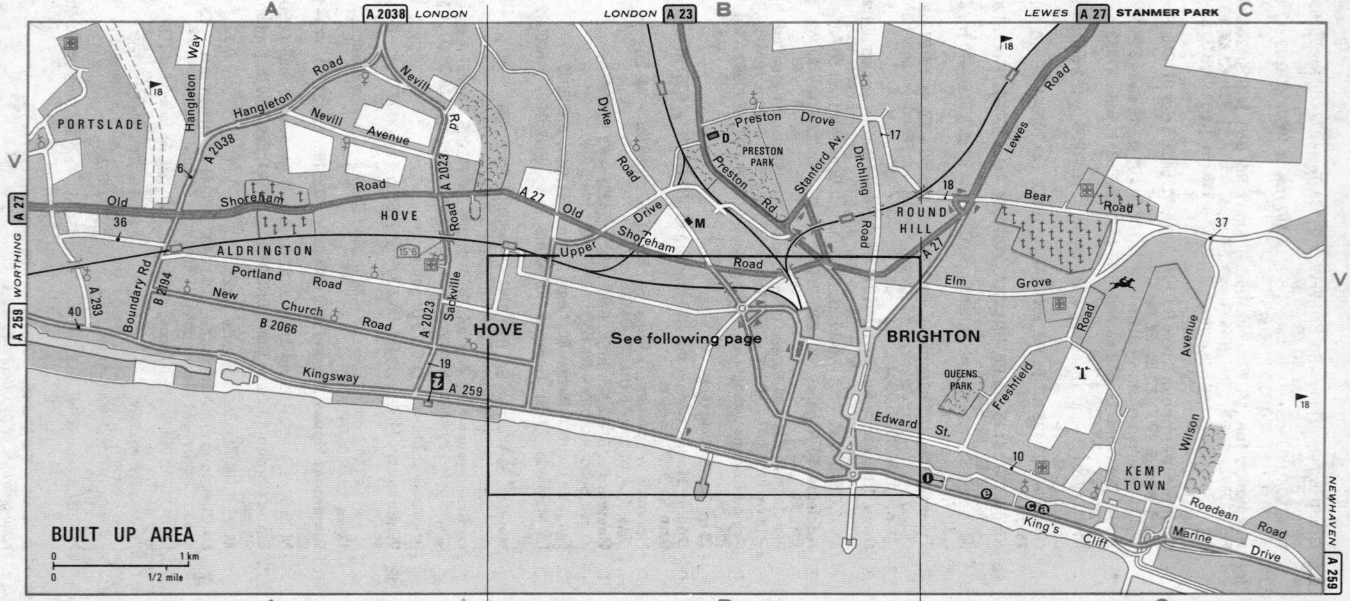

A 2038 LONDON · LONDON A 23 · LEWES A 27 STANMER PARK · A 27 WORTHING · A 259 WORTHING · NEWHAVEN A 259

PORTSLADE · HOVE · ALDRINGTON · BRIGHTON · ROUND HILL · KEMP TOWN · PRESTON PARK · QUEENS PARK

Hangleton Way · Hangleton Road · A 2038 · Nevill Rd · Nevill Avenue · Old Shoreham Road · A 27 · Upper Shoreham Road · Dyke Road · Drive · Preston Rd · Preston Drove · Stanford Av. · Ditchling Road · Lewes Road · Bear Road · Elm Grove · Road · Freshfield · Edward St. · Wilson Avenue · Roedean Road · Marine Drive · King's Cliff · A 2023 · Sackville Road · Portland Road · New Church Road · B 2066 · B 2194 · Boundary Rd · A 293 · Kingsway · A 259

See following page

BUILT UP AREA

0 — 1 km
0 — 1/2 mile

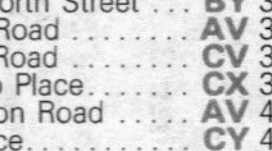
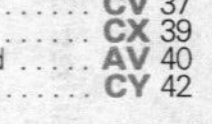

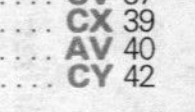
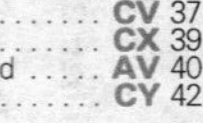
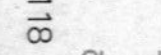

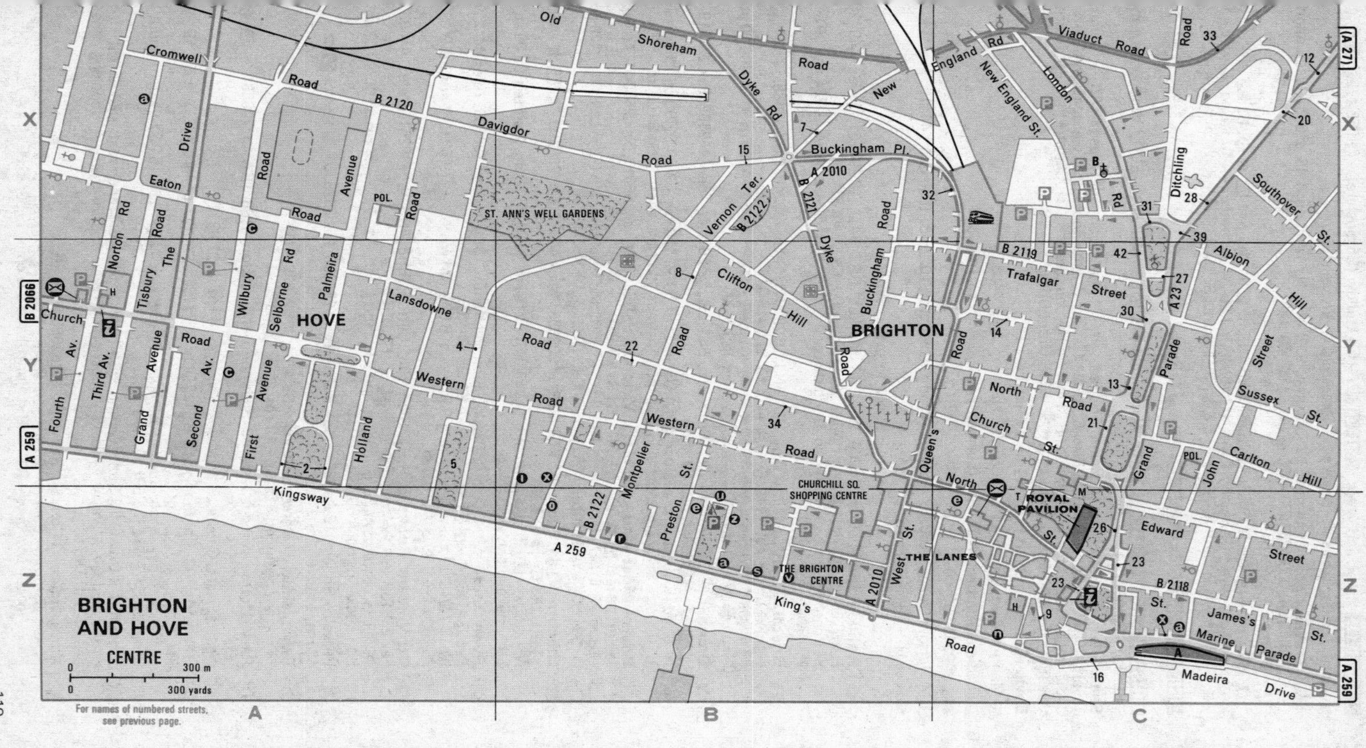

BRIGHTON
AND HOVE
CENTRE
0 300 m
0 300 yards
For names of numbered streets, see previous page.
HOVE
BRIGHTON
ROYAL PAVILION
THE LANES
CHURCHILL SQ. SHOPPING CENTRE
THE BRIGHTON CENTRE
ST. ANN'S WELL GARDENS
POL.
(A 27)
B 2066
A 259
A 259
X
Y
Z
A
B
C
Old Shoreham Road
Cromwell Road
B 2120
Davigdor Road
Dyke Rd
Dyke Road
New England Rd
New England St.
London Rd
Viaduct Road
Ditchling Road
Southover St.
Buckingham Pl.
A 2010
B 2121
Vernon Ter.
B 2122
Eaton Road
Norton Rd
Tisbury Road
The Drive
Wilbury Road
Selborne Rd
Palmeira Avenue
Lansdowne Road
Church Road
Third Av.
Fourth Av.
Grand Avenue
Second Av.
First Avenue
Holland Road
Western Road
Clifton Hill
Montpelier Road
Preston St.
Buckingham Road
Queen's Road
North Road
Church St.
North St.
West St.
Trafalgar Street
B 2119
Albion Hill
A 23
Grand Parade
Sussex St.
Street
Carlton Hill
John Street
Edward Street
B 2118
St. James's St.
Marine Parade
Madeira Drive
Kingsway
King's Road
A 2010
Road

BRIMFIELD Heref. and Worc. 403 404 L 27 – ✉ Ludlow (Shropshire) – ☎ 058 472.

♦London 149 – ♦Birmingham 41 – Hereford 21 – Shrewsbury 32 – Worcester 33.

- **Travelodge** without rest., Woofferton, SY8 4AL, N : ½ m. on A 49 ℘ 695, Reservations (Toll free) 0800 850950 – TV ♿ P. VISA.
32 rm 24.00/29.50 **t.**

- XX **Poppies** (at The Roebuck) with rm, SY8 4NE, ℘ 230 – rest TV ☎ P. VISA.
closed 2 weeks February, 1 week October and 25-26 December – **M** *(closed Sunday and Monday)* a la carte 19.75/25.90 **t.** 6.00 – **3 rm** 35.00/60.00 **t.**

BRIMSCOMBE Glos. 403 404 N 28 – see Stroud.

BRISTOL Avon 403 404 M 29 **The West Country G.** – pop. 413 861 – ECD : Wednesday and Saturday – ☎ 0272.

See : Site★★ – Clifton Suspension Bridge★★ AX – The Georgian House★★*AC* – Theatre Royal★★ CZ **T** – St. Mary Redcliffe Church★★ DZ – Bristol Zoological Gardens★★*AC* AX – Cathedral of SS Peter and Paul★★ AX **F** – Floating Harbour area★★ CZ – Clifton★★ AX – Industrial Museum★ CZ **M2** – Bristol Cathedral★ CZ – S.S Great Britain★ AX **B.**

Envir. : Clevedon Court★, W : 11 m. by A369 AX.

Mangotsfield, Carsons Rd ℘ 565501, NE : 6 m. by B 4465 BV.

Bristol Airport : ℘ 027 587 (Lulsgate) 4441 SW : 7 m. by A 38 AX.

℘ 0345 090700.

14 Narrow Quay ℘ 260767 – Bristol Airport, Lulsgate ℘ 027 587 (Lulsgate) 4441.

♦London 121 – ♦Birmingham 91.

Plans on following pages

- **Holiday Inn,** Lower Castle St., Old Market, BS1 3AD, ℘ 294281, Telex 449720, Fax 225838, – rm TV ☎ ♿ P – 600. AE VISA DY s
M (carving lunch) 15.95/17.25 **t.** and dinner a la carte 6.95 – 8.95 – **284 rm** 90.00/250.00 **st.**

- **Bristol Hilton,** Redcliffe Way, BS1 6NJ, ℘ 260041, Telex 449240, Fax 230089, – rm rest TV ☎ P – 400. AE VISA DZ r
M *(closed Saturday lunch)* 15.50 **t.** and a la carte 4.90 – 9.50 – **199 rm** 90.00/105.00 **st.** **2 suites** 175.00 **st.** – SB (weekends only) 125.00 **st.**

- **Grand** (Mt. Charlotte Thistle), Broad St., BS1 2EL, ℘ 291645, Telex 449889, Fax 227619 – TV ☎ – 600. AE VISA CY a
M 8.95/16.00 **st.** and a la carte 4.25 – 7.50 – **178 rm** 62.50/82.50 **st.**, **3 suites** 110.00 **st.** – SB (weekends only) (except Christmas and New Year) 77.00/82.00 **st.**

- **Bristol Moat House** (Q.M.H.), Victoria St., BS1 6HY, ℘ 255010, Fax 255040, – rm rest TV ☎ P – 200. AE VISA DZ a
closed 25 to 30 December – **M** 14.50/18.95 **t.** and a la carte 5.00 – 8.00 – **128 rm** 90.00/100.00 **t.**, **4 suites** 135.00/190.00 **t.**.

- **Unicorn** (Rank), Prince St., BS1 4QF, ℘ 230333, Telex 44315, Fax 230300 – TV ☎ – 300. AE VISA. CZ c
M 10.50/14.00 **st.** and a la carte – 7.95 – **215 rm** 49.00/75.00 **st.**, **2 suites** 95.00 **st.** – SB (weekends only) 85.00 **st.**

- **Avon Gorge** (Mt. Charlotte Thistle), Sion Hill, Clifton, BS8 4LD, ℘ 738955, Telex 444237 Fax 238125, ← – TV ☎ – 100. AE VISA AX x
M 10.75/13.00 **t.** and a la carte 3.90 – 6.50 – **74 rm** 67.50/79.50 **t.**, **2 suites** 95.00/160.00 **t.** – SB 79.00/120.00 **st.**

- **St. Vincent Rocks** (T.H.F.), Sion Hill, Clifton, BS8 4BB, ℘ 739251, Telex 444932 Fax 238139, ← – rm TV ☎ P – 50. AE VISA AX c
M *(closed Saturday lunch)* 16.95 **st.** and a la carte 3.95 – 7.00 – **46 rm** 65.00/90.00 **st.** – SB (weekends only) 80.00/90.00 **st.**

- Berkeley Square, 15 Berkeley Sq., BS8 1HB, ℘ 254000, Fax 252970 – rm TV ☎
42 rm, 1 suite. AX

- **Downlands,** 33 Henleaze Gdns, BS9 4HH, ℘ 621639 – TV AV s
M (by arrangement) 7.50 **st.** – **10 rm** 20.00/38.00 **st.**

- **Park House** without rest., 19 Richmond Hill, Clifton, BS8 1BA, ℘ 736331 – TV P
closed Easter, Christmas and Bank Holidays – **4 rm** 32.00 **st.** AX z

- XXX **Harvey's,** 12 Denmark St., BS1 5DQ, ℘ 277665, « 18C cellars » – . AE VISA
closed Saturday lunch, Sunday, Monday and Bank Holidays – **M** 15.95 **t.** (lunch) and a la carte 23.65/27.65 **t.** 4.50. CY c

- XX **Lettonie,** 9 Druid Hill, Stoke Bishop, BS9 1EW, ℘ 686456, French rest. – AE VISA
closed Sunday, Monday, 2 weeks August and 10 days at Christmas – **M** (booking essential) 12.50/18.95 **t.** AV a

- XX **Markwicks,** 43 Corn St., BS1 1HT, ℘ 262658 – VISA CY
closed Saturday, Sunday, 10 days at Easter, 2 weeks August, 10 days at Christmas and Bank Holiday Mondays – **M** 14.50 **st.** (lunch) and a la carte 19.50/26.95 **st.** 4.75.

XX **Du Gourmet,** 43 Whiteladies Rd, BS8 2LS, ℘ 736230 – AE VISA AX **v**
closed Sunday, Monday and 24 December-2 January – **M** a la carte 13.65/20.85 **t.** 3.50.

XX **Rajdoot,** 83 Park St., BS1 5PJ, ℘ 268033, Indian rest. – AE VISA CY **u**
closed lunch Sunday and Bank Holidays and 25-26 December – **M** 14.50 **t.** and a la carte 3.00.

XX **China Palace,** 18a Baldwin St., BS1 1SE, ℘ 262719, Chinese rest. – AE VISA
M 17.50 **t.** and a la carte 3.45. CY **x**

XX **La Taverna Dell'Artista,** 33 King St., BS1 4DZ, ℘ 297712, Italian rest. – AE VISA
closed Sunday, Monday, first 3 weeks August and Bank Holidays – **M** a la carte 8.85/19.20 **t.** 3.75. DY **s**

XX **Thai House,** 52 Park Row, BS1 5LH, ℘ 253079, Thai rest. – AE VISA CY **a**
closed Sunday, 23 to 27 December and 1 January – **M** 22.00 **st.** and a la carte.

X **Plum Duff,** 6 Chandos Rd, Redland, BS6 6PE, ℘ 238450 – VISA AX **n**
M *(closed Sunday dinner, Monday and 2 weeks Christmas)* (dinner only and Sunday lunch)/dinner 20.50 **t.**

X **Bistro Twenty One,** 21 Cotham Road South, Kingsdown, BS6 5TZ, ℘ 421744 – VISA
closed Saturday lunch, Sunday and 1 week Christmas – **M** (booking essential) a la carte 14.75/17.25 **t.** 3.25. AX **s**

X **Danton,** 2 Upper Byron Pl., The Triangle, BS8 1JY, ℘ 268314 – AE VISA
closed Saturday lunch, Sunday, 1 week Easter, and Bank Holidays – **M** a la carte 16.25/20.60 **t.** 3.85. AX **e**

X **Ganges,** 368 Gloucester Rd, Horfield, BS7 8TP, ℘ 245234, Indian rest. – AE VISA
closed 25 and 26 December – **M** 18.00 **t.** and a la carte. AV **e**

at Patchway N : 6 ½ m. on A 38 – BV – ✉ Bristol – 0454 Almondsbury :

Stakis Leisure Lodge Woodlands Lane, off A 38, BS12 4JF, ℘ 201144, Telex 445774, Fax 612022, – rm rest – 80. AE VISA
7.50 – **112 rm** 71.00/99.00 **t.** – SB 70.00/122.00 **st.**

at Almondsbury N : 7 ½ m. on A 38 – ✉ 0454 Almondsbury :

Aztec, Aztec West Business Park, BS12 4T5, S : 1 m. on A 38 ℘ 201090, Telex 444454, Fax 201593, squash – rm rest – 200
86 rm, **2 suites.**

at Hambrook NE : 5 ½ m. by M 32 on A 4174 – BV – ✉ 0272 Bristol :

Crest (T.H.F.), Filton Rd, BS16 1QX, ℘ 564242, Telex 449376, Fax 569735, park – rm rest – 500. AE VISA BX **o**
M *(closed Sunday lunch)* (carving rest.) 15.95/16.95 **st.** and a la carte – 9.50 – **193 rm** 85.00/115.00 **st.**, **4 suites** 195.00 **st.**.

at Winterbourne NE : 7 ½ m. by M 32 and A 4174 on B 4058 – ✉ 0454 Winterbourne :

Grange Resort, Northwood, BS17 1RP, NW : 2 m. by B 4057 on B 4427 ℘ 777333, Fax 777447, park – rm – 140
52 rm.

at Chelwood S : 8 ½ m. by A 37 – BX – on A 368 – ✉ Bristol – 0761 Compton Dando :

Chelwood House, BS18 4NH, SW : ¾ m. on A 37 ℘ 490730, Fax 490730, – rest AE VISA.
closed 2 weeks Christmas – **M** *(closed lunch Monday to Friday and Sunday dinner)* 16.50 **st.** and a la carte 4.00 – **11 rm** 59.00/85.00 **st.** – SB (weekends only) 97.00/107.00 **st.**

MICHELIN Distribution Centre, Pennywell Rd, BS5 0UD, ℘ **559802, Fax 553820** BX

UDI-VW 153 Cheltenham Rd ℘ 48051
MW Redcliffe Way ℘ 292402
ITROEN Wells Rd ℘ 832303
ITROEN, FIAT 724 Fishponds Rd ℘ 652556
AT 168-176 Coronation Rd ℘ 631101
ORD 175-185 Muller Rd, Horfield ℘ 513333
ORD College Green ℘ 293881
ONDA Whitby Rd ℘ 711890
ANCIA 33 Clevedon Rd ℘ 393673
AZDA, ALFA-ROMEO 676 Fishponds Rd ℘ 655439
ERCEDES-BENZ 20 Whitehouse St. ℘ 669331
ISSAN Feeder Rd ℘ 716181
EUGEOT-TALBOT College Green ℘ 260031
ENAULT Church Rd, Lawrence Hill ℘ 559074
ENAULT Station Rd, Kingswood ℘ 569911
ENAULT Marlborough St. ℘ 421816
OVER, SAAB Eastville ℘ 512121
OVER 74-80 Staple Hill Rd ℘ 654776
OVER 122-137 West St. ℘ 661481

ROVER, DAIMLER-JAGUAR, ROLLS-ROYCE 11-15 Merchants Rd, Clifton ℘ 730361
SAAB Clifton ℘ 743547
SEAT Fishponds Rd ℘ 655283
SKODA, SUBARU, HYUNDAI Fishponds Rd ℘ 659358
TOYOTA Gloucester Rd, Patchway ℘ 693704
TOYOTA High St., Staple Hill ℘ 571701
VAUXHALL-OPEL Avon St. ℘ 770411
VAUXHALL-OPEL Gloucester Rd ℘ 694331
VOLVO 84 Downend Rd ℘ 574474
VOLVO Berkeley Pl. ℘ 277355

ATS 68-72 Avon St. ℘ 711269
ATS 551 Gloucester rd, Horfield ℘ 514525/514549
ATS 58-60 Broad St., Staple Hill ℘ 564741/565396/564594/571483
ATS 34-38 St. Johns Lane, Bedminster ℘ 776418/770674

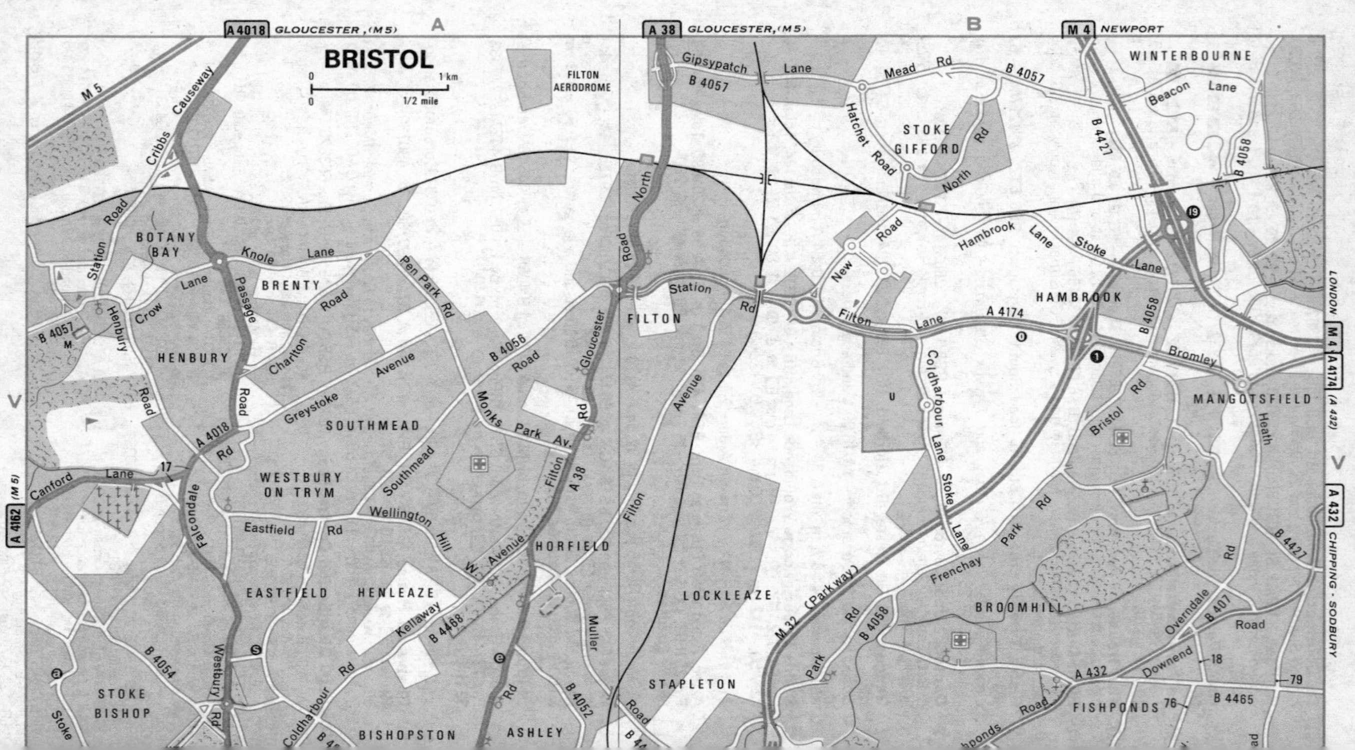

A 4018 GLOUCESTER, (M5)
A
A 38 GLOUCESTER, (M5)
B
M 4 NEWPORT
BRISTOL
0 1 km
0 1/2 mile
FILTON AERODROME
WINTERBOURNE
STOKE GIFFORD
HAMBROOK
MANGOTSFIELD
BOTANY BAY
BRENTY
HENBURY
SOUTHMEAD
FILTON
WESTBURY ON TRYM
HORFIELD
EASTFIELD
HENLEAZE
LOCKLEAZE
BROOMHILL
STAPLETON
STOKE BISHOP
BISHOPSTON
ASHLEY
FISHPONDS
M 5
Cribbs Causeway
Station Road
Knole Lane
Crow Lane
Passage Road
Henbury Road
B 4057
Charlton Road
Pen Park Rd
Greystoke Avenue
B 4056 Road
Monks Park Av.
Gloucester Rd
A 38
Filton Avenue
North Road
Gipsypatch Lane
B 4057
Mead Rd
Hatchet Road
North Rd
B 4427
Beacon Lane
B 4058
New Road
Hambrook Lane
Stoke Lane
Station Rd
Filton Lane
A 4174
Coldharbour Lane
Stoke Lane
B 4058
Bromley Heath
Bristol Rd
A 4018 Rd
Canford Lane
17
Falcondale Rd
Southmead Road
Wellington Hill
Eastfield Rd
W. Avenue
Kellaway Avenue
B 4468
Muller Road
M 32 (Park way)
Park Rd
B 4058
Frenchay Park Rd
Overndale Road
B 4407
Downend Road
18
79
A 432
B 4465
76
B 4427
Rd
B 4054
Westbury Rd
Coldharbour Rd
B 4052
Stoke
LONDON M 4 A 4174 (A 432)
A 432 CHIPPING - SODBURY
A 4162 (M 5)

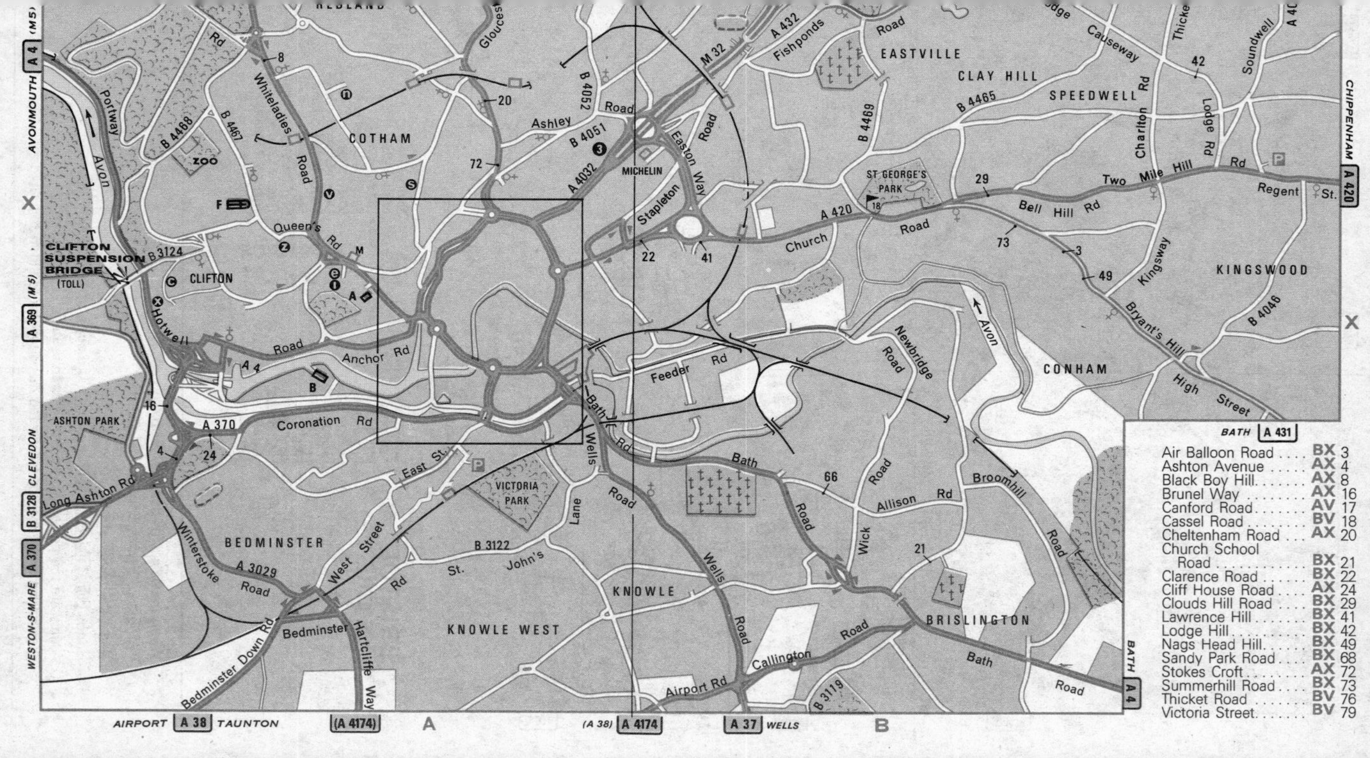
CHIPPENHAM A 420
BATH A 431
BATH A 4
A 37 WELLS
(A 38) A 4174
(A 4174)
AIRPORT A 38 TAUNTON
AVONMOUTH A 4 (M 5)
A 369 (M 5)
B 3128 CLEVEDON
A 370 WESTON-S-MARE
Air Balloon Road . . . BX 3
Ashton Avenue . . . AX 4
Black Boy Hill . . . AX 8
Brunel Way . . . AX 16
Canford Road . . . AV 17
Cassel Road . . . BV 18
Cheltenham Road . . . AX 20
Church School Road . . . BX 21
Clarence Road . . . BX 22
Cliff House Road . . . AX 24
Clouds Hill Road . . . BX 29
Lawrence Hill . . . BX 41
Lodge Hill . . . BX 42
Nags Head Hill . . . BX 49
Sandy Park Road . . . BX 68
Stokes Croft . . . AX 72
Summerhill Road . . . BX 73
Thicket Road . . . BV 76
Victoria Street . . . BV 79
EASTVILLE
CLAY HILL
SPEEDWELL
KINGSWOOD
CONHAM
COTHAM
CLIFTON
BEDMINSTER
KNOWLE
KNOWLE WEST
BRISLINGTON
ST GEORGE'S PARK
VICTORIA PARK
ASHTON PARK
CLIFTON SUSPENSION BRIDGE (TOLL)
ZOO
MICHELIN
Avon
A
B

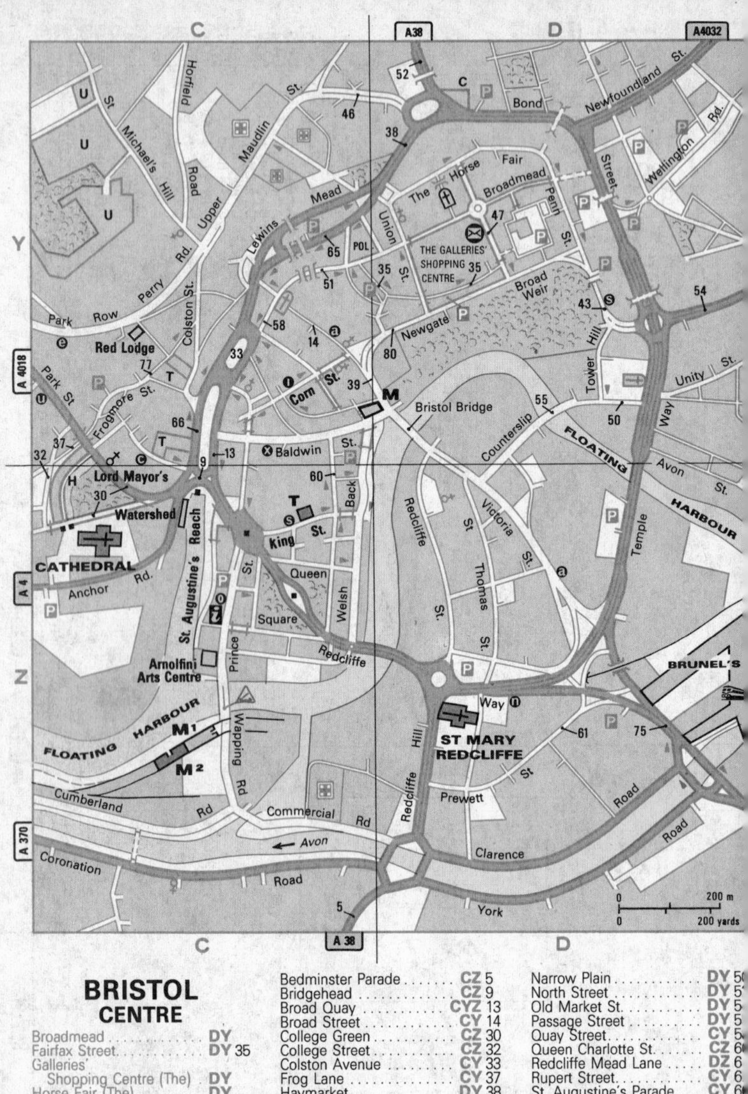

BRISTOL
CENTRE

Broadmead .... DY
Fairfax Street.............. DY 35
Galleries' Shopping Centre (The) . DY
Horse Fair (The) .... DY
Merchant Street .... DY 47
Nelson Avenue .... CY 51
Park Street.................. CY

Bedminster Parade .... CZ 5
Bridgehead .... CZ 9
Broad Quay .... CYZ 13
Broad Street .... CY 14
College Green .... CZ 30
College Street .... CZ 32
Colston Avenue .... CY 33
Frog Lane .... CY 37
Haymarket................. DY 38
High Street............... CDY 39
Lower Castle St. .... DY 43
Marlborough St. .... CDY 46

Narrow Plain .... DY 5
North Street .... DY 5
Old Market St. .... DY 5
Passage Street .... DY 5
Quay Street............... CY 5
Queen Charlotte St. .... CZ 6
Redcliffe Mead Lane ...... DZ 6
Rupert Street.............. CY 6
St. Augustine's Parade.... CY 6
Temple Gate .... DZ 7
Trenchard Street.......... CY 7
Wine Street............... DY 8

When travelling for business or pleasure
in England, Wales, Scotland and Ireland:

– use the series of five maps (nos 401, 402, 403, 404 and 405) at a scale of 1:400 000
– they are the perfect complement to this Guide as towns underlined in red on the maps will be found in this Guide.

BRIXHAM Devon 403 J 32 **The West Country G.** – pop. 15 171 – ECD : Wednesday – ☎ 080 45 (4 & 5 fig.) or 0803 (6 fig.).

Envir. : Berry Head★ (≤★★★), E : 2 m.

ℹ The Old Market House, The Quay ℘ 2861.

◆London 230 – Exeter 30 – ◆Plymouth 32 – Torquay 8.

- **Quayside,** 41-49 King St., TQ5 9TJ, ℘ 55751, Fax 882733, ≤ harbour – TV ☎ P. AE VISA. ✻
  closed Christmas and New Year – **M** 12.50/27.50 **t.** and a la carte 3.95 – **30 rm** 35.50/76.00 **st.** – SB 89.00 **st.**

FORD Churston Ferrers ℘ 842245
ROVER Milton St. ℘ 882474
SKODA 99 New Rd ℘ 882266

BROAD CAMPDEN Glos. – see Chipping Campden.

BROAD CHALKE Wilts. 403 404 O 30 – see Salisbury.

BROADSTAIRS Kent 404 Y 29 – pop. 21 551 (inc. St. Peter's) – ECD : Wednesday – ☎ 0843 Thanet.

See : Bleak House (stayed in by Charles Dickens) *AC*.

18, 18 North Foreland, Kingsgate, Broadstairs ℘ 62140.

ℹ Pierremont Hall, 67 High St. ℘ 68399.

◆London 78 – ◆Dover 21 – Maidstone 47.

- **Castlemere,** 15 Western Esplanade, CT10 1TD, ℘ 61566, ≤, – TV ☎ P. VISA
  M (bar lunch May-October)/dinner 11.50 **st.** 3.30 – **36 rm** 35.25/72.50 **st.** – SB (Thursday to Sunday) 70.50/79.00 **st.**
- **Bay Tree,** 12 Eastern Esplanade, CT10 1DR, ℘ 62502, Fax 860589, ≤ – rest TV P. VISA. ✻
  M 9.00 **st.** 4.00 – **11 rm** 19.00/38.00 **st.**
- XX **Marchesi,** 18 Albion St., CT10 1LU, ℘ 62481, ≤ – P. AE VISA
  closed Sunday dinner, Monday and 26 to 30 December – **M** 10.50/16.00 **t.** and a la carte 3.50.

AUDI-VW St. Peter's Rd ℘ 62333
HYUNDAI Ramsgate Rd ℘ 63531

Die Preise · Einzelheiten über die in diesem Führer angegebenen Preise finden Sie in der Einleitung.

BROADSTONE Dorset 403 404 O 31 – see Wimborne Minster.

BROADWATER Herts. – see Stevenage.

BROADWAY Heref. and Worc. 403 404 O 27 – pop. 1 931 – ECD : Thursday – ☎ 0386.

18 Willersey Hill ℘ 858997.

ℹ 1 Cotswold Court ℘ 852937 (summer only).

◆London 93 – ◆Birmingham 36 – Cheltenham 15 – Worcester 22.

- **Lygon Arms,** High St., WR12 7DU, ℘ 852255, Telex 338260, Fax 858611, « Part 15C inn », – TV ☎ P – 80. AE VISA
  M 19.00/28.00 **t.** and a la carte 22.25/29.00 **t.** – 8.00 – **61 rm** 100.00/145.00 **t.**, **5 suites** 220.00/295.00 **t.** – SB (except Christmas and New Year) 195.00/205.00 **st.**
- **Broadway,** The Green, WR12 7AB, ℘ 852401, – rm TV ☎ P. AE VISA. ✻
  M (buffet lunch Monday to Saturday)/dinner 16.50 **t.** and a la carte – **21 rm** 52.50/89.00 **t.** – SB (November-April) 78.00/86.00 **st.**
- **Collin House,** Collin Lane, WR12 7PB, NW : 1¼ m. by A 44 ℘ 858354, ≤, – P. VISA. ✻
  closed 24 to 28 December – **M** *(closed Sunday dinner to non-residents)* 12.50/17.00 **st.** and a la carte 4.00 – **7 rm** 40.00/76.00 **st.** – SB (November-March) 91.50/102.50 **st.**
- **Whiteacres** without rest., Station Rd, WR12 7DE, ℘ 852320, – rm TV P. ✻
  March-October – **6 rm** 28.00/40.00 **st.**
- **Windrush House,** Station Rd, WR12 7DE, ℘ 853577, – rest TV P. VISA
  M 12.00 **t.** – **4 rm** –/36.00 **t.**
- **Broadway Court** without rest., 89 High St., WR12 7AL, ℘ 852237 – P. ✻
  6 rm 25.00/80.00.
- XX **Hunters Lodge,** High St., WR12 7DT, ℘ 853247, – P. AE VISA
  closed Sunday dinner, Monday, first 2 weeks February and first 2 weeks August – **M** 13.00/19.50 **t.** and a la carte 4.00.

at Willersey (Glos.) N : 2 m. on B 4632 – ✉ ☎ 0386 Broadway :

- **Old Rectory** without rest., Church St., WR12 7PN, ℘ 853729, – rm TV ☎ P. VISA. ✻
  closed 1 week Christmas – **6 rm** 49.00/95.00 **t.**

at Willersey Hill (Glos.) E : 2 m. by A 44 – ✉ ⊛ 0386 Broadway :

Dormy House, WR12 7LF, ℘ 852711, Telex 338275, Fax 858636, – rm ☎ – 200. AE VISA
closed 25 and 26 December – **M** (bar lunch Saturday) 16.50/24.95 **t.** and a la carte 6.10 – **46 rm** 54.00/108.00 **t.**, **3 suites** 125.00/160.00 **t.** – SB 66.00/144.00 **st.**

at Buckland (Glos.) SW : 2 ¼ m. by B 4632 – ✉ ⊛ 0386 Broadway :

Buckland Manor , WR12 7LY, ℘ 852626, ≤, « Country house atmosphere » heated, , park, – ☎ . VISA.
closed 15 January-8 February – **M** a la carte 18.85/29.05 **t.** 3.85 – **10 rm** 125.00 210.00 **t.**

ROVER Willersey ℘ 852338

BROCKENHURST Hants. 403 404 P 31 – pop. 2 939 – ECD : Wednesday – ⊛ 0590 Lymington.

Sway Rd, Brockenhurst Manor ℘ 23332.

♦London 99 – Bournemouth 17 – ♦Southampton 14 – Winchester 27.

Balmer Lawn (Hilton), Lyndhurst Rd, on A 337, SO42 7ZB, junction A 337 and B 3055 ℘ 23116, Telex 477649, Fax 23864, ≤, , , heated, , , , squash – rm ☎ – 100. AE VISA
M *(bar lunch Monday to Saturday)/dinner* 15.00 **st.** 4.20 – **58 rm** 70.00/100.00 **st.** – SB (weekends only) 100.00/130.00 **st.**

Carey's Manor, Lyndhurst Rd, on A 337, SO42 7RH, ℘ 23551, Fax 22799, Dancing Friday and Saturday, , , , – rm ☎ – 150. AE VISA
M 11.95/19.95 **t.** and a la carte 4.95 – **(see also Le Blaireau** below) – **80 rm** 69.90 119.90 **t.** – SB 107.80/127.80 **st.**

Rhinefield House , Rhinefield Rd, SO42 7QB, W : 3 m. on Rhinefield Rd ℘ 22922 Telex 477617, Fax 22800, « Victorian country mansion », , , heated, , park, – rm ☎ – 80. AE VISA.
M 12.50/16.50 **st.** and a la carte 7.50 – **32 rm** 75.00/130.00 **st.** – SB 100.00 **st.**

Whitley Ridge , Beaulieu Rd, SO42 7QL, E : 1 m. on B 3055 ℘ 22354, Fax 22856, ≤ , – ☎ . AE VISA
M (bar lunch Monday to Saturday)/dinner 16.50 **t.** and a la carte 3.50 – **13 rm** 55.00 75.00 **t.**

Cottage, Sway Rd, S042 7SH, ℘ 0590 (Lymington) 22296, – . VISA.
M (bar lunch Monday to Saturday)/dinner 15.00 **t.** and a la carte 3.75 – **6 rm** 38.00 62.00 **t.** – SB (November-March) 72.00/76.00 **st.**

XXX **Le Poussin** with rm, 57-59 Brookley Rd, SO42 7RB, ℘ 23063, Fax 22912, French rest. . VISA
closed 3 weeks January and 1 week June – **M** *(closed Sunday dinner and Monday)* (booking essential) 15.00/30.00 **t.** and a la carte 4.50 – 2.50 – **4 rm** 30.00/55.00.

X **Le Blaireau** (at Carey's Manor H.), SO42 7RH, ℘ 23052, Fax 22799, French rest., – AE VISA
M 11.95/19.95 **t.** and a la carte 4.95.

HONDA 24 Brookley Rd ℘ 23464
MAZDA Brookley Rd ℘ 23122
PEUGEOT-TALBOT Waters Green ℘ 23113
ROVER Sway Rd ℘ 23344

BROMBOROUGH Merseyside 402 403 L 24 – pop. 14 901 – ✉ Wirral – ⊛ 051 Liverpool.

Raby Hall Rd ℘ 334 2155.

♦London 210 – Chester 14 – ♦Liverpool 6.5 – ♦Manchester 46.

Cromwell (Lansbury), High St., L62 7HZ, ℘ 334 2917, Telex 628225, Fax 346 1175, rm ☎ – 130. AE VISA
M 8.95/14.00 **t.** and a la carte – **31 rm** 64.00/77.00 **t.** – SB (weekends only) 60.00 72.00 **st.**

Dibbinsdale (B.C.B.), Dibbinsdale Rd, L63 0HJ, off Allport Rd ℘ 334 5171 – ☎ **19 rm.**

BROME Suffolk 404 X 26 – see Diss (Norfolk).

BROMLEY CROSS Greater Manchester 402 404 M 23 – see Bolton.

BROMPTON BY SAWDON North Yorks. 402 S 21 – pop. 1 827 – ✉ ⊛ 0723 Scarborough.

♦London 242 – ♦Kingston-upon-Hull 44 – Scarborough 8 – York 31.

XX **Brompton Forge**, YO13 9DP, ℘ 85409 –
closed Sunday dinner, Monday and 11 to 26 February – **M** (dinner only and Sunday lunch)/dinner 17.00 **st.** 4.25.

Great Britain and Ireland are covered entirely
at a scale of 16 miles to 1 inch by our map « Main roads » 986.

BROMSGROVE Heref. and Worc. 403 404 N 26 – pop. 24 576 – ECD : Thursday – ☎ 0527.
ℹ 47-49 Worcester Rd ℘ 31809.
♦London 117 – ♦Birmingham 14 – ♦Bristol 71 – Worcester 13.

Country Court (Stakis), Birmingham Rd, B61 0JB, N : 2½ m. on A 38 ℘ 447 7888, Telex 336976, Fax 447 7273, rm rest – 80. AE VISA.
M *(closed Saturday lunch)* a la carte 13.00/23.95 **st.** 7.00 – 8.25 – **131 rm** 74.00/84.00 **st.**, **10 suites** 94.00 **st.**

Perry Hall, 13 Kidderminster Rd, B61 7JN, ℘ 579976, Fax 575998, – – 60. AE VISA
M *(closed Saturday lunch)* 10.95 **st.** and a la carte – 7.00 – **55 rm** 57.00/80.00 **st.** – SB (weekends only) 64.00/84.00 **st.**

Pine Lodge (Best Western), 85 Kidderminster Rd, B61 9AB, W : 1 m. on A 448 ℘ 33033, Telex 335072, Fax 78981, – – 200. AE VISA
M *(closed Saturday lunch)* 13.50/14.50 **st.** and a la carte – **52 rm** 70.00/80.00 **st.**

Bromsgrove Country, Stoke Heath, B61 7JA, SW : 2 m. on Worcester Rd ℘ 35522, – . VISA.
closed 1 week Christmas and New Year – **M** *(closed Saturday and Sunday)* (dinner only) (residents only) 9.00 **st.** 2.50 – 4.50 – **9 rm** 35.00/46.00 **st.**

XXX **Grafton Manor** with rm, Grafton Lane, B61 7HA, SW : 1 ¾ m. by Worcester Rd ℘ 579007, Fax 575221, « 16C and 18C manor », , , park – . AE VISA.
M *(closed Saturday lunch)* 21.50/29.90 **t.** 4.95 – **7 rm** 88.00/115.00 **t.**, **2 suites** 165.00 **t.**

MITSUBISHI Saunders Rd ℘ 579877
PEUGEOT-TALBOT 184-186 Worcester Rd ℘ 575157
RENAULT 17-21 Worcester Rd ℘ 79898
VAUXHALL-OPEL 137 Birmingham Rd ℘ 71244

BROOK Hants. 403 404 P 31 – ECD : Tuesday – ✉ Lyndhurst – ☎ 0703 Southampton.
18, 18 Bramshaw Brook ℘ 813433, on B 3079.
♦London 92 – Bournemouth 24 – ♦Southampton 14.

Bell, SO43 7HE, ℘ 812214, Fax 813958, 18 – . AE VISA
M (bar lunch Monday to Saturday)/dinner 29.95 **t.** and a la carte 3.95 – **20 rm** 51.00/85.00 **t.** – SB 59.95/72.95 **st.**

BROOKMANS PARK Herts. 404 T 28 – pop. 4 020 – ☎ 0707 Potters Bar.
♦London 21 – Luton 21.

XX **Villa Rosa,** 3 Great North Rd, AL9 6LB, SE : 1 ¾ m. on A 1000 ℘ 51444, Italian rest. – . AE VISA
closed Saturday lunch and Sunday – **M** a la carte 14.00/22.05 **t.** 4.00.

BROUGHTON Lancs. 402 L 22 – see Preston.

BROXTED Essex – see Thaxted.

BROXTON Cheshire 402 403 L 24 – pop. 384 – ☎ 0829.
♦London 197 – ♦Birmingham 68 – Chester 12 – ♦Manchester 44 – Stoke-on-Trent 29.

Frogg Manor, Barn Hill, Nantwich Rd, CH3 9JH, on A 534 ℘ 782629, , , – . AE VISA
M 11.00/21.00 **st.** and a la carte 3.50 – 7.00 – **6 rm** 37.95/85.50 **st.** – SB 80.00/111.00 **st.**

Broxton Hall Whitchurch Rd, CH3 9JS, at junction A 41 with A 534 ℘ 782321, – . VISA.
closed 25 December – **M** *(closed Sunday dinner and Monday to non-residents)* 15.00/17.50 **st.** 4.50 – **10 rm** 50.00/70.00 **st.** – SB (weekends only) 86.00/96.00 **st.**

BRUSHFORD Somerset 403 J 30 – pop. 486 – ✉ ☎ 0398 Dulverton.
♦London 195 – Exeter 24 – Minehead 18 – Taunton 24.

Carnarvon Arms, TA22 9AE, ℘ 23302, Fax 24022, heated, , , park, – rest – 100. VISA
closed last 3 weeks February – **M** 8.50/15.75 **t.** 3.50 – **24 rm** 35.00/70.00 **t.**, **1 suite** 80.00 **t.** – SB 88.00/115.00 **st.**

BRUTON Somerset 403 404 M 30 – pop. 1 759 – ☎ 0749.
♦London 118 – ♦Bristol 27 – Bournemouth 44 – Salisbury 35 – Taunton 36.

X **Claire de Lune** with rm, 2-4 High St., BA10 0EQ, ℘ 813395 – . VISA.
closed last week August – **M** *(closed Sunday dinner and Monday)* (booking essential) (lunch by arrangement)/dinner 16.95 **st.** 4.50 – 2.50 – **2 rm** 25.00/35.00 **st.**

X **Truffles,** 95 High St., BA10 0AR, ℘ 812255
closed Monday – **M** (booking essential) 12.50/17.95 **t.** 4.00.

BRYHER Cornwall 403 ㉚ – see Scilly (Isles of).

BRYNBUGA = Usk.

BUCKDEN Cambs. 404 T 27 – pop. 2 605 – ✉ ☎ 0480 Huntingdon.

♦London 65 – Bedford 15 – ♦Cambridge 20 – Northampton 31.

- **Lion,** High St., PE18 9XA, ☎ 810313, Fax 811070, « Part 15C inn » – TV ☎ P. AE ① VISA
  M 8.95 **t.** (lunch) and a la carte 15.25/23.25 **t.** 2.75 – **15 rm** 52.00/68.00 **t.** – SB (weekends only) 85.00/110.00 **st.**
- **George,** Great North Rd, PE18 9XA, ☎ 810307, Fax 810307 – TV ☎ P – 30. AE ① VISA
  M *(closed Sunday dinner)* 15.00 **t.** and a la carte 4.95 – 3.50 – **15 rm** 50.00/55.00 **t.** – SB (weekends only) 59.50 **st.**

BUCKHURST HILL Essex 404 ⑬ – pop. 11 147 – ECD : Wednesday – ☎ 01 London.

♦London 13 – Chelmsford 25.

Plan : see Greater London (North-East)

- **Roebuck** (T.H.F.), North End, IG9 5QY, ☎ 505 4636, Fax 504 7826 – TV ☎ P – 100. AE ① VISA
  M 20.00 **st.** and a la carte 4.35 – 7.00 – **29 rm** 69.00/84.00 **st.** – SB (weekends only) 74.00 **st.**

BUCKINGHAM Bucks. 403 404 Q 27 – pop. 6 439 – ECD : Thursday – ☎ 0280.

Envir. : Claydon House★ (Rococo interior★★ : Chinese Room★★ staircase★★★, Florence Nightingale Museum) *AC*, SE : 8 m. – Stowe School (18C) (south front★, Marble Saloon★, park : monuments★ (18C), ≤★ from the Lake Pavilions) *AC*.

18 Tingewick Rd ☎ 813282.

♦London 64 – ♦Birmingham 61 – Northampton 20 – ♦Oxford 25.

- **Villiers, 24 Castle St., MK18 1BP, ☎ 822444, Fax 822113 – TV ☎ P – 9 rm.**

FORD Main St Tingewick ☎ (02804) 7071
ROVER Motorworks ☎ 812121
VAUXHALL-OPEL Chandos Rd ☎ 822892

BUCKLAND Glos. 403 404 O 27 – see Broadway (Heref. and Worc.).

BUCKLERS HARD Hants. 403 404 P 31 – see Beaulieu.

BUCKLOW HILL Cheshire 402 403 404 M 24 – see Knutsford.

BUCKNELL Shropshire 403 L 26 – ☎ 05474.

♦London 158 – ♦Birmingham 55 – Hereford 29 – Shrewsbury 31.

- **Bucknell House** without rest., SY7 0AD, on B 4367 ☎ 248, , park, – TV P
  February-November – **3 rm** 16.50/30.00 **t.**

BUDE Cornwall 403 G 31 **The West Country G.** – pop. 2 679 – ECD : Thursday – ☎ 0288.

See : The breakwater★★ – ≤ from Compass Point★.

Envir. : Poughill★ (Church★★) N : 2½ m. – at Poundstock★ (≤★★, church★★, Gildhouse★) S 4½ m. – Morwenstowe Church★ (cliffs★★) N : 11 m. – Stratton Church★, E : 1½ m. – Launcells Church★, E : 3 m. – Kilkhampton Church★, NE : 5½ m. – Jacobstowe Church★, S : 7 m.

18 Burn View ☎ 352006.

The Crescent car park ☎ 4240.

♦London 252 – Exeter 51 – ♦Plymouth 44 – Truro 53.

- **Camelot,** Downs View, EX23 8RS, ☎ 352361, Fax 355470, – rest TV ☎ P. VISA
  M (bar lunch)/dinner 12.00 **t.** and a la carte 3.50 – **21 rm** 25.00/45.00 **st.** – SB (except Bank Holidays) 54.00 **st.**
- **Bude Haven,** Flexbury Av., EX23 8NS, ☎ 352305, – TV P. VISA
  closed December – **M** (bar lunch)/dinner 7.00 **st.** 2.50 – **12 rm** 18.00/36.00 **st.** – SB (except June-September) 80.00/88.00 **st.**
- **Reeds**, Northcott Mouth rd, Poughill, EX23 9EL, NE : 1¼ m. ☎ 352841, – P.
  closed Tuesday to Friday – **M** (dinner only) (residents only) 19.50 **st.** 3.25 – **3 rm** 37.50/100.00 **st.**
- **Meva Gwin,** Upton, EX23 0LY, S : 1¼ m. on coast rd ☎ 352347, ≤ – rest TV P.
  May-November – **M** 7.50 **st.** 3.00 – **12 rm** 13.00/32.00 **st.**

FORD Bencoolen Rd ☎ 354616
ROVER Bencoolen Rd ☎ 352146

BUDLEIGH SALTERTON Devon 403 K 32 – ☎ 039 54.

♦London 215 – Exeter 16 – ♦Plymouth 55.

- **Long Range,** Vales Rd, EX9 6HS, by Raleigh Rd ☎ 3321, – rest TV.
  April-October – **M** 9.00 **st.** 2.50 – **7 rm** 19.50/39.00 **st.**

BUDOCK WATER Cornwall – see Falmouth.

BURNWELL Norfolk 404 X 26 – pop. 797 – ECD : Monday and Wednesday – ☏ 095 389.
♦London 102 – ♦Cambridge 51 – ♦Norwich 16.

Bunwell Manor ⨠, Bunwell St., NR16 1QU, NW : 1 m. ℘ 8304, 🌳 – TV ☎ P. AE VISA
M 11.00 **t.** and a la carte 🌢 3.50 – **10 rm** ☐ 40.00/60.00 **t.** – SB (except Christmas) 65.00/70.00 **st.**

BURBAGE Wilts. 403 404 O 29 – see Marlborough.
♦London 90 – ♦Bristol 53 – ♦Southampton 34 – Swindon 18.

BURFORD Oxon. 403 404 P 28 – pop. 1 371 – ECD : Wednesday – ☏ 099 382 (4 fig.) or 0993 (6 fig.).
See : St. John's Church★ (12C-14C).
Envir. : Swinbrook (church : Fettiplace Monuments★) 3 ½ m. – Cotswold Wildlife Park★ *AC*, S : 2 m. – Northleach : SS. Peter and Paul's Church : South Porch and the brasses★ (Perpendicular) NW : 7 ½ m.
18 ℘ 2149, S : ½ m. on A 361.
Sheep St. ℘ 3558.
♦London 76 – ♦Birmingham 55 – Gloucester 32 – ♦Oxford 20.

Bay Tree, Sheep St., OX8 4LW, ℘ 822791, Fax 823008, « 16C house, antique furnishings », 🌳 – ⇔ rest TV ☎ P. AE VISA
M 11.50/17.50 and a la carte 🌢 5.00 – **23 rm** ☐ 65.00/85.00, **2 suites** 105.00/150.00 – SB (November-March) 220.00/320.00 **st.**

Inn For All Seasons, The Barringtons, OX8 4TN, W : 3 ¼ m. on A 40 ℘ 045 14 (Windrush) 324, 🌳 – TV ☎ P. VISA. ⚘
M *(closed Sunday dinner)* (bar lunch Monday to Saturday)/dinner 14.95 **st.** 🌢 3.50 – **10 rm** ☐ 39.50/65.00 **st.** – SB 78.00 **st.**

Lamb Inn, Sheep St., OX8 4LR, ℘ 3155, « Part 14C inn, tastefully furnished », 🌳 – VISA
closed 25 and 26 December – **M** (bar lunch Monday to Saturday)/dinner 19.50 **t.** 🌢 3.75 – **16 rm** ☐ 35.00/75.00 **t.** – SB 82.00/96.00 **st.**

Andrews without rest., High St., OX8 4RJ, ℘ 3151, 🌳 – ⇔ rm TV. AE VISA. ⚘
9 rm ☐ 24.75/62.75 **st.**

at Fulbrook NE : ¾ m. on A 361 – ✉ ☏ 099 382 Burford :

Elm Farm House ⨠, Meadow Lane, OX8 4BW, ℘ 3611, 🌳 – ⇔ rm TV ☎ P. AE VISA. ⚘
closed 14 December-January – **M** 14.00 **st.** 🌢 3.25 – **7 rm** ☐ 27.00/52.00 **st.** – SB (except May-September) 54.00/70.00 **st.**

at Taynton NW : 1 ½ m. by A 424 – ✉ ☏ 099 382 Burford :

Manor Farm Barn ⨠ without rest., OX8 4UH, ℘ 2069, ≤, « Tastefully renovated barn », 🌳 – TV P. ⚘
closed 15 December-6 January – **3 rm** ☐ 28.00/48.00 **st.**

BURGHFIELD Berks. 403 404 Q 29 – see Reading.

BURLEY Hants. 403 404 O 31 – pop. 1 492 – ECD : Wednesday – ✉ Ringwood – ☏ 042 53.
9 Burley, Ringwood ℘ 2431.
♦London 102 – Bournemouth 17 – ♦Southampton 17 – Winchester 30.

Burley Manor ⨠, Ringwood Rd, BH24 4BS, ℘ 3522, Group Telex 41565, Fax 3227, ≤, heated, 🐎, 🌳 – ⇔ rm TV ☎ P – 🏛 80. AE VISA
M (bar lunch Monday to Saturday)/dinner a la carte approx. 15.00 **t.** – **30 rm** ☐ 60.00/85.00 **t.** – SB 90.00/100.00 **st.**

BURNHAM Bucks. 404 S 29 – ECD : Thursday – ☏ 062 86 (4 & 5 fig.) or 0628 (6 fig.).
18 Burnham Beeches, Green Lane ℘ 661150.
♦London 33 – ♦Oxford 37 – Reading 17.

Burnham Beeches Moat House (Q.M.H.) ⨠, Grove Rd, Burnham Beeches, SL1 8DP, NW : 1 m. by Britwell Rd ℘ 603333, Fax 603994, Lδ, ≘s, 🏊, 🌳, park, 🎾 – 🛗 TV ☎ P – 🏛 160
73 rm, 2 suites.

CITROEN 46-48 High St. ℘ 605255 | VAUXHALL-OPEL 71-73 Stomp Rd ℘ 4994

BURNHAM MARKET Norfolk 404 W 25 – pop. 943 – ☏ 0328 Fakenham.
♦London 128 – ♦Cambridge 71 – ♦Norwich 36.

Forbes, North St., PE31 8HG, ℘ 738824 – P. AE VISA
closed Sunday, Wednesday and mid January-March – **M** 8.75 **t.** and a la carte 🌢 3.50.

BURNHAM-ON-CROUCH Essex 404 W 29 – pop. 6 268 – ECD : Wednesday – ☎ 062 Maldon.

Creeksea ✆ 782282, W : 1 ¼ m. by B 1010.

◆London 52 – Chelmsford 19 – Colchester 32 – Southend-on-Sea 25.

XX **Contented Sole,** 80 High St., CM0 8AA, ✆ 782139
closed Sunday, Monday, 23 December-30 January and 14 to 30 July – **M** 9.75 **st.** (lunch and a la carte 19.45/26.45 **t.** 5.50.

BURNLEY Lancs. 402 N 22 – pop. 76 365 – ☎ 0282.

Envir. : Towneley Hall★ (16C-18C) SE : 1 m.

Towneley, Towneley Park, Todmorden Rd ✆ 51636, E : 1 ½ m. – Glen View ✆ 21045 – Marsden Park, Townhouse Rd, Walton Lane, Nelson ✆ 0282 (Nelson) 67525, N : 4 m.

Burnley Mechanics, Manchester Rd ✆ 30055.

◆London 236 – Bradford 32 – ◆Leeds 37 – ◆Liverpool 55 – ◆Manchester 25 – ◆Middlesbrough 104 – Preston 22 – ◆Sheffield 68.

Oaks, Colne Rd, Reedley, BB10 2LF, NE : 2 ½ m. on A 56 ✆ 414141, Telex 635309 Fax 33401, – rm – 120. VISA
M 19.75/29.50 **t.** and a la carte 4.75 – **58 rm** 70.00/100.00 **t.**

Rosehill House, Rosehill Av., Manchester Rd, BB11 2PW, ✆ 53931, – rm . VISA
M 14.50 **t.** and a la carte 3.80 – **18 rm** 36.50/52.00 **t.** – SB (weekends only) 60.00 **st.**

Travelodge without rest., Cavalry Barracks, Barracks Rd, BB11 4AS, W : ½ m. at junction of A 671 and A 679 ✆ 416039, Reservations (Toll free) 0800 850950 – . VISA
32 rm 24.00/29.50 **t.**

MAZDA Todmorden Rd ✆ 36131
RENAULT Trafalgar St. ✆ 33311
VAUXHALL Accrington Rd ✆ 27321
ATS Healey Wood Rd ✆ 22409/38423/51624

"Short Breaks" (SB)

De nombreux hôtels proposent des conditions avantageuses pour un séjour de deux nuits comprenant la chambre, le dîner et le petit déjeuner.

BURNSALL North Yorks. 402 O 21 – pop. 116 – ECD : Monday and Thursday – ✉ Skipton – ☎ 075 672.

◆London 223 – Bradford 26 – ◆Leeds 29.

Red Lion, BD23 6BU, ✆ 204 – .
M (dinner only and Sunday lunch)/dinner 10.00 **t.** 4.00 – **12 rm** 27.00/45.00 **t.** – SB (November-March) 50.00 **st.**

BURPHAM West Sussex 404 S 30 – see Arundel.

BURRINGTON Devon 403 I 31 – pop. 482 – ECD : Saturday – ☎ 0769 High Bickington.

◆London 260 – Barnstaple 14 – Exeter 28 – Taunton 50.

Northcote Manor (Best Western) , EX37 9LZ, NW : 1 m. ✆ 60501, Fax 60770, <, park, – rest . VISA
March-October – **M** (booking essential) 14.00/18.00 **t.** 6.50 – **11 rm** 55.00/136.00 **t.** – SB (March-October) 102.00/112.00 **st.**

BURSTALL Suffolk – see Ipswich.

BURTON-UPON-TRENT Staffs. 402 403 404 O 25 – pop. 59 040 – ECD : Wednesday – ☎ 0283.

Branston, Burton Rd ✆ 43207, SW : 1 ½ m. on A 5121 – Ashby Rd, East ✆ 68708, E : 3 m on A 50 – , Craythorne Road, Stretton ✆ 64329, N : 1 ½ m.

Town Hall, King Edward Square ✆ 45454.

◆London 128 – ◆Birmingham 29 – ◆Leicester 27 – ◆Nottingham 27 – Stafford 27.

Stanhope (Lansbury), Ashby Rd, DE15 0PU, SE : 2 ½ m. on A 50 ✆ 217954, Telex 347185 Fax 226199, – rm – 150. VISA.
M *(closed Saturday lunch)* 8.00/15.00 **t.** and a la carte 4.50 – **28 rm** 64.00/76.00 **t.** – SB (weekends only) 70.00/77.00 **st.**

Edgecote, 179 Ashby Rd, DE15 0LB, SE : 1 m. on A 50 ✆ 68966, – . VISA.
M (by arrangement) 10.00 **st.** 3.75 – **12 rm** 17.00/42.00 **st.** – SB (weekends only) 45.00/55.00 **st.**

at Stretton N : 3 ½ m. by A 50 off A 5121 – ✉ ☎ 0283 Burton-upon-Trent :

XXX **Dovecliff Hall** with rm, Dovecliff Rd, DE13 0DJ, ✆ 31818, <, « Carefully restored Georgian house », , park – . VISA.
M *(closed Monday lunch and Sunday dinner)* 12.50/29.50 **t.** – **6 rm** 70.00/90.00 **t.**

at Rolleston-on-Dove N : 3 ¾ m by A 50 on Rolleston Rd – ✉ 0283 Burton-upon-Trent :

XXX **Brookhouse Inn** with rm, Brookside, DE13 9AA, ☎ 814188, Fax 813644, « Tastefully furnished part 17C house », – TV ☎ P. AE VISA
closed 25 to 29 December – **M** *(closed Saturday lunch and Sunday dinner)* 9.25 **t.** (lunch) and a la carte 13.80/24.50 **t.** 3.50 – **19 rm** 59.00/79.00 **t.** – SB (weekends only) 80.00 **st.**

at Newton Solney NE : 3 m. by A 50 on B 5008 – ✉ 0283 Burton-upon-Trent :

Newton Park, DE15 0SS, ☎ 703568, Fax 703214, ←, – TV ☎ P – 100. AE VISA
closed 27 to 30 December – **M** *(closed lunch Bank Holidays)* 8.95/11.95 **st.** and a la carte 4.10 – 7.00 – **46 rm** 60.00/78.00 **st.** – SB (weekends only) 61.00/68.00 **st.**

at Branston SW : 1 ½ m. on A 5121 – ✉ 0283 Burton-upon-Trent :

Riverside Inn, Riverside Drive, off Warren Lane, DE14 3EP, ☎ 511234, Fax 511441, – TV ☎ P – 150. AE VISA
M 11.90/14.90 **t.** and a la carte – **20 rm** 53.00/64.00 **t.** – SB (weekends only) 85.90 **st.**

at Barton-under-Needwood SW : 5 m. by A 5121 on A 38 – ✉ 0283 Burton-Upon-Trent :

Travelodge without rest., A 38, Northbound, DE13 0ED, ☎ 716343, Reservations (Toll free) 0800 850950 – TV P. AE VISA
20 rm 24.00/29.50 **t.**

Travelodge without rest., Lichfield Rd, A 38 Southbound, DE13 8EJ, ☎ 716784, Reservations (Toll free) 0800 850950 – TV P. AE VISA.
40 rm 24.00/29.50 **t.**

CITROEN Tollgate ☎ 212454
FORD Horninglow St. ☎ 61081
NISSAN Scalpcliffe Rd ☎ 66677
RENAULT 118 Horninglow Rd ☎ 67811
ROVER Moor St. ☎ 45353
SCIMITAR, LOTUS, ALFA ROMEO Station Rd ☎ 813593
SKODA Woodside Rd ☎ 760363
VOLVO New St. ☎ 31331
VW-AUDI Tutbury Rd ☎ 31336

ATS All Saints Rd ☎ 65994/63170

BURY

Greater Manchester 402 N 23 403 ② 404 N 23 – pop. 61 785 – ECD : Tuesday – 061 Manchester.

Unsworth Hall, Blackford Bridge ☎ 766 2213 – Lowes Park, Hill Top ☎ 764 1231, NE : 2 m. by A 56 – Greenmount ☎ 020 488 (Tottington) 3712, N : 3 m.

♦London 211 – ♦Leeds 45 – ♦Liverpool 35 – ♦Manchester 9.

Normandie, Elbut Lane, Birtle, BL9 6UT, E : 3 m. by B 6222 ☎ 764 1170, Fax 764 4866, ← – TV ☎ P. AE VISA.
closed 26 December-7 January – **M** (see **Normandie rest.** below) – 6.75 – **24 rm** 55.00/79.00 **t.**

XXX **Normandie** (at Normandie H.), Elbut Lane, BL9 6UT, ☎ 764 1170, Fax 764 4866 – P. AE VISA
closed 26 December-7 January and Bank Holidays – **M** *(closed lunch Monday and Saturday and Sunday)* (booking essential) 18.50 **t.** (dinner) and a la carte 22.70/26.25 **t.**

ATS John St. ☎ 764 2830/6860

BURY ST. EDMUNDS

Suffolk 404 W 27 – pop. 30 563 – ECD : Thursday – 0284.

See : Abbey★★ – St. Mary's Church★ (15C) (the Angel roof★★).

Envir. : Ickworth House★ (18C) *AC*, SW : 3 m.

Fornham Park, Fornham St. Martin ☎ 63426, by A 134 on B 1106 – Tut Hill ☎ 755979, NW : 2 m. on B 1106 by A 45 – ☎ 84291, NW : 5 m. on A 1101 – Royal Worlington & Newmarket, Worlington ☎ 0638 (Newmarket) 712216, NW : 14 m. by A 11.

Athenaeum, Angel Hill ☎ 757082/764667 (evenings and weekends).

♦London 79 – ♦Cambridge 27 – ♦Ipswich 26 – ♦Norwich 41.

Angel, 3 Angel Hill, IP33 1LT, ☎ 753926, Telex 81630, Fax 750092 – rest TV ☎ P – 80. AE VISA
M 14.50 25.00 **st.** and a la carte – 7.00 – **39 rm** 63.00/105.00 **st.**, **1 suite** 150.00 **st.** – SB (weekends only and August) 110.00 **st.**

Kingshott's, 12 Angel Hill, IP33 1UZ, 704088, Fax 763133 – TV ☎. VISA.
M *(closed Sunday and Monday)* (lunch by arrangement)/dinner a la carte 17.95 **t.** 3.95 – **6 rm** 50.00/75.00 **t.**

Butterfly, Symonds Rd, IP32 7BW, SE : 1½ m. by A 1302 and A 134 at junction with A 45 760884, Fax 755476 – TV ☎ – 50. AE VISA.
M 10.00 **t.** and a la carte 3.25 – 5.00 – **50 rm** 57.00/80.00 **t.** – SB (weekends only) 67.00/70.00 **st.**

Suffolk (T.H.F.), 38 The Buttermarket, IP33 1DL, 753995, Fax 750973 – rm TV ☎ – 30. AE VISA
M 10.95/16.95 **st.** and a la carte 4.85 – 8.50 – **33 rm** 65.00/80.00 **st.**

Olde White Hart without rest., 35 Southgate St., IP33 2AZ, 755547 – TV ☎. AE VISA.
10 rm 38.00/48.00 **st.**

at Rougham Green SE : 4 m. by A 1302 and A 134 off A 45 – ✉ Bury St. Edmunds – 0359 Beyton:

Ravenwood Hall, IP30 9JA, on A 45 70345, Fax 70788, heated, park, – TV ☎ – 200. AE VISA
M 16.50 **t.** and a la carte 3.95 – **7 rm** 65.00/95.00 **t.** – SB (weekends only) 96.00/106.00 **st.**

at Bradfield Combust SE : 4½ m. on A 134 – ✉ Bury St. Edmunds – 028 486 Sicklesmere :

Bradfield House with rm, Sudbury Rd, IP30 0LR, 301, – TV ☎. VISA.
M *(closed Monday and Tuesday to non-residents and Sunday dinner)* (dinner only and Sunday lunch)/dinner 13.25 **st.** and a la carte 14.55/19.25 **st.** 4.25 – **4 rm** 40.00/55.00 **s.**

FIAT Barton Rd 750001
FORD 5 Fornham Rd 752332
ROVER 76 Risbygate St. 753101
VAUXHALL-OPEL Cotton Lane 755621
VOLVO, MAZDA Out Risbygate 762444
VW-AUDI Northern Way 763441

ATS Southgate Av., Mildenhall 713841/713891
ATS Unit 1, Ailwin Rd, Moreton Hall Ind. Est. 705610/703672

BUSHEY Herts. 404 S 29 – ✉ 081.

Moonlight on the Heath, Kemp Pl., 33b High St., WD2 1BD, 950 4001, Chinese rest. AE VISA.
M 17.50/30.00**st.** and a la carte 4.00.

BUTTERMERE Cumbria 402 K 20 – pop. 194 – ✉ Cockermouth – 059 685.

See : Lake★.

London 306 – Carlisle 35 – Kendal 43.

Bridge, CA13 9UZ, 266, – rest ☎
M (bar lunch)/dinner 14.00 **t.** – **22 rm** 48.50/92.00 **t.** – SB (winter only) 72.00/86.00 **st.**

BUXTON Derbs. 402 403 404 O 24 – pop. 19 502 – ECD : Wednesday – 0298.

Envir. : Tideswell (Parish Church★ 14C) NE : 9 m.

Buxton and High Peak, Townend 23453, NE : on A 6 – Cavendish, Gadley Lane 23494, ¾ m. Buxton Station.

The Cresent 25106/77889.

London 172 – Derby 38 – Manchester 25 – Stoke-on-Trent 24.

Lee Wood (Best Western), 13 Manchester Rd, SK17 6TQ, on A 5004 23002, Telex 669848, Fax 23228, – TV ☎ – 110. AE VISA.
closed 24 to 28 December – **M** (bar lunch Monday to Saturday)/dinner 17.50 **st.** and a la carte 4.00 – **38 rm** 56.00/74.00 **st.** – SB 80.00/94.00 **st.**

Hartington, 18 Broad Walk, SK17 6JR, 22638 – TV. VISA.
closed 15 to 21 July and 24 December-3 January – **M** 9.00 **t.** 3.50 – **17 rm** 18.00/48.00 **t.** – SB 50.00/63.00 **st.**

SAAB Leek Rd 2494

ATS Staden Lane off Ashbourne Rd 25608/25655

BWLCHTOCYN Gwynedd 402 403 G 25 – see Abersoch.

CADNAM Hants. 403 404 P 31 – pop. 1 882 – ECD : Wednesday – 0703 Southampton.

London 91 – Salisbury 16 – Southampton 8 – Winchester 19.

Walnut cottage without rest., Old Romsey Rd, SO4 2NP, off A 31 812275, – TV
closed 23 to 26 December – **3 rm** 21.00/33.00 **st.**

CAERDYDD = Cardiff.

CAERFFILI = Caerphilly.

CAERFYRDDIN = Carmarthen.

CAERGYBI = Holyhead.

CAERLEON Gwent 403 L 29 – see Newport.

CAERNARFON Gwynedd 402 403 H 24 – pop. 9 271 – ECD : Thursday – 0286 Llanwnda.
See : Castle★★★ (13C-14C) (Royal Welsh Fusiliers Regimental museum★) *AC* – City walls★.
Envir. : SE : Snowdon (ascent and ★★★) 1 h 15 mn by Snowdon Mountain Railway (*AC*) from Llanberis (Pass★★) SE : 13 m. – Dinas Dinlle★, SW : 5 m.
Llanfaglan 3783, SW : 2½ m.
Oriel Pendeitsh 672232 (summer only).
London 249 – Birkenhead 76 – Chester 68 – Holyhead 30 – Shrewsbury 85.

Seiont Manor, Llanrug, LL55 2AQ, E : 3 m. on A 4086 673366, Fax 2840, , park – – 100. *VISA*.
M *(closed Saturday lunch)* 15.00/22.50 **t.** and a la carte 3.65 – **28 rm** 70.00/135.00 **t.** – SB 110.00 **st.**

Pengwern, Saron, LL54 5UH, SW : 3¼ m. on Llandwrog rd 830717, « Working farm » – .
March-November – **M** (by arrangement) 9.00 **st.** – **3 rm** 16.00/32.00 **st.** – SB (except July and August) 48.00/49.00 **st.**

Isfryn, 11 Church St., LL55 1SW, 5628 –
March-November – **M** 8.00 **s.** – **6 rm** 15.00/34.00 **s.**

PEUGEOT Llanrug 673372
SEAT Groeslon 830562
ATS Bangor Rd 673110

CAERPHILLY (CAERFFILI) Mid Glam. 403 K 29 – pop. 28 681 – ECD : Wednesday – 0222.
See : Castle★★ (13C).
Mountain Lakes, Blaengwynlais 861128 – Castell Heights, Blaengwynlais 886666, SW : 2 m. – Mountain Road 883481.
Old Police Station, Park Lane 851378 (summer only).
London 157 – Cardiff 8 – Newport 11.

Hotels and restaurants see : Cardiff S : 8 m., ***Newport (Gwent)*** E : 11 m.

CALCOT Glos. – see Tetbury.

CALDBECK Cumbria 401 402 K 19 – pop. 606 – Wigton – 069 98.
London 308 – Carlisle 13 – Keswick 16 – Workington 23.

Parkend, Park End, CA7 8HH, SW : 1½ m. on B 5299 494, « Converted 17C farmhouse », – . *VISA*
M 12.95 **t.** 3.45 – **3 rm** 22.50/35.00 **t.** – SB 45.00/50.00 **st.**

CALLINGTON Cornwall 403 H 32 – pop. 2 579 – ECD : Wednesday – 0579 Liskeard.
London 252 – Exeter 51 – Penzance 67 – Plymouth 14.

Coachmakers Arms, Newport Sq., PL17 7AS, 82567 – . *VISA*.
M 12.90 **st.** and a la carte 3.00 – **4 rm** 23.50/37.00 **st.** – SB 50.00 **st.**

CALNE Wilts. 403 404 O 29 – pop. 10 235 – ECD : Wednesday – 0249.
London 91 – Bristol 33 – Swindon 17.

Chilvester Hill House, SN11 OLP, W : ¾ m. on A 4 813981, Fax 814217, heated, – . *VISA*.
M (booking essential) (dinner only) 22.00 **st.** 3.50 – **3 rm** 40.00/75.00 **st.**

ROVER Main Rd, Cherhill 812254
ATS Unit 4, Maundrell rd., Portmarsh Ind. Est. 821622

CALSTOCK Cornwall 403 H 32 – pop. 4 079 – ✉ – ☎ 0822 Tavistock.
♦London 246 – Exeter 48 – ♦Plymouth 22.

Danescombe Valley, Lower Kelly, PL18 9RY, W : ½ m. ☎ 832414, ≤ River Tama « Country house atmosphere » – ⇔ rest Ⓟ. AE. ✻
closed November-29 March – **M** *(closed Wednesday and Thursday)* (dinner only) 25.00 s 3.60 – **5 rm** ☐ 58.00/104.00 **st.**

CAMBERLEY Surrey 404 R 29 – pop. 45 108 – ECD : Wednesday – ☎ 0276.
Envir. : Sandhurst (Royal Military Academy : Royal Memorial Chapel★) NW : 1½ m.
18 Camberley Heath, Golf Drive ☎ 23258.
♦London 40 – Reading 13 – ♦Southampton 48.

Frimley Hall (T.H.F.), off Portsmouth Rd via Lime Av., GU15 2BG, E : ¾ m. off A 32 ☎ 28321, Telex 858446, Fax 691253, – ⇔ rm TV ☎ Ⓟ – 60. AE VISA
M 15.75/21.75 **st.** and a la carte – ☐ 7.60 – **66 rm** 70.00/90.00 **st.** – SB (weekends onl 74.00/94.00 **st.**

CAMBRIDGE Cambs. 404 U 27 – pop. 87 111 – ECD : Thursday – ☎ 0223.
See : Colleges Quarter★★★ : King's College★★ (King's Chapel★★★) Z – St. John's College★★ (Gateway★) Y – The Backs★★ YZ – Fitzwilliam Museum★★ *AC* Z **M1** – Trinity College★★ (Wre Library★★, Chapel★, Great Court and Gate★) Y – Clare College★ Z **B** – Senate House★ Z **S** Holy Sepulchre★ (12C round church) Y **E** – Jesus College (Chapel★) Y **K** – Kettle's Yard★ Y **M2** Queen's College★ (Cloister Court) Z.
Envir. : Anglesey Abbey (12C) (interior★★ and park★ *AC*) NE : 6 m. by A 1303 X and B 1102.
18 Dodford Lane ☎ 276169, N : 3 m. X. Cambridge Airport : ☎ 61133, E : 2 m. on A 1303
Wheeler St. ☎ 322640.
♦London 55 – ♦Coventry 88 – ♦Kingston-upon-Hull 137 – ♦Ipswich 54 – ♦Leicester 74 – ♦Norwich 61 – ♦Nottingham 8 – ♦Oxford 100.

Plan on next page

Garden House (Q.M.H.), Granta Pl., off Mill Lane, CB2 1RT, ☎ 63421, Telex 8146 Fax 316605, ≤, – ⇔ rest TV ☎ Ⓟ – 250. AE VISA. ✻ Z
M 15.50/18.50 **t.** and a la carte 7.20 – ☐ 7.00 – **118 rm** 75.00/265.00 **t.**

University Arms (De Vere), Regent St., CB2 1AD, ☎ 351241, Telex 817311, Fax 315256 TV ☎ Ⓟ – 200. AE VISA Z
M 11.00/15.00 **t.** and a la carte – **116 rm** ☐ 75.00/90.00 **st.**, **1 suite** 145.00 **st.** – SB (week ends only) 84.00 **st.**

Gonville, Gonville Pl., CB1 1LY, ☎ 66611, Fax 66611301 – rest TV ☎ Ⓟ – 50. AE VISA Z
closed 24 to 29 December – **M** 9.75/11.75 **st.** and a la carte 4.75 – **62 rm** ☐ 61.50 77.00 **st.** – SB (weekends only) 75.00/80.00 **st.**

Arundel House, 53 Chesterton Rd, CB4 3AN, ☎ 67701, Fax 67721 – ⇔ rest TV ☎ Ⓟ 35. AE VISA. ✻ Y
closed 25 and 26 December – **M** 7.95/11.75 **t.** and a la carte 4.80 – ☐ 1.85 – **88 rm** 26.50/65.00 **t.** – SB (weekends only) 72.50/79.50 **st.**

Centennial, 63-71 Hills Rd, CB2 1PG, ☎ 314652, Telex 817019, Fax 315443 – TV ☎ Ⓟ. AE VISA. ✻ X
closed 23 December-2 January – **M** 10.00/15.00 **t.** and a la carte 3.00 – **25 rm** ☐ 47.00 65.00 **t.** – SB (weekends only) 111.00/125.00 **st.**

Cambridge Lodge, 139 Huntingdon Rd, CB3 0DQ, ☎ 352833, Fax 355166, – TV ☎ Ⓟ AE VISA X
M *(closed Saturday lunch)* 15.95/20.50 **st.** and a la carte 4.25 – **11 rm** ☐ 45.00/90.00 **st.** – SB (October-March) (weekends only) 70.00/80.00 **st.**

Helen, 167-169 Hills Rd, CB2 2RJ, ☎ 246465, Fax 214406, – TV ☎ Ⓟ. VISA
closed 20 December-7 January – **M** *(closed Sunday dinner)* (bar lunch)/dinner 13.00 **st** 3.75 – **29 rm** ☐ 30.00/53.00 **st.** X

Midsummer House, Midsummer Common, CB4 1HA, ☎ 69299, « Riverside setting » – VISA Y
closed Saturday lunch and Sunday – **M** 29.00/42.50 **t.** 6.50.

Cafe Francais, 53 Castle Street, CB3 0AH, ☎ 60723, French rest. – AE VISA Y
closed 25 to 26 December and 1 to 2 January – **M** 19.45 **t.**

at Impington N : 2 m. on B 1049 at junction with A 45 – X – ✉ ☎ 0223 Cambridge :

Post House (T.H.F.), Lakeview, Bridge Rd, CB4 4PH, ☎ 237000, Telex 817123 Fax 233426, , , , – rest TV ☎ Ⓟ – 60. AE VISA
M 15.25/19.50 **st.** and a la carte 5.25 – ☐ 7.60 – **119 rm** 90.00/100.00 **st.**, **1 suite** 250.00/300.00 **st.** – SB (weekends only) 100.00/120.00 **st.**

at Fowlmere S : 8 ¾ m. by A 1309 – X – and A 10 on B 1368 – ✉ Royston (Herts.) – ☎ 076 382 Fowlmere :

Chequers Inn, High St., SG8 7SR, ☎ 369 – Ⓟ. AE VISA
closed Christmas Day – **M** 14.25/24.80 **st.** and a la carte 3.25.

Maguire's, High St., SG8 7SR, ☎ 444 – Ⓟ. AE VISA
closed Sunday dinner and 25 to 26 December – **M** 19.50 **t.** and a la carte 4.00.

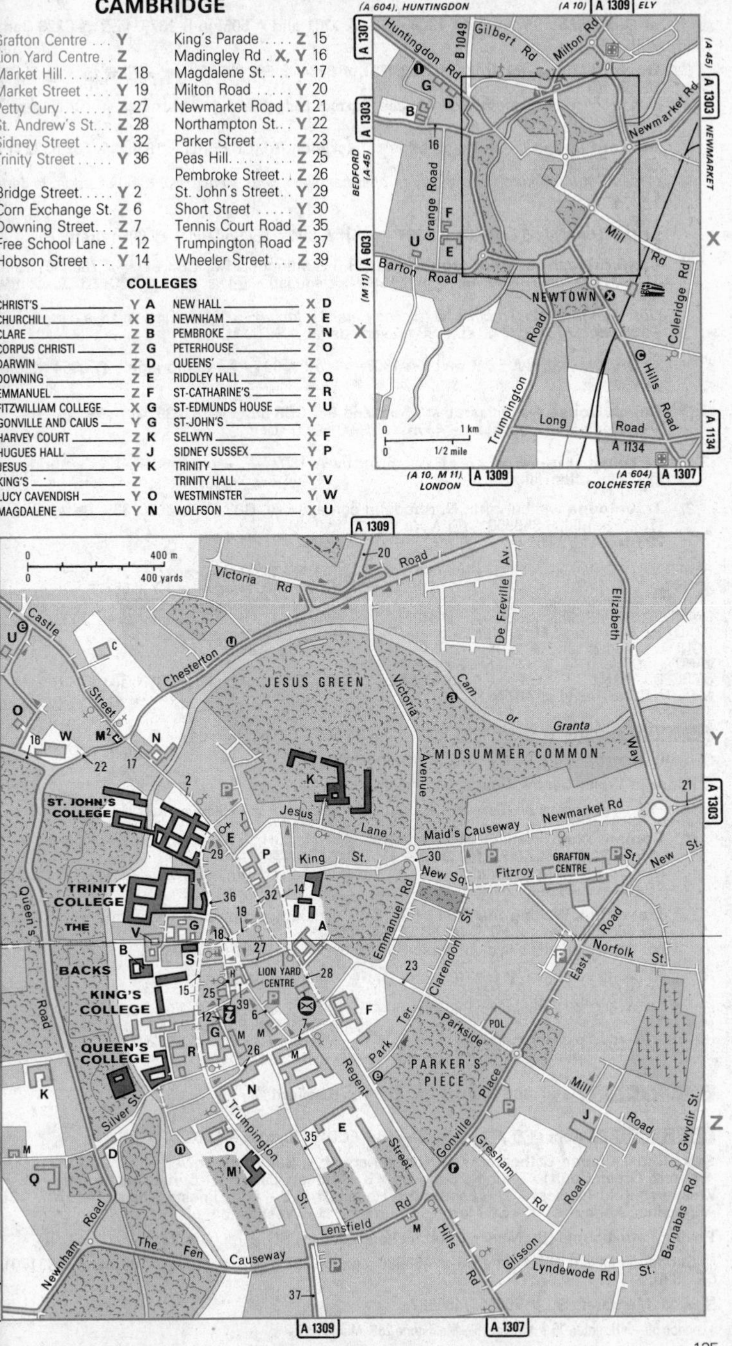
CAMBRIDGE
Grafton Centre ... Y
Lion Yard Centre .. Z
Market Hill .... Z 18
Market Street .... Y 19
Petty Cury .... Z 27
St. Andrew's St. .. Z 28
Sidney Street .... Y 32
Trinity Street ..... Y 36
Bridge Street ..... Y 2
Corn Exchange St. Z 6
Downing Street ... Z 7
Free School Lane . Z 12
Hobson Street ... Y 14
King's Parade ..... Z 15
Madingley Rd . X, Y 16
Magdalene St. ... Y 17
Milton Road ..... Y 20
Newmarket Road . Y 21
Northampton St. . Y 22
Parker Street ..... Z 23
Peas Hill .... Z 25
Pembroke Street . Z 26
St. John's Street . Y 29
Short Street ..... Y 30
Tennis Court Road Z 35
Trumpington Road Z 37
Wheeler Street ... Z 39
COLLEGES
CHRIST'S Y A
CHURCHILL X B
CLARE Z B
CORPUS CHRISTI Z G
DARWIN Z D
DOWNING Z E
EMMANUEL Z F
FITZWILLIAM COLLEGE X G
GONVILLE AND CAIUS Y G
HARVEY COURT Z K
HUGUES HALL Z J
JESUS Y K
KING'S Z
LUCY CAVENDISH Y O
MAGDALENE Y N
NEW HALL X D
NEWNHAM X E
PEMBROKE Z N
PETERHOUSE Z O
QUEENS' Z
RIDDLEY HALL Z Q
ST-CATHARINE'S Z R
ST-EDMUNDS HOUSE Y U
ST-JOHN'S Y
SELWYN X F
SIDNEY SUSSEX Y P
TRINITY Y
TRINITY HALL Y V
WESTMINSTER Y W
WOLFSON X U
(A 604), HUNTINGDON
(A 10) A 1309 ELY
(A 45) A 1303 NEWMARKET
BEDFORD (A 45) A 1303
A 1307
A 603 (M 11)
(A 10, M 11) LONDON A 1309
(A 604) COLCHESTER A 1307
A 1134
NEWTOWN
0 1 km
0 1/2 mile
0 400 m
0 400 yards
JESUS GREEN
MIDSUMMER COMMON
PARKER'S PIECE
ST. JOHN'S COLLEGE
TRINITY COLLEGE
THE BACKS
KING'S COLLEGE
QUEEN'S COLLEGE
LION YARD CENTRE
GRAFTON CENTRE
Cam or Granta

at Duxford S : 9½ m. by A 1309 – X – A 1301 and A 505 on B 1379 – ✉ ☎ 0223 Cambridge :

Duxford Lodge, Ickleton Rd, CB2 4RU, ☎ 836444, Fax 832271, – TV ☎ P – 25. AE VISA
closed 27 to 30 December – **M** (see **Duxford Lodge** below) – **16 rm** 45.00/85.00 **st.** – SB 92.00/110.00 **st.**

Duxford Lodge (at Duxford Lodge H.), Ickleton Rd, CB2 4RU, ☎ 836444, Fax 832271 – P. AE VISA
closed Saturday lunch and 3 days Christmas-New Year – **M** 16.50/18.50 **st.** and a la carte 4.00.

at Bar Hill NW : 5½ m. by A 1307 – X – off A 604 – ✉ Bar Hill – ☎ 0954 Crafts Hill :

Cambridgeshire Moat House (Q.M.H.), Huntingdon Rd, CB3 8EU, ☎ 780555, Telex 817141, Fax 780010, , , , 18, , , squash – TV ☎ P – 200. AE VISA
closed 24 to 26 December – **M** *(closed Saturday lunch)* 15.00/27.00 **st.** and a la carte 5.2 – **100 rm** 70.00/87.00 **st.** – SB (weekends only) 90.00 **st.**

at Dry Drayton NW : 5¾ m. by A 1307 – X – off A 604 – ✉ Cambridge – ☎ 0954 Madingley :

Coach House without rest., Scotland Rd, CB3 8BX, ☎ 782439, – P.
Mid March-mid December – **4 rm** 28.00/50.00 **st.**

at Lolworth Service Area NW : 6 m. by A 1307 – Y – on A 604 – ✉ Cambridge – ☎ 0954 Crafts Hill :

Travelodge without rest., Northbound carriageway, CB3 8DR, ☎ 781335, Reservations (Toll free) 0800 850950 – TV P. AE VISA.
20 rm 24.00/29.50 **t.**

BEDFORD, OPEL-VAUXHALL 137 Histon Rd ☎ 66751
CITROEN Newmarket Rd, Duxford ☎ 832136
DAIMLER-JAGUAR Cherry Hinton Rd ☎ 411114
FORD 350 New Market Rd ☎ 315435
HONDA Cheddars Lane ☎ 359151
LANCIA, SUZUKI, FIAT 315-349 Mill Rd ☎ 242222
MERCEDES-BENZ 121-129 Perne Rd ☎ 411511
NISSAN Babraham Rd ☎ 245456
RENAULT 217 Newmarket Rd ☎ 351616
ROVER 400 Newmarket Rd ☎ 65111
TOYOTA 1 Union Lane ☎ 356225
VAUXHALL-OPEL Elizabeth Way ☎ 321321
VOLVO Harston ☎ 870123
VW-AUDI 383 Milton Rd ☎ 424472

ATS 143 Histon Rd ☎ 61695 and 351431/2

CANNOCK Staffs. 402 403 404 N 25 – pop. 54 503 – ECD : Thursday – ☎ 0543.

18 Beau Desert, Hazel Slade ☎ 054 38 (Hednesford) 2773.

Prince of Wales Centre, Church St. ☎ 466543.

London 135 – Birmingham 20 – Derby 36 – Leicester 51 – Shrewsbury 32 – Stoke-on-Trent 28.

Roman Way, Watling St., Hatherton, WS11 1SH, SW : 1¼ m. by A 460 on A 5 ☎ 572121, Fax 502749 – TV ☎ P – 120. AE VISA
M *(closed Saturday lunch)* 7.50/11.50 **st.** and a la carte – **24 rm** 59.35/68.75 **st.** – SB (weekends only) 70.00 **st.**

Travel Inn, Walting St., WS11 1SJ, SW : 1 m. at junction of A 460 with A 5 ☎ 572721, Fax 466130 – rm TV P. AE VISA.
M (Beefeater grill) a la carte approx. 12.25 **t.** – 4.50 – **38 rm** -/27.50 **t.**

FORD PO Box 13 Watling St. ☎ 0922 (Cheslyn Hay) 417014
PEUGEOT-TALBOT 40 Longford Rd, Bridgetown ☎ 504111
ROVER Wolverhampton Rd ☎ 466646
VAUXHALL-OPEL Hatherton ☎ 466466
VW-AUDI Delta Way ☎ 506216

ATS Cannock Rd, Chadsmoor ☎ 4985/74580
ATS Cannock Rd, Heath Hayes ☎ 74200
ATS New Penkridge rd. ☎ 72662

CANON PYON Heref. and Worc. 403 L 27 – see Hereford.

CANTERBURY Kent 404 X 30 – pop. 34 546 – ECD : Thursday – ☎ 0227.

See : Christ Church Cathedral★★★ (Norman crypt★★, Bell Harry Tower★★, Great Cloister★★, ≤★ from Green Court) Y – King's School★ Y **B** – Mercery Lane★ Y – Christ Church Gate★ Y **A** – Weavers★ (old houses) Y **D** – Eastbridge Hospital★ Y **E** – Poor Priests Hospital★ Y **M1** – St. Augustines Abbey★★ Y **K** – St. Martin's Church★ Y **N** – West Gate★ Y **R**.

Envir. : Patrixbourne (St. Mary's Church : south door★) SE : 3 m. by A 2 Z.

18 Scotlands Hills, Littlebourne Rd ☎ 463586 Z and A 257 – 18 Broome Park, Barham ☎ 831701, SE : 8 m. Z.

34 St. Margarets St. ☎ 766567/455567.

London 59 – Brighton 76 – Dover 15 – Maidstone 28 – Margate 17.

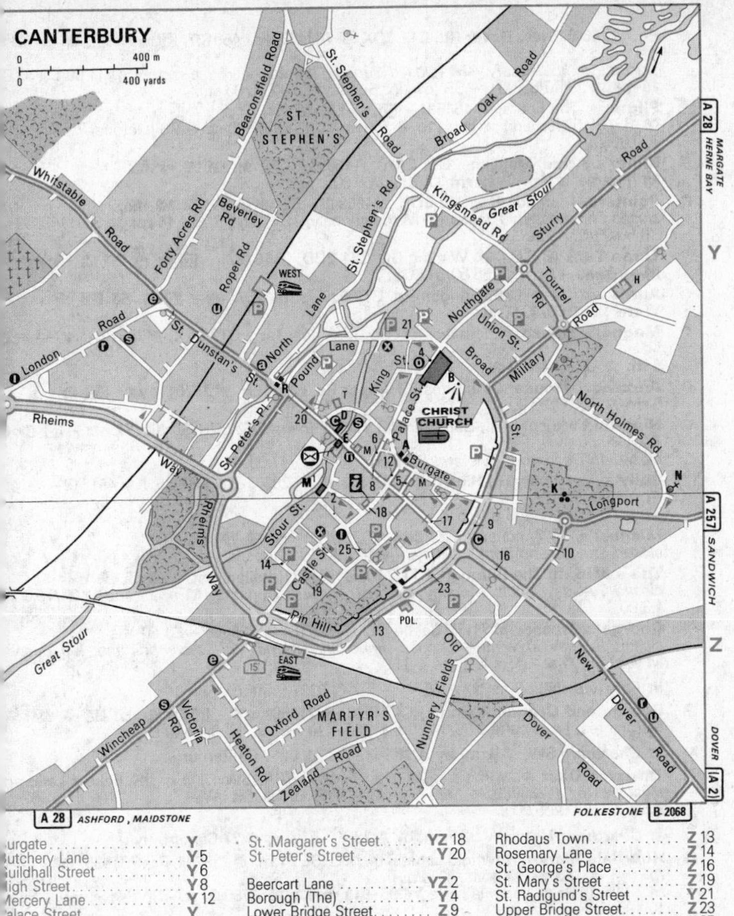

urgate . . . . . Y	St. Margaret's Street . . . . . YZ 18	Rhodaus Town . . . . . Z 13
utchery Lane . . . . . Y 5	St. Peter's Street . . . . . Y 20	Rosemary Lane . . . . . Z 14
uildhall Street . . . . . Y 6		St. George's Place . . . . . Z 16
igh Street . . . . . Y 8	Beercart Lane . . . . . YZ 2	St. Mary's Street . . . . . Z 19
ercery Lane . . . . . Y 12	Borough (The) . . . . . Y 4	St. Radigund's Street . . . . . Y 21
alace Street . . . . . Y	Lower Bridge Street . . . . . Z 9	Upper Bridge Street . . . . . Z 23
t. George's Street . . . . . Z 17	Lower Chantry Lane . . . . . Z 10	Watling Street . . . . . Z 25

County, High St., CT1 2RX, ✆ 766266, Telex 965076, Fax 451512 – lift TV ☎ P – 50. AE VISA. Y **n**
M (see **Sullys** below) – ☕ 7.50 – **72 rm** 66.00/85.00 **t.**, **1 suite** 160.00 **t.**.

Chaucer (T.H.F.), Ivy Lane, CT1 1TT, ✆ 464427, Telex 965096, Fax 450397 – rm TV ☎ P – 80. AE VISA Z **c**
M 9.50/13.75 **st.** and a la carte 4.35 – ☕ 7.50 – **45 rm** 64.00/85.00 **st.** – SB (except June-September) 70.00/100.00 **st.**

Falstaff (Lansbury), 8-12 St. Dunstan's St., CT2 8AF, ✆ 462138, Telex 96394, Fax 463525 – TV ☎ P – 40. AE VISA. Y **a**
M a la carte 11.65/20.15 **t.** – **24 rm** ☕ 63.00/77.00 **t.** – SB (weekends only) 78.00 **st.**

Thanington without rest., 140 Wincheap, CT1 3RY, ✆ 453227, – TV ☎ P. VISA Z **s**
10 rm ☕ 42.50/55.00 **st.**

Victoria (B.C.B.), 59 London Rd, CT2 8JY, ✆ 459333, – TV ☎ P. AE VISA. Y **i**
M (grill rest.) 15.00 **st.** – **34 rm** ☕ 42.00/70.00 **st.**

Canterbury, 71 New Dover Rd, CT1 3DZ, ✆ 450551, Telex 965809, Fax 450873 – lift TV ☎ P. AE VISA Z **u**
M 11.50/13.50 **st.** and a la carte 3.50 – **27 rm** ☕ 40.00/60.00 **st.** – SB (except summer and Christmas) 60.00/64.00 **st.**

Ebury, 65-67 New Dover Rd, CT1 3DX, 768433, Fax 459187, ... VISA Z
closed 1 to 15 January – **M** *(closed Sunday)* (dinner only) a la carte 9.70/11.50 **t.** 4.00 – **15 rm** 38.00/58.00 **t.** – SB (except Sunday) 60.00/70.00 **st.**

Pilgrims, The Friars, 464531 – ... VISA Y
M 6.00/8.50 **st.** and a la carte – **15 rm** 40.00/60.00 **st.** – SB (October-April) 90.0 100.00 **st.**

Miller's Arms, Mill Lane, CT1 2AA, 456057 – ... VISA Y
M (bar meals only) – **12 rm** 25.00/50.00.

Pointers, 1 London Rd, CT2 8LR, 456846 – ... VISA Y
closed Christmas-mid January – **M** (dinner only) 12.00 **st.** 3.25 – **14 rm** 30.00/52.00 t SB 50.00/62.00 **st.**

Three Tuns (B.C.B.), 24 Watling St., CT1 2UD, 767371 – ... VISA Z
M 15.00 **st.** – **7 rm** 35.50/51.50 **st.**

Ann's without rest., 63 London Rd, CT2 8JZ, 768767, ... VISA Y
17 rm 28.00/40.00 **st.**

Magnolia House without rest., 36 St. Dunstan's Terr., CT2 8AX, 765121, ... Y
6 rm 22.00/46.00 **st.**

Alexandra House without rest., 1 Roper Rd, CT2 7EH, 767011, ... Y
9 rm 15.00/32.00 **st.**

Highfield without rest., Summer Hill, Harbledown, CT2 8NH, 462772, ... VISA
by Rheims way Y
closed 15 December-2 February – **8 rm** 22.00/47.00.

XXX **Sully's,** (at County H.) High St., CT1 2RX, 766266, Telex 965076, Fax 451512 – ... VISA Y
M 14.00/18.00 **t.** and a la carte.

XX **Michael's,** 74 Wincheap, CT1 3RS, 767411 – ... VISA Z
closed Sunday and Bank Holidays – **M** 12.50/18.50 **st.** and a la carte 4.00.

XX **Tuo e Mio,** 16 The Borough, CT1 2JD, 761471, Italian rest. – ... VISA Y
closed Tuesday lunch, Monday and last 2 weeks August – **M** a la carte 11.25/19.00 s 3.00.

X **George's Brasserie,** 71-72 Castle St., CT1 2QD, 765658 – ... VISA Z
closed Sunday in winter, Sunday dinner in summer, 25 December and 1 January – **M** 5.00/35.00 **st.** and a la carte 3.50.

at Fordwich NE : 3 m. by A 28 – Y – 0227 Canterbury :

George and Dragon, King St., CT2 0DB, 710661, ... VISA
M (grill rest.) a la carte 6.85/14.50 **t.** 4.30 – **10 rm** 25.00/40.00 **t.**

at Chartham SW : 3 ¼ m. by A 28 – Z – 0227 Canterbury :

Thruxted Oast without rest., Mystole, CT4 7BX, SW : 1 ¼ m. by Bakers Lane ar Mystole Rd, 730080, ... VISA
3 rm 55.00/65.00 **s.**

at Chartham Hatch W : 3 ¼ m. by A 28 – Z – 0227 Canterbury :

Howfield Manor, Howfield Lane, CT4 7HQ, SE : 1 m. 738294, Fax 731535, ... 80. ... VISA
M 13.95/18.95 **st.** and a la carte 4.95 – **13 rm** 62.50/80.00 **st.** – SB (November-March) 100.00 **st.**

ALFA-ROMEO, LOTUS The Street, Boughton 751223
BMW Vauxhall Rd 454341
HONDA Vauxhall Rd 767781
HONDA Vauxhall Rd 767781
MERCEDES-BENZ Mill Rd, Sturry 710481
MITSUBISHI Westminster Rd 453314
PEUGEOT-TALBOT The Pavilion 451791
RENAULT Northgate 765561
ROVER, DAIMLER-JAGUAR 28-30 St. Peters St. 766161
SAAB Westminster Rd 769100
SUBARU, SEAT Island Rd 710431
TOYOTA Union St. 455553
VAUXHALL-OPEL Ashford Rd, Chartham 731331
VOLVO, MERCEDES-BENZ Mill Rd, Sturry 710481
YUGO Pound Lane 463349

ATS 29 Sturry Rd 464867/765021

CARBIS BAY Cornwall 403 D 33 – see St. Ives.

CARCROFT South Yorks. 402 403 404 Q 23 – see Doncaster.

Pleasant hotels and restaurants are shown in the Guide by a red sign.

Please send us the names of any where you have enjoyed your stay.

Your Michelin Guide will be even better.

... X

XXXXX ... X

CARDIFF **(CAERDYDD)** South Glam. 403 K 29 – pop. 262 313 – ECD : Wednesday – ☎ 0222.

See : Welsh Folk Museum★★ *AC* (St. Fagan's Castle) AV – Cardiff Castle★ *AC* BZ – National Museum of Wales★ BY **M2** – Llandaff Cathedral★ AV **B.**

Envir. : Caerphilly Castle★★ *AC*, N : 7 m. by A470 AV – Castell Coch★ *AC*, N : 5 m. by A470 AV.

⛳18 Dinas Powis ☎ 512727, W : 3 m. AY – ⛳18 Wenvoe ☎ 591094, W : 4 m. AY – ⛳18 Pantmawr Rd, Whitchurch ☎ 620125, NW : 3 m. AY – ⛳18 Radyr ☎ 842442, NW : 5 m. AY – ⛳18 St Mellons ☎ 0633 (St Mellons) 680401 – ⛳18 Creigian ☎ 890263 – ⛳18 Sherborne Av., Cyncoed ☎ 753067.

✈ Cardiff-Wales Airport ☎ 711111, Telex 497720 SW : 8 m. by A 48 AX – **Terminal :** Central Bus Station.

ℹ 8-14 Bridge St. ☎ 227281.

◆London 155 – ◆Birmingham 110 – ◆Bristol 46 – ◆Coventry 124.

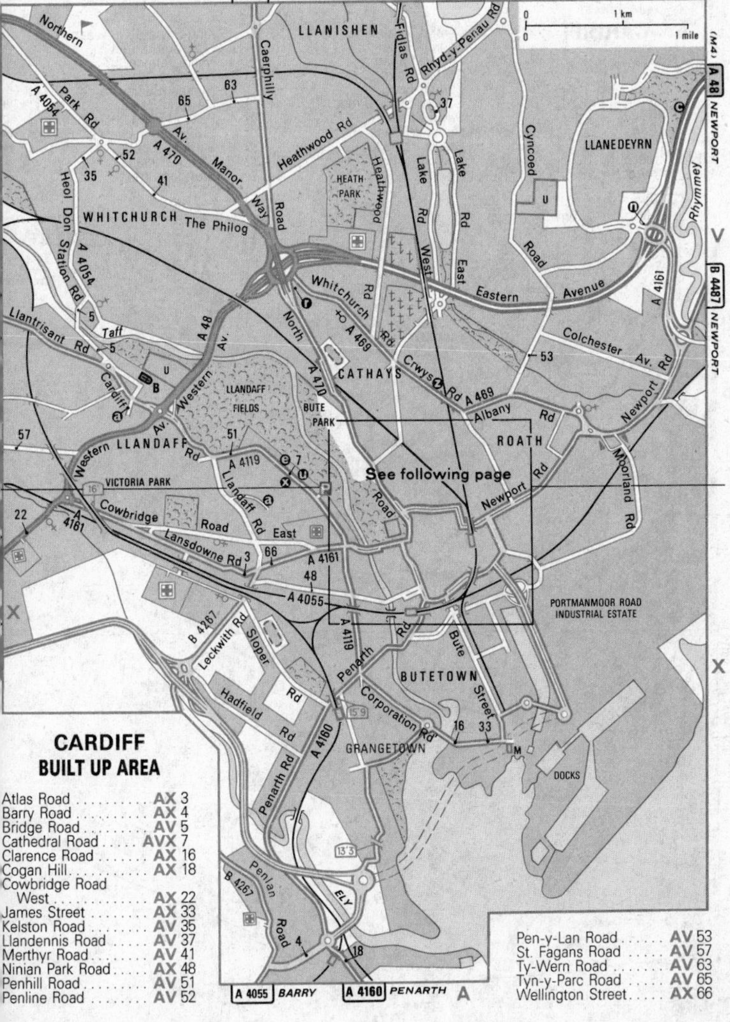

Great Britain and Ireland are covered entirely at a scale of 16 miles to 1 inch by our map «Main roads» 986.

Angel (Q.M.H.), Castle St., CF1 2QZ, ℰ 232633, Telex 498132, Fax 396212, – BZ
– 250. AE VISA
M *(closed Saturday lunch)* 15.00/18.00 **st.** and a la carte – 6.95 – **89 rm** 76.00/90.00 st
2 suites 105.00/176.00 **st.** – SB (weekends only) 99.00/110.00 **st.**

Holiday Inn, Mill Lane, CF1 1EZ, ℰ 399944, Group Telex 497365, Fax 395578, ,
squash – rm – 300. AE VISA BZ
M 15.95/16.95 **t.** and a la carte 6.50 – 9.95 – **178 rm** 88.00/110.00 **st.**, **4 suite**
232.00 **st.** – SB (weekends only) 106.00/139.00 **st.**

Park (Mt. Charlotte Thistle), Park Pl., CF1 3UD, ℰ 383471, Telex 497195, Fax 399309 –
– 300. AE VISA BZ
M 9.50/12.95 **st.** and a la carte 4.25 – **102 rm** 70.00/80.00 **st.**, **6 suites** 110.00/150.00 **st.**
SB (weekends only) 73.00 **st.**

CARDIFF

Duke Street .... **BZ** 26
High Street .... **BZ**
Queen Street .... **BZ**
St. David's Centre .... **BZ**
St. Mary Street .... **BZ**
Working Street .... **BZ** 67

Castle Street .... **BZ** 9
Cathays Terrace .... **BY** 10
Central Square .... **BZ** 12
Church Street .... **BZ** 14
City Hall Road .... **BY** 15
College Road .... **BY** 20
Corbett Road .... **BY** 21
Customhouse Street .... **BZ** 23
David Street .... **BZ** 25
Dumfries Place .... **BY** 28
Greyfriars Road .... **BY** 29
Guilford Street .... **BZ** 30
Hayes (The) .... **BZ** 32
King Edward VII Avenue .... **BY** 3
Mary Ann Street .... **BZ** 3
Moira Terrace .... **BZ** 4
Museum Avenue .... **BY** 4
Nantes (Boulevard de) .... **BY** 4
Newport Road .... **BY** 4
Penarth Road .... **BZ** 4
St. Andrews Place .... **BY** 5
St. John Street .... **BZ** 5
Station Terrace .... **BZ** 6
Stuttgart Street .... **BY** 6

Cardiff Moat House (Q.M.H.), Circle Way East, Llanedeyrn, CF3 7XF, NE : 3 m. on A 48 ☎ 732520, Telex 497582, Fax 549092, – rm rest – 200. AE VISA AV **n**
M 8.95/14.50 **t.** and a la carte – 7.50 – **142 rm** 65.00/86.00 **t.**, **2 suites** 120.00 **t.** – SB 72.00/126.00 **st.**

Celtic Bay, Schooner Way, Atlantic Wharf, Cardiff Bay, CF1 5RT, ☎ 465888, Fax 481491 – rest – 250. AE VISA BZ **x**
M *(closed Saturday lunch)* 12.95/16.25 **t.** and a la carte – **64 rm** 40.00/125.00 **t.** – SB (weekends only) 85.00/90.00 **st.**

Crest (T.H.F.), Castle St., CF1 2XB, ☎ 388681, Telex 497258, Fax 371495 – rm – 150. AE VISA BZ **i**
M 10.00/14.50 **t.** and a la carte – 7.95 – **157 rm** 75.00/87.00, **1 suite** 90.00/130.00 – SB 156.00/172.00 **st.**

Post House (T.H.F.), Pentwyn Rd, CF2 7XA, NE : 4 m. by A 48 ☎ 731212, Telex 497633, Fax 549147, – rm – 120. AE VISA on A 48 AV
M 13.95 **st.** (dinner) and a la carte 4.50 – 7.50 – **150 rm** 65.00/75.00 **st.** – SB (weekends only) 76.00 **st.**

Travelodge without rest., Circle Way East, Llanedeyrn, CF3 7ND, ☎ 549564, Reservations (Toll free) 0800 850950 – . AE VISA. AV **c**
32 rm 24.00/29.50 **t.**

Riverside, 53-59 Despencer St., Riverside, CF1 8RG, ☎ 378866, Fax 388306 – . AE VISA BZ **u**
M (bar lunch)/dinner a la carte 8.65/13.30 **t.** 2.75 – **36 rm** 38.50/75.00 **t.** – SB (weekends only) 50.00 **st.**

Campanile, Caxton Pl., Pentwyn, CF2 7HA, NE : 4 m. by A 48 ☎ 549044, Telex 497553 – rm . VISA on A 48 AV
M 9.40 **st.** and a la carte 2.60 – 3.95 – **47 rm** 33.00 **st.**

Penrhys without rest., 127 Cathedral Rd, CF1 9JB, ☎ 230548 – . VISA. AV **x**
13 rm 30.00/35.00 **st.**

Ferrier's, 130-132 Cathedral Rd, CF1 9LQ, ☎ 383413 – . AE VISA
closed 2 weeks Christmas-New Year – **M** (by arrangement) approx. 9.90 **t.** – **26 rm** 23.00/46.00 **t.** AV **e**

Annedd Lon without rest., 3 Dyfrig St., off Cathedral Rd, CF1 9LR, ☎ 223349 – . AV **u**
6 rm 14.00/32.00 **st.**

Trillium, 40 City Rd, CF2 3DL, ☎ 463665 – AE VISA BY **e**
closed lunch Saturday and Bank Holiday Mondays, Monday dinner and Sunday – **M** 12.50 **t.** (lunch) and a la carte 19.00/47.50 **t.**

Indian Ocean, 290 North Rd, Gabalfa, CF4 3BN, ☎ 621349, Indian rest. – . AE VISA AV **r**
M 11.95 **t.** (dinner) and a la carte approx. 18.70 **t.** 5.95.

Noble House, 9-11 St. David's House, Wood St., CF1 1ER, ☎ 388430, Chinese rest. – AE VISA BZ **e**
M 14.00 **t.** and a la carte approx. 9.80 **t.** 3.00.

Blas-ar-Gymru (A Taste of Wales), 48 Crwys Rd, CF2 4NN, ☎ 382132 – . AE VISA
closed Saturday lunch, Sunday, first two weeks January and Bank Holidays – **M** 16.95/17.95 **t.** and a la carte 3.50. AV **z**

Gibson's, 8 Romilly Cres., Canton, CF1 9NR, ☎ 341264, Bistro – AE VISA
closed dinner Sunday and Monday, Tuesday, 26 December and Bank Holidays – **M** (booking essential) 11.50/20.85 **t.** and a la carte 3.85. AX **a**

Armless Dragon, 97 Wyeverne Rd, Cathays, CF2 4BG, ☎ 382357 – AE VISA
closed Saturday lunch, Sunday, Christmas-New Year and Bank Holidays – **M** a la carte 12.50/18.50 **t.** 2.95. BY **n**

Thai House, 23 High St., CF1 2BZ, ☎ 387404, Thai rest. – AE VISA BZ **o**
closed Sunday, 23 to 29 December and 1 January – **M** 13.00/22.00 **st.** and a la carte.

at Thornhill N : S ¼ m. by A 470 on A 469 – ✉ Cardiff – 0222 Thornhill

New House Country, Caerphilly Rd, CF4 5UA, ☎ 520280, Fax 520324, park – – 40. AE VISA.
M 15.50/22.50 **st.** 3.75 – 5.00 **5 rm** 80.00/150.00 **t.**

at Castleton (Cas-Bach) (Gwent) NE : 7 m. on A 48 – AV – ✉ Cardiff – 0633 Castleton :

Wentloog Castle Resort, CF3 8UQ, ☎ 680591, Fax 681287, – . AE VISA
M *(closed Saturday lunch)* (grill rest.) 11.25 **st.** 4.50 – **55 rm** 55.50/70.00 **st.** – SB (weekends only) 50.00/75.00 **st.**

Travel Inn, Newport Rd, CF3 8UQ, ☎ 680070 – rm . AE VISA.
M (Beefeater grill) a la carte approx. 12.25 **t.** – 4.50 – **49 rm** 27.50 **t.**

ALFA-ROMEO Newport Rd, St. Mellons ℘ 777183
FORD 505 Newport Rd ℘ 490511
FORD 281 Penarth Rd ℘ 223100
RENAULT 325 Penarth Rd ℘ 383122
ROVER 52 Penarth Rd ℘ 343571

SKODA Braeval St. ℘ 485725
VAUXHALL-OPEL Sloper Rd ℘ 387221

ATS Hadfield Rd ℘ 228251/226336

CARDIFF WEST SERVICE AREA South Glam. – ✉ Pontycwn – ☎ 0222 Cardiff

Rank Motor Lodge whithout rest., CF7 8SB, M4 junction 33, ℘ 892255, Fax 892497 – rm TV ♿ P. AE VISA
50 rm 27.50/34.50 **st.**

CARDIGAN (ABERTEIFI) Dyfed 403 G 27 – pop. 3 815 – ECD : Wednesday – ☎ 0239.

Envir. : Mwnt (site★) N : 6 m. – Gwbert-on-Sea (cliffs ≤★) NW : 3 m. – Teifi Valley★, S : 3 m.

18 Gwbert-on-Sea ℘ 612035, NW : 3 m.

Theatre Mwldan, Bath House Rd ℘ 613230 (summer only).

◆London 250 – Carmarthen 30 – Fishguard 19.

Penbontbren Farm, Glynarthen, SA44 6PE, NE : 9 ½ m. by A 487 and Brongest rd ℘ 810248, park – TV ☎ ♿ P. VISA
M (dinner only) 12.50 **t.** and a la carte 3.15 – **10 rm** 27.00/52.00 **t.** – SB 59.00/66.00 **st.**

at St. Dogmaels W : 1 m. by A 487 on B 4568 – ✉ ☎ 0239 Cardigan :

Berwyn without rest., Cardigan Rd, SA43 3HS, ℘ 613555, ≤, – P.
March-October – **3 rm** 15.50/31.00 **s.**

FIAT St. Dogmaels ℘ 612025
ROVER, LAND-ROVER, RANGE ROVER, JAGUAR-DAILMER Aberystwyth Rd ℘ 612365

ATS 4 Bath House rd. ℘ 612917

CARLISLE

Botchergate .... **BZ**
Castle Street .... **BY** 6
English Street .... **BY** 13
Scotch Street .... **BY** 19

Annetwell Street .... **AY** 2
Bridge Street .... **AY** 3
Brunswick Street .... **BZ** 4
Caldcotes .... **AY** 5
Charlotte Street .... **AZ** 7
Chiswick Street .... **BY** 8
Church Street .... **AY** 10
Eden Bridge .... **BY** 12
Lonsdale Street .... **BY** 14
Lowther Street .... **BY** 15
Port Road .... **AY** 16
St. Aidan's Road .... **BY** 17
St. Nicholas Street .... **BZ** 18
Spencer Street .... **BY** 20
Tait Street .... **BZ** 21
Victoria Viaduct .... **ABZ** 24
West Tower Street .... **BY** 26
West Walls .... **ABY** 27
Wigton Road .... **AZ** 29

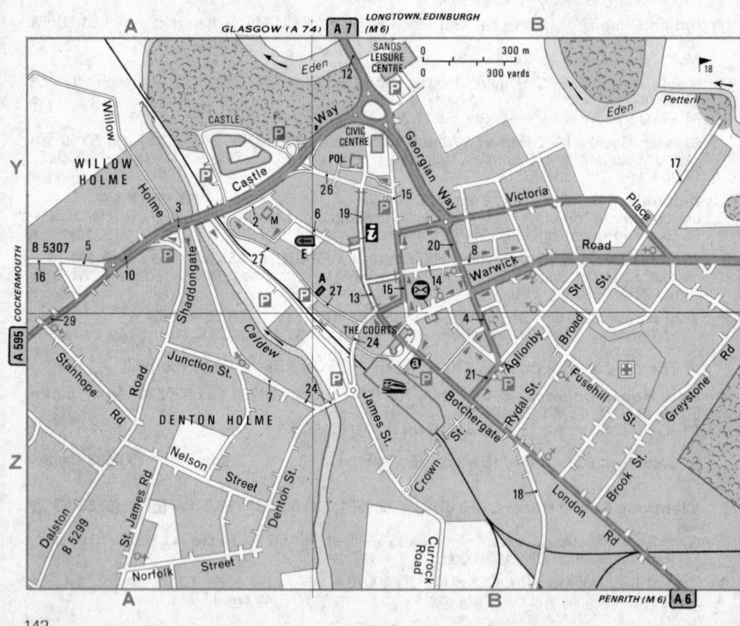

CARLISLE Cumbria 401 402 L 19 – pop. 72 206 – ECD : Thursday – ☎ 0228.

See : Cathedral★ (12C-14C) AY **E** – Tithe Barn★ BY **A**.

Envir. : Hadrian's Wall★★ (starts NE : 1½ m.) by B 5307 AY.

Aglionby ☎ 513303, E : ½ m. by A 69 BY – Stoney Holme ☎ 34856, E : 1 m. by St. Aidan's Rd BY.

☎ 022 873 (Crosby-on-Eden) 641, Telex 64476 by A 7 BY and B 6264 – **Terminal** : Bus Station, Lowther Street.

☎ 49433.

The Old Town Hall, Greenmarket ☎ 512444.

London 317 – Blackpool 95 – Edinburgh 101 – Glasgow 100 – Leeds 124 – Liverpool 127 – Manchester 122 – Newcastle-upon-Tyne 59.

Plan opposite

Cumbrian, Court Square, CA1 1QY, ☎ 31951, Telex 64287, Fax 47799 – rm ☎ – 300. AE VISA BZ **a**
M 12.50/16.50 **st.** and a la carte 4.50 – 7.50 – **105 rm** 70.00/85.00 **st.** – SB (weekends only) 76.00 **st.**

Cumbria Park, 32 Scotland Rd, CA3 9DG, N : 1 m. on A 7 ☎ 22887, Fax 514796 – ☎ – 100. AE VISA. by A 7 BY
closed 25 and 26 December – **M** 10.25/13.50 **t.** and a la carte 5.25 – **51 rm** 50.00/95.00 **t.** – SB (October-April) (weekends only) 71.00 **st.**

Swallow Hilltop, London Rd, CA1 2PQ, SE : 1 m. on A 6 ☎ 29255, Telex 64292, Fax 25238, – rm ☎ – 500. AE VISA by A 6 BZ
M 8.00/14.75 **st.** and a la carte 4.50 – **92 rm** 68.00/80.00 **st.**

at Kingstown N : 3 m. by A7 at junction 44– BY – of M 6 – ✉ ☎ 0228 Carlisle :

Crest (T.H.F.), Park House Rd, Kingstown, CA4 0HR, on A 7 ☎ 31201, Telex 64201, Fax 43178, – rm ☎ – 60. AE VISA
M *(closed Saturday lunch)* 8.25/14.95 **t.** and a la carte – 7.95 – **94 rm** 70.00/96.00 **t.** – SB (weekends only) 86.00/92.00 **st.**

at Crosby-on-Eden NE : 4½ m. by A 7 – BY – on B 6264 – ✉ Carlisle – ☎ 022 873 Crosby-on-Eden :

Crosby Lodge with rm, High Crosby, CA6 4QZ, ☎ 618, Fax 428, ←, « 18C country mansion », – rest ☎ . AE VISA.
closed 24 December-20 January – **M** *(closed Sunday dinner)* 17.75/25.00 **t.** and a la carte 5.00 – **11 rm** 60.00/80.00 **t.** – SB (October-April) (weekends only) 92.50/97.50 **st.**

at Faugh E : 8¼ m. by A 69 – BY – ✉ Carlisle – ☎ 022 870 Hayton :

String of Horses Inn, Heads Nook, CA4 9EG, ☎ 297, Fax 675, « Elaborately furnished 17C inn », heated – rest ☎ . AE VISA.
Accomodation closed 24 and 25 December – **M** *(closed Saturday lunch)* 9.95/14.95 **t.** and a la carte 3.50 – **14 rm** 60.00/150.00 **t.** – SB (October-April) 80.00/102.00 **st.**

at Wetheral SE : 6¼ m. by A 6 – BZ – ✉ Carlisle – ☎ 0228 Wetheral :

Crown (Best Western), CA4 8ES, on B 6263 ☎ 61888, Telex 64175, Fax 61637, , squash – rm ☎ – 175. AE VISA
M *(closed Saturday lunch)* 22.00/18.00 **st.** and a la carte 4.25 – **48 rm** 73.00/90.00 **st.**, **1 suite** 101.00 **st.**

CITROEN, SAAB Willowholme Estate ☎ 26617
FORD Hardwick Circus ☎ 24234
LADA Cecil St. ☎ 25051
LANCIA, SUZUKI King St. ☎ 47722
MERCEDES-BENZ Victoria Viaduct ☎ 41111
NISSAN Lowther St. ☎ 25555
RENAULT Church St. ☎ 22423
ROVER, DAIMLER-JAGUAR Rosehill Estate ☎ 24387
TOYOTA Lonsdale St. ☎ 42041
VAUXHALL-OPEL Viaduct Estate ☎ 29401
VOLVO Victoria Viaduct ☎ 28234

ATS Rosehill Ind. Est., Montgomery Way. ☎ 25277

CARLYON BAY Cornwall 403 F 33 – see St. Austell.

CARMARTHEN **(CAERFYRDDIN)** Dyfed 403 G 28 – pop. 13 860 – ECD : Thursday – ☎ 0267.

Blaenycoed Rd ☎ 87214, NW : 4 m.

Lammas St. ☎ 231557 (summer only).

London 220 – Fishguard 45 – Swansea 27.

Ivy Bush Royal (T.H.F.), 11-13 Spilman St., SA31 1LG, ☎ 235111, Telex 48520, Fax 234914, – rm ☎ – 200. AE VISA
M 8.50/12.50 **st.** and a la carte 4.95 – 7.00 – **76 rm** 58.00/72.00 **st.**, **1 suite** 95.00 **st.** – SB (weekends only and July-September) 64.00/90.00 **st.**

P.T.O. →

at Felingwm Uchaf NE : 7 m. by A 40 on B 4310 – ✉ ☎ 0267 Carmarthen :

Plough Inn, SA32 7PR, ℘ 290220 – TV P. AE VISA.
closed 25 and 26 December – **M** *(closed Sunday dinner)* 15.00/20.00 **st.** and a la cart
4.00 – **5 rm** 28.00/45.00 **st.**

at Nantgaredig E : 5 m. on A 40 – ✉ Carmarthen – ☎ 0267.

Four Seasons, Cwmtwrch Farm with rm, SA32 7NY, N : ¼ m. on B 4310 ℘ 29023
park – rest TV P
M (dinner only) 15.50 **st.** 3.00 – **6 rm** 28.00/40.00 **st.** – SB (October-June except Ban
Holidays) 60.00/62.00 **st.**

FIAT, VAUXHALL Pensarn ℘ 236633
FORD The Bridge ℘ 236482
NISSAN Penguin Court ℘ 237356
TOYOTA Priory St. ℘ 234171
ATS Pensarn Rd ℘ 236996/235456

CARNFORTH Lancs. 402 L 21 – pop. 7 140 – ECD : Thursday – ☎ 0524.
♦London 249 – ♦Blackpool 31 – ♦Carlisle 59 – Lancaster 6.

New Capernwray Farm, Capernwray, LA6 1AD, NE : 3 m. by B 6254 ℘ 734284,
– TV P
closed Christmas and New Year – **M** 16.50 **st.** – **3 rm** 34.50/53.00 **st.** – SB (November
April) (except Easter) 73.80/77.40 **st.**

CARTMEL Cumbria 402 L 21 – see Grange-over-Sands.

CAS-BACH = Castleton.

CAS-BLAIDD = Wolf's Castle.

CASNEWYDD-AR-WYSG = Newport.

CASTELL-NED = Neath.

CASTLE ACRE Norfolk 404 W 25 – pop. 777 – ☎ 076 05.
See : Priory★★ (ruins 11C - 14C) *AC.*
♦London 101 – King's Lynn 20 – ♦Norwich 31.

Hotels see : King's Lynn NW : 20 m., ***Swaffham*** S : 4 m.

CASTLE ASHBY Northants. 404 R 27 – pop. 142 – ✉ Northampton – ☎ 060 129 Yardle
Hastings.
♦London 76 – Bedford 15 – Northampton 11.

Falcon, NN7 1LF, ℘ 200, Telex 312207, Fax 673, – TV ☎ P. AE VISA.
M a la carte 16.10/25.95 **t.** 4.90 – **14 rm** 50.00/100.00 **st.** – SB (weekends only) 80.00
100.00 **st.**

CASTLE CARY Somerset 403 404 M 30 – pop. 2 599 – ECD : Thursday – ☎ 0963.
♦London 125 – ♦Bristol 28 – Taunton 31 – Yeovil 13.

George, Market Pl., BA7 7AH, ℘ 50761 – TV ☎ P. VISA
M *(closed Sunday and Monday)* (dinner only and Sunday lunch)/dinner 16.00 **t.** 4.00 –
16 rm 35.00/65.00 **st.** – SB 80.00/90.00 **st.**

Bond's with rm, Ansford Hill, Ansford, BA7 7JP, N : ¾ m. on A 371 ℘ 50464, – TV ☎
P. VISA.
closed 1 week at Christmas – **M** *(closed to non-residents Sunday and Monday)* (dinne
only) 16.95 **t.** and a la carte 3.50 – **7 rm** 36.00/68.00 **t.** – SB (except Christmas) 78.00
99.00 **st.**

CASTLE COMBE Wilts. 403 404 N 29 **The West Country G.** – pop. 347 – ✉ Chippenham –
☎ 0249.
See : Site★★.
♦London 110 – ♦Bristol 23 – Chippenham 6.

Manor House, SN14 7HR, ℘ 782206, Telex 449931, Fax 782159, « Part 14C mano
house in park », heated, , , – TV ☎ P – 25. AE VISA
M 16.50/35.00 **st.** and a la carte 7.00 – 7.50 – **35 rm** 95.00/200.00 **st.**, **1 suite** 150.00
250.00 **st.** – SB (November-March) (except Christmas-New Year and Easter) 150.00
210.00 **st.**

at Ford S : 1 ¾ m. – ✉ Chippenham – ☎ 0249 Castle Combe :

White Hart Inn, SN14 8RP, ℘ 782213, heated – TV P
11 rm.

at Nettleton Shrub W : 2 m. by B 4039 on Nettleton rd (Fosse Way) – ✉ Chippenham – ☎ 0249 Castle Combe :

Fosse Farmhouse, SN14 7NJ, ☎ 782286, – TV P. AE VISA
February-October – **M** 20.50 **t.** 3.50 – **6 rm** 35.00/75.00 **st.** – SB (except Bank Holidays) 110.00/125.00 **st.**

CASTLE DONINGTON Leics. 402 403 404 P 25 – pop. 5 854 – ✉ ☎ 0332 Derby.

East Midlands, ☎ 810621, Telex 37543.

London 123 – Birmingham 38 – Leicester 23 – Nottingham 13.

Donington Thistle (Mt. Charlotte Thistle), East Midlands Airport, DE7 2SH, SE : 3¼ m. by B 6540 on A 453 ☎ 850700, Telex 377632, Fax 850823, – rm rest TV ☎ P – 220. AE VISA
M 10.00/14.00 a la carte – 7.25 – **106 rm** 68.00/95.00 **st.**, **4 suites** 140.00 **st.** – SB 94.00 **st.**

Donington Manor, High St., DE7 2PP, ☎ 810253, Fax 850330 – TV ☎ P – 80. AE VISA
closed 27 to 30 December – **M** 6.50/8.50 **st.** and a la carte 3.50 – **37 rm** 49.50/65.00 **st.**

at Isley Walton SW : 1¾ m. by B 6540 on A 453 – ✉ Derby – ☎ 0332 Melbourne :

Park Farmhouse, Melbourne Rd, DE7 2RN, W : ¾ m. ☎ 862409, – TV ☎ P. AE VISA
closed 10 days Christmas-New Year – **M** a la carte 7.60/10.90 3.25 – **8 rm** 39.00/49.00 **st.**

VAUXHALL-OPEL Station Rd ☎ 810221

CASTLE HEDINGHAM Essex 404 V 28 – pop. 1 193 – ✉ Halstead – ☎ 0787.

London 53 – Cambridge 30 – Chelmsford 20 – Colchester 18.

Old School House, St. James St., CO9 3EW, ☎ 61370, – TV.
closed 25 December-1 January – **M** (by arrangement) 12.50 **st.** – **3 rm** 25.00/45.00 **s.** – SB 55.00/65.00 **st.**

CASTLETON Derbs 402 403 404 O 23 – pop. 881 – ECD : Wednesday – ✉ Sheffield (South Yorks.) – ☎ 0433 Hope Valley.

Envir. : Blue John Caverns★ *AC*, W : 1 m.

London 181 – Derby 49 – Manchester 30 – Sheffield 16 – Stoke-on-Trent 39.

Ye Olde Nags Head, S30 2WH, ☎ 20248, Fax 21604 – TV ☎ P. AE VISA.
M 10.55/15.50 **t.** and a la carte – **8 rm** -/80.00 **t.**

CASTLETON (CAS-BACH) Gwent 403 K 29 – see Cardiff (South Glam.).

CASTLETON North Yorks. 402 R 20 – ✉ Whitby – ☎ 0286 Guisborough.

London 258 – Middlesbrough 18 – York 61.

Moorlands, 55 High St., YO21 2DB, ☎ 660206, – rest TV P.
closed January and February – **M** a la carte 5.55/13.15 **t.** – **10 rm** 17.00/38.00 **t.**

CATLOWDY Cumbria 401 402 L 18 – ✉ Carlisle – ☎ 022 877 Nicholforest.

London 333 – Carlisle 16 – Dumfries 36 – Hawick 31 – Newcastle 65.

Bessietown Farm, CA6 5QP, ☎ 219, , park – P.
M (by arrangement) 11.00 **st.** – **5 rm** 22.50/75.00 **t.** – SB (November-February) (except Sunday, Christmas and New Year) 54.00/75.00 **st.**

CAWSTON Norfolk 404 X 25 – pop. 1 218 – ✉ ☎ 0603 Norwich.

London 122 – Cromer 15 – King's Lynn 42 – Norwich 13.

Grey Gables, Norwich Road, NR10 4EY, S : 1 m. ☎ 871259, – rest TV ☎ P. VISA
closed 25 and 26 December – **M** (lunch by arrangement)/dinner 20.00 **t.** 5.50 – **6 rm** 36.00/52.00 **t.** – SB 54.00/62.00 **st.**

CEINEWYDD = New Quay.

CHADDESLEY CORBETT Heref. and Worc. 403 404 N 26 –see Kidderminster.

CHADLINGTON Oxon. 403 404 P 28 – pop. 749 – ☎ 060 876.

♦London 74 – Cheltenham 32 – ♦Oxford 18 – Stratford-upon-Avon 25.

Manor ⛰, OX7 3LX, ☎ 711, ≤, 🌳, park – TV ☎ P. ⬚ VISA. ✗
M (dinner only) 24.50 **st.** 🍷 3.75 – **7 rm** ☐ 70.00/120.00 **st.**

Chadlington House, OX7 3LZ, ☎ 437, 🌳 – ⊁ rest TV P. ⬚ VISA. ✗
closed January and February – **M** (dinner only) 19.50 **t.** 🍷 4.00 – **11 rm** ☐ 25.00/100.00 **t.** – SB 75.00/90.00 **st.**

CHAGFORD Devon 403 I 31 **The West Country G.** – pop. 1 400 – ECD : Wednesday – ☎ 0647.

Envir. : Castle Drogo★ *AC*, NE : 2 m.

♦London 218 – Exeter 17 – ♦Plymouth 28.

Thornworthy House ⛰, Thornworthy, TQ13 8EY, SW : 3 m. by Fernworthy rd on Thornworthy rd ☎ 433297, ≤, « Country house atmosphere », 🌳, park, 🎾 – P
M (dinner only) 17.50 **t.** 🍷 3.00 – **6 rm** ☐ 30.00/65.00 **t.**

Claremont, 13 Mill St., TQ13 8AW, ☎ 433304 – TV 🚗. ✗
M 12.50 – **5 rm** ☐ 18.00/42.00.

Torr House ⛰, Thorn, TQ13 8DX, SW : 1 ½ m. by Fernworthy rd off Thornworthy rd ☎ 432228, 🌳 – ⊁ rest P. ⬚ AE VISA. ✗
M (dinner only) 12.50 **st.** 🍷 3.85 – **5 rm** ☐ 23.00/45.00 **t.** – SB (except Bank Holidays) 67.50/78.00 **st.**

at Sandy Park NE : 2 ¼ m. on A 382 – ✉ ☎ 0647 Chagford :

Mill End, TQ13 8JN, on A 382 ☎ 432282, Fax 433106, « Country house with water mill », 🎣, 🌳 – TV ☎ 🚗 P. ⬚ AE ◑ VISA
closed 12 to 22 December and 10 to 20 January – **M** (lunch by arrangement)/dinner 25.00 **t.** 🍷 5.00 – ☐ 8.50 – **17 rm** 30.00/65.00 **t.**

Great Tree (Best Western) ⛰, TQ13 8JS, on A 382 ☎ 432491, ≤, « Country house atmosphere », 🌳, park – ⊁ rest TV ☎ P. ⬚ AE ◑ VISA
M (bar lunch)/dinner 25.00 **st.** 🍷 3.50 – **12 rm** ☐ 44.00/88.00 **st.** – SB 96.00/110.00 **st.**

at Easton Cross NE : 1 ½ m. on A 382 – ✉ ☎ 064 73 Chagford :

Easton Court, TQ13 8JL, ☎ 433469, « 15C thatched house », 🌳 – TV ☎ P. ⬚ AE VISA
closed January – **M** *(dinner only)* 22.50 **t.** 🍷 2.95 – **7 rm** ☐ 46.00/68.00 **t.** – SB (except August, September and Bank Holiday weekends) 85.00/95.00 **st.**

CHALE I.O.W. – see Wight (Isle of).

CHALFONT ST.PETER Bucks. 404 S 29 – pop. 14 135 – ☎ 024 07.

⛳18 Harewood Downs, Cokes Lane, Chalfont St Giles ☎ 0494 (Chalfont St Giles) 762308.

♦London 24 – ♦Oxford 43.

XXX **Water Hall,** Amersham Rd, SL9 OPA, N : ½ m. on A 413 ☎ 3430, Chinese (Peking) rest. – P. ⬚ AE ◑ VISA
closed 25 December-7 January – **M** 16.00 **t.** and a la carte 🍷 4.00.

CHANCERY (RHYDGALED) Dyfed 403 H 26 – see Aberystwyth.

CHAPELTOWN North Yorks. 402 403 404 P 23 – see Sheffield.

CHARINGWORTH Glos. – see Chipping Campden.

CHARLBURY Oxon. 403 404 P 28 – pop. 2 637 – ☎ 0608.

♦London 72 – ♦Birmingham 50 – ♦Oxford 15.

Bell (Best Western), Church St., OX7 3AP, ☎ 810278, Fax 811447 – TV ☎ P – 🏛 50. ⬚ AE ◑ VISA
M 17.00 **t.** (lunch) and a la carte 17.50/26.50 **t.** 🍷 4.00 – **14 rm** ☐ 50.00/75.00 **t.** – SB 98.00 **t.**

CHARLECOTE Warw. 403 404 P 27 – see Stratford-Upon-Avon.

CHARLTON West Sussex 404 R 31 – see Chichester.

CHARMOUTH Dorset 403 L 31 – pop. 1 121 – ECD : Thursday – ✉ Bridport – ☎ 0297.

♦London 157 – Dorchester 22 – Exeter 31 – Taunton 27.

White House, 2 Hillside, The Street, DT6 6PJ, ☎ 60411 – TV ☎ P. ⬚ VISA. ✗
March-November – **M** 17.50 **st.** (dinner) and a la carte 6.90/15.80 **st.** 🍷 4.75 – **7 rm** ☐ 38.50/77.00 **st.** – SB 92.00/96.00 **st.**

⌂ **Hensleigh,** Lower Sea Lane, DT6 6LW, ☏ 60830 – ⊭ rest TV Ⓟ
closed December and January – **M** 8.00 **st.** – **10 rm** ☕ 20.00/40.00 **st.** – SB (except summer) 48.00/54.00 **st.**

⌂ **Newlands House,** Stonebarrow Lane, DT6 6RA, ☏ 60212, ⛱ – ⊭ TV Ⓟ
March-October – **M** 9.40 **t.** 🌢 3.00 – **12 rm** ☕ 17.50/41.00 **t.**

CHARTHAM Kent 404 X 30 – see Canterbury.

CHARTHAM HATCH Kent 404 X 30 – see Canterbury.

CHEDINGTON Dorset 403 L 31 – pop. 96 – ✉ Beaminster – ☎ 093 589 Corscombe.

♦London 148 – Dorchester 17 – Taunton 25.

🏛 **Chedington Court** ⛰, DT8 3HY, ☏ 265, Fax 442, ⩽ countryside, « Country house in landscaped gardens », park – TV ☎ Ⓟ. ⊡ AE VISA. ✻
closed Christmas and January – **M** (bar lunch) (residents only)/dinner 26.50 **st.** 🌢 3.40 – **10 rm** ☕ (dinner included) 82.00/160.00 **st.** – SB 130.00/160.00 **st.**

CHELFORD Cheshire 402 403 404 N 24 – see Macclesfield.

CHELMSFORD Essex 404 V 28 – pop. 91 109 – ECD : Wednesday – ☎ 0245.

⛳18 Channels, Belsteads Farm Lane, Little Waltham ☏ 440005, NE : 3½ m. off A 130.

ℹ County Hall, Market Rd ☏ 283400/283339.

♦London 33 – ♦Cambridge 46 – ♦Ipswich 40 – Southend-on-Sea 19.

🏛 **Saracens Head,** High St., CM1 1BE, ☏ 262368, Fax 262418 – TV ☎ – 🎤 80. ⊡ AE ⓞ VISA
M 15.00 **st.** 🌢 3.25 – ☕ 6.25 – **18 rm** ☕55.00/90.00 **st.**

🏛 **South Lodge,** 196 New London Rd, CM2 0AR, ☏ 264564, Telex 99452, Fax 492827 – TV ☎ Ⓟ – 🎤 40. ⊡ AE ⓞ VISA
M a la carte 13.25/20.00 **st.** 🌢 4.00 – ☕ 2.00 – **41 rm** 55.00/75.00 **st.**

🏠 **County,** 29 Rainsford Rd, CM1 2QA, ☏ 491911, Fax 492762 – TV ☎ Ⓟ – 🎤 150. ⊡ AE ⓞ VISA
closed 27 to 30 December – **M** 11.00/14.00 **t.** and a la carte – **52 rm** ☕ 20.00/75.00 **t.**

⌂ **Tanunda** without rest., 217-219 New London Rd, CM2 0AJ, ☏ 354295, ⛱ – TV ☎ Ⓟ. ⊡ VISA
closed 2 weeks Christmas and 2 weeks summer – **20 rm** ☕ 25.00/50.00 **st.**

✗ **Rose of India,** 30 Rainsford Rd, CM1 2QD, ☏ 352990, Indian rest. – ⊡ ⓞ VISA
M a la carte 9.90/11.15 **t.** 🌢 4.30.

at Great Baddow SE : 3 m. by A 130 – ✉ ☎ 0245 Chelmsford :

🏛 **Pontlands Park** ⛰, West Hanningfield Rd, CM2 8HR, ☏ 76444, Telex 995256, Fax 478393, ⩽, ♨, 🏊, ⛱, park – TV ☎ Ⓟ – 🎤 45. ⊡ AE ⓞ VISA. ✻
closed 1 to 7 January and Bank Holiday Mondays – **M** *(closed lunch Monday and Saturday and Sunday dinner)* 28.00/37.00 **t.** – ☕ 10.00 – **16 rm** 67.00/106.00 **t.**, **1 suite** 106.00 **t.**

CITROEN Galley Wood ☏ 268366/269465
FIAT Colchester Rd ☏ 450308
FORD 39 Robjohns Rd ☏ 264111
MERCEDES-BENZ Water House Lane ☏ 252255
RENAULT Southend Rd, Sandon ☏ 71113
ROVER 74 Main Rd, Broomfield ☏ 440571
VAUXHALL-OPEL Eastern Approach ☏ 466333
VAUXHALL-OPEL Moulsham Lodge ☏ 351611
VOLVO Colchester Rd, Springfield ☏ 468151

Ⓜ ATS 375 Springfield Rd ☏ 257795
ATS Chelmer Village Centre, Springfield ☏ 465676
ATS Town Centre, Inchbonnie Rd, South Woodham Ferrers ☏ 324999

CHELSWORTH Suffolk 404 W 27 – pop. 133 – ✉ Ipswich – ☎ 0449 Bildeston.

♦London 68 – Colchester 21 – ♦Ipswich 16.

🍺 **Peacock Inn,** The Street, IP7 7HU, ☏ 740758 – TV Ⓟ. ✻
M (buffet lunch)/dinner 12.00 **t.** and a la carte 🌢 3.60 – **5 rm** ☕ 20.00/38.00.

CHELTENHAM Glos. 403 404 N 28 – pop. 87 188 – ECD : Wednesday and Saturday – ☎ 0242.

See : Site★.

Envir. : Elkstone (Parish Church : doorway★ and arches★ 12C) SE : 7 m. by A 435 A – Sudeley Castle★ (12C - 15C) *AC*, NE : 6 m. by A 46. A.

⛳18 Cleeve Hill ☏ 024 267 (Bishop's Cleeve) 2025, N : 3 m. by A 46. A – ⛳18 Cotswold Hills, Ullenwood ☏ 522421, S : 3 m. A.

ℹ 77 Promenade ☏ 522878.

♦London 99 – ♦Birmingham 48 – ♦Bristol 40 – Gloucester 9 – ♦Oxford 43.

CHELTENHAM

Street	Grid	No.
High Street	BC	
Pittville Street	C	26
Portland Street	C	27
Promenade (The)	BC	28
Regent Arcade Shopping Centre	C	
Winchcombe Street	C	38
Berkeley Street	C	4
Clarence Road	C	5
Clarence Street	C	6
Crescent Terrace	B	7
Deep Street	A	9
Dunalley Street	C	10
Henrietta Street	C	13
High Street (PRESTBURY)	A	14
Keynsham Road	C	15
Knapp Road	B	16
Montpellier Avenue	B	17
Montpellier Walk	B	18
North Street	C	20
Norwood Road	B	21
Oriel Road	C	22
Regent Street	C	29
Rodney Road	C	30
Royal Well Road	BC	32
St. Margaret's Road	C	33
Sandford Mill Road	C	34
Sandford Terrace	C	35

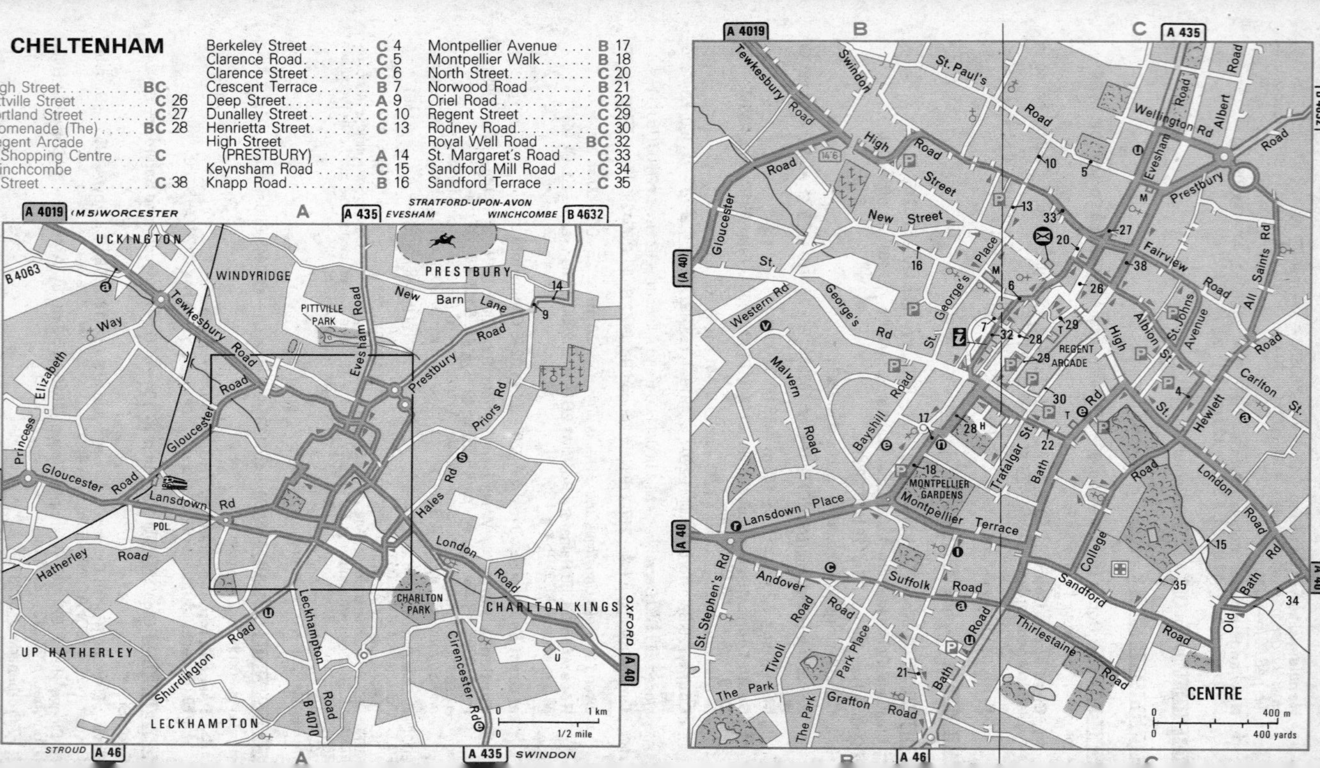

Queen's (T.H.F.), Promenade, GL50 1NN, ☏ 514724, Telex 43381, Fax 224145, – rm – 200. B n
M 17.50/27.50 **st.** and a la carte 4.50 – 7.60 – **77 rm** 80.00/100.00 **st.** – SB (weekends only) (except Christams) 120.00/140.00 **st.**

Golden Valley Thistle (Mt. Charlotte Thistle), Gloucester Rd, GL51 0TS, W : 2 m. on A 40 ☏ 232691, Telex 43410, Fax 221846, – rm rest – 220. by A 40 A
M 12.00/15.00 **t.** and a la carte 4.00 – 7.75 – **95 rm** 69.00/125.00 **st.**, **2 suites** 104.50/137.50 **st.** – SB 98.00/110.00 **st.**

Cheltenham Park, Cirencester Rd, Charlton Kings, GL53 8EA, ☏ 222021, Telex 437364, Fax 226935, – – 80. A e
M 25.00/30.00 **t.** and a la carte 4.40 – 8.00 – **41 rm** 78.00/220.00 **st.** – SB (weekends only) 96.00 **st.**

Lypiatt House, Lypiatt Rd, GL50 2QW, ☏ 224994, Fax 224996 – rest. B c
closed 22 December-3 January – **M** *(closed Saturday)* (dinner only) 16.00 **st.** – **10 rm** 35.00/68.00 **st.**

Stretton Lodge, Western Rd, GL50 3RN, ☏ 528724, – .
M (dinner only) (by arrangement) 12.50 **st.** 4.00 – **9 rm** 30.00/58.00 **st.** B v

Travel Inn, Tewkesbury Rd, Uckington, GL51 9SL, NW : 1 ¾ m. on A 4019 at junction with B 4063 ☏ 233847 – rm . A a
M (Beefeater grill) a la carte approx. 12.25 **t.** – 4.50 – **40 rm** -/27.50 **t.**

Lansdown (B.C.B.), Lansdown Rd, GL50 2LB, ☏ 522700 – B r
14 rm.

Hannaford's, 20 Evesham Rd, GL52 2AB, ☏ 515181 – . C u
M (by arrangement) 12.00 **st.** – **10 rm** 30.00/46.00 **st.**

Abbottslee, Priory Walk, GL52 6DU, ☏ 515255 – . C a
closed 6 January-11 February – **M** 9.00 **st.** 3.00 – **5 rm** 19.00/33.00 **st.**

Milton House without rest., 12 Royal Parade, Bayshill Rd, GL50 3AY, ☏ 582601, Fax 222326 – rm . B e
9 rm 28.75/48.00 **t.**

Beaumont House, 56 Shurdington Rd, GL53 0JE, ☏ 245986, – rest . A u
M (by arrangement) approx. 11.50 **t.** – **18 rm** 16.50/50.00 **st.** – SB (except summer) 50.00/73.00 **st.**

Hollington House, 115 Hales Rd, GL52 6ST, ☏ 519718, Fax 570280, – rm . A s
M (by arrangement) 9.95 **t.** 4.00 – **7 rm** 20.00/50.00 **t.**

Le Champignon Sauvage, 24-26 Suffolk Rd, GL50 2AQ, ☏ 573449 –
closed Saturday lunch, Sunday, 2 weeks June, 1 week Christmas-New Year, and Bank Holidays – **M** 24.85/25.95 **t.** 3.40. B a

Hussains, 37 Bath Rd., GL53 7HG, ☏ 226229, Indian rest. – C e

Finns, 143 Bath Rd, GL53 7LT, ☏ 232109. B u
closed Saturday lunch, Sunday and Bank Holiday Mondays – **M** 17.50/19.50 **t.**

Twelve, 12 Suffolk Par., GL50 2AB, ☏ 584544 – B i
closed Saturday lunch, Sunday dinner and Monday – **M** 9.95/19.75 **t.** and a la carte.

at Southam NE : 3 m. on B 4632– A – ✉ ☏ 0242 Cheltenham :

De La Bere (T.H.F), GL52 3NH, ☏ 237771, Telex 43232, Fax 236016, « Tudor manor house », heated, park, squash – rm .
M 12.00/18.00 **st.** and a la carte 5.00 – 8.00 – **56 rm** 70.00/90.00 **st.**, **1 suite** 110.00/120.00 **st.** – SB (weekends only) 100.00/110.00 **st.**

at Cleeve Hill NE : 4 m. on B 4632– A – ✉ Cheltenham – ☏ 0242 Bishop's Cleeve :

Rising Sun (Lansbury), GL52 3PX, ☏ 676281, Telex 437410, Fax 673069, ←, – – 50.
M 8.95/14.00 **t.** and a la carte – **24 rm** 63.00/76.00 **t.** – SB (weekends only) 76.00/92.00 **st.**

Redmond's with rm, GL52 3PR, ☏ 672017, ← – rest .
closed Sunday evening and first week January – **M** *(closed lunch Monday and Saturday and Sunday dinner)* 17.50/31.00 **st.** 4.00 – **4 rm** 45.00/65.00 **st.** – SB (weekdays only) 97.50 **st.**

at Shurdington SW : 3 ¾ m. on A 46 – A – ✉ ☏ 0242 Cheltenham :

Greenway, GL51 5UG, ☏ 862352, Fax 862780, ←, « Tastefully furnished Cotswolds country house, gardens », park – .
closed 27 December-11 January – **M** *(closed lunch Saturday and Bank Holidays)* 16.50/27.50 **t.** 4.50 – **18 rm** 95.00/195.00 **t.** – SB (except Christmas) 150.00/240.00 **st.**

Allards, Shurdington Rd, GL51 5XA, ☏ 862498, – .
M 12.00 **st.** – **11 rm** 21.00/48.00 **st.**

at Staverton W : 4 ¼ m. by A 40 and Staverton Airport rd – ✉ Cheltenham – ☎ 0452 Gloucester :

White House, Gloucester Rd, GL5 0FT, ☎ 713226, Telex 437382, Fax 857590 – TV ☎ P – 180. AE VISA. **M** 10.00/25.00 **st.** and a la carte 4.00 – 6.50 – **48 rm** 60.00/72.00 **st.**, **2 suites** 99.00 **st.**

CITROEN 16-28 Bath Rd ☎ 515391
FORD 71-93 Winchcombe St. ☎ 527061
HONDA 172 Leckhampton Rd ☎ 524348
LADA, PROTON Stoke Orchard ☎ 680428
LANCIA Swindon Rd ☎ 232167
MERCEDES-BENZ Princess Elizabeth Way ☎ 580777
MITSUBISHI 84 Fairview Rd ☎ 513880
RENAULT Montpellier Spa Rd ☎ 521651
ROLLS-ROYCE, BENTLEY Rutherford Way ☎ 515374
ROVER Princess Elizabeth Way ☎ 520441
SAAB, SUZUKI High St., Prestbury ☎ 224477
SEAT Charlton Kings ☎ 521131
SKODA Alderton ☎ 62220
SUBARU, ISUZU Bouncers Lane, Prestbury ☎ 235705
TOYOTA 38 Suffolk Rd ☎ 527778
VAUXHALL-OPEL 379 High St. ☎ 522666
VAUXHALL-OPEL Albion St. ☎ 525252
VOLVO Manor Rd ☎ 222400
VW-AUDI Oddington ☎ (0451) 30422
YUGO Coombe Hill ☎ 680817

ATS Chosen View Rd ☎ 521288
ATS 99-101 London Rd ☎ 519814

CHELWOOD Avon – see Bristol.

CHENIES Bucks. 404 S 28 – pop. 2 240 – ECD : Thursday – ✉ Rickmansworth (Herts.) – ☎ 092 78 Chorleywood.

♦London 30 – Aylesbury 18 – Watford 7.

Bedford Arms Thistle (Mt. Charlotte Thistle), WD3 6EQ, ☎ 3301, Telex 893939, Fax 4825, « 16C inn », – rm TV ☎ P. AE VISA
M a la carte 15.50/33.00 **t.** 6.00 – 7.90 – **10 rm** 68.00/85.00 **st.** – SB 76.00 **st.**

CHEPSTOW Gwent 403 404 M 29 – pop. 9 039 – ECD : Wednesday – ☎ 029 12 (4 & 5 fig.) or 0291 (6 fig.).

See : Castle★ (stronghold) *AC*.

18, 18 St Pierre ☎ 5261.

The Gatehouse, High St. ☎ 3772 (summer only).

♦London 131 – ♦Bristol 17 – ♦Cardiff 28 – Gloucester 34.

George (T.H.F.), Moor St., NP6 5DB, ☎ 625363, Fax 627418 – TV ☎ P – 40. AE VISA
M 8.50/15.00 **st.** and a la carte 4.50 – **15 rm** 55.00/70.00 **st.** – SB (weekends only) 84.00 **st.**

Beaufort, Beaufort Sq., NP6 5EP, ☎ 622497, Fax 627389 – TV ☎ P. AE VISA
M (bar lunch)/dinner 9.95 **st.** and a la carte 3.25 – **18 rm** 35.00/55.00 **st.** – SB (weekends only) 65.50 **st.**

Castle View, 16 Bridge St., NP6 5EZ, ☎ 70349, Fax 627397, – TV ☎. AE VISA
M 9.25 **st.** (lunch) and a la carte 2.75 – **11 rm** 44.50/66.00 **t.** – SB 68.00/80.00 **st.**

FORD Newport Rd ☎ 8155
PEUGEOT, TALBOT Tutshill ☎ 3131
ROVER Station Rd ☎ 3159

CHERITON BISHOP Devon 403 I 31 – pop. 587 – ECD : Wednesday – ✉ Exeter – ☎ 064 724.

♦London 211 – Exeter 10 – ♦Plymouth 51.

Old Thatch Inn, EX6 6HG, ☎ 24204 – TV P. VISA.
closed 3 to 16 November – **M** a la carte 6.00/8.75 **t.** 3.60 – **3 rm** 28.50/41.25 **t.**

CHESHAM Bucks. 404 S 28 – pop. 20 772 – ☎ 0494.

9 Maraud Grange, Chartridge ☎ 775919, NW : 2 m.

♦London 32 – Luton 25 – ♦Oxford 42.

Chesham Tandoori, 48 Broad St., HP5 3DX, ☎ 782669, Indian rest.

CHESTER Cheshire 402 403 L 24 – pop. 80 154 – ECD : Wednesday – ☎ 0244.

See : Site★★ – The Rows★★ – Cathedral★ – City Walls★.

Envir. : Chester Zoo★★ *AC*, N : 3 m. by A 5116.

18 Upton-by-Chester, Upton Lane ☎ 381183, by A 5116.
18 Vicars Cross, Littleton ☎ 335174, E : 2 m. by A 51.
18 Curzon Park ☎ 675130, S : 1 m.

ℹ Town Hall, Northgate St. ☎ 324324/317962 – Chester Visitor Centre, Vicars Lane ☎ 351609.

◆London 207 – Birkenhead 7 – ◆Birmingham 91 – ◆Liverpool 19 – ◆Manchester 40 – Preston 52 – ◆Sheffield 76 – ◆Stoke-on-Trent 38.

CHESTER

Bridge Street	3	Boughton	2	Lower Bridge Street	15
Eastgate Street	5	Frodsham Street	6	Nicholas Street	17
Northgate Street	18	Grosvenor Street	7	Parkgate Road	20
Watergate Street		Grosvenor Park Road	8	Pepper Street	21
		Handbridge	10	St. John Street	23
		Little St. John Street	12	St. Martins Way	24
		Liverpool Road	13	Vicar's Lane	25

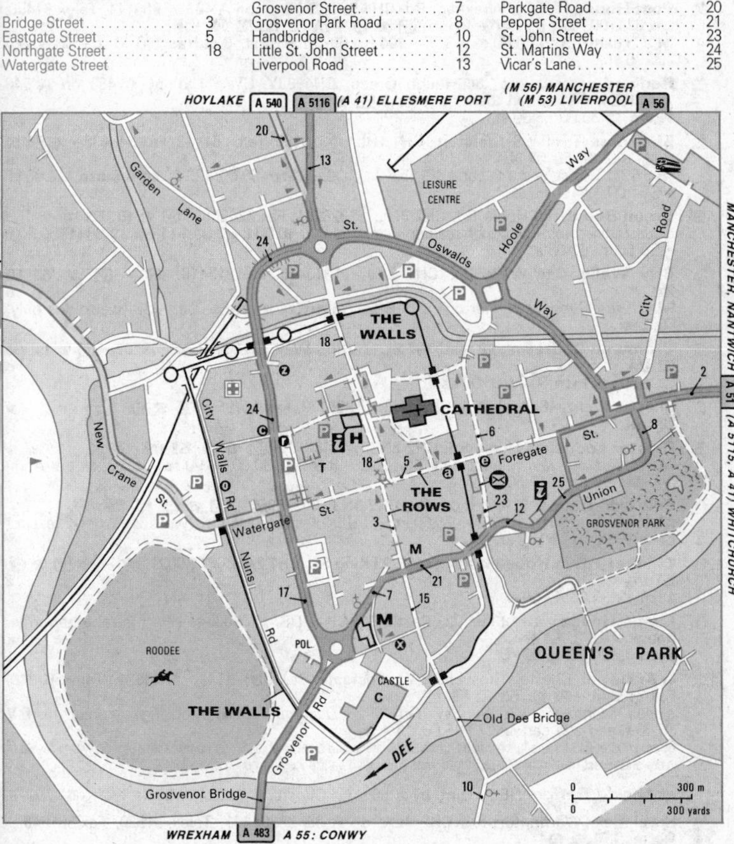

Chester Grosvenor, Eastgate St., CH1 1LT, ☎ 324024, Telex 61240, Fax 313246, – 200. AE VISA. a
closed 25 and 26 December – **M** – (see also **Arkle** below) – **La Brasserie** 12.50/17.50 **t.** and a la carte 6.50 – 8.50 – **82 rm** 110.00/185.00 **t.**, **3 suites** 225.00/325.00 **t.** – SB (weekends only) 135.00 **st.**

Crabwall Manor, Parkgate Rd, Mollington, CH1 6NE, NW : 2¼ m. on A 540 ☎ 851666, Telex 61220, Fax 851400, « Tastefully furnished manor of 16C origins », – rest – 90. AE VISA.
M 12.95/22.00 **t.** and a la carte 4.95 – 7.00 – **42 rm** 85.00/100.00 **t.**, **6 suites** 120.00/175.00 **t.** – SB (except Christmas and New Year) 137.00 **st.**

P.T.O. →

Mollington Banastre (Best Western), Parkgate Rd, CH1 6NN, NW : 2 m. on A 540 ℘ 851471, Telex 61686, Fax 851165, squash – rm – 250. AE VISA
M 10.50/17.50 **t.** and a la carte 8.95 – **62 rm** 73.00/95.00 **st.**, **2 suites** 105.00/125.00 **st.** – SB 102.00/112.00 **st.**

Chester International (Q.M.H.), Trinity St., CH1 2BD, ℘ 322330, Telex 61251, Fax 316118, – rm rest – 375. AE VISA r
M *(closed lunch Saturday and Bank Holidays)* 17.00/20.00 **st.** and a la carte 5.25 – **146 rm** 94.50/135.00 **st.**, **6 suites** 150.00/175.00 **st.** – SB (weekends only) 110.00 **st.**

Hoole Hall, Warrington Road, Hoole, CH2 3PD, NE : 2 m. on A 56 ℘ 350011, Telex 61292, Fax 320251 – rest – 100. AE VISA
M *(closed lunch Saturday and Bank Holidays)* 10.00/14.00 **t.** and a la carte 4.00 – **98 rm** 63.00/76.00 **t.**

Post House (T.H.F.), Wrexham Rd, CH4 9DL, S : 2 m. on A 483 ℘ 680111, Telex 61450, Fax 674100, – rm – 50. AE VISA
M a la carte 13.15/20.60 **st.** 3.75 – **104 rm** 69.00/79.00 **st.**, **3 suites** 110.00 **st.** – SB 80.00/100.00 **st.**

Redland without rest., 64 Hough Green, CH4 8JY, SW : 1 m. by A 483 on A 549 ℘ 671024, « Victorian town house » –
11 rm 35.00/55.00 **st.**

Blossoms (T.H.F.), St. John St., CH1 1HL, ℘ 323186, Telex 61113, Fax 346433 – – 100. AE VISA e
M 9.50/13.95 **st.** and a la carte 3.75 – 7.00 – **61 rm** 69.00/120.00 **st.**, **1 suite** 120.00 **st.** – SB 100.00/150.00 **st.**

Green Bough, 60 Hoole Rd, CH2 3NL, ℘ 326241, Fax 326265 – . VISA i
closed Christmas – **M** (lunch residents only)/dinner 10.00 **t.** 3.50 – **11 rm** 38.00/50.50 **t.** – SB 56.00/62.00 **st.**

City Walls, City Walls Rd, CH1 2LU, ℘ 313416, Fax 313416, – . AE VISA o
M *(closed Sunday)* (dinner only) 15.00 **t.** – **16 rm** 35.00/55.00 **t.** – SB (weekends only) 66.00 **st.**

Cromwell Court without rest., 5-7 St. Martin's Way, CH1 2NR, ℘ 349202 – . AE VISA c
4.50 – **11 rm** 30.00/50.00 **st.**

Chester Court, 48 Hoole Rd, CH2 3NL, ℘ 320779, Fax 44795 – v
20 rm.

Gloster Lodge, 44 Hoole Rd, CH2 3NL, ℘ 348410 – . VISA. v
M *(closed Sunday)* (dinner only) 10.50 **st.** – **8 rm** 30.00/36.50 **st.** – SB (October-April) (weekends only) 47.50 **st.**

Edwards House, 61-63 Hoole Rd, CH2 3NJ, ℘ 318055 – . VISA.
M 11.00 **st.** – **8 rm** 26.00/35.00 **st.** – SB (November-March) (weekends only) (except Bank Holidays) 50.00 **st.**

Chester Town House without rest., 23 King St., CH1 2AH, ℘ 350021, – . VISA z
4 rm 32.00/47.00 **st.**

Castle House without rest., 23 Castle St., CH1 2DS, ℘ 350354, « Part Elizabethan town house » – . VISA x
5 rm 20.00/40.00 **st.**

XXXX ✿ **Arkle** (at Chester Grosvenor H.), Eastgate St., CH1 1LT, ℘ 324024, Telex 61240, Fax 313246 – . AE VISA
closed Monday lunch, Sunday and 25-26 December – **M** (booking essential) 17.50/35.00 **t.** and a la carte 26.70/45.60 **t.** 4.75.
Spec. Lobster filled pasta leaves with Dublin Bay prawns and basil vinegar, French pot roasted pigeon with a royale of livers and forest mushrooms, Spiced red wine fruits with vanilla ice and Italian chocolate.

at Mickle Trafford NE : 2½ m. by A 56 – ✉ Chester – 0244 Mickle Trafford :

Royal Oak, Warrington Rd, CH2 4EX, on A 56 ℘ 301391, Telex 61536, Fax 301948 – rest
36 rm.

at Christleton E : 2 m. on A 41 – ✉ 0244 Chester :

Abbots Well, Whitchurch Rd, CH3 5QL, ℘ 332121, Telex 61561, Fax 335287, – rm – 200. AE VISA
M *(closed Saturday lunch)* 9.85/15.00 **st.** and a la carte 4.75 – 7.80 – **127 rm** 69.00/85.00 **st.** – SB 72.00/84.00 **st.**

at Rowton SE : 3 m. by A 41 – ✉ 0244 Chester :

Rowton Hall, Rowton Lane, CH3 6AD, ℘ 335262, Telex 61172, Fax 335464, – – 150. AE VISA
closed 25 and 26 December – **M** 10.00/14.00 **t.** and a la carte – **42 rm** 68.00/140.00 **t.** – SB (weekends only) 94.00/114.00 **st.**

MICHELIN Distribution Centre, Sandycroft Industrial Estate, Glendale Av., Sandycroft, Deeside, CH5 2QP, ☎ **537373, Fax 537453 by A 548**

BMW Chester Rd ☎ 311404
CITROEN Border House ☎ 682977
COLT Chester Rd ☎ 534347
DAIHATSU, MITSUBISHI Chester Rd ☎ 534347
DAIMLER-JAGUAR, ROLLS-ROYCE, RENAULT, LOTUS City Rd ☎ 390009
FIAT, SUZUKI, RENAULT Sealand Rd ☎ 390909
FORD Bridge Gate ☎ 20444
FORD Station Rd ☎ 813414
FORD Station Rd, Queensferry ☎ 813414
LADA Chester Rd ☎ 532322
MAZDA Sealand Rd ☎ 390000
MERCEDES-BENZ 36 Tarvin Rd ☎ 47441
NISSAN Hamilton Pl. ☎ 317661
ROVER Victoria Rd ☎ 381246
SAAB Western Av. ☎ 375744
SEAT 159 Boughton ☎ 310344
TOYOTA Welsh Rd ☎ 813633
VAUXHALL-OPEL Boughton ☎ 24611
VAUXHALL-OPEL 21-25 Garden Lane ☎ 46955
VAUXHALL-OPEL Parkgate Rd ☎ 372666
VOLVO Stadium Way ☎ 372199
VW-AUDI Sealand Rd ☎ 379889

ATS 7 Bumpers Lane, Sealand Trading Est. ☎ 375154

CHESTERFIELD Derbs. 402 403 404 P 24 – pop. 73 352 – ECD : Wednesday – ☎ 0246.

Envir. : Chatsworth★★★ : site★★, house★★★ (Renaissance), garden★★★ *AC*, W : 7 m. – Hardwick Hall★★ (16C) (Tapestries and embroideries★★) *AC*, SE : 8 m. – Bolsover Castle★ (17C) *AC*, E : 6 m. – Worksop (Priory Church : Norman nave★) NE : 14 m.

18 Tapton Park, Murray House, Crow Lane ☎ 475260.
18 Walton ☎ 279256, SW : 2 m. on A 263.
18 Murray House, Crow Lane ☎ 273887.
9 Stanedge, Walton Hay Farm ☎ 566156, SW : 5 m. by B 5057.

The Peacock Tourist Information and Heritage Centre, Low Pavement ☎ 207777.

London 152 – Derby 24 – Nottingham 25 – Sheffield 12.

Chesterfield (Best Western), Malkin St., S41 7UA, ☎ 271141, Telex 547492, Fax 220719, – TV ☎ P – 200. AE VISA
M 8.00/14.00 **st.** and a la carte 3.50 – **70 rm** 52.00/75.00 **st.**, **2 suites** 80.00 **st.** – SB (weekends only) 60.00/72.00 **st.**

AUDI-VW, PORSCHE Sheerbridge Ind Est. ☎ 260060
BMW Pottery Lane ☎ 208681
FIAT 300 Northwingfield Rd ☎ 850686
FORD Chatsworth Rd ☎ 209999
LADA 34 Chatsworth Rd ☎ 271029
ROVER 221 Sheffield Rd ☎ 220888
SEAT 361 Sheffield Rd ☎ 260383
SAAB, TOYOTA 2 Lockoford Lane ☎ 221100
VAUXHALL 464 Chatsworth Rd ☎ 279201
VAUXHALL Chesterfield Rd ☎ (0860) 295073
VAUXHALL, RENAULT Chesterfield Rd, Staveley ☎ 473286
VOLVO Whittington Moor ☎ 260100

ATS 512 Sheffield Rd ☎ 452281

In alta stagione, *e soprattutto nelle stazioni turistiche, è prudente prenotare con un certo anticipo.*
Avvertite immediatamente l'albergatore se non potete più occupare la camera prenotata.
Se scrivete ad un albergo all'estero, allegate alla vostra lettera un tagliando-risposta internazionale (disponibile presso gli uffici postali).

CHESTER-LE-STREET Durham 401 402 P 19 – pop. 34 776 – ECD : Wednesday – ☎ 0385 (6 fig.) or 091 (7 fig.).

Envir. : Lumley Castle★ (13C), E : 1 m. – Beamish (North of England open Air Museum★) *AC*, NW : 3 m.

18 Lumley Park ☎ 388 3218, E : 1 m. off B 1284 – 18 Roseberry Grange ☎ 370 0670, W : 3 m. on A 693.

London 275 – Durham 7 – Newcastle-upon-Tyne 8.

Lumley Castle, DH3 4NX, E : 1 m. on B 1284 ☎ 389 1111, Telex 537433, Fax 387 1437, « 13C castle », park – rm TV ☎ P
65 rm, **1 suite.**

MICHELIN Distribution Centre, Drum Rd Industrial Estate, Drum Rd, DH3 2AF, ☎ **410 7762**, Fax 492 0717

FORD 187 Front St. ☎ 388 4221
PEUGEOT Newfield ☎ 370 0355
ROVER Newcastle Rd ☎ 388 2267
VAUXHALL Hopgarth ☎ 388 0818

CHICHESTER West Sussex 404 R 31 – pop. 26 050 – ECD : Thursday – ☎ 0243.

See : Site★ – Cathedral★★ (11C-15C) BZ **A** – Market Cross★ BZ **B** – St. Mary's Hospital★ BY **D** – Pallant House★ BZ **E** – Mechanical Music and Doll Museum★, Church Rd.

Envir. : Fishbourne Roman Palace (mosaics★) *AC*, W : 2 m. AZ **R** – Weald and Downland open Air Museum★ N : 5 m. by A 286 AY.

18 Goodwood ☎ 774968, NE : 4½ m. off A 27 – 9 Golf Links Lane ☎ 602203, S : 7 m.

St. Peter's Market, West St. ☎ 775888.

London 69 – Brighton 31 – Portsmouth 18 – Southampton 30.

CHICHESTER

East Street . . . . BZ
North Street . . . . BYZ
South Street . . . . BZ

Birdham Road . . . . AZ 2
Bognor Road . . . . AZ 3
Cathedral Way . . . . AZ 4
Chapel Street . . . . BY 6
Chichester Arundel Road . . AY 7
Florence Road . . . . AZ 10
Hornet (The) . . . . BZ 12
Kingsham Road . . . . BZ 13
Lavant Road . . . . AY 14
Little London . . . . BY 15
Market Road . . . . BZ 16
Northgate . . . . BY 17
North Pallant . . . . BZ 19
Priory Lane . . . . BY 20
St. James's . . . . AZ 21
St. John's Street . . . . BZ 23
St. Martin's Square . . . . BY 24
St. Pancras . . . . BY 25
St. Paul's Road . . . . BY 27
Sherborne Road . . . . AZ 28
Southgate . . . . BZ 29
South Pallant . . . . BZ 31
Spitalfield Lane . . . . BY 32
Stockbridge Road . . . . AZ 33
Tower Street . . . . BY 35
Westhampnett Road . . . . . . AYZ 36

Dolphin and Anchor (T.H.F.), West St., PO19 1QE, ☎ 785121, Fax 533408 – ⇔ rm TV ☎ – 🚣 200. AE ⓪ VISA — BZ **a**
M 11.95/14.30 **st.** and a la carte 🍷 3.40 – ☕ 7.85 – **51 rm** 60.00/87.00 **st.** – SB 103.00/123.00 **st.**

Suffolk House, 3 East Row, PO19 1PD, ☎ 778899, Fax 787282, 🌳 – TV ☎. VISA. ✗ — BY **a**
M *(closed Sunday lunch)* (residents only) a la carte 15.20/21.95 **st.** 🍷 4.60 – **12 rm** ☕ 55.00/75.00 **st.**

Bedford, Southgate, PO19 1DP, ☎ 785766, Fax 533175 – TV ☎. AE ⓪ VISA — BZ **i**
M *(closed Sunday)* (dinner only) 12.50 **st.** 🍷 4.75 – **24 rm** ☕ 34.00/65.00 **st.** – SB (October-April) 66.00 **st.**

Crouchers Bottom, Birdham Rd, Apuldram, PO20 7EH, SW : 2 m. on A 286 AZ ☎ 784995, ←, 🌳 – ⇔ TV Ⓟ. VISA. ✗
closed 24 December-31 January – **M** (by arrangement) 17.00 **st.** 🍷 3.00 – **4 rm** ☕ 44.00/75.00 **st.**

Comme ça, 149 St. Pancras, PO19 1SH, ☎ 788724, French rest. – VISA — BZ **e**
closed Sunday dinner, Monday and Bank Holidays – **M** a la carte 16.05/19.65 **st.**

Confucius, 2 Cooper St., off South St., PO19 1EB, ☎ 783158, Chinese rest. — BZ **c**

at Charlton N : 6 ¼ m. by A 286 – AY – ✉ Chichester – ☎ 024 363 Singleton :

Woodstock House, PO18 0HU, ☎ 666, 🌳 – TV Ⓟ. ⓪ VISA
M (dinner only) a la carte 13.50/14.25 **t.** 🍷 3.50 – **11 rm** ☕ 32.50/64.00 **t.** – SB (except Bank Holidays) 65.00/75.00 **st.**

at Chilgrove N : 6 ½ m. by A 286 – AY – on B 2141 – ✉ Chichester – ☎ 0243.

White Horse Inn, 1 High St., PO18 9HX, ☎ 535219, Fax 359301, English rest. – Ⓟ. ⓪ VISA
closed Sunday dinner, Monday and 3 weeks February – **M** 15.00/22.50 **t.** 🍷 3.95.

at Goodwood NE : 3 ½ m. by A 27 – AY – on East Dean Rd – ✉ ☎ 0243 Chichester :

Goodwood Park, PO18 0QB, ☎ 775537, Telex 869173, Fax 533802, ≘s, 🏊, 🏌18, 🌳, 🎾, squash – TV ☎ ♿ Ⓟ – 🚣 100. AE ⓪ VISA
M 13.95/22.50 **st.** and a la carte 🍷 5.50 – **90 rm** ☕ 85.00/170.00 **st.** – SB (weekends only) 110.00/130.00 **st.**

at Bosham W : 4 m. by A 259 - AZ – ✉ ☎ 0243 Chichester :

Millstream, Bosham Lane, PO18 8HL, ☎ 573234, Fax 573459, 🌳 – TV ☎ Ⓟ. AE ⓪ VISA
M 14.80/21.00 **t.** 🍷 4.50 – **29 rm** ☕ 55.00/105.00 **t.** – SB 102.00/120.00 **st.**

Wishing Well Tandoori, Bosham Roundabout, PO18 8GP, N : ¾ m. on A 259 ☎ 572234, Indian rest. – Ⓟ. AE ⓪ VISA
closed Christmas Day – **M** 15.00/30.00 **t.** and a la carte 🍷 5.95.

FIAT Terminus Rd Ind Est ✆ 784844
FIAT Tangmere By-Pass (A 27) ✆ 773855
FORD The Hornet ✆ 788100
MERCEDES-BENZ Quarry Lane ✆ 776111
PEUGEOT-TALBOT 113 The Hornet ✆ 782293
RENAULT Delling Lane, Bosham ✆ 573271
ROVER Westhampnett Rd ✆ 781331
VAUXHALL-OPEL, NISSAN, CITROEN City Service Centre, Terminus Rd ✆ 774321
VW-AUDI 51-54 Bognor Rd ✆ 787684

ATS Terminus Rd Ind Est. ✆ 773100

CHIDDINGFOLD Surrey 404 S 30 – pop. 2 209 – 0428 Wormley.

◆London 45 – ◆Brighton 40 – Guildford 12.

XXX **Crown Inn** with rm, The Green, Petworth Rd, GU8 4TX, ✆ 682255, « 13C inn » – TV ☎ P. AE VISA
M 16.50 **t.** (lunch) and a la carte 15.90/23.70 **t.** 4.00 – 4.00 – **7 rm** 55.00/75.00 **st.**, **1 suite** 90.00 **st.**.

CHIDEOCK Dorset 403 L 31 – see Bridport.

CHILCOMPTON Somerset 403 404 M 30 – pop. 1 676 – ECD : Saturday – ✉ Bath – 0761 Stratton-on-the-Fosse.

◆London 125 – ◆Bristol 17 – Taunton 35.

Court, The Broadway, BA3 4SA, W : 1 ¼ m. on B 3139 ✆ 232237, – TV ☎ P
10 rm.

CHILGROVE West Sussex 404 R 31 – see Chichester.

CHILLINGTON Devon 403 I 33 – see Kingsbridge.

CHINNOR Oxon. 404 R 28 – pop. 5 432 – 0494 High Wycombe.

◆London 45 – ◆Oxford 19.

X **Sir Charles Napier Inn**, Sprigg's Alley, by Bledlow Ridge rd, OX9 4BX, SE : 2 ½ m. ✆ 483011, – P. AE VISA
closed Sunday dinner and Monday – **M** 15.50 **t.** (lunch) and a la carte 21.00/26.00 **t.** 4.50.

CHIPPENHAM Wilts. 403 404 N 29 **The West Country G.** – pop. 21 325 – ECD : Wednesday – 0249.

See : Yelde Hall★ *AC*.

Envir. : Biddestone★, W : 4 ½ m. – Sheldon Manor★ *AC*, W : 1 ½ m. – Bowood House★ *AC* (Library ≤★ of the Park) SE : 5 m.

18 Malmesbury Rd ✆ 652040.

The Neeld Hall, High St. ✆ 657733.

◆London 106 – ◆Bristol 27 – ◆Southampton 64 – Swindon 21.

Angel (Q.M.H.), 8 Market Pl., SN15 3HD, ✆ 652615, Fax 443210 – TV ☎ P – 50. AE VISA
M *(closed Saturday lunch)* 9.50/11.95 **t.** 5.00 – **44 rm** 55.00/95.00 **t.**

CITROEN Bristol Rd ✆ 444000
FIAT New Rd ✆ 655757
FORD Cocklebury Rd ✆ 653255
RENAULT London Rd ✆ 651131
SAAB London Rd ✆ 655871
TOYOTA London Rd ✆ 444888
VAUXHALL-OPEL 16-17 The Causeway ✆ 654321
VOLVO Malmesbury Rd ✆ 652016

ATS Cocklebury Rd ✆ 653541

CHIPPERFIELD Herts. 404 ㊷ – pop. 1 764 – ECD : Wednesday – ✉ 0923 Kings Langley.

◆ London 27 – Hemel Hempstead 5 – Watford 6.

Two Brewers (T.H.F.), The Common, WD4 9BS, ✆ 265266, Fax 261884 – TV ☎ P. AE VISA
M 13.50/17.50 **st.** and a la carte 4.75 – 7.00 – **20 rm** 75.00/95.00 **st.** – SB (weekends only) 80.00/84.00 **st.**

CHIPPING Lancs. 402 M 22 – pop. 1 376 – ✉ Preston – 0995.

◆London 233 – Lancaster 30 – ◆Leeds 54 – ◆Manchester 40 – Preston 12.

Gibbon Bridge Country House, PR3 2TQ, E : 1 m. on Clitheroe rd ✆ 61456, Fax 61277, ≤, – TV ☎ P. VISA.
M 8.00/14.00 **t.** and a la carte – **31 rm** 50.00/120.00 **t.** – SB 65.00/100.00 **st.**

CHIPPING CAMPDEN Glos. 403 404 O 27 – pop. 1 936 – ECD : Thursday – 0386 Evesham.

See : High Street★.

Envir. : Hidcote Manor Garden★★ *AC*, NE : 2 ½ m.

Woolstaplers Hall Museum, High St. ✆ 840289 (summer only).

◆London 93 – Cheltenham 21 – ◆Oxford 37 – Stratford-upon-Avon 12.

Cotswold House, The Square, GL55 6AN, 840330, Fax 840310, « Attractively converted Regency townhouse, staircase », – rest. closed 25 and 26 December – **M** (dinner only and Sunday lunch)/dinner 21.50 **t.** – **15 rm** 50.00/145.00 **t.** – SB 90.00/158.50 **st.**

Seymour House, High St., GL55 6AH, 840429, Fax 840369, « 100 year old grapevine in restaurant » – .
M 12.50/15.00 **st.** and a la carte 4.75 – 6.50 – **13 rm** 50.00/80.00 **st.**, **3 suites** 110.00/130.00 **st.** – SB (except 11 to 13 March, Christmas and New Year) 104.00/110.00 **st.**

Noel Arms, High St., GL55 6AT, 840317, Fax 841136 – .
M (bar lunch Monday to Saturday)/dinner 15.00 **t.** and a la carte 4.25 – **18 rm** 47.50/90.00 **t.** – SB 80.00/90.00 **st.**

Caminetto, Old Kings Arms Pantry, High St., GL55 6HR, 840934, Italian rest. – *closed Monday lunch, Sunday and 3 weeks March-April* – **M** a la carte 9.65/18.90 **t.** 4.25.

at Mickleton N : 3 ¼ m. by B 4035 and B 4081 on B 4632 – Chipping Campden – 0386 Mickleton :

Three Ways, GL55 6SB, 438429, Fax 438118, – – 60.
M (bar lunch Monday to Saturday)/dinner 16.50 **t.** – **40 rm** 39.00/72.00 **t.**

at Charingworth E : 3¼ m. by B 4081 and B 4085 – 038678 Paxford :

Charingworth Manor, GL55 6NS, on B 4085 555, Telex 333444, Fax 353, ←, « Early 14C manor house with Jacobean additions and 17C courtyard », , park – – 30.
M 15.50/24.50 **st.** and a la carte 4.50 – **18 rm** 80.00/125.00 **t.**, **1 suite** 195.00 **st.** – SB (except Christmas and Bank Holidays) 132.00/194.00 **st.**

at Broad Campden S : 1 ¼ m. by B 4081 – Chipping Campden – 0386 Evesham :

Malt House, GL55 6UU, 840295, Fax 841334, – .
closed 24 December-1 January – **M** *(closed Sunday)* (dinner only) 25.00 **t.** – **5 rm** 20.00/80.00 **t.**

CITROEN Sheep St. 840221
FORD High St. 840213
VAUXHALL Burford Rd 2461

Keine Aufnahme inden Michelin-Führer durch
– falsche Information oder
– Bezahlung!

CHIPPING NORTON Oxon 403 404 P 28 – 0608.

Southcombe 2383.

London 77 – Birmingham 44 – Gloucester 36 – Oxford 21.

Vittles, 7 Horse Fair, OX7 5AL, 644490.
closed Sunday and 25 January-7 February – **M** 12.50 **t.** and a la carte 4.00.

CHIPSTEAD Surrey 404 T 30 – pop. 7 177 (inc. Hooley and Woodmanster – 0737 Burgh Heath.

London 15 – Reigate 6.

Dene Farm, Outwood Lane, CR3 3NP, on B 2032 552661, – .
closed Saturday lunch, Sunday dinner, 26 December-8 January and 29 March – **M** 23.50/29.50 **t.** 5.00.

BMW Outwood Lane 556789

CHISELDON Wilts. 403 404 O 29 – see Swindon.

CHISLEHAMPTON Oxon. 404 Q 28 – Oxford – 0865 Stadhampton.

London 55 – Oxford 7.

Coach and Horses, OX9 7UX, 890255 –
9 rm.

CHITTLEHAMHOLT Devon 403 I 31 – pop. 259 – Umberleigh – 076 94.

London 216 – Barnstaple 14 – Exeter 28 – Taunton 45.

Highbullen, EX37 9HD, 561 (from Spring : 540561), Fax 492 (from Spring : 540492), ←, , , heated, , , , , park, , squash – rest.
M (bar lunch)/dinner 16.50 **st.** 4.00 – 3.00 – **35 rm** 45.00/90.00 **st.**

CHOLLERFORD Northumb. 401 402 N 18 – Hexham – 0434 Humshaugh.

London 303 – Carlisle 36 – Newcastle-upon-Tyne 21.

George (Swallow), NE46 4EW, 681611, Group Telex 53168, Fax 681727, ←, « Riverside gardens », , , – rm – 60.
M (buffet lunch Monday to Saturday)/dinner 14.95 **st.** and a la carte 5.50 – **50 rm** 63.00/97.00 **st.** – SB 85.00/96.00 **st.**

CHORLEY Lancs. 402 404 M 23 – pop. 33 465 – ECD : Wednesday – 025 72.

18 Duxbury Park 65380 – 18 Shaw Hill G & CC, Whittle-Le-Woods 69221, N : 1½m. – 18 Hall O'th'Hill Heath, Charnock 480263.

London 222 – Blackpool 30 – Liverpool 32 – Manchester 26.

Hartwood Hall, Preston Rd, PR6 7AX, on A 6 69966, Fax 41678 – TV – 100. VISA.
closed 25 to 29 December – **M** (bar lunch Saturday) a la carte 9.70/15.00 **st.** 5.50 – **22 rm** 40.00/60.00 **st.**

at Whittle-le-Woods N : 2 m. on A 6 – 025 72 Chorley :

Shaw Hill H. Golf and Country Club, Preston Rd, PR6 7PP, 69221, Fax 61223, 18 – TV – 60. VISA
M *(closed lunch Saturday and Bank Holidays)* 10.50/15.00 **t.** and a la carte – **22 rm** 77.00/87.50 **t.** – SB (weekends only) 80.00/135.00 **st.**

ATS 18 Westminster Rd 62000/65472

CHRISTCHURCH Dorset 403 404 O 31 – pop. 32 854 – ECD : Wednesday – 0202.

See : Site★ – Priory★.

Envir. : Hengistbury Head★ (★★) SW : 4 m. by B 3059.

9 Iford Bridge, Barrack Rd 473817, W: on A 5.

30 Saxon Sq. 471780.

London 111 – Bournemouth 6 – Salisbury 26 – Southampton 24 – Winchester 39.

King's Arms, 18 Castle St., BH23 1DT, 484117, Fax 471562 – rm TV – 200. VISA
M 7.65/12.00 **t.** 3.80 – **32 rm** 45.00/55.00 **t.** – SB (weekends only) 60.00/75.00 **st.**

Travel Inn, Somerford Rd, BH23 3QG, E : 2 m. by A 35 on B 3059 485376 – rm TV. VISA.
M (Beefeater grill) a la carte approx. 12.25 **t.** 4.30 – 4.50 – **38 rm** -/27.50 **t.**

Splinters, 12 Church St., BH23 1BW, 483454 – . VISA
closed Sunday – **M** (dinner only) a la carte 10.95/18.00 **t.** 4.25.

at Mudeford SE : 2 m. – 0202 Christchurch :

Avonmouth (T.H.F.), BH23 3NT, 483434, heated, – TV – 60
41 rm.

Waterford Lodge (Best Western), 87 Bure Lane, Friars CLiff, BH23 4DN, 0425 (Highcliffe) 272948, Fax 279130, – TV. VISA
M 9.95/14.50 **t.** and a la carte 3.50 – **20 rm** 47.00/80.00 **t.** – SB 80.00/98.00 **st.**

FORD Lyndhurst Rd 042 52 (Highcliffe) 71371
ROVER Highcliffe 042 52 (Highcliffe) 77703
VW-AUDI 105 Summerford Rd 476871

CHRISTLETON Cheshire 402 403 L 24 – see Chester.

CHURCHILL Oxon. 403 404 P 28 – pop. 421 – 0608 Kingham.

London 79 – Birmingham 46 – Cheltenham 29 – Oxford 23 – Swindon 31.

Forge House without rest., OX7 6NJ, 658173 – TV.
4 rm 25.00/50.00 **s.**

CHURCH STRETTON Shropshire 403 L 26 – pop. 2 932 – ECD : Wednesday – 0694.

18 Trevor Hill 722281.

Church St. 723133 (summer only).

London 166 – Birmingham 46 – Hereford 39 – Shrewsbury 14.

Mynd House, Ludlow Rd, Little Stretton, SY6 6RB, SW : 1 m. on B 4370 722212, Fax 724180, – TV. VISA
closed January and February – **M** (restricted lunch)/dinner 20.00 **t.** 5.00 – **7 rm** 30.00/62.00 **t.**, **1 suite** 67.00/75.00 **t.** – SB (except Bank Holidays) 65.00/104.00 **st.**

Willowfield, Lower Wood, All Stretton, SY6 6LF, NE : 2 ¼ m. by B 4370 069 45 (Leebstwood) 471, – TV.
March-October – **M** 14.00 **s.** – **5 rm** 27.00/40.00 **s.**

ATS Crossways 722526/722112

CHURT Surrey 404 R 30 – see Farnham.

CIRENCESTER Glos. 403 404 O 28 – pop. 13 491 – ECD : Thursday – 0285.

See : Site★ – St. John The Baptist Parish Church★ (Perpendicular) – Corinium Museum★.

Envir. : Chedworth *AC*, N : 7 m.

18 Cheltenham Rd 653939, N : 1 ½ m. on A 435.

Corn Hall, Market Pl. 654180.

London 97 – Bristol 37 – Gloucester 19 – Oxford 37.

Fleece (Best Western), Market Pl., GL7 2NZ, ☎ 658507, Fax 651017 – TV ☎ P – 30. AE VISA
M (bar lunch Monday to Saturday)/dinner 13.95/15.50 **t.** and a la carte 3.95 – ☕ 6.50 – **25 rm** 65.00/90.00 **t.** – SB 84.00/90.00 **st.**

Crown of Crucis, Ampney Crucis, GL7 5RS, E : 2¾ m. on A 417 ☎ 851806, Fax 851735 – TV ☎ P. AE VISA
M 10.00/25.00 **t.** and a la carte 4.00 – **26 rm** ☕ 45.00/60.00 **t.**

Wimborne House, 91 Victoria Rd, GL7 1ES, ☎ 653890 – TV P.
closed Christmas – **M** 7.00 **st.** – **5 rm** ☕ 25.00/30.00 **st.**

at Barnsley NE : 4 m. by A 429 on A 433 – ✉ Cirencester – ☎ 028 574 Bibury :

Village Pub, GL7 5EF, ☎ 421 – TV P. VISA
closed 25 December – **M** a la carte 8.05/14.15 **t.** 3.20 – **6 rm** ☕ 28.00/42.00 **st.**

at Ewen SW : 3 ¼ m. by A 429 – ✉ Cirencester – ☎ 0285 Kemble :

Wild Duck Inn, GL7 6BY, ☎ 770310, – TV ☎ P. AE VISA
M 10.00 **t.** and a la carte 3.00 – **9 rm** ☕ 48.00/65.00 **t.**, **1 suite** 75.00 **t.** – SB (weekend only) 75.00/90.00 **st.**

at Stratton NW : 1 ¼ m. on A 417 – ✉ ☎ 0285 Cirencester :

Stratton House, Gloucester Rd, GL7 2LE, ☎ 651761, Fax 640024, – TV ☎ P – 80. AE VISA
M 10.00/22.00 **st.** and a la carte – **25 rm** ☕ 55.00/80.00 **st.** – SB (except Christmas and Bank Holidays) 95.00 **st.**

CITROEN Perrotts Brook ☎ 028 583 (North Cerney) 219
FORD Chesterton Lane ☎ 640000
MITSUBISHI Love Lane ☎ 655799
RENAULT Gloucester Rd ☎ 658007
ROVER Tetbury Rd ☎ 652614
VAUXHALL Love Lane Trading Estate ☎ 653314

ATS 1 Mercian Close, Watermoor End ☎ 65776

"Short Breaks" (SB)

Zahlreiche Hotels bieten Vorzugspreise bei einem Aufenthalt von zwei Nächten.
Diese Preise umfassen Zimmer, Abendessen und Frühstück.

CLACTON-ON-SEA Essex 404 X 28 – pop. 39 618 – ECD : Wednesday – ☎ 0255.

See : Sea front (gardens)★.

23 Pier Av. ☎ 423400.

♦London 71 – Chelmsford 38 – Colchester 16.

Kingscliff, 55 Kings Par., Esplanade, Holland-on-Sea, CO15 5JB, NE : 1 ½ m. ☎ 812343 – TV ☎ P
15 rm.

CITROEN 67 Frinton Rd ☎ 812205
FORD Valleybridge Rd ☎ 432555
RENAULT St. Johns Rd ☎ 820287
ROLLS-ROYCE, BMW, MERCEDES Hayes Rd ☎ 473857/421834
ROVER 107 Old Rd ☎ 424128
VAUXHALL-OPEL 65 High St. ☎ 222444

ATS 46 High St. ☎ 420659

CLANFIELD Oxon. 403 404 P 28 – pop. 822 – ECD : Wednesday and Saturday – ☎ 036 781.

♦London 76 – ♦Oxford 20 – Swindon 17.

XXX **Plough at Clanfield** with rm, Bourton Rd, OX8 2RB, on A 4095 ☎ 222, Fax 596, « Small Elizabethan manor house », – TV ☎ P. AE VISA.
M 14.00/28.50 **t.** 8.00 – **6 rm** ☕ 66.00/110.00 **t.** – SB (except Christmas and New Year) 105.00/130.00 **st.**

CLAPHAM Beds. 404 S 27 – see Bedford.

CLAPPERSGATE Cumbria – see Ambleside.

CLAUGHTON Lancs. 402 M 21 – see Lancaster.

CLAVERING Essex 404 U 28 – pop. 1 076 – ☎ 0799 Saffron Walden.

♦London 44 – ♦Cambridge 25 – Colchester 44 – Luton 29.

X **Cricketers,** CB11 4QT, ☎ 550442, Fax 550882 – P. VISA
M (buffet lunch)/dinner 17.00 **t.** 3.80.

CLAWTON Devon 403 H 31 – pop. 300 – ✉ Holsworthy – ☎ 040 927 North Tamerton.

♦London 240 – Exeter 39 – ♦Plymouth 36.

Court Barn , EX22 6PS, W : ½ m. ☎ 219, – rm TV P. AE VISA
closed 1 to 7 January – **M** 8.95/17.00 **st.** and a la carte 3.00 – **8 rm** ☕ 30.00/64.00 **st.** – SB (except June and September) 76.00/80.00 **st.**

CLAYDON Suffolk 404 X 27 – pop. 2 516 – ✉ ☎ 0473 Ipswich.

◆London 78 – ◆Cambridge 50 – ◆Ipswich 4 – ◆Norwich 38.

Claydon Country House, Ipswich Rd, IP6 0AR, ☎ 830382, Fax 832476, – TV ☎ P. AE VISA.
closed Christmas Day – **M** *(closed Saturday lunch)* 12.50/12.95 **st.** and a la carte 4.25 – **14 rm** 36.50/59.50 **st.** – SB (weekends only) 57.50/62.50 **st.**

CLAYGATE Surrey 404 ㊷ – see Esher.

CLAYTON-LE-MOORS Lancs 402 M 22 – pop. 5 484 – ECD : Wednesday – ✉ ☎ 0254 Accrington.

◆London 232 – Blackburn 3.5 – Lancaster 37 – ◆Leeds 44 – Preston 14.

Dunkenhalgh, Blackburn Rd, BB5 5JP, W : 1 ½ m. on A 678 ☎ 398021, Telex 63282, Fax 872230, , , park – TV ☎ P – 400.
61 rm, 2 suites.

CLAYTON-LE-WOODS Lancs. – pop. 8 002 (inc. Cuerden) – ✉ Chorley – ☎ 0772 Leyland.

◆London 220 – ◆Liverpool 31 – ◆Manchester 26 – Preston 5.5.

Pines, Preston Rd, PR6 7ED, on A 6 ☎ 38551, Telex 67308, Fax 38551 (Extn : 302), – TV ☎ P. AE VISA.
closed 25 and 26 December – **M** 10.00/16.00 **st.** and a la carte 6.35 – **24 rm** 35.00/75.00 **st.** – SB 75.00 **st.**

CLAYWORTH Notts. 402 404 R 23 – pop. 275 – ✉ ☎ 0777 Retford.

◆London 150 – ◆Leeds 49 – Lincoln 26 – ◆Nottingham 38 – ◆Sheffield 29.

Royston Manor , St. Peters Lane, DN22 9AA, ☎ 817484, Fax 817155, <, – TV ☎ P
22 rm.

CLEARWELL Glos. – see Coleford.

CLEETHORPES Humberside 402 404 U 23 – pop. 33 238 – ECD : Thursday – ☎ 0472.

43 Alexandra Rd ☎ 200220.

◆London 171 – Boston 49 – Lincoln 38 – ◆Sheffield 77.

Plan : see Great Grimsby

Kingsway, Kingsway, DN35 0AE, ☎ 601122, Telex 527920, < – TV ☎ P – . AE VISA. BZ **a**
closed 25 and 26 December – **M** 11.00/14.00 **t.** and a la carte 3.50 – **50 rm** 54.00/79.00 **t.** – SB (weekends only) 82.00 **st.**

CLEEVE HILL Glos. 403 404 N 28 – see Cheltenham.

CLEY NEXT THE SEA Norfolk 404 X 25 – see Blakeney.

CLIFTON HAMPDEN Oxon. 403 404 Q 29 – see Abingdon.

CLIVEDEN Berks. 404 R 29 – see Maidenhead.

CLOWNE Derbs. 402 403 404 Q 24 – pop. 6 846 – ECD : Wednesday – ☎ 0246 Chesterfield.

◆London 156 – Derby 40 – Lincoln 35 – ◆Nottingham 30 – ◆Sheffield 12.

Van Dyk, Worksop Rd, S43 4TD, N : ¾ m. by A 618 on A 619 ☎ 810219, Fax 819566 – TV ☎ P – 80. AE VISA
M 15.40/25.00 **st.** and a la carte – **16 rm** 49.00/69.00 **st.**

CLUN Shropshire 403 KL 26 – pop. 817 – ✉ Craven Arms – ☎ 058 84.

◆London 178 – ◆Birmingham 60 – Shrewsbury 29.

XX **Old Post Office** with rm, 9 The Square, SY7 8JA, ☎ 687, < – VISA.
closed 27 January-13 March and 10 days Christmas – **M** *(closed Wednesday lunch, Monday and Tuesday except Bank Holidays)* (booking essential) (lunch by arrangement)/dinner a la carte 17.25/26.00 **t.** 5.50 – **2 rm** 22.00/40.00 **t.**

CLYST ST. GEORGE Devon – see Exeter.

COATHAM MUNDEVILLE Durham 402 P 20 – see Darlington.

COBHAM Kent 404 V 29 – ✉ ☎ 0474 Gravesend.

18 Silvermere, Redhill Rd ☎ 67275.

◆London 27 – Maidstone 13 – Rochester 6.

Leather Bottle (B.C.B.), The Street, DA12 3BZ, ☎ 814327, – TV ☎ P. AE VISA.
M 15.00 **st.** – **7 rm** 35.50/52.50 **st.**

COBHAM Surrey 404 S 30 – pop. 13920 – ECD : Wednesday – ☎ 0932.

Envir. : Wisley gardens** *AC*, SW : 4 m. by A 3 AZ.

♦London 24 – Guildford 10.

Plan : see Greater London (South-West)

Hilton National, Seven Hills Rd South, KT11 1EW, W : 1 ½ m. ✆ 64471, Telex 929196, Fax 68017, ≘s, ⛾, park, squash – |♦| ⇌ rm ▣ ☎ Ⓟ – 300. ⛁ AE ⓓ VISA. ✗
M *(closed Saturday lunch)* 14.50/24.50 **t.** and a la carte 5.00 – ☑ 9.95 – **149 rm** 95.00/145.00 **t.**, **3 suites** 165.00 **t.** by A 3 AZ

Cedar House, Mill Rd, KT11 3AN, ✆ 63424, – ⇌ rest ▣ ☎ Ⓟ. ⛁ AE VISA. ✗
closed 25 to 30 December – **M** *(closed Sunday and Monday)* (dinner only) 18.25 **t.** and a la carte 3.75 – **6 rm** ☑ 38.50/65.00 **t.** by A 307 AZ

at Stoke D'Aberon SE : 1 ½ m. on A 245 AZ – ✉ Cobham – ☎ 037 284 Oxshott :

Woodlands Park, Woodlands Lane, KT11 3QB, ✆ 3933, Telex 919246, Fax 2704, park, ✗ – |♦| ▤ rest ▣ ☎ Ⓟ – 200. ⛁ AE ⓓ VISA. ✗
M *(closed Saturday lunch)* 15.50/22.00 **st.** and a la carte – **58 rm** ☑ 95.00/105.00 **st.**, **1 suite** 110.00/180.00 **st.**

AUDI-VW 42 Portsmouth Rd ✆ 64493
BMW 18-22 Portsmouth Rd ✆ 67141
ROVER Stoke Rd ✆ 64244

COCKERMOUTH Cumbria 401 402 J 20 – pop. 7 074 – ECD : Thursday – ☎ 0900.

18 Embleton ✆ 059 681 (Bassenthwaite) 223, E : 3 m. off A 66.

Riverside Car Park, Market St. ✆ 822634.

♦London 306 – ♦Carlisle 25 – Keswick 13.

Trout, Crown St., CA13 0EJ, ✆ 823591, Fax 827514, – ▣ ☎ Ⓟ. ⛁ VISA
M 8.00/13.00 **t.** and a la carte 5.00 – **22 rm** ☑ 35.00/47.00 **t.** – SB (except Bank Holidays) (weekends only) 58.00/60.00 **st.**

at Great Broughton W : 2 ¾ m. by A 66 – ✉ ☎ 0900 Cockermouth :

Broughton Craggs, Graggs Rd, CA13 0XW, ✆ 824400, – ▣ ☎ Ⓟ. ⛁ AE ⓓ VISA. ✗
M 14.00 **st.** and a la carte 3.25 – **14 rm** ☑ 37.50/50.00 **st.**

BMW, VOLVO Derwent St. ✆ 823666
FORD Lorton St. ✆ 822033

COGGESHALL Essex 404 W 28 – pop. 3 505 – ECD : Wednesday – ✉ Colchester – ☎ 0376.

♦London 49 – Braintree 6 – Chelmsford 16 – Colchester 9.

White Hart, Market End, CO6 1NH, ✆ 561654, Fax 561789, « Part 14C Guild Hall » – ▣ ☎ Ⓟ. ⛁ AE ⓓ VISA. ✗
M *(closed Saturday lunch)* 12.50/14.75 **st.** and a la carte 4.75 – **16 rm** ☑ 60.00/120.00 **st.** – SB (weekends only) 80.00/100.00 **st.**

XX **Baumann's Brasserie**, 4-6 Stoneham St., CO6 1TT, ✆ 561453. ⛁ AE VISA
closed Saturday lunch, Sunday dinner and Monday – **M** 10.95 **t.** (lunch) and a la carte 15.00/21.75 **t.** 4.00.

COLCHESTER Essex 404 W 28 – pop. 87 476 – ECD : Thursday – ☎ 0206.

See : Castle and Museum*.

Envir. : Layer Marney (Marney Tower* 16C) SW : 7 m. – Stair Valley*, NE : 6 m.

18 Braiswick ✆ 852946, NW : ¾ m. – 18, 18 Keepers Lane, Leavenheath, Stoke by Nayland ✆ 262836, N : 7 m. – 9 Birch Grove, Layer Rd ✆ 34276, S : 2 m.

1 Queen St. ✆ 712920.

♦London 52 – ♦Cambridge 48 – ♦Ipswich 18 – Luton 76 – Southend-on-Sea 41.

Red Lion (Best Western), High St., CO1 1DJ, ✆ 577986, Fax 578207, « Part 15C inn » – ▣ ☎. ⛁ AE ⓓ VISA
closed 24 December-1 January – **M** 10.85/13.00 **st.** and a la carte 5.45 – **24 rm** 58.00/78.00 **st.** – SB (weekends only) 116.00/118.00 **st.**

George (Q.M.H.), 116 High St., CO1 1TD, ✆ 578494, Fax 761732, ≘s – ▣ ☎ Ⓟ – 80. ⛁ AE ⓓ VISA
M 7.25/10.25 **st.** 3.80 – **47 rm** ☑ 61.00/82.00 **st.**

AUDI-VW Wyncol Rd ℘ 855000
BMW Ipswich Rd ℘ 751100
CITROEN Butt Rd ℘ 576803
DAIHATSU Mersea Rd ℘ 570044
DAIMLER-JAGUAR Cowdrey Av. ℘ 764764
FERRARI, PORSCHE Auto Way, Ipswich Rd ℘ 855500
FIAT, SAAB Sheepen Rd ℘ 563311
FORD Magdalen St. ℘ 571171
HONDA, SEAT, MITSUBISHI, HYUNDAI ℘ 855455
LADA Clochester Rd, Elmstead Market ℘ 224499
LANCIA, MAZDA Bergholt Rd ℘ 844455
LAND-ROVER Cowdrey Ave. ℘ 764764
RELIANT London Rd
RENAULT 78 Military Rd ℘ 577295
ROVER East Gates ℘ 867484
ROVER Elmstead Rd ℘ 862811
SKODA Copford ℘ 210422
SUZUKI Maldon Rd ℘ 44233/579579
TALBOT-PEUGEOT Wimpole Rd ℘ 570197
TOYOTA Gosbecks Rd ℘ 46455
VAUXHALL-OPEL Ipswich Rd ℘ 844422
VOLVO Autoway, Ipswich Rd ℘ 855055
YUGO Barrack St. ℘ 760077

ATS East Hill ℘ 866484/867471
ATS 451 Ipswich Rd ℘ 841404
ATS Telford Way, Severalls Park Ind. Est. ℘ 845641

COLD CHRISTMAS Herts. – see Ware.

COLEFORD Glos. 403 404 M 28 – pop. 8 246 – ECD : Thursday – 0594 Dean.

Royal Forest of Dean, Lords Hills ℘ 32583, ½ m. on Parkend Rd.

Market Pl., Royal Forest of Dean ℘ 36307.

London 143 – Bristol 28 – Gloucester 19 – Newport 29.

Speech House (T.H.F.), Forest of Dean, GL16 7EL, NE : 3 m. on B 4226 ℘ 822607, Fax 823658, – rm. VISA
M 10.50/16.95 **st.** and a la carte 4.25 – 7.00 – **14 rm** 45.00/73.00 **st.** – SB 80.00/100.00 **st.**

Lambsquay, Perrygrove Rd, GL16 8QB, S : 1 m. on B 4228 ℘ 33127, – . VISA
closed January – **M** *(closed lunch Saturday and Sunday)* (bar lunch)/dinner a la carte 11.00/17.50 **t.** 3.50 – **9 rm** 28.00/63.00 **t.** – SB (except Bank Holidays) 56.00/68.00 **st.**

at Clearwell S : 2 m. by B 4228 – Coleford – 0594 Dean :

Wyndham Arms, GL16 8JT, ℘ 33666, Fax 36450 – . VISA
closed 25 and 26 December – **M** 13.00/14.25 **t.** and a la carte 4.60 – **17 rm** 35.00/70.00 **st.**

Tudor Farmhouse, GL16 8JS, ℘ 33046 – . VISA
M *(bar lunch)/dinner* 14.00 **st.** and a la carte 4.95 – **9 rm** 35.00/50.00 **st.**

FORD High St ℘ 32747
HYUNDAI, SUBARU Five Acres ℘ 33517 Market Pl. ℘ 32468

COLERNE Wilts. 403 404 M 29 – see Bath (Avon).

COLESHILL Warw. 403 404 O 26 – pop. 6 038 – ECD : Monday and Thursday – Birmingham – 0675.

Maxstoke Park, Castle Lane ℘ 462158, E : 2 m.

London 113 – Birmingham 8 – Coventry 11.

Coleshill (Lansbury), 152 High St., B46 3BG, ℘ 465527, Telex 497868, Fax 464013 – rm – 150. VISA.
M *(closed Saturday lunch)* 9.00/17.00 **t.** and a la carte 4.50 – **23 rm** 62.00/74.00 **t.** – SB (weekends only) 66.00/72.00 **st.**

COLLYWESTON Northants. 402 404 S 26 – see Stamford (Lincs.).

COLNE Lancs. 402 N 22 – pop. 19 094 – 0282.

Law Farm, Skipton Old Rd ℘ 863391 – Ghyll Brow, Barnoldswick ℘ 842466.

London 234 – Manchester 29 – Preston 26.

West Lynn Country House, Barrowford Rd, BB8 9QW, W : ½ m. on B 6247 ℘ 869199, Fax 869199, – . VISA.
M *(closed Sunday)* (dinner only) 16.50 **t.** 4.20 – **12 rm** 42.50/60.00 **t.**

ATS Corporation St. ℘ 864616

COLSTERWORTH Lincs. 402 404 S 25 – 0476 Grantham.

London 105 – Granthan 8 – Leicester 29 – Nottingham 32 – Peterborough 14.

Granada Lodge without rest., Granada Service Area, NG33 5JR, ℘ 860686, Fax 861078 – . VISA.
38 rm 27.50/29.50 **t.**

Travelodge without rest., South Witham, LE15 8AU, S : 3 m. by B 6403 on A 1 (Northbound carriageway) ℘ 586, Reservations (Toll free) 0800 850950 – . VISA.
32 rm 24.00/29.50 **t.**

COLTISHALL Norfolk 404 Y 25 – pop. 1 314 – ✉ ☎ 0603 Norwich.

◆London 133 – ◆Norwich 8.

- **Norfolk Mead** ⛰, Church St., NR12 7DN, ✆ 737531, heated, – TV ☎ P. AE VISA.
  closed 25 to 28 December – **M** *(closed Sunday dinner and Bank Holidays)* (dinner only an Sunday lunch)/dinner 19.50 **t.** and a la carte 🍷 3.50 – **10 rm** ☕ 49.00/65.00 **t.** – SB (excep Sunday and Monday) 89.00/99.00 **st.**

COLWYN BAY (BAE COLWYN) Clwyd 402 403 I 24 – pop. 27 002 – ECD : Wednesday – ☎ 0492.

See : Zoo★.

Envir. : Bodnant gardens★★ *AC*, SW : 6 m.

18 Abergele and Pensarn, Tan-y-Goppa Rd, Abergele ✆ 0745 (Abergele) 824034, E : 6 m. – 9 Old Colwyn, Woodland Av. ✆ 515581.

ℹ Station Rd. ✆ 530478 – The Promenade, Rhos-on-sea ✆ 48778 – Coach Park, Informatio Point, Princes Drive ✆ 534432.

◆London 237 – Birkenhead 50 – Chester 42 – Holyhead 41.

- **Norfolk House,** 36 Princes Drive, LL29 8PF, ✆ 531757, – rest TV ☎ P – 40 AE VISA
  M (bar lunch)/dinner a la carte 7.30/13.25 **t.** 🍷 4.00 – **24 rm** ☕ 43.00/59.00 **t.** – SB (week ends only) 72.00 **st.**
- **Hopeside,** 63-67 Prince's Drive, West End, LL29 8PW, ✆ 533244, Telex 61254 – rm TV ☎ P. AE VISA
  M 11.00/15.00 **t.** and a la carte 🍷 2.95 – **16 rm** ☕ 32.50/50.00 **st.** – SB 59.00/86.00 **st.**
- **Lyndale,** 410 Abergele Rd, Old Colwyn, LL29 9AB, E : 1 ¾ m. on A 547 ✆ 515429 – TV ☎ P. AE VISA.
  M (bar lunch Monday to Saturday)/dinner 16.00 **st.** 🍷 4.50 – **14 rm** ☕ 29.50/47.00 **t.** – SB 59.50/64.50 **st.**
- **West Point,** 102 Conway Rd, LL29 7LE, ✆ 530331, – TV P. VISA
  closed December and January – **M** 10.50 **st.** 🍷 2.95 – **10 rm** ☕ 14.50/34.00 **st.**

at Penmaenhead E : 2 ¼ m. on A 547 – ✉ ☎ 0492 Colwyn Bay :

- **Hotel 70°** (Best Western), Old Colwyn, LL29 9LD, ✆ 516555, Telex 61362, Fax 515565, ← TV ☎ P – 60. AE VISA
  M 11.50/18.75 **st.** and a la carte 🍷 5.95 – **43 rm** ☕ 52.00/75.00 **st.**, **1 suite** 85.00/95.00 **st.** – SB 79.00/99.00 **st.**

at Rhos-on-Sea (Llandrillo-yn-Rhos) NW : 1 m. – ✉ ☎ 0492 Colwyn Bay :

- **Ashmount,** 18 College Av., LL28 4NT, ✆ 45479 – TV ☎ P. AE VISA
  M (bar lunch Monday to Saturday) 8.50/9.50 **st.** and a la carte 🍷 3.30 – **18 rm** ☕ 29.00 48.50 **st.** – SB (October-April) 55.80 **st.**
- **Cabin Hill,** 12 College Av., LL28 4NT, ✆ 44568 – TV P.
  March-October – **M** 6.50 **st.** – **10 rm** ☕ 15.00/35.00 **st.** – SB (except Summer) 44.00 **st.**

FORD Conwy Rd ✆ 532201
PEUGEOT 268 Conwy Rd ✆ 44278
PORSCHE, MERCEDES Conny Rd ✆ 593555
ROVER 394 Abergele Rd ✆ 515292
VAUXALL Conwy Rd ✆ 530271
VW-AUDI Penrhyn Av. ✆ 46722

COLYTON Devon 403 K 31 **The West Country G.** – pop. 2 435 – ☎ 0297.

See : Site★ – St. Andrew's Church★.

◆London 160 – Exeter 23 – Lyme Regis 7.

- **Old Bakehouse,** Lower Church St., EX13 6ND, ✆ 52518, Fax 53700 – TV P. VISA
  M 8.00/19.50 **t.** and a la carte 🍷 4.75 – **8 rm** ☕ 22.00/44.00 **st.** – SB 54.00 **st.**
- **Grove,** South St., EX13 6ER, ✆ 52438, – rest P
  closed 15 December-4 January – **M** 7.50 **s.** 🍷 2.70 – **7 rm** ☕ 10.00/28.00 **s.**

COMBE MARTIN Devon 403 H 30 **The West Country G.** – pop. 2 279 – ECD : Wednesday – ✉ Ilfracombe – ☎ 0271.

ℹ Exmoor Park Information Office, Cross St. ✆ 883319 (summer only).

◆London 218 – Exeter 56 – Taunton 58.

- **Coulsworthy Country House** ⛰, EX34 0PD, SE : 2 ½ m. by A 399 on Hunters Inn r ✆ 882463, ←, « Country house atmosphere », heated, – rest TV P. VISA
  closed mid December-mid February – **M** *(closed Sunday dinner)* (dinner only and Sunda lunch)/dinner 20.00 **st.** 🍷 3.60 – **10 rm** ☕ 62.00/134.00 **st.** – SB 100.00/126.00 **st.**
- **Rone House,** King St., EX34 0AD, ✆ 883428, heated, – TV P. VISA
  closed November and January – **M** *(closed Monday)* (dinner only) 10.00 **t.** and a la cart 🍷 2.50 – **11 rm** ☕ 17.50/41.00 **t.** – SB (except August and Bank Holidays) 65.00/77.50 **st.**

VAUXHALL-OPEL Borough Rd ✆ 3257

CONGLETON Cheshire 402 403 404 N 24 – pop. 23 482 – ECD : Wednesday – ☎ 0260.

18 Peel Lane, Astbury ✆ 272772, S : 1m. – 9 Biddulph Rd ✆ 273540.

Town Hall, High St. ✆ 271095.

♦London 183 – ♦Liverpool 50 – ♦Manchester 25 – ♦Sheffield 46 – ♦Stoke-on-Trent 13.

Lion and Swan, Swan Bank, CW12 1JR, ✆ 273115, Fax 299270, « 16C inn » – TV ☎ P. AE VISA
M 8.95/13.95 **st.** and a la carte 3.75 – **21 rm** 52.50/105.00 **st.** – SB (weekends only) 70.00/85.00 **st.**

ATS Brookside ✆ 273720

CONISTON Cumbria 402 K 20 – pop. 1 713 – ☎ 053 94.

16 Yewdale Rd ✆ 41533 (summer only).

♦London 285 – ♦Carlisle 55 – Kendal 22 – Lancaster 42.

Sun, LA21 8HQ, ✆ 41248, ←, – rest TV ☎ P. VISA
M (bar lunch)/dinner 18.00 **t.** 6.95 – **11 rm** 30.00/70.00 **t.** – SB (November-31 March) 70.00/80.00 **st.**

CONSTANTINE BAY Cornwall 403 E 32 – see Padstow.

CONWY Gwynedd 402 403 I 24 – pop. 3 649 – ECD : Wednesday – ☎ 0492 Aberconway.

See : Site★ – Castle★★ (13C) *AC* – St. Mary's Church★ (14C).

Envir. : Bodnant Gardens★★ SE : 5 m Plas Mawr★★.

9 Penmaenmawr ✆ 623330, W : 4 m – 18 The Morfa, Conway ✆ 593400, W : 1 m. on A 55.

Conway Castle Visitor Centre, ✆ 592248 (summer only).

♦London 241 – Caernarfon 22 – Chester 46 – Holyhead 37.

Bryn Cregin Garden, Ty Mawr Rd, Deganwy, LL31 9UR, NE : 2 m. by A 55 on A 546 ✆ 585266, ←, – TV ☎ P. VISA.
closed January – **M** *(dinner only)* 20.00 **st.** and a la carte 5.00 – **16 rm** 48.00/88.00 **st.** – SB 80.00/100.00 **st.**

Castle (T.H.F.), High St., LL32 8DB, ✆ 592324, Fax 583351 – TV ☎ P – 25. AE VISA
M (bar lunch Monday to Saturday)/dinner 14.50 **st.** and a la carte 4.35 – 7.00 – **29 rm** 60.00/75.00 **st.** – SB 110.00/116.00 **st.**

Castle Bank, Mount Pleasant, LL32 8NY, ✆ 593888, ← – TV P. VISA.
closed January and February – **M** (dinner only and Sunday lunch)/dinner 13.00 **t.** 3.80 – **9 rm** 23.00/46.00 **t.** – SB 59.00/65.00 **st.**

at Roewen S : 3 m. by B 5106 – ✉ Conwy – ☎ 0492 Tyn-y-Groes :

Tir-y-Coed, LL32 8TP, ✆ 650219, ←, – rest TV P
closed Christmas and restricted service November-February – **M** 9.25 **t.** 3.25 – **7 rm** 22.75/41.50 **t.** – SB (October-April) 51.00/53.50 **st.**

at Tal-y-Bont S : 5¾ m. on B 5106 – ✉ Conwy – ☎ 049 269 Dolgarrog :

Lodge, LL32 8YX, ✆ 69766 – TV ☎ P. VISA
M *(closed Monday lunch)* 11.50 **st.** (dinner) and a la carte 3.75 – **10 rm** 27.50/45.00 **st.** – SB (November-Easter) 45.00/65.00 **st.**

COOKHAM Berks. 404 R 29 – pop. 5 865 – ECD : Wednesday and Thursday – ✉ Maidenhead – ☎ 062 85 Bourne End.

Envir. : Cliveden House★ (19C) (Park★★) *AC*, SE : 2 m.

18 Winter Hill, Grange Lane ✆ 27613, NW: 1 m. by B 4447.

♦London 32 – High Wycombe 7 – Reading 16.

Peking Inn, 49 High St., SL6 9SL, ✆ 20900, Chinese (Peking) rest. – AE VISA
M a la carte 16.50/24.90.

Cookham Tandoori, High St., SL6 9SL, ✆ 22584, Indian rest – AE VISA
M a la carte 16.50/29.50 3.50.

CITROEN High St. ✆ 22984

COPDOCK Suffolk 404 X 27 – see Ipswich.

Pleasant hotels and restaurants
are shown in the Guide by a red sign.

Please send us the names
of any where you have enjoyed your stay.

Your Michelin Guide will be even better.

...

XXXXX ... X

COPTHORNE West Sussex 404 T 30 – see Crawley.

CORBRIDGE Northumb. 401 402 N 19 – pop. 2 757 – ECD : Thursday – ☎ 043 471 (4 fig.) o 0434 (Hexham) (6 fig.).

Envir. : Corstopitum Roman Fort★ *AC*, NW : 1 ½ m.

Vicar's Pele Tower, Market Pl. ☎ 632815 (summer only).

♦London 300 – Hexham 3 – ♦Newcastle-upon-Tyne 18.

Riverside, Main St., NE45 5LE, ☎ 632942 – TV P
11 rm.

Clive House without rest., Appletree Lane, NE45 5DN, ☎ 632617, – rm TV ☎ P
VISA.
3 rm 28.00/38.00 **st.**

XXX **Ramblers Country House,** Tinklers Bank, Farnley, NE45 5RN, S : 1 m. on Riding Mil Rd ☎ 632424, German rest. – P. AE VISA
closed Sunday, Monday, 25-26 December and 1 January – **M** (lunch by arrangement) dinner a la carte 16.35/20.20 **st.** 3.25.

LANCIA Princes St. ☎ 606983

CORBY Northants. 404 R 26 – ✉ ☎ 0536.

Crest (T.H.F.), Rockingham Rd, NN17 1AE, ☎ 401348, Telex 341752, Fax 66383 – rm TV ☎ & P – 300. AE VISA
M *(closed lunch Saturday and Bank Holidays)* 10.50/16.95 **st.** and a la carte – 7.95 – **70 rm** 68.00/100.00 **st.** – SB (weekends only) 174.00/188.00 **st.**

CORFE CASTLE Dorset 403 404 N 32 – ✉ Wareham – ☎ 0929.

♦London 129 – Bournemouth 18 – Weymouth 23.

Mortons House, 45 East St., BH20 5EE, ☎ 480988, Fax 480820, « Elizabethan manor » – rest TV ☎ P. VISA.
closed Christmas and New Year – **M** 20.00**t** (dinner) and a la carte approx. 15.00 – **17 rm** 50.00/110.00 **t.**

CORNHILL-ON-TWEED Northumb. 401 402 N 17 – pop. 312 – ECD : Thursday – ☎ 0890 Coldstream.

♦London 345 – ♦Edinburgh 49 – ♦Newcastle-upon-Tyne 59.

Coach House, Crookham, TD12 4TD, E : 4 m. on A 697 ☎ 089 082 (Crookham) 293, – rest & P
25 March-25 November – **M** 12.50 **st.** – **9 rm** 19.00/52.00 **st.**

CORRIS Gwynedd 402 403 I 26 – see Machynlleth (Powys).

CORSE LAWN Heref. and Worc. – see Tewkesbury (Glos.).

CORSHAM Wilts. 403 404 N 29 **The West Country G.** – pop. 11 259 – ECD : Wednesday – ☎ 0249.

See : Corsham Court★★ *AC*.

18 Kingsdown ☎ 742530.

Arnold House, 31 High St. ☎ 714660 (summer only).

♦London 110 – ♦Bristol 22 – Swindon 25.

Rudloe Park, Leafy Lane, SN13 0PA, W : 2 m. by B 3353 on A 4 ☎ 0225 (Bath) 810555 Fax 811412, ←, – rest TV ☎ P – 30. AE VISA
M 15.00/17.50 **st.** and a la carte 5.25 – **11 rm** 60.00/90.00 **st.** – SB 105.00/115.00 **st.**

Methuen Arms, 2 High St., SN13 0HB, ☎ 714867, Fax 712004, – TV ☎ P. VISA.
M *(closed Sunday dinner)* 14.75 **t.** and a la carte 4.85 – **25 rm** 42.00/58.00 **st.** – SB 82.50/87.50 **st.**

FORD 101 Pickwick Rd ☎ 712166

COSGROVE Northants. – see Stony Stratford (Bucks.).

COSHAM Hants. 403 404 Q 31 – see Portsmouth and Southsea.

COUNTESTHORPE Leics. 403 404 Q 26 – pop. 6 133 – ☎ 0533 Leicester.

♦London 97 – ♦Coventry 25 – ♦Leicester 7 – Northampton 35.

XX **Old Bakery,** Main St., LE8 3QX, ☎ 778777 – P. VISA
closed Saturday lunch, Sunday dinner and Monday – **M** 8.95/15.50 **t.**

COUNTISBURY Devon – see Lynton.

COUNTY OAK West Sussex – see Crawley.

COVENTRY West Midlands 403 404 P 26 – pop. 318 718 – ECD : Thursday – ☎ 0203.

See : St. Michael's Cathedral★★★ (1962) : tapestry★★★ AV – Old Cathedral★ (ruins) AV **A** – St. John's Church★ (14C-15C) AV **B** – Old houses★ (16C-17C) AV **DEF**.

18 Finham Park ☎ 411123, S : 2½m. on A 444 BZ – 18 Beechwood Av. ☎ 713470, S : 1 ½ m. AZ – 9 Grange, Copsewood ☎ 451465 BY – 9 Sphinx, Siddeley Av. ☎ 451361 BY.

Coventry Airport : ☎ 301717, Telex 31646, S : 3 ½ m. by Coventry Rd BZ.

Central Library, ☎ 823311/823312.

London 100 – Birmingham 18 – Bristol 96 – Nottingham 52.

Plans on following pages

De Vere, Cathedral Sq., CV1 5RP, ☎ 633733, Telex 31380, Fax 225299 – 400. AE VISA AV **n**
M 12.50/18.00 **st.** and a la carte 5.00 – **180 rm** 81.50/116.00 **st.**, **10 suites** 124.00/150.50 **st.** – SB (weekends only) 60.00/80.00 **st.**

Brooklands Garage, Holyhead Rd, CV5 8HX, ☎ 601601, Fax 601277, – rest AE VISA. AY **e**
closed 24 December-2 January – **M** 22.20/27.70 **st.** and a la carte – **30 rm** 75.00/95.00 **st.**

Merrick Lodge, 80-82 St. Nicholas St., CV1 4BP, ☎ 553940, Fax 550112 – 150. AE VISA AV **a**
M 7.50/10.00 **t.** and a la carte – **26 rm** 36.00/55.00 **st.** – SB (weekends only) 60.00/100.00 **st.**

Campanile, Abbey Rd, Whitley, CV3 4BJ, SE : 2 ½ m. by A 423 and A 46 ☎ 639922, Fax 306898 – 30. VISA BZ **a**
M 9.40 **st.** and a la carte 2.60 – 3.95 – **50 rm** 33.00 **st.**

Victoria House without rest., 39 St. Patricks Rd, CV1 2LP, ☎ 221378 – AV **e**
5 rm 14.00/30.00 **s.**

Brymar without rest., 39a St. Patricks Rd, CV1 2LP, ☎ 225969 – . AV **e**
4 rm 14.00/38.00 **st.**

Baccara without rest., 20 Park Rd, CV1 2LD, ☎ 226530 – . AV **i**
7 rm 13.00/26.00 **s.**

Hearsall Lodge, 1-3 Broad Lane, Whoberley, CV5 7AA, W : 2 m. by B 4101 ☎ 674543 – . VISA AY **a**
M (by arrangement) 7.50 **st.** 3.75 – **18 rm** 26.00/40.00 **st.**

at Longford N : 4 m. on A 444 – ✉ ☎ 0203 Coventry :

Novotel, Wilsons Lane, CV6 6HL, ☎ 365000, Telex 31545, Fax 362422, heated – rest – 150. AE VISA BV **v**
M 11.00/12.00 **st.** and a la carte 5.15 – 6.50 – **100 rm** 54.00/58.00 **st.** – SB (weekends only) (except Christmas) 70.00/80.00 **st.**

at Walsgrave on Sowe NE : 3 m. on A 4600 – ✉ ☎ 0203 Coventry :

Crest (T.H.F.), Hinckley Rd, CV2 2HP, NE : ½ m. on A 4600 ☎ 613261, Telex 311292, Fax 621736, , , – rm rest – 425 BX **e**
145 rm, 2 suites.

Campanile, Wigston Rd off Hinckley Rd, CV2 2SD, NE : ½ m. by A 4600 ☎ 622311, Telex 317454, Fax 602362 – . VISA BX **a**
M 9.40 **st.** and a la carte 2.60 – 3.95 – **47 rm** 33.00 **st.**

at Ansty (Warw.) NE : 5 ¾ m. by A 4600 – BY – on B 4065 – ✉ ☎ 0203 Coventry :

Ansty Hall, CV7 9HZ, ☎ 612222, Fax 602155, « 17C mansion », , park –
19 rm.

at Brandon (Warw.) E : 6 m. on A 428 – BZ – ✉ ☎ 0203 Coventry :

Brandon Hall (T.H.F.) , Main St., CV8 3FW, ☎ 542571, Telex 31472, Fax 544909, park, squash – – 100. AE VISA
M 8.95/15.50 **st.** and a la carte 5.65 – 7.60 – **59 rm** 70.00/90.00 **st.**, **1 suite** 95.00/110.00 **st.**

at Willenhall SE : 3 m. on A 423 – ✉ ☎ 0203 Coventry :

Chace Crest (T.H.F.), London Rd, CV3 4EQ, ☎ 303398, Telex 311993, Fax 301816, – rm – 65. AE VISA BZ **u**
M *closed Saturday and Bank Holidays* 11.50/15.35 **st.** and a la carte – 8.25 – **67 rm** 72.00/84.00 **st.** – SB (weekends only) 148.00/180.00 **st.**

at Baginton (Warw.) S : 3 m. by A 444 off A 45 (off Westbound carriageway and Howes Lane turning) – ✉ ☎ 0203 Coventry :

Old Mill (B.C.B.), Mill Hill, CV8 2BS, ☎ 303588, Fax 307070, « Attractively converted corn mill », – . AE VISA. BZ **e**
M 15.00 **st.** – **20 rm** 58.50/71.00 **st.**

at Berkswell W : 6 ½ m. by B 4101 – AY – ✉ ☎ 0203 Coventry :

Nailcote Hall , Nailcote Lane, CV7 7DE, S : 1 ½ m. on B 4101 ☎ 466174, Fax 470720, – – 80. AE VISA
M 20.00 **t.** and a la carte – **20 rm** 85.00/105.00 **t.** – SB (weekends only) 200.00/240.00 **st.**

COVENTRY

- Broadgate . . . . AV 6
- Corporation Street . . . . AV
- Shopping Precincts . . . . AV

- Bayley Lane . . . . AV 3
- Bishop Street . . . . AV 5
- Burges . . . . AV 7
- Earl Street . . . . AV 10
- Fairfax Street . . . . AV 12
- Far Gosford Street . . . . . AV 13
- Gosford Street . . . . AV 15
- Greyfriars Lane . . . . AV 16
- Hales Street . . . . AV 17
- Hearsall Lane . . . . AV 21
- High Street . . . . AV 22
- Ironmonger Row . . . . AV 23
- Jordan Well . . . . AV 26
- Leicester Row . . . . AV 29
- Light Lane . . . . AV 30
- Little Park Street . . . . AV 31
- Primrose Hill Street . . . . . AV 34
- Queen Victoria Road . . . . AV 35
- St. Johns (Ringway) . . . . AV 38
- St. Nicholas (Ringway) . . AV 39
- Swanswell (Ringway) . . . AV 40
- Trinity Street . . . . AV 41
- Upper Well Street . . . . . . AV 43
- Vecqueray Street . . . . . . AV 45
- Victoria Street . . . . AV 46
- Warwick Row . . . . AV 49
- White Street . . . . AV 51
- Windsor Street . . . . AV 52
- White Friars (Ringway) . . AV 54

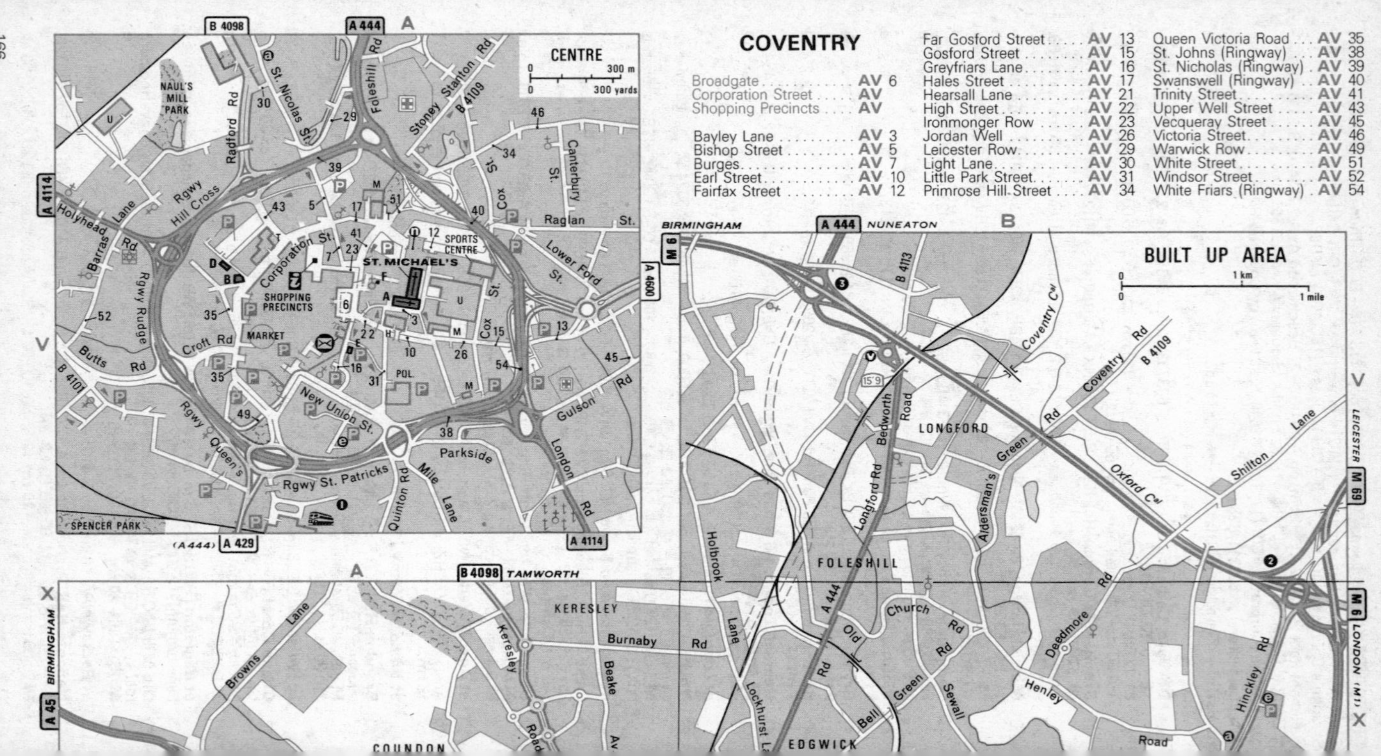

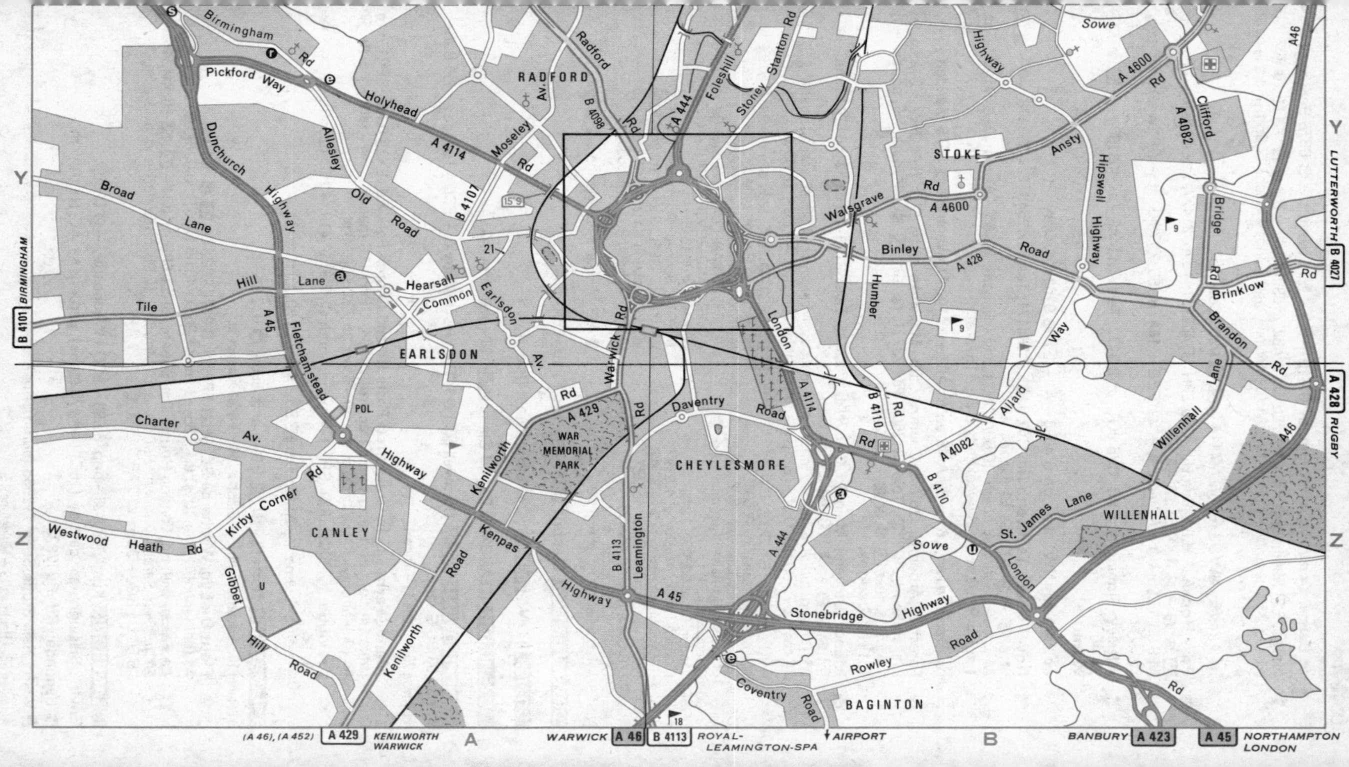

LUTTERWORTH B 4027
A 428 RUGBY
B 4101 BIRMINGHAM
(A 46), (A 452) A 429 KENILWORTH WARWICK
A
WARWICK A 46
B 4113 ROYAL-LEAMINGTON-SPA
AIRPORT
B
BANBURY A 423
A 45 NORTHAMPTON LONDON
Y
Z
Birmingham
Rd
Pickford Way
Holyhead
A 4114
Moseley
Rd
RADFORD
Av.
Radford
B 4098
Rd
A 444
Foleshill
Stoney
Stanton Rd
Sowe
Highway
A 4600
Rd
Clifford
A 4082
STOKE
Ansty
Hipswell
Highway
Bridge
Rd
Brinklow
Rd
Brandon
Rd
Lane
A46
Dunchurch
Highway
Allesley
Old
Road
B 4107
Broad
Lane
Hill
Lane
Hearsall
Common
Earlsdon
Tile
A 45
Fletchamstead
EARLSDON
Av.
Rd
Warwick
Rd
Walsgrave
Rd
A 4600
Binley
Road
A 428
Humber
Way
Allard
London
A 4114
B 4110
Rd
Daventry
Road
A 429
WAR MEMORIAL PARK
Rd
POL.
Charter
Av.
Highway
Kenilworth
CHEYLESMORE
Rd
A 4082
B 4110
Willenhall
A46
Kirby
Corner
Rd
CANLEY
Westwood
Heath
Rd
Gibbet
Hill
Road
Kenpas
Road
Kenilworth
B 4113
Leamington
A 444
Highway
A 45
Sowe
St. James
Lane
WILLENHALL
London
Stonebridge
Highway
Road
Rowley
Coventry
Road
BAGINTON
Rd

at Balsall Common W : 6 ¾ m. by B 4101 – AY – ✉ Coventry – ☎ 0676 Berkswell :

Haigs, 273 Kenilworth Rd, CV7 7EL, on A 452 ☎ 33004, – TV ☎ P. VISA.
closed 24 December-3 January – **M** (dinner only and Sunday lunch) 13.95 **t.** and a la carte 3.50 – **13 rm** 44.50/65.00 **t.**

at Allesley NW : 3 m. on A 4114 – ✉ ☎ 0203 Coventry :

Post House (T.H.F.), Rye Hill, CV5 9PH, ☎ 402151, Telex 31427, Fax 402235 – rm TV ☎ P – 120. VISA AXY **s**
M 9.95/13.95 **st.** and a la carte – 7.50 – **184 rm** 65.00/75.00 **st.** – SB (weekends only) 76.00 **st.**

Allesley, Birmingham Rd, CV5 9GT, ☎ 403272, Telex 311446, Fax 405190 – TV ☎ P – 400 AY **r**
90 rm.

at Keresley NW : 3 m. on B 4098 – AX – ✉ ☎ 0203 Coventry :

Royal Court, Tamworth Rd, CV7 8JG, ☎ 334171, Telex 312549, Fax 333478, – TV ☎ P – 200. VISA
M *(closed Saturday lunch)* 10.50/12.50 **t.** and a la carte 3.65 – **97 rm** 72.00/85.00 **st.**, **1 suite** 97.00 **st.** – SB (weekends only) 118.00 **st.**

at Meriden NW : 6 m. by A 45 on B 4102 – AX – ✉ Coventry – ☎ 0676 Meriden :

Forest of Arden H. Golf & Country Club, Maxstoke Lane, CV7 7HR, NW : 2 ¾ m. by Maxstoke rd ☎ 22335, Telex 312604, Fax 23711, , , , 18, , park, , squash – rm rest TV ☎ P – 275
151 rm, 2 suites.

Manor (De Vere), Main Rd, CV7 7NH, ☎ 22735, Telex 311011, Fax 22186, heated, – TV ☎ P – 300. VISA
M *(closed lunch Saturday and Bank Holiday Mondays)* 14.50 **st.** and a la carte 3.75 – **74 rm** 75.00/90.00 **st.** – SB (weekends only, July and August) 70.00 **st.**

BMW Holyhead Rd ☎ 591223
CITROEN Lockhurst Lane ☎ 686699
DAIHATSU Goodyers End Lane ☎ 362259
FIAT 324 Station Rd Balsall Common ☎ 0676 (Berkswell) 33145
FORD London Rd ☎ 502000
FORD Pickford Brook, Allesley ☎ 402177
JAGUAR Dunchurch Highway ☎ 404641
LADA, PROTON Brandon Rd ☎ 452777
MAZDA Browns Lane ☎ 402493
MERCEDES-BENZ Humber Rd ☎ 306234
NISSAN 105 Foleshill Rd ☎ 555399
PEUGEOT-TALBOT 136 Daventry Rd ☎ 503522
RELIANT 90 Paynes Lane ☎ 220475
ROVER Lockhurst Lane ☎ 688851
ROVER, LEYLAND DAF Warwick Rd ☎ 633661
ROVER, LAND-ROVER, RANGE-ROVER Kenpas Highway ☎ 411515
TOYOTA Bennetts Rd, Keresley ☎ 334204
VAUXHALL-OPEL Raglan St. ☎ 225361
VOLVO London Rd ☎ 303132
VW-AUDI Spon End ☎ 525555

ATS Mile Lane, Cheylesmore ☎ 228727

COWAN BRIDGE Cumbria 402 M 21 – see Kirkby Lonsdale.

COWES I.O.W. 403 404 PQ 31 – see Wight (Isle of).

COYCHURCH (LLANGRALLO) Mid Glam. 403 J 29 – see Bridgend.

CRACKINGTON HAVEN Cornwall 403 G 31 The West Country G. – ECD : Tuesday – ✉ Bude – ☎ 084 03 St. Gennys.

London 262 – Bude 11 – Truro 42.

Manor Farm , by Tresparrett Posts Rd and Church Park Rd, EX23 0JW, SE: 1 ¼ m. (take 1st right turn onto single track rd) ☎ 304, « Part 11C manor », , park – P.
M (dinner only) 10.00/15.00 **st.** 2.50 – **5 rm** 22.00/50.00 **st.**

Trevigue , EX23 0LQ, SE : 1 ¼ m. on South Cliff rd ☎ 418, « 16C farmhouse » – P.
March-September – **M** 12.00 **t.** 3.50 – **4 rm** 20.00/40.00 **t.**

CRANBORNE Dorset 403 404 O 31 – pop. 596 – ☎ 072 54.

London 107 – Bournemouth 21 – Salisbury 18 – Southampton 30.

Fleur De Lys, Wimborne St., BH21 5PP, on B 3078 ☎ 282 – TV P. VISA
M (bar lunch)/dinner 10.95 **t.** 3.55 – **8 rm** 26.00/40.00 **t.** – SB 50.00/60.00 **st.**

La Fosse with rm, London House, The Square, BH21 5PR, ☎ 604 – TV. VISA.
M *(closed Saturday lunch, Sunday and Monday)* 12.95 **t.** (dinner) and a la carte 19.95/25.50 **t.** 3.30 – **3 rm** 27.50/45.00 **t.**

CRANBROOK Kent 404 V 30 – pop. 3 593 – ECD : Wednesday – ☎ 0580.

Envir. : Sissinghurst : castle★ (16C) (≤★, 78 steps), gardens★★ *AC*, NE : 1 ½ m.

18 Benenden Rd ☎ 712833.

Vestry Hall, Stone St. ☎ 712538 (summer only).

London 53 – Hastings 19 – Maidstone 15.

Kennel Holt ⚘, Goudhurst Rd, TN17 2PT, NW : 2¼ m. by A 229 on A 262 ✆ 712032, Fax 712931, ≤, « Gardens » – TV ☎ P. VISA
M 16.75/19.75 ₫ 4.00 – ☐ 7.50 – **9 rm** 60.00/95.00 – SB 199.00/345.00 **st.**

Hartley Mount, TN17 3QX, S : ½ m. on A 229 ✆ 712230, – TV ☎ P. VISA
M (bar lunch)/dinner a la carte 14.40/20.00 **st.** ₫ 4.00 – **5 rm** ☐ 45.00/95.00 **st.** – SB (weekends only) 70.00 **st.**

Old Cloth Hall ⚘, TN17 3NR, E : 1 m. by Tenterden Rd ✆ 712220, ≤, « Tudor manor house, gardens », park, – TV P.
closed Christmas – **M** *(unlicensed)* (dinner only, residents only) 21.00 – **3 rm** ☐ 45.00/ 90.00.

at Sissinghurst NE : 1¾ m. by B 2189 on A 262 – ✉ ☎ 0580 Cranbrook :

Rankins, The Street, TN17 2JH, ✆ 713964 – VISA
closed Sunday dinner, Monday, Tuesday, last week May, 1 week October, and Bank Holidays – **M** 22.00/26.00 **t.** ₫ 4.00.

FORD Stone St. ✆ 712121 RENAULT Wilsley Pound ✆ 713262

CRANLEIGH Surrey 404 S 30 – pop. 10 967 – ECD : Wednesday – ☎ 0483.

Fernfell G CC, Barhatch Lane ✆ 276626.

◆London 42 – ◆Brighton 36 – Reading 36 – ◆Southampton 58.

Restaurant Bonnett, High St., GU6 8AE, ✆ 273889, French rest. – AE VISA
closed, Sunday dinner and Monday – **M** 14.00/26.00 **t.** ₫ 3.75.

CRANTOCK Cornwall 403 E 32 – see Newquay.

Questa Guida non contiene pubblicità a pagamento.

CRAVEN ARMS Shropshire 403 L 26 – ☎ 058 87 Little Brompton.

◆London 170 – ◆Birmingham 47 – Hereford 32 – Shrewsbury 21.

Old Rectory ⚘, Hopesay, SY7 8HD, W : 3¾ m. by B 4368 ✆ 245, ≤, « Part 17C », – TV P.
closed 23 to 30 December – **M** 14.00 **t.** – **3 rm** ☐ 38.00/56.00 **t.**

CRAWLEY West Sussex 404 T 30 – pop. 80 113 – ECD : Wednesday – ☎ 0293.

18 Cottesmore, Buchan Hill ✆ 28256, S : 4 m. on plan of Gatwick Z – 18 Rusper Rd, Ifield ✆ 20222, W : 1½ m. on plan of Gatwick Z – 18 Titmus Drive, Tilgate ✆ 30103, SE : 1½ m. on plan of Gatwick Z – 9 Gatwick Manor ✆ 24470, N : 5 m. on plan of Gatwick Y – 9 Horsham Rd, Pease Pottage ✆ 21706 Z.

◆London 33 – ◆Brighton 21 – Lewes 23 – Royal Tunbridge Wells 23.

Plan of enlarged Area : see Gatwick

Holiday Inn London Gatwick, Langley Drive, Tushmore Roundabout, RH11 7SX, ✆ 529991, Telex 877311, Fax 515913, – rm rest TV ☎ P – 200. AE VISA BY **n**
M 12.50/16.50 **st.** and a la carte – ☐ 8.95 – **221 rm** 89.00/120.00 **st.**, **2 suites** 125.00/ 195.00 **st.**.

George (T.H.F.), High St., RH10 1BS, ✆ 24215, Telex 87385, Fax 548565 – rm TV ☎ P – 35. AE VISA BY **o**
M *(closed Saturday lunch)* 9.50/13.95 **st.** and a la carte ₫ 4.95 – ☐ 7.00 – **86 rm** 75.00/ 98.00 **st.** – SB (weekends only) 90.00/100.00 **st.**

Goffs Park, Goffs Park Rd, Southgate, RH11 8AX, ✆ 35447, Group Telex 87415, Fax 542050, – TV ☎ P – 120 AZ **s**
64 rm.

at County Oak N : 1½ m. by A 2219 on A 23 – ✉ ☎ 0293 Crawley :

Gatwick Manor (B.C.B.), London Rd, RH10 2ST, ✆ 26301, – TV ☎ P – 200. AE VISA. Y **n**
M 15.00 **st.** – **30 rm** ☐ 70.00/77.00 **st.**

at Copthorne NE : 4½ m. on A 264 –BY – ✉ Crawley – ☎ 0342 Copthorne :

Copthorne Effingham Park, West Park Rd, RH10 3EU, ✆ 714994, Telex 95649, Fax 716039, ≤, 9, park – TV ☎ P – 500. AE VISA
M 17.95 **t.** (lunch) and a la carte ₫ 4.00 – ☐ 8.50 – **118 rm** 95.00/120.00 **t.**, **3 suites** 195.00 **t.**.

Copthorne London Gatwick (Best Western), Copthorne Rd, RH10 3PG, ✆ 714971, Telex 95500, Fax 717375, park, squash – rm TV ☎ P – 90. AE VISA.
M 14.75 **st.** and a la carte ₫ 4.50 – ☐ 9.00 – **224 rm** 90.00/115.00 **st.**, **5 suites** 185.00/ 195.00 **st.** – SB (weekends only) 115.00/135.00 **st.**

at Ifield NW : 2 m. by A 2219 off Ifield Av. – AY – ✉ ☎ 0293 Crawley :

Brooklyn Manor ⚘ without rest., Bonnetts Lane, RH11 0NY, ✆ 546024, – TV P. AE VISA.
closed 24 December-4 January – ☐ 3.00 – **11 rm** 18.00/40.00 **st.**

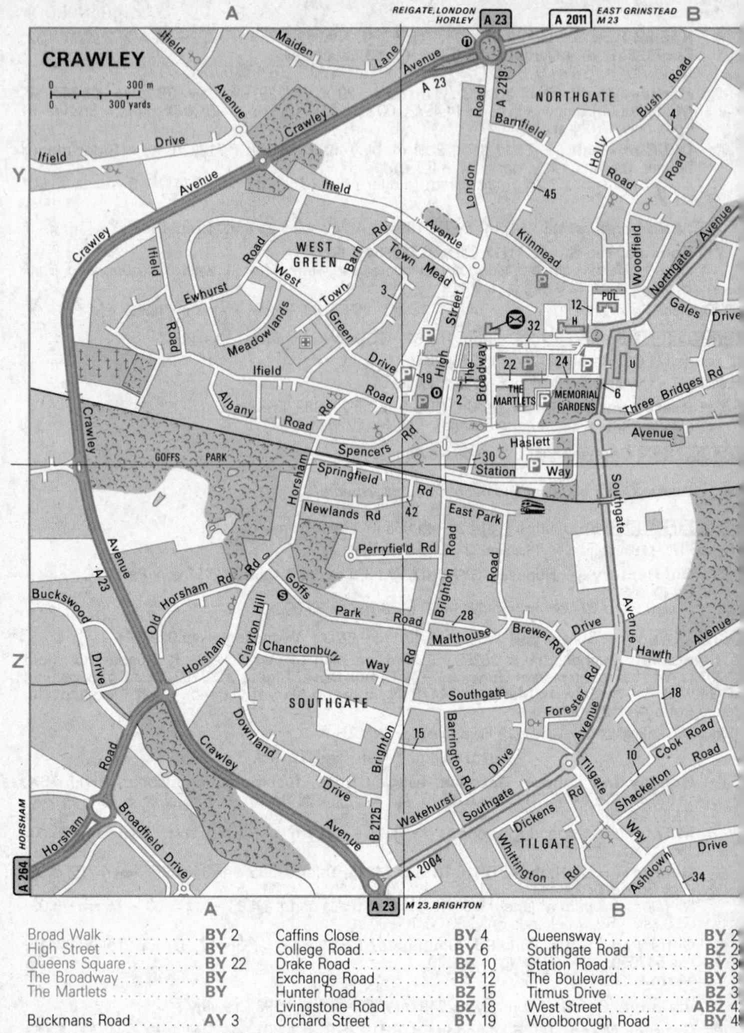

Broad Walk	BY 2	Caffins Close	BY 4	Queensway	BY 2
High Street	BY	College Road	BY 6	Southgate Road	BZ 2
Queens Square	BY 22	Drake Road	BZ 10	Station Road	BY 3
The Broadway	BY	Exchange Road	BY 12	The Boulevard	BY 3
The Martlets	BY	Hunter Road	BZ 15	Titmus Drive	BZ 3
		Livingstone Road	BZ 18	West Street	ABZ 4
Buckmans Road	AY 3	Orchard Street	BY 19	Woolborough Road	BY 4

CITROEN 163-165 Three Bridges Rd ℘ 25533
FORD Worth Park Av., Three Bridges ℘ 613361
PEUGEOT-TALBOT Barton ℘ 543232
RENAULT Orchard St. ℘ 23323
SKODA Balcombe Rd ℘ 882620
VW-AUDI Overdene Drive ℘ 515551

ATS Reynolds Rd, West Green ℘ 33151/2

CRAYKE North Yorks. – see Easingwold.

Besonders angenehme Hotels oder Restaurants sind im Führer rot gekennzeichnet.

Sie können uns helfen, wenn Sie uns die Häuser angeben, in denen Sie sich besonders wohl gefühlt haben.

Jährlich erscheint eine komplett überarbeitete Ausgabe aller Roten Michelin-Führer.

CREWE Cheshire 402 403 404 M 24 – pop. 59 097 – ECD : Wednesday – ☎ 0270.

Envir. : Sandbach (Two Crosses★ 7C, in Market Place) NE : 10 m.

Fields Rd ☎ 584227, E : 2¼ m. by A 534 – Queen7s Park ☎ 666724.

☎ 214343.

Market Hall, Earle St. ☎ 583191 ext 691.

London 174 – Chester 24 – Liverpool 49 – Manchester 36 – Stoke-on-Trent 15.

- **Crewe Arms,** Nantwich Rd, CW1 1DW, ☎ 213204, Fax 588615 – rm TV ☎ P – 80. **53 rm.**

FIAT Cross Green ☎ 500437
PEUGEOT-TALBOT 613 Crewe Rd, Wistaston ☎ 664111
VOLVO Earle St. ☎ 587711
VW-AUDI Oak St. ☎ 213241
ATS Gresty Rd ☎ 256285

CREWKERNE Somerset 403 L 31 **The West Country G.** – pop. 6 018 – ECD : Thursday – ☎ 0460.

Envir. : Cricket St. Thomas Wildlife Park★, W : 5 m. – Forde Abbey★, SW: 7 m. – Clapton Court Gardens★*AC*, S: 5 m.

London 145 – Exeter 38 – Southampton 81 – Taunton 20.

- **Old Parsonage,** 55-59 Barn St., TA18 8BP, W : ¼ m. by A 30 ☎ 73516 – TV ☎ P. AE VISA
  M *(closed Sunday dinner)* (lunch by arrangement)/dinner 12.95 **t.** and a la carte 3.00 – **10 rm** 46.50/68.00 **t.** – SB 86.00 **st.**
- **Broadview,** 43 East St., TA18 7AG, ☎ 73424, – rest TV P.
  M 8.50 – **3 rm** 22.50/29.00 – SB 46.00 **st.**

at Haselbury Plucknett NE : 2¾ m. by A 30 on A 3066 – ✉ ☎ 0460 Crewkerne :

- **Oak House,** North St., TA18 7RB, ☎ 73625, « 16C thatched cottage », – rest P
  Easter-October – **M** (by arrangement) 9.00 **st.** – **8 rm** 18.00/42.00 **st.**

Use this year's Guide.

CRICCIETH Gwynedd 402 403 H 25 – pop. 1 535 – ECD : Wednesday – ☎ 076 671 (4 fig.) or 0766 (6 fig.).

See : Castle ≤★★ *AC*.

Ednyfed Hill ☎ 522154.

The Sweet Stop, 47 High St. ☎ 523303.

London 249 – Caernarfon 17 – Shrewsbury 85.

- **Plas Isa,** Porthmadog Rd, LL52 0HP, ☎ 522443 – TV ☎ P. VISA
  closed 25 and 26 December – **M** *(closed Sunday dinner)* (dinner only and Sunday lunch)/dinner 10.50 **t.** and a la carte 3.95 – **12 rm** 27.50/65.00 **st.** – SB 55.00/65.00 **st.**
- **Glyn-y-Coed,** Porthmadog Rd, LL52 0HL, ☎ 522870 – TV P
  closed Christmas and New Year – **M** 9.00 **t.** 2.75 – **9 rm** 17.00/44.00 **t.**
- **Craig-y-Mor,** West Par., LL52 0EN, ☎ 522830, ≤ – TV ☎ P
  February-October – **M** 7.50 **st.** – **7 rm** 16.00/32.00 **st.** – SB 53.20/60.80 **st.**

AUDI-VW, MERCEDES-BENZ Caernarfon Rd ☎ 2516
FIAT Ala Rd, Pwllheli ☎ 612827
VOLVO Penamser Rd ☎ (Portmadoc) 3717

CRICK Northants. 403 404 Q 26 – see Rugby.

CRICKHOWELL Powys 403 K 28 – pop. 1 979 – ECD : Wednesday – ☎ 0873.

Envir. : Tretower Court and Castle★, NW : 2½ m.

Llangattock ☎ 810373.

London 169 – Abergavenny 6 – Brecon 14 – Newport 25.

- **Gliffaes Country House**, NP8 1RH, W : 3¾ m. by A 40 ☎ 0874 (Bwlch) 730371, Fax 730463, ≤, « Country house and gardens on the banks of the River Usk », park, – rest ☎ P. AE VISA.
  closed 31 December-15 March – **M** (buffet lunch)/dinner 15.25 **st.** and a la carte – **19 rm** 28.00/76.00 **st.** – SB 49.50/60.50 **st.**
- **Bear,** High St., NP8 1BW, ☎ 810408, Fax 811696 – TV ☎ P. AE VISA
  M *(closed Sunday)* (bar lunch)/dinner a la carte 14.45/19.40 **t.** 3.50 – **27 rm** 35.00/65.00 **t.**

CRICKLADE Wilts 403 404 O 29 – pop. 3 574 – ECD : Wednesday and Saturday – ☎ 0793 Swindon.

London 90 – Bristol 45 – Gloucester 27 – Oxford 34 – Swindon 6.

- **Cricklade H. & Country Club,** Common Hill, SN6 6HA, SW : 1 m. on B 4040 ☎ 750751, Fax 751767, ≤, park, – TV ☎ P – 80. AE VISA.
  M 12.00/18.00 **t.** and a la carte 4.50 – **47 rm** 75.00/95.00 **t.** – SB 85.00/90.00 **st.**

CRIPP'S CORNER East Sussex – see Sedlescombe.

CROMER Norfolk 404 X 25 – pop. 5 934 – ECD : Wednesday – ☎ 0263.

Royal Cromer, Overstand Rd ☎ 512884 – Mundesley, Links Rd ☎ 0263 (Mundesley) 720279, S : 7 m.

Town Hall, Prince of Wales Rd ☎ 512497.

♦London 132 – ♦Norwich 23.

- **Morden House,** 20 Cliff Av., NR27 0AN, ☎ 513396 – rest
  April-October and Christmas – **M** 9.50 **t.** 3.50 – **7 rm** 17.50/39.00 **t.** – SB (except Christmas) 46.00/50.00 **st.**
- **Danum House** without rest., 22 Pauls Lane, Overstrand, NR27 0PE, E : 1½ m. on B 1159 ☎ 026 378 (Overstrand) 327, –
  April-October – **6 rm** 14.00/28.00 **s.**
- **Birch House** without rest., 34 Cabbell Rd, NR27 9HX, ☎ 512521 – .
  7 rm 15.00/36.00 **s.**

CROOK Durham 401 402 O 19 – pop. 8 414 – ✉ ☎ 0388 Bishop Auckland.

Low Job's Hill ☎ 762429.

♦London 261 – ♦Carlisle 65 – ♦Middlesbrough 34 – ♦Newcastle-upon-Tyne 27.

- Helme Park Hall, DL13 4NW, NW : 3¼ m. by A 689 on A 68 ☎ 730970, ←, , park –
  10 rm.
- **Greenhead** without rest., Fir Tree, Bishop Auckland Rd, DL15 8BL, SW : 3½ m. by A 689 off A 68 ☎ 763143, « 18C house », – . VISA.
  6 rm 28.00/38.00 **st.**

CROSBY-ON-EDEN Cumbria 401 402 L 29 – see Carlisle.

CROSCOMBE Somerset 403 404 M 30 – see Shepton Mallet.

CROSSGATES Powys 403 J 27 – ✉ Llandrindod Wells – ☎ 059 787 Penybont.

♦London 172 – ♦Birmingham 81 – Hereford 39 – Shrewsbury 60.

- **Guidfa House,** LD1 6RF, ☎ 241, –
  M 11.00 **st.** 2.50 – **7 rm** 17.50/37.00 **st.**

CROSSHANDS Dyfed 403 H 28 – pop. 9 120 – ☎ 0269.

♦London 208 – Fishguard 63 – ♦Swansea 19.

- **Travelodge** without rest., SA14 6NW, on A 48 ☎ 845700, Reservations (Toll free) 0800 850950 – . AE VISA.
  32 rm 24.00/29.50 **t.**

CROWBOROUGH East Sussex 404 U 30 – pop. 17 008 – ECD : Wednesday – ☎ 0892 Tunbridge Wells.

♦London 45 – ♦Brighton 25 – Maidstone 26.

- **Winston Manor,** Beacon Rd, TN6 1AD, on A 26 ☎ 652772, Fax 665537, , – – 250. AE VISA
  M (closed Saturday lunch) 12.50/16.50 **t.** and a la carte 5.00 – **50 rm** 65.00/90.00 **t.** – SB (weekends only) 90.00 **st.**

FORD Crowborough Hill ☎ 652175
ROVER Beacon Rd ☎ 652777
TALBOT Church Rd ☎ 653424
ATS Church Rd ☎ 662100

CROWTHORNE Berks. 404 R 29 – pop. 19 166 – ECD : Wednesday – ☎ 0344.

♦London 42 – Reading 15.

- **Waterloo** (T.H.F.), Dukes Ride, RG11 7NW, on B 3348 ☎ 777711, Telex 848139, Fax 778913 – rm – 45. AE VISA
  M 10.25/22.00 **st.** and a la carte 4.35 – 7.00 – **58 rm** 74.00/80.00 **st.** – SB (weekends only) 80.00/90.00 **st.**
- **Dial House,** 62 Dukes Ride, RG11 6DL, ☎ 776941, Fax 777191, – rest . VISA.
  M (by arrangement) 12.50 **st.** 2.50 – **15 rm** 30.00/70.00 **st.** – SB (weekends only) 95.00/110.00 **st.**
- **Beijing,** 103 Old Wokingham Rd, RG11 6LH, NE : ¾ m. by A 3095 ☎ 778802, Chinese rest. – . AE VISA
  closed Sunday lunch and Bank Holidays – **M** approx. 17.80 **t.**

CROXDALE Durham –see Durham.

Europe

If the name of the hotel is not in bold type, on arrival ask the hotelier his prices.

CROYDE Devon 403 H 30 The West Country G. – ✉ Braunton – ☎ 0271.
♦London 232 – Barnstaple 10 – Exeter 50 – Taunton 61.

Kittiwell House, St. Mary's Rd, EX33 1PG, ℘ 890247, « 16C thatched Devon long-house » – ⇹ rm TV P. AE VISA
closed mid January-mid February – **M** (dinner only and Sunday lunch)/dinner 14.30 **t.** and a la carte 3.50 – **12 rm** 37.00/64.00 **t.** – SB (except summer and Bank Holidays) 140.00 **st.**

Whiteleaf, Hobbs Hill, EX33 1PN, ℘ 890266, – TV ☎ P. VISA
closed 2 weeks May and 2 weeks August – **M** (dinner only) 13.00 **st.** 3.90 – **5 rm** 29.00/48.00 **st.**

CRUDWELL Wilts. 403 404 N 29 – see Malmesbury.

CRUG-Y-BAR Dyfed 403 I 27 – ECD : Saturday – ✉ Llanwrda – ☎ 0558 Talley.
♦London 213 – Carmarthen 26 – ♦Swansea 36.

Glanrannell Park, SA19 8SA, SW : ½ m. by B 4302 ℘ 685230, ←, park – ⇹ rest P
April-October – **M** *(closed Sunday lunch)* (bar lunch)/dinner 17.50 **st.** 3.00 – **8 rm** 27.00/46.00 **st.** – SB (April-October) 66.00/74.00 **st.**

CRYMMYCH Dyfed 403 G 28 – ✉ Whitland – ☎ 099 47 Hebron.
♦London 245 – Carmarthen 25 – Fishguard 19.

Preseli Country House, SA34 0YP, S : 4 m. by A 478, on lane opposite disused quarry ℘ 419425, Fax 419425, ←, park – TV P
closed January – **M** (communal dining) 14.00 **st.** – **5 rm** (dinner included) 35.00/70.00 **st.** – SB 60.00/75.00 **st.**

CUCKFIELD West Sussex 404 T 30 – pop. 2 650 – ECD : Wednesday – ☎ 0444 Haywards Heath.
♦London 40 – ♦Brighton 15.

Ockenden Manor, Ockenden Lane, RH17 5LD, ℘ 416111, Fax 415549, « Part 16C manor », – TV ☎ P. AE VISA.
M 16.95/28.00 **t.** 4.50 – 3.00 – **20 rm** 70.00/145.00 **t.**, **2 suites** 145.00/155.00 **t.** – SB (weekends only) 115.00/135.00 **st.**

CUFFLEY Herts. 404 T 28 – pop. 4 875 – ECD : Thursday – ☎ 0707 Potters Bar.
♦London 16 – ♦Cambridge 44 – Luton 26.

XX **Gable House** with rm, 14-16 Newgate Street Village, SG13 8RA, N : 3 m. by B 157 ℘ 873899 – TV ☎. AE VISA
M 30.00 **t.** and a la carte 6.00 – 7.50 – **2 rm** 45.00 **t.**

CULLOMPTON Devon 403 J 31 – ☎ 0884.
♦London 197 – Exeter 15 – Taunton 29.

Toad Hall, Exeter Rd, EX15 1DY, S : ½ m. on B 3181 ℘ 32272, Fax 34568, – TV ☎ P – 200
18 rm.

CUMNOR Oxon. 403 404 P 28 – see Oxford.

CWMBRAN Gwent 403 K 29 – pop. 44 592 – ECD : Wednesday – ☎ 063 33.
Greenmeadow, Treherbert Rd ℘ 69321.
♦London 149 – ♦Bristol 35 – ♦Cardiff 17 – Newport 5.

Parkway, Cwmbran Drive, NP44 3UW, S : 1 m. by A 4051 ℘ 871199, Telex 497887, Fax 69160, , – ⇹ rm TV ☎ P – 300. AE VISA
M *(closed Saturday lunch)* 11.45 **st.** and a la carte 4.10 – **70 rm** 50.50/82.50 **st.**, **1 suite** 101.00/134.70 **st.** – SB (weekends only) 62.50 **st.**

ATS Station Rd ℘ 4964

DALLINGTON East Sussex 404 V 31 – pop. 286 – ✉ Heathfield – ☎ 042 482 Brightling.
♦London 59 – ♦Brighton 26 – Hastings 14 – Maidstone 34.

X **Little Byres,** Christmas Farm, Battle Rd, Wood's Corner, TN21 9LE, on B 2096 ℘ 230, « Converted timber framed barn », – P. VISA
closed Sunday – **M** (dinner only) 26.50 **t.** 3.95.

DARESBURY Cheshire 402 403 404 M 23 – pop. 353 – ✉ ☎ 0925 Warrington.
♦London 197 – Chester 16 – ♦Liverpool 22 – ♦Manchester 25.

Lord Daresbury (De Vere), Chester Rd, WA4 4BB, on A 56 ℘ 67331, Telex 629330, Fax 65615, , , squash – ⇹ rm TV ☎ P – 500. AE VISA
M 18.00 **st.** (lunch) and dinner a la carte 17.00/22.50 **st.** 4.95 – **138 rm** 60.00/110.00 **st.**, **3 suites** 150.00/170.00 **st.** – SB (weekends only) 95.00/105.00 **st.**

DARLINGSCOTT Warw. – see Shipston-on-Stour.

DARLINGTON Durham 402 P 20 – pop. 85 519 – ECD : Wednesday – 0325.

Blackwell Grange, Briar Close 464464, S : 1 m. on A 66 – Stressholme, Snipe Lane 353073, S : 2 m. on A 67 – Haughton Grange 463936, NE – Dinsdale Spa, Middleton St George 332222, SE : 5 m.

Tees-side Airport : 332811, E : 6 m. by A 67.

District Library, Crown St. 469858.

London 251 – Leeds 61 – Middlesbrough 14 – Newcastle-upon-Tyne 35.

Blackwell Grange Moat House (Q.M.H.), Blackwell Grange, DL3 8QH, SW : 2 m. on A 66 380888, Telex 587272, Fax 380899, rm 300. **M** a la carte 12.75/26.65 **st.** 4.00 – **95 rm** 76.00/100.00 **st.**, **3 suites** 150.00 **st.** – SB (weekends only) 108.00 **st.**

King's Head (Swallow), Priestgate, DL1 1NW, 380222, Telex 587112, Fax 382006 – 200. **M** *(closed Saturday lunch)* 10.50/13.00 **st.** and a la carte – **60 rm** 60.00/85.00 **st.** – SB (weekends only, July and August) 80.00 **st.**

White Horse, Harrowgate Hill, DL1 3AD, N : 2 ¼ m. on A 167 382121, Fax 355953 – rm – 50 **40 rm.**

Bishop's House, 38 Coniscliffe Rd, DL3 7RG, 382200 – *closed Saturday lunch and Sunday* – **M** 12.50/21.00 **t.** and a la carte 4.50.

Sardis, 196 Northgate, DL1 1QU, 461222 – *closed Sunday and 25-26 December* – **M** a la carte 8.70/15.80 **t.** 3.75.

Victor's, 84 Victoria Rd., DL1 5JW, 480818 – *closed Sunday, Monday and 1 week Christmas-New Year* – **M** 6.50/16.00 **t.** 3.50.

at Coatham Mundeville N : 4 m. by A 167 – 0325 Darlington :

Hall Garth Country House, DL1 3LU, 300400, Fax 310083, heated, rest – 300 **39 rm**, **1 suite.**

at Tees-side Airport E : 5 ½ m. by A 67 – 0325 Darlington :

St. George (Mt. Charlotte Thistle), DL2 1RH, 332631, Telex 587623, Fax 333851, squash – rm – 200. **M** *(closed Saturday lunch, Sunday dinner and Bank Holidays)* 8.95/13.00 **t.** and a la carte 4.40 – **58 rm** 55.00/75.00 **t.**, **1 suite** 85.00/90.00 **t.** – SB (weekends only) 70.00/80.00 **st.**

at Neasham SE : 6 ½ m. by A 66 off A 167 – 0325 Darlington :

Newbus Arms (Best Western), Hurworth Rd, DL2 1PE, W : ½ m. 721071 Fax 721770, squash – – 30. *closed 24 to 28 December* – **M** 16.50 **t.** and a la carte – **15 rm** 49.50/80.00 **st.** – SB 84.00/100.00 **st.**

at Headlam NW : 6 m. by A 67 – Gainford – 0325 Darlington :

Headlam Hall, DL2 3HA, 730238, ≤, « Part Jacobean mansion », park, – – 30. *closed 1 week Christmas* – **M** (lunch by arrangement)/dinner 20.00 **st.** and a la carte 3.2 – **17 rm** 43.00/62.00 **st.**, **3 suites** 62.00/72.00 **st.** – SB (weekend only) 72.00/80.00 **st.**

CITROEN 163 Northgate 468753
FIAT Woodland Rd 483251
FORD St. Cuthberts Way 467581
HONDA Chestnut St. 485141
LADA Albert Rd 485759
NISSAN Haughton Rd 462222
ROVER Croft Rd 488888
TOYOTA Neasham Rd. 482141
VAUXHALL Chestnut St. 466155
VAUXHALL-OPEL Whessoe Rd 466044
VOLVO Chestnut Street 353536
VW-AUDI 28-56 West Auckland Rd, Faverdale 353737

ATS Albert St., off Neasham Rd 46927 469693

DARTINGTON Devon 403 I 32 – see Totnes.

DARTMOUTH Devon 403 J 32 **The West Country G.** – pop. 5 282 – ECD : Wednesday and Saturday – 0803.

See : Site★★ (≤★) – Dartmouth Castle (≤★★★) *AC.*

Envir. : Start Point (≤★), S : 15 m. including 1 m. on foot.

11 Duke St. 4224.

London 236 – Exeter 36 – Plymouth 35.

Royal Castle, 11 The Quay, TQ6 9PS, ℘ 833033, Fax 835445, ≤ – TV ☎. VISA
M (bar lunch Monday to Saturday)/dinner 15.00 **t.** and a la carte 4.75 – **24 rm** 40.00/80.00 **t.** – SB 68.00/95.00 **st.**

Dart Marina (T.H.F.), Sandquay, TQ6 9PH, ℘ 832580, Fax 835040, ≤ – TV ☎ P. AE VISA
M 18.95 **st.** (dinner) and a la carte – 7.00 – **35 rm** 60.00/108.00 **st.** – SB 84.00/154.00 **st.**

Three Feathers without rest., 51 Victoria Rd, TQ6 9RT, ℘ 834694 – TV.
5 rm 15.00/30.00.

Mansion House, Mansion House St., TQ6 9AG, ℘ 835474
closed Tuesday lunch, Sunday, Monday, 1 week February and 3 weeks November – **M** a la carte 22.00/26.50 **t.** 4.00.

Carved Angel, 2 South Embankment, TQ6 9BH, ℘ 832465, ≤
closed Sunday dinner, Monday and January-early February – **M** 22.50/35.00 **st.** and a la carte 5.00.

at Stoke Fleming SW : 3 m. on A 379 – ✉ Dartmouth – 0803 Stoke Fleming :

Stoke Lodge, Cinders Lane, TQ6 0RA, ℘ 770523, ≤, heated, – TV ☎ P
M 8.25/13.95 **t.** and a la carte 3.50 – **24 rm** 35.00/55.00 **t.** – SB (except April-November) 64.00/68.00 **st.**

Endsleigh, New Rd, TQ6 0NR, ℘ 770381 – P
M (dinner only and Sunday lunch)/dinner 12.00 **t.** 3.00 – **7 rm** 17.50/40.00 **t.**

DAVENTRY Northants 404 Q 27 – 0327.

London 79 – Coventry 23 – Northampton 13 – Oxford 46.

Staverton Park, Staverton, NN11 6JT, SW : 2 ½ m. by A 45 on A 425 ℘ 705911, Fax 300821, ≤, – rm TV ☎ P – 300. AE VISA.
M 8.00/12.95 **t.** – **51 rm** 70.00/115.00 **t.**, **2 suites** 175.00 **t.** – SB (except Christmas and Bank Holidays) 139.00 **st.**

Penguin, London rd, NN11 4EN, SE : ¾ m. on A 45 at junction with A 361 ℘ 77333, Telex 312228, Fax 300420 – rm TV ☎ P – 300
146 rm, 2 suites.

DAWLISH Devon 403 J 32 The West Country G. – pop. 8 030 – ECD : Thursday and Saturday – 0626.

Warren ℘ 862255, E : 1 ½ m.

The Lawn ℘ 863589.

London 215 – Exeter 13 – Plymouth 40 – Torquay 11.

Langstone Cliff, Dawlish Warren, EX7 0NA, N : 2 m. by A 379 ℘ 865155, Fax 867166, heated, – TV ☎ P – 400. AE VISA
M 9.00/12.50 **st.** 3.60 – **64 rm** 40.00/70.00 **st.** – SB 86.00 **st.**

Lynbridge, 8 Barton Villas, The Bartons, EX7 9QJ, ℘ 862352, – rest P.
May-September – **M** 9.00 – **6 rm** 18.00/40.00 **st.**

DEAL Kent 404 Y 30 – pop. 26 548 – ECD : Thursday – 0304.

Walmer Kingsdown ℘ 373256 – Royal Cinque Ports, Golf Rd ℘ 374328.

Town Hall, High St. ℘ 369576.

London 78 – Canterbury 19 – Dover 8.5 – Margate 16.

Sutherland House, 186 London Rd, CT14 9PT, ℘ 362853 – rm P. VISA.
M (by arrangement) 25.00 **t.** 2.95 – **5 rm** 35.00/60.00 **t.**

Blencathra Country without rest., Kingsdown Hill, CT14 8EA, ℘ 373725, – TV P.
5 rm 15.00/34.00.

at Finglesham NW : 3 ½ m. by A 258 off North Bourne – ✉ 0304 Deal :

Finglesham Grange without rest., CT14 0NQ, NW : ¾ m. ℘ 611314, – P
closed Christmas-New Year – **3 rm** 22.50/40.00 **s.**

ATS 40 Gilford rd. ℘ 361543

DEDDINGTON Oxon. 403 404 Q 28 – pop. 1 617 – 0869.

London 72 – Birmingham 46 – Coventry 33 – Oxford 18.

Holcombe (Best Western), High St., OX5 4SL, ℘ 38274, Fax 37167, – TV ☎ P. AE VISA
M 16.95 **t.** and a la carte 4.95 – **17 rm** 54.00/88.00 **st.** – SB 86.00/94.00 **st.**

Tiffany's, Market Pl., OX5 4SE, ℘ 38813 – VISA
closed Sunday, Monday, last 2 weeks September and 1 week Christmas – **M** (dinner only) a la carte approx. 17.20 **t.** 3.50.

Les prix — Pour toutes précisions sur les prix indiqués dans ce guide, reportez-vous à l'introduction.

DEDHAM Essex 404 W 28 – pop. 1 905 – ECD : Wednesday – ✉ ☎ 0206 Colchester.
♦London 63 – Chelmsford 30 – Colchester 8 – ♦Ipswich 12.

Maison Talbooth without rest., Stratford Rd, CO7 6HN, W : ½ m. ☎ 322367, Group Telex 987083, Fax 322752, ≤, – TV ☎ P. VISA.
 5.50 – **9 rm** 95.00/145.00 **st.**, **1 suite** 145.00 **st.**.

Le Talbooth, Gun Hill, CO7 6HP, W : 1 m. ☎ 323150, Group Telex 987083, Fax 322752 ≤, « Tudor house in attractive riverside setting », – P. VISA
M 17.00 **t.** (lunch) and a la carte 28.00/36.30 **t.** 5.75.

Dedham Vale H. and Terrace Rest. with rm, Stratford Rd, CO7 6HW, W : ¾ m ☎ 322273, Group Telex 987083, Fax 322752, ≤, – TV ☎ P. VISA.
M *(closed Saturday lunch and Sunday dinner)* (buffet lunch)/dinner a la carte 17.25/26.75 5.25 – 5.00 – **6 rm** 70.00/95.00 **st.**

DERBY Derbs. 402 403 404 P 25 – pop. 218 026 – ECD : Wednesday – ☎ 0332.

See : Site★ – Museum and Art Gallery★ (Porcelain collection★, Wright of Derby collection★ YZ **M**.

Envir. : Kedleston Hall★★ (18C) *AC*, NW : 5 m. by Kedleston Rd X – Melbourne (St. Michael's Church : Norman nave★) S : 8 m. by A 514 X.

Shakespeare St., Sinfin ☎ 766323 X – Mickleover, Uttoxeter Rd ☎ 513339, W : 3 m. X – Kedleston Park ☎ 840035, N : 4 m. X – Chevin, Duffield ☎ 841864, N 5 m. X – Allestree Park Allestree ☎ 550616, N : 2 m. on A 6 X.

East Midlands, Castle Donington ☎ 810621, Telex 37543, SE : 12 m. by A 6 X.

Central Library, The Wardwick ☎ 290664.

♦London 132 – ♦Birmingham 40 – ♦Coventry 49 – ♦Leicester 29 – ♦Manchester 62 – ♦Nottingham 16 – ♦Sheffield 47 – ♦Stoke-on-Trent 35.

Plan opposite

Pennine (De Vere), Macklin St., DE1 1LF, ☎ 41741, Fax 294549 – TV ☎ – 300. VISA Z
M *(closed lunch Saturday, Sunday and Bank Holidays)* (carving lunch) 8.00 **st.** (lunch) and dinner a la carte 9.80/18.75 **st.** 4.50 – **94 rm** 60.00/75.00 **st.** SB (weekends only) 65.00 **st.**

Midland, Midland Rd, DE1 2SQ, ☎ 45894, Telex 378373, Fax 293522, – TV ☎ P 150. AE VISA Z
closed 25-26 December and 1 January – **M** *(closed Saturday lunch)* a la carte 10.85/18.35 – **60 rm** 60.00/90.00 **t.**

Gables, 119 London Rd, DE1 2QR, ☎ 40633, Fax 293502 – TV ☎ P – 150. AE VISA Z
closed 1 week Christmas – **M** 10.95 **st.** and a la carte 3.75 – **101 rm** 46.00/67.00 **st.** SB (weekends only) 54.95/59.95 **st.**

Oast House, Foresters Leisure Park, Ormaston Park Rd, DE3 8AG, ☎ 270027 Fax 270528 – TV ☎ & P – 40. AE VISA. X
M a la carte 12.95/20.95 **st.** – **25 rm** 39.90/59.90 **st.**

La Gondola with rm, 220 Osmaston Rd, DE3 8JX, ☎ 32895, Fax 384512 – TV ☎ P. VISA. X
closed Sunday – **M** (Dancing Saturday) 6.25/9.25 **t.** and a la carte 4.00 – **18 rm** 58.00/79.00 **t.**, **1 suite** 119.00/150.00 **t.**.

at Breadsall NE : 4 m. by A 52 off A 61 – ✉ ☎ 0332 Derby :

Breadsall Priory H. Golf & Country Club, Moor Rd, Morley, DE7 6DL, NE : 1 ¼ m. via Rectory Lane ☎ 832235, Telex 37409, Fax 833509, , , , 18, , , squash – rm TV ☎ & P – 90. AE VISA.
M *(closed Saturday lunch)* (carving lunch)/dinner 28.00 **st.** and a la carte – **92 rm** 80.00/105.00 **st.**

at Littleover SW : 2 ½ m. on A 5250 – ✉ ☎ 0332 Derby :

Crest (T.H.F.), Pastures Hill, DE3 7BA, ☎ 514933, Telex 377081, Fax 518668, – rm TV ☎ & P – 35. AE VISA X
M *(closed lunch Saturday and Bank Holiday Mondays)* 5.95/14.30 **st.** and a la carte – 7.95 – **64 rm** 73.00/99.00 **st.**, **2 suites** 120.00 **st.**.

AUDI-VW Sir Frank Whittle Rd ☎ 290022
BMW King St. ☎ 369511
CITROEN, DAIHATSU Alfreton Rd ☎ 381502
FORD Normanton Rd ☎ 40271
MAZDA 574-576 Burton Rd ☎ 369723
NISSAN Mansfield Rd ☎ 292525
PEUGEOT-TALBOT 4 Chequers Rd, Pentagon Island ☎ 361626
RENAULT 1263 London Rd, Alvaston ☎ 571847
ROVER Derwent St. ☎ 31166
SUZUKI 34-39 Duffield Rd ☎ 32706
TOYOTA St. Alkmunds Way ☎ 49536
VAUXHALL-OPEL Pentagon Island, Nottingham Rd ☎ 362661
VOLVO Kedleston Rd ☎ 32625

ATS Gosforth Rd off Ascot Drive ☎ 40854
ATS 67 Bridge St. ☎ 47327

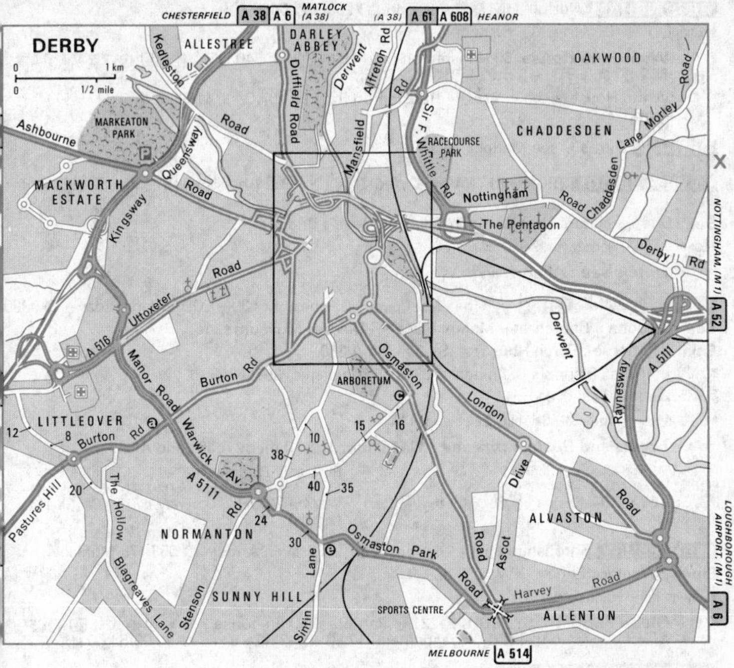

DERBY

Corn Market Z 13
Iron Gate Y 22
Shopping Centre Z
Victoria Street Z 39

Albert Street Z 2
Babington Lane Z 3
Bold Lane Y 4
Bradshaw Way Z 5
Cathedral Road Y 7
Chain Lane X 8
Charnwood Street Z 9
Church Street X 10
Corden Avenue X 12
Corporation Street YZ 14
Dairy House Road X 15
Douglas Street X 16
Duffield Road Y 17
East Street Z 18
Full Street Y 19
Hillsway X 20
Jury Street Y 23
Kenilworth Avenue X 24
King Street Y 25
Leopold Street Z 26
Market Place YZ 27
Midland Road Z 28
Mount Street X 29
Newdigate Street X 30
Normanton Road Z 31
Queen Street Y 32
St. Mary's Gate Z 33
St. Peter's Street Z 34
St. Thomas Road X 35
Sacheveral Street Z 36
Stafford Street Z 37
Upper Dale Road X 38
Walbrook Road X 40
Wardwick Z 41

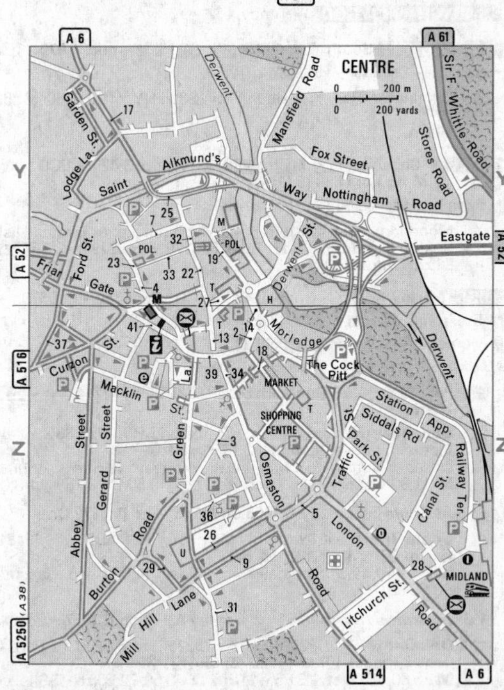

DERSINGHAM Norfolk 402 404 V 25 – pop. 3 263 – ✆ 0485.
♦London 110 – ♦Cambridge 53 – ♦Norwich 46.

- **Westdene House,** 60 Hunstanton Rd, PE31 6HQ, ✆ 540395, – TV P. VISA
M 7.50 **st.** 3.00 – **5 rm** 16.00/32.00 **st.**
- White House without rest., 44 Hunstanton Rd, PE31 6HQ, ✆ 41895 – P
4 rm.

DETHICK Derbs. – see Matlock.

DEVIL'S BRIDGE **(PONTARFYNACH)** Dyfed 403 I 26 – ✉ Aberystwyth – ✆ 097 085 Ponterwyd.
See : Site★ – Nature Trail (Mynach Falls and Devil's Bridge)★★.
♦London 230 – Aberystwyth 12 – Shrewsbury 66.

Hotels see : Aberystwyth W : 12 m.

DEVIZES Wilts. 403 404 O 29 **The West Country G.** – pop. 12 430 – ECD : Wednesday – ✆ 0380.
See : St. John's Church★★ – Market Place★ – Devizes Museum★ *AC*.
Envir. : Potterne : Porch House★★, S : 2 m. on A 360.
18 North Wilts., Bishop's Cannings ✆ 038 086 (Cannings) 257, N : 5 m.
Market Pl. ✆ 836618.
♦London 98 – ♦Bristol 38 – Salisbury 25 – Swindon 19.

Hotels and Restaurants see : Melksham, W : 10 m. by A 361 and A 365

AUDI-VW The Green ✆ 3667
FORD New Park St. ✆ 3456
PEUGEOT-TALBOT Chirton ✆ 038 084 (Chirton) 281
RENAULT Bath Rd ✆ 2032
SEAT Market Lavington ✆ 812761
VAUXHALL-OPEL Lydeway ✆ 038 084 (Chirton) 456

DIDDLEBURY Shropshire 403 L 26 – pop. 526 – ✉ Craven Arms – ✆ 058 476 Munslow.
Envir. : Wenlock Edge★, NW : 2½ m.
♦London 169 – ♦Birmingham 46.

- **Glebe Farm** , SY7 9DH, ✆ 221, « Part Elizabethan house », – rest TV P.
March-November – **M** (by arrangement) 12.50 **st.** 3.50 – **6 rm** 20.00/54.00 **st.**

DINBYCH-Y-PSYGOD = Tenby.

DINNINGTON South Yorks. 402 403 404 Q 23 – pop. 1 870 – ✉ Sheffield – ✆ 0909.
♦London 166 – Lincoln 37 – ♦Sheffield 12.

- Dinnington Hall , Falcon Way, S31 7NY, off B 6060 ✆ 569661, Fax 563411, – TV ☎ P
10 rm.

DISLEY Cheshire 402 403 404 N 23 – pop. 3 425 – ECD : Wednesday – ✉ Stockport – ✆ 066 32 (4 fig.) or 0663 (5 fig.).
♦London 187 – Chesterfield 35 – ♦Manchester 12.

- Moorside (Best Western) , Mudhurst Lane, Higher Disley, SK12 2AP, SE : 2 m. by Buxton Old Rd ✆ 64151, Telex 665170, Fax 62794, ≤ – TV ☎ P – 200.
88 rm, **2 suites.**

DISS Norfolk 404 X 26 – pop. 5 463 – ECD : Tuesday – ✆ 0379.
9 Stuston Common ✆ 642847.
Meresmouth, Mere St. ✆ 650523.
♦London 98 – ♦Ipswich 25 – ♦Norwich 21 – Thetford 17.

- Park (B.C.B.), 29 Denmark St., IP22 3LE, ✆ 642244, – TV ☎ P – .
17 rm.
- XX **Salisbury House** with rm, 84 Victoria Rd, IP22 3JG, ✆ 644738, « Stylishly decorated Victorian house, garden » – TV P. VISA.
closed Saturday lunch, Sunday, Monday, 2 weeks August and 1 week Christmas – **M** 11.00 **t.** (lunch) and a la carte 17.80/19.60 **t.** 3.75 – 3.00 – **2 rm** 35.00/62.00 **t.**

at Scole E : 2 m. by A 1066 on A 143 – ✉ ✆ 0379 Diss :

- **Scole Inn** (Best Western), Main St., IP21 4DR, ✆ 740481, Fax 740762, « 17C inn » – rm TV ☎ P. AE VISA
M *(closed lunch Saturday and Monday)* 14.50 **t.** and a la carte – **23 rm** 45.00/70.00 **st.** – SB 65.00/75.00 **st.**

at Brome (Suffolk) SE : 2¾ m. by A 143 on B 1077 – ✉ ✆ 0379 Eye :

- **Oaksmere** , IP23 8AJ, ✆ 870326, Fax 870051, « Part 16C country house and gardens », park – TV ☎ P. AE VISA.
M 15.00/18.00 **st.** 3.85 – **11 rm** 48.50/72.50 **st.** – SB (except Christmas) 108.00 **st.**

at South Lopham W : 5½ m. on A 1066 – ✉ Diss – ☎ 037 988 Bressingham :

Malting Farm ⛰, Blo' Norton Rd, IP22 2HT, ☎ 201, ≤, « Working farm » – ⊁ Ⓟ. ⛌
closed Christmas and New Year – **M** (by arrangement) – **3 rm** ☕ 20.00/32.00 **s.**

at Fersfield NW : 7 m. by A 1066 – ✉ Diss – ☎ 037 988 Bressingham :

Strenneth Farmhouse ⛰, Old Airfield Rd, IP22 2BP, ☎ 8182, ⛱ – Ⓟ. VISA
M 10.50 **st.** 🍷 2.50 – **9 rm** ☕ 17.00/44.00 **st.**

FORD Park Rd ☎ 642311
ROVER Victoria Rd ☎ 643141
VAUXHALL-OPEL 142-144 Victoria Rd ☎ 642241
ATS Shelfanger Rd ☎ 642861

DITTON PRIORS Shropshire 403 404 M 26 – pop. 550 – ✉ Bridgnorth – ☎ 074 634.
♦London 154 – ♦Birmingham 34 – Ludlow 13 – Shrewsbury 21.

Howard Arms, WV16 6SQ, ☎ 200, ⛱ – Ⓟ. VISA
closed Sunday dinner, Monday, 2 weeks August and 2 weeks September – **M** (dinner only and Sunday lunch)/dinner 24.00 **t.** 🍷 4.00.

DOCKING Norfolk 404 V 25 – pop. 1 193 – ✉ King's Lynn – ☎ 0485.
♦London 118 – ♦Cambridge 63 – ♦Norwich 39.

Holland House without rest., Chequers St., PE31 8LH, ☎ 518295, ⛱ – TV Ⓟ
closed 2 weeks Christmas-New Year – **5 rm** ☕ 14.00/28.00 **s.**

DODDISCOMBSLEIGH Devon – see Exeter.

Großbritannien und Irland
ein Atlas in drei Ausgaben :
Paperback, gebunden, spiralgebunden

DOLGELLAU Gwynedd 402 403 I 25 – pop. 2 261 – ECD : Wednesday – ☎ 0341.
Envir. : N : Precipice walk★★, Torrent walk★, Rhaiadr Ddu (Black waterfalls★), Coed-y-Brenin Forest★ – E : Bwlch Oerddrws★ on road★ from Cross Foxes Hotel to Dinas Mawddwy – S : Cader Idris (road★★ to Cader Idris : Cregenneu lakes) – Tal-y-Llyn Lake★★.
⛳9 Pencefn Rd ☎ 422603.
ℹ The Bridge ☎ 422888 (summer only).
♦London 221 – Birkenhead 72 – Chester 64 – Shrewsbury 57.

Royal Ship, Queen Sq., LL40 1AR, ☎ 422209 – lift TV Ⓟ
24 rm.

at Ganllwyd N : 5½ m. on A 470 – ✉ Dolgellau – ☎ 034 140 Ganllwyd :

Dolmelynllyn Hall ⛰, LL40 2HP, N : 5½ m. on A 470 ☎ 273, ≤, 🎣, ⛱ – ⊁ rest TV Ⓟ. AE VISA
closed December-February – **M** (lunch by arrangement)/dinner 16.95 **st.** 🍷 4.15 – **11 rm.**

at Llanfachreth NE : 3¾ m. by A 494 – ✉ ☎ 0341 Dolgellau :

Ty Isaf ⛰, LL40 2EA, ☎ 423261, ≤, « 17C Longhouse », ⛱ – ⊁ rm Ⓟ
M 9.50 **st.** – **3 rm** ☕ 30.00/40.00 **st.**

at Penmaenpool W : 2 m. on A 493 – ✉ ☎ 0341 Dolgellau :

George III, LL40 1YD, ☎ 422525, Fax 423565, ≤ Mawddach estuary and mountains – TV ☎ Ⓟ. AE VISA. ⛌
closed 2 weeks Christmas-New Year – **M** *(closed Sunday dinner to non-residents)* (bar lunch Monday to Saturday)/dinner a la carte 10.90/32.55 **t.** 🍷 3.70 – **12 rm** ☕ 55.00/84.70 **st.** – SB (November-April) (except Bank Holidays) 72.60/92.60 **st.**

at Bontddu W : 5 m. on A 496 (Barmouth Rd) – ✉ Dolgellau – ☎ 034 149 Bontddu :

Bontddu Hall, LL40 2SU, ☎ 661, Fax 284, ≤ Mawddach estuary and mountains, « Victorian mansion in large gardens » – ⊁ rest TV ☎ Ⓟ. AE ⓓ VISA. ⛌
Easter-October – **M** 7.95/19.50 **t.** and a la carte 🍷 3.50 – **19 rm** ☕ 42.50/70.00 **t.**, **3 suites** 90.00/115.00 **t.** – SB (Except Bank Holidays) 90.00/99.00 **st.**

Borthwnog Hall with rm, LL40 2TT, E : 1 m. on A 496 ☎ 271, ≤, « Part Regency house on banks of Mawddach estuary », ⛱, park – ⊁ rest TV Ⓟ. AE VISA. ⛌
M *(closed lunch Monday to Saturday except July and August)* (booking essential) 6.50/11.75 **t.** and a la carte 🍷 4.00 – **3 rm** ☕ 40.00/66.00 **t.** – SB 58.00/78.00 **st.**

FORD Arran Rd ☎ 423441
NISSAN Bala Rd ☎ 422681

DOLWYDDELAN Gwynedd 402 403 I 24 – pop. 480 – ECD : Thursday – ☎ 069 06.
♦London 232 – Holyhead 51 – Dolgellau 24 – LLandudno 27.

Elen's Castle, LL25 0EJ, on A 470 ☎ 207, ≤, 🎣, ⛱ – Ⓟ. AE ⓓ VISA. ⛌
M (bar lunch)/dinner 10.00 **s.** 🍷 3.90 – **10 rm** ☕ 18.00/42.00 **s.** – SB (except July and August) 50.80/54.80 **st.**

DONCASTER South Yorks. 402 403 404 Q 23 – pop. 74 727 – ECD : Thursday – ☎ 0302.

Crookhill Park, Conisbrough ☎ 0709 (Rotherham) 862979, W : 3 m. on A 630 – Doncaster Town Moor, The Belle Vue Club ☎ 535286 – Bawtry Rd, Bessacarr ☎ 868316, SE : 5 m. on A 638 – Hickleton ☎ 0709 (Rotherham) 892496, W : 6 m. on A 635 – Wheatley, Amthorpe Rd ☎ 831655, E : 3 m. – Thorne, Kirton Lane ☎ 0405 (Thorne) 812054.

Central Library, ☎ 734309.

London 173 – Kingston-upon-Hull 46 – Leeds 30 – Nottingham 46 – Sheffield 19.

Doncaster Moat House (Q.M.H.), Warmsworth, DN4 9UX, SW : 2 ¾ m. on A 630 ☎ 310331, Telex 547963, Fax 310197 – rest – . VISA
closed Christmas – **M** *(closed lunch Saturday and Bank Holidays)* 11.50/13.50 **st.** and a la carte – **70 rm** 69.00/89.00 **st.** – SB (weekends only) 72.00 **st.**

Grand St. Leger (Best Western), Racecourse Roundabout, Bennetthorpe, DN2 6AX, SE : 1 ½ m. on A 638 ☎ 329865, Fax 329865 – – 60. VISA.
M *(closed Saturday lunch and Sunday dinner)* 10.50/14.75 **st.** and a la carte – **13 rm** 59.50/70.00 **st.** – SB (weekends only) 70.00 **st.**

Punch's, Bawtry Rd, Bessacarr, DN4 7BS, SE : 3 m. on A 638 ☎ 370037, Telex 547137, Fax 532281 – rm – 40. VISA
M (grill rest.) a la carte 8.95/12.30 **st.** 3.00 – **24 rm** 35.50/55.50 **st.** – SB (weekends only) 57.00 **st.**

Danum (Swallow), High St., DN1 1DN, ☎ 342261, Telex 547533, Fax 329034 – – 300. VISA
M *(closed Saturday lunch)* 8.50/14.00 **st.** and a la carte 5.00 – **64 rm** 61.00/75.00 **st.** **2 suites** 80.00/95.00 **st.** – SB (weekends only and July) 70.00/85.00 **st.**

Ashlea without rest., 81 Thorne Rd, DN1 2ES, ☎ 363374 – . VISA.
12 rm 20.00/37.00 **st.**

at Rossington SE : 6 m. on A 638 – ☎ 0302 Doncaster :

Mount Pleasant, Great North Rd, DN11 0HP, on A 638 ☎ 868219, Fax 865130, – – 45. VISA.
closed Christmas Day – **M** 10.00 **st.** (dinner) and a la carte 11.30/20.30 **st.** 4.35 – **38 rm** 42.00/52.00 **st.**

at Carcroft NW : 6 ½ m. on A 1 – ☎ 0302 Doncaster :

Travelodge without rest., Great Norton Rd (Northbound carriageway), ☎ 330841, Reservations (Toll free) 0800 850950 – . VISA.
40 rm 24.00/29.50 **t.**

BMW Wheatley Hall Rd ☎ 369191
LANCIA Springwell Lane ☎ 854674
RENAULT Selby Rd, Thorne ☎ 0405 (Thorne) 8121100
TOYOTA Old Thorn Rd, Hatfield ☎ 840348
VW-AUDI York rd Roundabout ☎ 364141

ATS Carr Hill, Balby ☎ 367337/366997

DORCHESTER Dorset 403 404 M 31 **The West Country G.** – pop. 13 734 – ECD : Thursday – ☎ 0305.

See : Site★ – Dorset County Museum★*AC*.

Envir. : Bere Regis : St. John the Baptist Church★★★, NE : 11 m. by A 35 – Maiden Castle★★ (≤★) *AC*, SW : 2 m. by A 354 – Puddletown Church★, NE : 5 m. by A 35 – Athelhampton★*AC*, NE : 6 m. on A 35 – Moreton Church★, E : 10 m – Cerne Abbas★ N : 7 m.

Came Down ☎ 030 581 (Upwey) 2531, S : 2 m.

7 Acland Rd ☎ 67992.

London 135 – Bournemouth 27 – Exeter 53 – Southampton 53.

King's Arms, 30 High East St., DT1 1HF, ☎ 265353, Fax 260269 – – 80. VISA
M a la carte 12.20/22.75 **st.** 3.95 – **33 rm** 54.00/140.00 **st.**

Casterbridge without rest., 49 High East St., DT1 1HU, ☎ 264043 – . VISA.
closed 25 and 26 December – **15 rm** 28.00/56.00 **t.**

Yalbury Cottage, Lower Bockhampton, DT2 8PZ, S : 2 ¼ m. by B 3150 and Bockhampton rd ☎ 262382, – . VISA.
M *(closed Sunday dinner to non-residents)* (dinner only) 15.50/19.50 **st.** – **8 rm** 55.00/75.00 **st.** – SB (except summer) 87.50/98.00 **st.**

Mock Turtle, 34 High West St., DT1 1UP, ☎ 264011 – VISA
closed lunch Monday and Saturday and Sunday – **M** 10.50/18.95 **t.** 4.00.

CITROEN, LAND-ROVER, RANGE-ROVER Puddletown ☎ 845456
FORD Great Western Industrial Est. ☎ 62211
MERCEDES-BENZ Millers Close , The Grove ☎ 264494
PEUGEOT London Rd ☎ 66066
ROVER 21-26 Trinity St. ☎ 63031
VAUXHALL 6 High East St. ☎ 63913
VOLVO Bridport Rd ☎ 65555

ATS Unit 4, Great Western Ind. Centre ☎ 64756

Do not use yesterday's maps for today's journey.

DORCHESTER Oxon. 403 404 Q 29 – pop. 1 045 – ☎ 0865 Oxford.

See : Abbey Church★ (14C).

London 51 – Abingdon 6 – ◆Oxford 8 – Reading 17.

White Hart, 26 High St., OX10 7HN, ✆ 340074, Fax 341082, « Tastefully converted 17C coaching inn » – TV ☎ P. AE VISA. ✻
M 12.50/17.50 **t.** and a la carte 6.00 – **15 rm** 60.00/90.00 **st.**, **5 suites** 120.00/130.00 **st.** – SB (October-March) (weekends only) 85.00/95.00 **st.**

George, 23 High St., OX10 7HH, ✆ 340404, Fax 341620 – TV ☎ P – 40. AE VISA
closed 23 to 29 December – **M** 17.50/25.00 **t.** and a la carte 3.75 – **18 rm** 60.00/95.00 **t.** – SB (weekends only) 90.00/100.00 **st.**

DORDON Staffs. 402 403 404 P 26 – pop. 9 641 (inc. Polesworth) – ✉ ☎ 0827 Tamworth.

◆London 124 – ◆Birmingham 18 – ◆Coventry 19 – ◆Leicester 26.

Hall End Hall without rest., Watling St., B78 1SZ, on A 5 ✆ 899200, – P. ✻
3 rm -/25.00 **s.**

DORKING Surrey 404 T 30 – pop. 14 602 – ECD : Wednesday – ☎ 0306.

Envir. : Box Hill ≤★★, NE : 2½ m. – Polesden Lacey★★ (19C) *AC*, NW : 4½ m.

18 Betchworth Park, Reigate Rd ✆ 882052 – 18 Ockley ✆ 030 679 (Ockley) 555.

◆London 26 – ◆Brighton 39 – Guildford 12 – Worthing 33.

Burford Bridge (T.H.F.), Box Hill, RH5 6BX, N : 1½ m. on A 24 ✆ 884561, Telex 859507, Fax 880386, heated, – rm TV ☎ P – 250. AE VISA
M 15.00/18.50 **st.** and a la carte 4.50 – 7.50 – **48 rm** 82.50/135.00 **st.** – SB (weekends only) 114.00 **st.**

White Horse (T.H.F.), High St., RH4 1BE, ✆ 881138, Fax 887241, heated – rm TV ☎ P – 60. AE VISA
M 9.50/13.95 **st.** and a la carte 4.35 – 7.00 – **68 rm** 70.00/95.00 **st.**

Travelodge without rest., Reigate Rd, RH4 1QB, E : ½ m. on A 25 ✆ 740361, Reservations (Toll free) 0800 850950 – TV P. AE VISA. ✻
29 rm 24.00/29.50 **t.**

XX **Partners,** 2-4 West St., RH4 1BL, ✆ 882826 – . AE VISA
closed Saturday lunch and Sunday dinner – **M** 17.75/29.95 **t.** 4.50.

X **Le Bistro,** 84 South St., RH4 2EZ, ✆ 883239, French rest. – AE VISA
closed Saturday lunch, Sunday, 1 to 3 January and Bank Holidays – – **M** 8.90/11.95 **st.** and a la carte 4.65.

ROVER 105 South St. ✆ 882244 VAUXHALL-OPEL Reigate Rd ✆ 885022

DORMINGTON Heref. and Worc. – see Hereford.

DORRINGTON Shropshire 402 403 L 26 – see Shrewsbury.

DOULTING 403 404 M 30 – see Shepton Mallet.

DOVER Kent 404 Y 30 – pop. 33 461 – ECD : Wednesday – ☎ 0304.

See : Castle★★ (12C) (≤★) *AC* Y.

Envir. : Barfreston (Norman Church★ (11C) : carvings★★) NW : 6½ m. by A 2 Z – Bleriot Memorial, E : 1½ m. Z A.

Shipping connections with the Continent : to France (Boulogne and Calais) (P & O European Ferries) (Hoverspeed) – to France (Calais) (Sealink) – to Belgium (Oostende) (P & O European Ferries) (3 h 45 mn to 4 h) – to Belgium (Zeebrugge) (P & O European Ferries) (4 h to 4 h 30 mn).

to Belgium (Oostende) (P & O European Ferries, Jetfoil) (1 h 40 mn).

Townwall St. ✆ 205108.

◆London 76 – ◆Brighton 84.

Plan on next page

Dover Moat House (Q.M.H.), Townwall St., CT16 1SZ, ✆ 203270, Telex 96458, Fax 213230, – rm TV ☎ – 80. AE VISA Y z
M 16.50 **st.** and a la carte – 7.50 – **79 rm** 71.00/83.00 **st.** – SB (weekends only) 86.00/97.00 **st.**

Mildmay, 78 Folkestone Rd, CT17 9SF, ✆ 204278 – TV ☎ P. VISA. ✻ Y n
closed late January – **M** (bar lunch)/dinner a la carte 10.00/20.25 **st.** – **21 rm** 38.00/50.00 **st.**

Cliffe Court, 25-27 East Cliff, Marine Par., CT16 1LU, ✆ 211001, ≤ – TV ☎ P – . AE VISA. ✻ Z a
M 9.25 **t.** (dinner) and a la carte 3.75 – **25 rm** 28.00/41.00 **st.**

P.T.O. →

DOVER

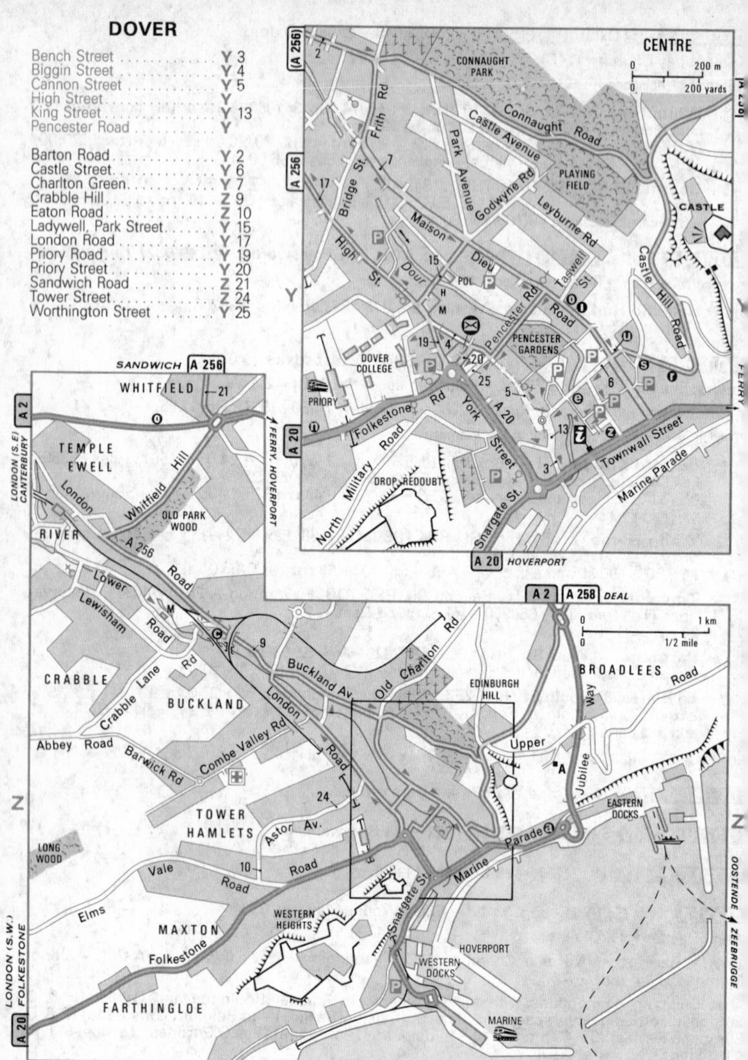

Travel Inn, Folkestone Rd, West Hougham, CT15 7AB, SW : 2 m. on A 20 ☎ 213339, Fax 214504 – ⇔ rm TV ♿ P. AE VISA.
M (Beefeater grill) a la carte approx. 12.25 **t.** – ☕ 4.50 – **30 rm** 27.50 **t.**

Hubert House, 9 Castle Hill Rd, CT16 1QW, ☎ 202253 – TV P. VISA — Y **s**
closed first 2 weeks October – **M** *(closed Sunday)* (dinner only) 8.50 **st.** and a la carte 🍷 3.50 – **8 rm** ☕ 21.00/36.00 **st.**

East Lee without rest., 108 Maison Dieu Rd, CT16 1RT, ☎ 210176 – ⇔ TV ☎. VISA.
4 rm ☕ 25.00/35.00 **st.** — Y **o**

Number One without rest., 1 Castle St., CT16 1QH, ☎ 202007, – TV.
5 rm ☕ 20.00/34.00. — Y **u**

Penny Farthing without rest., 109 Maison Dieu Rd, CT16 1RT, ☎ 205563 – ⇔ TV P.
6 rm ☕ 17.00/34.00 **s.** — Y **i**

↟ **Beulah House** without rest., 94 Crabble Hill, London Rd, CT17 0SA, ☏ 824615, 🌳 – 🚗 Ⓟ. 🚫 Z **c**
8 rm ☕ 17.00/34.00 **s.**

↟ **St. Martins and Ardmore** without rest., 17 Castle Hill Rd, CT16 1QW, ☏ 205938 – TV. 🚫 Y **r**
closed Christmas – **8 rm** ☕ 25.00/35.00 **st.**

✕ **Dino's,** 58 Castle St., CT16 1PJ, ☏ 204678, Italian rest. – AE ① VISA Y **e**
closed Monday and 3 weeks September-October – **M** a la carte 11.40/16.90 **t.** 🍷 3.60.

at St. Margaret's Bay NE : 4 m. by A 258 – Z – on B 2058 – ✉ ☎ 0304 Dover :

Cliffe Tavern, High St., CT15 6AT, ☏ 852400, 🌳 – TV Ⓟ
12 rm.

✕✕ **Wallet's Court** 🐦 with rm, West Cliffe, CT15 6EW, NW : ¾ m. on B 2058 ☏ 852424, « Part 17C manor house, 13C cellars », 🌳 – TV Ⓟ. VISA. 🚫
closed 24 to 27 December – **M** *(closed Sunday and Monday)* (dinner only) 25.00 **st.** 🍷 4.00 – **7 rm** ☕ 34.50/60.00 **st.**

at Whitfield NW : 3 ½ m. on A 256 – ✉ ☎ 0304 Dover :

Crest H. Dover (T.H.F.), Singledge Lane, CT16 3LF, ☏ 821222, Telex 965866, Fax 825576 – TV ☎ ♿ Ⓟ – 🎤 45. AE ① VISA. 🚫 Z **o**
M 9.90/15.05 **st.** and a la carte 🍷 4.50 – ☕ 7.95 – **67 rm** 72.00/82.00 **st.**

FORD Woolcomber St. ☏ 206518
RELIANT South Rd ☏ 206160
TOYOTA Poulton Close, Buckland Ind. Est. ☏ 201235
VW-AUDI 1 Crabble Hill ☏ 206710

DOWNTON Wilts. 403 404 O 31 – see Salisbury.

DRENEWYDD = Newtown.

DRENEWYDD YN NOTAIS **(NOTTAGE)** Mid Glam. – see Porthcawl.

DREWSTEIGNTON Devon 403 I 31 – ☎ 0647.
♦London 216 – Exeter 15 – ♦Plymouth 46

↟ **Hunts Tor House,** EX6 6QW, ☏ 21228 – 🚭 rest
March-November – **M** 16.50 **st.** 🍷 3.00 – ☕ 3.00 – **4 rm** 25.00/50.00 **st.**

DRIFFIELD Humberside 402 S 21 – see Great Driffield.

DRIFT Cornwall – see Penzance.

DROITWICH Heref. and Worc. 403 404 N 27 – pop. 18 025 – ECD : Thursday – ☎ 0905.
⛳18 Droitwich, Ford Lane ☏ 770129, N : 1 ½ m. by A 38.
ℹ Heritage Centre, St. Richards House, Victoria Sq ☏ 774312.
♦London 129 – ♦Birmingham 20 – ♦Bristol 66 – Worcester 6.

Raven, St. Andrews St., WR9 8DU, ☏ 772224, Group Telex 336673, 🌳 – 🛗 TV ☎ Ⓟ – 🎤 150. AE ① VISA
closed Christmas – **M** *(closed Saturday lunch and Sunday dinner)* 11.00/16.00 **st.** and a la carte 🍷 4.50 – ☕ 9.95 – **50 rm** 39.95/99.95 **st.**

St Andrews House, Worcester Rd, WR9 8AL, S : ¼ m. by A 38 ☏ 779677, 🌳 – TV ☎ Ⓟ – 🎤 80. AE ① VISA. 🚫
M (grill rest.) (lunch by arrangement)/dinner 18.00 **t.** 🍷 2.25 – **28 rm** ☕ 40.00/55.00 **t.** – SB (weekends only) 46.00 **st.**

Travelodge without rest., Rashwood Hill, WR9 8DA, NE : 1½ m. on A 38 ☏ 052 786 (Wychbold) 545, Reservations (Toll free) 0800 850950 – TV ♿ Ⓟ. AE VISA. 🚫
32 rm 24.00/29.50 **t.**

↟ Little Lodge Farm 🐦 without rest., Broughton Green, WR9 7EE, ☏ 052 784 (Hanbury) 305, « Attractive 17C timbered farmhouse », 🌳 – Ⓟ
3 rm.

FORD 141-149 Worcester Rd ☏ 772132
ROVER, LAND ROVER, LEYLAND DAF St. Georges Sq. ☏ 794000

DRONFIELD Derbs. 402 403 404 P 24 – pop. 22 641 – ECD : Wednesday – ✉ Sheffield (South Yorks) – ☎ 0246.
⛳18 Hallowes ☏ 413149.
♦ London 158 – Derby 30 – ♦ Nottingham 31 – ♦ Sheffield 6.

Manor, 10-15 High St., S18 6PY, ☏ 413971 – TV Ⓟ. AE ① VISA
M *(closed Sunday dinner)* 7.50/13.50 **t.** and a la carte 🍷 5.35 – **9 rm** ☕ 45.00/60.00 **t.** – SB (weekends only) 88.00/100.00 **st.**

DRY DRAYTON Cambs. – see Cambridge.

DUDLEY West Midlands 402 403 404 N 26 – ECD : Wednesday – ✉ ☎ 0384.

Himley Hall, Cabin, Himley Hall Park ☎ 0902 (Himley) 895207, W : 4½ m. on B 4176
Swindon, Bridgnorth Rd ☎ 0902 (Wombourne) 897031.

39 Churchill Precinct ☎ 50333.

♦London 132 – ♦Birmingham 10 – Wolverhampton 6.

Plan : see Birmingham p. 2

Himley House (B.C.B.), Himley, DY3 4LD, W : 4 m. by B 4176 on A 449 ☎ 0902 (Wolverhampton) 892468, Fax 892604, – TV ☎ P. AE VISA. AU
M (grill rest.) 15.00 **st.** and a la carte – **24 rm** 50.00/69.00 **st.**

Travelodge without rest., SW : 2 m. on A 461 ☎ 481579, Reservations (Toll free) 0800 85950 – TV & P. AE VISA.
32 rm 24.00/29.50 **t.**

ATS Oakeywell St. ☎ 238047

DULVERTON Somerset 403 J 30 **The West Country G.** – pop. 1 301 – ECD : Thursday – ☎ 0398

See : Site★.

Envir. : Tarr Steps★★, NW : 6 m. by B 3223.

♦London 198 – Barnstaple 27 – Exeter 26 – Minehead 18 – Taunton 27.

Ashwick House, TA22 9QD, NW : 3 m. by B 3223, Hawkridge rd and Ashwick rd ☎ 23868, ≤, « Country house atmosphere », – TV P.
M (dinner only and Sunday lunch)/dinner 20.00 **t.** 5.50 – **6 rm** (dinner included) 68.00/136.00 **st.** – SB 99.90/139.90 **st.**

DUNCHURCH Warw. 403 404 Q 26 – pop. 2 409 – ✉ ☎ 0788 Rugby.

♦London 90 – ♦Coventry 12 – ♦Leicester 24 – Northampton 26.

Travelodge without rest., London Rd, Thurslaston, CV23 9LG, NW : 2 ½ m. on A 4 ☎ 521538, Reservations (Toll Free) 0800 850950 – TV & P. AE VISA.
40 rm 24.00/29.50 **t.**

DUNSLEY North Yorks. – see Whitby.

DUNSTABLE Beds. 404 S 28 – pop. 48 436 – ECD : Thursday – ☎ 0582.

See : Priory Church of St. Peter (West front★).

Envir. : Whipsnade Park★ (zoo) ≤★★ *AC*, S : 3 m.

Dunstable Downs, Whipsnade Rd ☎ 604472, SW : 2 m. on B 4541 – Tilsworth, Dunstable Rd ☎ 0525 (Leighton Buzzard) 210721, N : 2 m. on A 5.

Vernon Pl. ☎ 471012.

♦London 40 – Bedford 24 – Luton 4.5 – Northampton 35.

Old Palace Lodge, Church St., LU5 4RT, ☎ 662201, Fax 696422 – rm rest TV ☎ P – 35. AE VISA
M *(closed Saturday lunch)* a la carte 18.70/25.20 **st.** – 7.95 – **49 rm** 69.50/90.00 **st.**

FIAT Poynters Rd ☎ 667742
FORD London Rd ☎ 667811
RENAULT Tring Rd ☎ 609605
ROVER 63 High St. South ☎ 666111
VAUXHALL-OPEL 7 The Green, Houghton Regis ☎ 864455
VW-AUDI Common Rd, Kensworth ☎ 872182

DUNSTER Somerset 403 J 30 **The West Country G.** – pop. 793 – ECD : Wednesday – ✉ Minehead – ☎ 0643.

See : Site★★ – Castle★★*AC* (upper rooms ≤★ from window) – Dunster Castle Water Mill★*AC* – Dovecote★ – St. Georges Church★.

Envir. : Exmoor National Park★★ (Dunkery Beacon★★★ – Tarr Steps Clapper Bridge★★ – Watersmeet★ – Valley of the Locks★) – Cleeve Abbey★★*AC*, SE : 5 m. on A 39.

♦London 184 – ♦Bristol 61 – Exeter 40 – Taunton 22.

Luttrell Arms (T.H.F.), 36 High St., TA24 6SG, ☎ 821555, Fax 821567, – TV ☎. AE VISA
M 8.95/16.50 **st.** and a la carte 4.35 – 7.00 – **27 rm** 60.00/85.00 **st.** – SB 100.00/126.00 **st.**

Exmoor House, 12 West St., TA24 6SN, ☎ 821268, – TV. AE VISA.
closed January and December – **M** (bar lunch residents only)/dinner 14.00 **st.** 2.70 – **6 rm** 31.50/48.00 **st.** – SB (February-November) 64.00/70.00 **st.**

***En saison,** surtout dans les stations fréquentées, il est prudent de retenir à l'avance.*
Cependant, si vous ne pouvez pas occuper la chambre que vous avez retenue, prévenez immédiatement l'hôtelier.
Si vous écrivez à un hôtel à l'étranger, joignez à vottre lettre un coupon-réponse international (disponible dans les bureaux de poste).

DURHAM Durham 401 402 P 19 – pop. 38 105 – ECD : Wednesday – ☎ 0385 (5 and 6 fig.) or 091 (7 fig.).

See : Cathedral★★★ (Norman) (Chapel of the Nine Altars★★) B – University (Gulbenkian Museum of Art and Archaeology★★ *AC*) by Elvet Hill Rd A – Castle★ (Norman chapel★) *AC* B.

⛳ Littleburn Farm, Langley Moor ✆ 378 0069, SW : 2 m. by A 690 A – ⛳ Mount Oswald, South Rd ✆ 386 5277 A – ⛳ Brancepeth Castle ✆ 378 0075, W : 4½ m. on A 690 A.

ℹ Market Pl. ✆ 384 3720.

♦London 267 – ♦Leeds 77 – ♦Middlesbrough 23 – Sunderland 12.

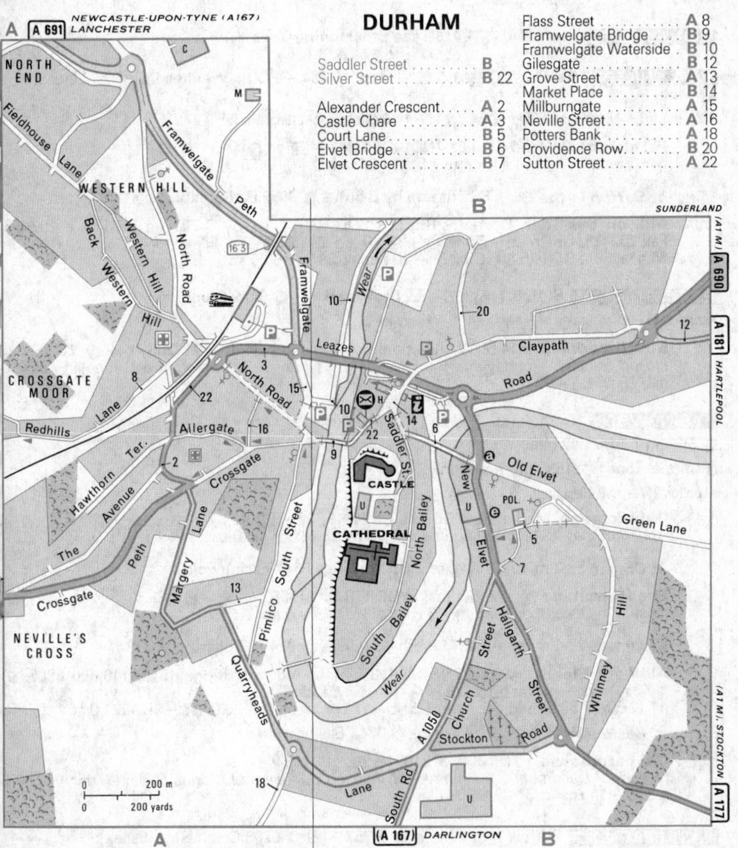

Royal County (Swallow), Old Elvet, DH1 3JN, ✆ 386 6821, Group Telex 538238, Fax 386 0704, – rm rest – 100. AE VISA B **a**
M 10.50/16.50 **st.** and a la carte 5.00 – **149 rm** 77.00/105.00 **st.**, **1 suite** 121.00/140.00 **st.** – SB (weekends only) 95.00/125.00 **st.**

Three Tuns (Swallow), New Elvet, DH1 3AQ, ✆ 386 4326, Fax 386 1406 – rm – 50. AE VISA B **e**
M *(closed Saturday lunch)* 8.75/13.50 **st.** and a la carte 5.00 – **48 rm** 59.00/76.00 **st.** – SB (weekends only) (except January-March) 82.00/90.00 **st.**

at Croxdale S : 3 m. by A 1050 on A 167 – B – ✉ ☎ 091 Tyneside :

Bridge Toby Hotel, DH1 3SP, ✆ 378 0524, Telex 538156 – – 50 – **46 rm.**

CITROEN Croxdale ✆ 0388 (Spennymoor) 814671
FORD Nevilles Cross ✆ 386 1155
HONDA Bearpark ✆ 386 2227
LADA Framwellgate Moor ✆ 386 9499
LANCIA 81 New Elvet ✆ 384 7777
MAZDA Framwellgate Moor ✆ 384 1925
ROVER Gilesgate Moor ✆ 386 7231
VAUXHALL Sacriston ✆ 371 0422
VW-AUDI 20 Alma Rd, Gilesgate Moor ✆ 386 7215

ATS Finchale Rd, Newton Hall ✆ 3841810
ATS Mill Rd, Langley Moor ✆ 378 0262

DUXFORD Cambs. 404 U 27 – see Cambridge.

DYFFRYN ARDUDWY Gwynedd 402 403 H 25 – pop. 1 122 (inc. Tal-y-bont) – 034 1 Ardudwy.

London 237 – Dolgellau 16 – Caernarfon 44.

Ael-Y-Bryn, LL44 2BE, on A 496 ℘ 701, Fax 682, – TV P. VISA
M (bar lunch)/dinner 12.00 **t.** and a la carte 3.50 – **8 rm** 30.00/50.00 **t.** – SB (September-April) 70.00/80.00 **st.**

MITSUBISHI Smithy Garage ℘ 279

EAGLESCLIFFE Cleveland 402 P 20 – see Stockton-on-Tees.

EARL SHILTON Leics. 403 404 Q 26 – pop. 16 484 – ECD : Wednesday – ✉ Leicester – 0455.

London 107 – Birmingham 35 – Coventry 16 – Leicester 9 – Nottingham 35.

Fernleigh, 32 Wood St., LE9 7ND, ℘ 847011 – TV ☎ P
M 8.75/12.00 **st.** and a la carte 3.50 – **27 rm** 40.00/55.00 **st.**

at Sutton in the Elms SE : 5½ m. by B 581 – 0455 Earl Shilton :

Mill on the Soar, Coventry Rd, LE9 6DQ, W : 1 m. by B 581 on B 4114 ℘ 282419 Fax 282419, Grill rest. – TV ☎ P – 40. AE VISA.
M a la carte 9.00/15.80 **st.** 2.95 – **20 rm** 38.00/46.00 **st.**

EARL STONHAM Suffolk 404 X 27 – ✉ Stowmarket – 0449 Stonham.

London 81 – Cambridge 47 – Ipswich 10 – Norwich 33.

Mr. Underhill's, IP14 5DW, Junction of A 140 and A 1120 ℘ 711206 – P. VISA
closed Sunday, Monday and Bank Holidays – **M** (lunch by arrangement) (booking essential) 29.50 **t.** 4.95.

EASINGWOLD North Yorks. 402 Q 21 – pop. 3 468 – ✉ York – 0347.

Stillington Rd ℘ 21486.

Chapel Lane ℘ 21530 (summer only).

London 217 – Middlesbrough 37 – York 14.

Old Vicarage, Market Pl., YO6 3AL, ℘ 21015, – TV P
April-October – **M** (by arrangement) – **7 rm** 16.00/30.00 **st.**

at Crayke E : 2 m. on Crayke rd – ✉ York – 0347 Easingwold :

The Hermitage without rest., YO6 4TB, ℘ 21635, <, – P.
closed 15 December-January – **3 rm** 15.00/33.00 **st.**

at Alne SW : 4 m. on Alne Rd – ✉ Aldwark – 034 73 Tollerton :

Aldwark Manor , YO6 2NF, SW : 3½ m. by Aldwark Bridge rd ℘ 8146, Fax 8867, <, 9, , park – rm TV ☎ P – 100. AE VISA
M 12.50/22.50 **st.** and a la carte 5.95 – **17 rm** 65.00/120.00 **st.** – SB 112.00 **st.**

at Raskelf W : 2¾ m. – ✉ York – 0347 Easingwold :

Old Farmhouse, , YO6 3LF, ℘ 21971 – P.
closed 22 December-31 January – **M** *(closed Sunday and Monday)* (dinner only) 13.50 **t.** 3.75 – **10 rm** 34.00/68.00 **t.**

EAST BERGHOLT Suffolk 404 X 28 – pop. 2 757 – ✉ 0206 Colchester (Essex).

London 59 – Colchester 9 – Ipswich 8.5.

Fountain House, The Street, CO7 6TB, ℘ 298232, « 15C cottage » – P. VISA
closed Saturday lunch, Sunday dinner, Monday, 1 week February and 2 weeks August – **M** 12.50/14.50 **t.**

EASTBOURNE

rndale Centre	V
rove Road	V
easide Rd.	V
outh Street	V
erminus Road	V
shford Road	V 2
edfordwell Road	V 3
hurch Street	Z 4
ornfield Road	V 5
evonshire Place	X 6
ildredge Road	V 7
ailsham Road	Y 8
igh Street	Z 9
ewes Road	Y 13
ismore Road	V 14
North Street	V 15
Polegate By-Pass	Y 18
St. Anthony's Avenue	Y 21
Station Road	Y 24
Susan's Road	V 25
The Goffs	Z 26
Trinity Trees	V 27
Upperton Road	V, Z 28

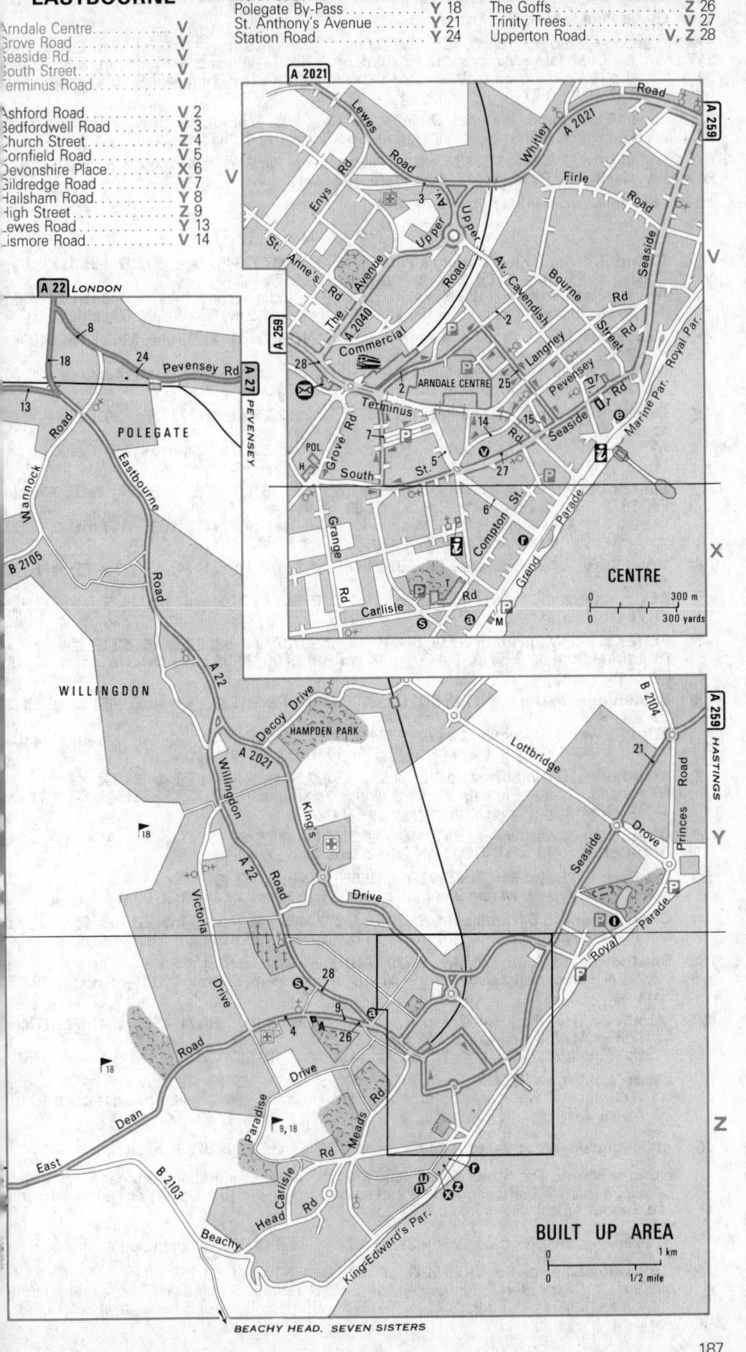

EASTBOURNE East Sussex 404 U 31 – pop. 86 715 – ECD : Wednesday – ☎ 0323.

See : Grand Parade★ X – Sea Front★.

Envir. : Beachy Head★★★ (cliff), ✻★, SW : 3 m. Z – Seven Sisters★ (cliffs) from Birling Gap SW : 5 m. Z – Charleston Manor★ AC, W : 8 m. by A 259 Z – W : scenic road★, from East Dean by A 259 Z up to Wilmington by West Dean – Wilmington : The Long Man★ : prehistoric giant figure, NW : 7 m. by A 27 Y.

18, 9 Royal Eastbourne, Paradise Drive ☎ 30412 Z – 18 Eastbourne Downs, East Dean Rd ☎ 20827, N : 1 m. on A 259 Z – 18 Willingdon, Southdown ☎ 410983, N : ½ m. by A 22 Y.

3 Cornfield Rd ☎ 411400/27432 – The Pier, Marine Parade, ☎ 411400 (summer only) at Pevensey, Castle Car Park ☎ 0323 (Eastbourne) 761444.

London 68 – Brighton 25 – Dover 61 – Maidstone 49.

Plan on preceding page

Grand (De Vere), King Edward's Par., BN21 4EQ, ☎ 412345, Telex 87332, Fax 412233, heated, – – 350. AE VISA Z
M (see also **Mirabelle rest.** below) 16.00/26.00 **st.** and a la carte 4.75 – **149 rm** 85.00/130.00 **st.**, **15 suites** 230.00/300.00 **st.** – SB (weekends only) 130.00/260.00 **st.**

Cavendish (De Vere), 37-40 Grand Par., BN21 4DH, ☎ 410222, Telex 87579, Fax 410941, – – 200. AE VISA X
M 15.00 **st.** (dinner) and a la carte 4.75 – **110 rm** 70.00/150.00 **st.**, **4 suites** 185.00/220.00 **st.** – SB (except Christmas and New Year) 120.00/195.00 **st.**

Queen's (De Vere), Marine Par., BN21 3DY, ☎ 22822, Telex 877736, Fax 30156, – – 150. AE VISA V
M 11.00/15.00 **t.** and a la carte – **106 rm** 70.00/120.00 **t.**, **2 suites** 140.00/200.00 **t.** – SB (weekends only) 100.00 **st.**

Lansdowne (Best Western), King Edward's Par., BN21 4EE, ☎ 25174, Telex 878624, Fax 39721, – – – 80. AE VISA Z
closed 1 to 12 January – **M** (a la carte lunch)/dinner 14.00 **st.** 5.00 – **130 rm** 43.50/89.00 **st.** – SB (except 6 May-26 October) 72.00/85.00 **st.**

Wish Tower, King Edward's Par., BN21 4EB, ☎ 22676, Fax 21474, – . AE VISA Z
M (buffet lunch Monday to Saturday) 10.50/15.95 **t.** 3.95 – **67 rm** 55.00/99.00 **t.** – SB 76.00/90.00 **st.**

Farrar's, 3-5 Wilmington Gdns, BN21 4JN, ☎ 23737, – . AE VISA
M (dinner only) 12.50 **st.** 4.90 – **44 rm** 33.00/60.00 **st.** – SB (November-April) 62.00 **st.** X

Brownings, 28 Upperton Rd, BN21 1JS, ☎ 24358, Fax 31288, heated – . AE VISA. Z
closed 3 weeks December-January – **M** *(closed Sunday dinner)* (dinner only and Sunday lunch)/dinner 14.95 **t.** and a la carte 2.95 – **10 rm** 32.00/60.00 **t.**

Mandalay, 16 Trinity Trees, BN21 3LE, ☎ 29222, – rest . VISA.
M *(closed Saturday lunch, Monday dinner and Sunday)* 10.00/13.95 **st.** 3.50 – **12 rm** 21.00/50.00 **st.** – SB (October-May) 55.00 **st.** V

Oban, King Edward's Par., BN21 4DS, ☎ 31581 – X
April-October – **M** 5.50/10.00 **t.** 4.00 – **30 rm** 22.00/44.00 **t.**

Far End, 139 Royal Par., BN22 7LH, ☎ 25666 – rest Y
March-September – **M** (by arrangement) 6.00 **st.** – **10 rm** 16.00/36.00 **st.**

Cherry Tree, 15 Silverdale Rd, BN20 7AJ, ☎ 22406 – rest . VISA. Z
M (by arrangement) 8.50 **t.** – **10 rm** 21.00/42.00 **t.** – SB (October-March) 48.50 **st.**

Southcroft, 15 South Cliff Av., BN20 7AH, ☎ 29071 – rest. Z
closed November and December – **M** (by arrangement) 6.00 **st.** 3.00 – **6 rm** 18.00/36.00 **st.**

XXXX **Mirabelle** (De Vere), (at Grand H.), King Edward's Par., BN21 4EQ, ☎ 410771, Telex 87332, Fax 412233 – . AE VISA Z
closed Sunday and Monday – **M** (booking essential) 16.00/26.00 **st.** and a la carte 4.75.

X **Byron's,** 6 Crown St., Old Town, BN21 1NX, ☎ 20171 – AE VISA Z
closed Sunday, 1 week at Christmas and Bank Holidays – **M** (dinner only) a la carte 15.10/20.70 **st.** 3.75.

at Jevington NW : 6 m. by A 259 – Z – on B 2105 – ✉ ☎ 032 12 Polegate :

XX **Hungry Monk,** The Street, BN26 5QF, ☎ 2178, « Part Elizabethan cottages », –
closed 24 to 26 December and Bank Holiday Mondays – **M** (booking essential) (dinner only and Sunday lunch)/dinner 19.50 **t.** 4.25.

at Wilmington NW : 6 ½ m. by A 22 on A 27 – Y – ✉ ☎ 032 12 Polegate :

Crossways, Lewes Rd, BN26 5SG, ☎ 2455, – . VISA.
closed 24 December-7 January – **M** *(closed dinner Sunday and Monday)* (dinner only) 20.90 **t.** 3.95 – **7 rm** 25.00/54.00 **t.** – SB (October-April) (weekdays only) 65.00/75.00 **st.**

CITROEN 8-14 Seaside ℘ 640139
FORD Lottbridge Drove ℘ 37171
PEUGEOT-TALBOT East Dean ℘ 423053
RENAULT 18 Lottbridge Drove ℘ 37233
ROVER, JAGUAR Meads Rd ℘ 30201
SUZUKI 85-89 Pevensey Bay Rd ℘ 761682
VAUXHALL-OPEL 336-8 Seaside ℘ 30663

ATS Langney Rise ℘ 761971

EAST BUCKLAND Devon 403 I 30 – see South Molton.

EAST CHINNOCK Somerset – see Yeovil.

EAST DEREHAM Norfolk 404 W 25 – pop. 11 798 – 0362 Dereham.

Quebec Rd ℘ 693122.

London 109 – Cambridge 57 – King's Lynn 27 – Norwich 16.

Phoenix (T.H.F.), Church St., NR19 1DL, ℘ 692276 – rm – 150. VISA
M 10.95 **st.** and a la carte – **23 rm** 40.00/45.00 **st.** – SB (weekends only) 72.00 **st.**

George (B.C.B.), Swaffham Rd, NR19 2AZ, ℘ 696801 –
8 rm.

King's Head, 42 Norwich St., NR19 1AD, ℘ 693842, Fax 693776, , – . VISA
M 14.50/15.00 **t.** and a la carte 3.50 – **15 rm** 37.50/49.50 **t.** – SB (October-April) (weekends only) 60.00/70.00 **st.**

FORD High St. ℘ 692281
ROVER Norwich Rd ℘ 692293
SEAT Two Oaks Garage Beetley ℘ 860219

Utilisez le guide de l'année.

EAST GRINSTEAD West Sussex 404 T 30 – pop. 23 867 – ECD : Wednesday – 0342.

Envir. : Hever Castle★ (13C-20C) and gardens★★ *AC*, NE : 10 m.

Boners Arms Rd Copthorne ℘ 712508 – Effingham Park ℘ 0342 (Copthorne) 716528.

London 32 – Brighton 29 – Eastbourne 33 – Lewes 21 – Maidstone 32.

Felbridge, London Rd, RH19 2BH, NW : 1 ½ m. on A 22 ℘ 326992, Telex 95156, Fax 410778, , heated, , – – 300. VISA
M 9.50/12.95 **t.** and a la carte – 6.95 – **50 rm** 70.00/85.00 **st.** – SB (weekends only) 94.00 **st.**

Woodbury House (Garden Room R.) with rm, Lewes Rd, RH19 3UD, SE : ½ m. on A 22 ℘ 313657, Fax 314801, – . VISA
M *(closed Saturday lunch and Sunday dinner)* 25.50 **t.** and a la carte **t.** 3.85 – **14 rm** 55.00/75.00 **t.** – SB (weekends only) 82.00/106.00 **st.**

at Gravetye SW : 4 ½ m. by B 2110 taking second turn left towards West Hoathly – ✉ East Grinstead – 0342 Sharpthorne :

Gravetye Manor, Vowels Lane, RH19 4LJ, ℘ 810567, Telex 957239, Fax 810080, <, « 16C manor house with gardens and grounds by William Robinson », , park – rest
.
M *(closed Christmas Night to non residents)* (booking essential) 19.00/22.00 **s.** and a la carte 24.50/33.30 **s.** 9.50 – 8.00 – **14 rm** 105.00/190.00 **s.**

FORD 220 London Rd ℘ 324344
VAUXHALL King St. ℘ 324666
ATS London Rd, North End ℘ 410740

EASTHAM Merseyside 402 403 L 24 – pop. 16 228 – ✉ Wirral – 051 Liverpool.

London 209 – Birmingham 45 – Chester 13 – Liverpool 7.5 – Manchester 45.

Travelodge without rest., New Chester Rd, Junction of M 53 and A 41, L62 9AQ, ℘ 327 2489, Reservations (Toll free) 0800 850950 – . VISA.
30 rm 24.00/29.50 **t.**

EAST HORNDON Essex – 0277 Brentwood.

London 21 – Chelmsford 13 – Southend-on-Sea 17.

Travelodge without rest., CM13 3LL, on A 127 (Eastbound carriageway) ℘ 810819, Reservations (Toll free) 0800 850950 – . VISA.
22 rm 24.00/29.50 **t.**

EAST HORSLEY Surrey 404 S 30 – pop. 5 864 – ECD : Thursday – ✉ Leatherhead – 048 65.

London 29 – Guildford 7.

Thatchers, Epsom Rd, KT24 6TB, on A 246 ℘ 4291, Fax 4222, heated, – rm
– 60. VISA
M *(closed Saturday lunch)* 20.00/35.00 **st.** and a la carte 3.75 – 6.50 – **59 rm** 75.00/95.00 – SB (weekends only) 84.00/94.00 **st.**

EASTLEIGH Devon 403 H 30 – see Bideford.

EASTLEIGH Hants. 403 P 31 – pop. 58 585 – ECD : Wednesday – 0703.

18 Fleming Park 612797.

Town Hall Centre, Leigh Rd 614646.

London 74 – Winchester 8 – Southampton 4.

Crest (T.H.F.), Leigh Rd, SO5 5PG, 619700, Telex 47606, Fax 643945, – rm rest – 250. AE VISA
M (bar lunch Saturday and Bank Holidays) 14.00/19.00 **st.** and a la carte 5.50 – 7.95 – **117 rm** 81.00/93.00 **st.**, **3 suites** 100.00/120.00 **st.**.

ATS Duttons Lane, Bishopstoke Rd 613027/613393

EAST MOLESEY Surrey 404 ㊷ – see Esher.

EASTON CROSS Devon 403 I 31 – see Chagford.

EASTON GREY Wilts. 403 404 N 29 – see Malmesbury.

EAST PORTLEMOUTH Devon 403 I 33 – see Kingsbridge.

EAST PRESTON West Sussex 404 S 31 – see Worthing.

EAST WITTERING West Sussex 404 R 31 – pop. 3 503 – 0243 Chichester.

London 74 – Brighton 37 – Portsmouth 25.

Clifford's Cottage, Bracklesham Lane, Bracklesham Bay, PO20 8JA, E : 1 m. by B 2179 on B 2198 670250, – . AE VISA
closed Sunday dinner, first week February and first 2 weeks November – **M** (dinner only and Sunday lunch)/dinner 14.95 **st.** and a la carte 3.75.

Utilizzate la Guida dell'anno in corso.

ECCLES Greater Manchester 402 403 404 M 23 – pop. 37 792 – 061 Manchester.

London 204 – Liverpool 31 – Manchester 4 – Preston 32.

Ashdene, 48 Wellington Rd, M30 9QW, 789 4762, Fax 787 8394 – . VISA.
M 8.25 **t.** 3.60 – **7 rm** 37.50/52.00 **t.**

ECCLESHALL Staffs. 402 403 404 N 25 – 0785.

London 149 – Birmingham 33 – Derby 40 – Shrewsbury 26 – Stoke-on-Trent 12.

St. George, Castle St., ST21 6DF, 850300, Fax 851452 – . AE VISA.
M 7.50/9.50 **st.** and a la carte – 5.25 – **10 rm** 48.00/70.00 **st.** – SB (weekends only) 75.00/95.00 **st.**

at High Offley SW : 4½ m. by A 519 – Stafford – 740785 Woodseaves :

Royal Oak, Grubb St., ST20 0NE, 284579 – . AE VISA
closed Sunday dinner, Monday, and Bank Holidays – **M** (dinner only and Sunday lunch)/dinner 20.25 **t.** 4.50.

EDENBRIDGE Kent 404 U 30 – pop. 7 674 – 0732.

18 Crouch House Rd 865097.

London 35 – Brighton 36 – Maidstone 29.

Honours Mill, 87 High Street, TN8 5AU, 866757, « Carefully renovated 18C mill » – VISA.
closed 1 week March, 2 weeks in June, 1 week after Christmas and Bank Holidays – **M** *(closed Saturday lunch, Sunday dinner and Monday)* 31.00 **st.** 4.25.

HONDA High St. 862031
ROVER Marlpit Hill 866202
ROVER, LAND-ROVER, FORD Stanford Rd, Hartfield End 863366
VAUXHALL-OPEL Station Rd 866822

EGERTON Greater Manchester 402 ㉑ 403 ② 404 ⑨ – see Bolton.

EGHAM Surrey 404 S 29 – pop. 21 337 – ECD : Thursday – 0784.

London 29 – Reading 21.

Runnymede, Windsor Rd, TW20 0AG, on A 308 436171, Telex 934900, Fax 436340, – – 350. AE VISA
M *(closed Saturday lunch)* (Dancing Saturday) 14.75/16.95 **t.** and a la carte 5.50 – 8.25 – **125 rm** 87.00/125.00 **st.** – SB (weekends only) 121.45/131.45 **st.**

Great Fosters, Stroude Rd, TW20 9UR, S : 1¼ m. by B 388 433822, Telex 944441, Fax 472455, , « Elizabethan mansion with extensive gardens », , heated, park, – – 50. AE VISA.
M 16.50/25.50 **t.** and a la carte 4.50 – **42 rm** 60.00/135.00 **t.**, **2 suites** 145.00 **t.**

XX **La Bonne Franquette,** 5 High St., TW20 9EA, ℘ 439494, French rest., – Ⓟ. AE ⓘ VISA
closed Saturday lunch and 25-26 December – **M** 21.50 **t.** and a la carte.

X Trattoria il Borgo, 15 The Precinct, TW20 9HN, ℘ 433544, Italian rest.

FERRARI Egham-by-pass ℘ 36431/36222 VOLVO The Causeway ℘ 36191

EGLWYSFACH Dyfed 403 I 26 – see Machynlleth (Powys).

EGTON BRIDGE North Yorks. – see Goathland.

ELLAND West Yorks. 402 O 22 –see Halifax.

ELSING Norfolk 404 X 25 – pop. 237 – ✉ Dereham – ☎ 036 283 Swanton Morley.
♦London 138 – Fakenham 12 – ♦Norwich 17.

Church Farm Motel, Church Farm, NR20 3EA, ℘ 8236, – TV ☎ Ⓟ
7 rm.

ELSTEAD Surrey 404 R 30 – pop. 2 633 – ☎ 0252.
♦London 43 – Guildford 9 – ♦Portsmouth 41.

XXX **Bentleys,** Elstead Mill, GU8 6LE, on B 3001 ℘ 703333, Fax 702310, « Converted water-mill », – Ⓟ. AE ⓘ VISA
closed Saturday lunch, Sunday dinner and Monday – **M** 14.50/18.50 **t.** and a la carte 4.25.

ELTERWATER Cumbria – see Ambleside.

ELY Cambs. 404 U 26 – pop. 9 006 – ECD : Tuesday – ☎ 0353.
See : Cathedral★★★ (11C-16C) (Norman nave★★★, lantern★★★).
Envir. : Wicken Fen★, 5 : 8½ m.
18 Cambridge Rd ℘ 2751.
Oliver Cromwell's House, 29 St. Mary's St. ℘ 662062.
♦London 74 – ♦Cambridge 16 – ♦Norwich 60.

Lamb (Q.M.H.), 2 Lynn Rd, CB7 4EJ, ℘ 663574, Fax 666350 – TV ☎ Ⓟ. AE ⓘ VISA
M 9.00/12.50 **t.** – **32 rm** 55.00/72.00 **t.** – SB 70.00/80.00 **st.**

Fenlands Lodge, Soham Rd, Stuntney, CB7 5TR, SE : 3 m. on A 142 ℘ 667047, Fax 667637 – TV ☎ Ⓟ. AE ⓘ VISA
M *(closed Sunday dinner)* 11.95 **t.** and a la carte – **9 rm** 45.00/57.00 **t.** – SB (weekends only) 68.00 **st.**

X **Old Fire Engine House,** 25 St. Mary's St., CB7 4ER, ℘ 662582, English rest., – Ⓟ
closed Sunday dinner, 2 weeks at Christmas and Bank Holidays – **M** (booking essential) a la carte 15.00/20.00 **t.**

X **Peking Duck,** 26 Fore Hill, CB7 4AF, ℘ 662948, Chinese rest. – AE
closed Tuesday lunch, Monday and 25-26 December – **M** a la carte 8.20/12.60 **t.** 4.00.

at Littleport N : 5¾ m. on A 10 – ✉ ☎ 0353 Ely :

XX **Fen House,** 2 Lynn Rd, CB6 1QG, ℘ 860645 – ⓘ VISA
(closed Sunday and Monday) – **M** (dinner only) a la carte 14.50/20.20 **st.** 3.75.

FIAT Lynn Rd ℘ 662981
FORD Southern By-pass ℘ 661181
VOLVO The Slade, Witcham ℘ 778403
VW-AUDI 16-18 St. Mary's St. ℘ 661272
ATS 11 Broad St. ℘ 662758/662801

EMPINGHAM Leics. 402 404 S 26 – see Stamford (Lincs.).

EMSWORTH Hants. 404 R 31 – pop. 17 604 (inc. Southbourne) – ECD : Wednesday – ☎ 0243.
♦London 75 – ♦Brighton 37 – ♦Portsmouth 10.

Brookfield, 93-95 Havant Rd, PO10 7LF, ℘ 373363, Fax 376342, – TV ☎ Ⓟ – 50. AE ⓘ VISA.
closed 24 December-2 January – **M** 11.50 **t.** and a la carte 3.95 – **41 rm** 52.00/63.00 **t.** – SB (weekends only) 65.00/70.00 **st.**

XXX **36 on the Quay,** The Quay, South St., PO10 7EG, ℘ 375592 – AE VISA
closed Monday lunch, Sunday, 2 weeks January and 2 weeks August – **M** 25.00/32.50 **t.** 6.50.

X **Spencer's,** 36 North St., PO10 7DG, ℘ 372744 – . VISA
closed Sunday and Monday – **M** (dinner only) 16.50 **t.**

"Short Breaks" (SB)

Molti alberghi propongono delle condizioni vantaggiose
per un soggiorno di due notti
comprendente la camera, la cena e la prima colazione.

EPPING Essex 404 U 28 – pop. 10 148 – ECD : Wednesday – ☏ 0378.

See : Forest★.

Envir. : Waltham Abbey (Abbey★) W : 6 m.

Theydon Bois ☏ 037 881 (Theydon Bois) 2279.

♦London 20 – ♦Cambridge 40 – Chelmsford 18.

Post House (T.H.F.), High Rd, Bell Common, CM16 4DG, S : 3⁄4 m. on B 1393 ☏ 73137, Telex 81617, Fax 560402, – rm – 90. VISA
M 10.75/14.50 **st.** and a la carte 4.35 – 7.50 – **82 rm** 74.00/84.00 **st.** – SB (weekends only) 76.00/96.00 **st.**

FORD 24 High St. ☏ 72281

RENAULT High Rd ☏ 72266

EPSOM Surrey 404 ㉚ – pop. 65 830 (inc. Ewell) – ECD : Wednesday – ☏ 037 27.

Envir. : Chessington Zoo★ *AC*, NW : 3½ m.

Longdown Lane South, South Epsom ☏ 23363 – Walton Heath, Tadworth ☏ 0737 (Tadworth) 812060.

♦London 17 – Guildford 16.

Plan : see Greater London (South-West)

White House, Downs Hill Rd, off Ashley Rd, KT18 5HW, ☏ 722472, – . VISA. by A 24 CZ
M 7.50 **st.** 3.50 – **15 rm** 39.50/58.00 **st.**

Epsom Downs, 9 Longdown Rd, KT17 3PT, ☏ 740643, Fax 723259 –
16 rm. by A 2022 CZ

River Kwai, 4 East St., KT17 1HH, ☏ 741475, Thai rest – VISA CZ **a**
M 10.00/15.00 **st.** and a la carte approx. 14.90 **st.** 3.40.

CITROEN Walton-on-the-Hill ☏ 073 781 (Tadworth) 3811
FIAT 38 Upper High St. ☏ 44444
FORD East St. ☏ 26246

NISSAN 5 Ruxley Lane, Ewell ☏ 081 394 1667
RENAULT Nonsuch Ind Est ☏ 28391
VW-AUDI Reigate Rd ☏ 073 73 (Burgh Heath) 60111

ERDINGTON West Midlands 403 404 O 26 – see Birmingham.

ERMINGTON Devon 403 I 32 – pop. 881 – ✉ Ivybridge – ☏ 0548 Modbury.

♦London 233 – Exeter 37 – ♦Plymouth 13 – Torquay 23.

Ermewood House, Totnes Rd, PL21 9NS, on B 3210 ☏ 830741, – rest . VISA
closed 2 weeks Christmas – **M** *(closed Sunday)* (dinner only) 16.50 **t.** 4.00 – **12 rm** 40.00/60.00 **t.** – SB (weekends only) 75.00/80.00 **st.**

ESHER Surrey 404 S 29 – pop. 46 688 (inc. Molesey) – ECD : Wednesday – ☏ 0372.

Thames Ditton, Marquis of Gransby, Portsmouth Rd ☏ 398 1551 Z – Moore Place, Portsmouth Rd ☏ 63533 BZ.

♦London 20 – ♦Portsmouth 58.

Plan : see Greater London (South-West)

Good Earth, 14-18 High St., KT10 9RT, ☏ 62489, Chinese rest. – BZ **e**

at East Molesey N : 2 m. by A 309 – ✉ East Molesey – ☏ 081 :

Le Chien Qui Fume, 107 Walton Rd, KT8 0DR, ☏ 979 7150, French rest. – VISA BY **c**
closed Sunday, February and Bank Holiday Mondays – **M** 30.00 **t.** and a la carte 3.80.

New Anarkali, 160 Walton Rd, KT8 OHP, ☏ 979 5072, Indian rest. – VISA
M a la carte approx 12.50 **t.** BY **a**

at Claygate SE : 1 m. by A 244 – ✉ ☏ 0372 Esher :

✿ **Les Alouettes,** 7 High St., KT10 OJW, ☏ 64882, French rest. – . VISA
closed Saturday lunch, Sunday, first 10 days January, last 2 weeks August and Bank Holidays – **M** 24.00/30.00 **t.** 4.50
Spec. Navarin de coquilles St. Jacques et langoustines, sauce iodée, Pavé de saumon d'Écosse rôti à l'unilateral, à la cassonade de tomate, Nougat glacé au tutti frutti. BZ **n**

Le Petit Pierrot, 4 The Parade, KT10 0NU, ☏ 65105, French rest. – VISA
closed Saturday lunch, Sunday, 25 August-1 September and Bank Holidays – **M** 13.75/18.50 **t.** 3.50. BZ **r**

ESKDALE GREEN Cumbria 402 K 20 – pop. 457 – ECD : Wednesday and Saturday – ✉ Holmrook – ☏ 094 03.

♦London 312 – ♦Carlisle 59 – Kendal 60.

Bower House Inn , CA19 1TD, W : 3⁄4 m. ☏ 244, – . VISA.
M (bar lunch)/dinner a la carte approx. 16.00 **t.** 3.80 – **22 rm** 38.50/52.00 **t.** – SB (weekends only) (except September, October and Bank Holidays) 65.00/80.00 **st.**

EVENLODE Glos. 403 404 O 28 – see Moreton-in-Marsh.
♦London 83 – ♦Birmingham 43 – Gloucester 34 – ♦Oxford 26.

EVERSHOT Dorset 403 404 M 31 – pop. 224 – ✉ Dorchester – ☎ 0935.
♦London 149 – Bournemouth 39 – Dorchester 12 – Salisbury 53 – Taunton 30 – Yeovil 10.

Summer Lodge ⛰, Summer Lane, DT2 0JR, ✆ 83424, Fax 83005, « Country house atmosphere », heated, ⚘, ⚔ – ☎ ♿ Ⓟ. VISA
closed 1 to 17 January – **M** 15.00/25.00 **t.** 4.25 – **17 rm** 60.00/150.00 **t.** – SB (except summer and Christmas) 125.00/150.00 **st.**

Acorn Inn, 28 Fore St., DT2 0JW, ✆ 83228 – TV ☎ Ⓟ. VISA
M a la carte 11.50/17.75 **t.** 3.95 – **8 rm** 28.00/90.00 **t.** – SB (except Bank Holidays) 70.00/95.00 **st.**

EVESHAM Heref. and Worc. 403 404 O 27 – pop. 15 069 – ECD : Wednesday – ☎ 0386.
ℹ The Almonry Museum, Abbey Gate ✆ 446944.
♦London 99 – ♦Birmingham 30 – Cheltenham 16 – ♦Coventry 32.

Evesham, Coopers Lane, off Waterside, WR11 6DA, ✆ 765566, Telex 339342, Fax 765443, ⛱, ⚘ – TV ☎ Ⓟ. AE ⓓ VISA
closed 25 and 26 December – **M** (buffet lunch)/dinner a la carte 14.20/21.45 **st.** 4.40 – **40 rm** 56.00/78.00 **st.** – SB (except weekdays in winter) 66.00/112.00 **st.**

Waterside, 56-59 Waterside, WR11 6JZ, ✆ 442420, ⚘ – ⚡ rest TV ☎ Ⓟ. AE VISA
M 11.50 **t.** and a la carte – **13 rm** 22.00/55.75 **t.** – SB (weekends only) 65.00/70.00 **st.**

at Harvington N : 3¾ m. by A 4184 and A435 off A439 – ✉ ☎ 0386 Evesham :

Mill at Harvington ⛰, Anchor Lane, WR11 5NR, SE : 1½ m. by A 439 ✆ 870688, Fax 870688, ≤, « 18C mill with riverside garden », heated, ⚓, ⚔ – TV ☎ Ⓟ. VISA. ✂
closed 24 to 27 December – **M** *(closed lunch Saturday and Monday)* 15.00/23.50 **t.** 3.90 – **15 rm** 54.00/78.00 **t.**

at Abbot's Salford N : 4¾ m. by A 4184 and A 435 on A 439 – ✉ ☎ 0386 Evesham :

Salford Hall, WR11 5UT, ✆ 871300, Telex 336682, Fax 871301, « Tudor mansion with early 17C extension and gatehouse », ≘, ⚘, ⚔ – ⚡ rest TV ☎ Ⓟ – 🏛 25. AE ⓓ VISA. ✂
closed Christmas and New Year – **M** 12.50/18.95 **t.** and a la carte 4.00 – **34 rm** 70.00/140.00 **t.**

FIAT 3 Cheltenham Rd ✆ 442301
FORD Four Pools Lane ✆ 442525
NISSAN Cheltenham Rd ✆ 47103/49580
PEUGEOT-TALBOT Broadway Rd ✆ 446261
VAUXHALL-OPEL Greenhill ✆ 442614
VW-AUDI Harvington ✆ 870612

ATS 6 Brick Kiln St. ✆ 765313

EWEN Glos. 403 404 O 28 – see Cirencester.

When looking for a quiet hotel
use the maps found in the introductory pages
or look for establishments with the sign ⛰ or ⛰.

EXETER Devon 403 J 31 **The West Country G.** – pop. 88 235 – ☎ 0392.
See : Site★★ – Cathedral★★ Z – Maritime Museum★★*AC* Z.
Envir. : Bicton Gardens★*AC* SE : 8 m. by B 3182 – at O'Hery St. Mary★, E : 12 m. by B 3183 : St. Mary's★★.
⛳18 Countess Wear ✆ 039 287 (Topsham) 4139, SE : 3 m. X – ⛳18 Downes Crediton ✆ 036 32 (Crediton) 3991, NW : 7½ m. by A 377 Y.
✈ Exeter Airport : ✆ 67433, Telex 42648, E : 5 m. by A 30 V – **Terminal** : St. David's and Central Stations.
ℹ Civic Centre, Paris St. ✆ 72434 – M 5 Service Area, Junction 30, Sandygate ✆ 437581.
♦London 201 – Bournemouth 83 – ♦Bristol 83 – ♦Plymouth 46 – ♦Southampton 110.

Plans on following pages

Forte (T.H.F.), Southernhay East, EX1 1QF, ✆ 412812, Telex 41717, Fax 413549, ⛹, ≘, ⛱ – 🛗 ⚡ rm ▤ rest TV ☎ ♿ Ⓟ – 🏛 80. AE ⓓ VISA Z a
M 12.95/18.50 **st.** and a la carte – 8.50 – **107 rm** 90.00/125.00 **st.** – SB (weekends only) 114.00/130.00 **st.**

Royal Clarence (Q.M.H.), Cathedral Yard, EX1 1HD, ✆ 58464, Group Telex 42919, Fax 439423 – 🛗 TV ☎ – 🏛 100. AE ⓓ VISA. ✂ Y z
M 15.00/17.50 **st.** and a la carte 6.00 – 7.50 – **53 rm** 75.00/90.00 **t.**, **3 suites** 120.00 **st.** – SB 99.00 **st.**

Buckerell Lodge (T.H.F.), Topsham Rd, EX2 4SQ, SE : 1 m. on B 3182 ✆ 52451, Telex 42410, Fax 412114, ⚘ – ⚡ rm TV ☎ ♿ Ⓟ – 🏛 50. AE ⓓ VISA X a
M (carving lunch Saturday) 9.50/16.00 **st.** and a la carte 4.50 – 7.95 – **54 rm** 72.00/84.00 **st.** – SB (weekends only) 72.00/94.00 **st.**

St. Olaves Court, Mary Arches St., EX4 3AZ, ✆ 217736, Fax 413054, – TV ☎ P. AE VISA. Z e
M 10.95/14.95 **t.** and a la carte 3.95 – **17 rm** 33.00/70.00 **t.** – SB (weekends only) 60.00 **st.**

Rougemont (Mt. Charlotte Thistle), Queen St., EX4 3SP, ✆ 54982, Telex 42455 Fax 420928 – TV ☎ P – 300. AE VISA Y
M 8.50/12.75 **st.** 3.80 – 6.50 – **92 rm** 60.00/69.50 **st.**, **2 suites** 99.00 **st.** – SB (except Christmas and New Year) 73.00 **st.**

Countess Wear Lodge (Q.M.H.), 398 Topsham Rd, EX2 6HE, S : 2½ m. at junction of A 379 and B 3182 ✆ 875441, Telex 42551, Fax 876174 – rm TV ☎ P – 185. AE VISA. – **M** *(closed lunch Saturday and Sunday and Bank Holidays)* a la carte 9.50/14.50 **st.** 4.50 – **44 rm** 51.00/65.00 **st.** – SB (weekends only) 60.00/72.00 **st.** X o

St. Andrews, 28 Alphington Rd, EX2 8HN, ✆ 76784 – TV ☎ P. AE VISA. *closed Christmas-New Year* – **M** (bar lunch)/dinner a la carte 9.70/14.65 **t.** 2.95 – **17 rm** 38.50/59.40 **t.** X c

Red House, 2 Whipton Village Rd, EX4 8AR, ✆ 56104, Fax 435708 – TV ☎ P. VISA
M 6.50/10.95 **st.** and a la carte 3.00 – **12 rm** 25.00/40.00 **st.** – SB (weekends only) 69.00/90.00 **st.** V

Park View without rest., 8 Howell Rd, EX4 4LG, ✆ 71772 – rm TV ☎ P. VISA
closed Christmas **15 rm** 16.00/45.00 **t.** V

at Huxham N : 5 m. by A 377 – V – off A 396 – ✉ Exeter – ✆ 0392 Stoke Canon :

Barton Cross, with rm, EX5 4EJ, ✆ 841245, Fax 50402, « Part 16C thatched cottage », – TV ☎ P. AE VISA.
M *(Sunday lunch residents only)* 16.75/20.75 **t.** – **6 rm** 62.50/82.50 **t.** – SB (weekends only) 94.00 **st.**

at Pinhoe NE : 2 m. by A 30 – V – ✉ ✆ 0392 Exeter :

Gipsey Hill, Gipsy Hill Lane, via Pinn Lane, EX1 3RN, ✆ 65252, Fax 64302, – rm TV ☎ P – 120. AE VISA
M 10.00/15.00 **t.** and a la carte 4.50 – **23 rm** 50.00/68.00 **t.**

EXETER
BUILT UP AREA

Blackboy Road . . . V 8
Buddle Lane . . . X 9
Butts Road . . . X 12
East Wonford Hill . . . X 17
Heavitree Road . . . VX 20
Hill Lane . . . V 21
Ladysmith Road . . . V 24
Marsh Barton Road . . . X 25
Mount Pleasant Road . . . V 29
North Street HEAVITREE . . . X 32
Old Tiverton Road . . . V 35
Polsloe Road . . . V 39
Prince Charles Road . . . V 41
Prince of Wales Road . . . V 42
St. Andrew's Road . . . V 48
Summer Lane . . . V 50
Sweetbriar Lane . . . VX 51
Trusham Road . . . X 52
Union Road . . . V 54
Whipton Lane . . . X 55
Wonford Road . . . X 57
Wonford Street . . . X 58

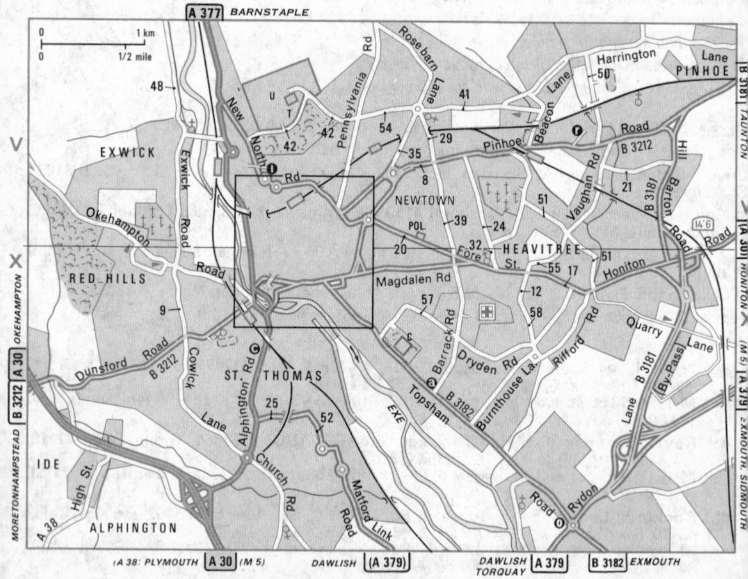

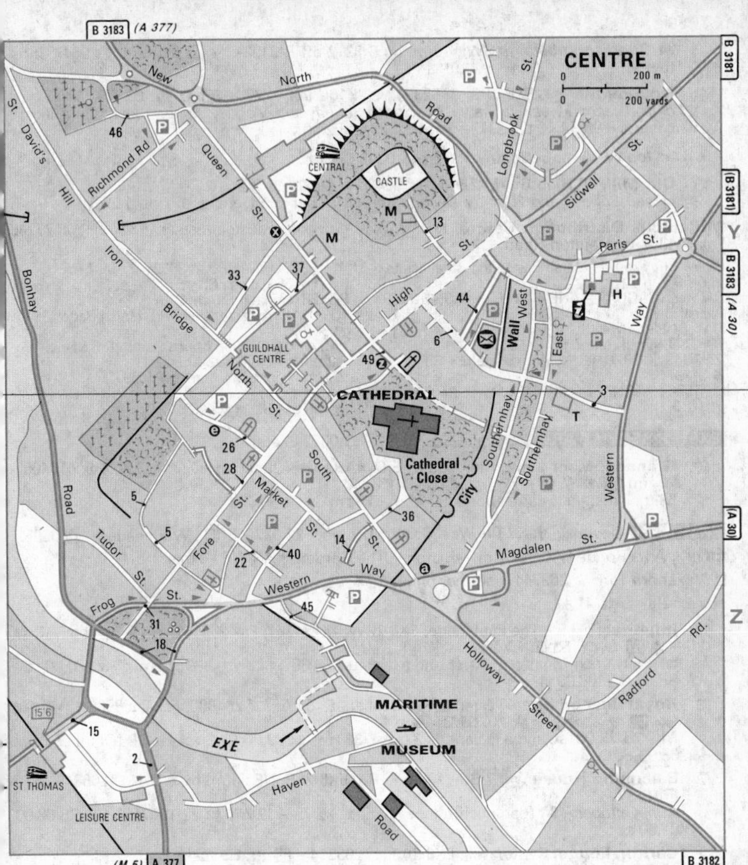

Bedford St. . . . . Y 6
Fore St. . . . . Z
High St. . . . . Y
Shopping Precinct . . . . Y

Alphington Rd . . . . Z 2
Barnfield Rd . . . . Z 3
Bartholomew Rd . . . . Z 5
Castle St. . . . . Y 13
Coombe St. . . . . Z 14
Corwick St. . . . . Z 15
Edmund St. . . . . Z 18
King St. . . . . Z 22
Mary Arches St. . . . . Z 26
Mint (The) . . . . Z 28
New Bridge St. . . . . Z 31
Northernhay St. . . . . Y 33
Palace Gate . . . . Z 36
Paul St. . . . . Y 37
Preston St. . . . . Z 40
Princesshay . . . . Y 44
Quay Hill . . . . Z 45
Queen's Terrace . . . . Y 46
St. Martin's Lane . . . . Y 49

at Whimple NE : 9 m. by A 30 – V – ✉ Exeter – ☎ 0404 Whimple :

Woodhayes, EX5 2TD, ✆ 822237, « Country house atmosphere », – ☎ – . *VISA*.
M (booking essential) (lunch by arrangement) 14.00/19.00 **st.** 3.80 – **6 rm** 55.00/75.00 **st.** – SB 98.00 **st.**

at Clyst St. George SE : 5 m. on A 376 – X – ✉ ☎ 0392 Exeter :

St. George and Dragon Toby, EX3 0QJ, ✆ 876121, – ☎ – 100
13 rm.

at Kennford S : 5 m. on A 38 – X – ✉ ☎ 0392 Exeter :

Exeter Court (Best Western), Kennford Services, EX6 7UX, ✆ 832121, Telex 42443, Fax 833590, – ☎ – 180. *VISA*
M 9.95/10.95 **t.** and a la carte 5.95 – **63 rm** 28.00/55.00 **t.** – SB 65.00/75.00 **st.**

Fairwinds, EX6 7UD, ✆ 832911 – ☎ . *VISA*.
closed 7 to 31 December – **M** (bar lunch)/dinner 10.65 **t.** 2.95 – **8 rm** 24.00/48.00 **t.** – SB 100.00/116.00 **st.**

at Doddiscombsleigh SW : 10 m. by B 3212 off B 3193– X – ✉ Exeter – ☎ 0647 Christow :

Nobody Inn ⛰, EX6 7PS, ☎ 52394, ≤, « 16C inn », 🌳 – TV ☎ P. VISA. ✂
closed second week January – **M** *(closed Sunday and Monday dinner)* (bar lunch)/dinner a la carte 8.90/14.10 **t.** 3.60 – **7 rm** 25.00/52.00 **t.**

at Ide W : 3 m. by A 30 – X – ✉ ☎ 0392 Exeter :

XX **Old Mill,** 20 High St., EX2 9RN, ☎ 59480 – P. AE VISA
closed Sunday and 25 to 27 December – **M** 7.95/11.95 **t.** and a la carte 2.75.

MICHELIN Distribution Centre, Kestrel Way, Sowton Industrial Estate, EX2 7LH, ☎ **77246,** Fax 444302 by Honiton Road VX

BMW Budlake Rd., Marsh Barton Industrial Estate ☎ 69595
DAIMLER-JAGUAR, LAND-ROVER, RANGE-ROVER Marsh Barton Rd ☎ 37152
FIAT 84-88 Sidwell St. ☎ 54923
FORD 9 Marsh Barton Rd ☎ 50141
IZUZU, SUBURU, HYUNDAI Alphinbrook Rd ☎ 57737
MERCEDES-BENZ Trusham Rd, Marsh Barton ☎ 77311
RENAULT Haven Rd ☎ 30321
ROVER 55 Sidwell St. ☎ 78342
ROVER Honiton Rd ☎ 68187
TOYOTA 37 Marsh Green Rd, Marsh Barton ☎ 34761
VAUXHALL-OPEL 8 Marsh Barton Rd, Marsh Barton Trading Estate ☎ 34851
VOLVO Longbrook Terr. ☎ 215691

ATS Exe St. ☎ 55465

EXETER SERVICE AREA Devon 403 J 31 – ✉ ☎ 0392 Exeter

Granada, Moor Lane, Sandygate, EX2 4AR, M 5 Junction 30 ☎ 74044, Fax 410406 – ⊁ rm TV ☎ & P – 🚶 70. AE VISA. ✂
M (grill rest.) a la carte approx. 12.00 **t.** – **76 rm** 35.00/39.00 **t.**

EXMOUTH Devon 403 J 32 The West Country G. – pop. 28 037 – ECD : Wednesday – ☎ 0395.

Envir. : A La Ronde★*AC*, N : 2 m. – Bicton★, The Gardens★*AC*, NE : 8 m.

Alexandra Terr. ☎ 263744 (summer only).

♦London 210 – Exeter 11.

Imperial (T.H.F.), The Esplanade, EX8 2SW, ☎ 274761, Fax 265161, ≤, heated, 🌳, ✂ – TV ☎ P. AE VISA
M (bar lunch)/dinner 20.00 **st.** and a la carte 4.35 – 7.00 – **57 rm** 60.00/80.00 **st.** – SB 96.00/108.00 **st.**

Royal Beacon (Best Western), The Beacon, EX8 2AF, ☎ 264886, Fax 268890, ≤, 🌳 – ⊁ TV ☎ P – 🚶 80. AE VISA
M 7.25/13.00 **st.** and a la carte 3.00 – **32 rm** 39.00/67.30 **st.** – SB (October-April) 68.00/80.00 **st.**

Balcombe House ⛰, 7 Stevenstone Rd, EX8 2EP, NE : 1 m. by A 376 ☎ 266349, 🌳 – TV P. ✂
April-October – **M** (bar lunch)/dinner 10.50 **t.** 2.75 – **12 rm** 22.10/50.80 **t.** – SB 63.90/67.50 **st.**

Carlton Lodge, Carlton Hill, EX8 2AJ, ☎ 263314 – TV P. VISA
M (bar lunch)/dinner 14.00 **t.** and a la carte 3.55 – **6 rm** 21.00/38.00 **t.** – SB (November-April) (except Bank Holidays) 45.00 **st.**

at Lympstone N : 3 m. by A 376 – ✉ ☎ 0395 Exmouth :

XXX **River House** with rm, The Strand, EX8 5EY, ☎ 265147, ≤ Exe Estuary – TV. AE VISA. ✂
M *(closed Sunday dinner, Monday and Bank Holidays)* 29.50 **t.** 4.10 – 5.50 – **2 rm** 50.00/66.00 **t.**

FORD Withycombe Village Rd ☎ 277633/272617
ROVER The Parade ☎ 272258

EYAM Derbs. 403 404 O 24 – pop. 923 – ✉ Sheffield (South Yorks.) – ☎ 0433 Hope Valley.

See : Celtic Cross★ (8C).

♦London 163 – Derby 29 – ♦Manchester 32 – ♦Sheffield 12.

Miners Arms, Water Lane, S30 1RG, ☎ 30853 – TV P. ✂
closed 25 and 26 December – **M** *(closed Sunday dinner and Monday)* 5.50/15.95 **t.** 4.50 – **6 rm** 24.00/40.00 **st.**

EYE Suffolk 404 X27 – ✉ ☎ 037 971.

Four Horseshoes, Thornham Magna, IP23 7HD, SW : 5 m. by B 1117 off A 140 ℘ 777, – TV ☎ P. AE VISA
M 10.50/13.50 **t.** and a la carte 4.25 – **8 rm** 36.50/49.50 **t.**

EYTON Heref. and Worc. – see Leominster.

FACCOMBE Hants. – see Hurstbourne Tarrant.

FAIRFORD Glos. 403 404 O 28 – pop. 2 408 – ECD : Saturday – ☎ 0285 Cirencester.
See : St. Mary's Church (stained glass windows** 15C-16C).
London 99 – Bristol 46 – Gloucester 28 – Oxford 27.

Hyperion House, London Rd, GL7 4AH, ℘ 712349, Fax 713126, – TV ☎ ♿ P. AE VISA
M (bar lunch)/dinner 20.00 **st.** 5.00 – **26 rm** 60.00/80.00 **st.** – SB (exept Christmas and New Year) 90.00 **st.**

ROVER The Bridge, Milton St. ℘ 712222

FAKENHAM Norfolk 404 W 25 – pop. 5 554 – ☎ 0328.
Fakenham ℘ 2867.
Red Lion House, 37 Market Pl. ℘ 51981 (summer only).
London 108 – King's Lynn 22 – Norwich 27.

Crown (B.C.B.), 6 Market Pl., NR21 9BP, ℘ 51418 – TV ☎ P.
M (grill rest.) – **11 rm.**

PEUGEOT Norwich Rd ℘ 864035 VAUXHALL Greenway Lane ℘ 862200

FALMOUTH Cornwall 403 E 33 **The West Country G.** – pop. 17 810 – ECD : Wednesday – ☎ 0326.
See : Site* – Pendennis Castle* (≤**) *AC* B.
Envir. : Glendurgan Garden** *AC*, S : 3 ½ m. by Swanpool Rd A – Helston Flora Day Flurry Dance**, SW : 11 m. by A 39 A – Mawnan Parish Church*, (≤**), SW : 4 m. by Trescobeas Rd A – at Gweek, Seal Sanctuary*, setting* *AC*, SW : 8 m. by A 39 A – Carn Brea (≤*), NW : 9 m. by A 39 A – at Wendron, Poldark Mine*, W : 9 m. by A 39 A – at Culdrose, Cornwall Aero Park* *AC*, SW : 10 m. by A 39 A – at Redruth, Tolgus Tin Streaming* *AC*, NW : 11 m. by A 39 A.
18 Swanpool Rd ℘ 311262 A – 9 Budock Vean Hotel ℘ 250288 A.
28 Killigrew St. ℘ 312300.
London 308 – Penzance 26 – Plymouth 65 – Truro 11.

Plan on next page

Greenbank, Harbourside, TR11 2SR, ℘ 312440, Telex 45240, Fax 211362, ≤ harbour – TV ☎ P. AE VISA A a
closed 23 December-13 January – **M** 8.50/14.50 **t.** and a la carte 4.50 – **43 rm** 33.00/120.00 **t.** – SB (weekends only) 88.00/94.00 **st.**

Royal Duchy, Cliff Rd, TR11 4NX, ℘ 313042, Fax 319420, ≤, – TV ☎ P. AE VISA B a
M 8.00/14.00 **t.** and a la carte – **45 rm** 50.00/88.00 **t.**, **2 suites** 96.00/175.00 **t.** – SB (except Easter, spring Bank Holiday and Christmas) 79.00/97.00 **st.**

Penmere Manor (Best Western), Mongleath Rd, TR11 4PN, ℘ 211411, Telex 45608, Fax 317588, heated, – rest TV ☎ P. AE VISA A e
closed 24 to 28 December – **M** (bar lunch)/dinner 17.50 **st.** and a la carte 18.75/27.25 **st.** 3.50 – **39 rm** 45.00/99.00 **st.** – SB 88.00/125.00 **st.**

St. Michael's of Falmouth, Gyllyngvase Beach, Seafront, TR11 4NB, ℘ 312707, Telex 45540, Fax 319147, ≤, – TV ☎ P – 50. AE VISA A z
M (bar lunch Monday to Saturday)/dinner 15.00 **t.** and a la carte 3.85 – **70 rm** 49.50/114.00 **t.** – SB (October – May) 42.00/49.00 **st.**

Crill Manor, Roscarrack Rd, TR11 5BL, SW : 2 ½ m. by Swanpool Rd ℘ 211880, Fax 211229, heated, – TV ☎ P. VISA. by Boslowick Rd A
M 16.50 **t.** and a la carte 3.75 – **11 rm** (dinner included) 39.50/125.00 **t.**

Broadmead, 66-68 Kimberley Park Rd, TR11 2DD, ℘ 315704 – TV ☎ P. VISA
closed Christmas and New Year – **M** (dinner only) 10.50/13.25 **t.** 3.75 – **12 rm** 18.00/42.00 **t.** – SB (except summer) 44.00/54.00 **st.** A u

Gyllyngvase House, Gyllyngvase Rd, TR11 4DJ, ℘ 312956, – rest TV ☎ P
Closed 1 November-28 February – **M** (bar lunch)/dinner 8.50 **t.** 3.50 – **15 rm** 14.50/35.00 **t.** B s

Tresillian House, 3 Stracey Rd, TR11 4DW, ℘ 312425 – rest TV ☎ P. A n
March-September – **M** 12.00 **t.** 3.00 – **12 rm** 20.00/40.00 **t.**

Esmond, 5 Emslie Rd, TR11 4BG, ℘ 313214 – TV. B e
May-October – **M** (by arrangement) – **7 rm** 13.00/27.00 **st.**

Rosemullion, Gyllyngvase Hill, TR11 4DF, ℘ 314690 – P B c
13 rm.

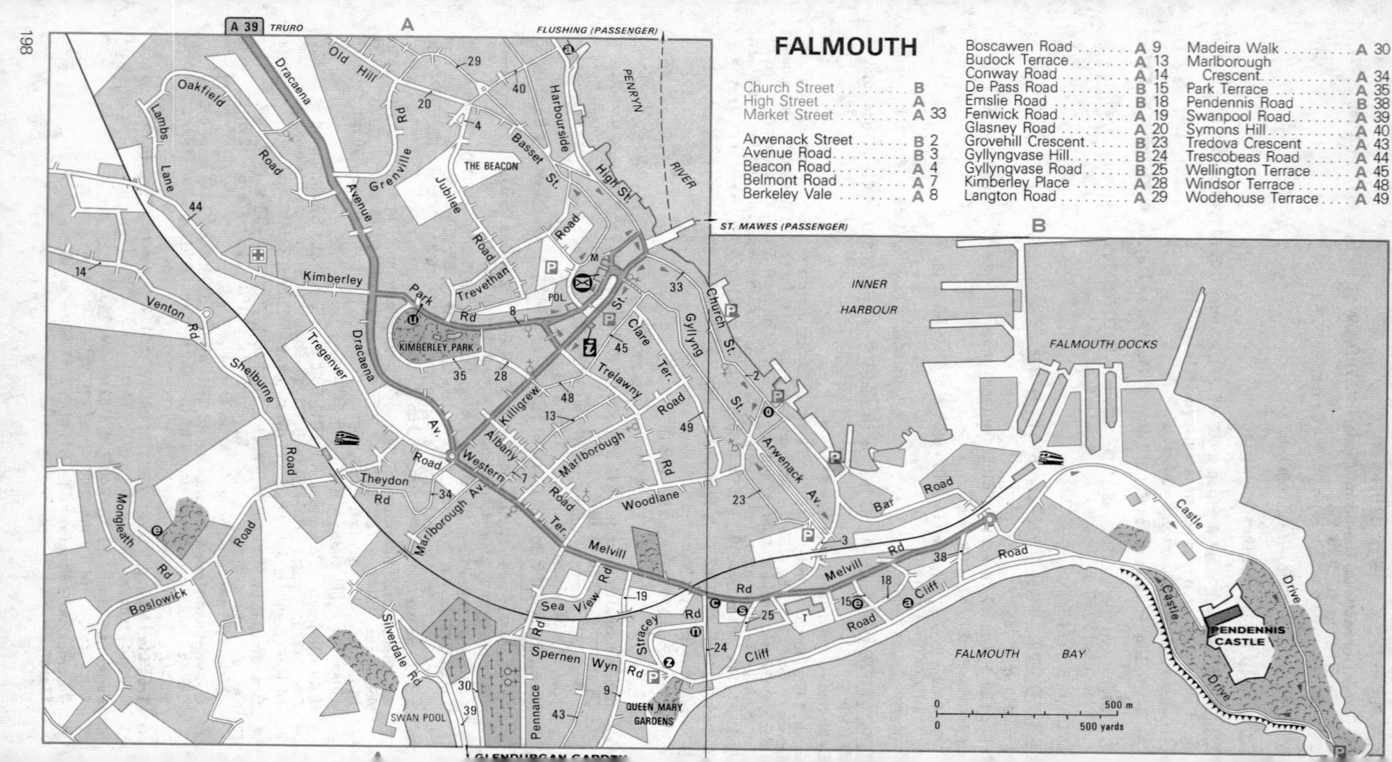
FALMOUTH
Church Street B
High Street A
Market Street A 33
Arwenack Street B 2
Avenue Road B 3
Beacon Road A 4
Belmont Road A 7
Berkeley Vale A 8
Boscawen Road A 9
Budock Terrace A 13
Conway Road A 14
De Pass Road B 15
Emslie Road B 18
Fenwick Road A 19
Glasney Road A 20
Grovehill Crescent B 23
Gyllyngvase Hill B 24
Gyllyngvase Road B 25
Kimberley Place A 28
Langton Road A 29
Madeira Walk A 30
Marlborough Crescent A 34
Park Terrace A 35
Pendennis Road B 38
Swanpool Road A 39
Symons Hill A 40
Tredova Crescent A 43
Trescobeas Road A 44
Wellington Terrace A 45
Windsor Terrace A 48
Wodehouse Terrace A 49
A 39 TRURO
A
B
FLUSHING (PASSENGER)
ST. MAWES (PASSENGER)
PENRYN
RIVER
INNER
HARBOUR
FALMOUTH DOCKS
FALMOUTH BAY
PENDENNIS CASTLE
THE BEACON
KIMBERLEY PARK
QUEEN MARY GARDENS
SWAN POOL
POL
Dracaena Avenue
Old Hill
Grenville Rd
Oakfield Road
Lambs Lane
Jubilee Road
Basset St.
Harbourside
High St.
Trevethan Rd
Kimberley Park Rd
Venton Rd
Tregenver
Dracaena Av.
Shelburne Road
Theydon Rd
Western Ter.
Killigrew St.
Clare Ter.
Trelawny Road
Gyllyng St.
Church St.
Arwenack Av.
Albany Road
Marlborough Rd
Woodlane
Marlborough Av.
Melvill Rd
Bar Road
Castle Drive
Cliff Road
Sea View Rd
Stracey Rd
Spernen Wyn Rd
Pennance Rd
Silverdale Rd
Mongleath Rd
Boslowick Road
0 500 m
0 500 yards

XX **Livingstones,** Maenporth Beach, TR11 5HN, SW : 2½ m. by Swanpool Rd ✆ 250251 – A
P. VISA
closed Sunday dinner and Monday – **M** 10.50/21.50 **t.** and a la carte.

X Hannan Tandoori, 47 Arwenack St., TR11 3JH, ✆ 317391, Indian rest. – rest. VISA B o

at Mawnan Smith SW : 5 m. by Trescobeas Rd – A – – ✉ ☎ 0326 Falmouth :

Meudon ⑤, TR11 5HT, E : ½ m. via Carwinion Rd ✆ 250541, Telex 45478, Fax 250543, « ≤ Terraced gardens landscaped by Capability Brown », park – TV ☎ P. VISA
closed January-mid February – **M** 18.00/35.00 **t.** and a la carte 4.50 – **30 rm** 65.00/132.00 **t.**, **2 suites** 154.00/188.00 **t.** – SB (exept August and September) 110.00/120.00 **st.**

Budock Vean Golf and Country House ⑤, TR11 5LG, ✆ 250288, Fax 250892, ≤, , park, – TV ☎ P.
closed 3 January-1 March – **M** (bar lunch)/dinner 16.75 **st.** and a la carte 3.50 – **57 rm** 65.00/130.00 **t.**, **1 suite** 150.00/170.00 **t.**.

Nansidwell Country House ⑤, TR11 5HU, SE : ¼ m. via Carwinion Rd ✆ 250340, Fax 250440, ≤, « Country house atmosphere, gardens », park, – TV ☎ P. VISA
closed 28 December-1 February – **M** 10.00/25.00 **t.** and a la carte 19.00/21.75 **t.** 4.25 – 3.50 – **13 rm** 60.00/120.00 **t.**

Trelawne ⑤, Maenporth Rd, TR11 5HS, E : ¾ m. via Carwinion Rd ✆ 250226, Fax 250909, – rest TV ☎ P. VISA
closed 29 December-5 March – **M** (bar lunch)/dinner 15.50/16.25 **t.** 3.90 – **14 rm** 36.00/72.00 **t.** – SB (except March to October) 69.00/73.00 **st.**

at Budock Water W : 2¼ m. by Trescobeas Rd – ☎ 0326 Falmouth :

Penmarvah Manor ⑤, TR11 5ED, S : ¾ m. ✆ 250277, – TV ☎ P. VISA.
M 8.50/12.00 **t.** and a la carte 2.75 – **8 rm** 35.00/60.00 **t.** – SB (October-March) (except Christmas and New Year) 100.00 **st.** A

BMW Falmouth Rd, Penryn ✆ 032 67 (Penryn) 2641
FORD Ponsharden ✆ 72011
ATS Dracaena Av. ✆ 319233

Le Guide change,
changez de guide Michelin tous les ans.

FAREHAM Hants. 403 404 Q 31 – pop. 55 563 (inc. Portchester) – ECD : Wednesday – ☎ 0329.

Envir. : Portchester castle★ (ruins 3C - 12C), Keep ≤★ *AC*, SE : 2½ m.

Ferneham Hall, Osborn Rd ✆ 221342.

◆London 77 – ◆Portsmouth 9 – ◆Southampton 13 – Winchester 19.

Red Lion (Lansbury), East St., P016 0BP, ✆ 822640, Telex 86204, Fax 823579, – rm TV ☎ & P – 100. VISA.
M a la carte 10.95/20.15 **t.** – **44 rm** 67.00/79.00 **t.** – SB (weekends only) 68.00 **st.**

Avenue House without rest., 22 The Avenue, PO14 1NS, ✆ 232175, – TV ☎ & P. VISA
10 rm 32.00/49.00 **t.**

ROVER Newgate Lane ✆ 282811
ATS Queens Rd ✆ 234941/280032

FARLINGTON Hants. – see Portsmouth and Southsea.

FARNBOROUGH Hants. 404 R 30 – pop. 48 063 – ECD : Wednesday – ☎ 0252.

See : St. Michael's Abbey church★ (19C) (Imperial crypt *AC*).

Southwood, Ively Rd ✆ 548700, W : 1 m.

Country Library, Pinehurst Av. ✆ 513838.

◆London 41 – Reading 17 – ◆Southampton 44 – Winchester 33.

Queen's (T.H.F.), Lynchford Rd, GU14 6AZ, S : 1½ m. on Farnborough Rd (A 325) ✆ 545051, Group Telex 859637, Fax 377210, , – rm TV ☎ P – 150. VISA
M 24.00 **st.** and a la carte 4.35 – 7.50 – **110 rm** 75.00/110.00 **st.** – SB (weekends only) 76.00/96.00 **st.**

Falcon, Farnborough Rd, GU14 6TH, S : ¾ m. on A 325 ✆ 545378, Fax 522539 – TV ☎ P – . VISA.
M 12.50/15.50 **st.** 4.00 – **30 rm** 55.00/65.00 **st.**

FORD Elles Rd ✆ 544344

FARNE ISLANDS Northumb. 401 402 P 17.

See : Islands★★ (Sea Bird Sanctuary and grey seals, by boat from Seahouses *AC*).

Hotels see : Bamburgh.

FARNHAM Surrey 404 R 30 – pop. 34 541 – ECD : Wednesday – ☎ 0252.

See : Castle keep (12C) (square tower★) *AC*.

Envir. : Birdworld★ (zoological bird gardens) *AC*, SW : 3½ m.

The Sands ☎ 025 18 (Runfold) 3163, E : 1 m. – Farnham Park ☎ 715216.

Locality Office, South St. ☎ 0483 (Godalming) 861111.

♦London 45 – Reading 22 – ♦Southampton 39 – Winchester 28.

Bush (T.H.F.), The Borough, GU9 7NN, ☎ 715237, Telex 858764, Fax 733530 – rm ☎ – 48. VISA
M *(closed Saturday lunch)* 10.50/14.50 **st.** and a la carte 4.35 – 7.00 – **68 rm** 65.00/98.00 **st.** – SB (weekends only) (except Christmas and New Year) 84.00/89.00 **st.**

Bishop's Table (Best Western), 27 West St., GU9 7DR, ☎ 710222, Telex 94016743, Fax 733494 – ☎. VISA
closed 26 December-6 January – **M** *(closed Saturday lunch)* 15.00/27.00 **t.** and a la carte 4.70 – **18 rm** 70.00/85.00 **t.** – SB (weekends only) 95.00 **st.**

Trevena House, Alton Rd, GU10 5ER, SW : 1¾ m. on A 31 ☎ 716908, Fax 722583 – ☎. VISA
closed Christmas and first week January – **M** *(closed Sunday to non-residents)* (bar lunch, residents only)/dinner a la carte 10.00/14.45 **t.** 3.60 – **20 rm** 45.00/65.00 **st.** – SB 66.00/76.00 **st.**

XX Chik's, 68 Castle St., GU9 7LN, ☎ 715666, Chinese (Peking, Szechuan) rest.

XX Krug's, 84 West St., GU9 7EN, ☎ 723277, Austrian rest.

at Seale E : 4 m. on A 31 – ✉ Farnham – ☎ 025 18 Runfold :

Hog's Back, GU10 1EX, on A 31 ☎ 2345, Telex 859352, Fax 3113 – rm ☎ – 150. VISA
M 12.50/14.50 **st.** and a la carte 4.75 – 7.00 – **75 rm** 77.50/97.50 **st.**

at Frensham S : 3 m. on A 287 – ✉ Farnham – ☎ 025 125 Frensham :

Mariners, Millbridge, GU10 3DJ, N : 1 m. on A 287 ☎ 2050, Fax 2649 – ☎
21 rm.

at Churt S : 5¾ m. on A 287 – ✉ Farnham – ☎ 025 125 Frensham :

Frensham Pond, GU10 1QB, N : 1½ m. by A 287 ☎ 3175, Telex 858610, Fax 2631, « Lake-side setting », squash – ☎ –
19 rm.

Pride of the Valley (Best Western), Tilford Rd, GU10 2LE, E : 1½ m. via Hale House Lane ☎ 0428 (Hindhead) 605799, Telex 858893, Fax 605875 – ☎. VISA
M 12.00 **t.** and a la carte – **12 rm** 54.50/85.00 **st.**, **1 suite** 55.00/80.00 **st.** – SB (weekends only) 82.00/98.00 **st.**

ROVER, DAIMLER-JAGUAR East St. ☎ 716201 VW-AUDI West St. and Crondall Lane ☎ 715616

FARRINGTON GURNEY Avon 403 404 M 30 – pop. 587 – ✉ Bristol – ☎ 0761 Temple Cloud.

♦London 132 – Bath 13 – ♦Bristol 12 – Wells 8.

Country Ways, Marsh Lane, BS18 5TT, ☎ 52449, Fax 53360 – ☎. VISA
closed Christmas – **M** a la carte 17.05/19.70 **st.** 3.50 – **6 rm** 49.00/65.00 **st.**

at Ston Easton S : 1¼ m. on A 37 – ✉ Bath – ☎ 076 121 Chewton Mendip :

Ston Easton Park, BA3 4DF, ☎ 631, Fax 377, « Palladian country house », park – ☎. VISA
M 22.00/32.00 **t.** 5.00 – 6.50 – **19 rm** 95.00/285.00 **t.**, **2 suites** – SB (November-April) 170.00/240.00 **st.**

FAR SAWREY Cumbria 402 L 20 – see Hawkshead.

FARTHING CORNER SERVICE AREA Kent – ✉ Gillingham – ☎ 0634 Medway.

Farthing Corner Motorway Services ☎ 360323.

♦London 39 – Canterbury 22 – Maidstone 11.

Farthing Corner Lodge (Rank) without rest., ME8 8PW, at Farthing Corner Service Area on M 2 ☎ 377337 – VISA
58 rm 27.50/34.50 **st.**

Do not mix up :

Comfort of hotels : ... ,

Comfort of restaurants : XXXXX X

Quality of the cuisine : ✿✿✿, ✿✿, ✿, **M**

FAUGH Cumbria – see Carlisle.

FAVERSHAM Kent 404 W 30 – pop. 15 914 – ECD : Thursday – ☎ 0795.
Fleur de Lis Heritage Centre, 13 Preston St. ☎ 534542.
London 52 – Dover 26 – Maidstone 21 – Margate 25.

XX **Read's,** Painter's Forstal, ME13 0EE, SW : 2¼ m. by A 2 ☎ 535344 – P. AE VISA
closed Sunday, Monday, 25 to 26 December and last 2 weeks August – **M** 12.50/26.00 **st.** and a la carte 5.00.

at Boughton SE : 3 m. by A 2 – ✉ Faversham – ☎ 0227 Canterbury :

White Horse, The Street, ME13 9AX, ☎ 751343, Fax 751090 – TV ☎ P. AE VISA
M a la carte 13.75/16.95 **st.** 3.50 – **13 rm** 38.50/50.00 **st.** – SB (weekends only) 70.00/75.00 **st.**

at Sheldwich S : 2¾ m. on A 251 – ✉ ☎ 0795 Faversham :

Throwley House, Ashford Rd, ME13 0LT, ☎ 539168, « 18C country house », – TV ☎ P. AE VISA
M (*closed Saturday lunch* 18.50/27.50 **t.** 5.50 – 9.00 – **6 rm** 80.00/100.00 **t.** – SB 139.00/150.00 **st.**

FORD West St. ☎ 532255

ATS 20 North Lane, Faversham ☎ 534039

FAWKHAM Kent – see Brands Hatch.

FAWLEY Bucks. 404 R 29 – see Henley-on-Thames (Oxon.).

FELINDRE FARCHOG (VELINDRE) Dyfed 403 F 27 – see Newport (Dyfed).

FELINGWM UCHAF Dyfed – see Carmarthen.

FELINHELI = Port Dinorwic.

We suggest:
For a successful tour, that you prepare it in advance.
Michelin maps and guides will give you much useful information on route planning, places of interest, accommodation, prices etc.

FELIXSTOWE Suffolk 404 Y 28 – pop. 24 207 – ECD : Wednesday – ☎ 0394.
18 Ferry Rd ☎ 286834.
Shipping connections with the Continent : to Belgium (Zeebrugge) (P & O European ferries).
to Harwich (Orwell & Harwich Navigation Co.) 7 daily (except Saturday and Sunday) (15 mn).
Sea Front ☎ 276770.
London 84 – Ipswich 11.

Orwell Moat House (Q.M.H.), Hamilton Rd, IP11 7DX, ☎ 285511, Group Telex 987676, Fax 670687, – rest TV ☎ P – 200. AE VISA
M 15.50/18.00 **t.** and a la carte 6.00 – 8.00 – **55 rm** 62.50/80.00 **t.**, **3 suites** 85.00/90.00 **t.** – SB (weekends only) (except Christmas) 85.00/90.00 **st.**

Brook, Orwell Rd, IP11 7PS, ☎ 278441, Fax 670422 – TV ☎ P – 30
25 rm.

Marlborough, Sea Rd, IP11 8BJ, ☎ 285621, Telex 987047, Fax 670724, – TV ☎ P – 100. AE VISA
M 8.95/10.95 **t.** and a la carte 4.90 – 5.50 – **47 rm** 39.50/65.00 **t.**

FORD Undercliffe Rd West ☎ 286339
PEUGEOT High Rd West ☎ 272363
ROVER Crescent Rd ☎ 283221
VAUXHALL-OPEL Garrison Lane ☎ 284792

ATS 4-8 Sunderland Rd, Carr Rd Ind. Est. ☎ 675604
ATS St. Andrews Rd ☎ 277596/277888

FELMINGHAM Norfolk 404 Y 25 – see North Walsham.

FENNY BRIDGES Devon – ✉ ☎ 0404 Honiton.
London 166 – Exeter 12.

Greyhound Inn (B.C.B.), EX14 0BJ, on A 30 ☎ 850380, « 17C thatched inn », – TV ☎ P. AE VISA.
M 15.00 **st.** – **10 rm** 36.50/49.50 **st.**

Fenny Bridges Inn, EX14 0BQ, ☎ 850218, Fax 850920, – rm TV ☎ P
5 rm.

FERNDOWN Dorset 403 404 O 31 – pop. 23 921 – ECD : Wednesday – ☎ 0202.

♦London 108 – Bournemouth 6 – Dorchester 27 – Salisbury 23.

Dormy (De Vere), New Rd, BH22 8ES, on A 347 ☎ 872121, Telex 418301, Fax 895388, squash – TV ☎ P – 230. AE VISA
M 12.50/20.00 **t.** and a la carte – **125 rm** 90.00/145.00 **t.**, **5 suites** 170.00/270.00 **t.** – SB (weekends only) 130.00 **st.**

CITROEN Ringwood Rd ☎ 893589
MITSUBISHI Victoria Rd ☎ 871131
TOYOTA Ringwood Rd ☎ 872201
VAUXHALL-OPEL Wimborne Rd East ☎ 872055
VOLVO 539 Ringwood Rd ☎ 872212

FERSFIELD Norfolk – see Diss.

FINDON West Sussex 404 S 31 – see Worthing.

FINGLESHAM Kent – see Deal.

FISHBOURNE I.O.W. 403 404 Q 31 – Shipping Services : see Wight (Isle of).

Si vous écrivez à un hôtel à l'étranger,
joignez à votre lettre un coupon-réponse international.
(disponible dans les bureaux de poste).

FISHGUARD (ABERGWAUN) Dyfed 403 F 28 – pop. 2 903 – ECD : Wednesday – ☎ 0348.

Envir. : Porthgain (cliffs ★★★) SW : 10 m. – Goodwick (←★★) NW : 1½ m. – Strumble Head (←★★ from the lighthouse) NW : 5 m. – Trevine (←★★) SW : 8 m. – Bryn Henllan (site★) NE 5 m.

to Ireland (Rosslare) (Sealink) 1-2 daily (except Monday) (3 h 30 mn).

4 Hamilton St. ☎ 873484 (summer only).

♦London 265 – ♦Cardiff 114 – Gloucester 176 – Holyhead 169 – Shrewsbury 136 – ♦Swansea 76.

Plas Glyn-Y-Mel, Lower Town, SA65 9LY, ☎ 872296, ←, park – TV P. VISA
M (bar lunch)/dinner 16.00/17.00 **t.** and a la carte 4.00 – **6 rm** 38.00/70.00 **t.**

Cartref, 13-19 High St., SA65 9AW, ☎ 872430 – P. VISA.
M 12.50 **st.** 4.00 – **13 rm** 22.00/60.00 **st.** – SB 50.00/70.00 **st.**

at Pontfaen SE : 5½ m. by B 4313 – ☎ 0239 Newport :

Tregynon Country Farmhouse, Gwaun Valley, SA65 9TU, E : 3½ m. ☎ 820531, – TV P – 40.
M (dinner only) 16.00 **t.** and a la carte – **8 rm** 23.00/46.00 **t.** – SB (November-mid March) 52.00/61.00 **st.**

at Llanychaer SE : 2¼ m. on B 4313 – ✉ ☎ 0348 Fishguard :

Penlan Oleu with rm, SA65 9TL, SE : 2 m. by B 4313 on Puncheston rd ☎ 881314, ←, « Converted farmhouse », – rest P. VISA.
closed 25 and 26 December – **M** *(closed Saturday lunch)* (booking essential) a la carte 11.00/15.50 **st.** 3.00 – **5 rm** 18.00/36.00 **st.**

at Welsh Hook SW : 7½ m. by A 40 – ✉ Haverfordwest – ☎ 0348 Letterston :

Stone Hall with rm, SA62 5NS, ☎ 840212, Fax 840815, « Part 14C manor house with 17C extension », – TV P. AE VISA.
closed 2 weeks December – **M** *(closed Monday November-March)* (lunch by arrangement)/dinner 12.00/13.50 **t.** and a la carte 3.75 – **5 rm** 35.00/46.00 **t.**

at Goodwick (Wdig) NW : 1½ m. – ✉ ☎ 0348 Fishguard :

Fishguard Bay, Quay Rd, SA64 0BT, ☎ 873571, Telex 48602, Fax 873030, park – TV ☎ P – 300. AE VISA
M (bar lunch Monday to Saturday)/dinner 14.00 **st.** and a la carte 3.10 – **62 rm** 33.00/80.00 **st.** – SB (October-April) 60.00/65.00 **st.**

Glanmoy, SA64 0JX, E : 1¼ m. by A 487 ☎ 872844, – TV P. VISA.
M *(closed Monday)* 10.00 **st.** and a la carte – **3 rm** 25.00/53.00 **st.** – SB 29.00/34.50 **st.**

FORD Clive Rd ☎ 872253

FLAMSTEAD Herts. 404 S 28 – pop. 1 407 – ✉ St. Albans – ☎ 0582 Luton.

♦London 32 – Luton 5.

Hertfordshire Moat House (Q.M.H.), London Rd, AL3 8HH, on A 5 ☎ 840840, Fax 842282 – TV ☎ P – 120. AE VISA
M (bar lunch Saturday) 15.00/16.00 **t.** and a la carte – **95 rm** 85.00/150.00 **t.** – SB (weekends only) (except 25 to 31 December) 90.00 **st.**

FLEET Hants. 404 R 30 – pop. 27 406 – ECD : Wednesday – 0252.

Minley Rd ✆ 616443.

Gurkha Sq., Fleet Rd ✆ 811151.

London 46 – Guildford 14 – Reading 16 – ◆Southampton 42.

Lismoyne, Church Rd, GU13 8NA, ✆ 628555, Fax 811761, – TV ☎ P. AE VISA
M 11.75/12.75 **st.** and a la carte 4.20 – **44 rm** 62.00/80.00 **st.** – SB (weekends only) 121.30/148.10 **st.**

ROVER 66 Albert St. ✆ 613303 — ATS 113-115 Kings Rd ✆ 616412/620028

FLEETWOOD Lancs. 402 K 22 – pop. 27 899 – ECD : Wednesday – 039 17.

Fleetwood, Princes Way ✆ 3114, W : 1 m.

to the Isle of Man : Douglas (Isle of Man Steam Packet Co.) July-August, 2 weekly (3 h 20 mn).

Wyne Borough Council, The Esplanade ✆ 71141(summer only).

◆London 245 – ◆Blackpool 10 – Lancaster 28 – ◆Manchester 53.

North Euston, The Esplanade, FY7 6BN, ✆ 6525, Fax 77842 – TV ☎ P – 200. AE VISA.
M *(closed Saturday lunch)* 8.00/12.00 **t.** and a la carte 3.75 – **56 rm** 37.00/53.00 **t.** – SB (weekends only) (except September, October and Bank Holidays) 65.00 **st.**

FORD Hatfield Av. ✆ 2292 — ATS 238 Dock St. ✆ 71211/2

FLITWICK Beds. 404 S 27 – pop. 8 421 – 0525.

Beadlow Manor Hotel ✆ 0525 (Sheffield) 60800, 7 ½ m.

◆London 45 – Bedford 13 – Luton 12 – Northampton 28.

Flitwick Manor, Church Rd, off Dunstable Rd, MK45 1AE, ✆ 712242, Fax 712242 (ext 55), ≤, « 18C manor house », park, – TV ☎ P. AE VISA
M 12.95/21.00 **t.** and a la carte 24.30/48.75 **t.** 6.50 – **15 rm** 75.00/180.00 **t.**

FOLKESTONE Kent 404 X 30 – pop. 42 949 – ECD : Wednesday and Saturday – 0303.

See : Site★.

Envir. : The Warren★ (cliffs) E : 2 m. by A 20 X – Acrise Place★ *AC*, NW : 6 m. by A 260 X.

Sene Valley Folkestone Hythe ✆ 68513.

Shipping connections to France (Boulogne) (Sealink) (5-6 daily) (1 h 50 mn).

Harbour St. ✆ 58594.

◆London 76 – ◆Brighton 76 – ◆Dover 8 – Maidstone 33.

Plan on next page

Clifton, The Leas, CT20 2EB, ✆ 851231, Fax 851231, ≤, – TV ☎ – 120. AE VISA — Z **r**
M 10.25/16.00 **st.** and a la carte 3.75 – **80 rm** 42.50/115.00 **st.** – SB 75.50/83.00 **st.**

Wards, 39 Earls Av., CT20 2HB, ✆ 45166 – TV ☎ P – 40. AE VISA.
M *(closed Sunday dinner)* 10.00/12.95 **t.** and a la carte 3.80 – **10 rm** 39.50/79.50 **t.** – SB (weekends only) 80.00/105.00 **st.** — X **c**

Banque without rest., 4 Castle Hill Av., CT20 2QT, ✆ 53797 – TV ☎. AE VISA
12 rm 22.00/44.00 **st.** — Z **z**

La Tavernetta, Leaside Court, Clifton Gdns, CT20 2ED, ✆ 54955, Italian rest. – AE VISA — Z **n**
closed Sunday and Bank Holidays – **M** a la carte 12.90/16.85 **t.** 3.85.

Emilio, 124a Sandgate Rd, CT20 2BW, ✆ 55762, Italian rest. – AE VISA — Z **u**
M 7.50 **t.** and a la carte approx. 15.10 **t.** 3.60.

Paul's, 2a Bouverie Rd West, CT20 2RX, ✆ 59697 – VISA — Z **e**
closed Sunday lunch – **M** a la carte approx. 12.45 **t.** 3.50.

India, 1 Old High St., CT20 1RJ, ✆ 59155, Indian rest. – AE VISA — YZ **i**
closed Monday and 25-26 December – **M** 7.50/11.50 **t.** and a la carte 4.25.

COLT, MITSUBISHI 1-3 Park Rd ✆ 275114
RENAULT Sandgate Rd ✆ 55331
ROVER 141-143 Sandgate Rd ✆ 850066
VAUXHALL Sandgate Rd ✆ 53103
VAUXHALL Caesars Way, Cheriton ✆ 53103
YUGO Cheriton High St. ✆ 275795
ATS 318-324 Cheriton Rd ✆ 275198/275121

Gli alberghi o ristoranti ameni sono indicati nella guida con un simbolo rosso.
Contribuite a mantenere la guida aggiornata segnalandoci gli alberghi ed i ristoranti dove avete soggiornato piacevolmente.

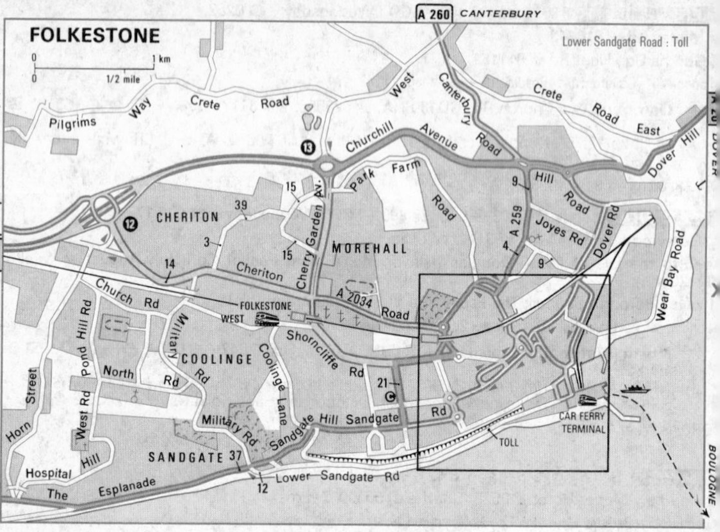

FOLKESTONE

Lower Sandgate Road : Toll

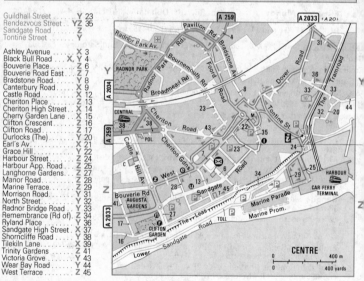

Guildhall Street . . . . Y 23
Rendezvous Street . . . YZ 35
Sandgate Road . . . . . Z
Tontine Street . . . . . Y

Ashley Avenue . . . . . X 3
Black Bull Road . . . X, Y 4
Bouverie Place . . . . . Z 6
Bouverie Road East . . . Z 7
Bradstone Road . . . . . Y 8
Canterbury Road . . . . . X 9
Castle Road . . . . X 12
Cheriton Place . . . . . . Z 13
Cheriton High Street . . X 14
Cherry Garden Lane . . X 15
Clifton Crescent . . . . . Z 16
Clifton Road . . . . Z 17
Durlocks (The) . . . . . . Y 20
Earl's Av. . . . . X 21
Grace Hill . . . . Y 22
Harbour Street . . . . . . Z 24
Harbour App. Road . . . Z 25
Langhorne Gardens . . . Z 27
Manor Road . . . . Z 28
Marine Terrace . . . . . . Z 29
Morrison Road . . . . . . Y 31
North Street . . . . Y 32
Radnor Bridge Road . . Y 33
Remembrance (Rd of) . Z 34
Ryland Place . . . . Y 36
Sandgate High Street . X 37
Shorncliffe Road . . . . . Y 38
Tilekiln Lane . . . . X 39
Trinity Gardens . . . . . Z 41
Victoria Grove . . . . . . Y 43
Wear Bay Road . . . . . . Y 44
West Terrace . . . . Z 45

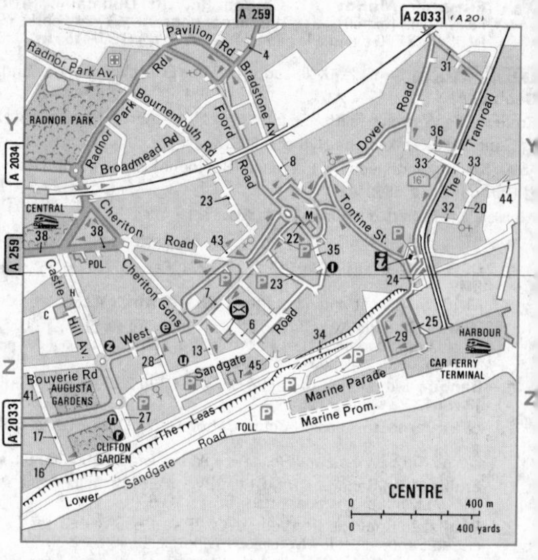

CENTRE

Alle Michelin-Straßenkarten werden ständig überarbeitet und aktualisiert.

FONTWELL West Sussex – ✉ Arundel – ☎ 0243 Eastergate.

Little Chef Complex ℘ 543269.

◆London 60 – Chichester 6 – Worthing 15.

Travelodge without rest., BN18 0SB, at A 27/29 roundabout ℘ 683973, Reservations (Toll free) 0800 850950 – TV & P. AE VISA.
32 rm 24.00/29.50 **t.**

FORD Wilts. – see Castle Combe.

FORDINGBRIDGE Hants. 403 404 O 31 – pop. 3 026 – ECD : Thursday – ☎ 0425.
See : St. Mary's Church★ (13C).
Envir. : Breamore House★ (Elizabethan) *AC*, N : 2 m.
London 101 – Bournemouth 17 – Salisbury 11 – Winchester 30.

XX **Hour Glass,** Salisbury Rd, Burgate, SP6 1LX, N : 1 m. on A 338 ☎ 652348, « 14C thatched cottage » – P. VISA
closed Sunday dinner, Monday, 2 weeks March, 1 week November and 1 January – **M** 15.95 **t.** (dinner) and a la carte 3.75.

at Stuckton SE : 1 m. by B 3078 – ✉ ☎ 0425 Fordingbridge :

X **Three Lions,** Stuckton Rd, SP6 2HF, ☎ 652489 – P. VISA
closed Sunday, Monday, January, 2 weeks July-August and Christmas – **M** a la carte 9.50/25.20 **t.** 3.95.

at Rockbourne NW : 4 m. by B 3078 – ✉ Fordingbridge – ☎ 072 53 Rockbourne :

Shearings, SP6 3NA, ☎ 256, « Picturesque 16C thatched cottage », – P.
closed mid December-mid February – **M** 16.50 **st.** – **3 rm** 19.50/39.00 **st.**

FORDWICH Kent 404 X 30 – see Canterbury.

FOREST ROW East Sussex 404 U 30 – pop. 3 842 – ECD : Wednesday – ☎ 034 282.
Royal Ashdown Forest, Chapel Lane ☎ 4866.
London 35 – Brighton 26 – Eastbourne 30 – Maidstone 32.

Chequers Inn, The Square, RH18 5ES, ☎ 4394, Fax 5454 – TV ☎ P. AE VISA.
5.00 – **17 rm** 40.00/65.00 **st.** – SB (weekends only) 80.00 **st.**

at Wych Cross S : 2½ m. on A 22 – ✉ ☎ 034 282 Forest Row :

Roebuck, RH18 5JL, ☎ 3811, Fax 4790, – TV ☎ P – 100. AE VISA
M 16.50/19.50 **st.** 4.50 – 7.00 – **28 rm** 60.00/80.00 **st.**

Pour visiter une ville ou une région : utilisez les Guides Verts Michelin.

FORTON SERVICE AREA Lancs. – ✉ ☎ 0524 Lancaster.

Rank Motor Lodge without rest., LA2 9DU, ☎ 792227 – TV P. AE VISA
41 rm 27.50/34.50 **st.**

FOSSEBRIDGE Glos. 403 404 O 28 – pop. 1 706 – ✉ ☎ 0285.
London 88 – Gloucester 23 – Oxford 31 – Swindon 21.

Fossebridge Inn, GL54 3JS, ☎ 720721, Fax 720793, « Attractively furnished », – TV ☎ P. AE VISA
M 24.50 **t.** and a la carte – **12 rm** 47.50/75.00 **t.** – SB 84.00/94.00 **st.**

FOUR MARKS Hants. 403 404 Q 30 – pop. 2 429 – ✉ ☎ 0420 Alton.
London 58 – Guildford 24 – Reading 29 – Southampton 24.

Travelodge without rest., 156 Winchester Rd, GU34 5HZ, on A 31 ☎ 62659, Reservations (Toll free) 0800 850950 – TV P. AE VISA.
31 rm 24.00/29.50 **t.**

FOWEY Cornwall 403 G 32 The West Country G. – pop. 2 092 – ECD : Wednesday – ☎ 0726.
See : Site★★.
The Post Office, 4 Custom House Hill ☎ 833616.
London 277 – Newquay 24 – Plymouth 34 – Truro 22.

Marina, The Esplanade, PL23 1HY, ☎ 833315, ≤ Fowey river and harbour, – rest TV ☎. AE VISA
March-October – **M** (bar lunch)/dinner 14.00 **t.** and a la carte 3.00 – **11 rm** 29.00/68.00 **t.** – SB 66.00/90.00 **st.**

Carnethic House, Lambs Barn, PL23 1HQ, NW : ¾ m. on A 3082 ☎ 833336, heated, – rm TV P. AE VISA
closed December and January – **M** (bar lunch)/dinner 10.00 **st.** 3.00 – **8 rm** 27.50/50.00 **st.** – SB (except July and August) 55.00/60.00 **st.**

Ocean View without rest., 24 Tower Park, PL23 1JB, ☎ 832283, ≤,
March-September – **4 rm** 16.00/34.00 **s.**

Ashley House without rest., The Esplanade, PL23 1HY, ☎ 832310 – rest TV
6 rm.

XX **Food for Thought,** 4 Town Quay, PL23 1AT, ☎ 832221, ≤ – VISA
closed Sunday, January and February – **M** (booking essential) (dinner only) 16.50 **t.** and a la carte 21.50/30.00 **t.** 3.50.

at Golant N : 3 m. by B 3269 – ✉ ☎ 0726 Fowey :

Cormorant, PL23 1LL, ☎ 833426, ≤ River Fowey, – TV ☎ P
11 rm.

at Bodinnick-by-Fowey E : ¼ m. via car ferry – ✉ Fowey – ☎ 072 687 Polruan :

Old Ferry Inn, PL23 1LX, ℘ 870237, ≤ Fowey Estuary and town, « Part 16C inn » – P. VISA
M *(closed November-March)* (bar lunch)/dinner 18.00 **st.** 4.20 – **10 rm** 30.00/70.00 s

FOWLMERE Cambs. 404 U 27 – see Cambridge.

FOWNHOPE Heref. and Worc. 403 404 M 27 – pop. 1 362 – ✉ Hereford – ☎ 043 277.
London 132 – Cardiff 46 – Hereford 6 – Gloucester 27.

Green Man Inn, HR1 4PE, ℘ 243, Fax 207, – TV ☎ P. VISA
M (bar lunch)/dinner 15.00 **st.** and a la carte 3.75 – **15 rm** 28.00/39.50 **st.** SB 60.50 **st.**

Bowens Country, HR1 4PS, on B 4224 ℘ 430, – rest TV P. VISA.
closed Christmas – **M** (by arrangement) – **12 rm** 19.00/44.00 **t.** – SB 52.00/57.50 **st.**

FRAMLINGHAM Suffolk 404 X 27 – pop. 1 830 – ECD : Wednesday – ✉ Woodbridge ☎ 0728.
See : Castle ramparts★ (Norman ruins) *AC.*
London 92 – Ipswich 19 – Norwich 42.

Crown (T.H.F.), Market Hill, IP13 9AN, ℘ 723521, Fax 724274, « 16C inn » – TV ☎ P. AE VISA
M 14.00 **st.** and a la carte 4.35 – 7.00 – **14 rm** 50.00/99.00 **st.** – SB 94.00/114.00 **st.**

FORD Market Hill ℘ 723215

Die Preise	Einzelheiten über die in diesem Führer angegebenen Preise finden Sie in der Einleitung.

FRAMPTON-ON-SEVERN Glos. 403 404 M 28 – ☎ 0452 Gloucester.
London 121 – Bristol 48 – Gloucester 14.

Savery's, The Green, GL2 7EA, ℘ 740077 – VISA
closed Sunday, Monday and 25-26 December – **M** (dinner only) 25.95 **st.** 3.50.

FRANKLEY West Midlands 403 404 ⑲ – see Birmingham.

FRANT Kent 404 U 30 – see Royal Tunbridge Wells.

FRENSHAM Surrey 404 R 30 – see Farnham.

FRESHWATER BAY I.O.W. 403 404 P 31 – see Wight (Isle of).

FRESSINGFIELD Suffolk 404 X 26 – pop. 831 – ✉ Eye – ☎ 037 986.
London 103 – Ipswich 30 – Norwich 23.

Fox and Goose, IP21 5PB, ℘ 247 – P. AE VISA
closed Sunday dinner, Tuesday, 2 weeks January-February and 2 weeks September – **M** (booking essential) 17.00 **t.** and a la carte 5.50.

FRIETH Bucks. – see Henley-on-Thames (Oxon.).

FRILFORD Oxon 403 404 P28-29 – see Abingdon.

FRIMLEY Surrey 404 R 30 – ✉ ☎ 0276 Camberley.
London 39 – Reading 17 – Southampton 47.

Ancient Raj, 9 The Parade, High St., ℘ 26042, Indian rest..

at Frimley Green SE : 1¼ m. by Church Rd – ✉ Camberley – ☎ 0252 Deepcut :

Lakeside International, Wharf Rd, GU16 6JR, ℘ 838000, Telex 858095, ≤, – TV ☎ P –
96 rm.

FRINTON-ON-SEA Essex 404 X 28 – pop. 12 507 (inc. Walton) – ECD : Wednesday – ☎ 0255.
The Esplanade ℘ 764618.
London 72 – Chelmsford 39 – Colchester 17.

Maplin, 3 The Esplanade, CO13 9EL, ℘ 673832, ≤, heated – TV ☎ P. AE VISA
closed January – **M** 13.75/14.75 **st.** and a la carte 4.60 – **11 rm** 44.00/84.00 **st.**

Uplands, 41 Hadleigh Rd, CO13 9HQ, ℘ 674889, – rm P.
closed Christmas – **M** (by arrangement) 10.00 – **8 rm** 17.50/46.00.

FIAT Connaught Ave. ℘ 679123
PEUGEOT-TALBOT Thorpe Rd ℘ 674383
ROVER, FORD Connaught Av. ℘ 674311
TOYOTA Frinton Rd, Kirby Cross ℘ 679191
VOLVO, SEAT Connaught Av. ℘ 679123/674341
Yugo High St., Walton ℘ 675768

FRODSHAM Cheshire 402 403 404 L 24 – pop. 9 143 – ✉ Warrington – ☎ 0928.
♦London 203 – Chester 11 – ♦Liverpool 21 – ♦Manchester 29 – ♦Stoke-on-Trent 42.

Old Hall, Main St., WA6 9LY, ✆ 32052, Telex 629794, Fax 39046, heated – TV ☎ P. AE VISA
M 12.50/18.50 **st.** and a la carte – **21 rm** 40.00/70.00 **st.**, **1 suite** 65.00/85.00 **st.** – SB (weekends only) 80.00/90.00 **st.**

ATS 63 Main St. ✆ 33555

FULBROOK Oxon. 403 404 P 28 – see Burford.

FULWOOD Lancs. 402 L M 22 – see Preston.

GAINSBOROUGH Lincs. 402 404 R 23 – pop. 20 326 – ECD : Wednesday – ☎ 0427.
See : Old Hall★★ (15C) *AC*.
18 Thonock ✆ 613088, N : 1 m. by A 159.
♦London 150 – Lincoln 19 – ♦Nottingham 42 – ♦Sheffield 34.

Hotels and Restaurant see : Bawtry NW : 12 m., ***Scunthorpe*** NE : 17 m.

FORD Lea Rd ✆ 810018
ROVER North St. ✆ 612251
VAUXHALL-OPEL 35 Trinity St. ✆ 611570

GALMPTON Devon – ✉ ☎ 0803 Brixham.
♦London 229 – ♦Plymouth 32 – Torquay 6.

Lost and Found, Maypool, TQ5 0ET, by Greenway Rd ✆ 842442, ≤River Dart and valley, – TV ☎ P – **16 rm.**

GANLLWYD Gwynedd 402 403 I 25 – see Dolgellau.

GARFORTH West Yorks. 402 P 22 – see Leeds.

GATESHEAD Tyne and Wear 401 402 P 19 – pop. 91 429 – ECD : Wednesday – ☎ 091 Tyneside.
18 Ravensworth, Mossheaps, Wrekenton ✆ 487 6014/487 2843 – 18 Heworth, Gingling Gate ✆ 469 2137, SE.
Central Library, Prince Consort Rd ✆ 477 3478.
♦London 282 – Durham 16 – ♦Middlesbrough 38 – ♦Newcastle-upon-Tyne 1 – Sunderland 11.

Plan : see Newcastle-upon-Tyne

Metropark, Metro Centre, NE11 9XF, ✆ 493 2233, Fax 493 2030, – rm TV ☎ P – 450. AE VISA AX **e**
M 13.25/15.00 **t.** and a la carte 4.00 – 7.95 – **150 rm** 57.95/98.45 **st.**

Springfield, Durham Rd, NE9 5BT, S : ½ m. on A 6127 ✆ 477 4121, Fax 477 7213 – rm TV ☎ P – 150 – **60 rm.** BX **s**

Swallow, High West St., NE8 1PE, ✆ 477 1105, Telex 53534, Fax 478 7214, – rm TV ☎ P – 200. AE VISA BX **r**
M *(closed Saturday lunch)* 11.00/16.50 **st.** and a la carte 5.00 – **103 rm** 68.00/125.00 **st.** – SB (weekends only) 80.00/85.00 **st.**

FORD Eslington Park ✆ 460 7464
NISSAN Lobley Hill Rd ✆ 460 0000
PEUGEOT-TALBOT Team Valley ✆ 482 6969
ROVER Low Fell ✆ 487 2118
TOYOTA St. James Sq. ✆ 490 0112
VAUXHALL St James Sq. ✆ 477 8595
ATS Earlsway/First Av., Team Valley Trading Est. ✆ 4910081

GATWICK AIRPORT West Sussex 404 T 30 – ✉ West Sussex – ☎ 0293 Gatwick.
✈ ✆ 0293 (Crawley) 28822/31299 and ✆ 081 (London) 759 4321.
International Arrivals Concourse ✆ 560108.
♦ London 29 – ♦Brighton 28.

Plan on next page

London Gatwick Airport Hilton, Gatwick Airport, RH6 0LL, ✆ 518080, Telex 877021, Fax 28980, – rm TV ☎ – 450. AE VISA Y **u**
M 13.50/22.90 **st.** and a la carte 6.95 – 9.95 – **549 rm** 115.00/125.00 **st.**, **3 suites** 185.00/295.00 **st.**.

Gatwick Penta, Povey Cross Rd ✉Horley (Surrey), RH6 0BE, ✆ 820169, Telex 87440, Fax 820259, squash – rm TV ☎ P – 150. AE VISA Y **a**
M *(closed Saturday lunch)* 13.00/16.25 **st.** and a la carte 4.40 – 7.75 – **256 rm** 95.00/110.00 **st.**, **4 suites** 205.00/220.00 **st.** – SB (weekends only) 281.50 **st.**

Post House (T.H.F.), Povey Cross Rd ✉Horley (Surrey), RH6 0BA, ✆ 771621, Telex 877351, Fax 771054, – rm TV ☎ P – 100. AE VISA Y **c**
M *(closed Saturday lunch)* 10.50/14.50 **st.** and a la carte 4.35 – 8.00 – **216 rm** 80.00/90.00 **st.**

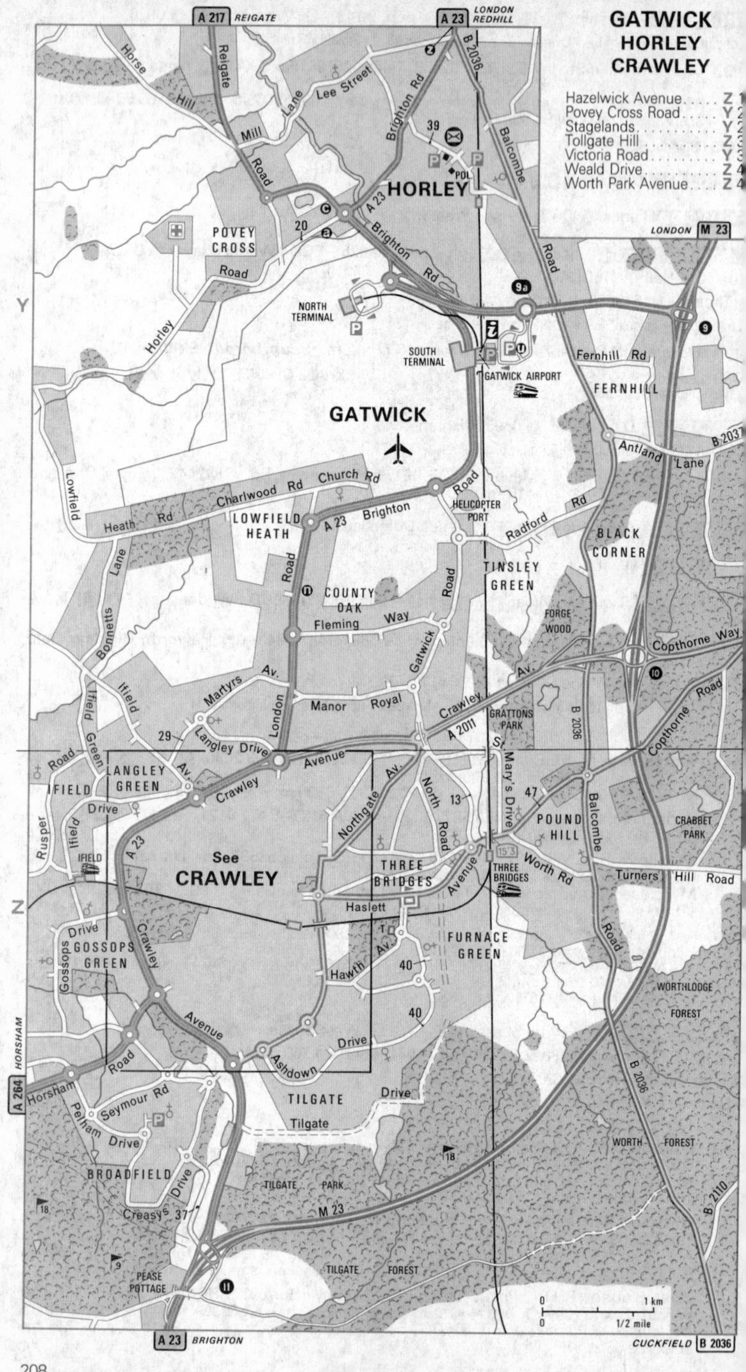

GATWICK
HORLEY
CRAWLEY
Hazelwick Avenue Z 1
Povey Cross Road Y
Stagelands Y
Tollgate Hill Z
Victoria Road Y
Weald Drive Z 4
Worth Park Avenue Z 4
A 217 REIGATE
A 23 LONDON REDHILL
LONDON M 23
A 264 HORSHAM
A 23 BRIGHTON
CUCKFIELD B 2036
HORLEY
POVEY CROSS
NORTH TERMINAL
SOUTH TERMINAL
GATWICK AIRPORT
GATWICK
FERNHILL
LOWFIELD HEATH
HELICOPTER PORT
BLACK CORNER
TINSLEY GREEN
COUNTY OAK
FORGE WOOD
GRATTONS PARK
LANGLEY GREEN
IFIELD
POUND HILL
CRABBET PARK
See CRAWLEY
THREE BRIDGES
FURNACE GREEN
GOSSOPS GREEN
WORTHLODGE FOREST
TILGATE
WORTH FOREST
BROADFIELD
TILGATE PARK
PEASE POTTAGE
TILGATE FOREST
Horse Hill
Reigate Road
Mill Lane
Lee Street
Brighton Rd
Balcombe Road
Horley Road
Fernhill Rd
Antland Lane
B 2037
Lowfield Heath Rd
Charlwood Rd
Church Rd
A 23 Brighton Road
Radford Rd
Bonnetts Lane
Fleming Way
Gatwick Road
Copthorne Way
Copthorne Road
Ifield Green
Ifield Av.
Martyrs Av.
Manor Royal
Crawley Av.
A 2011
London Road
Langley Drive
Rusper Road
Ifield Drive
Crawley Avenue
Northgate Av.
North Road
St. Mary's Drive
Worth Rd
Turners Hill Road
Haslett Avenue
Hawth Av.
Gossops Drive
Crawley Avenue
Ashdown Drive
Tilgate Drive
Horsham Road
Seymour Rd
Pelham Drive
Creasys Drive
M 23
B 2036
B 2110
1 km
1/2 mile

GERRARDS CROSS Bucks. 404 S 29 – pop. 19 447 (inc. Chalfont St.Peter) – ECD : Wednesday – ✆ 0753.

Chalfont Park ✆ 883263.

London 22 – Aylesbury 22 – Oxford 36.

Bull (De Vere), Oxford Rd, SL9 7PA, on A 40 ✆ 885995, Telex 847747, Fax 885504 – rest – 200. AE VISA
M 19.00/20.00 **st.** and a la carte – **96 rm** 95.00/135.00 **st.**, **2 suites** 175.00 **st.** – SB (weekends only) 96.00 **st.**

Ethorpe (B.C.B.), Packhorse Rd, SL9 8HY, ✆ 882039, Fax 887012 – TV. AE VISA.
M 15.00 **st.** – **29 rm** 69.00/84.00 **st.**

Monsoon, 1a Packhorse Rd, SL9 7QA, ✆ 888910, Indian rest. – AE VISA
M 12.00/15.00 **t.** (dinner) and a la carte approx. 11.45 3.25.

BMW 31-33 Station Rd ✆ 889606 PEUGEOT-TALBOT Oxford Rd ✆ 882545

GILLAN Cornwall 403 E 33 **The West Country G.** – see Helford.

GILLINGHAM Dorset 403 404 N 30 – pop. 5 379 – ✆ 0747.

London 116 – Bournemouth 34 – Bristol 46 – Southampton 52.

Stock Hill House, Wyke, SP8 5NR, W : 1½ m. on B 3081 ✆ 823626, « Victorian country house », park – rest TV. VISA.
M *(closed Sunday dinner and Monday)* (lunch by arrangement) 20.00/27.00 **t.** 5.00 – **8 rm** (dinner included) 80.00/160.00 **t.**

GISBURN Lancs. 402 N 22 – pop. 435 – ECD : Wednesday – ✉ Clitheroe – ✆ 020 05.

London 243 – Manchester 37 – Preston 25.

Stirk House, BB7 4LJ, SW : 1 m. on A 59 ✆ 581, Telex 635238, Fax 744, squash – TV – 250
50 rm.

GISLINGHAM Suffolk 404 X 27 – pop. 589 – ✉ Eye – ✆ 037 983 Mellis.

London 93 – Cambridge 45 – Ipswich 20 – Norwich 30.

Old Guildhall, Mill St., IP23 8JT, ✆ 361 – TV.
closed January – **M** (by arrangement) 9.50 **t.** 3.50 – **4 rm** 37.50/45.00 **st.** – SB 60.00 **st.**

GITTISHAM Devon 403 K 31 – pop. 233 – ECD : Thursday – ✉ ✆ 0404 Honiton.

London 164 – Exeter 14 – Sidmouth 9 – Taunton 21.

Combe House, EX14 0AD, ✆ 42756, Fax 46004, <, « Country house atmosphere », park – TV. AE VISA
closed Sunday and Monday January-February – **M** (bar lunch, residents only)/dinner a la carte 21.25/26.25 **st.** 4.00 – **14 rm** 55.50/110.50 **st.**, **1 suite** 119.50 **st.**.

GLASTONBURY Somerset 403 L 30 **The West Country G.** – pop. 6 751 – ECD : Wednesday – ✆ 0458.

See : Site★★ – Abbey★★ *AC* – St. John the Baptist Church★★ – Somerset Rural Life Museum★ *AC* – Glastonbury Tor★ (<★★★).

1 Marchant's Buildings, Northload St. ✆ 32954 (summer only).

London 136 – Bristol 26 – Taunton 22.

George and Pilgrims Resort, 1 High St., BA6 9DP, ✆ 31146, « Part 15C inn » – rest TV
12 rm.

Number Three with rm, 3 Magdalene St., BA6 9EW, ✆ 32129, « Georgian house » – rest TV. AE VISA.
closed first 3 weeks January – **M** *(closed Sunday and Monday)* (booking essential) (dinner only) 30.00 **t.** 4.00 – 5.50 – **6 rm** 50.00/70.00 **t.**

at West Pennard E : 3½ m. on A 361 – ✉ ✆ 0458 Glastonbury :

Red Lion, BA6 8NN, ✆ 32941 – TV. AE VISA.
M a la carte 6.25/14.75 **t.** – **7 rm** 30.00/45.00 **t.** – SB (October-March) (weekends only) 60.00 **st.**

RENAULT Beckery Rd ✆ 34370

Pleasant hotels and restaurants are shown in the Guide by a red sign.

Please send us the names of any where you have enjoyed your stay.

Your Michelin Guide will be even better.

... XXXXX ... X

GLEMSFORD Suffolk 404 V 27 – pop. 2 406 – ✉ Sudbury – ☎ 0787.
♦London 65 – ♦Cambridge 32 – Colchester 21 – ♦Ipswich 28.

XX **Barretts,** 31 Egremont St., CO10 7SA, ℘ 281573 – ⓟ. AE VISA
closed Sunday dinner and Monday – **M** (dinner only and Sunday lunch)/dinner a la carte 23.85/27.85 **st.**

GLEN PARVA Leics. – see Leicester.

GLEWSTONE Heref. and Worc. – see Ross-on-Wye.

GLOOSTON Leics. – see Market Harborough.

GLOSSOP Derbs. 402 403 404 O 23 – pop. 29 923 – ECD : Wednesday – ☎ 0457.
⛳9 Sheffield Rd ℘ 3117, E : 1 m. by A 577.
ℹ Station Fourcourt, Norfolk St. ℘ (045 74) 5920.
♦London 194 – ♦Manchester 18 – ♦Sheffield 25.

Wind in the Willows ⛰, Derbyshire Level, SK13 9PT, off A 57 ℘ 868001, – TV ☎ ⓟ. AE VISA.
M *(closed Christmas and New Year)* (dinner only) 19.50 **st.** 4.50 – **8 rm** 53.00/95.00 **st**

For maximum information from town plans: consult the conventional signs key.

GLOUCESTER Glos. 403 404 N 28 – pop. 106 526 – ECD : Thursday – ☎ 0452.
See : Site★ – Cathedral★★ (12C-14C) (Great Cloister★★★ 14C) Y – Docks★ Y – Bishop Hooper's Lodging (Folk Museum)★ (15C) Y **M.**
⛳18 Gloucestershire Hotel, Matson Lane ℘ 25653, S : 2 m. Z.
ℹ St Michael's Tower, The Cross ℘ 421188/504273.
♦London 106 – ♦Birmingham 52 – ♦Bristol 38 – ♦Cardiff 66 – ♦Coventry 57 – Northampton 83 – ♦Oxford 48 – ♦Southampton 98 – ♦Swansea 92 – Swindon 35.

Plan opposite

Crest (T.H.F.), Crest Way, Barnwood, GL4 7RX, E : 3 m. on A 417 ℘ 613311, Telex 437273, Fax 371036, ⛹, ≘s, ⛾ – ⇔ rm TV ☎ ♿ ⓟ – 🎤 100. AE ⓓ VISA
M *(closed Saturday lunch)* 12.50/17.50 **st.** and a la carte – ☕ 7.95 – **122 rm** 80.00/92.00 **st.**, **1 suite** 120.00/160.00 **st.** – SB (weekends only and August) 176.00/188.00 **st.** by A 417 Z

Gloucester H. and Country Club, Robinswood Hill, Matson Lane, GL4 9EA, SE : 3 m. by B 4073 ℘ 25653, Telex 43571, Fax 307212, ⛹, ≘s, ⛾, ⛳18, 🎾, squash – ⇔ rm TV ☎ ⓟ – 🎤 180. AE ⓓ VISA Z c
M *(closed Saturday lunch)* 13.50/17.50 **st.** and a la carte 4.90 – ☕ 7.00 – **102 rm** 77.50/87.50 **st.**, **5 suites** 120.00 **st.** – SB (except Easter, Christmas and New Year) 109.00 **st.**

New County, Southgate St., GL1 2DU, ℘ 307000, Fax 500487 – TV ☎ – 🎤 130 **31 rm.**

Travel Inn, Tewkesbury Rd, Longford, GL2 9BE, N : 1 ¾ m. on A 38 Z ℘ 23519 – ⇔ rm TV ♿ ⓟ. AE ⓓ VISA.
M (Beefeater grill) a la carte approx. 12.25 **t.** – ☕ 4.50 – **40 rm** -/27.50 **t.**

X **College Green,** 7-11 College St., GL1 2NE, ℘ 20739 – AE VISA Y a
closed Sunday to Tuesday and Bank Holidays – **M** (dinner only and Sunday lunch)/dinner 15.50/22.00 **st.** and a la carte 4.00.

at Upton St. Leonards SE : 3½ m. by B 4073 – Z – ✉ ☎ 0452 Gloucester :

Hatton Court, Upton Hill, GL4 8DE, S : ¾ m. on B 4073 ℘ 617412, Group Telex 437334, Fax 612945, ←, ⛾ heated, – ▤ rest TV ☎ ⓟ – 🎤 30. AE ⓓ VISA.
M 30.00 **t.** (lunch) and a la carte 21.15/27.70 **t.** 7.00 – **46 rm** ☕ 72.00/110.00 **t.** – SB (exept Christmas and New Year) 105.00/120.00 **st.**

at Witcombe SE : 7 m. by A 40 and A 417 – ✉ ☎ 0452 Gloucester :

Travel Inn, GL3 4SS, on A 417 ℘ 862521 – ⇔ rm TV ♿ ⓟ. AE ⓓ VISA.
M (Beefeater grill) a la carte approx. 12.25 **t.** – ☕ 4.50 – **39 rm** -/27.50 **t.**

at Quedgeley SW : 2 ¾ m. by A 430 on B 4008 – Z – ✉ ☎ 0452 Gloucester :

The Retreat without rest., 116 Bristol Rd, GL2 6NA, ℘ 728296, ⛾ heated, – TV ☎ ⓟ.
11 rm ☕ 15.00/34.00 **st.**

AUDI-VW Eastern Av. ℘ 25177
BMW Kingsholm Rd ℘ 23456
CITROEN 143 Westgate St. ℘ 23252
FIAT Quedgeley ℘ 720107
LAND-ROVER, RANGE-ROVER Wotton-under-Edge ℘ 0453 (Dursley) 844131
NISSAN Eastern Av. ℘ 423691
PEUGEOT-TALBOT, FIAT Bristol Rd ℘ 29755
RENAULT St. Oswalds Rd ℘ 305051
ROVER Mercia Rd ℘ 29531
SAAB Montpelier ℘ 22404
TOYOTA London Rd ℘ 21555
VAUXHALL Cole Av. ℘ 26711
VAUXHALL Priory Rd ℘ 24912
VAUXHALL Shepherd Rd, Cole Av. ℘ 26711
VOLVO Shepherd Rd ℘ 25291

ATS St. Oswald's Rd ℘ 27329

GLOUCESTER

astgate Shopping Centre . . . . Y
astgate Street . . . . . . Y 10
orthgate Street . . . . . . Y 16
outhgate Street . . . . Y

arnwood By-Pass . . . . . Z 3
lack Dog Way . . . . Y 5
ommercial Road . . . . . . Y 6
otteswold Road . . . . Z 8
erby Road . . . . Z 9
reat Western Road . . . . Y 12
eathville Road . . . . Y 13
ng Edward's Avenue . . Z 14
ower Westgate Street . . Y 15
arkend Road . . . . Z 17
arliament Street . . . . . . Y 18
itt Street . . . . Y 19
uay Street . . . . Y 20
oyal Oak Road . . . . Y 21
t. Aldate Street . . . . Y 22
t. Johns Lane . . . . Y 23
outhern Avenue . . . . Z 24
pa Road . . . . Y 26
troud Road . . . . Z 28
redworth Road . . . . Z 30
Vorcester Street . . . . Y 31

A 40
A 38
A 417
St. Oswald's Rd
Westgate
CATHEDRAL
London Road
The Quay
POL.
St.
EASTGATE SHOPPING CENTRE
THE DOCKS
Southgate
Brunswick Rd
Bruton Way
CENTRAL
LEISURE CENTRE
Park Road
Barton St.
B 4073
0 200 m.
0 200 yds
A 430 (A 38)
(A 430)
Y

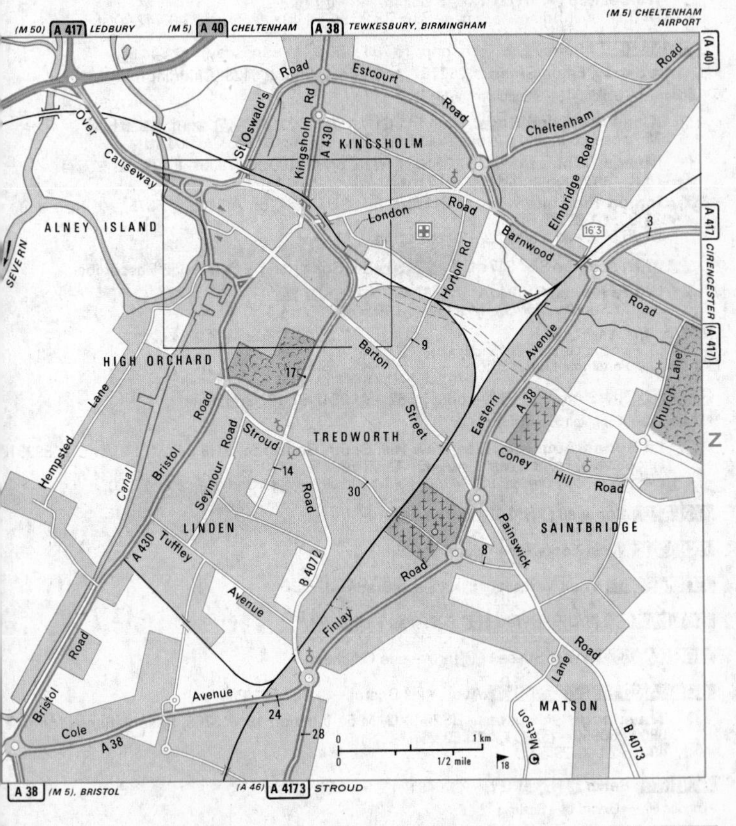

GLYN CEIRIOG Clwyd 402 403 K 25 – ✉ Llangollen – ☎ 069 172.
♦London 194 – Shrewsbury 30 – Wrexham 17.

Golden Pheasant ⑤, Llwynmawr, LL20 7BB, ℘ 281, Telex 35664, ≤, ☞ – TV ☎ P. AE ① VISA
M 9.50/16.95 **t.** 4.50 – **18 rm** 33.50/103.00 **st.** – SB (except Easter and Christma 104.00/147.00 **st.**

GOATHLAND North Yorks. 402 R 20 – pop. 442 – ECD : Wednesday and Saturday – ☎ 0947 Whitby.
♦London 248 – ♦Middlesbrough 36 – York 38.

Mallyan Spout ⑤, The Common, YO22 5AN, ℘ 86206, ☞ – TV ☎ P. AE ① VISA
M (dinner only and Sunday lunch)/dinner 25.00 **t.** and a la carte 4.00 – **24 rm** 55.0 100.00 **t.**

Whitfield House ⑤, Darnholm, YO22 5LA, NW : ¾ m. ℘ 86215, ☞ – rest
closed mid November-mid January – **M** 12.50 **t.** 4.00 – **9 rm** 19.50/39.00 **t.** – SB (except summer) 50.00/55.00 **st.**

Heatherdene ⑤, The Common, Y022 5AN, ℘ 86334, ≤, ☞ – rest TV P
April-October – **M** 8.00 – **6 rm** 13.50/30.00.

Prudom House ⑤, The Common, YO22 5AN, ℘ 86368, ≤ – rest
closed mid November-December – **7 rm** (dinner included) 15.50/36.00 **st.**

at Egton Bridge NW : 4¾ m. – ✉ ☎ 0947 Whitby :

Horseshoe ⑤, YO21 1XE, ℘ 85245, ☞ – TV P. AE.
M (bar lunch)/dinner a la carte 7.55/13.00 **st.** 4.40 – **6 rm** 28.00/42.00 **st.**

GODALMING Surrey 404 S 30 – pop. 18 758 – ECD : Wednesday – ☎ 048 68.
18 West Surrey, Enton Green ℘ 21275 – 9 Chiddingfold ℘ 0428 (Chiddingfold) 53237.
♦London 38 – Guildford 5 – ♦Southampton 51.

Kings Arms and Royal, High St., GU7 1EB, ℘ 21545 – TV ☎ P. VISA.
M *(closed Sunday)* a la carte 11.35/17.65 **t.** – **16 rm** 45.00/55.00 **st.**

Meads, 65 Meadrow, GU7 3HS, N : ½ m. on A 3100 ℘ 21800 – TV P. AE VISA
M (by arrangement) 8.20 **t.** – **15 rm** 23.00/48.00 **t.**

XXX **Inn on the Lake** with rm, Ockford Rd, GU7 1RH, on A 3100 ℘ 5575, ☞ – TV ☎ P 80. AE ① VISA
M 25.50 **t.** and a la carte – **20 rm** 45.00/80.00 **t.**

at Hascombe SE : 3½ m. on B 2130 – ✉ Godalming – ☎ 048 632 Hascombe :

X **White Horse,** GU8 4JA, ℘ 258, ☞ – P. AE VISA
closed Sunday dinner – **M** a la carte 15.50/22.05 **t.** 4.50.

NISSAN The Wharf ℘ 5201
RENAULT Farncombe ℘ 7743/23169
VAUXHALL Portsmouth Rd ℘ 5666
ATS Meadrow ℘ 21845/22219

GODSTONE Surrey 404 T 30 – pop. 2 567 – ☎ 0342 South Godstone.
♦London 22 – ♦Brighton 36 – Maidstone 28.

XXX **La Bonne Auberge,** Tilburstow Hill, South Godstone, RH9 8JY, S : 2¼ m. ℘ 892318 Fax 893435, French rest., ☞ – P. AE ① VISA
closed Sunday dinner and Monday – **M** 21.50/27.75 **st.** and a la carte 4.20.

GOLANT Cornwall 403 G 32 – see Fowey.

GOLCAR West Yorks. – see Huddersfield.

GOMERSAL West Yorks. 402 O 22 – see Bradford.

GOODWICK (WDIG) Dyfed 403 F 27 – see Fishguard.

GOODWOOD West Sussex 404 R 31 – see Chichester.

GORDANO SERVICE AREA Avon – ✉ Bristol – ☎ 027 581 Pill

Travelodge without rest., BS20 9XG, M 5 : junction 19 ℘ 3709, Reservations (Toll free) 0800 850950 – TV & P. AE VISA.
40 rm 24.00/29.50 **t.**

GORING Berks 403 404 Q 29 – ☎ 0491.
♦London 56 – ♦Oxford 16 – Reading 12.

X **Leatherne Bottel,** RG8 0HS, N : 1½ m. by B 4009 ℘ 872667, ≤, « Thames-side setting » – P. AE VISA
closed Christmas Day – **M** a la carte 12.70/21.70 **t.**

GORLESTON-ON-SEA Norfolk 404 Z 26 – see Great Yarmouth.

GOSFORTH Tyne and Wear 401 402 P 18 – see Newcastle-upon-Tyne.

GOUDHURST Kent 404 V 30 – pop. 2 673 – ECD : Wednesday – ✉ Cranbrook – ☎ 0580.
◆London 45 – Hastings 22 – Maidstone 13.

Star and Eagle (Lansbury), High St., TN17 1AL, ☎ 211512, « 14C inn » – TV ☎ P. AE VISA
M a la carte 18.75/22.68 **t.** 4.50 – **11 rm** 50.00/66.00 **t.**

GOVETON Devon 403 I 33 – see Kingsbridge.

GRAMPOUND Cornwall 403 F 33 – ✉ Truro – ☎ 0726 St. Austell.
◆London 287 – Newquay 16 – ◆Plymouth 44 – Truro 8.

XX **Eastern Promise,** 1 Moor View, TR2 4RT, ☎ 883033, Chinese rest. – P. AE VISA
closed Wednesday – **M** (booking essential) (dinner only) a la carte 14.50 **t.** (dinner) and a la carte 3.00.

GRANGE-IN-BORROWDALE Cumbria 402 K 20 – see Keswick.

GRANGE-OVER-SANDS Cumbria 402 L 21 – pop. 3 864 – ECD : Thursday – ☎ 044 84 (4 fig.) or 053 95 (5 fig.).
Envir. : Cartmel (Priory Church★ 12C chancel★★) NW : 3 m.
18 Meathop Rd ☎ 63180, ½ m. from station – 9 Grange Fell, Cartmel Rd ☎ 32536.
Victoria Hall, Main St. ☎ 34026 (summer only).
◆London 268 – Kendal 13 – Lancaster 24.

Graythwaite Manor , Fernhill Rd, LA11 7JE, ☎ 32001, ← gardens and sea, « Extensive flowered gardens », park, – TV ☎ P. VISA.
M 10.50/20.00 **t.** 3.00 – **22 rm** 37.50/80.00 **st.** – SB 80.00/98.00 **st.**

Netherwood , Lindale Rd, LA11 6ET, ☎ 32552, ←, , park – TV ☎ P
M 9.50/14.50 **t.** and a la carte 3.95 – **23 rm** 32.75/67.50 **t.** – SB (November-March) 60.00 **st.**

at Witherslack NE : 5 m. by B 5277 off A 590 – ✉ ☎ 044 852 Witherslack :

Old Vicarage , Church Rd, LA11 6RS, ☎ 52381, Telex 668230, Fax 52373, , – TV ☎ P. AE VISA
closed Christmas week – **M** (booking essential) (dinner only) 25.00 **t.** 6.00 – **13 rm** 50.00/130.00 **t.**

at Cartmel NW : 3 m. – ✉ Grange-over-Sands – ☎ 044 854 (3 fig.) or 053 95 (5 fig.) Cartmel :

Aynsome Manor , LA11 6HH, NE : ½ m. ☎ 36653, « Country house atmosphere », – rest TV ☎ P. AE VISA
closed 2 to 28 January – **M** *(closed Sunday dinner to non-residents)* (dinner only and Sunday lunch)/dinner 8.95/17.00 **t.** 4.00 – **13 rm** 28.00/56.00 **t.** – SB (22 October-9 May) 67.00/73.00 **st.**

XX **Uplands** with rm, Haggs Lane ✉ Cartmel, LA11 6HD, E : 1 m. ☎ 36248, ←, – rest TV ☎ P. VISA
closed 1 January-24 February – **M** *(closed Monday)* (booking essential) 12.50/21.00 **t.** 4.50 – **5 rm** (dinner included) 67.00/110.00 **t.** – SB (November-April) (weekdays only) 98.00/110.00 **st.**

BMW Lindale Hill ☎ 3751
SUBARU, SEAT Lindale Corner ☎ 2282
VW-AUDI Lindale ☎ 4242

GRANTHAM Lincs. 402 404 S 25 – pop. 30 700 – ECD : Wednesday – ☎ 0476.
See : St. Wulfram's Church★ (13C).
Envir. : Belton House★ (Renaissance) *AC*, NE : 2 m. – Belvoir Castle★★ (19C) (interior★) W : 8 m.
Stoke Rochford, Great North Rd ☎ 047 683 (Great Ponton) 275, S : 6 m. on A 1 – 18 Belton Lane, Londonthorpe Rd ☎ 63355.
The Museum, St. Peters Hill ☎ 66444.
◆London 113 – ◆Leicester 31 – Lincoln 29 – ◆Nottingham 24.

Angel and Royal (T.H.F.), High St., NG31 6PN, ☎ 65816, Fax 67149, « Part 13C » – rm TV ☎ P – 30. AE VISA
M 9.95/14.95 **st.** – 7.50 – **28 rm** 69.00/95.00 **st.**, **1 suite** 95.00 **st.** – SB (weekends only) 74.00/80.00 **st.**

at Barkston N : 3¾ m. on A 607 – ✉ Grantham – ☎ 0400 Loveden :

XX **Barkston House** with rm, NG32 2NH, ☎ 50555, , – TV ☎ P. AE VISA.
closed 2 weeks June-July and 1 week Christmas – **M** *(closed lunch Monday and Saturday, Sunday and Bank Holiday Mondays)* 10.00 **t.** (lunch) and a la carte 3.25 – **2 rm** 40.00/58.00 **t.** – SB (weekends only) 75.00 **st.**

at Great Gonerby NW : 2 m. on B 1174 – ✉ ☎ 0476 Grantham :

XX **Harry's Place,** 17 High Street, NG31 8JS, ℘ 61780 – VISA
closed Monday, Sunday and Bank Holidays – **M** (booking essential) a la carte 27.50/37.00 **t.** 7.00.

at Grantham Service Area NW : 3 m on B 1174 at junction with A 1 – ✉ ☎ 0476 Grantham :

Travelodge without rest., NG32 2AB, ℘ 77500, Reservations (Toll free) 0800 850950 – TV ♿ P. AE VISA.
40 rm 24.00/29.50 **t.**

FORD 30-40 London Rd ℘ 65195
NISSAN Barrowby High Rd ℘ 64443
PEUGEOT-TALBOT 66 London Rd ℘ 62595
RENAULT London Rd ℘ 61338
TOYOTA Great Ponton ℘ 047 683 (Great Ponton) 261
VOLVO Barrowby Rd ℘ 64114
VW-AUDI, SUBARU, CITROEN Spittlegate ℘ 66416

ATS East St. ℘ 590222
ATS Elmer St. South ℘ 590444

GRASMERE Cumbria 402 K 20 – ECD : Thursday – ☎ 096 65.

See : Dove Cottage★ plan of Ambleside AY **A.**

Red Bank Rd ℘ 245 (summer only).

◆London 282 – ◆Carlisle 43 – Kendal 18.

Plans : see Ambleside

Wordsworth, Stock Lane, LA22 9SW, ℘ 592, Telex 65329, Group Telex 65329, Fax 765, , – rest TV ☎ P – 100. AE VISA. BZ **s**
M 16.50/27.00 **t.** and a la carte 4.00 – **35 rm** 46.50/114.00 **t.**, **2 suites** 160.00 **t.** – SB (1 November-end March) (except Christmas and New Year) 90.00/112.00 **st.**

Michaels Nook Country House, LA22 9RP, NE : ½ m. off A 591 ℘ 496, Group Telex 65329, Fax 765, ≤ mountains and countryside, « Antiques and gardens » – rest TV ☎ P. AE VISA. AY **n**
M (booking essential) 24.00/35.00 **t.** 6.15 – **12 rm** (dinner included) 100.00/264.00 **st.**, **2 suites** 288.00/340.00 **st.**.

Swan (T.H.F.), LA22 9RF, on A 591 ℘ 551, ≤, – TV ☎ P. AE VISA AY **r**
M 10.50/20.00 **st.** and a la carte 4.50 – 8.50 – **36 rm** 70.00/86.00 **st.** – SB 100.00/134.00 **st.**

White Moss House, Rydal Water, LA22 9SE, S : 1½ m. on A 591 ℘ 295, , – rest TV ☎ P. BY **v**
March-November – **M** (booking essential) (dinner only) 25.00 **st.** 3.50 – **6 rm** (dinner included) 73.00/150.00 **st.** – SB (November and March except Easter) 120.00/140.00 **st.**

Rothay Garden, Broadgate, LA22 9RJ, ℘ 334, Fax 723, – rest TV ☎ P. VISA
M 11.90/16.50 **t.** 2.95 – **21 rm** (dinner included) 45.00/110.00 **t.** – SB (November-Easter) (weekdays only) 81.00/90.00 **st.** AY **e**

Oak Bank, Broadgate, LA22 9TA, ℘ 217, – rest TV ☎ P. VISA BZ **e**
closed mid December-mid February – **M** (bar lunch)/dinner 15.00 **t.** 3.50 – **14 rm** 30.00/80.00 **t.** – SB (except Easter-November) 60.00/66.00 **st.**

Grasmere, Broadgate, LA22 9TA, ℘ 277, – TV ☎ P. VISA BZ **r**
closed January – **M** (dinner only) 14.50 **t.** 3.50 – **12 rm** 30.00/70.00 **t.** – SB (November-March) 56.00/59.00 **st.**

Bridge House, Stock Lane, LA22 9SN, ℘ 425, – P. VISA. BZ **n**
Mid March-mid November – **M** 12.50 **t.** 3.50 – **12 rm** (dinner included) 35.00/70.00 **t.** – SB 66.00/70.00 **st.**

Lancrigg Vegetarian Country House, Easedale Rd, LA22 9QN, W : ½ m. on Easedale Rd ℘ 317, ≤, , park – rest TV P. AY **u**
M 14.50 **t.** 3.25 – **10 rm** (dinner included) 45.00/60.00 **t.** – SB (November-April) (weekdays only) 60.00/80.00 **st.**

Banerigg without rest., Lake Rd, LA22 9PW, S : ¾ m. on A 591 ℘ 204, ≤, – P. AY **a**
March-November – **6 rm** 16.50/35.00 **st.**

Rothay Lodge, White Bridge, LA22 9RH, ℘ 341, – P. AY **o**
April-October – **M** (by arrangement) 8.50 **st.** – **6 rm** 17.50/37.00 **st.**

GRASSINGTON North Yorks. 402 O 21 – pop. 1 220 – ECD : Thursday – ✉ Skipton – ☎ 0756

Grassington National Park Centre, Hebden Rd ℘ 752748 (weekends but not evenings).

◆London 240 – Bradford 30 – Burnley 28 – ◆Leeds 37.

Grassington House, 5 The Square, BD23 5AQ, ℘ 752406, Fax 752135 – TV P. VISA
closed mid week November and January – **M** *(closed Monday and October-May)* 15.00 **t.** and a la carte 3.50 – 2.00 – **11 rm** 27.50/70.00 **t.** – SB (winter only) (weekdays only) 70.00/90.00 **st.**

Ashfield House, BD23 5AE, ☏ 752584, – rest TV P.
closed November-mid February – **7 rm** (dinner included) 32.00/67.00 **st.** – SB 57.00/63.00 **st.**

Lodge, 8 Wood Lane, BD23 5LU, ☏ 752518 – rest P
March-October and weekends in December – **M** 8.50 **st.** – **7 rm** 19.00/36.00 **st.**

at Threshfield SW : ½ m. on B 6265 – ✉ Skipton – ☎ 0756 Grassington :

Wilson Arms, Station Rd, BD23 5ET, ☏ 752666, Fax 752666, – rest TV ☎ P. AE VISA
M 8.50/13.95 **t.** and a la carte 3.95 – **14 rm** 36.00/72.00 **t.** – SB (except Christmas and New Year) 93.00 **st.**

Greenways, Wharfeside Av., BD23 5BS, ☏ 752598, ←, – rest P
April-October – **M** (by arrangement) 10.50 **st.** 4.00 – **5 rm** 18.00/36.00 **st.**

GRAVESEND Kent 404 V 29 – pop. 53 450 – ECD : Wednesday – ☎ 0474.

Singlewell Rd ☏ 568035 – Rochester Cobham Park, Park Pale ☏ 047 482 (Shorne) 3411, : 3 m.

to Tilbury (Sealink) frequent services daily (5 mn).

10 Parrock St. ☏ 337600.

London 25 – Dover 54 – Maidstone 16 – Margate 53.

Overcliffe, 15-16 Overcliffe, DA11 0EF, ☏ 322131, Telex 965117, Fax 536737 – TV ☎ P. AE VISA
M (dinner only) 25.00 **st.** and a la carte 3.95 – **29 rm** 58.00/80.00 **st.**

Cromer without rest., 194 Parrock St., DA12 1EW, ☏ 361935 – TV P
11 rm.

ROVER The Grove ☏ 322111
SKODA Meopham ☏ 813562
VW-AUDI Old Rd West ☏ 357925

Michelin puts no plaque or sign on the hotels and restaurants mentioned in this Guide.

GRAVETYE East Sussex – see East Grinstead.

GRAYSHOTT Hants. 404 R 30 – pop. 2 048 – ✉ Hindhead (Surrey) – ☎ 042 873 Hindhead.

See : Devils Punch Bowl (←★).

London 47 – Chichester 23 – Farnham 9 – Guildford 14 – Portsmouth and Southsea 31.

Woods, Headley Rd, GU26 6LB, ☏ 605555 – AE VISA
closed Sunday and Monday – **M** (dinner only) a la carte 22.30/26.60 **st.** 3.45.

MASSERATI Headley Rd ☏ 5363/6545

GREASBY Merseyside 402 ㉜ 403 ⑫ – pop. 44 272 – ✉ Wirral – ☎ 051 Liverpool.

London 220 – Liverpool 9.

Twelfth Man Lodge without rest., Greasby Rd, L69 2PP, ☏ 677 5445, Fax 678 5085 – TV ☎ P. AE VISA
M a la carte 6.50/9.25 **t.** – 4.50 – **30 rm** -/38.50 **t.**

GREAT AYTON North Yorks. 402 Q 20 – pop. 4 690 – ✉ ☎ 0642 Middlesbrough.

High Green ☏ 722835 (summer only).

London 245 – Leeds 63 – Middlesbrough 7 – York 48.

Ayton Hall, with rm, Low Green, TS9 6BW, ☏ 723595, Fax 722149, « Tasteful decor », – TV ☎ P. AE VISA.
M 10.95/20.50 **t.** and a la carte – **9 rm** 77.00/115.00 **t.** – SB (weekends only) 95.00/125.00 **st.**

GREAT BADDOW Essex 404 V 28 – see Chelmsford.

GREAT BARR West Midlands 403 404 O 26 – see Birmingham.

GREAT BROUGHTON Cumbria 401 402 J 19 – see Cockermouth.

GREAT BROUGHTON North Yorks. 402 Q 20 – ✉ ☎ 0642 Middlesborough.

London 241 – Leeds 61 – Middlesborough 10 – York 54.

Wainstones, 31 High St., TS9 7EW, ☏ 712268, Fax 711560 – TV ☎ P. VISA.
M 10.50/12.50 **st.** and a la carte 3.35 – **16 rm** 34.50/49.50 **st.** – SB (weekends only) 59.00 **st.**

at Ingleby Greenhow E : 2½ m. on Ingleby Greenhow rd – ✉ ☎ 0642 Great Ayton :

Manor House Farm, Ingleby Greenhow, TS9 6RB, SE : 4¼ m. by B 1257 ☏ 722384, ←, – P.
M 11.50 **st.** 3.50 – **3 rm** 19.50/36.00 **st.**

GREAT DRIFFIELD Humberside 402 S 21 – pop. 8 970 – ECD : Wednesday – ✉ York – ☎ 0377.

Envir. : Sledmere House★ NW : 7½ m.

Driffield, Sunderlandwick ☎ 43116 – Hainsworth Park, Brandesburton ☎ 542362.

◆London 201 – ◆Kingston-upon-Hull 21 – Scarborough 22 – York 29.

Bell (Best Western), 46 Market Pl., YO25 7AP, ☎ 46661, Fax 43228, squash – res TV ☎ & P – 150. AE VISA.
M (dinner only Monday to Saturday and Sunday lunch)/dinner 10.00 **st.** and a la carte 3.00 – **13 rm** 57.00/78.00 **t.**, **1 suite** 83.00 **t.** – SB (weekends only) 120.00 **st.**

at North Dalton SW : 7 m. by A 164 and A 163 on B 1246 – ✉ York – ☎ 037 781 Middleton-on-the-Wolds :

Star Inn, Warter Rd, YO25 9UX, ☎ 688 – TV ☎ P
7 rm.

GREAT DUNMOW Essex 404 V 28 – pop. 4 026 – ECD : Wednesday – ☎ 0371.

Council Offices, High St. ☎ 4533.

◆London 42 – ◆Cambridge 27 – Chelmsford 13 – Colchester 24.

XXX **Starr** with rm, Market Pl., CM6 IAX, ☎ 874321, Fax 876337 – rm TV ☎ P. AE VISA
M (closed Saturday lunch and Sunday dinner) 18.00/30.00 **t.** 5.75 – **8 rm** 55.00/110.00 **t.**

BMW 81 High St. ☎ 872884
RENAULT Weatherfield ☎ 850225

GREAT GONERBY Lincs. 402 404 S 25 – see Grantham.

GREAT GRIMSBY Humberside 402 404 T 23 – pop. 91 532 – ECD : Thursday – ☎ 0472.

Envir. : Thornton Curtis (St. Lawrence's Church★ : Norman and Gothic) NW : 16 m. by A 18 Y and B 1211 – Thornton Abbey (ruins 14C) : the Gatehouse★ *AC*, NW : 18 m. by A 18 Y and B 1211.

Littlecoates Rd ☎ 342823.

Humberside Airport : ☎ 0652 (Barnetby)688456, W : 13 m. by A 8 Y.

Central Library, Town Hall Square ☎ 240410.

◆London 172 – Boston 50 – Lincoln 36 – ◆Sheffield 75.

Plan opposite

Humber Royal (T.H.F.), Littlecoates Rd, DN34 4LX, ☎ 350295, Telex 527776, Fax 241354 ≤, – rm TV ☎ P – 285. AE VISA Y c
M 11.50/16.50 **st.** and a la carte 5.95 – 7.95 – **52 rm** 68.00/102.00 **st.** – SB (weekends only) 74.00/78.00 **st.**

Crest (T.H.F.), St. James Sq., DN31 1EP, ☎ 359771, Telex 527741, Fax 241427, – TV ☎ P – 65. AE VISA AZ r
closed 25 to 30 December – **M** 7.95/15.75 **st.** and a la carte 4.20 – 7.95 – **125 rm** 61.00/73.00 **st.** – SB (weekends only) 70.00/74.00 **st.**

Yarborough, Bethlehem St., DN31 1LY, ☎ 242266, Fax 242266 – TV ☎ P – 100. AE VISA AZ c
M (bar lunch Monday to Saturday)/dinner 10.00 **st.** and a la carte 3.50 – **51 rm** 35.00/45.00 **st.**

XX **Regines,** 2 Osborne St., DN31 1EY, ☎ 356737 – VISA AZ a
M (dinner only) 10.95 **t.** and a la carte 3.50.

BMW Laceby Rd ☎ 276666
FIAT Wellowgate ☎ 355951
FORD Corporation Rd ☎ 358941
HONDA Moody Lane ☎ 356417
MERCEDES-BENZ Bradley Cross Rd ☎ 276777
MITSUBISHI Rendel St. ☎ 362021
NISSAN 210-212 Victoria St. ☎ 353572 and 41281
RENAULT Chelmsford Av. ☎ 70111
ROVER 415 Victoria St. ☎ 356161
SAAB 226 Victoria St. ☎ 348527
TOYOTA Cromwell Rd ☎ 352191
VAUXHALL 123 Cromwell Rd ☎ 346066
VAUXHALL-OPEL Brighowgate ☎ 358486
VW-AUDI Convamore Rd ☎ 355451

ATS 2 Abbey Rd ☎ 358151

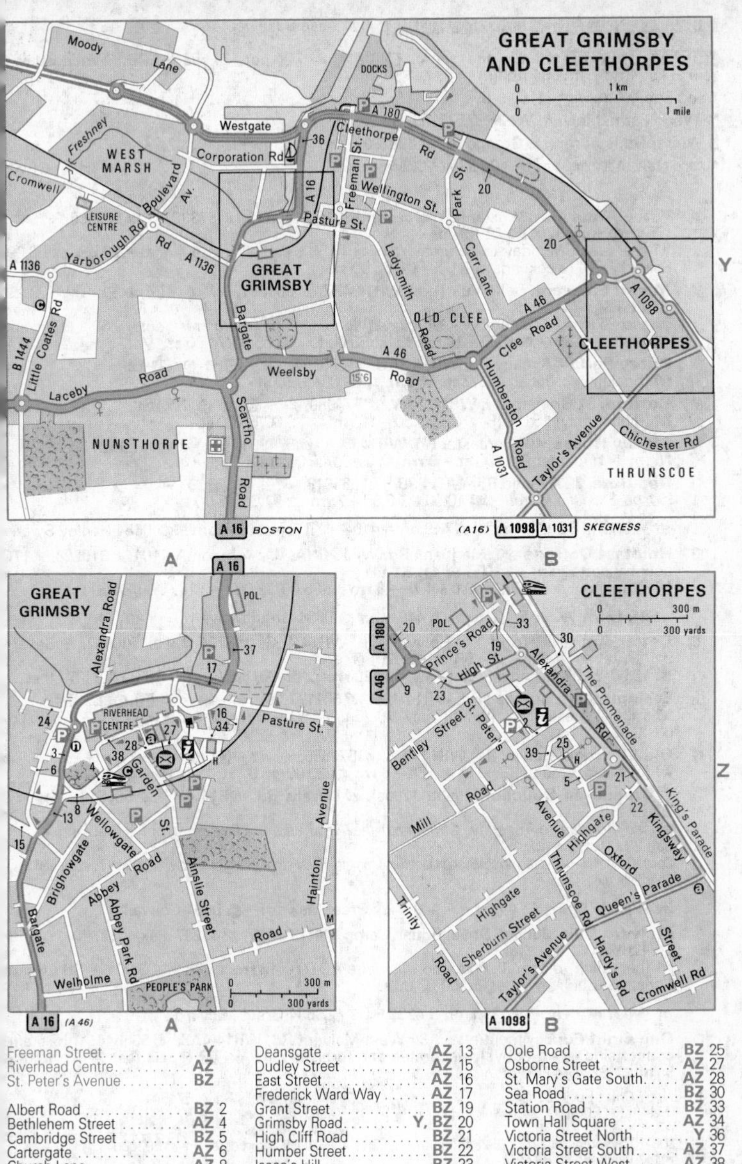

GREAT HANWOOD Shropshire 402 403 L 25 – see Shrewsbury.

GREAT HOCKHAM Norfolk 404 W 26 – pop. 557 – ✉ Attleborough – ☎ 095 382.

♦London 86 – ♦Cambridge 41 – ♦Norwich 23.

⌂ **Church Cottage** without rest., Breckles, NR17 1EW, N : 1 ½ m. by A 1075 ℘ 286, heated, ⟡, ⟡ – Ⓟ. ⟡
closed 20 December-5 January – **3 rm** ☕ 15.00/30.00.

GREAT LONGSTONE Derbs. 402 403 404 O 24 – see Bakewell.

GREAT MALVERN Heref. and Worc. 403 404 N 27 – pop. 30 153 – ECD : Wednesday – 068 45 (4 fig.) or 0684 (6 fig.).

See : Priory Church★ (11C) B **B.**

Wood Farm, Malvern Wells ℘ 573905, S : 2 m..

Winter Gdns Complex, Grange Rd ℘ 892289.

◆London 127 – ◆Birmingham 34 – ◆Cardiff 66 – Gloucester 24.

Plan opposite

Foley Arms (Best Western), Worcester Rd, WR14 4QS, ℘ 573397, Fax 569665, ≤, – 120. B a
M (bar lunch Monday to Saturday)/dinner 13.50 **t.** and a la carte 4.00 – **26 rm** 56.00/85.00 **t.** – SB (weekends only) 80.00/100.00 **st.**

Mount Pleasant, Belle Vue Terr., WR14 4PZ, ℘ 561837, ≤, – – 100. B e
closed 25 and 26 December – **M** *(closed Sunday dinner to non residents)* 9.50/11.50 **t.** and a la carte 3.95 – 5.00 – **14 rm** 39.50/53.00 **t.** – SB 65.00/74.00 **st.**

Priory Park, 4 Avenue Rd, WR14 3AG, ℘ 565194, – . B x
M (booking essential) 16.00 **st.** – **6 rm** 39.00/68.00 **st.**

Cotford, 51 Graham Rd, WR14 2JW, ℘ 574680, – . B c
M (dinner only) 15.00/18.00 **st.** 3.50 – **16 rm** 25.00/50.00 **st.**

Sidney House, 40 Worcester Rd, WR14 4AA, ℘ 574994, ≤ – rest . B s
M (by arrangement) 15.00 **st.** – **8 rm** 17.00/46.00 **st.**

Red Gate, 32 Avenue Rd, WR14 3BJ, ℘ 565013, – . B
closed 2 weeks March – **M** 10.50 **t.** 3.00 – **7 rm** 21.00/42.00 **t.**

at Welland SE : 4½ m. by A 449 on A 4104 – ✉ Great Malvern – 0684 Hanley Swan :

Holdfast Cottage , Marlbank Rd, WR13 6NA, W : ¾ m. on A 4104 ℘ 310288, « 17C country cottage », – . A x
M (dinner only) 16.00/22.00 **t.** 4.75 – **8 rm** 36.00/72.00 **t.** – SB 76.00/84.00 **st.**

at Malvern Wells S : 2 m. on A 449 – ✉ 0684 Great Malvern :

Cottage in the Wood , Holywell Rd, WR14 4LG, ℘ 573487, Fax 560662, ≤ Severn and Evesham Vales, – . A z
M 10.50/24.00 **st.** and a la carte 4.40 – **20 rm** 55.00/105.00 **st.** – SB 69.00/107.00 **st.**

Essington , Holywell Rd, WR14 4LQ, ℘ 561177, ≤, – rest . A e
M (booking essential) (dinner only) 13.75 **t.** 4.50 – **9 rm** 27.00/52.00 **t.** – SB 65.00/68.00 **st.**

Old Vicarage, Hanley Rd, WR14 4PH, ℘ 572585, ≤, – A c
M (by arrangement) 13.50 **st.** 4.50 – **6 rm** 30.00/46.00 **st.**

✿ **Croque-en-Bouche** (Marion Jones), 221 Wells Rd, WR14 4HF, ℘ 565612 – . A u
closed Sunday to Tuesday, Christmas and New Year – **M** (dinner only) (booking essential) 29.00 **st.** 4.40
Spec. Cannelloni with crab, avocado, coriander and tomato, Roast smoked leg of lamb with bulgar, spinach and mint, Chocolate mousse cake.

at Wynds Point S : 4 m. on A 449 – ✉ Great Malvern – 0684 Colwall :

Malvern Hills, Jubilee Drive, British Camp, WR13 6DW, ℘ 40237, Fax 40327, – . A s
M (bar lunch)/dinner 18.00 **t.** and a la carte 3.60 – **16 rm** 38.00/60.00 **t.** – SB (except Christmas and New Year) 80.00/85.00 **st.**

at West Malvern W : 2 m. on B 4232 – ✉ 0684 Great Malvern :

One Eight Four without rest., 184 West Malvern Rd, WR14 4AZ, ℘ 566544, ≤ hills and countryside, « Attractively decorated and furnished » – . A a
5 rm 22.25/41.00 **s.**

CITROEN 62 Court Rd ℘ 573391
DAIHATSU, ALFA ROMEO 2 Cowleigh Rd ℘ 892747
FORD 203-207 Worcester Rd ℘ 892345
HONDA 157 Wells Rd ℘ 892792
RENAULT Wells Rd ℘ 574541
VAUXHALL Linktop ℘ 573336
VOLVO Pickersleigh Rd ℘ 892255
VW-AUDI Worcester Rd ℘ 892606

GREAT MALVERN

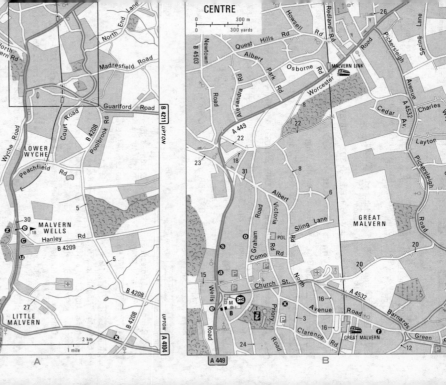

Church Street . . . . B
Wells Road . . . . B

Albert Road South . . . . . B 3
Blackmore
  Park Road . . . . A 5
Clerkenwell Crescent . . . B 6
Cockshot Road . . . . B 8
Court Road . . . . B 12
Croft Bank . . . . A 13
Happy Valley
  off St. Ann's Road . . . B 15
Imperial Road . . . . B 16
Jubilee Drive . . . . A 17
Lygon Bank . . . . B 18
Madresfield Road . . . . . . B 20
Moorlands Road . . . . B 22
North Malvern Road . . . . B 23
Orchard Road . . . . B 24
Richmond Road . . . . B 26
Upper Welland
  Road . . . . A 27
Walwyn Road . . . . A 29
Wells Road . . . . A 30
Zetland Road . . . . B 31

Town plans
roads most used
by traffic and those
on which guide listed
hotels and restaurants
stand are fully drawn;
the beginning only
of lesser roads
is indicated.

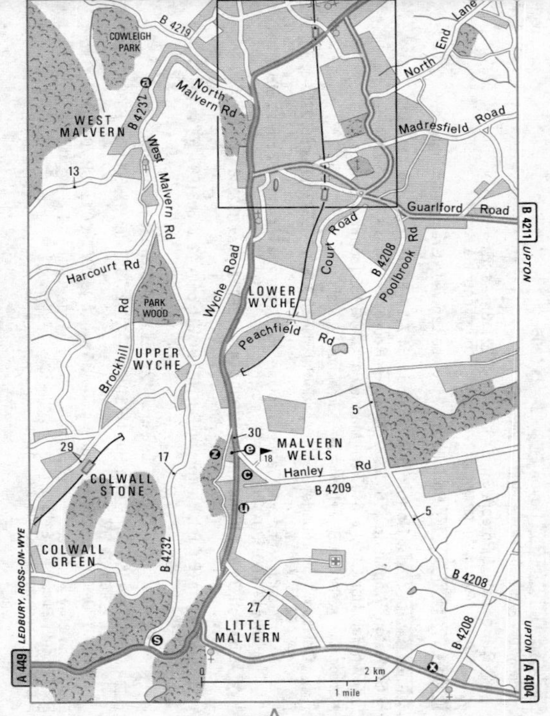

GREAT MILTON Oxon. 403 404 Q 28 – see Oxford.

GREAT MISSENDEN Bucks. 404 R 28 – pop. 7 429 (inc. Prestwood) – ECD : Thursday – 024 06.

London 34 – Aylesbury 10 – Maidenhead 19 – Oxford 35.

XX **Graziemille** (at Cock and Rabbit Inn), The Lee, HP16 9LZ, N : 2½ m. by A 41 024 020 (The Lee) 512, Italian rest., – rest . AE VISA
closed Sunday dinner and Monday – **M** (bar lunch Monday to saturday)/dinner a la carte 14.95/24.70 **t.** 3.70.

GREAT OFFLEY Herts. 404 S 28 – Hitchen – 0462.

London 40 – Bedford 14 – Cambridge 29 – Luton 6.

Red Lion (Lansbury), Kings Walden Rd, SG5 3DZ, 76281, – TV . AE VISA
M 20.00 **t.** 3.75 – **5 rm** 50.00/65.00 **st.** – SB (weekends only) 120.00/135.00 **st.**

GREAT RISSINGTON Glos. – see Bourton-on-the-Water.

GREAT SNORING Norfolk 404 W 25 – pop. 180 – Fakenham – 0328 Fakenham.

London 115 – Cambridge 68 – Norwich 28.

Old Rectory, Barsham Rd, NR21 0HP, 820597, « Country house atmosphere » – TV . AE .
closed 23 to 26 December – **M** (booking essential) (dinner only) 18.00 **t.** – **7 rm** 40.00/145.00 **t.** – SB (November-March) 97.00 **st.**

GREAT TEW Oxon. 403 404 P 28 – 060 883.

London 75 – Birmingham 50 – Gloucester 42 – Oxford 21.

Falkland Arms without rest., OX7 4DB, 653, « 17C inn in picturesque village » – rm TV .
4 rm 28.00/35.00 **st.**

GREAT TORRINGTON Devon 403 H 31 – 0805.

London 228 – Exeter 36 – Plymouth 51 – Taunton 57.

X **Rebecca's,** 8 Potacre St., EX38 8BH, 22113 – VISA
closed Monday lunch and Sunday – **M** 18.50 **st.** and a la carte.

GREAT WITCHINGHAM Norfolk 404 X 25 – see Lenwade Great Witchingham.

GREAT YARMOUTH Norfolk 404 Z 26 – pop. 54 777 – ECD : Thursday – 0493.

18 Gorleston, Warren Rd 661802 – 18 Beach House, Caister-on-Sea 720421.

Town Hall, Hall Quay 846345 – Marine Par. 842195 (summer only).

London 126 – Cambridge 81 – Ipswich 53 – Norwich 20.

Carlton, 1-5 Kimberley Terr., Marine Par., NR30 3JE, 855234, Fax 852220 – TV . AE VISA
M (bar lunch Monday to Saturday)/dinner 15.00 **st.** and a la carte – **92 rm** 50.00/70.00 t – **3 suites** 90.00/130.00 **t.**

Linwood, 74-75 Marine Parade, NR30 2DH, 852427, Fax 852336 – TV
24 rm.

Two Bears (B.C.B.), Southtown Rd, NR31 OHU, on A 12 603198 – TV
11 rm.

at Gorleston-on-Sea S : 3 m. on A 12 – 0493 Great Yarmouth :

Cliff (Best Western), Cliff Hill, NR31 6DH, 662179, Telex 975608, Fax 653617, – TV . AE VISA
M 10.50/12.50 **t.** and a la carte 4.50 – **34 rm** 49.00/83.00 **t.** – SB 70.00/100.00 **st.**

FIAT North Quay 844266
FORD South Gates Rd 844922
FORD 134 Lowestoft Rd, Gorleston-on-Sea 664151

ATS Suffling Rd 858211

GREETHAM Leics – see Stamford.

GRETA BRIDGE Durham 402 O 20 – ☎ 0833 Teesdale.
♦London 253 – ♦Carlisle 63 – ♦Leeds 63 – ♦Middlesbrough 32.

Morritt Arms, DL12 9SE, ✆ 27232, Fax 27570, – ☎ P. VISA
M (bar lunch Monday to Saturday)/dinner 19.00 **st.** 3.50 – **23 rm** 42.00/65.00 **st.** – SB 75.00/85.00 **st.**

GRIMSBY Humberside 402 404 T 23 – see Great Grimsby.

GRIMSTON Norfolk – see King's Lynn.

GRINDLEFORD Derbs. 402 403 404 P 24 – ✉ Sheffield (South Yorks.) – ☎ 0433 Hope Valley.
♦London 165 – Derby 31 – ♦Manchester 34 – ♦Sheffield 10.

Maynard Arms, Main Rd, S30 1HP, ✆ 30321, ≤, – ☎ P – 100. VISA
M 10.00/16.00 **t.** – **13 rm** 50.00/69.00 **t.** – SB 76.00/90.00 **st.**

GRINDLETON Lancs. 402 M 22 – pop. 1 451 (inc. West Bradford) – ✉ ☎ 020 07 Bolton-by-Bowland.
♦London 241 – ♦Blackpool 38 – Lancaster 25 – ♦Leeds 45 – ♦Manchester 33.

Harrop Fold Country Farmhouse, Harrop Fold, BB7 4PJ, N : 2 ¾ m. by Slaidburn Rd ✆ 600, ≤, « 17C Longhouse » – rest ☎ P
7 rm.

GRIZEDALE Cumbria 402 K 20 – see Hawkshead.

GUILDFORD Surrey 404 S 30 – pop. 61 509 – ECD : Wednesday – ☎ 0483.
See : Cathedral★ (1961) Z **A.**
Envir. : Clandon Park★★ (Renaissance House) *AC*, E : 3 m. by A 246 Z.
High Path Rd, Merrow ✆ 575243 – Puttenham ✆ 810498.
Guildford House Gallery, 155 High St. ✆ 444007.
♦London 33 – ♦Brighton 43 – Reading 27 – ♦Southampton 49.

Plan on next page

Post House (T.H.F.), Egerton Rd, GU2 5XZ, ✆ 574444, Telex 858572, Fax 302960, – rm ☎ P – 120. VISA Z **v**
M 13.50/16.50 **st.** and a la carte 4.35 – 9.50 – **111 rm** 95.00/105.00 **st.**, **2 suites** 110.00/140.00 **st.** – SB (weekends only) 94.00/100.00 **st.**

Manor at Newlands, Newlands Corner, GU4 8SE, E : 5½ m. by A 246 on A 25 Z ✆ 222624, Fax 211389, , park – ☎ P – 100. VISA.
closed 25 to 31 December – **M** 13.00/16.50 **t.** and a la carte 4.00 – **20 rm** 90.00/115.00 **t.** – SB (weekends only) 95.00 **st.** on A 25 Z

Café de Paris, 35 Castle St., GU1 3UQ, ✆ 34896, French rest. – VISA Y **u**
closed Saturday lunch, Sunday and Bank Holidays – **M** 9.95 **t** and a la carte 3.95.

at Shere E : 5 ¾ m. on A 25 – Z – ✉ Guildford – ☎ 048 641 Shere :

Frederick's, Gomshall Lane, GU5 9HE, ✆ 2168 – P. VISA
closed Saturday lunch, Sunday dinner and Monday – **M** 11.50/18.75 **t.** 3.50.

at Bramley S : 3 m. on A 281 – Z – ✉ ☎ 0483 Guildford :

Bramley Grange (Best Western), Horsham Rd, GU5 0BL, ✆ 893434, Telex 859948, Fax 893835, , – ☎ P – 150. VISA.
M *(closed Saturday lunch)* 16.00/19.50 **t.** and a la carte 4.75 – **48 rm** 70.00/150.00 **st.** – SB (weekends only) 95.00/105.00 **st.**

Le Berger, 4a High St., GU5 0HB, ✆ 894037, .

FORD Woodbridge Meadow ✆ 60601
MERCEDES-BENZ Aldershot Rd ✆ 60751
RENAULT Walnut Tree Close ✆ 577371
ROVER, JAGUAR, ROLLS-ROYCE Woodbridge Rd ✆ 69231
TOYOTA Pitch Pl. Worplesdon ✆ 234242
VAUXHALL Woking Rd ✆ 37731

Besonders angenehme Hotels oder Restaurants sind im Führer rot gekennzeichnet.
Sie können uns helfen, wenn Sie uns die Häuser angeben, in denen Sie sich besonders wohl gefühlt haben.
Jährlich erscheint eine komplett überarbeitete Ausgabe aller Roten Michelin-Führer.

...

XXXXX ... X

GUILDFORD

Friary Centre	Y
High Street	Y
Market Street	Y 18
North Street	Y
Bedford Road	Y 2
Bridge Street	Y 3
Castle Street	Y 5
Chertsey Street	Y 6
College Road Link	Y 7
Commercial Road	Y 8
Eastgate Gardens	Y 9
Friary Bridge	Y 12
Ladymead	Z 13
Leapale Lane	Y 15
Leapale Road	Y 16
Leas Road	Y 17
Mary Road	Y 19
Midleton Road	Z 20
Millbrook	Y 21
New Inn Lane	Z 22
One Tree Hill Road	Z 24
Onslow Street	Y 25
Park Street	Y 27
Quarry Street	Y 28
Stoughton Road	Z 30
Trood's Lane	Z 31
Tungsgate	Y 33
Warwick's Bench	Y 34
Woodbridge Road	Z 37

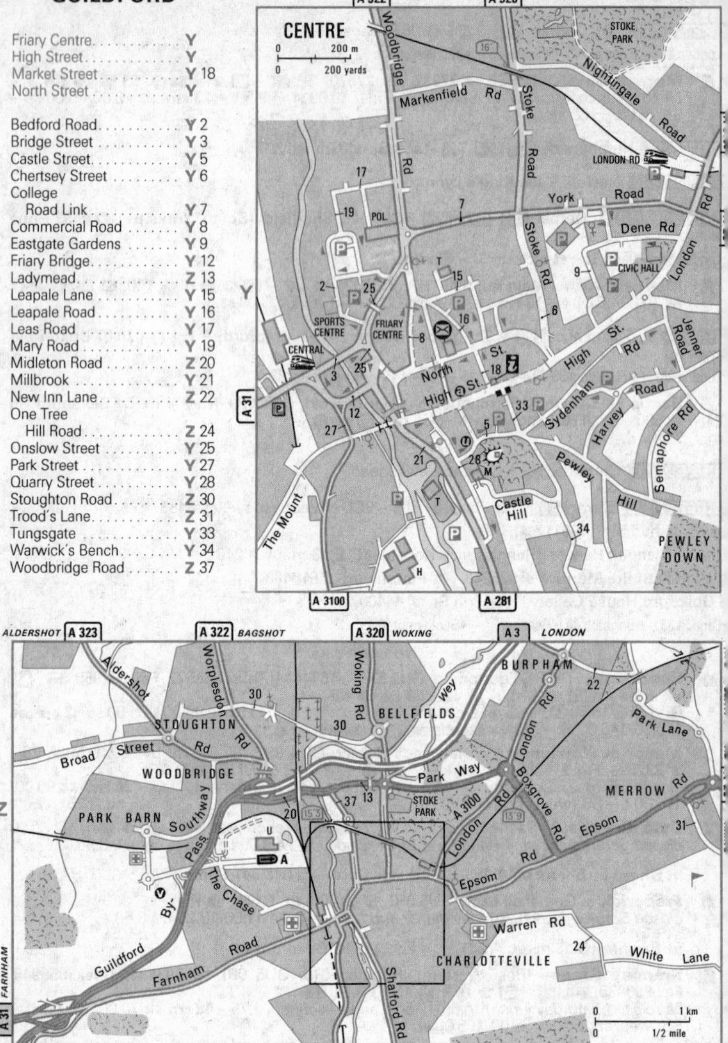

Pour un bon usage des plans de ville, voir les signes conventionnels.

GUIST Norfolk 404 W 25 – **pop. 209** – ✉ Fakenham – ☎ 036 284 Foulsham.

♦London 119 – ♦Cambridge 67 – King's Lynn 29 – ♦Norwich 20.

XX **Tollbridge,** Dereham Rd, NR20 5NU, S : ½ m. on B 1110 ☎ 359, ⩽, « Attractive setting on banks of River Wensum », ⛱ – ⟷ rm ☎ Ⓟ. AE VISA
closed Sunday dinner, Monday and first 3 weeks January – **M** (booking essential) (dinner only and Sunday lunch)/dinner 18.50/21.50 **t.** 🍷 3.60.

FORD Oak St. ☎ 0328 (Fakenham) 2317
PEUGEOT Norwich Rd ☎ 0328 (Fakenham) 864035
VAUXHALL-OPEL Greenway Lane ☎ 0328 (Fakenham) 862200

GULWORTHY Devon 403 H 32 – see Tavistock.

GUNNISLAKE Cornwall 403 H 32 The West Country G. – pop. 2 154 – ECD : Wednesday – ☎ 0822 Tavistock.

Envir. : Cotehele House** *AC*, SW : 2½ m.

London 244 – Bude 37 – Exeter 43 – Plymouth 20 – Tavistock 5.

Cornish Inn, The Square, PL18 9BW, ☎ 832475 – TV P. AE VISA
M 15.00 **t.** and a la carte 2.25 – **6 rm** 18.00/39.00 **t.**

HACKNESS North Yorks. 402 S 21 – see Scarborough.

HADLEIGH Suffolk 404 W 27 – pop. 5 858 – ☎ 0473.

Toppesfield Hall ☎ 822922.

London 72 – Cambridge 49 – Colchester 17 – Ipswich 10.

Edgehill, 2 High St., IP7 5AP, ☎ 822458, – TV ☎ P
closed 24 to 28 December – **M** (By arrangement) 12.50 **st.** 4.10 – **9 rm** 33.00/66.00 **st.** – SB (Except Bank Holidays) 60.00/80.00 **st.**

Gables, 63-67 Angel St., IP7 5EY, ☎ 827169, – rm TV ☎ P.
closed 24 to 26 December – **M** (dinner only) 16.00/21.00 **st.** 2.00 – **4 rm** 20.00/56.00 **st.** – SB (except August) 60.00/80.00 **st.**

HAGLEY W. Midlands 403 404 N 26 – See Stourbridge.

HAILSHAM East Sussex 404 U 31 – pop. 12 774 – ECD : Thursday – ✉ ☎ 0323.

Area Library, Western Rd ☎ 840604.

London 57 – Brighton 23 – Eastbourne 7 – Hastings 20.

Boship Farm, Lower Dicker, BN27 4AT, NW : 3 m. by A 295 on A 22 ☎ 844826, Telex 878400, Fax 843945, heated, – rm TV ☎ P – 120. AE VISA
M *(closed Saturday lunch)* 11.25 **st.** (lunch)/dinner a la carte 14.00/20.00 **st.** – **46 rm** 55.00/65.00 **st.**, **2 suites** 65.00/75.00 **st.** – SB (weekends only) 75.00/110.00 **st.**

at Magham Down NE : 2 m. by A 295 on A 271 – ✉ Hailsham – ☎ 0323 Eastbourne :

Olde Forge, BN27 1PN, ☎ 842893 – TV P. AE VISA
closed 24 December-2 January – **M** *(closed lunch and Wednesday dinner to non-residents)* 10.50 **t.** (dinner) and a la carte 11.50/18.50 **t.** 3.50 – **8 rm** 25.00/44.00 **st.** – SB (October-March) 55.00 **st.**

Prices — For full details of the prices quoted in the guide, consult the introduction.

HALE Greater Manchester 402 403 404 M 23 – see Altrincham.

HALEBARNS Greater Manchester – see Altrincham.

HALIFAX West Yorks. 402 O 22 – pop. 76 675 – ECD : Thursday – ☎ 0422.

Halifax Bradley Hall, Holywell Green ☎ 374108 – West End, Highroad Well ☎ 353608, : 3 m. – Ryburn, Norland ☎ 831355, S : 3 m.

The Piece Hall ☎ 368725.

London 205 – Bradford 8 – Burnley 21 – Leeds 15 – Manchester 28.

Holdsworth House, Holmfield, HX2 9TG, N : 3 m. by A 629 ☎ 240024, Telex 51574, Fax 245174, « Part 17C house », – TV ☎ P – 30. AE VISA
closed 23 to 30 December – **M** *(closed lunch Saturday, Sunday and Bank Holidays)* a la carte 16.45/25.85 **st.** 4.25 – **36 rm** 70.00/85.00 **st.**, **4 suites** 85.00/100.00 **st.** – SB (weekends only) 150.00/170.00 **st.**

Milans, 6 Carlton Pl., HX1 2SB, ☎ 330539, Telex 517587 – TV ☎
22 rm.

at Elland S : 3½ m. by A 629 – ✉ ☎ 0422 Halifax :

Berties Bistro, 7-9 Town Hall Buildings, HX5 OEU, ☎ 371724 –
closed Monday and 25-26 December – **M** (dinner only) a la carte 10.90/15.45 **st.** 3.40.

FIAT Skircoat Rd ☎ 53701
FORD Skircoat Rd ☎ 365790
ESO Rochdale Rd ☎ 365036
RENAULT Hanson Lane ☎ 59442
VAUXHALL Northgate ☎ 362851
VAUXHALL-OPEL 7 Horton St. ☎ 365846
VOLVO 31 Pellon New Rd ☎ 361961
VW-AUDI Denholme Gate Rd, Hipperholme ☎ 205611

ATS Hope St. ☎ 365892/360819

HALLAND East Sussex 404 U 31 – ECD : Wednesday – ✉ Lewes – ☎ 082 584.

London 48 – Brighton 16 – Eastbourne 16 – Royal Tunbridge Wells 19.

Halland Forge, BN8 6PW, on A 22 ☎ 456, Fax 773, , park – TV ☎ P. AE VISA
M 9.95/15.50 **t.** and a la carte 4.00 – 7.25 – **20 rm** 42.50/53.50 **t.** – SB 73.00/80.00 **st.**

HALSE TOWN Cornwall 403 D 33 – see St. Ives.

HALTWHISTLE Northumb. 401 402 M 19 – pop. 3 522 – ☎ 0434.
Greenhead ☎069 (Greenhead) 72367, W : 3 m.
Sycamore St. ☎ 320351 (summer only).
♦London 335 – ♦Carlisle 22 – ♦Newcastle 37.

Ashcroft without rest., Lantys Lonnen, NE49 0DA, ☎ 320213, – P.
closed 21 December-26 January – **6 rm** 16.00/32.00.

HAMBLETON Leics. – see Oakham.

HAMBROOK Avon 403 404 M 29 – see Bristol.

HAMPTON LOADE Shropshire –see Bridgnorth.

HAMSTEAD MARSHALL Berks. 403 404 P 29 – see Newbury.

HAMSTERLEY Durham 401 402 O 19 – ✉ ☎ 0388 Bishop Auckland.
♦London 260 – ♦Carlisle 75 – ♦Middlesbrough 30 – ♦Newcastle upon Tyne 22.

Grove House, Hamsterley Forest, DL13 1NL, W : 3 ¾ m. via Bedburn ☎ 88203, – P.
closed August, Christmas and New Year – **M** 8.50 **st.** – **4 rm** 22.00/44.00 **st.**

HANDFORTH Cheshire 402 403 404 N 23 – see Wilmslow.

HANLEY Staffs. 402 403 404 N 24 – see Stoke-on-Trent.

HANMER Clwyd 402 403 L 25 – ✉ Whitchurch – ☎ 094 874.
♦London 237 – Chester 26 – Shrewsbury 27 – ♦Stoke-on-Trent 28.

Hanmer Arms, SY13 3DE, ☎ 532, Fax 532 – TV ☎ P. AE VISA
M 8.00/12.50 **t.** and a la carte 3.90 – **7 rm** 35.00/50.00 **t.**, **4 suites** 45.00/50.00 **t.** – SB (Weekends only) 55.00/60.00 **st.**

HANWOOD Shropshire 402 403 L 25 – see Shrewsbury.

HAREWOOD West Yorks. 402 P 22 – pop. 3 429 – ✉ Leeds – ☎ 0532.
♦London 214 – Harrogate 9 – ♦Leeds 10 – York 20.

Harewood Arms, Harrogate Rd, LS17 9LH, on A 61 ☎ 886566, Fax 886064, – TV ☎ P. AE VISA
M 10.50/15.50 **t.** and dinner a la carte 3.95 – **24 rm** 58.00/78.00 **t.**

HARBERTONFORD Devon 403 I 32 – ✉ Totnes – ☎ 080 423.
♦London 228 – Exeter 28 – ♦Plymouth 24 – Torquay 13.

The Old Mill Country House, TQ9 7SW, NW : 1 ¼ m. ☎ 349, – TV ☎ P. AE VISA
M (bar lunch)/dinner 14.95/21.40 **t.** and a la carte – **7 rm** 30.00/58.00 **t.** – SB 130.00 155.00 **st.**

HARLECH Gwynedd 402 403 H 25 – pop. 1 292 – ECD : Wednesday – ☎ 0766.
See : Castle★★ (13C) *AC*, site and ≤ from the castle★.
Envir. : Llanbedr (Cwm Bychan★) S : 3½ m. – Vale of Ffestiniog★, NE : 9 m.
Royal St. David's ☎ 780203.
High St. ☎ 780658 (summer only).
♦London 241 – Chester 72 – Dolgellau 21.

Maes-y-Neuadd, Talsarnau, LL47 6YA, NE : 3½ m. by B 4573 ☎ 780200, Fax 780211 ≤, « Part 14C country house », , park – rest TV ☎ P. AE VISA
closed 6 to 17 December – **M** (booking essential) 13.50/23.00 **t.** and a la carte 4.60 – **14 rm** 38.50/116.00 **t.**, **1 suite** 90.00/130.00 **t.** – SB 100.00/165.00 **st.**

Gwrach Ynys, LL47 6TS, N : 2 ¼ m. on A 496 ☎ 780742, – rest P
closed December-February – **M** 8.00 **st.** – **7 rm** 15.00/34.00 **st.** – SB 44.00/50.00 **st.**

The Cemlyn, High St., LL46 2YA, ☎ 780425, ≤ Harlech Castle, Cardigan Bay and Lleyn Peninsula – VISA
Easter-mid October – **M** (lunch by arrangement)/dinner 17.50 **t.** 4.00.

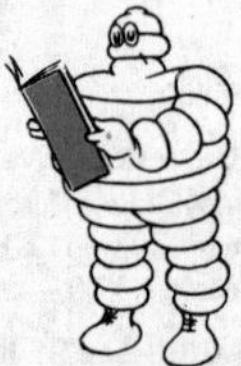

HARLOW Essex 404 U 28 – pop. 79 150 – ECD : Wednesday – 0279.
Canons Brook, Elizabeth Way 21482.
London 22 – Cambridge 37 – Ipswich 60.

Churchgate Manor (Best Western), Churchgate St., Old Harlow, CM17 0JT, E : 3¼ m. by A 414 and B 183 420246, Telex 818289, Fax 437720, – 170.
M *(closed Saturday lunch)* 16.95 **t.** (dinner) and a la carte 17.00/24.50 **t.** 4.50 – **85 rm** 75.00/120.00 **t.** – SB (weekends only)(except Christman) 84.00/96.00 **st.**

Harlow Moat House (Q.M.H.), Southern Way, CM18 7BA, SE : 2¼ m. by A 1025 on A 414 22441, Telex 81658, Fax 635094 – rm – 225
120 rm.

Green Man (T.H.F.), Mulberry Green, Old Harlow, CM17 0ET, E : 2¼ m. by A 414 and B 183 442521, Telex 817972, Fax 626113 – – 50.
M *(closed Saturday lunch and Bank Holidays)* 12.50/14.50 **st.** and a la carte 4.70 – 8.00 – **55 rm** 67.00/89.00 **st.**

Travel Inn, Cambridge Rd, Old Harlow, CM20 2EP, NE : 3¼ m. by A 414 on A 1184 442545 – rm .
M (Beefeater grill) a la carte approx. 12.25 **t.** – 4.50 – **38 rm** -/27.50 **t.**

FORD Edinburgh Way 21166
VOLVO The High Harlow 39541
ATS 14 Burnt Mill 21965

HARNHAM Wilts. 403 404 O 30 – see Salisbury.

HAROME North Yorks. – see Helmsley.

***In alta stagione,** e soprattutto nelle stazioni turistiche, è prudente prenotare con un certo anticipo.*
Avvertite immediatamente l'albergatore se non potete più occupare la camera prenotata.
Se scrivete ad un albergo all'estero, allegate alla vostra lettera un tagliando-risposta internazionale (disponibile presso gli uffici postali).

HARPENDEN Herts. 404 S 28 – pop. 28 589 – ECD : Wednesday – 0582.
Hammonds End 712580 – East Common 712856.
London 32 – Luton 6.

Harpenden Moat House (Q.M.H.), 18 Southdown Rd, AL5 1PE, 764111, Telex 826938, Fax 769858, – rm – 100
51 rm, 3 suites.

Glen Eagle, 1 Luton Rd, AL5 2PX, 760271, Fax 460819, – rest – 50.
M *(closed Saturday lunch)* 16.00/18.00 **st.** and a la carte – **51 rm** 77.00/143.00 **st.**

Chef Peking, 5-6 Church Green, 769358, Chinese (Peking, Szechuan) rest. – .
M a la carte 13.40/24.50 **t.** 3.50.

FORD, RELIANT, SCIMITAR 100 Southdown Rd 15217
MERCEDES-BENZ Station Rd 64311
RENAULT 44-46 Cold Harbour Lane 0582 (Luton) 460545
ROVER Lower Luton Rd 66463
VAUXHALL-OPEL Luton Rd 0582 (Luton) 460111

HARROGATE North Yorks. 402 P 22 – pop. 63 637 – ECD : Wednesday – 0423.
Envir. : Fountains Abbey*** (ruins 12C-13C, floodlit in summer), Studley Royal Gardens** – Fountains Hall* (17C) *AC*, NW : 9 m. by A 61 AY – Harewood House** S : 10½ m. by A 61 BZ.
Forest Lane Head 863158, E : 2 m. on A 59 BY – Follifoot Rd, Pannal 871641, S : 2½ m. CZ – Oakdale 567162, NE : ½ m. CY – Crimple Valley, Hookstone Wood Rd 883485, by A 661 CZ.
Royal Baths Assembly Rooms, Crescent Rd 525666.
London 211 – Bradford 18 – Leeds 15 – Newcastle-upon-Tyne 76 – York 22.

Plan on next page

Old Swan (Q.M.H.), Swan Rd, HG1 2SR, 500055, Telex 57922, Fax 501154, park, – – 400 AY **e**
127 rm, 10 suites.

Majestic (T.H.F.), Ripon Rd, HG1 2HU, 568972, Telex 57918, Fax 502283, , squash – rm – 300. AY **c**
M *(closed Saturday lunch)* 15.00/19.50 **st.** and a la carte 4.75 – 8.30 – **146 rm** 80.00/115.00 **st.**, **10 suites** 135.00/160.00 **st.** – SB (weekends only) 120.00/140.00 **st.**

Moat House International (Q.M.H.), Kings Rd, HG1 1XX, 500000, Telex 57575, Fax 524435, – rm – 300. BY **x**
M 15.00/25.00 **st.** and a la carte – **205 rm** 90.00/108.00 **st.**, **9 suites** 160.00 **st.** – SB (weekends only) 79.00 **st.**

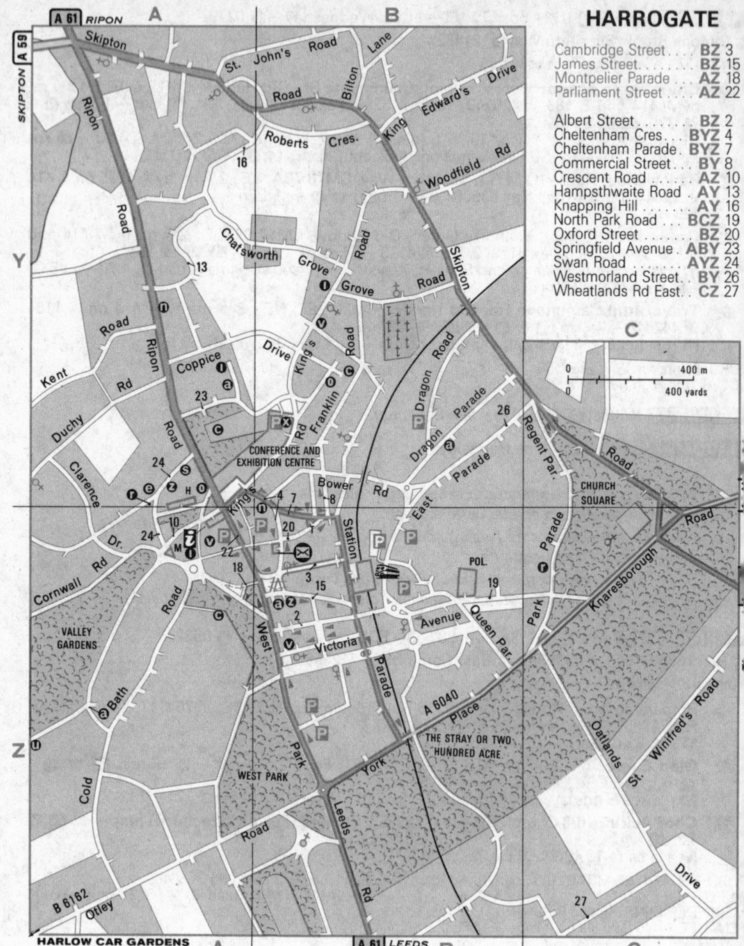

Crown (T.H.F.), Crown Pl., HG1 2RZ, ✆ 567755, Telex 57652, Fax 502284 – |♦| ⋡ rm TV ☎ P – 🏔 350. AE VISA AZ i
M 10.00/15.50 **st.** and a la carte – ☕ 8.00 – **116 rm** 77.00/100.00 **st.**, **5 suites** 145.00 **st.** – SB 94.00/102.00 **st.**

Imperial, Prospect Pl., HG1 1LA, ✆ 565671, Telex 57606, Fax 500082 – |♦| TV ☎ P – 🏔 150. AE VISA BZ a
M 9.00/14.50 **st.** and a la carte – **84 rm** ☕ 70.00/90.00 **st.**, **1 suite** 150.00 **st.** – SB 70.00/89.00 **st.**

St. George (Swallow), 1 Ripon Rd, HG1 2SY, ✆ 561431, Telex 57995, Fax 530037, ≘s, – |♦| TV ☎ P – 🏔 150. AE VISA AY o
M 12.50/18.00 **st.** and a la carte 🍷 3.75 – **92 rm** ☕ 80.00/107.00 **st.**, **1 suite** 180.00/190.00 **st.** – SB 92.00/97.00 **st.**

Studley, 28 Swan Rd, HG1 2SE, ✆ 560425, Telex 57506, Fax 530967 – |♦| ▤ rest TV ☎ P. AE VISA. ✱ AZ x
M *(closed lunch Saturday and Bank Holidays)* 20.75 **t.** (dinner) and a la carte 🍷 3.35 – **34 rm** ☕ 59.00/89.00 **st.**, **2 suites** 70.00/90.00 **st.** – SB (weekends only) 75.00 **st.**

Balmoral, 16-18 Franklin Mount, HG1 5EJ, ✆ 508208, Fax 530652, « Antique furnishings » – TV ☎ P. AE VISA BY v
M (bar lunch residents only)/dinner 27.50 **st.** 🍷 4.00 – ☕ 6.00 – **19 rm** 54.00/74.00 **st.**, **1 suite** 95.00/130.00 **st.** – SB (weekends only) 88.00/128.00 **st.**

Grants, Swan Rd, HG1 2SS, 560666, Fax 502550 – rest. **M** (bar lunch Monday to Saturday)/dinner 13.95 **t.** and a la carte 3.95 – **37 rm** 65.00/120.00 **t.** – SB 75.00/85.00 **st.** AY **s**

Hospitality Inn (Mt. Charlotte Thistle), Prospect Pl., West Park, HG1 1LB, 564601, Telex 57530, Fax 507508 – BZ **v**
M 8.50/14.50 **t.** – 6.75 – **71 rm** 60.00/79.50 **st.**, **5 suites** 70.00/135.00 **st.** – SB (weekends only) 70.00/85.00.

Fern, Swan Rd, HG1 2SS, 523866, Telex 57583, Fax 501825 – – 35
32 rm, 2 suites. AY **z**

Alexandra Court without rest., 8 Alexandra Rd, HG1 5JS, 502764 – BY **o**
12 rm 30.00/46.00 **st.**

Beech without rest., 1 Esplanade, HG2 0LN, 531431 – AZ **c**
11 rm 32.00/49.00 **t.**

Green Park, Valley Drive, HG2 0JT, 504681, Fax 530811 – rest – 40. AZ **a**
M (bar lunch)/dinner 10.75 **t.** and a la carte – **43 rm** 45.00/63.00 **t.** – SB (weekends only) 68.50 **st.**

Gables, 2 West Grove Rd, HG1 2AD, 505625 – BY **i**
M (lunch by arrangement)/dinner a la carte approx. 9.50 **t.** 3.15 – **9 rm** 25.00/50.00 **t.** – SB 62.00/70.00 **st.**

Britannia Lodge, 16 Swan Rd, HG1 2SA, 508482 – rest
M 7.00/13.00 **t.** 3.50 – **12 rm** 42.00/58.00 **t.** – SB 142.00 **st.** AYZ **r**

Ashwood House without rest., 7 Spring Grove, HG1 2HS, 560081 – rm
closed 24 December-1 January – **9 rm** 18.00/44.00 **t.** AY **a**

Stoney Lea without rest., 13 Spring Grove, HG1 2HS, 501524 – AY **i**
26 February-21 December – **6 rm** 25.00/38.00 **st.**

Garden House, 14 Harlow Moor Drive, HG2 0JX, 503059 – rest AZ **u**
M 8.50 **st.** 3.00 – **7 rm** 20.00/40.00 **st.** – SB (November-April) (weekends only) 53.00 **st.**

Alexa House without rest., 26 Ripon Rd, HG1 2JJ, 501988 – AY **n**
closed 22 December-6 January – **13 rm** 21.00/42.00 **st.**

Arden House, 69-71 Franklin Rd, HG1 5EH, 509224 – BY **c**
closed 20 December-1 January – **M** 10.75 **st.** 3.50 – **14 rm** 19.50/35.00 **st.**

Daryl House, 42 Dragon Par., HG1 5DA, 502775 – BY **a**
closed 1 week Christmas – **M** 7.00 **st.** – **6 rm** 12.00/20.00 **st.**

Knox Mill House without rest., Knox Mill Lane, HG3 2AE, N : 1 ½ m. by A 61 AY
560650, –
3 rm 32.00.

Shabab, 1 John St., HG1 1JZ, 500250, Indian rest. – BZ **z**

Grundy's, 21 Cheltenham Cres., HG1 1DH, 502610 – BYZ **n**
closed Sunday 2 weeks January-Febuary, 2 weeks August and Bank Holidays – **M** (dinner only) 11.75 **t.** and a la carte 3.50.

Millers, 1 Montpellier Mews, HG1 2TC, 530708 – AZ **v**
closed Monday dinner, Sunday and 2 weeks August – **M** 30.50 **t.** (dinner) and a la carte 9.65/17.50 **t.** 5.10.

Drum and Monkey, 5 Montpellier Gdns, HG1 2TF, 502650, Seafood –
closed Sunday and 24 December-3 January – **M** (booking essential) a la carte 11.05/19.05 **t.** AZ **v**

at Beckwithshaw W : 2 ½ m. on B 6162 – AZ – 0423 Harrogate :

Sandringham, HG2 0NN, 500722, , « Antiques » – rest
M *(closed Sunday dinner)* 13.50/21.00 **t.** 3.90 – **6 rm** 45.00/110.00 **t.** – SB 90.00/110.00 **st.**

at Markington NW : 8 ¾ m. by A 61 –AY– 0423 Harrogate :

Hob Green , HG3 3PJ, SW : ½ m. 770031, Group Telex 57780, Fax 771589, , « Country house in extensive parkland », –
M (bar lunch Monday to Saturday)/dinner 14.75/17.70 **t.** 4.75 – **11 rm** 65.00/85.00 **t.**, **1 suite** 105.00 **t.** – SB 110.00 **st.**

CITROEN Cheltenham Mount 568151
MERCEDES Leeds Rd, Pannal 879236
RENAULT Stacey Houses, Pannal 879231
ROVER, DAIMLER-JAGUAR 91 Leeds Rd 871263
VW-AUDI Ripon Rd 505141
ATS Leeds Rd, Pannal 879194

Bitte beachten Sie die Geschwindigkeitsbeschränkungen in Großbritannien
- 60 mph (= 96 km/h) außerhalb geschlossener Ortschaften
- 70 mph (= 112 km/h) auf Straßen mit getrennten Fahrbahnen und Autobahnen.

HARTFORD Cheshire 402 403 404 M 24 – pop. 4 000 – ☎ 0606 Northwich.

Delamere Forest ☎ 0606 (Sandiway) 882807, SW : 2 m.

♦London 188 – Chester 15 – ♦Liverpool 31 – ♦Manchester 25.

Hartford Hall, 81 School Lane, CW8 1PW, ☎ 75711, Fax 782285, – TV ☎ P – 35 AE VISA.
M *(closed Saturday lunch)* – **20 rm** 65.00/90.00 **t.**, **1 suite** 80.00/100.00 **t.**

AUDI-VW Station Rd, Northwich ☎ 0606 (Northwich) 46061
CITROEN Manchester Rd, Northwich ☎ 0606 (Northwich) 43816
FORD Chesterway, Northwich ☎ 0606 (Northwich) 46141
PEUGEOT-TALBOT 322 Chester Rd ☎ 0606 (Sandiway) 888188
RENAULT Runcorn Rd, Barnton ☎ 0606 (Northwich) 77137
VAUXHALL-OPEL 9 London Rd, Northwich ☎ 0606 (Northwich) 43434

HARTINGTON Derbs. 402 403 404 O 24 – ✉ Buxton – ☎ 0298 Buxton.

♦London 168 – Derby 36 – ♦Manchester 40 – ♦Sheffield 34 – Stoke-on-Trent 22.

Biggin Hall, Biggin, SK17 0DH, SE : 2 m. by B 5054 ☎ 84451, ←, « 17C hall », – rest TV P. VISA.
closed midweek in winter – **M** 13.50 **st.** 3.50 – 3.00 – **11 rm** 30.00/75.00 **st.**

HARTLEPOOL Cleveland 402 Q 19 – pop. 91 749 – ECD : Wednesday – ☎ 0429.

Seaton Carew, Tees Rd ☎ 266249 – Castle Eden and Peterlee ☎ 836220 – Hart Warren ☎ 274398.

Teesside Airport ☎ 0325 (Darlington) 332811, SW : 20 m.

Civic Centre, Victoria Rd ☎ 266522.

♦London 263 – Durham 19 – ♦Middlesbrough 9 – Sunderland 21.

Grand, Swainson St., TS24 8AA, ☎ 266345, Fax 265217 – TV ☎ – 50. AE VISA
closed 25-26 December and 1 January – **M** *(closed lunch Saturday and Bank Holiday Mondays)* 5.75/7.75 **t.** and a la carte – **47 rm** 39.50/119.95 **t.**

at Seaton Carew SE : 2 m. on A 178 – ☎ 0429 Hartlepool :

Krimo's, 8 The Front, TS25 1BS, ☎ 266120 – VISA
closed Saturday lunch, Sunday, Monday,and first 2 weeks August – **M** 8.50 **st.** (lunch) and a la carte 12.40/18.00 **st.** 3.10.

AUDI-VW Brenda Rd ☎ 221619
CITROEN Longhill Ind. Est. ☎ 233031
FORD Stockton Rd ☎ 869000
MAZDA Westview Rd ☎ 236783
ROVER York Rd ☎ 274431
VAUXHALL Oxford Rd ☎ 273672
ATS York Rd ☎ 275552

We suggest:
For a successful tour, that you prepare it in advance.
***Michelin maps** and **guides** will give you much useful information on route planning, places of interest, accommodation, prices etc.*

HARTOFT END North Yorks. 402 R 21 – pop. 62 – ✉ Pickering – ☎ 075 15 Lastingham.

♦London 243 – Scarborough 26 – York 32.

Blacksmith's Arms, YO18 8EN, ☎ 331, ←, – TV ☎ P. VISA.
M 12.50/19.50 **t.** 4.25 – **14 rm** 48.00/75.00 **t.** – SB (November-March) (except Christmas and New Year) 78.00/86.00 **st.**

HARVINGTON 403 404 027 – see Evesham.

HARWICH and DOVERCOURT Essex 404 X 28 – pop. 17 245 – ECD : Wednesday – ☎ 0255.

Parkeston Rd ☎ 424331.

Shipping connections with the Continent : to Germany (Hamburg) (Scandinavian Seaways) – to Denmark (Esbjerg) (Scandinavian Seaways) – from Parkeston Quay to The Netherlands (Hoek van Holland) (Sealink) – to Sweden (Göteborg) (Scandinavian Seaways).

to Felixstowe (Orwell & Harwich Navigation Co.) 7 daily (except Saturday and Sunday) (15 mn).

Parkeston Quay ☎ 506139.

♦London 78 – Chelmsford 41 – Colchester 20 – ♦Ipswich 23.

Tower, Main Rd, Dovercourt, CO12 3PJ, ☎ 504952, Fax 504952 – TV ☎ P. AE VISA
closed 25 to 27 December – **M** 8.50 **t.** (lunch) and a la carte 9.60/21.90 **t.** – **15 rm** 35.00/54.00 **t.**

Cliff, Marine Par., Dovercourt, CO12 3RE, ☎ 503345, ← – TV ☎ P – 200. AE VISA
closed 25 and 26 December – **M** 9.00/9.50 **t.** and a la carte 3.25 – **26 rm** 45.00/55.00 **t.** **1 suite** 65.00/75.00 **t.** – SB (weekends only)75.00 **st.**

XX **Pier at Harwich** with rm, The Quay, CO12 3HH, ℘ 241212, Group Telex 987083, ≤, Seafood – TV ☎ P. VISA. ✗
Accommodation closed 24 to 26 December – **M** (*closed dinner 25 and 26 December*) 14.50 **t.** (lunch) and a la carte 16.00/24.20 **t.** 5.45 – ☐ 4.50 – **6 rm** 50.00/70.00 **st.** – SB 75.50 **st.**

ORD, VAUXHALL-OPEL Station Rd, Dovercourt ℘ 242222
KODA 113 High St., Dovercourt ℘ 502537
ATS 723 Main Rd, Dovercourt ℘ 508314

HASCOMBE Surrey – see Godalming.

HASELBURY PLUCKNETT Somerset 403 L 31 – see Crewkerne.

HASLEMERE Surrey 404 R 30 – pop. 10 544 – ECD : Wednesday – ☎ 0428.

nvir. : Petworth House★★★ (17C) (paintings★★★ and carved room★★★) *AC*, SE : 11 m.

London 47 – ◆Brighton 46 – ◆Southampton 44.

Lythe Hill, Petworth Rd, GU27 3BQ, E : 1 ½ m. on B 2131 ℘ 651251, Telex 858402, Fax 644131, ≤, park, ✗ – TV ☎ P – 50. AE VISA
M 16.00 **t.** and a la carte (see also **Auberge de France** below) 5.50 – ☐ 7.00 – **27 rm** 74.00/135.00 **t.**, **13 suites** 110.00/150.00 **t.** – SB (weekends only) 99.00 **st.**

XXX **Auberge de France** (at Lythe Hill H.), Petworth Rd, GU27 3BQ, E : 1 ½ m. on B 2131 ℘ 651251, Telex 858402, Fax 644131, ≤, French rest., « Tudor building », – P. AE VISA
closed Monday – **M** (dinner only and Sunday lunch)/dinner 17.50/28.00 **t.** and a la carte 5.50.

XXX ✿ **Morels,** (Morel) 23-27 Lower St., GU27 2NY, ℘ 51462, French rest. – AE ⓓ VISA
closed Saturday lunch, Sunday, Monday, last 2 weeks February, 2 weeks September and Bank Holidays except Easter – **M** 19.00/23.00 **t.** and a la carte approx. 30.00 **t.** 5.00.
Spec. Andouillette de homard, jus au basilic, Poulet fermier farci au crabe et gingembre, Marquise aux deux chocolats.

X **Shrimptons,** 2 Grove Cottages, Midhurst Rd, Kingsley Green, GU27 3LF, SW : 1 ¼ m. on A 286 ℘ 3539 – AE ⓓ VISA
closed Saturday lunch, Sunday, 25 March, 25-26 December, 1 January and Bank Holidays – **M** 13.50/19.50 **t.** and a la carte 17.50/24.20 **t.** 6.00.

ORD Havenford ℘ 3222
EUGEOT-TALBOT High St. ℘ 52552
ROVER Grayswood Rd ℘ 2303
VW-AUDI Hindhead Rd ℘ 53811

HASSOP Derbs. – see Bakewell.

HASTINGS and ST. LEONARDS East Sussex 404 V 31 – pop. 74 979 – ☎ 0424.

See : Norman Castle (ruins) ✳★★ *AC* BZ – Alexandra Park★ AY – White Rocks gardens ≤★ ABZ
· Public Museum and Art Gallery (Pottery★, Durbar Hall★) BZ **M.**

18 Beauport Park, St. Leonards, ℘ 52977, NW : 3 m. by B 2159 AY.

4 Robertson Terr. ℘ 718888 – The Fishmarket ℘ 722022 (summer only).

London 65 – ◆Brighton 37 – Folkestone 37 – Maidstone 34.

Plan on next page

Beauport Park (Best Western), Battle Rd, TN38 8EA, NW : 3½ m. at junction A 2100 and B 2159 ℘ 851222, Telex 957126, Fax 852465, ≤, « Formal garden », heated, park, ✗ – rest TV ☎ P – 80. AE ⓓ VISA by B 2159 AY
M 14.00/16.00 **st.** and a la carte 3.90 – **23 rm** ☐ 50.00/85.00 **st.** – SB (weekends only)- 72.00/84.00 **st.**

Cinque Ports, Summerfields, Bohemia Rd, TN34 1ET, ℘ 439222, Telex 957584, Fax 437277 – TV ☎ P – 120 AZ **a**
40 rm.

Norton Villa without rest., Hill St., Old Town, TN34 3HU, ℘ 428168, ≤, – TV P. ✗
4 rm ☐ 18.00/38.00 **s.** BY **n**

Chimes, 1 St. Matthews Gdns, Silverhill, TN38 0TS, ℘ 434041, – TV. ✗ AY **a**
9 rm.

XX **Röser's,** 64 Eversfield Pl., TN37 6DB, ℘ 712218 – AE ⓓ VISA BZ **i**
closed Saturday lunch, Sunday, Monday and first 3 weeks January – **M** 14.95 **st.** (lunch) and a la carte 18.05/26.20 **st.**

FORD Bohemia Rd ℘ 422727
MITSUBISHI Sedlescombe Rd North ℘ 440511
PEUGEOT-TALBOT Bexhill Rd ℘ 431276
RENAULT 109-111 Sedlescombe Rd North ℘ 432982
ROVER 5-9 Western Rd ℘ 721111
VAUXHALL 36-39 Western Rd, St. Leonards ℘ 424545
VOLVO 100 Battle Rd ℘ 423451
ATS Menzies Rd, St. Leonards-on-Sea ℘ 427780/424567

HASTINGS AND ST. LEONARDS

Street	Grid	No.
King's Road	AZ	22
London Road	AZ	
Norman Road	AZ	
Queen's Road	BZ	
Robertson Street	BZ	27
Wellington Place	BZ	35
Bourne (The)	BY	4
Cambridge Gardens	BZ	5
Castle Street	BZ	7
Castle Hill Road	BZ	8
Cornwallis Gardens	BZ	9
Cornwallis Terrace	BZ	10
Denmark Place	BZ	13
Dorset Place	BZ	15
Gensing Road	AZ	16
George Street	BY	18
Grosvenor Crescent	AY	19
Harold Place	BZ	20
Marine Court	AZ	23
Rock-a-Nore Road	BY	30
St. Helen's Park Road	BY	31
Sedlescombe Road South	AY	32
Silchester Road	AZ	33
Warrior Square	AZ	34
Wellington Square	BZ	36
White Rock Road	BZ	38

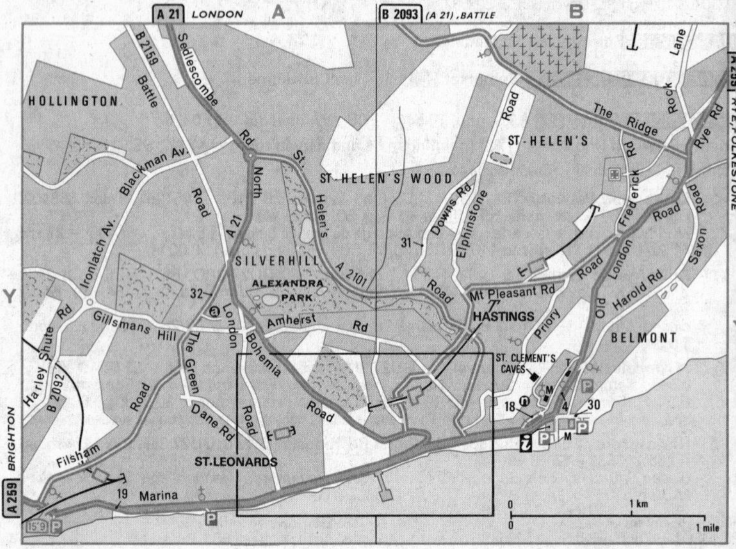

A 21 LONDON — A — B 2093 (A 21), BATTLE — B

HOLLINGTON
B 2159
Battle
Road
Sedlescombe
Rd
North
A 21
Blackman Av.
Ironlatch Av.
St. Helen's
ST-HELEN'S WOOD
SILVERHILL
ALEXANDRA PARK
A 2101
Downs Rd
Elphinstone
Road
ST-HELEN'S
The Ridge
Rock Lane
Rye Rd
Frederick Rd
London Road
Old London Road
Saxon Road
Harold Rd
Mt Pleasant Rd
Priory
HASTINGS
BELMONT
ST. CLEMENT'S CAVES
Gillsmans Hill
Amherst Rd
London
The Green
Bohemia
Road
Harley Shute Rd
B 2092
Road
Dane Rd
ST.LEONARDS
Filsham
Marina
BRIGHTON
A 259
A 259 FOLKESTONE, RYE
0 — 1 km
0 — 1 mile
Y

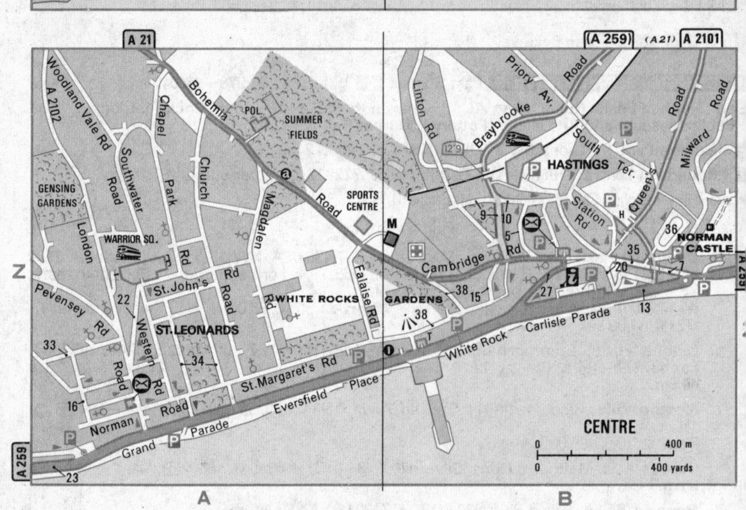

This Guide is not a comprehensive list of all hotels and restaurants, nor even of all good hotels and restaurants in Great Britain and Ireland.

Since our aim is to be of service to all motorists, we must show establishments in all categories and so we have made a selection of some in each.

HATCH BEAUCHAMP Somerset 403 K 30 – see Taunton.

HATFIELD Herts. 404 T 28 – pop. 33 174 – ECD : Monday and Thursday – 0707.
See : Hatfield House★★ *AC* (gardens★ and Old Palace★).
Bedwell Park, Essendon ℘ 42624, E : 3 m. – 18 Brookmans Park ℘ 52487, S : 3 m.
London 27 – Bedford 38 – ◆Cambridge 39.

Hazel Grove, Roehyde Way, AL10 9AF, S : 2 m. by B 6426 on A 1001 ℘ 275701, Telex 916580, Fax 266033, – TV ☎ ♿ P – 120. AE VISA
M *(closed Saturday lunch)* 15.00 **st.** (dinner) and a la carte – **76 rm** 65.00/85.00 **st.**

Comet, 301 St. Albans Rd West, AL10 9RH, SW : 1 m. by A 1057 at junction with A 1 ℘ 265411, Fax 264019 – TV ☎ P – 35. AE VISA.
M *(closed Saturday lunch and Sunday dinner)* 11.95 **st.** and a la carte 5.00 – 7.00 – **57 rm** 62.50/82.50 **st.**

ALFA-ROMEO By-Pass ℘ 264521
ROVER 1 Great North Rd ℘ 264366
LANCIA, SUZUKI 42 Beaconsfield Rd ℘ 271226

HATFIELD HEATH Essex. 404 U 28 – see Bishop's Stortford (Herts.).

HATHERLEIGH Devon 403 H 31 – pop. 1 355 – ECD : Wednesday – ✉ 0837 Okehampton.
at Okehampton, Tors Rd, ℘ 52113, SE : 7 m.
London 230 – Exeter 29 – ◆Plymouth 38.

The Tally Ho, 14 Market St., EX20 3JN, ℘ 810306, – TV. VISA.
M *(closed Wednesday and Sunday)* 12.50 **st.** (dinner) and a la carte 3.75 – 2.50 – **3 rm** 22.00/40.00 **st.**

Pressland Country House, EX20 3LW, S : 2 m. on A 386 ℘ 810347, – P
4 rm.

at Sheepwash NW : 5½ m. by A 3072 – ✉ Beaworthy – 040 923 Black Torrington :

Half Moon Inn, The Square, EX21 5NE, ℘ 376, « 17C inn », – TV ☎ P. VISA
closed January – **M** (dinner only) 15.00 **t.** 3.25 – **14 rm** 23.00/46.00 **t.**

HATHERSAGE Derbs. 402 403 404 P 24 – pop. 1 966 – ECD : Wednesday – ✉ Sheffield (South Yorks.) – 0433 Hope Valley.
◆London 165 – ◆Manchester 33 – ◆Sheffield 10.

George (Lansbury), Main Rd, S30 1BB, ℘ 50436, Telex 547196, Fax 50099 – rm TV ☎ P – 30. AE VISA.
M 9.50/17.00 **t.** and a la carte 4.50 – **18 rm** 64.00/78.00 **t.** – SB (weekends only) 84.00/94.00 **st.**

Highlow Hall without rest., S30 1AX, S : 1½ m. by B 6001 on Abney rd ℘ 50393, ←, – P
6 rm.

HATTON Warw. – see Warwick.

HAVANT Hants. 404 R 31 – pop. 50 098 – ECD : Wednesday – 0705.
18 Rowlands Castle, Links Lane ℘ 412216, N : 3 m.
1 Park Rd South ℘ 480024.
◆London 70 – ◆Brighton 39 – ◆Portsmouth 9 – ◆Southampton 22.

Bear (Lansbury), 15 East St., PO9 1AA, ℘ 486501, Telex 869136, Fax 470551 – rm TV ☎ P – 100. AE VISA.
M 9.45 **t.** (lunch) and a la carte 10.55/19.45 **t.** – **42 rm** 67.00/79.00 **t.** – SB (weekends only) 72.00 **st.**

FORD New Rd ℘ 482161
ATS 60-62 Bedhampton Rd ℘ 483018/451570

HAVERFORDWEST (HWLFFORDD) Dyfed 403 F 28 – pop. 13 572 – ECD : Thursday – 0437.
Envir. : SW : Martin's Haven ★★ – St. Ann's Head★★ by Dale ←★.
18 Arnolds Down ℘ 763565.
40 High St. ℘ 763110 (summer only).
◆London 250 – Fishguard 15 – ◆Swansea 57.

Mariners, Mariners Sq., SA61 2DU, ℘ 763353, Fax 764258 – TV ☎ P. AE VISA
closed 26-27 December and 1 January – **M** (bar lunch)/dinner 10.00/17.50 **t.** 3.75 – **32 rm** 39.00/74.00 **t.** – SB (weekends only) 66.00/76.00 **st.**

Sutton Lodge, Portfield Gate, SA62 3LN, W : 3 m. by B 4327 and B 4341 off Sutton rd ℘ 768548, Fax 760826, ← – rest TV P
closed January and February – **M** *(closed Sunday)* (dinner only) 17.50 **t.** 3.25 – **6 rm** 35.00/70.00 **t.** – SB (October-March) 82.50/85.50 **st.**

FORD Dew St. ℘ 763772
RENAULT Fishguard Rd ℘ 762468
ROVER, DAIMLER-JAGUAR Salutation Sq. ℘ 764511
VAUXHALL-OPEL Perrotts Rd ℘ 762717
ATS Back Lane, Prendergast ℘ 763756/7

HAWES North Yorks. 402 N 21 – pop. 1 177 – ☎ 0969.

National Park Centre, Station Yard ☎ 667450 (summer only).

London 253 – Kendal 27 – Leeds 72 – York 65.

- **Simonstone Hall**, Simonstone, DL8 3LY, N : 1 ½ m. on Muker rd ☎ 66725 Fax 667741, ≤, « Country house atmosphere », – TV P. VISA
  M (bar lunch Monday to Saturday)/dinner 24.50 **t.** and a la carte 4.10 – **10 rm** 48.60 115.00 **t.** – SB 110.00/140.00 **st.**
- **Rookhurst Georgian Country House**, Gayle, DL8 3RT, S : ½ m. ☎ 667454, « Antique furnishings », – TV P.
  closed Christmas and New Year – **M** (residents only) (dinner only Tuesday to Saturday) 16.00/26.00 **t.** – **5 rm** 40.00/106.00 **t.**
- **Stone House**, Sedbusk, DL8 3PT, N : 1 m. by Muker rd on Askrigg rd ☎ 66757 Fax 667720, – rest TV P. VISA
  closed January – **M** (dinner only) 12.95 **t.** 3.50 – **15 rm** 25.00/60.00 **t.** – SB (Mid October-Easter) 68.50/77.50 **st.**
- **Herriot's,** Main St., DL8 3QU, ☎ 667536 – TV. VISA
  closed November-February except Christmas and New Year – **M** a la carte 10.20/12.85 3.30 – **6 rm** 28.50/41.00 **t.** – SB (February-May) 54.00 **st.**
- **Cockett's** with rm, Market Pl., DL8 3RD, ☎ 667312 – TV. VISA
  M (dinner only) 14.95 **st.** 4.00 – **8 rm** 21.50/45.00 **st.**

HAWKCHURCH Devon 403 L 31 – see Axminster.

HAWKHURST Kent 404 V 30 – pop. 3 192 – ECD : Wednesday – ☎ 0580.

Envir. : Bodiam Castle★★, SE : 3 ½ m. – Bedgebury Pinetum★ *AC*, NW : 2 m.

High St. ☎ 752396.

London 47 – Folkestone 34 – Hastings 14 – Maidstone 19.

- **Tudor Court** (Best Western), Rye Rd, TN18 5DA, E : ¾ m. on A 268 ☎ 752312 Fax 753966, ≤, « Gardens » – rm TV ☎ P – 50. AE VISA
  M 12.50/13.50 **st.** and a la carte 4.50 – **18 rm** 51.50/87.00 **st.** – SB (except Christmas and New Year) 106.00/111.00 **st.**

HAWKRIDGE Somerset 403 J 30 – ✉ Dulverton – ☎ 064 385 Winsford.

London 203 – Exeter 32 – Minehead 17 – Taunton 32.

- **Tarr Steps**, TA22 9PY, NE : 1 ½ m. ☎ 293, ≤, park – P. VISA
  Mid March-December – **M** (bar lunch Monday to Saturday)/dinner 17.00 **t.** 3.15 – **14 rm** 31.00/62.00 **t.**

HAWKSHEAD Cumbria 402 L 20 – pop. 660 – ECD : Thursday – ✉ Ambleside – ☎ 096 66.

Main Car Park ☎ 525 (summer only).

London 283 – Carlisle 52 – Kendal 19.

- **Field Head House**, Outgate, LA22 0PY, N : 1 m. by B 5285 off B 5286 ☎ 240, ≤, – P
  closed mid January-mid February – **M** *(closed Tuesday)* (dinner only) 20.00 **st.** – **7 rm** (dinner included) 57.50/115.00 **st.**
- **Queen's Head,** Main St., LA22 0NS, ☎ 271 – TV ☎. AE VISA.
  M (bar lunch)/dinner a la carte 11.50/17.75 **t.** 3.95 – **12 rm** 22.00/46.00 **t.**
- **Highfield House**, Hawkshead Hill, LA22 0PN, W : ½ m. on B 5285 (Coniston rd) ☎ 344, ≤ Kirkstone Pass and Fells, – rest TV P
  closed 23 to 28 December – **M** 11.50 **st.** – **11 rm** 26.00/54.00 **st.** – SB (November-March) 54.90/69.30 **st.**
- **Ivy House,** Main St., LA22 0NS, ☎ 204 – P
  closed November and December – **M** 8.75 **t.** 2.80 – **11 rm** 17.25/21.75 **t.**
- **Rough Close**, LA22 0QF, S : 1 ½ m. on Newby Bridge rd ☎ 370, – rest P. VISA.
  April-October – **M** 9.50 **t.** 4.00 – **6 rm** (dinner included) 28.50/59.00 **t.**

at Near Sawrey SE : 2 m. on B 5285 – ✉ Ambleside – ☎ 096 66 Hawkshead :

- Garth, LA22 0JZ, ☎ 373, – TV P
  7 rm.

at Far Sawrey SE : 2 ½ m. on B 5285 – ✉ Ambleside – ☎ 096 62 Windermere :

- **West Vale,** LA22 0LQ, ☎ 2817, ≤ – P.
  M 8.00 **t.** 3.00 – **8 rm** 15.00/34.00 **t.**

at Grizedale SW : 2 ¾ m. – ✉ Ambleside – ☎ 096 66 Hawkshead :

- **Grizedale Lodge** with rm, LA22 0QL, ☎ 532 – TV P. VISA.
  closed 2 January-14 February – **M** *(closed Monday lunch)* (bar lunch)/dinner 15.50 **t.** – **6 rm** 34.00/52.00 **t.** – SB (except April-October) 66.00/75.00 **st.**
- Hunt Tor House, EX6 6QW, ☎ 228 – **4 rm.**

HAWORTH West Yorks. 402 O 22 – pop. 5 041 – ECD : Tuesday – ✉ Keighley – ☎ 0535.
See : Brontë Parsonage Museum★ AC.
2-4 West Lane ☎ 42329.
London 213 – Burnley 22 – ◆Leeds 22 – ◆Manchester 34.

- **Old White Lion,** 6 West Lane, BD22 8DU, ☎ 42313 – TV ☎ P. AE VISA.
  M (bar lunch)/dinner 8.00 **st.** and a la carte 3.80 – **12 rm** 29.50/42.50 **st.** – SB (weekends only) 47.50 **st.**
- **Ferncliffe,** Hebden Rd, BD22 8RS, ☎ 43405, ← – TV P. VISA
  M (by arrangement) 14.05 **st.** 3.50 – **6 rm** 19.00/40.00 **st.** – SB (November-February) (weekends only) 45.00/50.00 **st.**
- **Weaver's** with rm, 15 West Lane, BD22 8DU, ☎ 43822 – TV ☎. AE VISA.
  closed 2 weeks June-July and 2 weeks Christmas-New Year – **M** *(closed dinner Sunday and Monday)* (dinner only and Sunday lunch in winter) 10.50 **t.** and a la carte 3.50 – **3 rm** 40.50/52.00 **t.**

HAYDOCK Merseyside 402 403 404 M 23 – pop. 17 372 – ✉ Newton-le-Willows – ☎ 0942 Ashton-in-Makerfield.
London 198 – ◆Liverpool 17 – ◆Manchester 18.

- **Haydock Thistle** (Mt. Charlotte Thistle), Penny Lane, WA11 9SG, NE : ½ m. on A 599 ☎ 272000, Fax 711092, – rm rest TV ☎ P – 300. AE VISA
  M 15.00/40.00 and a la carte 4.50 8.50 – **135 rm** 72.00/105.00 **st.**, **4 suites** 115.00/130.00 **st.**
- **Post House** (T.H.F.), Lodge Lane, WA12 0JG, NE : 1 m. on A 49 ☎ 717878, Telex 677672, Fax 718419, – rm TV ☎ P – 50. AE VISA
  M 10.95/13.95 **st.** and a la carte 4.35 – 7.50 – **143 rm** 69.00/89.00 **st.**
- **Travelodge** without rest., Piele Rd, WA11 9TL, on A 580 ☎ 272055, Reservations (Toll free) 0800 850950 – TV P. AE VISA.
  40 rm 24.00/29.50 **t.**

ATS Legh Rd, St. Helens ☎ 50551

HAYLING ISLAND Hants. 404 R 31 – pop. 12 410 – ECD : Wednesday – ☎ 0705.
Ferry Rd ☎ 463712.
Seafront, Beachlands ☎ 467111 (summer only).
London 77 – ◆Brighton 45 – ◆Southampton 28.

- **Post House** (T.H.F.), Northney Rd, PO11 0NQ, ☎ 465011, Telex 86620, Fax 466468, ←, – rm TV ☎ P – 180. AE VISA
  M *(closed Saturday lunch)* 10.95/11.95 **st.** and a la carte 4.35 – 7.50 – **96 rm** 69.00/89.00 **st.**
- **Cockle Warren Cottage,** 36 Seafront, PO11 9HL, ☎ 464961, heated – rm TV ☎ P. VISA.
  M (dinner only) 19.50 **st.** 3.50 – **5 rm** 35.45/52.70 **st.**

HAY-ON-WYE Powys 403 K 27 – pop. 1 578 – ECD : Tuesday – ☎ 0497.
The Car Park ☎ 820144 (summer only).
London 154 – Brecon 16 – Hereford 21 – Newport 62.

- **Swan** (Best Western), Church St., HR3 5DQ, ☎ 821188, Fax 821424, – rest TV ☎ P – 100. AE VISA
  M (bar lunch)/dinner 24.00 **st.** and a la carte 4.00 – **19 rm** 35.00/75.00 **st.** – SB (except Christmas-New Year and Bank Holidays) 45.00/50.00 **st.**

FORD Broad St. ☎ 820548
FORD 2-10 Thorn Rd, Hendon ☎ 899181
ROVER, LAND-ROVER, RANGE-ROVER Church St. ☎ 820404

HAYTOR Devon – see Bovey Tracey.

HAYTOR VALE Devon – see Bovey Tracey.

HEACHAM Norfolk 402 404 V 25 – see Hunstanton.

HEADLAM Durham – see Darlington.

HEALEY North Yorks. 402 O 21 – see Masham.

HEATHFIELD East Sussex 404 U 31 – pop. 4 848 – ✉ ☎ 0435.
◆London 51 – ◆Brighton 23 – Eastbourne 16.

- **Risingholme** without rest., 38 High St., TN21 8LS, ☎ 864525, – TV P.
  3 rm 30.00/45.00.

ATS Unit 1, Dainton House, Battle rd., Nr Bovey Tracey ☎ 834692

HEATHROW AIRPORT – see Hillingdon (Greater London).

HEBDEN BRIDGE West Yorks. 402 N 22 – pop. 4 167 – ECD : Tuesday – ✉ ☎ 0422 Halifax.

Mount Skip, Wadsworth ☎ 842896, N : 1 m.

1 Bridge Gate ☎ 843831.

London 223 – Burnley 13 – Leeds 24 – Manchester 25.

Carlton, Albert St., HX7 8ES, ☎ 844400, Fax 843117 – 100. AE VISA
M 8.95/14.95 **t.** 3.25 – **18 rm** 49.00/69.00 **t.** – SB 80.00/86.00 **st.**

HEDON Humberside 402 T 22 – ✉ ☎ 0482 Kingston-upon-Hull.

London 189 – Kingston upon Hull 6 – Lincoln 60 – York 34.

Kingstown, Hull Rd, HU12 9DJ, W : 1 m. on A 1033 ☎ 890461, Fax 890713 – VISA.
M *(closed Sunday dinner)* 10.95 **st.** and a la carte 2.95 – **18 rm** 55.00/78.00 **st.**

HELFORD Cornwall 403 E 33 – ✉ Helston – ☎ 032 623 Manaccan.

London 324 – Falmouth 15 – Penzance 22 – Truro 27.

Riverside with rm, TR12 6JU, ☎ 443, Fax 443, ≤, « Converted cottages in pictur-esque setting », –
Mid February-October – **M** (dinner only) 26.00 **st.** 4.50 **6 rm** 65.00/100.00 **st.**

at Gillan SE : 3 m. – ✉ Helston – ☎ 032 623 Manaccan :

Tregildry , TR12 6HG, ☎ 378, ≤ Gillan Creek, sea, – VISA
Easter-mid October – **M** (bar lunch)/dinner 15.00 **t.** 4.50 – **10 rm** 40.00/60.00 **t.**

HELMSLEY North Yorks. 402 Q 21 – pop. 1 399 – ECD : Wednesday – ☎ 0439.

See : Castle★ (ruins 12C) *AC*.

Envir. : Rievaulx Abbey★★ (ruins 12C-13C) *AC*, NW : 2½ m. – Byland Abbey★ (ruins 12C) SW 6 m. by Ampleforth.

Ampleforth College, 56 High St. ☎ 70678.

Town Hall, Market Pl. ☎ 70173 (summer only).

London 234 – Middlesbrough 29 – York 24.

Black Swan (T.H.F.), Market Pl., YO6 5BJ, ☎ 70466, Fax 70174, « 16C inn », – rm
AE VISA
M 12.95/38.00 **st.** and a la carte 8.50 – 8.00 – **44 rm** 75.00/200.00 **st.** – SB 130.00/150.00 **st.**

Feversham Arms (Best Western), 1 High St., YO6 5AG, ☎ 70766, heated, , –
– 30. AE VISA
M (bar lunch Tuesday to Saturday)/dinner 25.00 **t.** and a la carte 4.00 – **18 rm** 45.00/80.00 **t.** – SB (except Christmas) 76.00/96.00 **st.**

Feathers, Market Pl., YO6 5BH, ☎ 70275, – AE VISA.
closed 23 December-1 February – **M** (bar lunch Monday to Saturday)/dinner 19.50 **st.** and a la carte 3.95 – **17 rm** 24.00/57.00 **st.** – SB 65.00/74.00 **st.**

Laskill Farm, NW : 6¼ m. on B 1257 ☎ 268, « Woking farm », –
M (by arrangement) (communal dining) 10.00 **st.** – **6 rm** 14.00/36.00 **st.**

Beaconsfield without rest., Bondgate, YO6 5BW, ☎ 71346 –
6 rm 23.00/38.00 **s.**

at Harome E : 2¾ m. by A 170 – ✉ York – ☎ 0439 Helmsley :

Pheasant, YO6 5JG, ☎ 71241, – rest
closed January, February and Christmas – **M** (bar lunch)/dinner 17.50 **t.** 3.00 – **12 rm** (dinner included) 48.00/106.00 **t.**, **2 suites** 80.00/120.00 **t.** – SB (November-mid May) 79.00/85.00 **t.**

at Nawton E : 3¼ m. on A 170 – ✉ York – ☎ 0439 Helmsley :

Plumpton Court, High St., YO6 5TT, ☎ 71223, –
Mid March-October – **M** 8.00 **st.** – **8 rm** 26.25/36.50 **st.**

at Nunnington SE : 6¼ m. by A 170 off B 1257 – ✉ York – ☎ 043 95 Nunnington :

Ryedale Lodge with rm, YO6 5XB, W : 1 m. ☎ 246, ≤, « Converted railway station », – rest VISA.
(closed 3 weeks January) – **M** (dinner only) 25.00 **t.** 4.50 – **7 rm** 50.00/85.00 **t.** – SB 108.00/120.00 **st.**

HEMEL HEMPSTEAD Herts. 404 S 28 – pop. 80 110 – ECD : Wednesday – ☎ 0564.

Little Hay, Box Lane, Bovington ☎ 833798, off A 41 – Boxmoor, 18 Box Lane ☎ 42434, W 1 m. on B 4505.

Pavilion Box Office, Marlowes ☎ 64451.

London 30 – Aylesbury 16 – Luton 10 – Northampton 46.

Post House (T.H.F.), Breakspear Way, HP2 4UA, E : 2 ½ m. on A 414 ✆ 51122, Telex 826902, Fax 211812, – rm – 90.
M *(closed Saturday lunch)* 9.95/11.95 **st.** and a la carte 4.35 – 7.50 – **107 rm** 69.00/89.00 **st.** – SB (weekends only) 76.00 **st.**

Casanova, 75 Waterhouse St., HP1 1ED, ✆ 47482, Italian rest. –
closed Saturday lunch, Sunday and Bank Holidays – **M** a la carte 12.30/19.25 **t.** 3.75.

at Bourne End W : 2 ¼ m. on A 41 – ✉ Hemel Hempstead – ✆ 044 27 Berkhamsted :

Hemel Hempstead Moat House (Q.M.H.), London Rd, HP1 2RJ, ✆ 871241, Fax 866130 – rm – 100.
M *(closed Saturday lunch, 29 March and Bank Holiday Mondays)* 10.95 **st.** and a la carte 3.95 – **61 rm** 63.00/75.00 **st.** – SB (weekends only) 67.00/82.00 **st.**

IAT, VAUXHALL-OPEL Two Waters Rd ✆ 51212
ORD Redbourne Rd ✆ 63013
EUGEOT-TALBOT Queensway ✆ 54561/50401
OVER London Rd ✆ 42841
TOYOTA Waterend ✆ 51466
ATS Lyon Way, Hatfield Rd, St. Albans ✆ 52314/5
ATS Grimston Rd, St. Albans ✆ 35174

HENDY-GWYN = Whitland.

HENLADE Somerset – see Taunton.

HENLEY-IN-ARDEN Warw. 403 404 O 27 – pop. 2 636 – ECD : Thursday – ✆ 0564.
London 104 – Birmingham 15 – Stratford-upon-Avon 8 – Warwick 8.5.

Ashleigh House without rest., Whitley Hill, B95 5DL, E : 1 ¾ m. on B 4095 ✆ 792315, –
10 rm 38.00/55.00 **st.**

Le Filbert Cottage, 64 High St., B95 5BX, ✆ 792700, French rest. –
closed Sunday, Monday, 25-26 December, 1 January and Bank Holiday Mondays – **M** a la carte 17.10/26.40 **t.**

HENLEY-ON-THAMES Oxon. 404 R 29 – pop. 10 910 – ECD : Wednesday – ✆ 0491.
Envir. : Greys Court★ *AC*, NW : 2 ½ m.
Badgemore Park ✆ 572206 – Harpsden ✆ 573304 – Huntercombe, Nuffield ✆ 641207.
Town Hall, Market Place ✆ 578034 (summer only).
London 40 – Oxford 23 – Reading 9.

Red Lion, Hart St., RG9 2AR, ✆ 572161, Fax 410039 – – 50.
M 24.00 **t.** (lunch) and a la carte 18.70/25.10 **t.** 5.00 – 6.50 – **26 rm** 37.00/93.50 **st.** – SB (weekends only) 122.00/162.00 **st.**

Slow Boat, 25 Duke St., RG9 1UR, ✆ 410001, Chinese (Peking) rest. –.

Chef Peking, 10 Market Pl., RG9 2AH, ✆ 578681, Chinese (Peking) rest. –
closed 24 to 27 December – **M** a la carte approx. 9.80 **t.**

Little Angel, Remenham, RG9 2LS, E : ¼ m. on A 423 ✆ 574165 –
closed Sunday dinner and Monday – **M** 20.00/30.00 **st.** and a la carte 3.50.

at Fawley (Bucks.) N : 3 ½ m. by A 4155 – ✉ Henley-on-Thames – ✆ 049 163 Turville Heath :

Walnut Tree, Fawley Green, RG9 6JE, ✆ 360 –
M a la carte approx. 13.50 **t.**

at Stonor N : 4 m. by A 423 on B 480 – ✉ Henley-on-Thames – ✆ 049 163 Turville Heath :

Stonor Arms with rm, RG9 6HE, ✆ 345, –
M (dinner only and Sunday lunch)/dinner 28.95/33.20 **t.** – **7 rm** -/90.00 **t.**, **2 suites** 135.00 **t.**

at Frieth (Bucks.) NE : 7 ½ m. by A 4155 – ✉ Henley-on-Thames – ✆ 0494 High Wycombe :

Yew Tree, RG9 6RJ, ✆ 882330 –
M 13.95/16.95 **t.** and a la carte 5.95.

BMW 49 Station Rd ✆ 577933
FIAT 66 Bell St. ✆ 573077
FORD Station Rd ✆ 578331
RENAULT Binfield Heath Rd ✆ 574255

HEREFORD Heref. and Worc. 403 L 27 – pop. 48 277 – ECD : Thursday – ☎ 0432.

See : Cathedral★★ (12C-13C) (the Mappa Mundi★ 13C) A **A** – The Old House★ (17C) A **B**.

Envir. : Abbey Dore★ (12C-17C) SW : 12 m. by A 465 B.

⛳18 Ravens Causeway, Wormsley ☎ 71219 by A 438 B – ⛳18 Belmont House, Belmont ☎ 277445 by A 465 B.

ℹ Townhall Annexe, St. Owens St. ☎ 268430.

◆London 133 – ◆Birmingham 51 – ◆Cardiff 56.

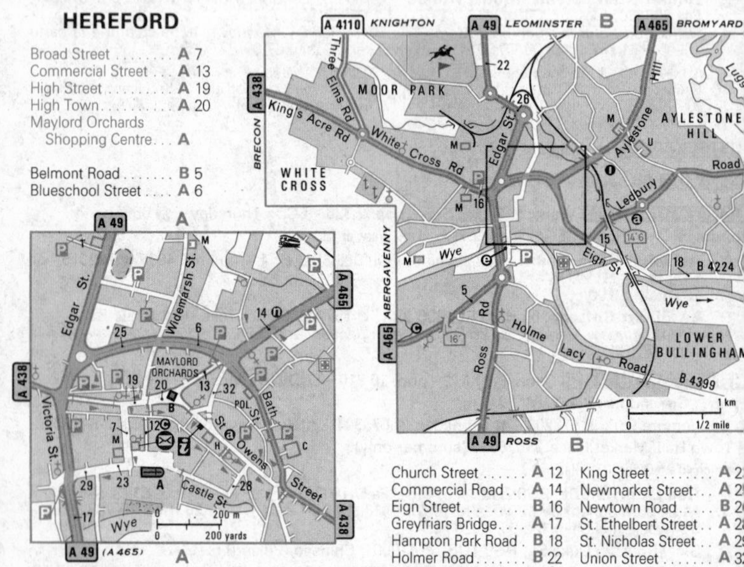

Broad Street	**A** 7
Commercial Street	**A** 13
High Street	**A** 19
High Town	**A** 20
Maylord Orchards Shopping Centre	**A**
Belmont Road	**B** 5
Blueschool Street	**A** 6
Church Street	**A** 12
Commercial Road	**A** 14
Eign Street	**B** 16
Greyfriars Bridge	**A** 17
Hampton Park Road	**B** 18
Holmer Road	**B** 22
King Street	**A** 2
Newmarket Street	**A** 2
Newtown Road	**B** 2
St. Ethelbert Street	**A** 2
St. Nicholas Street	**A** 2
Union Street	**A** 3

🏨 **Hereford Moat House** (Q.M.H.), Belmont Rd, HR2 7BP, SW : 1 ½ m. on A 46 ☎ 354301, Fax 275114 – TV ☎ ♿ P – 🏛 300. AE VISA — B
M *(closed Saturday lunch)* 10.50/16.00 **st.** and a la carte 🍷 5.00 – **60 rm** ☕ 63.00/85.00 **t.** – SB (weekends only) 80.00/90.00 **st.**

🏨 **Collins House,** 19 St. Owens St., HR1 2JR, ☎ 272416 – 🚭 rest TV ☎. AE VISA. ✗ — A
M (booking essential) 22.15/32.85 **st.** – **4 rm** 65.00/90.00 **st.**

🏨 **Merton,** Commercial Rd, HR1 2BD, ☎ 265925, Fax 354983 – TV ☎. AE VISA. ✗ — A
closed 26 December-3 January – **M** *(closed Sunday and Bank Holidays to non-residents)* 12.50/15.00 **t.** and a la carte 🍷 4.25 – **18 rm** ☕ 41.50/70.00 **t.**, **1 suite** 64.00/70.00 **t.** – SB (weekends only) 80.00 **st.**

🏨 **Travel Inn,** Holmer Rd, Holmer, HR4 9RS, N : 1¾ m. on A 49 – 🚭 rm TV ♿ P. AE VISA. ✗
M (Beefeater grill) a la carte approx. 12.25 **t.** – ☕ 4.50 – **40 rm** -/27.50 **t.**

🏠 **Somerville,** 12 Bodenham Rd, HR1 2TS, ☎ 273991, 🌳 – 🚭 rest TV ☎ P. VISA
M 12.80 **st.** – **10 rm** ☕ 23.00/47.00 **st.** – SB (October-March) (weekends only) 47.50/49.50 **st.** — B

🏠 **Ferncroft,** 144 Ledbury Rd, HR1 2TB, ☎ 265538, 🌳 – TV P. VISA. ✗ — B
closed mid December-early January – **M** 10.00 **st.** 🍷 3.00 – **11 rm** ☕ 25.00/45.00 **t.**

✗ **Fat Tulip,** Old Wye Bridge, 2 St. Martin's St., HR2 7RE, ☎ 275808 – AE VISA — B
closed Saturday lunch, Sunday and 2 weeks Christmas – **M** a la carte 18.45/24.20 **st.**

✗ **96,** 96 East St., HR1 2LW, ☎ 59754 – VISA — A
closed Sunday, Monday, 1 week Christmas, 2 weeks summer and Bank Holidays – **M** (dinner only) a la carte 15.45/18.90 **t.** 🍷 3.00.

at Canon Pyon N : 7 m. on A 4110–B– ✉ Hereford – ☎ 043 271 Canon Pyon :

🏠 Hermitage 🌿 without rest., HR4 8NR, S : 1 m. on A 4110 ☎ 0432 (Hereford) 760317, Vale of Hereford, 🌳 – P
3 rm.

at Dormington E : 5 ¼ m. on A 438 – B – ✉ ☎ 0432 Hereford :

Dormington Court, HR1 4DA, ✆ 850370, – TV P. VISA
M 13.00/19.00 **t.** and a la carte 3.00 – **6 rm** 24.00/56.00 **t.** – SB 60.00/80.00 **st.**

at Much Birch S : 5 ½ m. on A 49 – B – ✉ Hereford – ☎ 0981 Golden Valley :

Pilgrim, Ross Rd, HR2 8HJ, on A 49 ✆ 540742, Telex 35332, Fax 540620, ←, – TV ☎ P – 45. AE VISA.
M (bar lunch Monday to Saturday)/dinner 22.50 **t.** and a la carte 4.50 – **20 rm** 54.00/68.00 **st.** – SB 90.00 **st.**

at Ruckhall W : 5 m. by A 49 off A 465 – B – ✉ Eaton Bishop – ☎ 0981 Golden Valley :

Ancient Camp Inn , HR2 9QX, ✆ 250449, ← River Wye and countryside, « Tastefully renovated inn » – TV ☎ P. VISA.
M *(closed Sunday dinner and Monday)* (bar lunch)/dinner a la carte 10.95/16.50 **t.** 4.35 – **4 rm** 30.00/52.50 **t.**

BMW White Cross Rd ✆ 272589
CITROEN 38 St. Martin St. ✆ 272545
DAIHATSU, ALFA-ROMEO ✆ 054 46 (Eardisley) 441
FIAT Bath St. ✆ 274134
FORD Commercial Rd ✆ 276494
HONDA Steels Corner ✆ 267151
LADA Whitestone ✆ 850464
LAND-ROVER, RANGE-ROVER Muchcowarne ✆ 053 186 (Bosbury) 746
PEUGEOT-TALBOT 101-105 St. Owen St. ✆ 276268
RELIANT, SKODA Bridge St. ✆ 272341
SAAB Kings Acre Rd ✆ 266974
TOYOTA Mill St. ✆ 276727
VAUXHALL Blackfriars St. ✆ 352352
VOLVO Harrow Rd ✆ 276275
VW-AUDI Roman Rd ✆ 352424

ATS 6 Kyrle St. ✆ 265491

"Short Breaks" (SB)

De nombreux hôtels proposent des conditions avantageuses pour un séjour de deux nuits comprenant la chambre, le dîner et le petit déjeuner.

HERNE BAY Kent 404 X 29 – pop. 26 523 – ECD : Thursday – ☎ 0227.

Envir. : Reculver (church twin towers★ *AC*) E : 3 m.

Herne Bay, Eddington ✆ 374097.

Band Stand, Central Parade ✆ 361911.

London 63 – Dover 24 – Maidstone 32 – Margate 13.

Northdown, 14 Cecil Park, CT6 6DL, ✆ 372051, – TV ☎ P.
M (by arrangement) 7.50 **st.** 3.00 – **5 rm** 16.00/36.00 **st.**

L'Escargot, 22 High St., CT6 5LH, ✆ 372876 – VISA
closed lunch Saturday and Monday, Sunday, first week January and last two weeks September – **M** 9.30/10.90 **t.** and a la carte 4.05.

FORD Sea St. ✆ 374939
MAZDA Canterbury Rd ✆ 374772
SKODA Express Garage ✆ 364077

HERSTMONCEUX East Sussex 404 U 31 – pop. 2 246 – ☎ 032 181 (4 fig.) or 0323 (6 fig.).

See : Castle (15C) (home of the Royal Greenwich Observatory) site and grounds★★ *AC*.

Envir. : Michelham Priory (site★) *AC*, SW : 6 m.

London 63 – Eastbourne 12 – Hastings 14 – Lewes 16.

Sundial, Gardner St., BN27 4LA, ✆ 832217, French rest., « Converted 16C cottage », – P. AE VISA
closed Sunday dinner, Monday, 6 August-7 September and 25 December-20 January – **M** 14.50/22.50 **t.** and a la carte 4.25.

FIAT Cowbeech ✆ 833321
ROVER Boreham St. ✆ 832353

HERTINGFORDBURY Herts. 404 T 28 – pop. 658 – ✉ ☎ 0992 Hertford.

London 26 – Luton 18.

White Horse (T.H.F.), Hertingfordbury Rd, SG14 2LB, ✆ 586791, Fax 550809, – rm TV ☎ P – 60. AE VISA
M 10.95/13.95 **st.** and a la carte 3.95 – 7.00 – **42 rm** 65.00/85.00 **st.** – SB (weekends only) 84.00 **st.**

HETHERSETT Norfolk 404 X 26 – see Norwich.

HETTON North Yorks. – pop. 115 – ✉ Skipton – ☎ 075 673 Cracoe.

London 237 – Burnley 25 – Leeds 33.

Angel Inn, BD23 6LT, ✆ 263, « Attractive 18C inn » – P. VISA
closed Sunday dinner – **M** (dinner only and Sunday lunch)/dinner 17.95 **t.** 3.75.

HEXHAM Northumb. 401 402 N 19 – pop. 8 914 – ECD : Thursday – ☎ 0434.

See : Abbey Church★ (13C) (Saxon Crypt★★, Leschman chantry★).

Envir. : Hadrian's Wall★★ with its forts and milecastles – Housesteads Fort★, museum★, NW : 14 m.

18 Spital Park ✆ 602057 – 18 Slaley ✆ 673691 – 9 Tynedale, Tyne Green.

ℹ The Manor Office, Hallgate ✆ 605225.

◆London 304 – ◆Carlisle 37 – ◆Newcastle-upon-Tyne 21.

Beaumont, Beaumont St., NE46 3LT, ✆ 602331, Fax 602331 – rm TV ☎ – . AE VISA.
closed 25-26 December and 1 January – **M** 10.00/16.00 **t.** and a la carte 3.00 – **23 rm** 42.00/66.00 **st.** – SB (weekends only) 60.00 **st.**

County, Priestpopple, NE46 1PS, ✆ 602030 – TV ☎. AE VISA
M 8.25 **t.** (lunch) and dinner a la carte 9.75/19.25 **t.** 3.50 – **9 rm** 38.00/50.00 **t.** – SB (weekdays only) (except summer) 65.00 **st.**

MAZDA Tyne Mills Ind. Est. ✆ 607091
PEUGEOT-TALBOT Haugh Lane ✆ 604527
RENAULT, AUDI-VW Station Garage ✆ 606781
ROVER Alemouth Rd ✆ 605151
SUZUKI Priestpopple ✆ 603615
VAUXHALL Parkwell ✆ 602411
VOLVO Dere Park ✆ 605825

ATS Haugh Lane ✆ 602394

HEYSHAM Lancs. 402 L 21 – ECD : Wednesday – ☎ 0524.

18 Trumacar Park ✆ 51011.

to the Isle of Man : Douglas (Isle of Man Steam Packet Co.) (3 h 45 mn to 4 h 30 mn).

◆London 251 – ◆Blackpool 33 – ◆Carlisle 74 – Lancaster 8.

HIGHAM Suffolk 404 W 28 – pop. 142 – ✉ Colchester – ☎ 020 637.

◆London 55 – Colchester 10 – ◆Ipswich 11.

Old Vicarage without rest., CO7 6JY, ✆ 248, ≤, « 16C former vicarage », , , , – TV P
4 rm 20.00/45.00 **st.**

HIGH HALDEN Kent 404 W 30 – see Tenterden.

HIGH OFFLEY Staffs. 402 403 404 N 25 – see Eccleshall.

HIGHWORTH Wilts. 403 404 O 29 – pop. 8 020 – ☎ 0367 Faringdon.

◆London 88 – Gloucester 33 – ◆Oxford 25 – Swindon 5.

Inglesham Forge, Inglesham, SN6 7QY, N : 2½ m. by A 361 ✆ 52298 – P. AE VISA
closed lunch Monday and Saturday, Sunday, August and Christmas-New Year – **M** 19.50/25.50 **t.** and a la carte 4.75.

HIGH WYCOMBE Bucks. 404 R 29 – pop. 69 575 – ECD : Wednesday – ☎ 0494.

Envir. : Hughenden Manor★ (site★, Disraeli Museum) *AC*, N : 1 m. – West Wycombe (Manor House★ (18C) *AC*, St. Lawrence's Church : from the tower 74 steps, *AC*, ★) NW : 2½ m.

18 Flackwell Heath ✆ 062 85 (Flackwell Heath) 20027 – 18 Penn Rd, Hazlemere ✆ 714722, NE : 3 m. on B 474.

ℹ 6 Cornmarket ✆ 421892/28652.

◆London 34 – Aylesbury 17 – ◆Oxford 26 – Reading 18.

Crest (T.H.F.), Crest Rd, HP11 1TL, SW : 1½ m. by A 404 ✆ 442100, Telex 83626, Fax 439071 – rm rest TV ☎ P – 100. AE VISA.
M 12.95/14.95 **t.** and a la carte – 7.95 – **110 rm** 82.00/130.00 **st.**

Alexandra, Queen Alexandra Rd, HP11 2JX, ✆ 463494, Fax 463560 – TV ☎ P. AE VISA.
M *(closed Friday to Sunday and Bank Holidays)* (dinner only) a la carte approx. 13.00 **t.** – **28 rm** 66.00/110.00 **st.**

MICHELIN Distribution Centre, Thomas Rd, Wooburn Green, HP10 0PE, ✆ 06285 (Bourne End) 27472, Fax 819082

TOYOTA Littleworth Rd, Downley ✆ 35811
VAUXHALL London Rd ✆ 30021/445181/27494
VAUXHALL West Wycombe Rd ✆ 32545
VOLVO London Rd ✆ 34511

ATS Copyground Lane ✆ 25101/438019

HILLSFORD BRIDGE Devon – see Lynton.

HILTON PARK SERVICE AREA West Midlands – ✉ Wolverhampton – ☎ 0922 Cheslyn Hay

Rank Motor Lodge without rest., M6 between junctions 10 A and 11, WV11 2DR, ✆ 414100, Fax 418762 – TV P. AE VISA
60 rm 27.50/34.50 **st.**

HINCKLEY Leics. 402 403 404 P 26 – pop. 35 510 – ECD : Thursday – ☎ 0455.

Leicester Rd ℘ 615124, NE : 1½ m. on A 47.

Hinckley Library, Lancaster Rd ℘ 30852.

London 103 – Birmingham 31 – Coventry 12 – Leicester 14.

Hinckley Island, Watling St., LE10 3JA, SE : 3 m. by A 447 on A 5 ℘ 631122, Telex 34691, Fax 634536, rest – 400. AE VISA
M 12.95 **st.** (lunch) and a la carte 14.25/29.50 **st.** – 6.75 – **380 rm** 69.00/95.00 **st.** – SB (weekends only) 76.00 **st.**

Sketchley Grange (Best Western), Sketchley Lane, Burbage, LE10 3HU, SE : 2 m. by A 447 ℘ 251133, Fax 631384, – – 250
33 rm.

AUDI-VW 94-106 Upper Bond St. ℘ 637934
CITROEN Shilton Rd, Barwell ℘ 845091
FORD Watling St. ℘ 38911
NISSAN Roston Drive ℘ 632023
PEUGEOT-TALBOT London Rd ℘ 637152
RENAULT New Building ℘ 635379
SUBARU, ISUZU The Square, Wolvey ℘ 220761
VAUXHALL-OPEL 38 Derby Rd ℘ 636551
VOLVO Station Rd ℘ 632478

ATS 5 Leicester Rd ℘ 632022/635835

HINDON Wilts. 403 404 N 30 – pop. 489 – ECD : Saturday – ✉ Salisbury – ☎ 0747.

London 107 – Bath 28 – Bournemouth 40 – Salisbury 15.

Lamb at Hindon, SP3 6DP, ℘ 89573, Fax 89605, – rest . AE VISA.
M 17.50/15.00 **t.** and a la carte 4.50 – **15 rm** 25.00/65.00 **t.** – SB 80.00/110.00 **st.**

HINTLESHAM Suffolk 404 X 27 – see Ipswich.

HINTON CHARTERHOUSE Avon – see Bath.

HINWICK Beds. – see Wellingborough (Northants.).

HITCHIN Herts. 404 T 28 – pop. 33 480 – ECD : Wednesday – ☎ 0462.

Hitchin Library, Paynes Park ℘ 434738.

London 40 – Bedford 14 – Cambridge 26 – Luton 9.

Lord Lister, Park St., SG4 9AH, ℘ 432712, Fax 432712 – . AE VISA.
M (lunch by arrangement)/dinner 11.50 **t.** and a la carte 3.00 – **21 rm** 37.00/57.00 **t.** – SB (weekends only) 58.00/68.00 **st.**

at Little Wymondley SE : 2½ m. on A 602 – ✉ Hitchin – ☎ 0438 Stevenage :

XX **Redcoats Farmhouse** with rm, Redcoats Green, SG4 7JR, S : ½ m. by A 602 ℘ 729500, Telex 83343, Fax 723322, « Part 15C farmhouse », – . AE VISA.
closed 1 week Christmas – **M** *(closed Sunday and Bank Holiday Mondays)* 25.00 **t.** and a la carte 3.50 – **14 rm** 35.00/88.00 **st.** – SB (weekends only) 101.00/131.00 **st.**

CITROEN High St., Graveley ℘ 0438 (Stevenage) 316177
ROVER Queen St. ℘ 50311

HOATH Kent – pop. 436 – ✉ Canterbury – ☎ 022 786 Chislet.

London 67 – Canterbury 6 – Margate 13.

Knaves Ash Country Inn, CT3 4JT, ℘ 343 – rm
4 rm.

HOCKLEY HEATH Warw. 403 404 O 26 – pop. 3 507 – ✉ Solihull – ☎ 0564 Lapworth.

London 117 – Birmingham 11 – Coventry 17.

XXX **Nuthurst Grange** with rm, Nuthurst Grange Lane, B94 5NL, S : ¾ m. by A 3400 ℘ 783972, Telex 333485, Fax 783919, <, – . AE VISA.
closed Christmas – **M** *(closed Saturday lunch)* 17.50/32.50 **t.** 6.75 – 7.90 – **8 rm** 85.00/109.00 **t.** – SB (weekends only) 140.00 **st.**

HODNET Shropshire 402 403 404 M 25 – pop. 1 343 – ☎ 0630.

London 166 – Birmingham 50 – Chester 32 – Stoke-on-Trent 22 – Shrewsbury 14.

Bear, Shrewsbury St., TF9 3NH, ℘ 84214, Fax 84351 – . VISA.
M a la carte 8.25/13.00 **t.** 3.25 – **6 rm** 35.00/54.00 **t.**

HOLDENBY Northants. – see Northampton.

HOLFORD Somerset 403 K 30 – pop. 266 – ✉ Bridgwater – ☎ 027 874.

Envir. : Stogursey Priory Church★★, W : 4½ m.

London 171 – Bristol 48 – Minehead 15 – Taunton 22.

Combe House, TA5 1RZ, S : 1 m. ℘ 382, « Country house atmosphere », , – rest . AE VISA.
April-October – **M** (dinner only) 16.00 **t.** 3.95 – **22 rm** 30.00/80.00 **t.** – SB (except summer) 57.00/72.00 **st.**

HOLME West Yorks. – see Holmfirth.

HOLMES CHAPEL Cheshire 402 403 404 M 24 – pop. 4 672 – ✉ Crewe – ☎ 0477.
♦London 181 – Chester 25 – ♦Liverpool 41 – ♦Manchester 24 – ♦Stoke-on-Trent 20.

Holly Lodge, 70 London Rd, CW4 7AS, on A 50 ✆ 37033, Fax 35823 – TV ☎ P – 110 ... VISA
closed 26 to 30 December – **M** *(closed Saturday lunch)* 8.45/12.65 **t.** and a la carte 3.75 – **33 rm** 51.00/62.00 **st.** – SB (weekends only) 111.50/151.50 **st.**

Old Vicarage, Knutsford Rd, Cranage, CW4 8EF, NW : ½ m. on A 50 ✆ 32041 – rm ☎ P
23 rm.

at Twemlow Green NE : 1 ¾ m. on A 535 – ✉ ☎ 0477 Holmes Chapel :

Yellow Broom, Macclesfield Rd, CW4 8BL, ✆ 33289 – P. AE VISA
closed Sunday dinner – **M** (dinner only and Sunday lunch) (booking essential) 18.50/22.50 **t.** 5.00.

at Brereton SE : 2 m. on A 50 – ✉ Sandbach – ☎ 0477 Holmes Chapel :

Bear's Head, Newcastle Rd, CW11 9RS, ✆ 35251, – TV ☎ P. AE VISA.
M *(closed Sunday dinner)* 9.75 **t.** (lunch)/dinner a la carte 12.95/20.00 **t.** 4.50 – **23 rm** 45.50/70.00 **t.**

HOLMFIRTH West Yorks. 402 404 O 23 – pop. 21 148 – ECD : Tuesday – ✉ Huddersfield – ☎ 0484.
ℹ 49-51 Huddersfield Rd ✆ 684992/687603.
♦London 195 – ♦Leeds 23 – ♦Manchester 25 – ♦Sheffield 22.

Old Bridge, HD7 1DA, ✆ 681212, Fax 687978 – TV ☎ P. AE VISA
closed Christmas Night – **M** 15.00/19.00 **t.** and a la carte 3.75 – **20 rm** 43.00/55.00 **t.** – SB (weekends only) 65.00/80.00 **st.**

at Holme SW : 2½ m. on A 6024 – ✉ Huddersfield – ☎ 0484 Holmfirth :

Holme Castle, HD7 1QG, ✆ 686764, ← – TV P. VISA.
M (by arrangement) 20.00 **t.** 3.40 – **8 rm** 30.00/60.00 **t.**

HOLMROOK Cumbria 402 J 20 – ✉ ☎ 094 04.
♦London 314 – Kendal 52 – Workington 24.

Carleton Green without rest., Saltcoats Rd, CA19 1YX, S : 1 m. by A 595 ✆ 608, – P
closed Christmas-New Year – **7 rm** 15.00/26.00 **s.**

HOLT Norfolk 404 X 25 – pop. 2 502 – ECD : Thursday – ☎ 0263.
♦London 124 – King's Lynn 34 – ♦Norwich 22.

Feathers (B.C.B.), 6 Market Pl., NR25 6BW, ✆ 712318 – TV ☎ P
13 rm.

Yetmans, 37 Norwich Rd, NR25 6SA, ✆ 713320
closed Monday, Tuesday and 3 weeks January – **M** 17.50/25.00 **t.** and a la carte.

ATS Hempstead Rd Ind Est. ✆ 712015

HOLYHEAD (CAERGYBI) Gwynedd 402 403 G 24 – pop. 12 569 – ECD : Tuesday – ☎ 0407.
Envir. : South Stack (cliffs★) W : 3½ m. – Rhosneigr (site★) SE : 13 m.
to Ireland (Dun Laoghaire) (Sealink) 2 daily; (3 h 30 mn) – to Ireland (Dublin) (B & I Line) 2-4 daily (3 h 30 mn-4 h.).
ℹ Marine Sq., Salt Island Approach ✆ 2622.
♦London 269 – Birkenhead 94 – ♦Cardiff 215 – Chester 88 – Shrewsbury 105 – ♦Swansea 190.

HOLY ISLAND Northumb. 401 402 O 16 – pop. 190 – ☎ 0289 Berwick-upon-Tweed.
See : Castle (16C) ←★★ *AC* – Priory★ (ruins 12C) *AC.*
♦London 342 – Berwick-upon-Tweed 13 – ♦Newcastle-upon-Tyne 59.

Hotels see : Berwick-upon-Tweed NW : 13 m.

HOLYWELL (TREFFYNNON) Clwyd 402 403 K 24 – pop. 11 101 – ECD : Wednesday – ☎ 0352.
Holywell, Brynford ✆ 710040.
♦London 217 – Chester 19 – ♦Liverpool 34.

Stamford Gate, Halkyn Rd, CH8 7SJ, ✆ 712942, Fax 713309 – TV P. VISA.
M 7.50/14.00 **t.** and a la carte 3.50 – **12 rm** 32.00/46.00 **st.**

Travelodge without rest., Halkyn, CH8 8RF, SE : 3½ m. on A 55 (westbound carriageway) ✆ 780952, Reservations (Toll free) 0800 850950 – TV P. AE VISA.
31 rm 24.00/29.50 **t.**

FORD Holway ✆ 711838 ROVER Halkyn Rd ✆ 711711

HONITON Devon 403 K 31 The West Country G. – pop. 6 490 – ECD : Thursday – ☎ 0404.

See : All Hallows Museum★ *AC.*

Envir. : Farway Countryside Park (<★) *AC*, S : 3 m.

Angel Hotel car park, High St. ☎ 43716 (summer only).

◆London 186 – Exeter 17 – ◆Southampton 93 – Taunton 18.

at Wilmington E : 3 m. on A 35 – ✉ Honiton – ☎ 040 483 Wilmington :

Home Farm, EX14 9JR, ☎ 278, « Part 16C thatched farm », – TV ☎ P
14 rm.

at Weston W : 2 m. by A 30 – ✉ ☎ 0404 Honiton :

Deer Park, EX14 0PG, ☎ 41266, Fax 46598, <, heated, park, squash – TV ☎ P. AE VISA.
M 14.00/22.50 **st.** and a la carte 4.50 – **28 rm** 35.00/120.00 **st.** – SB (weekends only) 100.00/140.00 **st.**

HOOK Hants. 404 R 30 – pop. 2 562 – ECD : Thursday – ☎ 0256.

◆London 47 – Reading 13 – ◆Southampton 35.

Basingstoke Country, Nately Scures, RG27 9JS, W : 1 m. on A 30 ☎ 764161, Telex 859981, Fax 768341, – rm rest TV ☎ P – 125. AE VISA
M *(closed Saturday lunch and Sunday dinner)* 17.50/19.50 **st.** and a la carte 3.50 – 7.50 – **69 rm** 82.00/110.00 **st.**, **1 suite** 120.00/150.00 **st.** – SB (weekends only) 100.00/150.00 **st.**

Raven (Lansbury), Station Rd, RG27 9HS, ☎ 722541, Telex 858901, Fax 768677, – rm TV ☎ P – 100. AE VISA.
M a la carte 11.95/18.45 **t.** – **38 rm** 67.00/79.00 **t.** – SB (weekends only) 64.00 **st.**

White Hart, London Rd, RG27 9DZ, on A 30 ☎ 762462, Fax 768351, – TV ☎ P. AE VISA
M *(closed Sunday)* – **20 rm** 55.50/65.50 **st.**

Oaklea, London Rd, RG27 9LA, on A 30 ☎ 762541, – P
M 10.00 **st.** 1.80 – **10 rm** 22.50/47.00 **st.**

HOPE COVE Devon 403 I 33 – see Salcombe.

HOPTON WAFERS Shropshire 403 404 M 26 – pop. 948 – ✉ Kidderminster – ☎ 0299 Cleobury Mortimer.

◆London 150 – ◆Birmingham 32 – Shrewsbury 38.

Crown Inn, DY14 0NB, on A 4117 ☎ 270372, Fax 271127 – TV ☎ P. VISA
M *(closed Sunday dinner and Monday)* 12.95 **st.** 2.50 – 4.50 – **8 rm** 29.50/39.50 **st.** – SB (except Christmas and New Year) 65.00 **st.**

HOPWOOD West Midlands – ✉ – ☎ 021 Birmingham

Westmead (Lansbury), Redditch Rd, B48 7AL, on A 441 ☎ 445 1202, Telex 335956, Fax 445 6163 – rm rest TV ☎ P – 150. AE VISA
M 8.95/14.00 **t.** and a la carte – **58 rm** 74.00/87.00 **t.**

HORLEY Surrey 404 T 30 – pop. 17 700 – ECD : Wednesday – ☎ 029 34 (4 and 5 fig.) or 0293 (6 fig.).

◆London 27 – ◆Brighton 26 – Royal Tunbridge Wells 22.

Plan : see Gatwick

Chequers Thistle (Mt. Charlotte Thistle), Brighton Rd, RH6 8PH, ☎ 786992, Telex 877550, Fax 820625, – rm TV ☎ P – 70. AE VISA.
M 10.00/15.00 **st.** and a la carte – 7.75 – **78 rm** 72.00/95.00 **st.**

FORD Reigate Rd, Hookwood ☎ 820110 | ROVER Massetts Rd ☎ 785176

HORNDON ON THE HILL Essex 404 V 29 – ☎ 0375 Stanford-le-Hope.

◆London 24 – Chelmsford 21 – Gravesend 8 – Southend-On-Sea 14.

Hill House with rm, High Rd, SS17 8LD, ☎ 642463, Fax 361611 – TV ☎ P. VISA.
closed 25 to 31 December – **M** *(closed Sunday and Monday)* 13.95/17.95 **t.** and a la carte 4.20 – 5.25 – **10 rm** 35.00/45.00 **t.**

HORNING Norfolk 404 Y 25 – pop. 1 033 – ECD : Wednesday – ✉ Norwich – ☎ 0692.

◆London 122 – Great Yarmouth 17 – ◆Norwich 11.

Petersfield House, Lower St., NR12 8PF, ☎ 630741, Fax 630745, – TV ☎ P. AE VISA
M 12.00/14.00 **t.** and a la carte 4.50 – **18 rm** 52.00/66.00 **t.** – SB 86.00/96.00 **st.**

Swan (B.C.B.), Lower St., NR12 8AH, ☎ 630316, <, « Riverside setting » – TV ☎ P. AE VISA.
M 15.00 **st.** – **11 rm** 42.50/49.50 **st.**

HORNS CROSS Devon 403 H 31 – ECD : Wednesday – ✉ Bideford – ☎ 023 75.
◆London 237 – Barnstaple 15 – Exeter 48.

Foxdown Manor, Foxdown, EX39 5PJ, S : 1 m. ☎ 325, ≤, « Country house atmosphere », heated, park, – TV ☎ P
7 rm, **1 suite.**

at Parkham S : 2 m. – ✉ Bideford – ☎ 023 75 Horns Cross :

Penhaven Country, EX39 5PL, ☎ 711, park – rest TV ☎ P. VISA
M 7.50/12.50 **t.** and a la carte 4.10 – **13 rm** 48.50/107.00 **t.**

HORSFORTH West Yorks. 402 P 22 – see Leeds.

HORSHAM West Sussex 404 T 30 – pop. 38 356 – ECD : Monday and Thursday – ☎ 0403.
Mannings Heath ☎ 210168.
Horsham Museum, The Causeway ☎ 211661.
◆London 39 – ◆Brighton 23 – Guildford 20 – Lewes 25 – Worthing 20.

Ye Olde King's Head, 35 Carfax Rd, RH12 1EG, ☎ 53126 – rest TV ☎ P. VISA
M *(closed Sunday dinner)* 9.35/13.50 **t.** and a la carte 4.20 – **42 rm** 49.50/72.00 **t.** – SB (weekends only)64.00 **st.**

at Lower Beeding SE : 3 ½ m. on A 281 – ✉ Horsham – ☎ 040 376 (3 fig.) or 0403 (6 fig.) Lower Beeding :

South Lodge, Brighton Rd, RH13 6PS, on A 281 ☎ 891711, Telex 877765, Fax 891766, ≤, park, – TV ☎ P – 80. VISA.
M 17.50/30.00 **t.** and a la carte 5.75 – 9.00 – **36 rm** 70.00/125.00 **t.**, **3 suites** 150.00/210.00 **t.** – SB (weekends only) 160.00/180.00 **st.**

Cisswood House, Sandygate Lane, RH13 6NF, ☎ 891216, Fax 891621, – TV ☎ P – 200. VISA.
closed 1 week August and 2 weeks Christmas – **M** 25.00 **t.** and a la carte 4.00 – 5.50 – **32 rm** 62.00/95.00 **st.**, **2 suites** 135.00 **st.**

CITROEN Guildford Rd ☎ 61393
FIAT Brighton Rd ☎ 65637
FORD The Bishopric ☎ 54331
RENAULT 108 Crawley Rd ☎ 61146
ROVER Springfield Rd ☎ 54311
TOYOTA Slinfold ☎ 790766
VAUXHALL-OPEL Broadbridge Heath ☎ 56464
VOLVO Guildford Rd ☎ 56381

ATS Rear of Brighton Rd Filling Station. ☎ 67491/51736

HORSHAM ST. FAITH Norfolk 404 X 25 – see Norwich.

HORTON Dorset 403 404 O 31 – see Wimborne Minster.

HORTON Northants. 404 R 27 – ✉ ☎ 0604 Northampton.
◆London 66 – Bedford 18 – Northampton 6.

French Partridge, Newport Pagnell Rd (B 526), NN7 2AP, ☎ 870033 – P
closed Sunday, Monday, 2 weeks Easter, 3 weeks mid July-August and 2 weeks Christmas – **M** (dinner only) (booking essential) 20.00 **st.** 4.50.

HORTON-CUM-STUDLEY Oxon. 403 404 Q 28 – ECD : Wednesday – ✉ Oxford – ☎ 086 735 Stanton St. John.
◆London 57 – Aylesbury 23 – ◆Oxford 7.

Studley Priory, OX9 1AZ, ☎ 203, Fax 613, ≤, « Converted priory in park », – TV ☎ P – 25. VISA.
M 22.00/30.00 **st.** 7.50 – **18 rm** 75.00/130.00 **st.**, **1 suite** 150.00/175.00 **st.** – SB (except Christmas and New Year) 105.00/140.00 **st.**

HOUGHTON CONQUEST Beds. 404 S 27 – see Bedford.

HOVE East Sussex 404 T 31 – see Brighton and Hove.

HOVINGHAM North Yorks. 402 R 21 – pop. 310 – ECD : Thursday – ✉ York – ☎ 0653.
◆London 235 – ◆Middlesbrough 36 – York 25.

Worsley Arms, YO6 4LA, ☎ 628234, Fax 628130, – TV ☎ P. VISA
M 9.50/18.50 **t.** and a la carte – **14 rm** 52.00/93.00 **t.** – SB (November-April) (except Bank Holidays) 72.00/92.00 **t.**

***En saison,** surtout dans les stations fréquentées, il est prudent de retenir à l'avance.*
Cependant, si vous ne pouvez pas occuper la chambre que vous avez retenue, prévenez immédiatement l'hôtelier.
Si vous écrivez à un hôtel à l'étranger, joignez à votre lettre un coupon-réponse international (disponible dans les bureaux de poste).

HOWDEN Humberside 402 R 22 – pop. 3 227 – ECD : Thursday – ☎ 0430.

See : St. Peter's Church★ (12C-14C).

Boothferry, Spaldington Lane ☎ 430364, N : 2½ m. by B 1228.

◆London 196 – ◆Kingston-upon-Hull 23 – ◆Leeds 37 – York 22.

- Bowmans, Bridgegate, DN14 7JG, ☎ 430805 – TV ☎ P.
  13 rm.

HOWEY Powys – see Llandrindod Wells.

HOWTOWN Cumbria – see Ullswater.

HUDDERSFIELD West Yorks. 402 404 O 23 – pop. 147 825 – ECD : Wednesday – ☎ 0484.

18 Thick Hollins Hall, Meltham ☎ 850227, SW : 5 m. – 18 Bradley Park, off Bradley Rd ☎ 539988, N : 3 m. – 18 Woodsome Hall, Fenay Bridge ☎ 602971, SE : 6 m. – 18 Outlane, Slack Lane ☎ 0422 (Ryburn) 374762, W : 4 m. – 18 Meltham, Thick Hollins Hall ☎ 850227, W : 5 m. – 18 Fixby Hall. Lightbridge Rd ☎ 420110 – 9 Hemyslow, Marsden ☎ 844253.

3-5 Albion St. ☎ 430808.

◆London 191 – Bradford 11 – ◆Leeds 15 – ◆Manchester 25 – ◆Sheffield 26.

- Pennine Hilton, Ainley Top, HD3 3RH, NW : 2½ m. at junction A 629 and A 640 ☎ 0422 (Elland) 375431, Telex 517346, Fax 0422 (Elland) 310067, – rm rest TV ☎ P –
  119 rm.
- George, St. George's Sq., HD1 1JA, ☎ 515444, Fax 435056 – rm TV ☎ P – 170
  60 rm, 1 suite.
- **Briar Court,** Halifax Rd, Birchencliffe, HD3 3NT, NW : 2 m. on A 629 ☎ 519902, Telex 518260, Fax 431812 – TV ☎ P – 90. AE VISA.
  M 12.50 **t.** (dinner) and a la carte – **48 rm** 60.00/90.00 **t.**
- Cote Royd, 7 Halifax Rd, HD3 3AN, ☎ 547588, – TV ☎ P
  21 rm.
- **Huddersfield,** 37-47 Kirkgate, HD1 1QT, ☎ 512111, Telex 51575, Fax 435262 – TV ☎ P. AE VISA
  M *(closed Sunday dinner)* 6.50/10.50 **st.** and a la carte 4.40 – **40 rm** 30.00/80.00 **st.**
- **Elm Crest** without rest., 2 Queens Rd, HD2 2AG, ☎ 530990 – P. VISA.
  8 rm 22.00/60.00 **st.**
- XX **Pisces,** 84 Fitzwilliam St., HD1 5BD, ☎ 516773, Seafood – VISA
  closed Sunday, 25 December, 1 January and Bank Holiday Mondays – **M** 13.50 **t.** (dinner) and a la carte 14.25/33.15 **t.**

at Golcar W : 3½ m. by A 62 on B 6111 – ✉ ☎ 0484 Huddersfield :

- XX **Weaver's Shed,** Knowl Rd, HD7 4AN, via Scar Lane ☎ 654284, « Converted 18C woollen mill » – P. AE VISA
  closed Saturday lunch, Sunday, Monday, first 2 weeks January and last 2 weeks July – **M** 8.95 **t.** and a la carte 14.85/19.20 **t.**

at Outlane NW : 4 m. on A 640 – ✉ Huddersfield – ☎ 0422 Elland :

- **Old Golf House** (Lansbury), New Hey Rd, HD3 3YP, ☎ 379311, Telex 51324, Fax 372694 – rm TV ☎ P – 70. AE VISA.
  M 9.50/14.50 **t.** and a la carte 4.50 – **50 rm** 75.00/88.00 **t.** – SB (weekends only) 62.00/66.00 **st.**

BMW Wakefield Rd ☎ 515515
DAIMLER-JAGUAR, LAND-ROVER, RANGE-ROVER Northgate ☎ 535251
ROVER Southgate ☎ 535341
TOYOTA Fartown ☎ 514514
VAUXHALL-OPEL 386 Leeds Rd ☎ 518700
VOLVO Northgate ☎ 531362
VW-AUDI Bradford Rd ☎ 542001

ATS Leeds Rd ☎ 534441

HULL Humberside 402 S 22 – see Kingston-upon-Hull.

HUNGERFORD Berks. 403 404 P 29 – pop. 4 488 – ECD : Thursday – ☎ 0488.

Envir. : Littlecote House★★ *AC*, NW : 3½ m.

18 West Berkshire, Chaddleworth ☎ 048 82 (Chaddleworth) 574, N : 2½ m.

◆London 74 – ◆Bristol 57 – ◆Oxford 28 – Reading 26 – ◆Southampton 46.

- **Bear,** 17 Charnham St., RG17 0EL, on A 4 ☎ 682512, Fax 684357, – TV ☎ P – 100. AE VISA
  M 13.95/17.95 **t.** and a la carte – 6.50 – **41 rm** 60.00/90.00 **t.** – SB (weekends only) 84.00 **st.**
- **Marshgate Cottage,** Marsh Lane, RG17 0QX, W : ¾ m. by Church St. ☎ 682307, Fax 685475 – TV ☎ P. VISA.
  closed 24 December-21 January – **M** (by arrangement) 17.00 **st.** – **9 rm** 23.50/45.50 **st.**

BMW, SUZUKI Bath Rd ☎ 82772

HUNMANBY North Yorks. 402 T 21 – pop. 2 623 – ✉ Filey – ☎ 0723 Scarborough.

♦London 198 – ♦Kingston-upon-Hull 40 – Scarborough 9 – York 41.

- **Wrangham House,** 10 Stonegate, YO14 0NS, ☎ 891333, – rm TV P. VISA.
  M (dinner only) 11.50 **t.** and a la carte – **13 rm** (dinner included) 30.00/60.00 **t.** – SB 77.00/82.00 **st.**

HUNSTANTON Norfolk 402 404 V 25 – pop. 3 990 – ECD : Thursday – ☎ 0485.

Envir. : Holkham Hall★★ (18C) *AC*, W : 14 m.

Hunstanton ☎ 2811, N : 1½ m. by A 149.

The Green ☎ 2610.

♦London 120 – ♦Cambridge 60 – ♦Norwich 45.

- **Le Strange Arms,** Golf Course Rd, PE36 6JJ, N : 1 m. by A 149 ☎ 534411, Fax 534724, – TV ☎ P – 100. VISA
  M 16.95 **st.** and a la carte – **40 rm** 48.00/80.00 **st.** – SB (except Christmas and New Year) 85.00/95.00 **st.**
- **Claremont,** 35 Greevegate, PE36 6AF, ☎ 533171 – .
  M 10.50 **st.** 2.50 – **7 rm** 16.00/43.00 **st.**
- **Deepdene,** 29 Avenue Rd, PE36 5BW, ☎ 2460, Fax 2460, – TV P.
  closed October – **M** 13.50 **st.** – **9 rm** 22.50/45.00 **st.**
- **Pinewood,** 26 Northgate, PE36 6AP, ☎ 533068 – TV P. VISA
  closed Christmas – **M** (by arrangement) 8.95 **t.** 4.20 – **8 rm** 25.00/36.00 **t.** – SB (October-July) 40.00/50.00 **st.**

at Heacham S : 3 m. by A 149 – ✉ King's Lynn – ☎ 0485 Heacham :

- **Holly Lodge,** Lynn Rd, PE31 7HY, ☎ 70790, « Country house atmosphere », – P. VISA.
  closed January and February – **M** *(closed Sunday)* (dinner only) a la carte 17.50/21.00 **t.** 3.50 – **6 rm** 50.00/80.00 **st.**

CITROEN, ISUZU Southend Rd ☎ 2508 — ROVER 12 Lynn Rd ☎ 33435

HUNSTRETE Avon 403 404 M 29 – see Bath.

HUNTINGDON Cambs. 404 T 26 – pop. 14 395 – ECD : Wednesday – ☎ 0480.

See : Cromwell Museum – All Saint's Church (interior★).

Envir. : Hinchingbrooke House★ (Tudor mansion-school) W : 1 m. – Ramsey (Abbey Gatehouse★ 15C) NE : 11½ m.

St Ives ☎ 64459, E : 5 m.

Huntingdon Library, Princes St. ☎ 425831.

♦London 69 – Bedford 21 – ♦Cambridge 16.

- **Old Bridge,** 1 High St., PE18 6TQ, ☎ 52681, Telex 32706, Fax 411017 – TV ☎ P – 45. VISA
  M 20.00/22.00 **st.** and a la carte – **26 rm** 67.50/110.00 **st.**
- **George** (T.H.F.), George St., PE18 6AB, ☎ 432444, Fax 453130 – rm TV ☎ P – 150. VISA
  M 14.50/17.50 **st.** and a la carte 4.50 – 7.50 – **24 rm** 69.00/90.00 **st.** – SB (weekends only) 84.00/94.00 **st.**

BMW Stutley Rd ☎ 459551
ROVER St. Peters Rd ☎ 456441
VAUXHALL-OPEL Brookside ☎ 52694
ATS Nursery Rd ☎ 451031/451515

HURLEY-ON-THAMES Berks. 404 R 29 – ECD : Wednesday – ✉ Maidenhead – ☎ 0628 Littlewick Green.

♦London 38 – ♦Oxford 26 – Reading 12.

- **Ye Olde Bell,** High St., SL6 5LX, ☎ 825881, Fax 825939, « Part 12C inn », – TV ☎ P – 100. VISA
  M 14.50/17.50 **st.** and a la carte – 6.50 – **32 rm** 70.00/90.00 **st.**, **3 suites** 115.00 **t.** – SB (weekends only) 84.00/121.00 **st.**

HURSTBOURNE TARRANT Hants. 403 404 P 30 – pop. 709 – ✉ Andover – ☎ 0264.

♦London 77 – ♦Bristol 77 – ♦Oxford 38 – ♦Southampton 33.

- **Esseborne Manor**, SP11 0ER, NE : 1½ m. on A 343 ☎ 76444, Fax 76473, – TV ☎ P. VISA.
  M 15.50/29.25 **t.** 5.30 – **12 rm** 75.00/115.00 **t.**

at Faccombe N : 3½ m. by A 343 – ✉ Andover – ☎ 026 487 Linkenholt :

- **Jack Russel**, SP11 0DS, ☎ 315 – TV P. VISA.
  M 12.75 **t.** 4.00 – **3 rm** 25.00/45.00 **st.**

Per usare bene le piante di città, vedere i segni convenzionali.

HURST GREEN Lancs. 402 M 22 – ✉ Whalley – ☎ 025 486 Stonyhurst.

♦London 236 – Blackburn 12 – Burnley 13 – Preston 12.

Shireburn Arms, Whalley Rd, BB6 9QJ, ℘ 518, ⇐ – TV ☎ P. VISA
closed 1 to 3 January – **M** a la carte 12.45/21.95 **st.** 4.00 – **15 rm** 41.50/69.50 **t.** – SB 74.00/116.00 **st.**

HUSBANDS BOSWORTH Leics. 403 404 Q 26 – pop. 889 – ✉ Lutterworth – ☎ 0858 Market Harborough.

♦London 88 – ♦Birmingham 40 – ♦Leicester 14 – Northampton 17.

XX Fernie Lodge with rm, Berridges Lane, LE17 6LE, ℘ 880551, Fax 88014 – rest TV ☎ P
7 rm.

HUTTON-LE-HOLE North Yorks. 402 R 21 – see Lastingham.

HUXHAM Devon – see Exeter.

HUYTON Merseyside 402 403 L 23 – see Liverpool.

HWLFFORDD = Haverfordwest.

HYTHE Kent 404 X 30 – pop. 13 118 – ECD : Wednesday – ☎ 0303.

See : St. Leonard's Church (⩽★ from the churchyard) – Canal.

Hythe Imperial, Prince's Parade ℘ 67441.

Prospect Rd Car Park ℘ 267799 (summer only).

♦London 68 – Folkestone 6 – Hastings 33 – Maidstone 31.

Hythe Imperial (Best Western), Princes Par., CT21 6AE, ℘ 267441, Telex 965082, Fax 264610, ⩽, squash – TV ☎ P – 220. AE VISA
M 16.50/20.50 **st.** and a la carte 4.00 – **94 rm** 70.00/130.00 **st.**, **6 suites** 160.00 **st.** – SB (weekends only) (except Bank Holidays) 100.00/160.00 **st.**

Stade Court (Best Western), West Par., CT21 6DT, ℘ 68263, Telex 965082, Fax 264610, ⩽ – TV ☎ P – 35
39 rm.

FORD Stade St. ℘ 67726

SAAB 215 Seabrook Rd ℘ 38467

North is at the top on all town plans.

IBSTONE Bucks – ✉ High Wycombe – ☎ 049 163 Turrill Heath.

♦London 39 – ♦Oxford 20 – Reading 19.

Fox of Ibstone Country, HP14 3GG, ℘ 722, Fax 8873 – TV ☎ P. AE VISA
M *(closed Sunday dinner and Monday lunch)* 18.00/22.00 **t.** and a la carte 3.50 – **9 rm** 44.00/72.00 **st.** – SB (weekends only) 90.00 **st.**

IFFLEY Oxon – see Oxford.

IDE Devon 403 J 31 – see Exeter.

IFIELD West Sussex – see Crawley.

ILFRACOMBE Devon 403 H 30 **The West Country G.** – pop. 9 966 – ECD : Thursday – ☎ 0271.

See : Capstone Hill★ (⩽★) – Hillsborough (⩽★★) – St. Nicholas' Chapel *AC* (⩽★).

Hele Bay ℘ 62176, E : 1 m.

Access to Lundy Island from Hartland Point by helicopter ℘ 062 882 (Littlewick Green) 3431.

to Lundy 2-3 weekly (summer only) (Lundy Co.).

The Promenade ℘ 63001.

♦London 223 – Exeter 54 – Taunton 61.

St. Helier, Hillsborough Rd, EX34 9QQ, ℘ 864906 – TV P. VISA
May-September – **M** (dinner only) 7.00 **st.** 3.00 – **23 rm** 20.00/40.00 **st.**

PEUGEOT-TALBOT West Down ℘ 63104

RENAULT Northfield Rd ℘ 62075

ILKLEY West Yorks. 402 O 22 – pop. 13 060 – ECD : Wednesday – ☎ 0943.

Ben Rhydding, High Wood ℘ 608759 – Myddleton ℘ 607277.

Station Rd ℘ 602319.

♦London 210 – Bradford 13 – Harrogate 17 – ♦Leeds 16 – Preston 46.

Rombalds, 11 West View, Wells Rd, LS29 9JG, ℘ 603201, Telex 51593, Fax 816586 – TV ☎ P. AE VISA
closed 27 to 30 December – **M** (dinner only) a la carte 17.75/26.50 **st.** 3.60 – **11 rm** 58.00/95.00 **t.**, **4 suites** 110.00/135.00 **st.** – SB (except September, October and Bank Holidays) 120.00/160.00 **st.**

Grove, 66 The Grove, LS29 9PA, ✆ 600298 – TV P. VISA
closed 23 December-3 January – **M** (bar lunch)/dinner 12.50 **st.** and a la carte 4.00 – **6 rm** 33.00/48.00 **st.**

Cow and Calf, Moor Top, LS29 8BT, SE : 1¼ m. ✆ 607335, ←, – TV ☎ P. AE VISA
closed Christmas – **M** 7.50/14.50 **t.** and a la carte 4.75 – **17 rm** 55.00/75.00 **t.** – SB 80.00/95.00 **st.**

Moorview, 104 Skipton Rd, LS29 9HE, W : ¼ m. on A 65 ✆ 600156, ←, – TV P.
closed 2 weeks Christmas-New Year – **M** (by arrangement) 10.00 **st.** **14 rm** 26.00/46.00 **st.**

XXX ✿ **Box Tree,** 35-37 Church St., LS29 9DR, ✆ 608484, Fax 816793, « Ornate decor » – AE VISA
closed Sunday dinner, Monday, 25-26 December and 1 January – **M** (booking essential) (dinner only and Sunday lunch)/dinner 18.50/30.00 **st.** and a la carte approx. 30.00 **st.** 5.95.
Spec. Dodine of duck, shallot and thyme marmalade, Fillet of sea bass with scallops and champagne, Timbale of strawberries.

FORD Leeds Rd ✆ 603261
PEUGEOT-TALBOT Bridge Lane ✆ 608966
VAUXHALL Skipton Rd ✆ 607606
VAUXHALL-OPEL Bradford Rd, Menston ✆ 0943 (Menston) 76122

ILLOGAN Cornwall 403 E 33 – pop. 11 782 – ✉ ☎ 0209 Redruth.
◆London 305 – Falmouth 14 – Penzance 17 – Truro 11.

Aviary Court ⛰, Mary's Well, TR16 4QZ, NW : ¾ m. by Alexandra Rd ✆ 842256, – TV ☎ P. AE
M *(closed Sunday dinner to non-residents)* (bar lunch Monday to Saturday residents only)/dinner 9.50 **t.** and a la carte 3.75 – **6 rm** 36.50/51.00 **t.**

Europe

Wenn der Name eines Hotels dünn gedruckt ist,
hat uns der Hotelier Preise
und Öffnungszeiten nicht angegeben.

IMPINGTON Cambs. – see Cambridge.

INGATESTONE Essex 404 V 28 – pop. 6 150 – ECD : Wednesday – ☎ 0277.
◆London 27 – Chelmsford 6.

Ivy Hill, Ivy Barn Lane, Margaretting, CM4 0EW, NE : 2 ¼ m. by A 12 ✆ 353040, Fax 355038, heated, , – TV ☎ P. AE VISA
M (bar lunch)/dinner 12.50 **t.** 3.50 – 6.95 – **18 rm** 64.00/94.00 **t.** – SB (weekends only) 76.00 **st.**

INGHAM Lincs. 404 S 23 – ✉ Lincoln – ☎ 0522.

XX **Moulin Maison,** The Mill House, Clifftop, LN1 2YQ, ✆ 730130, – P. VISA
closed Sunday to Tuesday – **M** (dinner only) 16.50/19.50 **t.**

INGLEBY GREENHOW North Yorks. 402 Q 20 – see Great Broughton.

INGLETON North Yorks. 402 M 21 – pop. 1 769 – ✉ Carnforth – ☎ 052 42.
Envir. : Ribblehead Viaduct★ NE : 6 m.
Community Centre car park, ✆ 41049 (summer only).
◆London 266 – Kendal 21 – Lancaster 18 – ◆Leeds 53.

Moorgarth Hall Country House, New Road, LA6 3HL, SE : ¼ m. on A 65 ✆ 41946, ←, – rm TV P
8 rm.

Pines Country House, New Rd, LA6 3HN, NW : ¼ m. on A 65 ✆ 41252, – TV P
M 10.50 **st.** 3.30 – **4 rm** 22.00/36.00 **st.**

INSTOW Devon 403 H 30 – see Bideford.

IPSWICH Suffolk 404 X 27 – pop. 129 661 – ECD : Monday and Wednesday – ☎ 0473.
See : St. Margaret's Church (the roof★) X **A** – Christchurch Mansion (Wolsey Art Gallery★) X **B** – Pykenham House★ (16C) X **E**.
Envir. : Stour Valley★ (Flatford Mill★) (SW : from Ipswich by A 137 Z).
18 Rushmere Heath ✆ 727109, E : 2 m. Y – 18, 9 Purdis Heath ✆ 728941, E : 3 m. Z – 9 Bucklesham Rd ✆ 726821.
Ipswich Airport ✆ 720111.
Town Hall, Princes St. ✆ 258070.
◆London 76 – ◆Norwich 43.

IPSWICH

Butter Market . . . . X 9
Carr Street . . . . X 10
Corn Hill . . . . X 16
Tavern Street X
Westgate Street . . . . X 52

Argyle Street . . . . X 2
Back Hamlet . . . . Z 3
Birkfield Drive . . . . Z 5
Bond Street . . . . X 6
Bridgwater Road . . . . Z 7
Chevallier Street . . . . Y 13
College Street . . . . X 15
Dogs Head Street . . . . . . X 18
Ellenbrook Road . . . . Z 19
Falcon Street . . . . X 21
Fore Hamlet . . . . Z 22
Franciscan Way . . . . X 24
Friars Street . . . . X 25
Grey Friars Road . . . . X 26
Grove Lane . . . . YZ 28
Handford Road . . . . . . X, Y 30
Lloyds Avenue . . . . X 31
Lower Orwell Street . . . . X 32
Northgate Street . . . . X 33
Orwell Place . . . . X 34
Queen Street . . . . X 37
St. Helen's Street . . . . X, Y 39
St. Margarets Street . . . . X 40
St. Nicholas Street . . . . . X 41
St. Peter's Street . . . . X 42
Salthouse Street . . . . X 43
Scrivener Drive . . . . Z 45
Silent Street . . . . X 46
Upper Orwell Street . . . . X 49
Waterworks Street . . . . . X 51
Yarmouth Road . . . . Y 54

Europe

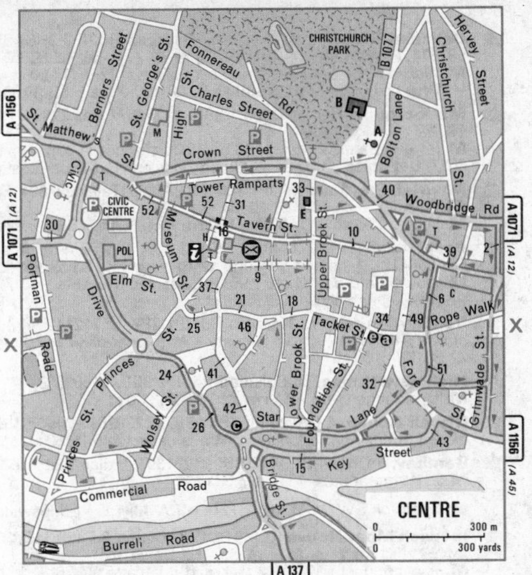

If the name of the hotel
is not in bold type,
on arrival ask the hotelier his prices.

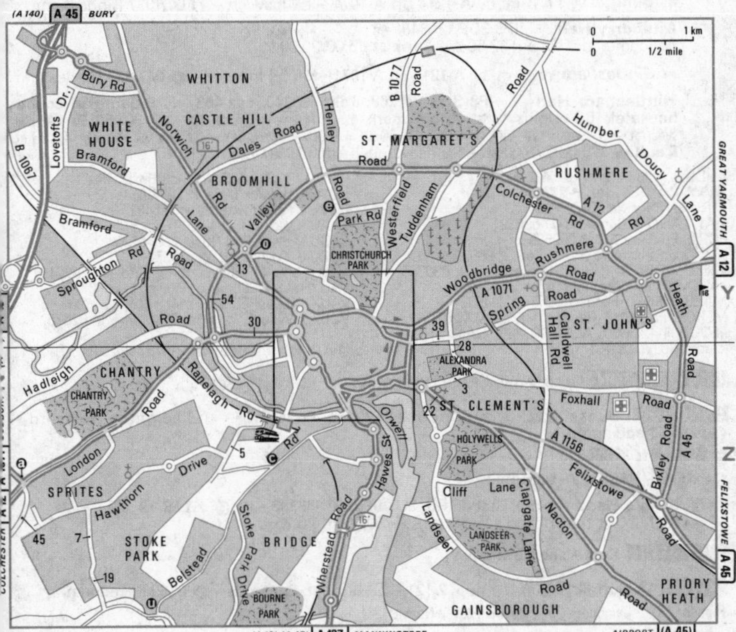

Belstead Brook (Best Western), Belstead Rd, IP2 9HB, SW : 2 ½ m. ℘ 684241, Telex 987674, Fax 681249, ⋘, park – TV ☎ P – 50. AE VISA. Z u
M *(closed lunch Saturday and Bank Holidays)* 12.95/14.50 **st.** and a la carte 4.00 – 6.95 – **27 rm** 65.00/85.00 **st.**, **6 suites** 90.00/110.00 **st.** – SB (weekends only) 72.00/110.00 **st.**

Marlborough, Henley Rd, IP1 3SP, ℘ 257677, Fax 226927, ⋘ – TV ☎ P – 40. AE VISA Y e
M *(closed Saturday lunch)* 13.50/19.00 **t.** and a la carte 5.50 – 7.00 – **21 rm** 63.00/85.00 **t.**, **1 suite** 95.00 **t.** – SB (weekends only) (except Christmas) 85.00 **st.**

Novotel, Greyfriars Rd, IP1 1UP, ℘ 232400, Telex 987684, Fax 232414 – rm rest TV ☎ P – 200. AE VISA X c
M 11.50/20.00 **st.** – 6.50 – **100 rm** –/56.00 **st.** – SB (weekends only) 72.00 **st.**

Post House (T.H.F.), London Rd, IP2 0UA, SW : 2¼ m. on A 12 ℘ 690313, Telex 987150, Fax 680412, heated – TV ☎ P – 110. AE VISA Z a
M *(closed Saturday lunch)* 9.95/15.00 **st.** and a la carte – 7.50 – **118 rm** 65.00/90.00 **st.** – SB (weekends only) 70.00/85.00 **st.**

Bentley Tower, 172 Norwich Rd, IP1 2PY, ℘ 212142 – TV P. VISA. Y o
closed 24 December to 4 January – **M** (dinner only) 14.50 **t.** and a la carte 4.00 – **10 rm** 38.00/48.00 **st.**

Highview House, 56 Belstead Rd, IP2 8BE, ℘ 688659, ⋘ – TV ☎ P. AE VISA. Z c
M (by arrangement) – **11 rm** 28.00/43.00 **st.**

XX **Orwell House,** 4 Orwell Pl., IP4 1BB, ℘ 230254 – . AE VISA X e
closed Sunday and Monday – **M** a la carte 17.45/28.60 **st.**

XX **Bombay,** 6 Orwell Pl., IP4 1BB, ℘ 251397, Indian rest. – AE VISA X a
M a la carte approx. 12.95 **t.** 3.00.

at Copdock SW : 4 m. by A 1214 off A 1071 Z – ✉ Ipswich – 047 386 Copdock :

Ipswich Moat House (Q.M.H.), Old London Rd, IP8 3JD, ℘ 444, Telex 987207, Fax 801, – TV ☎ P – 350. AE VISA
M (carving lunch) 12.00/12.75 **t.** and a la carte 4.25 – 7.50 – **74 rm** 69.00/95.00 **t.** – SB (weekends only) 78.00 **st.**

at Burstall W : 4½ m. by A 1214 off A 1071 – ✉ Ipswich – 047 387 Hintlesham

Mulberry Hall, IP8 3DP, ℘ 348, ⋘, – P.
M (communal dining) 12.50 **s.** – **3 rm** 15.00/30.00 **s.**

at Hintlesham W : 5 m. by A 1214 on A 1071 – Y – ✉ Ipswich – 047 387 Hintlesham :

Hintlesham Hall, IP8 3NS, ℘ 268, Telex 98340, Fax 463, ←, « Georgian country house of 16C origins », 18, ⋘, park, – rest TV ☎ P – 30. AE VISA
M *(closed Saturday lunch)* 18.50/37.50 **st.** 8.00 – 6.50 – **27 rm** 80.00/140.00 **st.**, **6 suites** 175.00/275.00 **st.** – SB (November-April) 165.00/250.00 **st.**

AUDI-VW 88 Princes St. ℘ 214231
BMW West End Rd ℘ 212456
CITROEN Norwich Rd ℘ 253173
FIAT, LANCIA Burrel Rd ℘ 690321
FORD Princess St. ℘ 252525
HONDA Felixstowe Rd, Nalton ℘ 88591
ISUZU, SUBARU Lower Rd, Baylham ℘ 830265
LAND-ROVER Sproughton Rd ℘ 463021
MAZDA, SEAT Fuchsia Lane ℘ 724535
MERCEDES-BENZ Raneleigh Rd ℘ 232232
PEUGEOT-TALBOT, ALFA-ROMEO, DAIHATSU Derby Rd ℘ 720101
RENAULT 301-305 Norwich Rd ℘ 43021
ROVER Barrack Lane ℘ 254202
ROVER Felixstowe Rd ℘ 725431
SAAB Dales Rd ℘ 42547
SKODA West End Rd ℘ 255461
SUZUKI Foxhall Rd ℘ 728377
TOYOTA 301-305 Woodbridge Rd ℘ 719221
VAUXHALL-OPEL Knightsdale Rd ℘ 43044
VAUXHALL-OPEL St. Helens St. ℘ 256363
VOLVO Woodbridge Rd, Rushmere ℘ 626767

ATS White Elm St. ℘ 217157/252815

ISLEY WALTON Leics. – see Castle Donington.

IVINGHOE Bucks. 404 S 28 – pop. 2 517 (inc. Pitstone) – ✉ Leighton Buzzard – 0296 Cheddington.

9 Wellcroft ℘ 668696.

♦London 42 – Aylesbury 9 – Luton 11.

XXX **King's Head** (T.H.F.), Station Rd, LU7 9EB, ℘ 668388 – P. AE VISA
M 17.50 **st.** (lunch) and a la carte 19.25/30.95 **st.** 6.25.

IVY HATCH Kent – see Sevenoaks.

IXWORTH Suffolk 404 W 27 – pop. 2 121 – ✉ Bury St. Edmunds – 0359 Pakenham.

♦London 85 – ♦Cambridge 35 – ♦Ipswich 25 – ♦Norwich 36.

XX **Theobalds,** 68 High St., IP31 2HJ, ℘ 31707 – VISA
closed lunch Saturday and Monday, Sunday dinner and Bank Holidays – **M** 13.50/24.50 **t.** 4.25.

JERVAULX ABBEY North Yorks. – see Masham.

JEVINGTON East Sussex 404 U 31 – see Eastbourne.

KENDAL Cumbria 402 L 21 – pop. 23 710 – ECD : Thursday – ☎ 0539.

See : Abbot Hall Art Gallery (Museum of Lakeland Life and Industry★) AC.

Envir. : Levens Hall★ (Elizabethan) AC and Topiary Garden★ AC, SW : 5½ m.

18 The Heights ✆ 724079 – 9 The Riggs ✆ 0587 (Sedbergh) 20993, E : 9 m.

Town Hall, Highgate ✆ 725758.

London 270 – Bradford 64 – Burnley 63 – Carlisle 49 – Lancaster 22 – Leeds 72 – Middlesbrough 77 – Newcastle-upon-Tyne 104 – Preston 44 – Sunderland 88.

- **Woolpack** (Swallow), Stricklandgate, LA9 4ND, ✆ 723852, Telex 728256, Fax 728608 – rm TV ☎ P – 100. AE VISA
  M (carving lunch)/dinner 15.00 **t.** and a la carte 4.00 – **53 rm** 62.00/85.00 **st.** – SB 78.00/95.00 **st.**
- **Garden House,** Fowling Lane, LA9 6PH, NE : ½ m. by A 685 ✆ 731131, Fax 760064, – TV ☎ P. AE VISA.
  closed 1 to 8 January – **M** *(closed Sunday dinner to non-residents)* (lunch residents only)/dinner 16.95 **st.** 3.70 – **10 rm** 47.00/63.00 **st.** – SB 80.00/90.00 **st.**
- **Lane Head House** , LA9 5RJ, S : 1¾ m. on A 6 ✆ 731283, ≤, – TV ☎ P. VISA.
  closed November – **M** 16.00 **st.** 4.25 – **7 rm** 38.00/65.00 **st.**
- XX **Castle Dairy,** 26 Wildman St., LA9 6EN, ✆ 721170, English rest., « Part 13C and 16C »
  closed Sunday, Monday, Tuesday and August – **M** (booking essential) (dinner only) 16.00 3.00.

at Underbarrow W : 3½ m. on Crosthwaite rd – ✉ Kendal – ☎ 044 88 Crosthwaite :

- XX **Tullythwaite House** , LA8 8BB, S : ¾ m. by Brigsteer rd ✆ 397, – P. VISA
  closed Sunday to Tuesday and February – **M** (dinner only and Sunday lunch)/dinner 22.50 **t.** 3.00.

FIAT 113 Stricklandgate ✆ 20967
FORD Mintsfeet Ind. Est. ✆ 23534
FORD, MERCEDES-BENZ Ings ✆ 0539 (Staveley) 821442
RENAULT Kirkland ✆ 22211
VAUXHALL Sandes Av. ✆ 24420
VOLVO Station Rd ✆ 31313
VW-AUDI, NSU, PORSCHE Longpool ✆ 24331

ATS Mintsfeet Est. ✆ 721559/723802

Die Preise Einzelheiten über die in diesem Führer angegebenen Preise finden Sie in der Einleitung.

KENILWORTH Warw. 403 404 P 26 – pop. 18 782 – ECD : Monday and Thursday – ☎ 0926.

See : Castle★ (12C) AC.

18 Crew Lane ✆ 54296.

Library, 11 Smalley Pl. ✆ 52595/50708.

London 102 – Birmingham 19 – Coventry 5 – Warwick 5.

- **De Montfort** (De Vere), The Square, CV8 1ED, ✆ 55944, Telex 311012, Fax 57830 – TV ☎ P – 250. AE VISA
  M 12.00/14.75 **st.** and a la carte – **94 rm** 80.00/120.00 **st.**, **1 suite** 180.00 **st.**.
- **Castle Laurels,** 22 Castle Rd, CV8 1NG, ✆ 56179 – rest TV ☎ P. .
  closed 24 December-2 January – **M** (by arrangement) 7.95 **t.** 2.85 – **12 rm** 24.00/39.00 **t.**
- **Abbey,** 41 Station Rd, CV8 1JD, ✆ 512707 – TV.
  M 7.50 **st.** – **7 rm** 16.00/34.00 **st.**
- XX **Bosquet,** 97a Warwick Rd, CV8 1HP, ✆ 52463, French rest. – AE VISA
  closed Sunday, Monday and last week July-first 2 weeks August – **M** (lunch by arrangement)/dinner 17.50/26.00 **t.** 4.00.
- XX **Diment,** 121-123 Warwick Rd, CV8 1HP, ✆ 53763 – P. AE VISA
  closed Saturday lunch, Sunday, Monday, 1 week Easter, first 3 weeks August and Bank Holidays – **M** 11.20 **t.** (lunch) and a la carte 14.40/20.40 **t.** 4.25.
- X **Portofino,** 14 Talisman Sq., CV8 1JB, ✆ 57186, Italian rest. – AE VISA
  M *(closed Monday lunch, Sunday and Bank Holidays)* 9.00/19.50 **t.** and a la carte 3.95.

SUZUKI Whitemoor Rd ✆ 513131
TOYOTA, CITROEN Warwick Rd ✆ 54722

KENNFORD Devon 403 J 32 – see Exeter.

KERESLEY West Midlands 403 404 P 26 – see Coventry.

KESWICK Cumbria 402 K 20 – pop. 4 777 – ECD : Wednesday – ☎ 076 87.

See : Derwent Water★★ Y.

Envir. : Castlerigg (stone circle) ★, E : 2 m. Y A.

18 Threlkeld Hall ✆ 83324, E : 4 m. by A 66 Y.

Moot Hall, Market Sq. ✆ 72645.

London 294 – Carlisle 31 – Kendal 30.

Keswick, Station Rd, ←, – ▯ rest TV ☎ P **66 rm.** Z **a**

Brundholme Country House ⛰, Brundholme Rd, CA12 4NL, ℘ 74495, ←, – rest TV ☎ P. VISA Y **e**
closed 21 December-1 February – **M** 12.00/20.00 **t.** and a la carte – **11 rm** ☐ 56.00/115.00 **t.** – SB (except September, October and Bank Holidays) 85.00/105.00 **st.**

Grange Country House ⛰, Manor Brow, Ambleside Rd, CA12 4BA, ℘ 72500, ←, – rest TV ☎ P. VISA. Y **u**
21 March-3 November – **M** (bar lunch)/dinner 14.75 **st.** 4.00 – **11 rm** ☐ 38.00/61.00 **st.** – SB 66.00/78.00 **st.**

KESWICK

Main Street .... Z
Station Street ...... Z

Bank Street .... Z 2
Borrowdale Road .. Z 3
Brackenrigg Drive .. Z 5
Brundholme Road . Y 6
Chestnut Hill ...... Y 8
Church Street ...... Z 10
Crosthwaite Road .. Y 12
Derwent Street .... Z 13
High Hill .... Z 14
Manor Brow .... Y 17
Market Square .... Z 18
Otley Road .... Z 20
Police Station Court .... Z 22
Ratcliffe Place ..... Z 23
St. Herbert Street .... Z 24
Standish Street .... Z 25
Station Street ..... Z 26
The Crescent .... Z 27
The Hawthorns .... Y 29
The Headlands .... Z 31
Tithebarn Street ... Z 32

North is at the top on all town plans.

Les plans de villes sont disposés le Nord en haut.

A 66 WORKINGTON COCKERMOUTH
A 591 CARLISLE
PENRITH, M 6
A 66
By-Pass
Greta
PORTINSCALE
Derwent
B 5292
BRAITHWAITE
29
8
17
A
A 591
WINDERMERE
Brockle Beck
LINGHOLM GARDENS
GREAT WOOD
Road
DERWENTWATER
Borrowdale
Y
Newlands Beck
BRANDELHOW PARK
HOGS EARTH
BORROWDALE
DERWENT FELLS
Derwent
Watendlath Beck
GRANGE
0 1 km
0 1/2 mile
ROSTHWAITE B 5289 BUTTERMERE

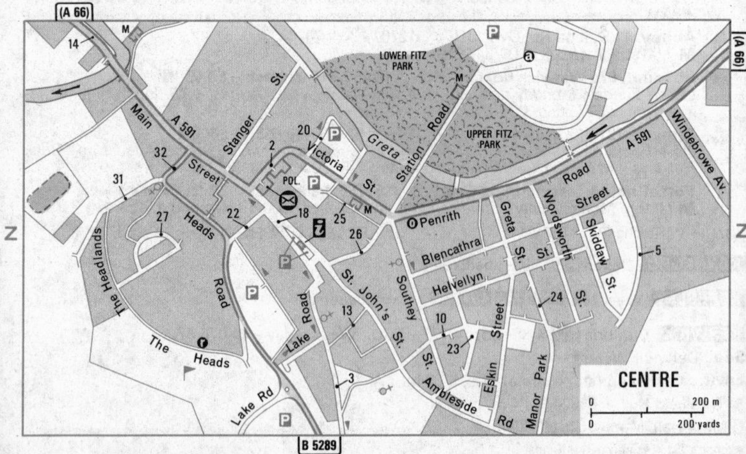

Dale Head Hall, Thirlmere, CA12 4TN, SE : 5 3/4 m. 72478, Lake Thirlmere, – rest. by A 591 Y
M (dinner only) 13.75 **st.** 4.50 – **9 rm** 45.50/85.00 **st.** – SB 86.50/105.50 **st.**

Gales Country House, Underskiddaw, CA12 4PL, NW : 1 3/4 m. on Ormathwaite rd 72413, – rest. by A 591 Y
April-October – **M** (dinner only) 14.00 **st.** 3.90 – **13 rm** 24.00/48.00 **st.**

Lyzzick Hall, Underskiddaw, CA12 4PY, NW : 2 1/2 m. 72277, heated, – by A 591 Y
closed February – **M** 12.00/18.00 **t.** and a la carte 3.50 – **20 rm** 24.00/48.00 **t.** – SB (November-January) 64.00/70.00 **st.**

Highfield, The Heads, CA12 5ER, 72508, – rest Z **r**
April-October – **M** 10.50 **t.** 4.00 – **19 rm** 15.50/46.00 **t.**

Brackenrigg Country House, Thirlmere, CA12 4TF, SE : 3 m. 72258, – .
April-October – **M** 12.50 – **6 rm** 20.00/47.00. by A 591 Y

Linnett Hill, 4 Penrith Rd, CA12 4HF, 73109 – rm. Z **o**
M 14.00 **t.** 4.00 – **8 rm** 20.00/36.00 **t.** – SB (November-March) (except Bank Holidays) 65.50/73.00 **st.**

Lairbeck, Vicarage Hill, CA12 5QB, 73373, – rest.
M 11.00 **t.** 2.65 – **15 rm** 20.00/46.00 **st.** – SB (winter-spring) 47.00/53.00 **st.** Y **a**

at Borrowdale S : 3 1/4 m. on B 5289 – Keswick – 076 87 Borrowdale :

Stakis Lodore Swiss, CA12 5UX, 77285, Telex 64305, Fax 77343, Derwent Water and mountains, heated, park, squash – rest. Y **n**
closed January – **M** 10.00/19.50 **t.** and a la carte – 7.50 – **70 rm** 68.00/99.00 **t.**, **1 suite** 135.00 **t.** – SB 106.00/130.00 **st.**

Greenbank, CA12 5UY, 77215, – rm. Y **z**
closed December – **10 rm** (dinner included) 27.50/59.00 **st.** – SB (winter only) 49.00/53.00 **st.**

at Grange-in-Borrowdale S : 4 3/4 m. by B 5289 – Keswick – 076 87 Borrowdale :

Borrowdale Gates Country House, CA12 5UQ, 77204, – . Y **s**
M (bar lunch Monday to saturday)/dinner 16.50 **t.** 4.50 – **23 rm** (dinner included) 52.50/100.00 **t.** – SB (November-March) (except Easter and Christmas) 68.00/78.00 **st.**

at Rosthwaite S : 6 m. on B 5289 – Y – Keswick – 076 87 Borrowdale :

Hazel Bank, CA12 5XB, 77248, – rest.
March-8 November – **M** 11.50 **st.** 3.50 – **9 rm** (dinner included) 32.00/64.00 **st.**

Royal Oak, CA12 5XB, 77214 – rest.
closed December – **M** 8.00 **st.** 3.00 – **12 rm** (dinner included) 28.00/64.00 **st.**

at Seatoller S : 8 m. on B 5289 – Y – Keswick – 076 87 Borrowdale :

Seatoller House, Borrowdale, CA12 5XN, 77218, Borrowdale, –
April-October – **M** (by arrangement) 8.00 **st.** 5.00 – **9 rm** 19.50/36.00 **st.**

at Portinscale W : 1 1/2 m. by A 66 – 076 87 Keswick :

Derwent Cottage, CA12 5RF, 74838, – rest. Y **x**
Mid March-mid November – **M** 13.00 **st.** 3.20 – **5 rm** 45.00/50.00 **st.**

Swinside Lodge, Newlands, CA12 5UE, S : 1 1/2 m. on Grange Rd 72948, Catbells and Newlands Valley, – rest. Y **c**
closed December-January – **M** 19.00 **t.** – **8 rm** 35.00/61.00 **t.** – SB (November and February-April) 36.00/44.00 **st.**

at Braithwaite W : 2 m. by A 66 on B 5292 – Y – Keswick – 0768778 Braithwaite :

Middle Ruddings, CA12 5RY, on A 66 436, – . Y **v**
M (bar lunch)/dinner 17.50 **t.** 3.60 – **13 rm** 36.00/63.80 **t.** – SB (winter only) (weekends only) 70.00/85.80 **st.**

Cottage in The Woods, Whinlatter Pass, CA12 5TW, NW : 1 3/4 m. on B 5292 409, – .
March-November – **M** (bar lunch)/dinner 13.00 **st.** 2.50 – **7 rm** 39.50/53.00 **st.** – SB (March and November) 58.00/60.00 **st.**

at Thornthwaite W : 3 1/2 m. by A 66 – Keswick – 059 682 Braithwaite :

Thwaite Howe, CA12 5SA, 281, Skiddaw and Derwent Valley, – rest Y **i**
March-October – **M** 10.95 **st.** 2.50 – **8 rm** 35.00/50.00 **st.** – SB (March, July and August except Bank Holidays) 60.00 **st.**

FIAT Lake Rd 72064 ROVER High Hill 72768

KETTLEWELL North Yorks. 402 N 21 – pop. 361 (inc. Starbotton) – ECD : Tuesday and Thursday – ✉ Skipton – ☎ 075 676.
♦London 237 – Bradford 33 – ♦Leeds 40.

Cam Lodge, BD23 5QU, ☎ 276, –
4 rm.

at Starbotton NW : 1 ¾ m. on B 6160 – ✉ Skipton – ☎ 075 676 Kettlewell :

Hilltop Country, BD23 5HY, ☎ 321, « 17C stone built house », – rm
mid March-mid November – **M** (by arrangement) 14.00 **st.** 2.45 – **5 rm** 38.00/48.00 **st.**

KEXBY North Yorks. – see York.

KEYSTON Cambs. 404 S 26 – pop. 252 (inc. Bythorn) – ✉ Huntingdon – ☎ 080 14 Bythorn.
♦London 75 – ♦Cambridge 29 – Northampton 24.

Pheasant Inn, Village Loop Rd, PE18 0RE, ☎ 241 – . AE VISA
closed dinner 25 and 26 December – **M** 19.60 **st.**

KIDDERMINSTER Heref. and Worc. 403 404 N 26 – pop. 50 385 – ECD : Wednesday – ☎ 0562.
Russel Rd ☎ 822303 – Churchill Lane, Blakedown ☎ 700200, N : 3 m. on A 453 – Habberley, Trimpley ☎ 746756, NW : 3 m.
♦London 139 – ♦Birmingham 17 – Shrewsbury 34 – Worcester 15.

Gainsborough House, Bewdley Hill, DY11 6BS, SW : 1 m. on A 456 ☎ 820041, Telex 333058, Fax 66179, – rm rest – 250
42 rm.

at Stone SE : 2 ½ m. on A 448 – ✉ Kidderminster – ☎ 0562 Chaddesley Corbett :

Stone Manor, DY10 4PJ, ☎ 777555, Telex 335661, Fax 777834, ←, , park, – – 250. AE VISA
M 11.25/16.25 **t.** and a la carte 4.00 – 7.50 – **53 rm** 62.75/90.00 **t.** – SB (weekends only) 191.00 **st.**

at Chaddesley Corbett SE : 4 ½ m. by A 448 – ✉ Kidderminster – ☎ 0562 Chaddesley Corbett :

Brockencote Hall, DY10 4PY, on A 448 ☎ 777876, Telex 333431, ←, « 19C mansion in park » – . AE VISA
closed 26 December-mid January – **M** *(closed Saturday lunch, Sunday dinner and Bank Holiday Mondays)* 29.50 **st.** – **8 rm** 57.00/115.00 **st.** – SB 125.00/149.00 **st.**

BMW Mustow Green ☎ 056 283 (Chaddesley Corbett) 811
CITROEN, FIAT Worcester Rd ☎ 820202
FORD Worcester Rd ☎ 820028
LADA, PROTON Plimsoll St. ☎ 822145
PEUGEOT-TALBOT Mill St. ☎ 824961
ROVER Churchfields ☎ 752566
SKODA Mill St. ☎ 823708
VAUXHALL-OPEL Churchfields ☎ 68427
VOLVO Stourport Rd ☎ 515832
VW-AUDI Worcester Rd ☎ 823660

ATS Park St. ☎ 744668/744843

KIDLINGTON Oxon. 403 404 Q 28 – see Oxford.

KILSBY Northants. 403 404 Q 26 – see Rugby (Warw.).

KILVE Somerset – pop. 324 – ☎ 027 874 Holford.
♦London 172 – ♦Bristol 49 – Minehead 13 – Taunton 23.

Meadow House, Sea Lane, TA5 1EG, ☎ 546, « Country house atmosphere », – rest . AE VISA.
closed 1 week Christmas – **M** (dinner only) 18.00 **st.** 3.90 – **4 rm** 51.00/74.00 **st.**, **4 suites** 84.00 **st.** – SB (except Bank Holidays) 95.00/114.00 **st.**

Hood Arms, TA5 1EA, ☎ 210, – . VISA
closed Christmas Day – **M** 10.00/15.00 **t.** and a la carte 2.50 – **5 rm** 32.00/55.00 **t.** – SB (weekends only) 65.00/75.00 **st.**

KINGHAM Oxon. 403 404 P 28 – pop. 576 – ECD : Wednesday – ☎ 060 871.
♦London 81 – Gloucester 32 – ♦Oxford 25.

Mill House, OX7 6UH, ☎ 8188, Fax 492, – . AE VISA.
M 12.95/17.50 **t.** and a la carte – **21 rm** 45.00/92.00 **t.** – SB 105.00/127.00 **st.**

KINGSBRIDGE Devon 403 I 33 **The West Country G.** – pop. 4 164 – ECD : Thursday – ☎ 0548.
See : Site★ – Boat Trip to Salcombe★★ *AC.*
Thurlestone ☎ 560405.
The Quay ☎ 3195.
♦London 236 – Exeter 36 – ♦Plymouth 20 – Torquay 21.

Kings Arms, Fore St., TQ7 1AB, ☎ 852071, Fax 852977, – – 100. VISA
M a la carte 10.35/16.75 **t.** – **11 rm** 30.00/55.00 **t.** – SB (November-April) 57.50/62.50 **st.**

at Goveton NE : 2 ½ m. by A 381 – ✉ ☎ 0548 Kingsbridge :

Buckland-Tout-Saints ⅁, TQ7 2DS, ✆ 853055, Fax 856261, ≤, « Queen Anne mansion », ⚘, park – ⇔ rest TV ☎ P. AE VISA. ✻
closed January-mid February – **M** (booking essential) 25.00/35.00 **st.** 4.75 – **12 rm** 88.00/165.00 **st.** – SB 155.00/215.00 **st.**

at Chillington E: 5 m. on A 379 – ✉ ☎ 0548 Kingsbridge :

White House, TQ7 2JX, ✆ 580580, ⚘ – ⇔ rest TV P
April-October and 23 to 31 December – **M** (bar lunch residents only)/dinner approx. 11.00 **st.** 2.50 – **8 rm** 26.95/59.00 **st.**

Chillington Inn, TQ7 2JS, ✆ 580244 – TV. AE VISA
M *(closed Monday)* (bar lunch)/dinner 12.50 **t.** and a la carte 3.75 – **3 rm** 21.00/38.00 **t.** – SB (October-June) 60.00 **st.**

at Torcross E : 7 m. on A 379 – ✉ ☎ 0548 Kingsbridge :

The Venture, TQ7 2TQ, ✆ 580314, ≤ – TV. ✻
March-September – **M** 10.50 **st.** 3.50 – **5 rm** 18.95/36.90 **st.**

at East Portlemouth S : 9 ¼ m. by A 379 – ✉ ☎ 054 884 Salcombe :

Gara Rock ⅁, TQ8 8PH, SE : 1 ¼ m. by Rickham rd ✆ 2342, Fax 3033, ≤, heated, ⚘, ⚔ – ⇔ rest TV ☎ P. VISA
Easter-October – **M** (bar lunch)/dinner 13.50 **st.** and a la carte – **16 rm** 40.00/86.00 **t.**, **6 suites** 90.00/135.00 **t.**.

at Thurlestone W : 4 m. by A 381 – ✉ ☎ 0548 Kingsbridge :

Thurlestone ⅁, TQ7 3NN, ✆ 560382, Fax 561069, ≤, heated, 9, ⚘, park, ⚔, squash – |♦| ⇔ rest ▤ rest TV ☎ P – 90. VISA
closed 4 to 18 January – **M** 9.75/21.00 **st.** and a la carte 4.75 – **68 rm** 43.00/152.00 **st.** – SB (11 November-23 March) 98.00/130.00 **st.**

at Bantham W : 5 m. by A 379 – ✉ ☎ 0548 Kingsbridge :

Sloop Inn, TQ7 3AJ, ✆ 560489 – TV P
M a la carte 8.80/12.10 **t.** – **5 rm** 30.00/44.00 **t.** – SB 57.00/63.00 **st.**

ROVER The Quay ✆ 852323 — ATS Union Rd ✆ 853247

KINGSEY Bucks. – see Thame (Oxon.).

KINGSKERSWELL Devon 403 J 32 – pop. 3 471 – ✉ Torquay – ☎ 0803.

♦London 219 – Exeter 21 – ♦Plymouth 33 – Torquay 4.

Pitt House, 2 Church End Rd, TQ12 5DS, ✆ 873374, « 15C thatched dower house », ⚘ – ⇔ P. AE VISA
closed Sunday, 2 weeks January-February and 2 weeks August-September – **M** (dinner only) a la carte 17.80/24.20 **t.** 4.90.

KING'S LYNN Norfolk 402 404 V 25 – pop. 37 323 – ECD : Wednesday – ☎ 0553.

See : St. Margaret's Church★ (17C, chancel 13C) – St. Nicholas' Chapel★ (Gothic).

Envir. : Houghton Hall★★ (18C) *AC*, NE : 15 m. – Sandringham House★ and park★★ *AC*, NE : 6 m. – Holkham Hall★★ – Oxburgh Hall★★ – St. Peter's Church★.

18 Castle Rising ✆ 87656, NE : 4 m. by A 164.

The Old Gaol House, Saturday Market Place ✆ 763044.

♦London 103 – ♦Cambridge 45 – ♦Leicester 75 – ♦Norwich 44.

Duke's Head (T.H.F.), Tuesday Market Pl., PE30 1JS, ✆ 774996, Telex 817349, Fax 763556 – |♦| ⇔ rm TV ☎ P – 180. AE VISA
M 5.75/14.25 **st.** and a la carte 4.35 – 7.60 – **72 rm** 60.00/80.00 **st.**

Knights Hill (Best Western), Knights Hill Village, PE30 3HQ, NE : 4 ½ m. on A 148 at junction with A 149 ✆ 675566, Telex 818118, Fax 675568 – TV ☎ P – 300. AE VISA
M 14.95 **st.** (dinner) and a la carte – 6.00 – **58 rm** 55.00/78.00 **st.** – SB 96.00 **st.**

Butterfly, Beveridge Way, PE30 4NB, S : 2 ¼ m. by Hardwick Rd at junction of A 10 and A 47 ✆ 771707, Telex 818313, Fax 768027 – ⇔ rest TV ☎ P – 50. AE VISA. ✻
M 10.00 **t.** and a la carte 3.25 – 5.00 – **50 rm** 57.00/114.00 **t.** – SB (weekends only) 67.00/70.00 **st.**

Globe (B.C.B.), Tuesday Market Pl., PE30 1EZ, ✆ 772617 – TV ☎ P. AE VISA. ✻
M 15.00 **st.** – **40 rm** 42.00/59.50 **st.**

Russet House, 53 Goodwins Rd, PE30 5PE, ✆ 773098, ⚘ – ⇔ rest TV ☎ P. AE VISA. ✻
closed 23 December-14 January – **M** 10.50 **t.** – **12 rm.**

Garbo's, 7 Saturday Market Place, ✆ 773136 – VISA
closed Sunday and Monday – **M** (dinner only) a la carte 11.95/18.45 **st.** 3.95.

at Grimston NE : 6 ¼ m. by A 148 – ✉ King's Lynn – ☎ 0485 Hillington :

Congham Hall 🙗, Lynn Rd, PE32 1AH, ✆ 600250, Telex 81508, Fax 601191, ≤, « Georgian manor house », heated, park, – rest ☎ . AE VISA.
M *(closed lunch Saturday)* 14.50/35.00 **t.** 5.00 – 2.00 – **12 rm** 70.00/110.00 **t.**, **2 suites** 145.00/165.00 **t.** – SB (weekends only) 150.00/205.00 **st.**

at Tottenhill S : 5 ¼ m. on A 10 – ✉ ☎ 0553 Kings Lynn :

Oakwood House, PE33 0RH, ✆ 810256, – . VISA
M 10.00 **st.** 3.95 – **10 rm** 22.00/44.00 **st.** – SB (except Christmas and New Year) 58.00/64.00 **st.**

RELIANT, MAZDA Valingers Rd ✆ 772255
RENAULT Hardwick Rd ✆ 772644
ROVER, LAND-ROVER, RANGE-ROVER Scania Way ✆ 763133
TOYOTA Tottenhill ✆ 810306
VAUXHALL-OPEL North St. ✆ 773861

ATS 4 Oldmeadow Rd, Hardwick Rd Trading Est. ✆ 774035

KING'S NORTON West Midlands 402 ⑩ 404 ⑳ – see Birmingham.

KINGSTEIGNTON Devon 403 J 32 – ✉ ☎ 0626 Newton Abbot.

♦London 223 – Exeter 17 – ♦Plymouth 33 – Torquay 7.

Passage House, Hackney Lane, TQ12 3QH, S : ½ m. ✆ 55515, Fax 63336, ≤, – ☎ – 150. AE VISA.
M 8.50/13.75 **t.** and a la carte – **38 rm** 63.00/75.00 **t.**, **1 suite** 115.00 **t.** – SB 90.00 **st.**

KINGSTON Devon 403 I 33 – pop. 317 – ✉ ☎ 0548 Kingsbridge.

♦London 237 – Exeter 41 – ♦Plymouth 11.

Trebles Cottage 🙗, TQ7 4PT, ✆ 810268, – . VISA
M 11.50 **st.** – **5 rm** 35.00/44.00 **st.**

KINGSTON-UPON-HULL Humberside 402 S 22 – pop. 322 144 – ECD : Monday and Thursday – ☎ 0482 Hull.

Envir. : Burton Constable Hall★ (16C) *AC*, NE : 8 m. by A 165 Z.

Ganstead Park, Longdales Lane, Coniston ✆ 811280, NE : 4 ½ m. Z – Springhead Park, Willerby Rd ✆ 656309, W : by Spring Bank West Z – Sutton Park, Salthouse Rd ✆ 74242, E : 3 m. Z – The Hall, 27 Packman Lane, Kirk Ella ✆ 653026, W : 5 m. Z.

Humberside Airport : ✆ 0652 (Barnetby) 688456, S : 19 m. by A 63 Z and A 15 via Humber Bridge – **Terminal** : Coach Service.

Shipping connections with the Continent : to The Netherlands (Rotterdam) and Belgium (Zeebrugge) (North Sea Ferries).

Central Library, Albion St. ✆ 223344 – King George Dock, Hedon Rd ✆ 702118 – 75-76 Carr Lane ✆ 223559.

♦London 183 – ♦Leeds 61 – ♦Nottingham 94 – ♦Sheffield 68.

Plan opposite

Marina Post House (T.H.F.), Castle St., HU1 2BX, ✆ 225221, Telex 592777, Fax 213299, – rm ☎ – 100. AE VISA — Y **n**
M 10.25/14.50 **st.** and a la carte 3.75 – 7.50 – **99 rm** 69.00/110.00 **st.** – SB (weekends only) 76.00/133.00 **st.**

Stakis Paragon, Paragon St., HU1 3PJ, ✆ 26462, Telex 592431, Fax 213460 – rm ☎ – — Y **e**
125 rm.

Campanile, Beverley Rd, Freetown Way, HU2 9AN, ✆ 25530, Telex 592840 – ☎ – . VISA — X **a**
M 9.40 **st.** and a la carte 2.60 – **49 rm** 33.00 **st.**

Earlsmere, 76-78 Sunnybank, off Spring Bank West, HU3 1LQ, ✆ 41977 – — Z **i**
closed Christmas – **M** (by arrangement) 12.00 **st.** 3.00 – **15 rm** 18.40/40.25 **st.**

Ashford without rest., 125 Park Av., HU5 3EX, ✆ 492849 – . — Z **a**
closed Christmas and New Year – **6 rm** 15.00/28.00 **s.**

Parkwood, 113 Princes Av., HU5 3JL, ✆ 445610 – ☎. VISA — Z **c**
M (by arrangement) 11.20 **st.** – **9 rm** 19.50/42.00 **st.** – SB (weekends only) 37.00 **st.**

Cerutti's, 10 Nelson St., HU1 1XE, ✆ 28501, Fax 587597, Seafood – . VISA
closed Saturday lunch, Sunday, 10 days Christmas and Bank Holidays – **M** a la carte 17.50/23.75 **t.** 4.80. — Y **o**

at North Ferriby W : 7 m. on A 63 – Z – ✉ Kingston-upon-Hull – ☎ 0482 Hull :

Crest (T.H.F.), Ferriby High Rd, HU14 3LG, ✆ 645212, Telex 592558, Fax 643332 – rm ☎ – 100. AE VISA
M *(closed Saturday lunch)* 17.95/24.95 **st.** and a la carte – 7.95 – **101 rm** 70.00/82.00 **t.** – SB (weekends only) 76.00/82.00 **st.**

KINGSTON-UPON-HULL

Street	Grid	No.
Carr Lane	Y	
George Street	X	
Jameson Street	XY	
King Edward Street	Y	19
Paragon Street	Y	29
Prospect Street	X	
Whitefriargate	Y	49
Albion Street	X	2
Bond Street	X	3
Caroline Street	X	6
Commercial Road	Y	8
County Road North	Z	9
Dock Office Row	X	10
Dock Street	X	12
Fairfax Avenue	Z	13
Ferensway	XY	14
Great Union Street	X	15
Grimston Street	X	16
Humber Dock Street	Y	17
Jarratt Street	X	18
Lockwood Street	X	21
Lowgate	Y	23
Market Place	Y	24
Maybury Road	Z	25
Prince's Avenue	Z	31
Prince's Dock Street	Y	32
Queen's Road	Z	33
Queen Street	Y	35
Queen's Dock Avenue	X	36
Reform Street	X	37
St. Mark's Street	X	40
Sculcoates Bridge	X	42
Southcoates Avenue	Z	43
Southcoates Lane	Z	44
Waterhouse Lane	Y	47
Wilberforce Drive	X	50
Worship Street	X	52

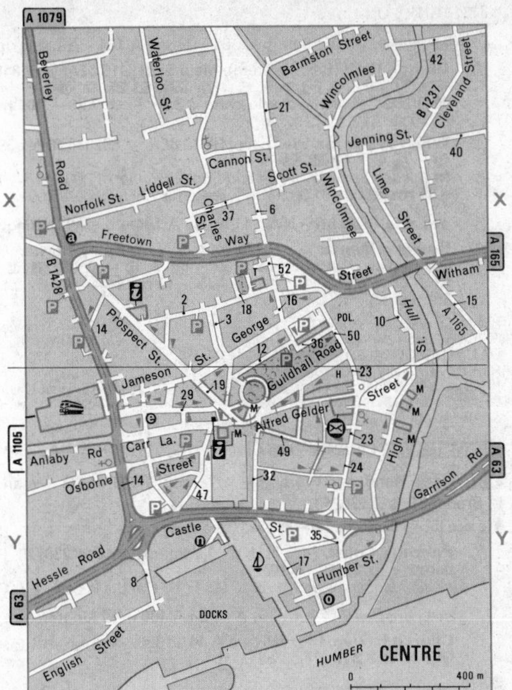

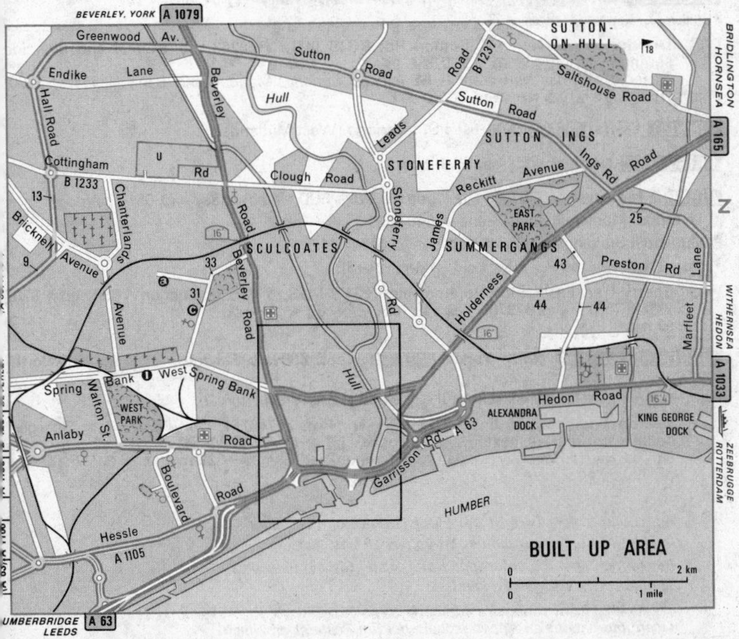

BEVERLEY, YORK A 1079

SUTTON-ON-HULL

BRIDLINGTON HORNSEA

A 165

Z

WITHERNSEA HEDON

A 1033

ZEEBRUGGE ROTTERDAM

HUMBERBRIDGE LEEDS A 63

BUILT UP AREA

2 km

1 mile

at Willerby NW : 5 m. by A 63 – Z – off A 164 – ✉ Kingston-upon-Hull – ☎ 0482 Hull

Grange Park (Best Western), Main St., HU10 6EA, ☏ 656488, Telex 592773, Fax 655848, – – TV ☎ – 300. AE VISA
M 15.00/22.50 **t.** and a la carte 3.75 – 7.50 – **109 rm** 51.00/92.00 **st.** – SB 85.00/95.00 **st.**

Willerby Manor, Well Lane, HU10 6ER, ☏ 652616, Telex 592629, Fax 653901, – TV ☎ – 450. AE VISA
M *(closed Saturday lunch and Sunday dinner)* 11.00/15.75 **t.** and a la carte 5.50 – 6.95 – **35 rm** 59.00/78.00 **t.** – SB (weekends only) 79.00/85.00 **st.**

at Little Weighton NW : 11 m. by A 164 – Z – ✉ Cottingham – ☎ 0482 Hull :

Rowley Manor , HU20 3XR, SW : ½ m. by Rowley Rd ☏ 848248, Fax 849900, ≤, « Georgian manor house », – TV ☎ – 60. AE VISA
M 14.95 **t.** and a la carte **t.** 4.15 – **16 rm** 44.00/85.00 **t.** – SB (weekends only) 80.00/85.00 **st.**

BMW Citadel Way ☏ 25071
FIAT 96 Boothferry Rd ☏ 506976
FIAT, PEUGEOT-TALBOT Witham ☏ 24131
FORD 172 Anlaby Rd ☏ 25732
HONDA 576 Springbank West ☏ 51250
PEUGEOT-TALBOT Kirkwell ☏ 659362
SAAB Anlaby Rd ☏ 23773
TOYOTA Clarence St. ☏ 20039
VAUXHALL-OPEL 230-236 Anlaby Rd ☏ 23681
VW-AUDI 170 Anlaby Rd ☏ 23631

ATS Great Union St. ☏ 29044
ATS Scott St. ☏ 29370/225502

KINGSTOWN Cumbria – see Carlisle.

KINGTON Heref. and Worc. 403 K 27 – pop. 2 040 – ECD : Wednesday – ☎ 0544.

18 Bradnor Hill ☏ 230340.

London 152 – Birmingham 61 – Hereford 19 – Shrewsbury 54.

Penrhos Court, HR5 3LH, E : 1 ½ m. on A 44 ☏ 230720, Fax 230754, « Converted 18C barn » – AE VISA
closed January-March – **M** 10.00/17.50 **t.** and a la carte 7.00.

st Lyonshall E : 2½ m . by A 44 on A 480 – ✉ Kington – ☎ 054 48 Lyonshall :

Church House, HR5 3HR, on A 44 ☏ 350, – rest .
M 7.50 **st.** – **3 rm** 17.50/32.00 **st.**

ATS 20-22 Bridge St. ☏ 230350

KINTBURY Berks. 403 404 P 29 – pop. 2 034 – ✉ Newbury – ☎ 0488.

London 73 – Newbury 6 – Reading 23.

Dundas Arms with rm, Station Rd, RG15 0UT, ☏ 58263, ≤, « Canal and riverside setting », – TV ☎ . AE VISA.
closed Christmas-New Year – **M** *(closed Sunday, Monday and Bank Holidays)* 18.00/26.00 **t.** 4.50 – **5 rm** 50.00/60.00 **t.**

KINVER Staffs. 403 404 N 26 – see Stourbridge (West Midlands).

KIRBY HILL North Yorks. – see Richmond.

KIRKBY Merseyside 402 403 L 23 – pop. 52 825 – ECD : Wednesday – ☎ 051 Liverpool.

18 Liverpool Municipal, Ingoe Lane ☏ 546 5435.

Municipal Buildings, Cherry field Drive ☏ 443 4024.

London 214 – Blackpool 54 – Liverpool 7 – Manchester 31.

Cherry Tree, East Lancs. Rd, Knowsley, L34 9HA, S : 1 ½ m. at junction A 580 and A 5207 ☏ 546 7531, Telex 629769, Fax 549 1069 – TV ☎ –
50 rm.

KIRKBY FLEETHAM North Yorks. 402 P 20 – pop. 406 (inc. Fencote) – ✉ ☎ 0609 Northallerton.

London 236 – Leeds 46 – Middlesbrough 31 – Newcastle-upon-Tyne 51 – York 37.

Kirkby Fleetham Hall , DL7 0SU, N : 1 m. ☏ 748711, Fax 748747, ≤, « Georgian country house », heated, , , park – TV ☎ . AE VISA
M (bar lunch Monday to Saturday)/dinner 25.00 4.95 – **22 rm** 75.00/175.00 **st.** – SB 150.00 **st.**

*Es ist empfehlenswert, **in der Hauptsaison** und vor allem in Urlaubsorten, Hotelzimmer im voraus zu bestellen.*
Benachrichtigen Sie sofort das Hotel, wenn Sie ein bestelltes Zimmer nicht belegen können.
Wenn Sie an ein Hotel im Ausland schreiben, fügen Sie Ihrem Brief einen internationalen Antwortschein bei (im Postamt erhältlich).

KIRKBY LONSDALE Cumbria 402 M 21 – pop. 1 557 – ECD : Wednesday – ✉ Carnforth – ☎ 05242.

Casterton Rd ☎ 72085, 1 m. on Sedbergh Rd.

24 Main St. ☎ 71437.

London 259 – Carlisle 62 – Kendal 13 – Lancaster 17 – Leeds 58.

Pheasant Inn, Casterton, LA6 2RX, NE : 1¼ m. on A 683 ☎ 71230, – rest TV ☎ & P. VISA
M (bar lunch Monday to Saturday)/dinner 10.50/18.00 **t.** 3.50 – **10 rm** 35.00/55.00 **t.** – SB 70.00/80.00 **st.**

at Cowan Bridge (Lancs.) SE : 2 m. on A 65 – ✉ Carnforth – ☎ 052 42 Kirkby Lonsdale :

Hipping Hall, LA6 2JJ, SE : ½ m. on A 65 ☎ 71187, – TV P. VISA
March-November – **M** *(closed Sunday)* (communal dining) (booking essential) (dinner only) 15.00 **st.** – **5 rm** 46.00/58.00 **st.**, **2 suites** 68.00 **st.**.

Cobwebs Country House, Leck, LA6 2HZ, NE : ¼ m. ☎ 72141, Fax 72141 – rest TV ☎ P. VISA.
April-December – **M** *(closed Sunday)* (booking essential) (dinner only) 17.00 **st.** 3.50 – **5 rm** 30.00/50.00 **st.**

at Lupton NW : 3¾ m. on A 65 – ✉ Carnforth – ☎ 044 87 Crooklands :

Lupton Tower with rm, LA6 2PR, ☎ 400, ←, vegetarian rest., – P.
M (booking essential) (dinner only) 13.50 **st.** 3.50 – **6 rm** 18.50/37.00 **t.** – SB (January-March) (weekdays only) 52.00/60.00 **st.**

KIRKBYMOORSIDE North Yorks. 402 R 21 – pop. 2 227 – ECD : Thursday – ☎ 0751.

Manor Vale ☎ 31525.

London 244 – Scarborough 26 – York 33.

George and Dragon, 17 Market Pl., YO6 6AA, ☎ 31637, – TV ☎ P
22 rm.

NISSAN Pickering Rd ☎ 31551
VAUXHALL-OPEL Piercy End ☎ 31434
RENAULT New Rd ☎ 31401

KIRKBY STEPHEN Cumbria 402 M 20 – pop. 1 518 – ECD : Thursday – ☎ 076 83.

Envir. : Brough (Castle ruins 12C-14C : keep ※★ *AC*) N : 4 m.

Market Sq. ☎ 71199 (summer only).

London 285 – Carlisle 48 – Kendal 24.

King's Arms, Market Sq., CA17 4QN, ☎ 71378, – ☎ P. VISA
closed Christmas Day – **M** 7.75/16.50 **t.** 4.00 – **9 rm** 24.50/47.50 **t.** – SB (November-early May) (except Bank Holidays) 60.00 **st.**

KIRKHAM Lancs. 402 L 22 – pop. 8 393 – ✉ Preston – ☎ 0772.

London 240 – Blackpool 9 – Preston 7.

Cromwellian, 16 Poulton St., PR4 2AB, ☎ 685680. AE VISA
closed Sunday dinner, Monday, 1 week February and 2 weeks June – **M** (dinner only and Sunday lunch)/dinner 18.95/21.95 **t.** 4.25.

KIRKLINGTON North Yorks. 402 P 21 – ✉ Bedale – ☎ 0845 Thirsk.

London 229 – Leeds 32 – Middlesborough 35 – York 30.

Dower House without rest., DL8 2LX, ☎ 567271, – TV P
closed 20 December-2 January – **3 rm** 20.00/40.00 **st.**

KIRKOSWALD Cumbria 401 402 L 19 – pop. 730 – ✉ Penrith – ☎ 076 883 Lazonby.

London 300 – Carlisle 23 – Kendal 41 – Lancaster 58.

Prospect Hill, CA10 1ER, N : ¾ m. ☎ 500, ←, « Converted 18C farm buildings », – P
9 rm.

KNAPTON Norfolk – see North Walsham.

KNARESBOROUGH North Yorks. 402 P 21 – pop. 12 910 – ECD : Thursday – ☎ 0423 Harrogate.

Boroughbridge Rd ☎ 863219, N : 1½ m.

Market Place ☎ 866886 (summer only).

London 217 – Bradford 21 – Harrogate 3 – Leeds 18 – York 18.

Dower House (Best Western), Bond End, HG5 9AL, ☎ 863302, Telex 57202, Fax 867665, – TV ☎ P – 70. AE VISA
closed 24 to 26 December – **M** *(closed Saturday lunch)* 16.50 **t.** (dinner) and a la carte 4.50 – **31 rm** 42.50/88.00 **t.**, **1 suite** 100.00 **t.**

FORD York Place ☎ 862291

KNIGHTON (TREFYCLAWDD) Powys 403 K 26 – ☎ 0547.

Little Ffrydd Wood ☎ 528646, SW : ½ m.

The Old School ☎ 528753.

London 162 – Birmingham 59 – Hereford 31 – Shrewsbury 35.

Milebrook House, Ludlow Rd, Milebrook, LD7 1LT, E : 2 m. on A 4113 ☎ 528632, – TV P. VISA.
M *(closed Monday lunch)* (bar lunch)/dinner 16.95 **t.** and a la carte 4.25 – **6 rm** 39.50/53.00 **t.**

KNIGHTWICK Heref. and Worc. 403 404 M 27 – pop. 82 – ECD : Wednesday – ✉ Worcester – ☎ 0886.

London 132 – Hereford 20 – Leominster 18 – Worcester 8.

Talbot, WR6 5PH, on B 4197 ☎ 21235, , squash – TV ☎ P. VISA
closed 24 and 25 December – **M** a la carte 9.95/16.00 **st.** 2.50 – **10 rm** 20.00/47.50 **st.**

KNOWLE West Midlands 403 404 O 26 – ✉ Solihull – ☎ 0564.

Bridgewater, 2110 Warwick Rd, B93 0EE, S : 1 ½ m. on A 4141 ☎ 771177, Fax 770141 – rest ☎ P. AE VISA.
M 14.50/24.50 **t.** and a la carte 4.50 – 10.00 – **20 rm** 40.00/80.00 **t.** – SB (weekends only) 75.00 **st.**

KNOWLE Devon – see Braunton.

KNOWL HILL Berks. 404 R 29 – ✉ Twyford – ☎ 062 882 Littlewick Green.

London 38 – Maidenhead 5 – Reading 8.

Bird in Hand, Bath Rd, RG10 9UP, ☎ 6622, Fax 6748, – TV ☎ P. AE VISA.
M *(closed dinner 25 and 26 December)* 15.00/16.50 **st.** and a la carte 4.50 – **15 rm** 65.00/85.00 **st.** – SB (weekends only) 80.00 **st.**

at Warren Row NW : 1 m. – ✉ Wargrave – ☎ 062 882 Littlewick Green :

Warrener Inn with rm, RG10 8QS, ☎ 2803, Fax 6055, – TV ☎ P. VISA.
closed first week January – **M** *(closed Saturday lunch and Sunday)* 24.00/36.00 **t.** 9.00 – **5 rm** 75.00/85.00 **t.**

La Grande-Bretagne et l'Irlande sont maintenant couvertes
par un atlas disponible en trois versions :
broché, relié et à spirale.

KNUTSFORD Cheshire 402 403 404 M 24 – pop. 13 628 – ECD : Wednesday – ☎ 0565.

Envir. : Tatton Hall★ (Georgian) and gardens★★ *AC*, N : 2 m. – Jodrell Bank (Concourse building-radiotelescope *AC*) SE : 8 ½ m.

Council Offices, Toft Rd ☎ 2611.

London 187 – Chester 25 – Liverpool 33 – Manchester 18 – Stoke-on-Trent 30.

Cottons, Manchester Rd, WA16 0SU, NW : 1 ½ m. on A 50 ☎ 650333, Telex 669931, Fax 755351, , , , – rm TV ☎ P – 200. AE VISA
M *(closed Saturday lunch)* 14.00/30.00 **st.** (dinner) and a la carte 4.50 – **77 rm** 89.00/115.00 **st.**, **9 suites.**

Royal George (B.C.B.), King St., WA16 6EE, ☎ 4151, Fax 4955 – TV ☎ P – 80. AE VISA.
M 15.00 **st.** – **31 rm** 59.00/73.50 **st.**

Longview, 55 Manchester Rd, WA16 0LX, ☎ 632119, Fax 653204 – TV ☎ P
closed Christmas and New Year – **M** *(closed Sunday dinner)* (lunch by arrangement)/dinner 15.00 **st.** 3.75 – **23 rm** 31.50/55.00 **st.** – SB (weekends only) 65.00 **st.**

Travelodge without rest., A 556 Chester Rd, Tabley, WA16 0PP, NW : 2 ¾ m. by A 5033 on A 556 ☎ 52187, Reservations (Toll free) 0800 850950 – TV P. AE VISA.
32 rm 24.00/29.50 **t.**

La Belle Epoque with rm, 60 King St., WA16 6DT, ☎ 3060, French rest., « Art nouveau » – TV. AE VISA.
closed first week January – **M** *(closed Sunday and Bank Holidays)* (dinner only) (booking essential) a la carte 15.50/24.50 **t.** – 3.50 – **5 rm** 33.00/45.00 **st.**

at Bucklow Hill NW : 3 ½ m. at junction A 556 and A 5034 – ✉ Knutsford – ☎ 0565 Bucklow Hill :

Swan Inn (De Vere), Bucklow Hill, Chester Rd, WA16 6RD, ☎ 830295, Telex 666911, Fax 830614 – TV ☎ P – 50. AE VISA
M *(closed Saturday lunch)* 13.75/14.75 **st.** and a la carte 5.00 – **70 rm** 55.00/65.00 **st.** – SB (weekends only, July and August) 60.00/80.00 **st.**

FORD Garden Rd ☎ 4141
PEUGEOT Toft Rd ☎ 4294
VOLVO Park Lane, Pickmere ☎ 056 589 (Pickmere) 3254

ATS Malt St. ☎ 52224

LACOCK Wilts. 403 404 N 29 **The West Country G.** – pop. 1 289 – ✉ Chippenham – ☎ 024 973.

See : Site★ – Lacock Village : High St.★, St. Cyriac Church★, Fox Talbot Museum of Photography★ *AC* – Lacock Abbey★ *AC*.

◆London 109 – Bath 16 – ◆Bristol 30 – Chippenham 3.

X **Sign of the Angel** with rm, 6 Church St., SN15 2LA, ☎ 230, English rest., « 14C inn in National Trust village », 🌳 – TV ☎. AE VISA
closed 22 December-6 January – **M** *(closed Saturday lunch and Sunday dinner)* 22.00/27.50 **t.** 3.50 – **8 rm** 65.00/90.00 **t.** – SB (except weekends in summer) 115.00 **st.**

LAKE VYRNWY Powys 402 403 J 25 – ✉ ☎ 069 173 Llanwddyn.

◆London 204 – Chester 52 – Llanfyllin 10 – Shrewsbury 40.

Lake Vyrnwy, SY10 0LY, ☎ 692, Fax 259, ← Lake Vyrnwy, « Country house atmosphere », 🌳, park, 🎾 – TV ☎ 🚗 P. AE VISA
M 9.75/16.75 **t.** – **29 rm** 39.75/72.50 **t.**, **1 suite** 95.50 **t.** – SB (except Bank Holidays) 72.50/119.00 **st.**

LALESTON Mid Glam. 403 J 29 – see Bridgend.

LAMORNA COVE Cornwall 403 D 33 – ECD : Thursday – ✉ ☎ 0736 Penzance.

Envir. : Land's End★★, W : 7 ½ m.

◆London 323 – Penzance 5 – Truro 31.

Hotels see : **Penzance** NE : 5 m.

LAMPHEY Dyfed – see Pembroke.

LANCASTER Lancs. 402 L 21 – pop. 43 902 – ECD : Wednesday – ☎ 0524.

See : Castle★.

18 Ashton Hall, Ashton-with-Stodday ☎ 751247, S : 2 ½ m. on A 588 – 9 Lansil, Caton Rd ☎ 39269 – 9 Robin Lane, Bentham ☎ 052 42 (Bentham) 61018.

7 Dalton Sq. ☎ 32878.

◆London 252 – ◆Blackpool 26 – Bradford 62 – Burnley 44 – ◆Leeds 71 – ◆Middlesbrough 97 – Preston 26.

Post House (T.H.F.), Waterside Park, Caton Rd, LA1 3RA, NE : 1 ½ m. on A 683 ☎ 65999, Telex 65363, Fax 841265, 🌳 – rm TV ☎ P – 120. AE VISA
M 10.50/15.00 **st.** and a la carte 4.35 – 7.50 – **117 rm** 69.00/79.00 **st.** – SB (April-September and weekends only October-March) 80.00/86.00 **st.**

Royal Kings Arms, Market St., CA1 1HP, ☎ 32451, Telex 65481, Fax 841698 – TV ☎ P – 70. AE VISA
M (bar lunch)/dinner 11.00 **st.** and a la carte – **55 rm** 49.00/75.00 **st.** – SB 60.00/70.00 **st.**

Edenbreck House without rest., Sunnyside Lane, off Ashfield Av., LA1 5ED, via Meeting House Lane ☎ 32464, 🌳 – TV P
5 rm 35.00/40.00 **st.**

at Claughton NE : 6 ¾ m. on A 683 – ✉ ☎ 052 42 Kirkby Lonsdale :

Old Rectory, LA2 9LA, on A 683 ☎ 21455, 🌳 – TV ☎ P. AE VISA.
M a la carte 17.75/39.75 **t.** – 6.95 – **12 rm** 43.95/75.95 **t.** – SB 96.00/100.00 **st.**

FORD Parliament St. ☎ 63553
HYUNDAI, PONY Brookhouse ☎ 0524 (Caton) 770501
NISSAN Scotsforth Rd ☎ 36162
ROVER King St. ☎ 32233

LANGSTONE Gwent 403 L 29 – see Newport.

LANREATH Cornwall 403 G 32 – pop. 449 – ✉ Looe – ☎ 0503.

◆London 269 – ◆Plymouth 26 – Truro 34.

Punch Bowl Inn, PL13 2NX, ☎ 20218, 🌳 – TV P. VISA
M (bar lunch Monday to Saturday)/dinner 8.50 **t.** and a la carte 2.90 – **14 rm** 17.50/48.00 **t.**

LANSALLOS Cornwall 403 G 32 – ✉ Fowey – ☎ 0726 St. Austell

◆London 273 – ◆Plymouth 30.

Carneggan House, Lanteglos-by-Fowey, PL23 1NW, NW : 2 m. on Polruan rd ☎ 870327, ←, 🌳 – TV P
3 rm.

LARKFIELD Kent 404 V 30 – see Maidstone.

When in a hurry use the ***Michelin Main Road Maps*** *:*
970 *Europe,* 980 *Greece,* 984 *Germany,* 985 *Scandinavia-Finland,*
986 *Great Britain and Ireland,* 987 *Germany-Austria-Benelux,* 988 *Italy,*
989 *France,* 990 *Spain-Portugal and* 991 *Yugoslavia.*

LASTINGHAM North Yorks. 402 R 21 – pop. 108 – ECD : Wednesday – ✉ York – ☎ 075 15.
◆London 244 – Scarborough 26 – York 32.

Lastingham Grange ♨, YO6 6TH, ☎ 345, ≤, « Country house atmosphere », ⛱ – ⛔ rest 📺 ☎ ℗. AE ⓓ. ✻
closed December-February – **M** (bar lunch Monday to Saturday)/dinner 18.95 **t.** 🍾 3.25 – **12 rm** ☕ 45.50/93.00 **t.** – SB 102.00/117.75 **st.**

at Hutton-le-Hole W : 2 m. – ✉ York – ☎ 075 15 Lastingham :

Hammer and Hand, YO6 6UA, ☎ 300 – ⛔ rm 📺
3 rm.

Barn, YO6 6UA, ☎ 311 – ℗. 🅂 VISA. ✻
closed January and February – **M** 10.00 **st.** 🍾 3.50 – **8 rm** ☕ 16.00/40.00 **st.**

LAVENHAM Suffolk 404 W 27 – pop. 1 658 – ECD : Wednesday – ✉ Sudbury – ☎ 0787.
See : Site★★ – SS. Peter and Paul's Church : the Spring Parclose★ (Flemish).
ℹ Market Pl. ☎ 248207.
◆London 66 – ◆Cambridge 39 – Colchester 22 – ◆Ipswich 19.

Swan (T.H.F.), High St., CO10 9QA, ☎ 247477, Telex 987198, Fax 248286, « Part 14C timbered inn », ⛱ – 📺 ☎ ℗ – 🏛 40. 🅂 AE ⓓ VISA
M 14.00/19.50 **st.** and a la carte – ☕ 8.60 – **44 rm** 81.00/107.00 **st.**, **3 suites** 119.00/141.00 **st.** – SB 133.95/162.00 **st.**

Angel Corner, 17 Market Pl., CO10 9RH, ☎ 247168, « 15C former woolmerchant's house », ⛱
closed December and January – **M** (by arrangement) 11.00 **st.** – **3 rm** ☕ 15.50/31.00 **st.**

XX **Great House** with rm, Market Pl., CO10 9QZ, ☎ 247431, « Part 14C timbered house » – 📺 ☎. 🅂 VISA
closed January – **M** *(closed Sunday dinner and Monday)* 11.90/13.95 **t.** and a la carte 🍾 6.00 – **1 rm** ☕ 50.00/68.00 **t.**, **3 suites** 68.00/78.00 **t.** – SB (weekdays only except Monday) 93.90/123.90 **st.**

at Brent Eleigh SE : 2½ m. by A 1141 – ✉ Sudbury – ☎ 0787 Lavenham :

Street Farm without rest., CO10 9NU, ☎ 247271, ⛱ – ⛔ ℗. ✻
March-November – **3 rm** ☕ 20.00/35.00 **s.**

PEUGEOT-TALBOT Sudbury Rd ☎ 247228

LEA Lancs. – see Preston.

LEAMINGTON SPA Warw. 403 404 P 27 – see Royal Leamington Spa.

LEATHERHEAD Surrey 404 T 30 – pop. 42 399 – ☎ 0372.
⛳ Kingston Rd ☎ 843966, N : 1¼ m. on A 244 – ⛳ Tyrells Wood ☎ 376025.
◆London 23 – ◆Brighton 43 – Guildford 15 – Maidstone 41.

XX **Le Pelerin,** Hawk's Hill, Guildford Rd, KT22 9AL, ☎ 373602, Seafood – ▤ ℗. 🅂 AE ⓓ VISA
M 8.95/11.95 **t.** and a la carte 🍾 4.95.

ATS 85a and 89 Kingston Rd ☎ 372003

LEDBURY Heref. and Worc. 403 404 M 27 – pop. 4 985 – ECD : Wednesday – ☎ 0531.
See : Church Lane★.
Envir. : Birtsmorton Court★ (15C) *AC*, SE : 7 m.
ℹ St. Katherine's, High St. ☎ 2461.
◆London 119 – Hereford 14 – Newport 46 – Worcester 16.

Feathers, High St., HR8 1DS, ☎ 5266, Fax 2001, « Tastefully decorated timbered 16C inn », squash – 📺 ☎ ℗ – 🏛 60. 🅂 AE ⓓ VISA
M (bar lunch Monday to Saturday)/dinner a la carte 15.20/22.95 **st.** – **11 rm** ☕ 54.50/76.50 **st.** – SB (weekends only) 110.00 **st.**

at Wellington Heath N : 2 m. by B 4214 – ✉ ☎ 0531 Ledbury :

Hope End ♨, Hope End, HR8 1JQ, N : ¾ m. ☎ 3613, « Georgian house, gardens », ⛱, park – ⛔ rest ☎ ℗. 🅂 VISA. ✻
closed Monday, Tuesday and December-February – **M** (booking essential) (dinner only) 27.50 **t.** 🍾 5.00 – **9 rm** ☕ 96.00/132.00 **t.** – SB 163.00/177.00 **st.**

FORD New St. ☎ 2261/4733 | ROVER The Homend ☎ 5561

"Short Breaks" (SB)

Zahlreiche Hotels bieten Vorzugspreise bei einem Aufenthalt von zwei Nächten.
Diese Preise umfassen Zimmer, Abendessen und Frühstück.

LEE Devon 403 H 30 – ✉ ☎ 0271 Ilfracombe

- **Lee Bay** 🏨, EX34 8LP, ☏ 863503, ≤, Fб, 🏊, heated, 🌳, park – TV ☎ P **57 rm.**
- **Lee Manor** 🏨, EX34 8LR, ☏ 863920, 🌳, park – TV P. ✱ *Easter-mid October* – **M** (dinner only) 10.95 **t.** and a la carte 🍷 4.00 – **11 rm** ☐ (dinner included) 35.00/92.00 **t.**

LEEDS West Yorks. 402 P 22 – pop. 445 242 – ECD : Wednesday – ☎ 0532.

See : Site★ – City Art Gallery★ DZ M.

Envir. : Temple Newsam House★ (17C) (interior★★) *AC*, E : 4 m. CX D – Kirkstall Abbey★ (ruins 12C) *AC*, NW : 3 m. BV.

18, 18 The Temple Newsam, Temple Newsam Rd, Halton ☏ 645624, E : 3 m. CX – 18 Gotts Park, Armley Ridge Rd, ☏ 636600, W : 2 m. BV – 18 Middleton Park Municipal, Ring Rd, Middleton ☏ 709506, S : 3 m. CX – 18 Scarcroft, Syke Lane ☏ 892263, N : 7 m. by A 58 C – 18 Sand Moor, Alwoodley Lane ☏ 681685, N : 5 m. by A 61 C – 18 Howley Hall, Scotchman Lane, Morley ☏ 0924 (Morley) 472432, SW : 4 m. on B 6123 – 9 Roundhay, Park Lane ☏ 662695, N : 4 m. C.

✈ Leeds and Bradford Airport : ☏ 509696, Telex 557868, NW : 8 m. by A 65 and A 658 BV.

i 19 Wellington St. ☏ 462454/462455.

♦London 204 – ♦Liverpool 75 – ♦Manchester 43 – ♦Newcastle-upon-Tyne 95 – ♦Nottingham 74.

Plans on following pages

- **Leeds Hilton**, Neville St., LS1 4BX, ☏ 442000, Telex 557143, Fax 433577 – |♯| ✱ rm ▤ TV ☎ ♿ P – 🏛 400. AE ① VISA DZ r
  M 11.50/15.50 **t.** and a la carte 🍷 4.70 – ☐ 11.75 – **225 rm** 95.00/110.00 **st.**, **3 suites** 135.00/155.00 **st.**
- **Queen's** (T.H.F.), City Sq., LS1 1PL, ☏ 431323, Telex 55161, Fax 425154 – |♯| ✱ rm TV ☎ ♿ – 🏛 600. AE ① VISA DZ a
  M 12.00/15.00 **st.** and a la carte 🍷 4.00 – ☐ 9.00 – **183 rm** 90.00/100.00 **st.**, **5 suites** 150.00/200.00 **st.** – SB (except Christmas) 80.00 **st.**
- **Golden Lion** (Mt. Charlotte Thistle), Lower Briggate, LS1 4AE, ☏ 436454, Fax 429327 – |♯| TV ☎ – 🏛 80. AE ① VISA DZ v
  M *(closed Sunday lunch)* 11.25 13.25/17.95 **st.** (dinner) and a la carte **t.** – **89 rm** ☐ 60.00/70.00 **st.** – SB (weekends only) 67.00 **st.**
- **Merrion** (Mt. Charlotte Thistle), Merrion Centre, 17 Wade Lane, LS2 8NH, ☏ 439191, Telex 55459, Fax 423527 – |♯| TV ☎ P – 🏛 80. AE ① VISA DZ x
  M 12.25 **t.** and a la carte 🍷 4.10 – ☐ 7.25 – **120 rm** 70.95/76.40 **t.** – SB 82.50/166.10 **st.**
- **Butlers**, 40 Cardigan Rd, Headingley, LS6 3AG, ☏ 744755, Fax 744755 – TV ☎ P. AE VISA AY a
  M *(closed Sunday dinner)* (lunch by arrangement)/dinner a la carte 10.30/17.55 **st.** 🍷 2.50 – **8 rm** ☐ 49.50/61.50 **st.**
- **Aragon**, 250 Stainbeck Lane, LS7 2PS, ☏ 759306, 🌳 – TV P. AE ① VISA CV c
  closed Christmas-New Year – **M** 7.95 **s.** – **13 rm** ☐ 20.35/39.50 **s.**
- **Ash Mount**, 22 Wetherby Rd, Oakwood, LS8 2QD, ☏ 658164, 🌳 – TV P CV u
  closed 1 week Christmas – **M** (by arrangement) 5.00 **st.** – **13 rm** ☐ 17.50/38.00 **st.**
- **Pinewood**, 78 Potternewton Lane, LS7 3LW, ☏ 622561, 🌳 – ✱ rest TV. ✱ AY s
  closed Christmas-New Year – **M** (by arrangement) 9.00 **st.** 🍷 3.00 – **10 rm** ☐ 31.00/46.00 **st.**
- XXX **Mandalay**, 8 Harrison St., LS1 6PA, ☏ 446453, Indian rest. – ▤. AE ① VISA DZ e
  closed Sunday lunch, 25-26 December and 1 January – **M** 12.50 **t.** and a la carte.
- X **Sang Sang**, 7 The Headrow, LS1 6PN, ☏ 468664, Chinese rest. – AE ① VISA DZ u
  closed Bank Holidays – **M** (restricted lunch)/dinner a la carte 7.30/10.10 **t.** 🍷 2.75.

at Seacroft NE : 5½ m. at junction of A 64 and A 6120 – ✉ ☎ 0532 Leeds :

- **Stakis Windmill**, Ring Rd, LS14 5QP, ☏ 732323, Telex 55452, Fax 323018 – |♯| ▤ rest TV ☎ P – 🏛 300. AE ① VISA CV a
  M 7.95/13.95 **t.** – ☐ 7.50 – **99 rm** 70.00/92.00 **t.** – SB 74.00/116.00 **st.**

at Garforth E : 6 m. at junction of A 63 and A 642– CV – ✉ ☎ 0532 Leeds :

- Hilton National, Wakefield Rd, LS25 1LH, ☏ 866556, Telex 556324, Fax 868326, 🏊 – ✱ rm TV ☎ ♿ P – 🏛
  141 rm.

at Pudsey W : 5¾ m. by A 647 – ✉ Leeds – ☎ 0274 Bradford :

- X **Aagrah**, Bradford Rd, on A 647 ☏ 668818, Indian rest. – P. AE ① VISA BV e
  closed 25 December – **M** (dinner only and Sunday lunch) a la carte 5.45/12.10 **t.** 🍷 2.85.

at Horsforth NW : 5 m. by A 65 off A 6120 – ✉ ☎ 0532 Leeds :

- XXX **Low Hall**, Calverley Lane, LS18 5EF, ☏ 588221, « Elizabethan manor », 🌳 – P. VISA
  closed Saturday lunch, Sunday and Monday – **M** 11.50/19.50 **t.** and a la carte. BV a
- XX Roman Garden, Hall Lane, Hall Park, LS18 5JY, ☏ 587962, ≤, Italian rest. – P BV i

LEEDS AND BRADFORD

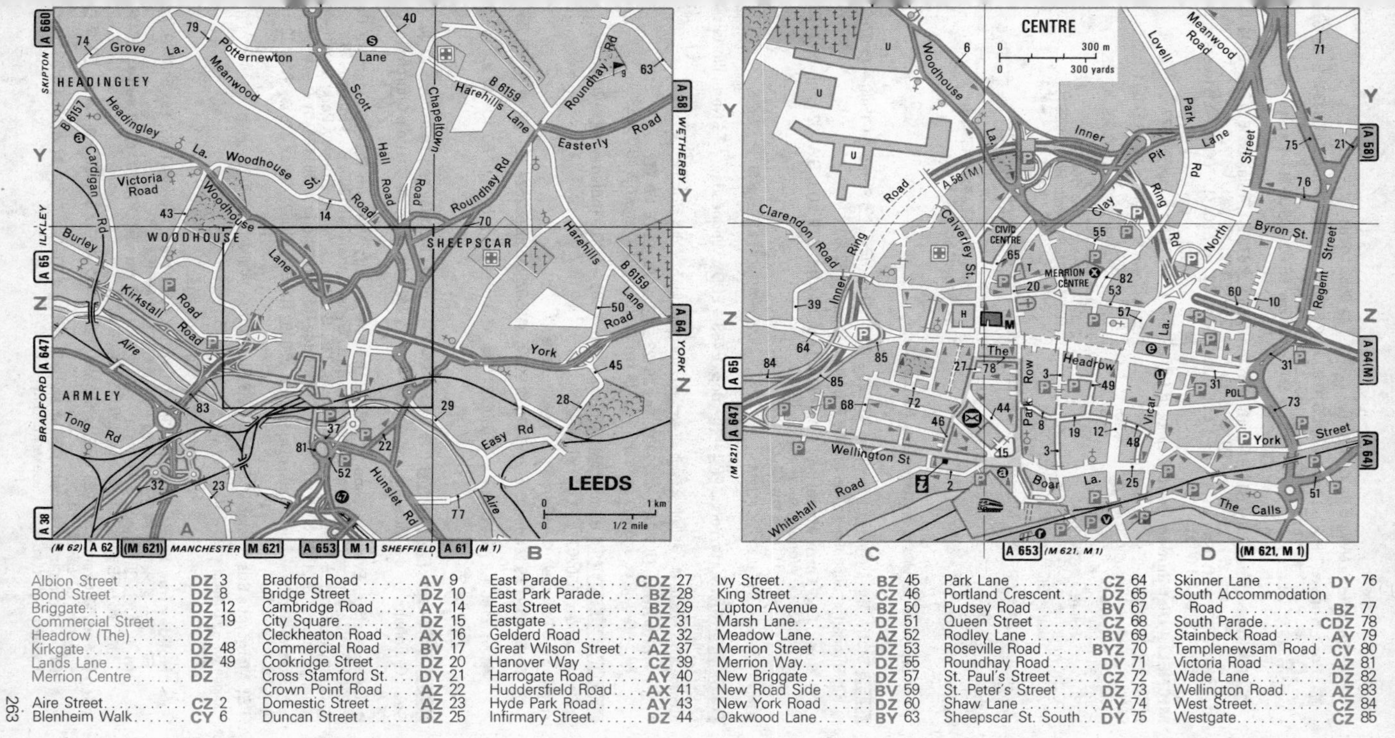

Albion Street . . . . DZ 3
Bond Street . . . . DZ 8
Briggate . . . . DZ 12
Commercial Street . . . . DZ 19
Headrow (The) . . . . . . DZ
Kirkgate . . . . DZ 48
Lands Lane . . . . DZ 49
Merrion Centre . . . . . . DZ

Aire Street . . . . CZ 2
Blenheim Walk . . . . CY 6
Bradford Road . . . . AV 9
Bridge Street . . . . DZ 10
Cambridge Road . . . . . AY 14
City Square . . . . DZ 15
Cleckheaton Road . . . . AX 16
Commercial Road . . . . BV 17
Cookridge Street . . . . . DZ 20
Cross Stamford St. . . . . DY 21
Crown Point Road . . . . AZ 22
Domestic Street . . . . . AZ 23
Duncan Street . . . . . . DZ 25
East Parade . . . . CDZ 27
East Park Parade . . . . . BZ 28
East Street . . . . BZ 29
Eastgate . . . . DZ 31
Gelderd Road . . . . . . AZ 32
Great Wilson Street . . . AZ 37
Hanover Way . . . . CZ 39
Harrogate Road . . . . . AY 40
Huddersfield Road . . . . AX 41
Hyde Park Road . . . . . AY 43
Infirmary Street . . . . . DZ 44
Ivy Street . . . . BZ 45
King Street . . . . CZ 46
Lupton Avenue . . . . . . BZ 50
Marsh Lane . . . . DZ 51
Meadow Lane . . . . AZ 52
Merrion Street . . . . . . DZ 53
Merrion Way . . . . DZ 55
New Briggate . . . . DZ 57
New Road Side . . . . . . BV 59
New York Road . . . . . . DZ 60
Oakwood Lane . . . . . . BY 63
Park Lane . . . . CZ 64
Portland Crescent . . . . DZ 65
Pudsey Road . . . . BV 67
Queen Street . . . . CZ 68
Rodley Lane . . . . BV 69
Roseville Road . . . . . . BYZ 70
Roundhay Road . . . . . . DY 71
St. Paul's Street . . . . . CZ 72
St. Peter's Street . . . . . DZ 73
Shaw Lane . . . . AY 74
Sheepscar St. South . . DY 75
Skinner Lane . . . . DY 76
South Accommodation Road . . . . BZ 77
South Parade . . . . CDZ 78
Stainbeck Road . . . . . . AY 79
Templenewsam Road . CV 80
Victoria Road . . . . AZ 81
Wade Lane . . . . DZ 82
Wellington Road . . . . . AZ 83
West Street . . . . CZ 84
Westgate . . . . CZ 85

at Bramhope NW : 8 m. on A 660 – BV – ✉ 0532 Leeds :

Post House (T.H.F.), Leeds Rd, LS16 9JJ, ☎ 842911, Telex 556367, Fax 843451, – rm – 180. VISA
M 19.95 **st.** and a la carte – 7.60 – **126 rm** 85.00/100.00 **st.**, **1 suite** 150.00 **st.** – SB (weekends only) 90.00/104.00 **st.**

Parkway, Otley Rd, LS16 8AG, S : 2 m. on A 660 ☎ 672551, Telex 556614, Fax 674410, – rm – 250. VISA
M 10.95/14.00 **st.** and a la carte 4.95 – 7.50 – **103 rm** 79.00/120.00 **st.** – SB (weekends only) 36.00/41.00 **st.**

MICHELIN Distribution Centre, Gelderd Rd, LS12 6EU, ☎ 793911, Fax 794577 BX

ALFA-ROMEO Domestic St. ☎ 468141
BMW Sheepscar Way ☎ 620641
FORD 83 Roseville Rd ☎ 455955
FORD 54 Dolly Lane ☎ 421222
FORD Whitehall Rd ☎ 634222
MAZDA York Rd ☎ 480093
PEUGEOT South Milford ☎ 0977 (South Milford) 682714
PEUGEOT-TALBOT, CITROEN Meadow Rd ☎ 444531
PORSCHE, SAAB, MAZDA Apperley Lane, Yeadon ☎ 0532 (Rawdon) 502231
RENAULT Regent St. ☎ 430837
ROVER Town St., Stanningley ☎ 571811
ROVER Water Lane ☎ 438091
ROVER, DAIMLER-JAGUAR, ROLLS-ROYCE, BENTLEY Roseville Rd ☎ 432731
TOYOTA Regent St. ☎ 444223
VAUXHALL 123 Hunslet Rd ☎ 439911
VAUXHALL-OPEL Armley Rd ☎ 434554
VOLVO Harrogate Rd ☎ 694666
VOLVO Wellington Rd ☎ 436412
VW-AUDI Gelderd Rd ☎ 633431

ATS Cross Green Lane ☎ 459423
ATS 2 Regent St. ☎ 430652

Les plans de ville sont disposés le Nord en haut.

LEEK Staffs. 402 403 404 N 24 – pop. 19 689 – ECD : Thursday – ✉ Stoke-on-Trent – 0782.

Big Birchall ☎ 385889 – Newcastle Rd, Walbridge ☎ 383060.

Bank End Farm Motel, Longsdon, Leek Old Rd, ST9 9QJ, SW : 2 ½ m. by A 53 ☎ 383638, « Working farm », –
M 16.00 **st.** 3.00 – **8 rm** 22.50/33.00 **st.**

FORD Chatfields, Sneyol St. ☎ 383114
VAUXHALL-OPEL Broad St. ☎ 399605

LEEMING BAR North Yorks. 402 P 21 – pop. 1 468 – ECD : Wednesday – ✉ Northallerton – 0677 Bedale.

♦London 235 – ♦Leeds 44 – ♦Middlesbrough 30 – ♦Newcastle-upon-Tyne 52 – York 37.

White Rose, DL7 9AY, ☎ 22707, Fax 25123 – VISA
M 5.10/9.50 **st.** and a la carte 3.40 – **18 rm** 25.00/40.00 **st.** – SB 48.00 **st.**

LEE-ON-THE-SOLENT Hants. 403 404 Q 31 – pop. 7 068 – ECD : Thursday – 0705.

Brune Lane ☎ 550207.

♦London 81 – ♦Portsmouth 13 – ♦Southampton 15 – Winchester 23.

Belle Vue, 39 Marine Par. East, PO13 9BW, ☎ 550258, Fax 552624, – VISA
M 15.00 **st.** 3.75 – **24 rm** 60.00/72.00 **st.** – SB (weekends only) 82.50/104.50 **st.**

NISSAN High St. ☎ 551785

LEICESTER Leics. 402 403 404 Q 26 – pop. 324 394 – ECD : Monday and Thursday – 0533.

See : Guildhall★ BY **B** – Museum and Art Gallery★ CY **M2** – St. Mary de Castro's Church★(12C) BY **A**.

Leicestershire, Evington Lane ☎ 736035, E : 2 m. AY – Western Park, Scudamore Rd ☎ 876158, W : 4 m. AY – Humberstone Heights, Gypsy Lane ☎ 761905, E : 3 m. by A 47 AX – Oadby, Leicester Road Racecourse ☎ 700326, S : 2 m. AZ – Rothley Park, Westfield Lane, Rothley ☎ 302019, N : 6 m. AX – Cambridge Rd, Whetstone ☎ 861424, by A 426 AZ.

East Midlands Airport : Castle Donington ☎ 0332 (Derby) 810621, Telex 37543, NW : 22 m. by A 50 AX and M1.

St. Margaret's Bus Station ☎ 532353 – 2-6 St. Martin's Walk ☎ 511300.

♦London 107 – ♦Birmingham 43 – ♦Coventry 24 – ♦Nottingham 26.

Plans on following pages

Holiday Inn, 129 St. Nicholas Circle, LE1 5LX, ☎ 531161, Telex 341281, Fax 513169, – rm – 250. VISA BY c
M 10.00/15.25 **st.** and a la carte – 8.00 – **187 rm** 75.00/100.00 **st.**, **1 suite** 150.00/180.00 **st.** – SB (weekends only) 129.00/134.00 **st.**

Grand, 73 Granby St., LE1 6ES, ☎ 555599, Telex 342244, Fax 544736 – rm – 450. VISA CY o
M *(closed Saturday lunch)* 11.95 **st.** and a la carte 4.00 – 7.00 – **91 rm** 75.00/92.50 **st.**, **1 suite** 110.00 **st.** – SB (weekends only) 132.00/145.00 **st.**

LEICESTER

BUILT UP AREA

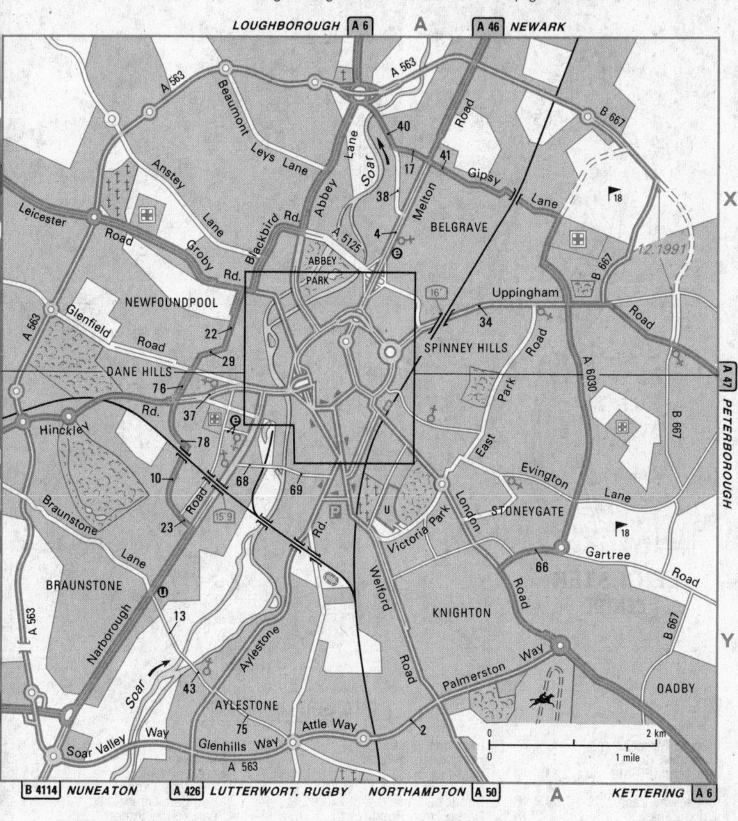

Belmont (Best Western), De Montfort St., LE1 7GR, ℘ 544773, Telex 34619, Fax 470804 – rm – 150. VISA CY **c**
closed 24 to 27 December – **M** *(closed Saturday lunch)* 13.00/15.00 **t.** and a la carte 5.00 – **68 rm** 67.00/90.00 **st.** – SB (weekends only) 76.00/83.00 **st.**

St. James, Abbey St., LE1 3TE, ℘ 510666, Telex 342434, Fax 515183 – 150. VISA CX **a**
M *(closed Sunday lunch)* 8.40/12.50 **st.** and a la carte 3.25 – 6.50 – **73 rm** 62.00/93.00 **st.** – SB (weekends only) 72.00/76.00 **st.**

Spindle Lodge, 2 West Walk, LE1 7NA, ℘ 551380 – CY **r**
closed 21 December-1 January – **M** (by arrangement) approx. 10.85 **st.** – **13 rm** 21.00/40.50 **st.**

Seaforth, 12 Westcotes Drive, LE3 0QR, ℘ 554895 – AY **c**
closed 25 and 26 December – **M** (by arrangement) 6.50 **st.** – **4 rm** 22.00/33.00 **s.**

Scotia, 10 Westcotes Drive, LE3 0QR, ℘ 549200, – AY **e**
M (by arrangement) approx. 10.25 **t.** 3.00 – **16 rm** 20.00/40.00 **t.**

Curry House, 64 London Rd, LE2 0QD, ℘ 550688, Indian rest.. VISA
closed 25-26 December – **M** a la carte 10.40/18.10. CY **e**

Water Margin, 76-78 High St., LE1 5YP, ℘ 516422, Chinese (Canton) rest. – VISA BY **x**
M 6.50/19.00 **t.** and a la carte 3.50.

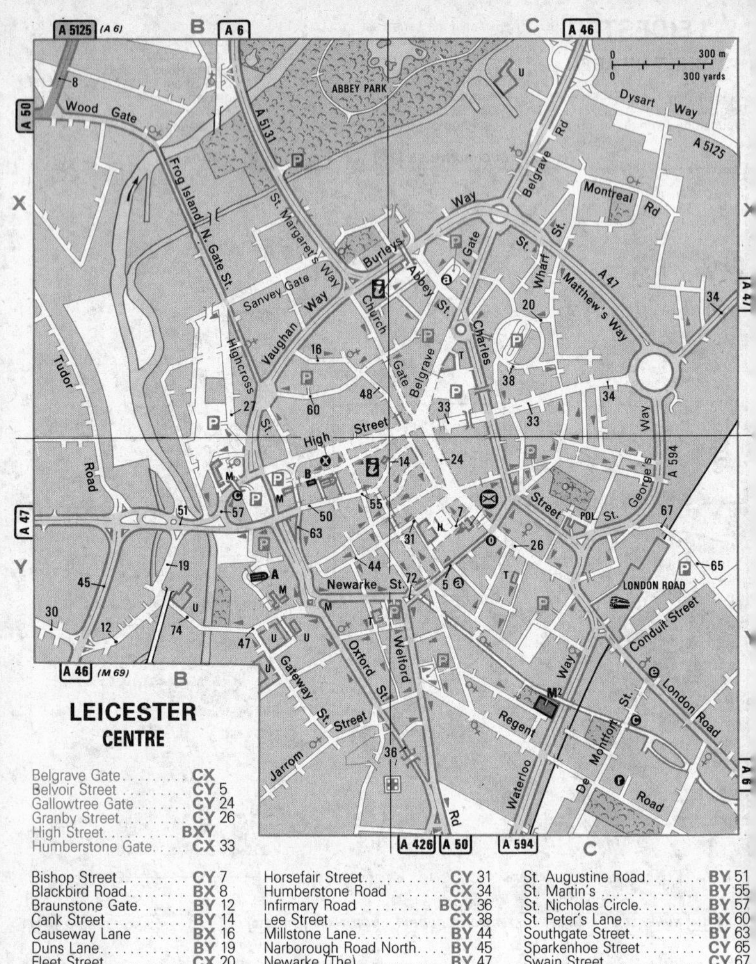

LEICESTER
CENTRE

Belgrave Gate CX
Belvoir Street .... CY 5
Gallowtree Gate .... CY 24
Granby Street .... CY 26
High Street .... BXY
Humberstone Gate .... CX 33

Bishop Street	CY 7	Horsefair Street	CY 31	St. Augustine Road	BY 51
Blackbird Road	BX 8	Humberstone Road	CX 34	St. Martin's	BY 55
Braunstone Gate	BY 12	Infirmary Road	BCY 36	St. Nicholas Circle	BY 57
Cank Street	BY 14	Lee Street	CX 38	St. Peter's Lane	BX 60
Causeway Lane	BX 16	Millstone Lane	BY 44	Southgate Street	BY 63
Duns Lane	BY 19	Narborough Road North	BY 45	Sparkenhoe Street	CY 65
Fleet Street	CX 20	Newarke (The)	BY 47	Swain Street	CY 67
Great Central Street	BX 27	New Bond Street	BCX 48	Welford Place	CY 72
Hinckley Road	BY 30	Peacock Lane	BY 50	Western Boulevard	BY 74

X Casa Romana, 5 Albion St., LE1 6GD, ℘ 541174, Italian rest. — CY a
M (booking essential).

X **Curry Pot,** 78-80 Belgrave Rd, ℘ 538256, Indian rest. – AE VISA — AX e
closed Sunday lunch – **M** a la carte 10.95/18.40 **t.**

at Rothley N : 5 m. by A 6 –AX– on B 5328 – ✉ 0533 Leicester :

Rothley Court (T.H.F), Westfield Lane, LE7 7LG, W : ½ m. on B 5328 ℘ 374141, Telex 342811, Fax 374483, ≤, « Part 12C house and chapel », – TV ☎ P – 100. AE VISA
M 10.50/18.50 **st.** and a la carte 4.50 – 7.60 – **35 rm** 70.00/90.00 **st.**, **1 suite** 120.00 **st.** – SB (weekends only) 94.00 **st.**

Limes, 35 Mountsorrel Lane, LE7 7PS, ℘ 302531 – TV ☎ P. VISA.
closed 23 December-3 January – **M** (by arrangement) 16.00 **st.** – **11 rm** 35.00/50.00 **st.**

at Thrussington NE : 10 m. by A 46 –AX– ✉ Leicester – 0664 Melton Mowbray :

Travelodge without rest., Green Acres Filling Station, LE7 8TF, on A 46 (southbound carriageway) ℘ 424525, Reservations (Toll free) 0800 850950 – TV P. AE VISA. – **32 rm** 24.00/29.50 **t.**

at Oadby SE : 3 ½ m. by A 6 on A 5096 – ✉ ☎ 0533 Leicester :

Leicestershire Moat House (Q.M.H.), Wigston Rd, LE2 5QE, ✆ 719441, Fax 720559 – rm – 250
57 rm.

at Glen Parva S : 4 ½ m. on A 426 – ✉ ☎ 0533 Leicester :

Glen Parva Manor, The Ford, Little Glen Rd, LE2 9TL, E : ½ m. on A 5096 ✆ 774604, – . VISA
closed Saturday lunch, Sunday dinner and 25-26 December – **M** 11.50/19.50 **t.** and a la carte 4.00.

at Whetstone S : 5 ½ m. by A 426 – AY – ✉ ☎ 0533 Leicester :

Old Vicarage, 123 Enderby Rd, LE8 3JH, ✆ 771195 – . VISA.
closed Saturday lunch, Sunday and Bank Holidays – **M** a la carte 14.00/23.75 **st.** 4.00.

at Braunstone SW : 2 m. on A 46 – BY – ✉ ☎ 0533 Leicester :

Country Court (Stakis), LE3 2WQ, SW : 1 ¾ m. on A 46 ✆ 630066, Telex 34429, Fax 630627, , , , – rm rest – 80. VISA
M *(closed lunch Saturday and Bank Holidays)* a la carte 14.85/21.95 **t.** 6.00 – 7.75 – **131 rm** 74.00/84.00 **t.**, **10 suites** 95.00 **t.**

Post House (T.H.F.), Braunstone Lane East, LE3 2FW, ✆ 630500, Telex 341009, Fax 823623 – rm – 160. VISA AY **u**
M *(closed Saturday lunch)* 11.00/14.00 **st.** and a la carte 3.95 – 7.50 – **172 rm** 67.00/89.00 **st.** – SB (weekends only) 76.00 **st.**

at Narborough SW : 6 m. by A 46 – AY – and A 5096 on B 4114 – ✉ ☎ 0533 Leicester :

Charnwood, 48 Leicester Rd, LE9 5DF, ✆ 862218, Fax 750119, – . VISA
M *(closed Saturday lunch and Sunday dinner)* 20.00/25.00 **st.** and a la carte 4.00 – **20 rm** 45.00/60.00 **st.**

at Leicester Forest East W : 3 m. on A 47 – AY – ✉ ☎ 0533 Leicester :

Leicester Forest Moat House (Q.M.H.), Hinckley Rd, LE3 3GH, ✆ 394661, Fax 394952 – – 100
34 rm.

Red Cow without rest., Hinckley Rd, LE3 3PG, ✆ 387878, Fax 387878 –
31 rm.

AUDI-VW Dover St. ✆ 556262
CITROEN Lee Circle ✆ 25285
FORD Belgrave Gate ✆ 510111
FORD Conduit St. ✆ 544301
HONDA 33 St. Matthews Way ✆ 516281
NISSAN Abbey Lane ✆ 666861
PORSCHE Coventry Rd at Narborough ✆ 848270
RENAULT, ROLLS-ROYCE, BENTLEY Welford Rd ✆ 548757
ROVER Leicester Rd ✆ 881601
ROVER Parker Drive ✆ 352587
ROVER 60-62 North Gate St. ✆ 628612
ROVER Abbey Lane ✆ (05336) 669393
SKODA 177 Leicester Rd Mount Sorrel ✆ 303055
TALBOT-PEUGEOT 91 Abbey Lane ✆ 661501
VAUXHALL Main St., Evington ✆ 730421
VOLVO 459 Aylestone Rd ✆ 831052

ATS 16 Wanlip St. ✆ 624281
ATS 31 Woodgate ✆ 625611

LEIGH Heref. and Worc. – see Worcester.

LEIGH DELAMERE SERVICE AREA Wilts. – ✉ Chippenham – ☎ 0666 Malmesbury

Granada Lodge without rest., M 4 between junctions 18 and 17 (Eastbound Carriageway), SN14 6LB, ✆ 837097, Fax 837112 – . VISA.
35 rm 27.50/29.50 **st.**

LEIGHTON BUZZARD Beds. 404 S 28 – pop. 29 554 – ECD : Thursday – ☎ 0525.

Plantation Rd ✆ 373811, N : 1 m.

London 47 – Bedford 20 – Luton 12 – Northampton 30.

Swan, High St., LU7 7EA, ✆ 372148, Fax 370444 – – 40. VISA.
M 15.00/19.50 **t.** and a la carte 3.75 – **38 rm** 72.00/80.00 **t.** – SB (except Christmas and New Year) (weekends only) 75.00/100.00 **st.**

ALFA-ROMEO Victoria Rd, Linslade ✆ 371102
ROVER 2 Leighton Rd ✆ 373022

ATS Unit C, Camden Ind Est., 83 Lake St. ✆ 376158/379238

LENWADE-GREAT WITCHINGHAM Norfolk 404 X 25 – ECD : Wednesday – ✉ ☎ 0603 Norwich.

♦London 121 – Fakenham 14 – ♦Norwich 10.

- Lenwade House, Fakenham Rd, NR9 5QP, ☎ 872288, ≤, heated, park, squash – TV ☎ P
  14 rm.

LEOMINSTER Heref. and Worc. 403 L 27 – pop. 8 637 – ECD : Thursday – ☎ 0568.

See : Priory Church★ (14C) (the north aisle★ 12C).

Envir. : Berrington Hall★ (Georgian) *AC*, N : 3 m. – Croft Castle★ (15C) *AC*, NW : 6 m.

Leominster, Ford Bridge ☎ 2863, S : 3 m. on A 49.

6 School Lane ☎ 6460.

♦London 141 – ♦Birmingham 47 – Hereford 13 – Worcester 26.

- **Talbot** (Best Western), West St., HR6 8EP, ☎ 6347 – TV ☎ P – 150. AE VISA.
  M 11.50/17.50 **t.** and a la carte – **23 rm** 43.00/80.00 **t.** – SB 80.00/88.00 **st.**
- **Withenfield,** South St., HR6 8JN, ☎ 2011, – TV ☎ P. VISA.
  M (booking essential for non-residents) (lunch by arrangement)/dinner 13.75 **st.** 3.50 – **4 rm** 39.00/62.00 **st.** – SB 70.00/75.00 **st.**

at Stoke Prior SE : 2 m. by A 44 – ✉ ☎ 0568 Leominster :

- **Wheelbarrow Castle** with rm, HR6 0NB, on Leominster rd ☎ 2219, heated – TV P. AE VISA
  closed 25 December – **M** a la carte 12.10/17.20 **t.** 2.50 – **3 rm** 25.00/35.00 **t.**

at Eyton NW : 2 m. by B 4361 – ✉ ☎ 0568 Leominster :

- **The Marsh**, HR6 0AG, ☎ 3952 (from Spring : 613952), « Part 14C », – rm TV ☎ P. AE VISA.
  M (bar lunch)/dinner 30.00 **st.** 7.50 – **5 rm** 80.00/110.00 **st.** – SB 140.00/150.00 **st.**

FORD 4 Etnam St. ☎ 2060
PEUGEOT-TALBOT The Bargates ☎ 2337
RENAULT South St. ☎ 611879
ATS Market Mill, Dishley St. ☎ 2679/4114

"Short Breaks"

Many hotels now offer a special rate for a stay of 2 nights which includes dinner, bed and breakfast.

LEONARD STANLEY Glos. 403 404 N 28 – see Stroud.

LETCHWORTH Herts. 404 T 28 – pop. 31 146 – ECD : Wednesday – ☎ 0462.

Letchworth ☎ 683203.

♦London 40 – Bedford 22 – ♦Cambridge 22 – Luton 14.

- **Broadway Toby,** The Broadway, SG6 3NZ, ☎ 480111, Telex 82425, Fax 481563 – TV ☎ P – 180. AE VISA.
  closed 24 December-2 January – **M** (grill rest.) a la carte approx. 7.50 **t.** 3.50 – **35 rm** 60.00/70.00 **t.**

FORD 18-22 Station Rd ☎ 83722
HONDA Norton Way North ☎ 78191
ROVER Works Rd ☎ 73161
VW-AUDI Norton Way North ☎ 686341
ATS Unit 21, Jubilee Trade Centre, Works Rd ☎ 670517

LEWDOWN Devon 403 H 32 – ☎ 056 683.

♦London 238 – Exeter 37 – ♦Plymouth 22.

- **Lewtrenchard Manor**, EX20 4PN, S : ¾ m. by Lewtrenchard rd ☎ 256, Fax 332, « 17C manor house and gardens », park – rest TV ☎ P. AE VISA
  closed 7 January-1 February – **M** (lunch by arrangement)/dinner 28.00 **t.** and a la carte 5.00 – **8 rm** 70.00/130.00 **t.**

LEWES East Sussex 404 U 31 – pop. 14 499 – ECD : Wednesday – ☎ 0273.

See : Site★.

Envir. : Glynde Place (pictures★) *AC*, E : 3 ½ m. – Firle Place★ (mansion 15C-16C) *AC*, SE : 4 ½ m. – Ditchling Beacon ≤★, W : 7 ½ m. – Glyndebourne Opera Festival (May-August) *AC*, E : 3 m.

Chapel Hill ☎ 473245, Opp. Junction Cliffe High/South St.

32 High St. ☎ 471600/483448.

♦London 53 – Brighton 8 – Hastings 29 – Maidstone 43.

- **Shelleys** (Mt. Charlotte Thistle), High St., BN7 1XS, ☎ 472361, Fax 483152, – TV ☎ P – 50. AE VISA
  M 12.50/15.50 **t.** and a la carte 5.50 – 7.50 – **21 rm** 60.00/110.00 **t.** – SB (except May-August) 99.00/108.00 **st.**

Millers without rest., 134 High St., BN7 1XS, ✆ 475631, – TV.
closed mid December-mid January – **3 rm** 30.00/42.00 **st.**

Hillside without rest., Rotten Row, BN7 1TN, ✆ 473120, – .
3 rm 14.00/30.00 **s.**

FORD Station St. ✆ 474461
ROVER Brooks Rd ✆ 473186
VW Western Rd ✆ 473221

ATS 18 North St. ✆ 477972/3

LEYLAND Lancs. 402 L 22 – pop. 36 694 – ECD : Wednesday – 0772.

Envir. : Rufford Old Hall★ SW : 6 ½ m.

Wigan Rd ✆ 421359.

London 220 – Liverpool 31 – Manchester 32 – Preston 6.

Penguin, Leyland Way, PR5 2JX, E : ¾ m. on B 5256 ✆ 422922, Telex 677651, Fax 622282 – rm TV – 220. AE VISA
M 7.95/11.25 **st.** and a la carte 5.95 – 6.50 – **93 rm** 52.00/70.00 **st.** – SB 70.00/90.00 **st.**

PEUGEOT-TALBOT Golden Hill Lane ✆ 23416
SKODA Wigan Rd ✆ 423797

ATS Leyland Lane ✆ 431021/2

LICHFIELD Staffs. 402 403 404 O 25 – pop. 25 408 – ECD : Wednesday – 0543.

See : Cathedral★★ (12C-14C).

Donegal House, Bore St. ✆ 252109.

London 128 – Birmingham 16 – Derby 23 – Stoke-on-Trent 30.

George, Bird St., WS13 6PR, ✆ 414822, Fax 415817 – rm TV – 100. AE VISA
M 9.85/13.15 **st.** and a la carte **st.** 4.40 – 7.00 – **38 rm** 59.00/66.00 **st.** – SB (weekends only) 24.50/34.00 **st.**

Little Barrow, Beacon St., WS13 7AR, ✆ 414500 – TV – 50.
24 rm.

Angel Croft, 3 Beacon St., WS13 7AA, ✆ 258737, Fax 415605, – TV – 30. VISA.
closed 25 and 26 December – **M** *(closed Sunday dinner)* 16.25/18.00 **t.** 4.00 – **19 rm** 30.00/70.00 **t.**

Oakleigh House, 25 St. Chad's Rd, WS13 7LZ, ✆ 262688, – rest TV . VISA.
M *(closed Sunday and Monday)* (dinner only) a la carte 17.50 **t.** 3.25 – **10 rm** 34.00/52.00 **t.**

Gaialands without rest., 9 Gaiafields Rd, off Bulldog Lane, WS13 7LT, ✆ 263764, – .
4 rm 17.00/36.00 **s.**

XX **Thrales,** 40-44 Tamworth St. (corner of Backcester Lane), WS13 6JJ, ✆ 255091 – VISA
closed Saturday lunch, Sunday dinner, 26 to 30 December and Bank Holiday Mondays – **M** 7.95/24.00 **st.** and a la carte.

FORD Birmingham Rd ✆ 414566
NISSAN Birmingham Rd ✆ 414404
ROVER St. John St. ✆ 414451

ATS Eastern Av. ✆ 414200

LIFTON Devon 403 H 32 – pop. 966 – ECD : Tuesday – 0566.

London 238 – Bude 24 – Exeter 37 – Launceston 4 – Plymouth 32.

Arundell Arms (Best Western), Fore St., PL16 0AA, on A 30 ✆ 84666, Fax 84494, , – rest TV – 50. AE VISA
closed 4 days at Christmas – **M** 14.00/22.00 **t.** and a la carte 5.00 – **29 rm** 51.00/83.00 **t.** – SB 80.00/121.00 **st.**

LINCOLN Lincs. 402 404 S 24 – pop. 79 980 – ECD : Wednesday – 0522.

See : Site★ – Cathedral★★★ (11C-15C) (Angel Choir★★, Library : Magna Carta*AC*) Y – High Bridge★★ Z 9 – Usher Gallery★★ YZ **M1** – Jews House★ (12C) Y – Castle★ (11C)*AC* Y.

Envir. : Doddington Hall★ (Elizabethan) *AC*, SW : 7 m. by A 15 Z and A 46.

Carholme, Carholme Rd ✆ 36811, 1 m. from town centre – Canwick Park, Washingborough Rd ✆ 22166, S : 1 m. – Lincoln ✆ 042 771 (Torksey) 210, W : 12 m. – Millfield, Laughterton ✆ 042 771 (Torksey) 255, W : 12 m.

Humberside Airport : ✆ 0652 (Barnetby) 688456, N : 32 m. by A 15 Y.

9 Castle Hill ✆ 529828 – 21 The Cornhill ✆ 512971.

London 140 – Bradford 81 – Cambridge 94 – Kingston-upon-Hull 44 – Leeds 73 – Leicester 53 – Norwich 104 – Nottingham 38 – Sheffield 48 – York 82.

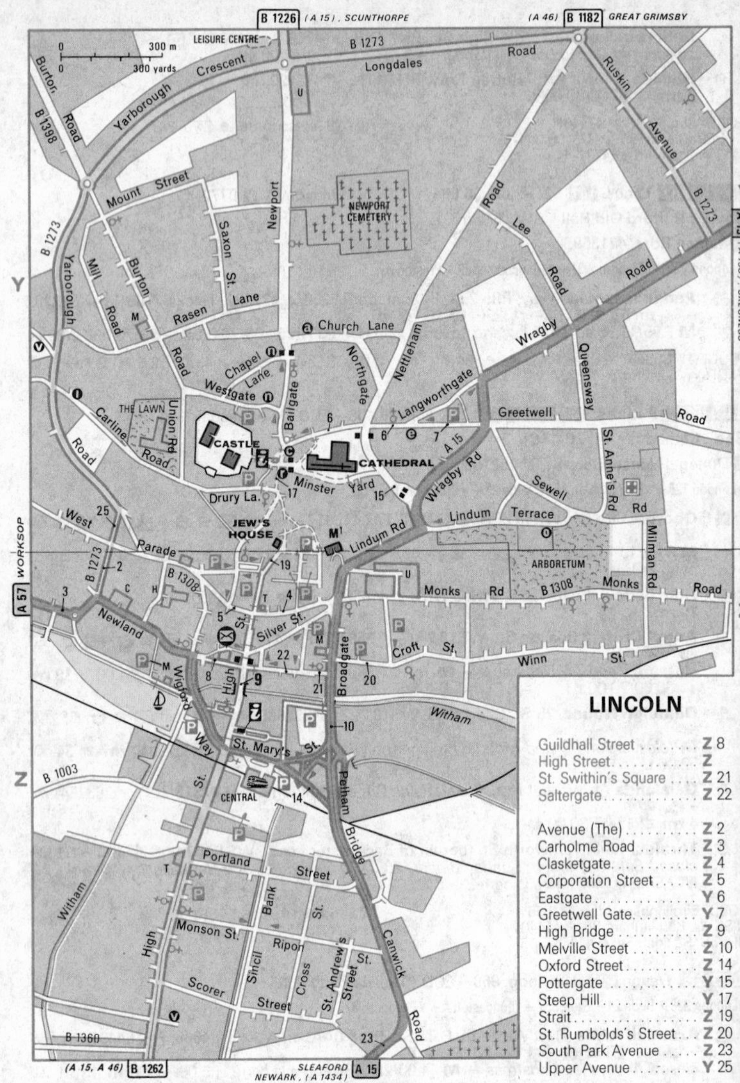

White Hart (T.H.F.), Bailgate, LN1 3AR, ✆ 526222, Telex 56304, Fax 531798, « Antique furniture » – ⇕ ⇔ rm TV ☎ 🚗 Ⓟ – 🏊 90. AE ⓓ VISA Y
M 12.50/17.95 **st.** and a la carte 🍷 9.50 – ☕ 8.00 – **36 rm** 75.00/95.00 **st.**, **13 suites** 125.00/160.00 **st.** – SB (weekends only) 104.00/114.00 **st.**

D'Isney Place without rest., Eastgate, LN2 4AA, ✆ 538881, Fax 511321, 🛏 – TV ☎. AE ⓓ VISA Y
18 rm ☕ 38.00/68.00 **t.**

Hillcrest, 15 Lindum Terr., LN2 5RT, ✆ 510182, <, 🛏 – TV ☎ Ⓟ. VISA Y
closed 22 December-2 January – **M** *(closed Sunday lunch)* (bar lunch)/dinner a la carte 9.35/13.30 **t.** – **17 rm** ☕ 36.50/49.50 **t.** – SB (weekends only) 64.00 **st.**

Minster Lodge without rest., 3 Church Lane, LN2 1QJ, ✆ 513220, Fax 513220 – TV ☎ Ⓟ. VISA. ✻ Y
5 rm ☕ 43.00/48.00 **t.**

Woodcocks, Burton Lane End, Saxilby Rd, LN1, NW : 3½ m. on A 57 ℘ 703000, – TV ☎ P
8 rm. by A 57 Z

Carline without rest., 3 Carline Rd, LN1 1HN, ℘ 530422 – TV P Y i
closed Christmas and New Year – **11 rm** 13.00/31.00 **st.**

Fircroft, 396-398 Newark Rd, LN6 8RX, SW : 2 m. on A 1434 ℘ 526522 – TV P
15 rm. by A 15 Z

Rowan Lodge without rest., 58 Pennell St., LN5 7TA, ℘ 529589 – P. Z v
4 rm 13.50/24.00 **st.**

Tennyson, 7 South Park Av., LN5 8EN, ℘ 521624 – TV P. AE VISA.
closed Christmas and New Year – **M** 11.00 **st.** 3.60 – **8 rm** 27.00/40.00 **st.** – SB 50.00/52.00 **st.** by A 158 Z

ABC without rest., 126 Yarborough Rd, LN1 1HP, ℘ 543560 – TV. Y v
closed 25 and 26 December – **8 rm** 18.00/28.00 **st.**

Harveys, 1 Exchequer Gate, Castle Sq., LN2 1PZ, ℘ 510333 – VISA Y r
closed Sunday dinner – **M** 12.50/23.50 **t.** 3.50.

Newport Arch, 50 Bailsgate, LN1 3AR, ℘ 45006, Chinese rest. Y n

Jews House, Jews House, 15 The Strait, LN2 1JD, ℘ 24851 « 12C town house » – VISA
closed Sunday and 2 weeks January-February – **M** 9.50 **t.** (lunch) and a la carte 11.40/16.40 **t.** 3.95. YZ x

at Washingborough E : 3 m. by B 1188 – Z – on B 1190 – ✉ 0522 Lincoln :

Washingborough Hall, Church Hill, LN4 1BE, ℘ 790340, – TV ☎ P – 50. AE VISA
M (bar lunch Monday to Saturday)/dinner 16.00 **t.** 3.00 – **12 rm** 42.00/75.00 **t.** – SB (except Christmas and New Year) 66.00/82.00 **st.**

at Branston SE : 3 m. on B 1188 – Z – 0522 Lincoln :

Moor Lodge, Sleaford Rd, LN4 1HU, ℘ 791366, Fax 510720 – TV ☎ & P – 160
25 rm.

MICHELIN Distribution Centre, Tritton Rd, LN6 7RX, ℘ 684023, Fax 500973 by A 1180 Z

BMW South Park Av. ℘ 521345
CITROEN 300 Wragby Rd ℘ 531195
DAIMLER-JAGUAR 116 High St. ℘ 513410
FIAT 314 Wragby Rd ℘ 534805
FORD Wragby Rd ℘ 530101
HONDA, LANCIA Wragby Rd ℘ 531735
LADA Newark Rd, North Hykeham ℘ 681242
MAZDA Tritton Rd ℘ 681094
MITSUBISHI Tritton Rd ℘ 500880
RENAULT 25 Wragby Rd ℘ 521252
ROVER Outer Circle Rd ℘ 535771
SAAB 247 Lincoln Rd ℘ 500200
TALBOT-PEUGEOT 477 High St. ℘ 529131
VAUXHALL Outer Circle Rd ℘ 527127
VOLVO 314 Wragby Rd ℘ 29462/3
VW-AUDI 223 Newark Rd ℘ 531881

ATS Crofton Rd, Allenby Rd Trading Est. ℘ 527225
ATS Newmark Rd, North Hykeham ℘ 684510

LIPHOOK Hants. 404 R 30 – pop. 4 697 – 0428.

Old Thorns, Longmoor Rd ℘ 724555.

London 50 – Guildford 17 – ♦Portsmouth 27.

Milland Place, Milland, GU30 7JW, S : 2 m. by A 3 ℘ 042 876 (Milland) 633, Fax 643, ≤, « Garden » – TV ☎ P. AE VISA.
M 15.00/19.50 **t.** and a la carte – 8.50 – **17 rm** 80.00/95.00 **t.**, **1 suite** 130.00 **t.** – SB (weekends only) 110.00/135.00 **t.**

Old Thorns, Longmoor Rd, GU30 7PE, W : 1 m. on B 2131 ℘ 724555, Fax 725036, 18, – TV ☎ P – 60. AE VISA.
M (see **Nippon-Kan** below) – 4.50 – **32 rm** 82.00/105.00 **t.**

Nippon-Kan (at Old Thorns H.), Longmoor Rd, GU30 7PE, W : 1 m. on B 2131 ℘ 724555, Fax 725036, Japanese rest., – P. AE VISA
M 40.00 **t.** and a la carte.

LISKEARD Cornwall 403 G 32 **The West Country G.** – pop. 6 213 – ECD : Wednesday – 0579.

See : Church★.

Envir. : St. Neot★ (Church★★) NW : 5 m.

London 261 – Exeter 59 – ♦Plymouth 18 – Truro 37.

Well House, St. Keyne, PL14 4RN, S : 3½ m. on St. Keyne Well Rd ℘ 42001, ≤, heated, – TV ☎ P. AE VISA
M *(closed Monday to non-residents)* 21.00/27.50 **t.** 3.50 – 9.00 – **7 rm** 60.00/110.00 **t.** – SB (November-March) 115.00/137.50 **st.**

Old Rectory, Duloe Rd, St. Keyne, PL14 4RL, S : 3¼ m. on B 3254 ℘ 42617, – rest TV P. VISA
closed Christmas – **M** (dinner only) (residents only) a la carte 9.50/15.90 **st.** 3.00 – **8 rm** 20.00/54.00 **st.** – SB (October-March) 60.00 **st.**

ATS 10 Dean St. ℘ 45489/45247

LITTLE CHALFONT Bucks. 404 S 29 – pop. 4 093 – ☎ 0494.

Lodge Lane, Amersham ☎ 4877.

London 31 – Luton 20 – Oxford 37.

XX **Dynasty 1,** 9 Nightingales Corner, HP7 9PZ, ☎ 764038, Chinese (Peking) rest. – AE VISA
M 18.00/28.00 **t.** and a la carte 15.00/25.00 **t.**

PEUGEOT 4 White Lion Rd ☎ 764666

LITTLE HAVEN Dyfed 403 E 28 – ECD : Thursday – ✉ Haverfordwest – ☎ 0437 Broad Haven

London 258 – Haverfordwest 8.

Haven Fort, Settlands Hill, SA62 3LA, ☎ 781401, ≤ St. Brides Bay, – P.
late March-mid October – **M** (bar lunch)/dinner 13.50 3.50 – **15 rm** 21.50/42.00 **t.**

Pendyffryn without rest., SA62 3LA, ☎ 781337, ≤ – TV P.
Easter-September – **7 rm** 16.50/37.00 **t.**

LITTLE LANGDALE Cumbria 402 K 20 – see Ambleside.

LITTLEOVER Derbs. 402 403 404 P 25 – see Derby.

LITTLE PETHERICK Cornwall 403 F 32 – see Padstow.

LITTLEPORT Cambs 404 U 26 – see Ely.

LITTLE SINGLETON Lancs. – see Blackpool.

LITTLE THORNTON Lancs. 402 L 22 – see Blackpool.

LITTLE WALSINGHAM Norfolk 404 W 25 – ✉ Walsingham – ☎ 0328 Fakenham.

London 117 – Cambridge 67 – Cromer 21 – Norwich 32.

White Horse Inn, Fakenham Rd, East Barsham, NR21 0LU, S : 2 ¼ m. on B 110
☎ 820645 – TV P. VISA.
M *(closed Tuesday lunch, Sunday dinner and Monday)* 9.25 **t.** (lunch) and a la carte – **3 rm**
30.00/52.00 **t.** – SB (November-April) (weekends only) 48.00/78.00 **st.**

X **Old Bakehouse** with rm, 33-35 High St., NR22 6BZ, ☎ 820454. VISA.
closed 3 weeks January, February, 1 week June and 2 weeks October-November – **M**
(closed Sunday and Monday) (dinner only) a la carte 14.55/17.75 **t.** 4.00 – **3 rm** 18.00
36.00 **t.**

LITTLE WEIGHTON Humberside 402 S 22 – see Kingston-upon-Hull.

LITTLE WYMONDLEY Herts. 404 T 28 – see Hitchin.

Besonders angenehme Hotels oder Restaurants
sind im Führer rot gekennzeichnet.
Sie können uns helfen, wenn Sie uns die Häuser angeben,
in denen Sie sich besonders wohl gefühlt haben.
Jährlich erscheint eine komplett überarbeitete Ausgabe
aller Roten Michelin-Führer.

... XXXXX ... X

LIVERPOOL Merseyside 402 403 L 23 – pop. 538 809 – ECD : Wednesday – ☎ 051.

See : Site★ – Walker Art Gallery★★ DY M2 – Liverpool Cathedral★★ EZ – Metropoltan Cathedr of Christ the King★★ (1967) EY Z – Albert Dock★ CZ – Merseyside Martime Museum★ *AC* CZ M – Tate Gallery Liverpool★ CZ.

Envir. : Speke Hall★ (16C) *AC*, SE : 8 m. by A 561 BX.

Dunnings Bridge Rd, Bootle ☎ 928 6196, N : 5 m. by A 5036 AV – Allerton Park ☎ 428 104 S : 5 m. by B 5180 BX – Lee Park, Childwall Valley Rd ☎ 487 3882, E : 7 m. by B 5178 BX West Derby, Yee Tree Lane ☎ 228 1540, E : 2 m. by A 580 BV – Woolton, Doe Park, Spek Rd ☎ 486 1601 BX – Liverpool municipal, Ingoe Lane, Kirkby ☎ 546 5435 BV.

Liverpool Airport : ☎ 486 8877, Telex 629323, SE : 6 m. by A 561 BX – **Terminal** : Pier Head

to Ireland (Dun Laoghaire) (Sealink) 1 daily (9 h) – to Belfast (Belfast Ferries) 1 daily – t Douglas (Isle of Man Steam Packet Co.) (summer only) (4 h).

to Birkenhead (Merseyside Transport) frequent services daily (7-8 mn) – to Wallase (Merseyside Transport) frequent services daily (7-8 mn).

29 Lime St. ☎ 709 3631 – Atlantic Pavilion, Albert Dock ☎ 708 8854.

London 219 – Birmingham 103 – Leeds 75 – Manchester 35.

Town plans : Liverpool pp. 2-5

Liverpool Moat House (Q.M.H.), Paradise St., L1 8JD, ✆ 709 0181, Telex 627270, Fax 709 2706, – ☎ – 400. AE VISA DZ n
M *(closed Saturday lunch)* 14.00/17.25 **st.** and a la carte 7.45 – **244 rm** 77.50/99.00 **t.**, **7 suites** 180.00/230.00 **t.** – SB (weekends only) 87.00/118.00 **st.**

Atlantic Tower (Mt. Charlotte Thistle), 30 Chapel St., L3 9RE, ✆ 227 4444, Telex 627070, Fax 236 3973, ☎ – 120. AE VISA CY r
M *(closed Saturday lunch)* 14.50/14.95 **t.** and a la carte 4.40 – 6.95 – **216 rm** 67.50/75.00 **st.**, **10 suites** 125.00/150.00 **st.** – SB 72.00 **st.**

St. George's (T.H.F.), St. John's Precinct, Lime St., L1 1NQ, ✆ 709 7090, Telex 627630, Fax 709 0137 – rm ☎ – 200. AE VISA DY v
M 10.95 **st.** and a la carte 3.75 – 7.60 – **153 rm** 60.00/81.00 **st.**, **2 suites** 87.00/95.00 **st.**

Trials, 56-62 Castle St., L2 7LQ, ✆ 227 1021, Telex 626125, Fax 236 0110 – ☎. AE VISA. CY e
M *(closed Saturday lunch and Sunday)* 10.95 **t.** (lunch)/dinner a la carte 12.70/20.35 **t.** 6.95 – 7.50 – **20 rm** 98.00/150.00 **t.**

Crest (T.H.F.), Lord Nelson St., L3 5QB, ✆ 709 7050, Telex 627954, Fax 709 2193 – rm ☎ – 500. AE VISA DY i
M *(closed lunch Saturday and Sunday)* 8.00/15.00 **st.** and a la carte 6.50 – 7.95 – **155 rm** 64.00/76.00 **st.**, **1 suite** 80.00/95.00 **st.** – SB (weekends only) 74.00/82.00 **st.**

XXX **L'Oriel,** Oriel Chambers, 14 Water St., L2 8TD, ✆ 236 5025 – AE VISA CY o
closed 25-26 December and 1 January – **M** *(closed lunch Saturday, Sunday and Bank Holidays)* 12.25/14.25 **t.** and a la carte 4.10.

XXX **Churchill's,** Churchill House, Tithebarn St., L2 2PB, ✆ 227 3877 – AE VISA CY a
closed Saturday lunch, Sunday and Bank Holidays – **M** 12.00/14.00 **t.** and a la carte.

at Bootle N : 5 m. by A 565 – AV – ✉ 051 Liverpool :

Park (De Vere), Park Lane West, L30 3SU, on A 5036 ✆ 525 7555, Telex 629772, Fax 525 2481 – ☎ – 50. AE VISA
M 6.00/9.95 **t.** and a la carte 3.50 – **58 rm** 49.50/62.00 **t.** – SB (weekends only) 60.00 **st.**

at Huyton E : 7 m. by M 62 on A 5058 – ✉ 051 Liverpool :

Derby Lodge, Roby Rd, L36 4HD, ✆ 480 4440, Telex 629371, Fax 480 8132, – ☎. AE VISA.
M *(closed Saturday lunch)* 10.50/12.00 **st.** and a la carte 3.70 – **19 rm** 70.00/84.00 **t.**

at Aigburth SE : 4 m. on A 561 – BX – ✉ 051 Liverpool :

Grange, 14 Holmefield Rd, L19 3PG, ✆ 427 2950, Fax 427 9055, – rest ☎. AE VISA.
M (dinner only and Sunday lunch)/dinner 16.95 **t.** and a la carte 4.30 – **25 rm** 48.80/65.25 **st.** – SB (weekends only) 89.15 **st.**

BMW Scotland Rd ✆ 207 7213
BMW Aigburth Rd ✆ 427 8086
CITROEN Ullet Rd ✆ 727 1414
FIAT East Prescot Rd ✆ 228 9151
FIAT Tonon St. ✆ 708 8224
FORD Linacre Lane ✆ 922 0070
FORD Lunts Heath Rd ✆ 424 5781
FORD Speke Hall Rd ✆ 486 2233
HONDA Berry St. ✆ 709 1475
JAGUAR Queens Drive ✆ 220 4557
LADA Washington Par. ✆ 922 0481
MAZDA Longmoor Lane ✆ 525 6733
MAZDA Southport Rd ✆ 520 2282
MERCEDES Duke St. ✆ 227 4171
MITSUBISHI Woolton Rd ✆ 737 2138
NISSAN Mersey Rd ✆ 924 6575
NISSAN Mill Lane ✆ 254 1010
NISSAN Northway ✆ 531 7105
PEUGEOT-TALBOT Pilch Lane ✆ 489 4433
PEUGEOT-TALBOT Coronation Rd ✆ 924 6575
RENAULT, SEAT Edge Lane ✆ 228 4737
ROVER 72-74 Coronation Rd ✆ 924 6411
ROVER Kensington ✆ 263 0661
ROVER Long Lane ✆ 523 3737
SAAB 574 Aigburth Rd ✆ 427 3500
SUZUKI Duke St. ✆ 708 5656
TOYOTA Gale Rd ✆ 546 8228
VAUXHALL-OPEL 215 Knowsley Rd ✆ 922 7585
VAUXHALL-OPEL Derby Rd ✆ 933 7575
VOLVO Fox St. ✆ 207 4364
VW-AUDI Moor Lane, Thornton ✆ 931 2861
VW-AUDI Edge Lane ✆ 228 0919
YUGO Millfoot Rd ✆ 486 2840

ATS 15/37 Caryl St. ✆ 709 8032
ATS De Silva St., Huyton ✆ 489 8386/7
ATS 190-194 St. Mary's Rd, Garston ✆ 427 3665
ATS 73-77 Durning Rd, Wavertree ✆ 263 7604
ATS 46-50 Lightbody St. ✆ 207 4618
ATS Musker St., Crosby ✆ 931 3166

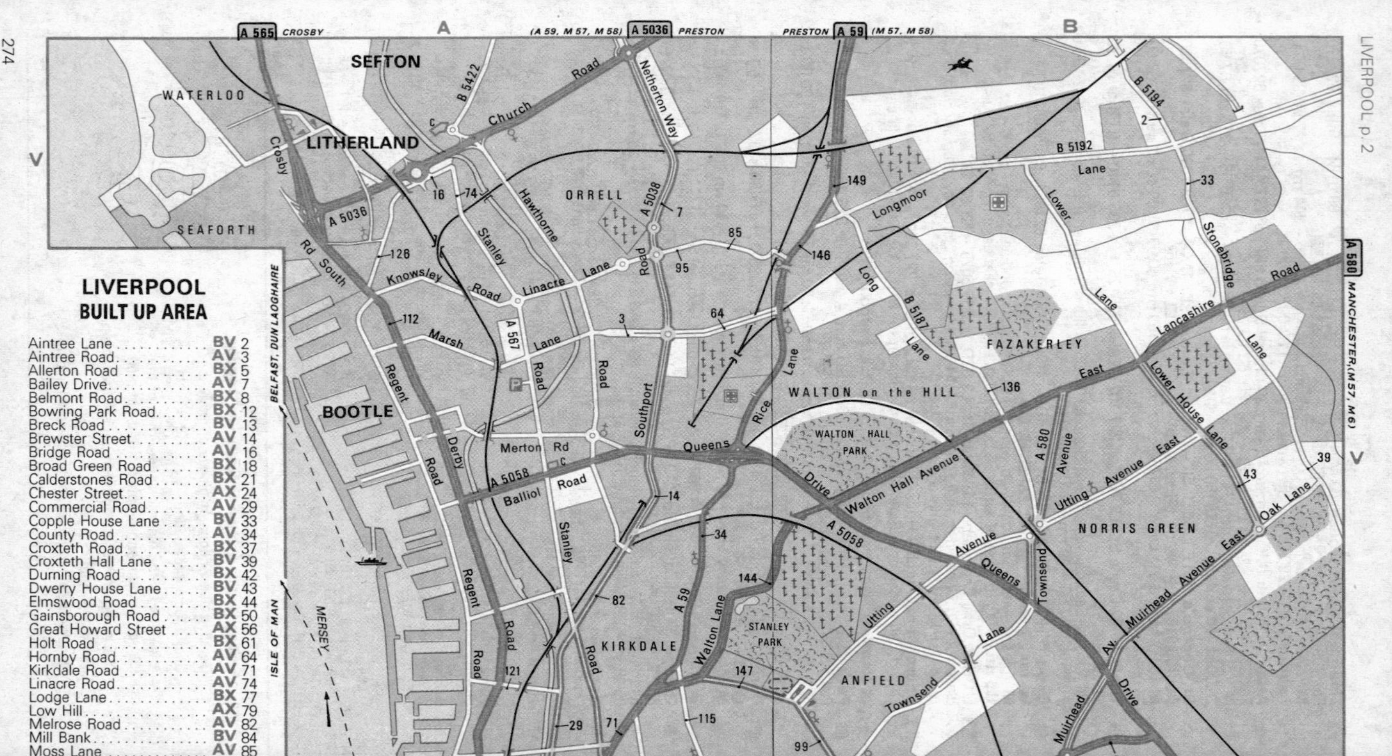

LIVERPOOL
BUILT UP AREA

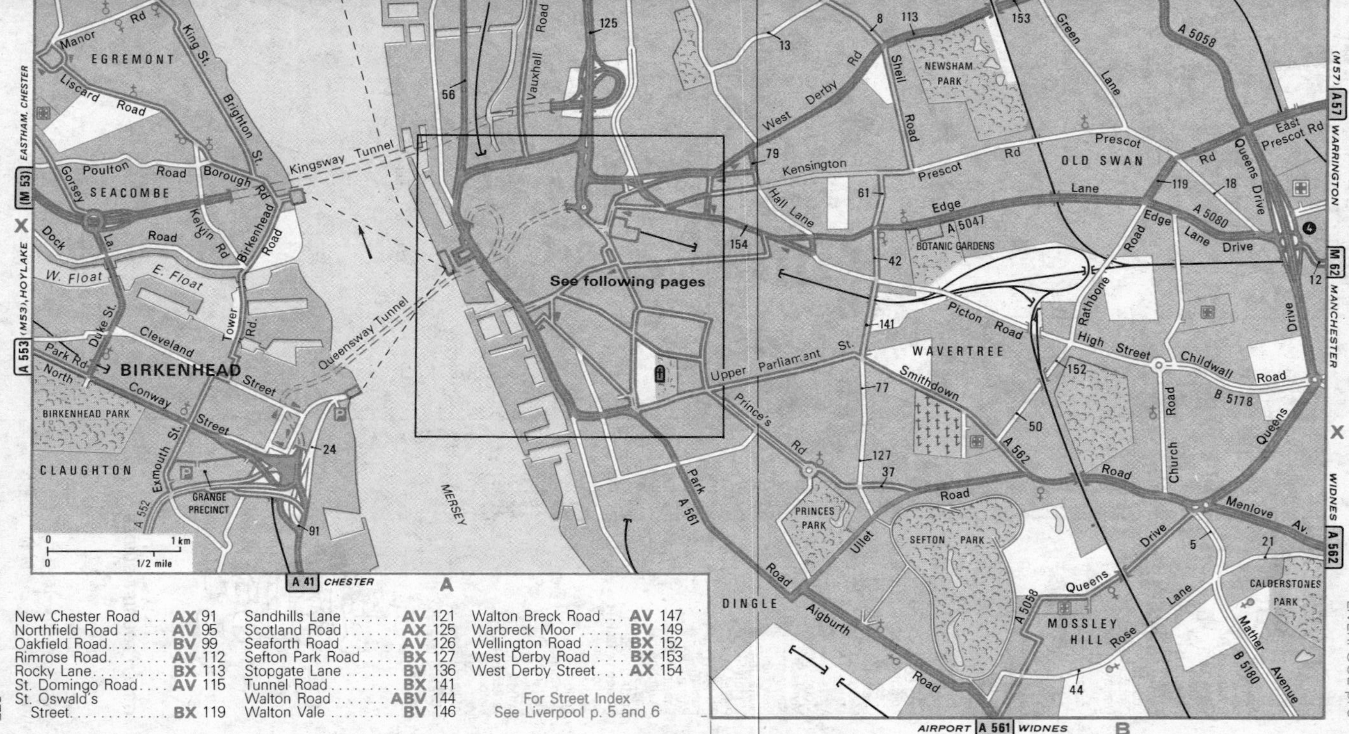

New Chester Road . . . AX 91	Sandhills Lane . . . . AV 121	Walton Breck Road . . . AV 147
Northfield Road . . . . . AV 95	Scotland Road . . . . AX 125	Warbreck Moor . . . . . BV 149
Oakfield Road . . . . BV 99	Seaforth Road . . . . AV 126	Wellington Road . . . . BX 152
Rimrose Road . . . . AV 112	Sefton Park Road . . . . BX 127	West Derby Road . . . . BX 153
Rocky Lane . . . . BX 113	Stopgate Lane . . . . BV 136	West Derby Street . . . . AX 154
St. Domingo Road . . . . AV 115	Tunnel Road . . . . BX 141	
St. Oswald's Street . . . . BX 119	Walton Road . . . . ABV 144	
	Walton Vale . . . . BV 146	

For Street Index
See Liverpool p. 5 and 6

LIVERPOOL
CENTRE

Argyle St.	DZ	6
Blackburne Pl.	EZ	11
Brunswick Rd.	EY	19
Canning Pl.	CZ	23
Churchill Way	DY	25
Clarence St.	EYZ	26
College Lane	DZ	28
Commutation Row	DY	30
Cook St.	CY	32
Crosshall St.	DY	36
Daulby St.	EY	40
Erskine St.	EY	45
Fontenoy St.	DY	48
Forrest St.	DZ	49
George's Dock Gate	CY	51
Grafton St.	DZ	53
Great Charlotte St.	DY	54
Great Howard St.	CY	56
Hatton Garden	DY	57
Haymarket	DY	58
Hood St.	DY	62
Houghton St.	DY	65
Huskisson St.	EZ	66
James St.	CY	68
King Edward St.	CY	69
Knight St.	EZ	72
Leece St.	EZ	73
Liver St.	CDZ	76
Mansfield St.	DEY	80
Mathew St.	CDY	81
Moss St.	EY	86
Mount St.	EZ	88
Myrtle St.	EZ	89
Newington	DZ	92
New Quay	CY	93
North John St.	CY	96
Norton St.	DY	97
Parker St.	DY	103
Pitt St.	DZ	104
Prescot St.	EY	105
Prince's Rd	EZ	107
Ranelagh St.	DY	108
Richmond St.	DY	109
Roe St.	DY	114
St. James Pl.	EZ	117
St. John's Lane	DY	118
School Lane	DYZ	122
Scotland Pl.	DY	123
Sefton St.	DZ	129
Seymour St.	EY	130
Skelhorne St.	DY	133
Stanley St.	CDY	135
Suffolk St.	EZ	137
Tarleton St.	DY	139
Victoria St.	DY	143
Water St.	CY	150
William Brown St.	DY	156
York St.	DZ	157

A 565
C
A 5038
A 5036
Pall
Vauxhall
Leeds Street
A 5053
Road
Y
Bath Street
Old Hall Street
A 565
Mall
St.
Tithebarn
MOURFIELDS
Chapel St.
Dale
Castle St.
St Nicholas Place
Royal Liver Building
Cunard Building
Port of Liverpool Bldg.
Pier Head
The Strand
Lord
JAMES ST.
QUEENSWAY TUNNEL
Strand St.
Wapping
TATE GALLERY
ALBERT DOCK
M1
Britannia Pavillion
Z
MERSEY
0 300 m
0 300 yards
C

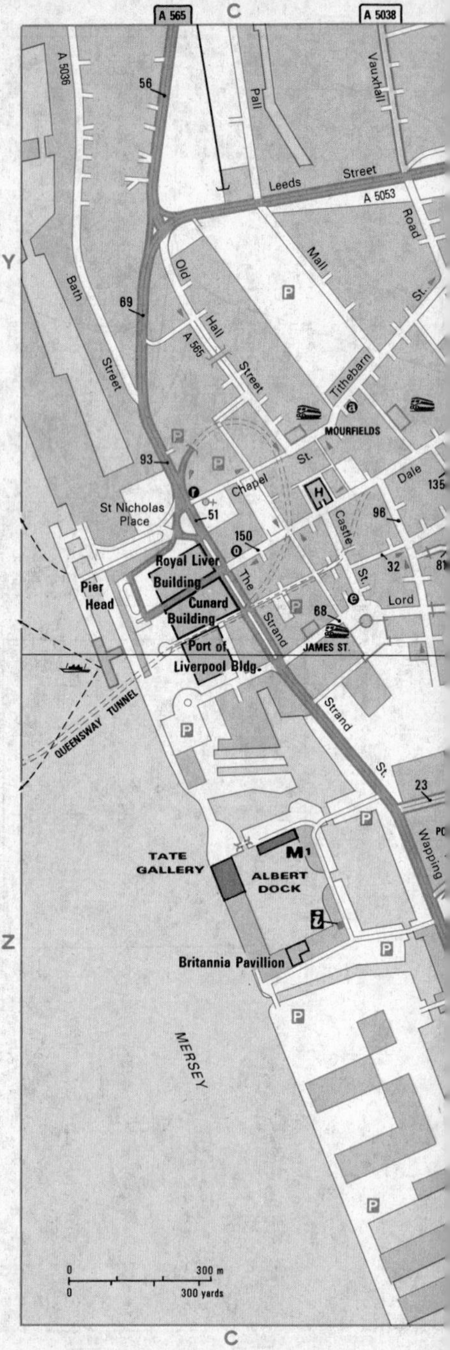

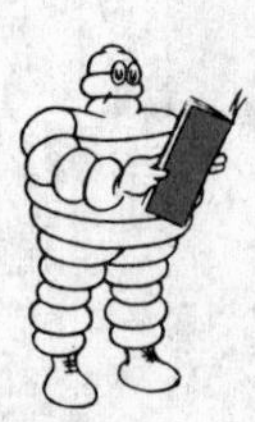

GREEN TOURIST GUIDES

Picturesque scenery, buildings
Attractive routes
Touring programmes
Plans of towns and buildings.

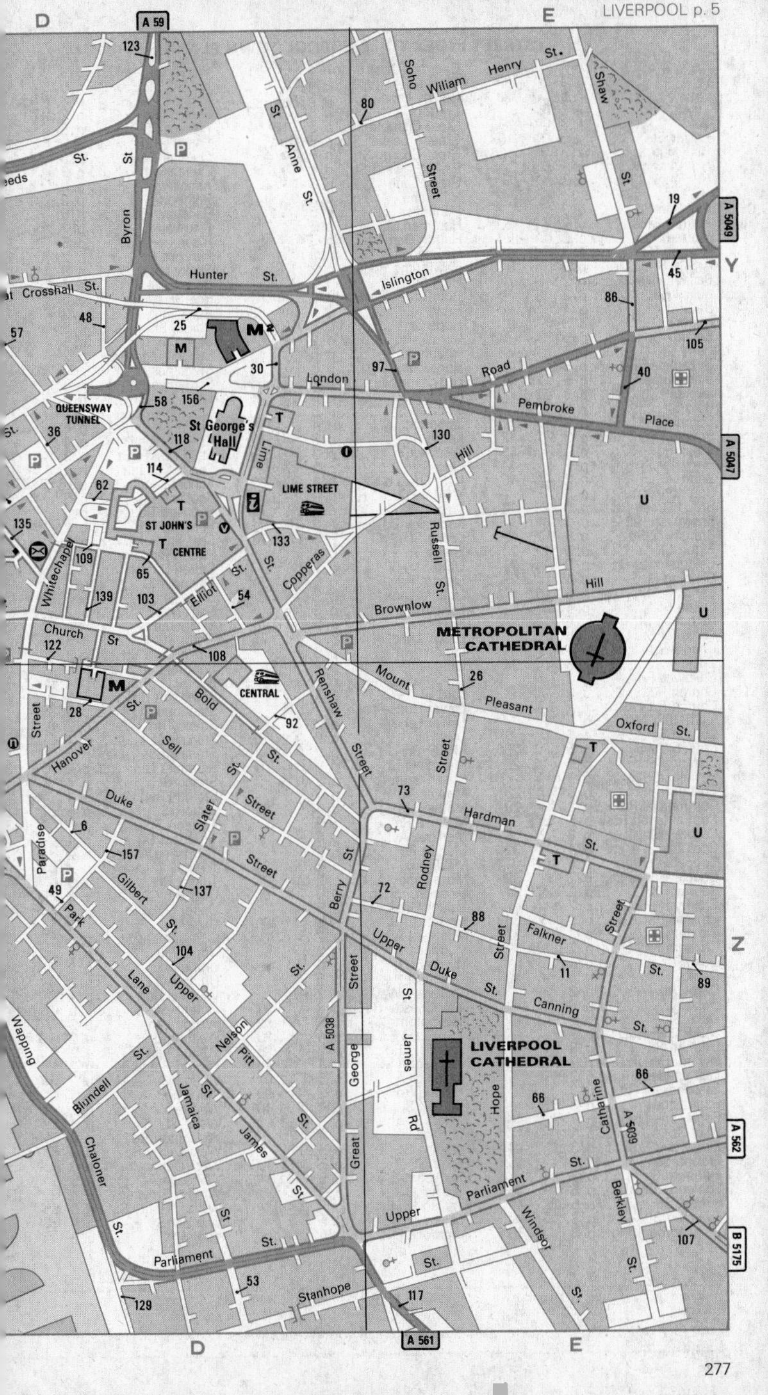
D
E
A 59
123
Soho
William
Henry
St.
Shaw
80
St.
Anne
St.
Street
St.
Leeds
St.
Byron
St.
19
A 5049
Y
Hunter
St.
Islington
45
Crosshall
St.
86
48
25
105
57
M
M
30
97
London
Road
40
QUEENSWAY
TUNNEL
58
156
Pembroke
Place
St George's
Hall
T
St.
36
118
130
Hill
A 5047
Lime
114
LIME STREET
U
62
T
ST JOHN'S
135
Russell
St.
109
T
CENTRE
65
133
Copperas
St.
Whitechapel
139
103
Elliot
St.
54
Hill
Brownlow
U
Church
St
METROPOLITAN
CATHEDRAL
122
108
M
Renshaw
Mount
26
28
CENTRAL
Bold
St.
Pleasant
Oxford
St.
92
Street
Hanover
Sell
St.
St.
Street
T
Street
73
Duke
Slater
St.
Street
Hardman
U
6
Paradise
157
Street
St.
T
Gilbert
Street
137
Berry
Rodney
St.
49
72
88
Street
Falkner
Z
Park
St.
104
Upper
Street
St.
89
11
Upper
Duke
St.
Lane
Canning
St.
Wapping
Nelson
St.
A 5038
James
Pitt
LIVERPOOL
CATHEDRAL
St.
66
St
Blundell
George
Hope
66
Catharine
A 5039
Jamaica
St.
Rd
A 562
Chaloner
James
Great
St.
Parliament
St.
Berkley
St
Windsor
Upper
107
St.
St.
Parliament
St.
St.
St.
53
Stanhope
B 5175
129
117
A 561
D
E

STREET INDEX TO LIVERPOOL TOWN PLANS

Street	Page	Square	No.
Bold St.	p. 5	DZ	
Church St.	p. 5	DY	
Lime St.	p. 5	DY	
London Rd	p. 5	DEY	
Lord St.	p. 4	CDY	
Parker St.	p. 5	DY	103
Ranelagh St.	p. 5	DY	108
Renshaw St.	p. 5	DEZ	
St. Johns Centre	p. 5	DY	

Street	Page	Square	No.
Aigburth Rd	p. 3	BX	
Aintree Lane	p. 2	BV	2
Aintree Rd	p. 2	AV	3
Allerton Rd	p. 3	BX	5
Argyle St.	p. 5	DZ	6
Bailey Drive	p. 2	AV	7
Balliol Rd	p. 2	AV	
Bath St.	p. 4	CY	
Belmont Rd	p. 3	BX	8
Berkley St.	p. 5	EZ	
Berry St.	p. 5	DZ	
Birkenhead Rd	p. 3	AX	
Blackburne Pl.	p. 5	EZ	11
Blundell St.	p. 5	DZ	
Bold St.	p. 5	DZ	
Borough Rd	p. 3	AX	
Bowring Park Rd	p. 3	BX	12
Breck Rd	p. 3	ABX	13
Brewster St.	p. 2	AV	14
Bridge Rd.	p. 2	AV	16
Brighton St.	p. 3	AX	
Broad Green Rd	p. 3	BX	18
Brownlow Hill	p. 5	DEY	
Brunswick Rd	p. 5	EY	19
Byron St.	p. 5	DY	20
Calderstones Rd	p. 3	BX	21
Canning Pl.	p. 4	CZ	23
Canning St.	p. 5	EZ	
Castle St.	p. 4	CY	
Catharine St.	p. 5	EZ	
Chaloner St.	p. 5	DZ	
Chapel St.	p. 4	CY	
Chester St.	p. 3	AX	24
Childwall Rd	p. 3	BX	
Church Rd	p. 3	BX	
Church Rd LITHERLAND	p. 2	AV	
Church St.	p. 5	DY	
Churchill Way	p. 5	DY	25
Clarence St.	p. 5	EYZ	26
Cleveland St.	p. 3	AX	
College Lane	p. 5	DZ	28
Commercial Rd	p. 2	AV	29
Commutation Row	p. 5	DY	30
Conway St.	p. 3	AX	
Cook St.	p. 4	CY	32
Copperas Hill	p. 5	DE	
Copple House La.	p. 2	BV	33
County Rd	p. 2	AV	34
Crosby Rd South	p. 2	AV	
Crosshall St.	p. 5	DY	36
Croxteth Rd	p. 3	BX	37
Croxteth Hall Lane	p. 2	BV	39
Dale St.	p. 4	CDY	
Daulby St.	p. 5	EY	40
Derby Rd	p. 2	AV	
Duke St.	p. 5	DZ	
Duke St. BIRKENHEAD	p. 3	AX	
Durning Rd	p. 3	BX	42
Dwerry House Lane	p. 2	BV	43
East Lancashire Rd	p. 2	BV	
East Prescot Rd	p. 3	BX	
Edge Lane	p. 3	BX	
Edge Lane Drive	p. 3	BX	
Elliot St.	p. 5	DY	
Elmswood Rd	p. 3	BX	44
Erskine St.	p. 5	EY	45
Exmouth St.	p. 3	AX	
Fontenoy St.	p. 5	DY	48
Forrest St.	p. 5	DZ	49
Freeman St.	p. 3	AX	
Gainsborough Rd	p. 3	BX	50
George's Dock Lane	p. 4	CY	51
Gilbert St.	p. 5	DZ	
Gorsey Lane	p. 3	AX	
Grafton St.	p. 5	DZ	53
Great Charlotte St.	p. 5	DY	54
Great Crosshall St.	p. 5	DY	
Great George St.	p. 5	DY	
Great Howard St.	p. 4	CY	56
Green Lane	p. 3	BX	
Hall Lane	p. 3	BX	
Hannover St.	p. 5	DZ	
Hardman St.	p. 5	EZ	
Hatton Garden	p. 5	DY	57
Haymarket	p. 5	DY	58
Hawthorne Rd	p. 2	AV	
High St.	p. 3	BX	
Holt Rd	p. 3	BX	61
Hood St.	p. 5	DY	62
Hope St.	p. 5	EZ	
Hornby Rd	p. 2	AV	64
Houghton St.	p. 5	DY	65
Hunter St.	p. 5	DY	
Huskisson St.	p. 5	EZ	66
Islington	p. 5	EY	
Jamaica St.	p. 5	DZ	
James St.	p. 4	CY	68
Kelvin Rd	p. 3	AX	
Kensington	p. 3	BX	
King St.	p. 3	AX	
King Edward St.	p. 4	CY	69
Kirkdale Rd.	p. 2	AV	71
Knight St.	p. 5	EZ	72
Knowsley Rd	p. 2	AV	
Leece St.	p. 5	EZ	73
Leeds St.	p. 4	CY	
Lime St.	p. 5	DY	
Linacre Rd	p. 2	AY	74
Linacre Lane	p. 2	AV	
Liscard Rd	p. 3	AX	
Liver St.	p. 5	DZ	76
Lodge Lane	p. 3	BX	77
London Rd	p. 5	DEY	
Long Lane	p. 2	BV	
Longmoor Lane	p. 2	BV	
Lord St.	p. 4	CDY	
Lower House Lane	p. 2	BV	
Lower Lane	p. 2	BV	
Low Hill	p. 3	AX	79
Manor Rd	p. 2	AX	
Mansfield St.	p. 5	DEY	80
Marsh Lane	p. 2	AV	
Mather Av.	p. 3	BX	
Mathew St.	p. 4	CDY	81
Melrose Rd	p. 2	AV	
Menlove Av.	p. 3	BV	
Merton Rd	p. 2	AV	
Mill Bank	p. 2	BV	84
Moss Lane	p. 2	AV	85
Moss St.	p. 5	EY	86
Mount Pleasant	p. 5	EZ	
Mount St.	p. 5	EZ	88
Muirhead Av.	p. 2	BV	
Muirhead Av. East	p. 2	BV	
Myrtle St.	p. 5	EZ	89
Nelson St.	p. 5	DZ	
Netherton Way	p. 2	AV	
New Chester Rd	p. 3	AX	91
Newington	p. 5	DZ	92
New Quay	p. 4	CY	93
Northfield Rd	p. 2	AV	95
North John St.	p. 4	CY	96
Norton St.	p. 5	EY	97
Oakfield Rd	p. 2	BV	99
Old Hall St.	p. 4	CY	101
Oxford St.	p. 5	EZ	
Pall Mall	p. 4	CY	
Paradise St.	p. 5	DZ	
Parker St.	p. 5	DY	103
Park Lane	p. 5	DZ	
Park Rd.	p. 3	AX	
Park Rd North	p. 3	AX	
Parliament St.	p. 5	DZ	
Pembroke Pl.	p. 5	EY	
Picton Rd	p. 3	BX	
Pitt St.	p. 5	DZ	10
Poulton Rd	p. 3	AX	
Prescot Rd	p. 3	BX	
Prescot St.	p. 5	EY	10
Prince's Rd	p. 5	EZ	10
Queens Drive	p. 3	BX	
Queensway	p. 3	AX	
Ranelagh St.	p. 5	DY	1
Rathbone Rd	p. 3	BX	
Renshaw Rd.	p. 5	DZ	
Rice Lane	p. 2	AV	
Richmond St.	p. 5	DY	10
Rimrose Rd	p. 2	AV	11
Rocky Lane	p. 3	BX	11
Rodney St.	p. 5	EZ	
Roe St.	p. 5	DY	11
Rose Lane	p. 3	BX	
Russel St.	p. 5	DY	
St. Anne St.	p. 5	DY	
St. Domingo Rd.	p. 2	AV	11
St. James Pl.	p. 5	EZ	11
St. James Rd	p. 5	EZ	
St. James St.	p. 5	DZ	
St. John's Lane	p. 5	DY	11
St. Johns Centre	p. 5	DY	
St. Nicholas Pl.	p. 4	CY	
St. Oswald's St.	p. 3	BX	11
Sandhills Lane	p. 2	AV	12
School Lane	p. 5	DYZ	12
Scotland Pl.	p. 5	DY	12
Scotland Rd	p. 3	AX	12
Seaforth Rd	p. 2	AV	12
Seel St.	p. 5	DZ	
Sefton Park Rd.	p. 3	BX	12
Sefton St.	p. 3	DZ	12
Seymour St.	p. 5	EY	13
Shaw St.	p. 5	EY	13
Sheil Rd	p. 3	BX	
Skelhorne St.	p. 5	EY	13
Slater St.	p. 5	DZ	
Smithdown Rd.	p. 3	BX	
Soho St.	p. 5	EY	
South John St.	p. 4	CYZ	
Southport Rd	p. 2	AV	
Stanhope St.	p. 5	DZ	
Stanley Rd	p. 2	AV	
Stanley St.	p. 4	CDY	13
Stonebridge Lane	p. 2	BV	
Stopgate Lane	p. 2	BV	13
Strand St.	p. 4	CZ	
Strand (The)	p. 4	CY	
Suffolk St.	p. 5	DZ	13
Tarleton St.	p. 5	DY	13
Tithebarn St.	p. 4	CY	
Townsend Av.	p. 2	BV	
Townsend Lane	p. 2	BV	
Tunnel Rd.	p. 3	BX	14
Ullet Rd	p. 3	BX	
Upper Duke St.	p. 5	EZ	
Upper Parliament St.	p. 5	EZ	
Upper Pitt	p. 5	DZ	
Utting Av.	p. 2	AV	
Utting Av. East	p. 2	BV	
Vauxhall Rd	p. 4	CY	
Victoria St.	p. 5	DY	143
Walton Lane	p. 2	AV	
Walton Rd	p. 2	ABV	144
Walton Vale	p. 2	BV	146
Walton Breck Rd	p. 2	AV	147
Walton Hall Av.	p. 2	BV	
Wapping	p. 4	CDZ	
Warbreck Moor	p. 2	BV	149
Water St.	p. 4	CY	150
Wellington Rd	p. 3	BX	152
West Derby Rd	p. 3	BX	153
West Derby St.	p. 3	AX	154
Whitechapel	p; 5	DY	
William Brown St.	p. 5	DY	156
William Henry St.	p. 5	EY	
Windsor St.	p. 5	EZ	
York St.	p. 5	DZ	157

The names of main shopping streets are indicated in red at the beginning of the list of streets.

IZARD Cornwall 403 E 34 **The West Country G.** – ☎ 0326 The Lizard.

ee : Lizard Peninsula★.

nvir. : Kynance Cove★★★, NW : 1 ½ m. – Landewednack★, Church★, E : ½ m. – Cury★, hurch★, N : 6 ½ m. – Cadgwith★, NE : 4 m. – Ruan Minor (Church★), NE : 4 m. – Gunwalloe shing Cove★, NW : 9 m. – Mawgan In Meneage Church★, N : 10 m.

London 326 – Penzance 24 – Truro 29.

- **Housel Bay**, Housel Cove, TR12 7PG, ☎ 290417, Fax 290359, ≤ Housel Cove, – TV ☎ P. AE VISA
  closed 1 January-10 February – **M** (bar lunch Monday to Saturday)/dinner 19.00 **st.** 3.50 – **23 rm** 26.00/72.00 **st.** – SB 60.00/93.00 **st.**
- **Penmenner House**, Penmenner Rd, TR12 7NR, ☎ 290370, ≤, – TV P. VISA.
  M 9.35 **st.** 3.10 – **8 rm** 20.65/56.00 **st.** – SB (October-March) 48.00/54.70 **st.**
- **Parc Brawse House**, Penmenner Rd, TR12 7NR, ☎ 290466, ≤, – rest P. VISA – *March-mid November* – **M** 7.50 **s.** – **6 rm** 14.50/39.00 **s.**

LANARMON DYFFRYN CEIRIOG Clwyd 402 403 K 25 – pop. 137 – ✉ Llangollen – ☎ 069 176. ♦London 196 – Chester 33 – Shrewsbury 32.

- **West Arms**, LL20 7LD, ☎ 665, Fax 262, – rm P – 60. AE VISA
  M (bar lunch Monday to Saturday)/dinner 17.50 **t.** 3.75 – **12 rm** 45.00/80.00 **t.**, **2 suites** 60.00/120.00 **t.** – SB 70.00/80.00 **st.**
- **Hand**, LL20 7LD, ☎ 666, Fax 262, – rm P. AE VISA.
  M (bar lunch Monday to Saturday)/dinner 15.95 **t.** 4.25 – **13 rm** 41.00/64.00 **t.**, **1 suite** 80.00 **t.** – SB 90.00 **st.**

LANBEDR Gwynedd 402 403 H 25 – pop. 486 – ECD : Wednesday – ☎ 034 123.

London 262 – Holyhead 54 – Shrewsbury 100.

- **Pensarn Hall**, LL45 2HS, N : ¾ m. on A 496 ☎ 236, ≤, – TV P. VISA.
  March-October – **M** (dinner only) 9.50 **st.** 3.00 – **7 rm** 22.00/40.00 **t.** – SB (March-May and October) 45.00/50.00 **st.**
- **Ty Mawr**, LL45 2NH, ☎ 440, – TV P
  M (bar lunch)/dinner a la carte approx. 12.85 **st.** – **10 rm** 25.00/56.00 **st.** – SB 68.00/72.00 **st.**

LLANBEDROG Gwynedd 402 403 G 25 – ✉ ☎ 0758 Pwllheli.

♦London 263 – Caernarfon 25 – Dolgellau 43.

- **Penarwel Country House**, LL53 7NN, NE : ½ m. on A 499 ☎ 740719, « Edwardian country house », – TV P.
  closed January – **M** (bar lunch)/dinner 11.50 **st.** and a la carte 2.65 – **7 rm** 25.00/48.00 **st.**

LLANBERIS Gwynedd 403 H 24 – pop. 1 809 – ECD : Wednesday – ☎ 0286.

Amgueddfa'r Gogledd/Museum of the North ☎ 870765 (summer only).

♦London 243 – Caernarfon 7 – Chester 65 – Shrewsbury 78.

- XX **Y Bistro,** 43-45 High St., LL55 4EU, ☎ 871278. VISA
  closed Sunday and Monday – **M** (booking essential) (dinner only) 22.00 **t.** 4.00.

FIAT Cwm-Y-Go ☎ 870234

LLANDEILO Dyfed 403 I 28 – pop. 1 598 – ECD : Thursday – ☎ 0558.

Envir. : Talley (Abbey and lakes★) N : 7 m.

18 Glynhir, Llandybie, nr. Ammanford ☎ 0269 (Llandybie) 850472.

♦London 218 – Brecon 34 – Carmarthen 15 – ♦Swansea 25.

- Cawdor Arms, Rhosmaen St., SA19 6EN, ☎ 823500 – TV ☎ P – **17 rm.**

at Rhosmaen N : 1 m. on A 40 – ✉ ☎ 0558 Llandeilo :

- XX **Plough Inn** with rm, SA19 6NP, ☎ 823431, Fax 823969, Italian rest., – TV ☎ P – 40. VISA. – *closed 25 and 26 December* – **M** *(closed Sunday dinner)* a la carte 10.10/20.00 **t.** – 3.00 – **12 rm** 30.00/45.00 **t.**

ATS Towy Terr., Ffairfach ☎ 822567

LLANDELOY Dyfed – see St. Davids.

LLANDOWROR Dyfed 403 G 28 – see St. Clears.

LLANDRILLO Clwyd 402 403 J 25 – pop. 477 – ✉ Bala – ☎ 049 084.

♦London 210 – Chester 40 – Dolgellau 26 – Shrewsbury 46.

- **Tyddyn Llan Country House**, LL21 0ST, ☎ 264, Fax 264, « Example of 18C rural architecture », – ☎ P. VISA
  M *(closed lunch Monday and Tuesday to non residents)* (bar lunch Wednesday to Saturday)/dinner 21.00 **st.** 5.00 – **10 rm** 42.50/73.00 **st.** – SB (except Christmas) 95.00/101.00 **st.**

LLANDRILLO-YN-RHOS (RHOS-ON-SEA) Clwyd – see Colwyn Bay.

LLANDRINDOD WELLS Powys 403 J 27 – pop. 4 232 – ECD : Wednesday – 0597.

Envir. : Elan Valley★★ W : from Llandrindod Wells.

18 2010, E : 1 m.

Town Hall 2600/822600.

♦London 204 – Brecon 29 – Carmarthen 60 – Shrewsbury 58.

Metropole, Temple St., LD1 5DY, 822881, Telex 35237, Fax 824828, rm – 300. VISA
M 9.50/16.50 **st.** and a la carte 3.00 – **120 rm** 45.00/68.00 **st.**, **2 suites** 72.00/90.00 **s** – SB 85.00/88.00 **st.**

Charis, Pentrosfa, LD1 5NL, S : ¾ m. by A 483 824732, – rest
April-October – **M** (by arrangement) 6.50 **st.** – **4 rm** 13.00/30.00 **st.**

at Howey S : 1 ½ m. on A 483 – 0597 Llandrindod Wells :

Three Wells Farm, LD1 5PB, NE : ½ m. 822484, « Working farm », rest
M 6.50 2.50 – **10 rm** 13.50/30.00 **t.**, **4 suites** 19.00/42.00 **t.** – SB (October-May) 39.00 52.00 **st.**

Holly Farm, LD1 5PP, W : ½ m. 822402, « Working farm », – rest
3 rm.

Corven Hall, LD1 5RE, S : ½ m. by A 483 on Hundred House rd 823368, rest
closed December – **M** 8.00 **st.** 3.00 – **10 rm** 22.50/29.00 **st.** – SB (except June-September) 37.00/41.00 **st.**

AUDI-VW Doldowlod 810376

Michelin n'accroche pas de panonceau aux hôtels et restaurants qu'il signale.

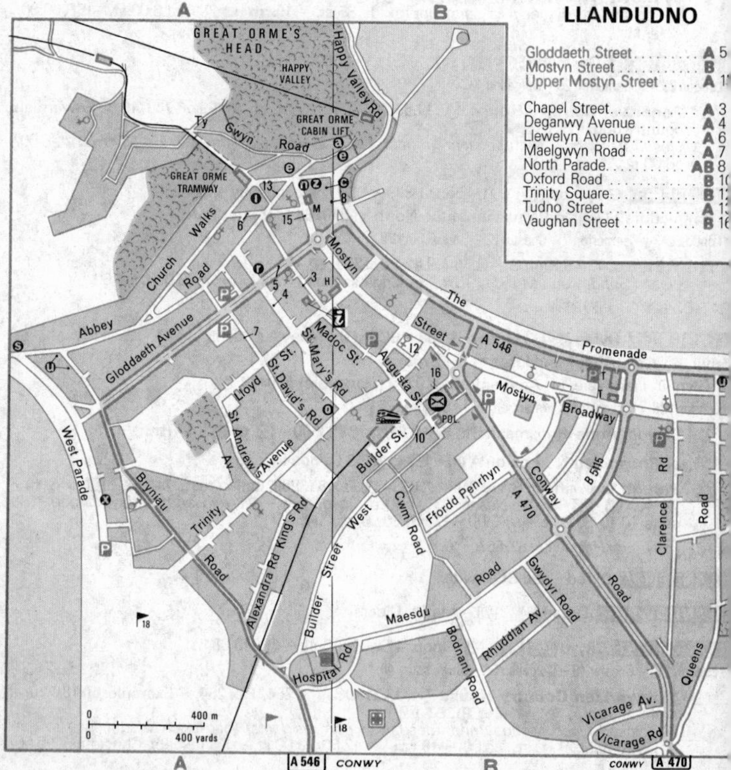

LLANDUDNO Gwynedd 402 403 I 24 – pop. 13 202 – ECD : Wednesday except summer – 0492. **See** : Great Orme's Head (<** from the summit) by Ty-Gwyn Rd A – Tour of the Great Orme's Head**.

Rhos-on-Sea Residential, Penryn Bay 49641, by A 546 A – 72 Bryniau Rd, West Shore 75325 A – Hospital Rd 76450 B. Chapel St. 76413.

London 243 – Birkenhead 55 – Chester 47 – Holyhead 43.

Plan opposite

Bodysgallen Hall, LL30 1RS, SE : 2 m. on A 470 B 584466, Telex 617163, Fax 582519, < gardens and mountains, « Part 17C and 18C hall with terraced gardens », park, – rest – 25. AE VISA.
M (booking essential) 16.50/28.75 **st.** 5.00 – 8.50 – **19 rm** 85.00/135.00 **st.**, **9 suites** 148.00/193.00 **st.** – SB (November-April) (except Bank Holidays) 160.00/180.00 **st.**

St. Tudno, North Parade, LL30 2LP, 874411, Telex 61400, Fax 860407, – rest rest. AE VISA. A c
closed 1 to 15 January – **M** 10.50/21.00 **t.** and a la carte 3.95 – **21 rm** 49.50/105.00 **t.** – SB 78.00/118.00 **st.**

Empire, 73 Church Walks, LL30 2HE, 860555, Telex 617161, Fax 860791, heated, – rest – 25. AE VISA. A e
closed 2 weeks Christmas-New Year – **M** (bar lunch Monday to Saturday)/dinner 18.50 **st.** and a la carte 4.50 – **56 rm** 45.00/100.00 **st.** – SB 70.00/120.00 **st.**

Annex: **Empire (No 72),** 72 Church Walks, LL30 2HE, 860555, Telex 617161, Fax 860791, « Victoriana » – . AE VISA. A e
closed 2 weeks Christmas-New Year – **M** (see **Empire H.**) – **8 rm** 55.00/100.00 **st.** – SB 97.50/120.00 **st.**

Gogarth Abbey, West Shore, LL30 2QY, 76211, <, , – . AE VISA A s
M 12.00/17.50 **st.** 4.00 – **39 rm** 41.00/104.00 **st.**, **1 suite** 70.00/110.00 **st.** – SB 70.00/110.00 **st.**

Dunoon, Gloddaeth St., LL30 2DW, 860787 – . VISA A r
Mid March-October – **M** 7.50/10.00 **st.** 3.75 – **56 rm** 29.00/58.00 **st.** – SB 50.00/68.00 **st.**

Belle Vue, 26 North Par., LL30 2LP, 879547, < – . AE VISA B e
April-October – **M** (bar lunch)/dinner 8.00 **t.** and a la carte 3.50 – **17 rm** 24.00/52.00 **t.** – SB (April and October) 54.00/64.00 **st.**

Bryn-y-Bia Lodge, Bryn-y-Bia Rd, Craigside, LL30 3AS, E : 1 ½ m. on A 546 49644, – rest . AE VISA by A 546 B
M (bar lunch)/dinner 15.50 **t.** and a la carte 3.75 – **13 rm** 28.00/52.00 **t.** – SB 62.00/82.00 **st.**

Bromwell Court, Promenade, 6 Craig-y-Don Par., LL30 1BG, 78416 – . VISA. – **M** (bar lunch)/dinner 9.00 **st.** 3.50 – **11 rm** 23.00/42.00 **st.** – SB 48.00 **st.** B u

Headlands, Hill Terr., LL30 2LS, 77485, < – rest . VISA AB a
closed January and February – **M** (bar lunch)/dinner 13.50 **t.** 2.75 – **17 rm** 23.00/46.00 **t.** – SB (except summer) 57.00 **t.**

Chandos, 6 Church Walks, LL30 2HD, 878848 – rest . VISA A z
closed mid December-mid January – **M** 8.00 **t.** 3.75 – **8 rm** 15.00/35.00 **t.** – SB (Mid September-Easter) 39.00 **st.**

Craiglands, 7 Carmen Sylva Rd, LL30 1LZ, E : 1 m. by A 546 and B 5115 75090 – . by A 546 B
April-October – **M** (by arrangement) – **6 rm** 14.50/30.00 **s.** – SB 35.00/40.00 **st.**

Sunnymede, West Par., West Shore, LL30 2BD, 77130 – . VISA A x
March-November – **M** 12.00 **t.** 3.50 – 7.50 – **18 rm** 20.00/44.00 **st.** – SB (except summer) 55.00/64.00 **st.**

Leamore, 40 Lloyd St., LL30 2YG, 75552 – rest . A o
closed Christmas – **M** 8.50 **st.** 5.00 – **12 rm** 14.00/34.00 **st.** – SB 46.00/52.00 **st.**

Clontarf, 1 Great Orme's Rd, West Shore, LL30 2AR, 77621 – rest . A u
10 rm.

Tan Lan, Great Ormes Rd, West Shore, LL30 2AR, 860221 – . VISA A u
mid March-October – **M** 10.00 **t.** 3.95 – **18 rm** 20.00/44.00 **t.** – SB 50.00/54.00 **st.**

Buile Hill, 46 St. Mary's Rd, LL30 2UE, 76972, – rest AB o
March-November – **M** 7.50 **st.** 2.40 – **13 rm** 15.00/45.00 **st.** – SB (except summer) 52.00/60.00 **st.**

XX **Richard at Lanterns,** 7 Church Walks, LL30 2HD, 77924 – . VISA A n
closed Sunday and Monday – **M** (dinner only) 16.95 **st.**

XX **La Mouette** (at Merrion H.), Promenade, 860378, 860022, Fax 860378 – AE VISA
closed Sunday, Monday, February and 2 weeks August – **M** 15.00/22.50 **t.** and a la carte 3.50. B x

X **No. 1,** 1 Old Rd, LL30 2HA, 75424, Bistro.. VISA A i
closed Monday lunch, Sunday and 2 weeks January – **M** a la carte 9.70/15.00 **t.** 4.50.

AUDI-VW Builders St. West 75401
BMW Conway Rd 82441
CITROEN Herkomer Rd 77607
DAIHATSU Conway Rd 74490
HONDA Ffordd Mael Gnyn 653491/593939
LADA Conway Rd 83172
RENAULT, ROVER The Promenade 85171/78003

LLANDYBIE Dyfed 403 H 28 – pop. 2 813 – ✉ Ammanford – ☎ 0269.

Glynhir ☎ 850472.

◆London 210 – Brecon 38 – Carmarthen 19 – ◆Swansea 41.

Mill at Glynhir ⊗, SA18 2TE, SE : 2¼ m. by A 483 and Glynhir Rd ☎ 850672, ⊡, 🌳 – TV ☎ Ⓟ. ⊡ VISA
closed Christmas-New Year – **M** (dinner only) 15.00 **st.** – **11 rm** ⊒ 29.00/68.00 **st.** – SB (September-March) 62.00/68.00 **st.**

X **The Cobblers,** 3 Church St., SA18 3HZ, ☎ 850540 – ⊡ VISA
closed Thursday lunch, Sunday and Monday – **M** 16.50 **t.** and a la carte 🍷 2.50.

LLANELLI Dyfed 403 H 29 – pop. 45 336 – ECD : Tuesday – ☎ 0554.

Envir. : Kidwelly (Castle★) *AC*, NW : 9 m.

◆London 206 – Carmarthen 20 – ◆Swansea 11.

Diplomat, Felinfoel Rd, SA15 3PJ, NE : 1 m. on A 476 ☎ 756156, Fax 751649, Lб, ≘s, ⊡ – |♦| TV ☎ Ⓟ – 🔬 300. ⊡ AE ⓘ VISA
M 19.95/19.50 **st.** and a la carte 🍷 4.20 – **31 rm** ⊒ 49.00/59.00 **st.**

FORD Chapel St. ☎ 750142
ROVER Vauxhall Rd ☎ 773371
ATS Coldstream St. ☎ 750435

LLANELWY = St. Asaph.

LLANERCHYMEDD Gwynedd 402 403 G 24 – pop. 613 – ✉ ☎ 0248.

◆London 262 – Bangor 18 – Caernarfon 23 – Holyhead 15.

Llwydiarth Fawr ⊗, LL71 8DF, N : ¾ m. on B 5111 ☎ 470321, ≤, « Georgian farmhouse », 🌳 – ⇤ TV Ⓟ. ⊁
closed Christmas – **M** (by arrangement) 7.50 **st.** – **4 rm** ⊒ 15.00/35.00 **st.** – SB 50.00 **st.**

Drws-Y-Coed ⊗, LL71 8AD, E : 2½ m. by B 5111 on Benllech rd ☎ 470473, ≤ – TV Ⓟ. ⊁
closed December – **M** 7.50 **s.** – **4 rm** ⊒ 20.00/32.00 **s.** – SB 47.00 **st.**

LLANFACHRETH Gwynedd 402 403 I 25 – see Dolgellau.

LLANFAIR-YM-MUALLT = Builth Wells.

LLANFIHANGEL Powys 402 403 J 25 – see Llanfyllin.

LLANFYLLIN Powys 402 403 K 25 – pop. 1 210 – ECD : Friday – ☎ 069 184.

Council Offices ☎ 8868 (summer only).

◆London 188 – Chester 42 – Shrewsbury 24 – Welshpool 11.

Bodfach Hall ⊗, SY22 5HS, NW : 1 m. on B 4391 ☎ 272, ≤, 🌳, park – TV Ⓟ. ⊡ AE ⓘ VISA
March-mid November – **M** *(closed Sunday dinner)* (dinner only and Sunday lunch)/dinner 13.50 **t.** – **9 rm** ⊒ 28.50/57.00 **t.** – SB 66.00/73.00 **st.**

at LLanfihangel SW : 5 m. by A 490 and B 4393 on B 4382 – ✉ ☎ 069 184 LLanfyllin :

Cyfie Farm ⊗, SY22 5JE, S : 1½ m. by B 4382 ☎ 451, ≤, « Working farm, restored 17C longhouse », 🌳 – Ⓟ. ⊁
M 8.00 **st.** – **2 rm** ⊒ 18.00/30.00 **st.**, **1 suite** 36.00 **st.** – SB (except summer) 84.00/104.00 **st.**

LLANGAMMARCH WELLS Powys 403 J 27 – ECD : Wednesday – ☎ 059 12.

◆London 200 – Brecon 17 – Builth Wells 8.

Lake ⊗, LD4 4BS, E : ¾ m. ☎ 202, Fax 457, ≤, 🎣, 🌳, park, 🎾 – ⇤ rest TV ☎ Ⓟ. ⊡ AE VISA
closed January – **M** (bar lunch Monday to Saturday)/dinner 19.50 **st.** – **10 rm** ⊒ 65.00/85.00 **st.**, **9 suites** 110.00 **st.** – SB 120.00 **st.**

LLANGEFNI Gwynedd 402 403 H 24 – pop. 4100 – ECD : Tuesday – ✉ ☎ 0248.

Llangefni ☎ 880326.

◆London 256 – Chester 75 – Caernarfon 17 – Holyhead 17.

Tre-Ysgawen Hall ⊗, LL77 7UR, N : 4 ¼ m. by B 5110 and B 5111 via Tregaian ☎ 750750, Fax 750035, ≤, « Victorian mansion », 🌳 – TV ☎ Ⓟ – 🔬 100. ⊡ AE VISA. ⊁
M 12.50/21.00 **t.** and a la carte – ⊒ 6.00 – **19 rm** 71.50/127.50 **t.**

Nant Yr Odyn, Llanfawr, LL77 7YE, SW : 1¼ m. at junction of A 5 and A 5114 ☎ 723354 – TV ☎ Ⓟ. ⊡ VISA. ⊁
M *(closed Sunday dinner to non-residents)* (lunch by arrangement)/dinner 12.00 **t.** and a la carte 🍷 3.60 – **14 rm** ⊒ 32.50/60.00 **t.** – SB (except Bank Holidays) 72.00/80.00 **st.**

RENAULT Industrial Estate ☎ 724141
VAUXHALL Argraig Service Station ☎ 750126
ATS Industrial Est. ☎ 750397

LLANGOLLEN Clwyd 402 403 K 25 – pop. 2 546 – ECD : Thursday – 0978.

See : Plas Newydd★ (the house of the Ladies of Llangollen) *AC*.

Envir. : Horseshoe Pass★, NW : 4½ m. – Chirk Castle★ (gates★)*AC*, SE : 7½ m.

Vale of Llangollen, Holyhead Rd 860040, E : 1½ m.

Town Hall, 860828.

London 194 – Chester 23 – Holyhead 76 – Shrewsbury 30.

Bryn Howel, LL20 7UW, E : 2¾ m. on A 539 860331, Fax 860119, ≤, – 300. AE VISA
closed Christmas Day – **M** *(closed Saturday lunch)* 10.00/15.00 **t.** 4.00 – **38 rm** 55.00/85.00 **t.** – SB (weekends only) 105.00.

Wild Pheasant, Berwyn Rd, LL20 8AP, on A 5 860629, Fax 861837, –
33 rm.

Royal (T.H.F.), Bridge St., LL20 8PG, 860202, Fax 861824, ≤, – rm – 80. AE VISA
M (bar lunch Monday to Saturday)/dinner 15.00 **st.** 4.35 – **33 rm** 45.00/55.00 **st.** – SB (except Christmas and New Year) 62.00/72.00 **st.**

Ty'n-y-Wern, LL20 7PH, E : 1 m. on A 5 860252, ≤, – . VISA
– **12 rm** 32.00/42.00 **st.**

Caesar's, Deeside Lane, LL20 8PN, 860133, ≤ – VISA
closed Sunday and Christmas – **M** (dinner only) 17.50 **st.**

FORD Berwyn St. 860270

LLANGURIG Powys 403 J 26 – pop. 620 – ECD : Thursday – Llanidloes – 055 15.

London 188 – Aberystwyth 25 – Carmarthen 75 – Shrewsbury 53.

Old Vicarage, SY18 6RN, 280 –
March-October – **M** 9.00 **st.** 2.95 – **4 rm** 14.00/34.00 **st.**

LLANGYBI Gwent – see Usk.

LLANGYNIDR Powys 403 K 28 – pop. 846 – Crickhowell – 0874 Bwlch.

London 174 – Abergavenny 14 – Brecon 11 – Newport 30.

Red Lion, NP8 1NY, 730223, « 15C inn » – . VISA.
M *(closed Sunday dinner and Monday)* a la carte 11.70/14.35 **st.** 4.00 – **5 rm** 30.00/50.00 **st.**

LLANILLTUD FAWR = Llantwit Major.

LLANNEFYDD Clwyd 402 403 J 24 – Denbigh – 074 579.

London 225 – Chester 37 – Shrewsbury 63.

Hawk and Buckle Inn, LL16 5ED, 249, ≤ – . VISA.
M (bar lunch)/dinner 15.00 **t.** and a la carte – **10 rm** 38.00/48.00 **t.** – SB (weekends only) 60.00 **st.**

ROVER Denbigh Rd 227

LLANRHIDIAN West Glam. – see Swansea.

LLANRWST Gwynedd 402 403 I 24 – pop. 2 908 – ECD : Thursday – 0492.

See : Gwydir Castle★.

Envir. : Capel Garmon (Burial Chamber★) SE : 6 m.

London 230 – Holyhead 50 – Shrewsbury 66.

Maenan Abbey, N : 2½ m. on A 470, LL26 0UL, 049 269 (Dolgarrog) 247, –
12 rm.

Meadowsweet, Station Rd, LL26 0DS, 640732, ≤ – rest . VISA
M (dinner only) 27.50 **t.** 3.85 – **10 rm** 37.50/75.00 **t.** – SB (except Bank Holidays) 80.00/100.00 **st.**

at Trefriw NW : 2 m. on B 5106 – 0492 Llanrwst :

Hafod House, LL27 0RQ, 640029, Fax 641351 – . AE VISA.
M (lunch by arrangement)/dinner 14.75 **t.** 3.45 – **6 rm** 29.50/59.00 **t.** – SB 70.00/85.00 **st.**

FORD Betws Rd 640684 ROVER Kerry Garage 640381

LLANSANFFRAID GLAN CONWY Gwynedd – pop. 1 935 – 0492 Colwyn Bay.

London 241 – Colwyn Bay 4 – Holyhead 42.

Old Rectory , LL28 5LF, on A 470 580611, Fax 584555, ≤ Conwy estuary, « Georgian country house with antique furnishings », – . VISA.
closed 7 December-1 February – **M** (dinner only) 22.50 **st.** 5.90 – **4 rm** 47.50/80.00 **st.**

LLANTWIT MAJOR **(LLANILLTUD FAWR)** South Glam. 403 J 29 – pop. 13 375 (inc. St. Athan) – ☎ 044 65.

♦London 175 – ♦Cardiff 18 – ♦Swansea 33.

- **West House,** West St., CF6 9SP, ☎ 792406, – TV ☎ P. AE VISA
  M 10.50 **t.** (dinner) and a la carte 13.90/17.75 **t.** 2.95 – **16 rm** 37.00/47.00 **t.** – SB (weekends only) 57.50/77.50 **st.**

TOYOTA 2 Colhugh St. ☎ 3466

LLANWENARTH Gwent – see Abergavenny.

LLANWRTYD WELLS Powys 403 J 27 – pop. 528 – ECD : Wednesday – ☎ 059 13.

See : Cambrian Mountains-: road★★, from Llanwrtyd to Tregaron.

Envir. : Rhandir-mwyn (≤★ of Afon Tywi Valley) SW: 12 m.

♦London 214 – Brecon 32 – Carmarthen 39.

- **Lasswade Country House,** Station Rd, LD5 4RW, ☎ 515, ≤, – rest TV ☎ P. AE VISA
  M 15.50 **st.** 3.95 – **7 rm** 32.50/52.00 **st.** – SB 66.00/71.00 **st.**

LLANYCHAER Dyfed 403 F 28 – see Fishguard.

LLWYDAFYDD Dyfed 403 G 27 – see Newquay.

LLYSWEN Powys 403 K 27 – pop. 168 – ✉ Brecon – ☎ 0874.

♦London 188 – Brecon 8 – ♦Cardiff 48 – Worcester 53.

- **Llangoed Hall** , LD3 0YP, NW : 1 ¼ m. on A 470 ☎ 754525, Fax 754545, ≤, « Edwardian mansion by Sir Clough Williams-Ellis of 17C origins », , , park, – rest TV ☎ P. AE VISA.
  M 17.50/32.50 **t.** 4.75 – **18 rm** 85.00/115.00 **t.**, **5 suites** 175.00 **t.**
- **Griffin Inn,** LD3 0UR, on A 470 ☎ 754241, – ☎ P. AE VISA
  closed February – **M** *(closed Sunday dinner to non-residents)* a la carte 8.65/14.95 **st.** 4.65 – **8 rm** 25.00/60.00 **st.** – SB (October-March) 70.00/85.00 **st.**

LOFTUS Cleveland 402 R 20 – pop. 5 626 – ECD : Wednesday – ✉ Saltburn-by-the-Sea – ☎ 0287 Guisborough.

♦London 264 – ♦Leeds 73 – ♦Middlesbrough 17 – Scarborough 36.

- Grinkle Park , Easington, TS13 4UB, SE : 3 ½ m. by A 174 ☎ 40515, Fax 41278, ≤, , park, – TV ☎ P
  20 rm.

LOLWORTH Cambs. – see Cambridge.

London

404 folds ㊷ to ㊹ – **London G.** – pop. 7 566 620 – ✆ 071 or 081: see heading of each area

✈ Heathrow, ✆ (081) 759 4321, Telex 934892, p. 8 AX – **Terminal** : Airbus (A1) from Victoria, Airbus (A2) from Paddington – Underground (Piccadilly line) frequent service daily.

✈ Gatwick, ✆ 0293 (Crawley) 28822 and ✆ 081 (London) 668 4211, Telex 877725, p. 9 : by A 23 EZ and M 23 – **Terminal** : Coach service from Victoria Coach Station (Flightline 777, hourly service) – Railink (Gatwick Express) from Victoria (24 h service).

✈ London City Airport ✆ (071) 589 5599, Telex 264731, p. 7 : HV.

✈ Stansted, at Bishop's Stortford, ✆ 0279 (Bishop's Stortford) 680800, Telex 818708, NE : 34 m. p. 7 : by M 11 JT and A 120.

British Airways, Victoria Air Terminal : 115 Buckingham Palace Rd, SW1, ✆ (071) 834 9411, p. 32 BX.

🚗 Euston and Paddington ✆ 0345 090700.

ℹ National Tourist Information Centre, Victoria Station Forecourt, SW1, ✆ (071) 730 3488.
British Travel Centre, 12 Regent St., Piccadilly Circus, SW1 ✆ (071) 730 3400.
London Tourist Board and Convention Bureau Telephone Information Services ✆ (071) 730 3488.

Sights
Curiosités – Le curiosità
Sehenswürdigkeiten

HISTORIC BUILDINGS AND MONUMENTS

Palace of Westminster★★★ : House of Lords★★, Westminster Hall★★ (hammerbeam roof★★★), Robing Room★, Central Lobby★, House of Commons★, Big Ben★, Victoria Tower★ p. 26 LY – Tower of London★★★ (Crown Jewels★★★, White Tower or Keep★★★, St. John's Chapel★★, Beauchamp Tower★) p. 27 PVX.

Banqueting House★★ p. 26 LX – Buckingham Palace★★ (Changing of the Guard★★, Royal Mews★★) p. 32 BVX – Kensington Palace★★ p. 24 FX – Lincoln's Inn★★ p. 33 EV – London Bridge★★ p. 27 PVX – Royal Hospital Chelsea★★ p. 31 FU – St. James's Palace★★ p. 29 EP – South Bank Arts Centre ★★ (Royal Festival Hall★, National Theatre★, County Hall★) p. 26 MX – The Temple★★ (Middle Temple Hall★) p. 22 MV – Tower Bridge★★ p. 27 PX.

Albert Memorial★ p. 30 CQ – Apsley House★ p. 28 BP – Burlington House★ p. 29 EM – Charterhouse★ p. 23 NOU – Commonwealth Institute★ p. 24 EY – Design Centre★ p. 29 FM – George Inn★, Southwark p. 27 PX – Gray's Inn★ p. 22 MU – Guildhall★ (Lord Mayor's Show★★) p. 23 OU – Imperial College of Science and Technology★ p. 30 CR – Dr Johnson's House★ p. 23 NUV **A** – Lancaster House★ p. 29 EP – Leighton House★ p. 24 EY – Linley Sambourne House★ p. 24 EY – Mansion House★ (plate and insignia★★) p. 23 PV **P** – The Monument★ (✻★) p. 23 PV **G** – Old Admiralty★ p. 26 KLX – Royal Exchange★ p. 23 PV **V** – Royal Opera Arcade★ (New Zealand House) p. 29 FGN – Royal Opera House★ (Covent Garden) p. 33 DX – Somerset House★ p. 33 EXY – Staple Inn★ p. 22 MU **Y** – Stock Exchange★ p. 23 PUV – Theatre Royal★ (Haymarket) p. 29 GM – Westminster Bridge★ p. 26 LY.

CHURCHES

The City Churches

St. Paul's Cathedral★★★ (Dome ⩽★★★) p. 23 NOV.

St. Bartholomew the Great★★ (vessel★) p. 23 OU **K** – St. Dunstan-in-the-East★★ p. 23 PV **F** – St. Mary-at-Hill★★ (plan★, woodwork★★) p. 23 PV **B** – Temple Church★★ p. 22 MV.

All Hallows-by-the-Tower (font cover★★ brasses★) p. 23 PV **Y** – Christ Church★ p. 23 OU **E** – St. Andrew Undershaft (monuments★) p. 23 PV **A** – St. Bride★ (steeple★★) p. 23 NV **J** – St. Clement Eastcheap (panelled interior★★) p. 23 PV **E** – St. Edmund the King and Martyr (tower and spire★) p. 23 PV **D** – St-Giles Cripplegate★ p. 23 OU **N** – St. Helen Bishopsgate★ (monuments★★) p. 23 PUV **R** – St. James Garlickhythe (tower and spire★, sword rests★) p. 23 OV **R** – St. Katherine Cree (sword rest★) p. 23 PV **J** – St. Magnus the Martyr (tower★, sword rest★) p. 23 PV **K** – St. Margaret Lothbury★ (tower and spire★, woodwork★, screen★, font★) p. 23 PU **S** – St. Margaret Pattens (woodwork★) p. 23 PV **N** – St. Martin Ludgate (tower and spire★, door cases★) p. 23 NOV **B** – St. Mary Abchurch★ (tower and spire★, dome★, reredos★) p. 23 PV **X** – St. Mary-le-Bow (tower and steeple★★) p. 23 OV **G** – St. Michael Paternoster Royal (tower and spire★) p. 23 OV **D** – St. Nicholas Cole Abbey (tower and spire★) p. 23 OV **F** – St. Olave★ p. 23 PV **S** – St. Peter upon Cornhill (screen★) p. 23 PV **L** – St. Stephen Walbrook★ (tower and steeple★, dome★), p. 23 PV **Z** – St. Vedast (tower and spire★, ceiling★), p. 23 OU **E**.

Other Churches

Westminster Abbey★★★ (Chapel of Edward the Confessor★★, Henry VII Chapel★★★, Chapter House★★) p. 26 LY.

Southwark Cathedral★★ p. 27 PX.

Queen's Chapel★ p. 29 EP – St Clement Danes★ p. 33 EX – St. James's★ p. 29 EM – St. Margaret's★ p. 26 LY **A** – St. Martin-in-the-Fields★ p. 33 DY – St. Paul's★ (Covent Garden) p. 33 DX – Westminster Roman Catholic Cathedral★ p. 26 KY **B**.

PARKS

Regent's Park★★★ p. 21 HI (terraces★★), Zoo★★★.

Hyde Park★★ p. 25 GHV **X** – St. James's Park★★ p. 26 KXY.

Kensington Gardens★ pp. 20-21 FGX (Orangery★ **A**).

STREETS AND SQUARES

The City★★★ p. 23 NV.

Bedford Square★★ p. 22 KLU – Belgrave Square★★ p. 32 AVX – Burlington Arcade★★ p. 29 DM – The Mall★★ p. 29 FP – Piccadilly★★ p. 29 EM – The Thames★★ pp. 25-27 – Trafalgar Square★★ p. 33 DY – Whitehall★★ (Horse Guards★) p. 26 LX.

Barbican★ p. 23 OU – Bloomsbury★ p. 22 LMU – Bond Street★ pp. 28-29 CK-DM – Canonbury Square★ p. 23 NS – Carlton House Terrace★ p. 29 GN – Charing Cross★ p. p. 33 DY – Cheyne Walk★ p. 25 GHZ – Fitzroy Square★ p. 22 KU – Jermyn Street★ p. 29 EN – Merrick Square★ p. 27 OY – Montpelier Square★ p. 31 EQ – Piccadilly Arcade★ p. 29 DEN – Portman Square★ p. 28 AJ – Queen Anne's Gate★ p. 26 KY – Regent Street★ p. 29 EM – St. James's Square★ p. 29 FN – St. James's Street★ p. 29 EN – Sheperd Market★ p. 28 CN – Strand★ p. 33 DY – Trinity Church Square★ p. 27 OY – Victoria Embankment★ p. 33 DEXY – Waterloo Place★ p. 29 FN.

MUSEUMS

British Museum★★★ p. 22 LU – National Gallery★★★ p. 29 GM – Science Museum★★★ p. 30 CR – Tate Gallery★★★ p. 26 LZ – Victoria and Albert Museum★★★ p. 31 DR.

Courtauld Institute Galleries★★ (Somerset House) p. 33 EXY – Museum of London★★ p. 23 OU **M** – National Portrait Gallery★★ p. 29 GM – Natural History Museum★★ p. 30 CS – Queen's Gallery★★ p. 32 BV – Wallace Collection★★ p. 28 AH.

Clock Museum★ (Guidhall) p. 22 OU – Geological Museum★ p. 30 CR – Imperial War Museum★ p. 27 NY – London Transport Museum★ p. 33 DX – Madame Tussaud's★ p. 21 IU **M** – Museum of Mankind★ p. 29 DM – National Army Museum★ p. 31 FU – Percival David Foundation of Chinese Art★ p. 22 KLT **M** – Sir John Soane's Museum★ p. 22 MU **M** – Wellington Museum★ p. 28 BP.

OUTER LONDON

Hampton Court p. 8 BY (The Palace★★★, gardens★★★) – **Kew** p. 9 CX Royal Botanic Gardens★★★ : Palm House★★, Temperate House★, Kew Palace or Dutch House★★, Orangery★, Pagoda★, Japanese Gateway★ – Windsor (Castle★★★) p. 4 : by M 4 AV.

Blackheath p. 11 HX terraces and houses★, Eltham Palace★ **A** – **Brentford** p. 8 BX Syon Park★★, gardens★ – **Chiswick** p. 9 CV Chiswick Mall★★, Chiswick House★ **D**, Hogarth's House★ **E** – **Greenwich** pp. 10 and 11 : Cutty Sark★★ GV **F**, National Maritime Museum★★ (Queen's House★★) GV **M**, Royal Naval College★★ (Painted Hall★, the Chapel★) GV **G**, Old Royal Observatory★ (Meridian Building : collection★★) HV **K**, Ranger's House★ GX **N** – **Hampstead** Kenwood House★★ (Adam Library★★, paintings★★) p. 5 EU **P**, Fenton House★ p. 20 ES – Hendon★ p. 5, Royal Air Force Museum★★ CT **M** – **Hounslow** p. 8 BV Osterley Park★★ – **Lewisham** p. 10 GX Horniman Museum★ **M** – **Richmond** pp. 8 and 9 : Richmond Park★★, ✻★★★ CX, Richmond Bridge★★ BX **R**, Richmond Green★★ BX **S** (Maids of Honour Row★★, Trumpeter's House★), Asgill House★ BX **B**, Ham House★★ BX **V**.

Dulwich p. 10 Dulwich College Picture Gallery★ FX **X** – **Shoreditch** p. 6 FU Geffrye Museum★ **M** – **Tower Hamlets** p. 6 GV St. Katharine Dock★ **Y** – **Twickenham** p. 8 BX Marble Hill House★ **Z**, Strawberry Hill★ **A**.

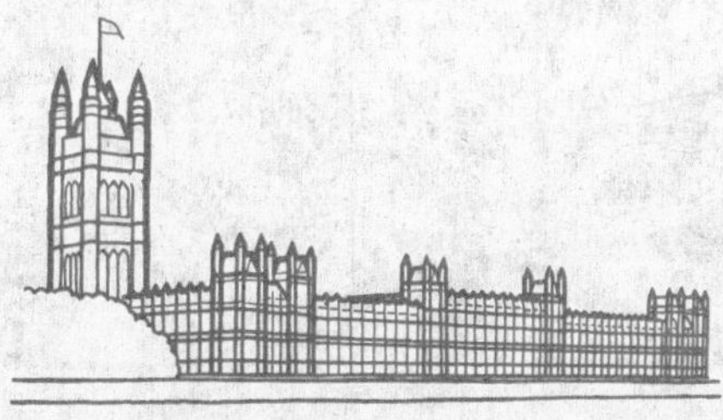

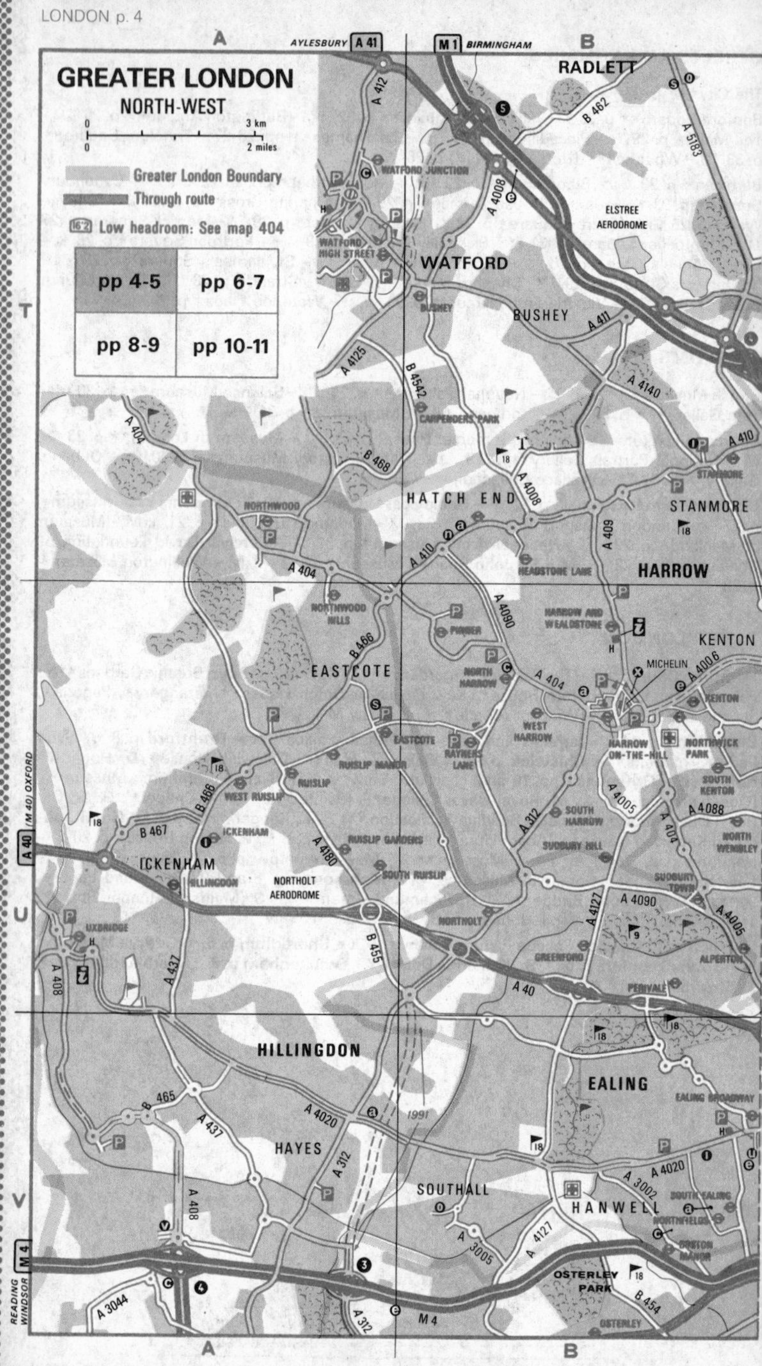
GREATER LONDON
NORTH-WEST
Greater London Boundary
Through route
Low headroom: See map 404
pp 4-5
pp 6-7
pp 8-9
pp 10-11
AYLESBURY A 41
M 1 BIRMINGHAM
RADLETT
WATFORD JUNCTION
ELSTREE AERODROME
WATFORD HIGH STREET
WATFORD
BUSHEY
CARPENDERS PARK
HATCH END
NORTHWOOD
STANMORE
HEADSTONE LANE
HARROW
NORTHWOOD HILLS
PINNER
HARROW AND WEALDSTONE
KENTON
MICHELIN
EASTCOTE
NORTH HARROW
WEST HARROW
RAYNERS LANE
HARROW ON-THE-HILL
NORTHWICK PARK
RUISLIP MANOR
RUISLIP
WEST RUISLIP
SOUTH KENTON
SOUTH HARROW
ICKENHAM
RUISLIP GARDENS
SUDBURY HILL
NORTH WEMBLEY
ICKENHAM
HILLINGDON
NORTHOLT AERODROME
SOUTH RUISLIP
SUDBURY TOWN
NORTHOLT
UXBRIDGE
GREENFORD
ALPERTON
PERIVALE
A 40 (M 40) OXFORD
HILLINGDON
EALING
EALING BROADWAY
HAYES
SOUTHALL
HANWELL
SOUTH EALING
NORTHFIELDS
BOSTON MANOR
OSTERLEY PARK
OSTERLEY
M 4
READING WINDSOR

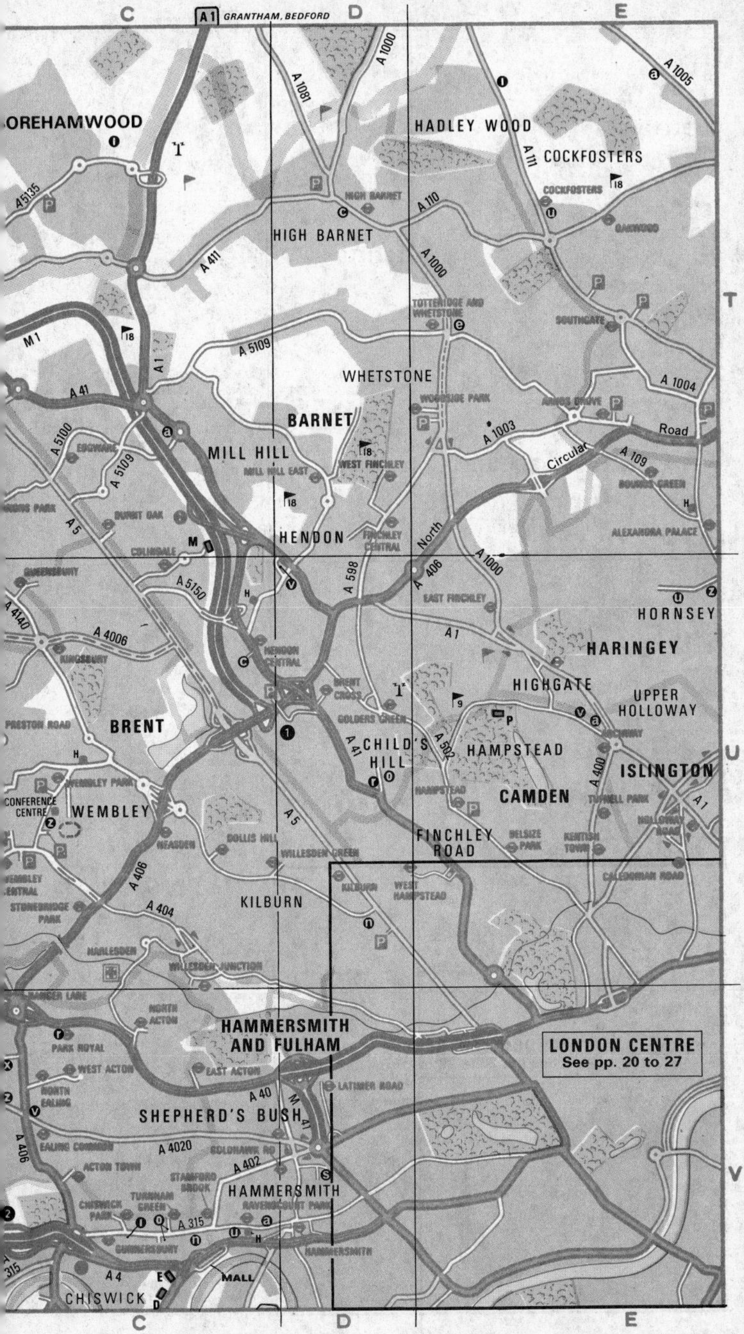

C D E

A 1 GRANTHAM, BEDFORD

BOREHAMWOOD
HADLEY WOOD
COCKFOSTERS
HIGH BARNET
WHETSTONE
BARNET
MILL HILL
HENDON
HORNSEY
HARINGEY
HIGHGATE
UPPER HOLLOWAY
BRENT
CHILD'S HILL
HAMPSTEAD
ISLINGTON
WEMBLEY
CONFERENCE CENTRE
CAMDEN
FINCHLEY ROAD
KILBURN
HAMMERSMITH AND FULHAM
SHEPHERD'S BUSH
HAMMERSMITH
CHISWICK
MALL

A 1000
A 1081
A 1005
A 111
A 110
A 5135
A 411
A 1000
A 5109
A 1004
A 41
A 1003
A 109
A 5100
A 5109
A 5
M 1
A 1
North Circular Road
A 1000
A 598
A 406
A 5150
A 4140
A 4006
A 1
A 41
A 502
A 400
A 1
A 5
A 406
A 404
A 40
M 41
A 4020
A 402
A 406
A 315
A 4
A 315

T
U
V

LONDON CENTRE
See pp. 20 to 27

C D E

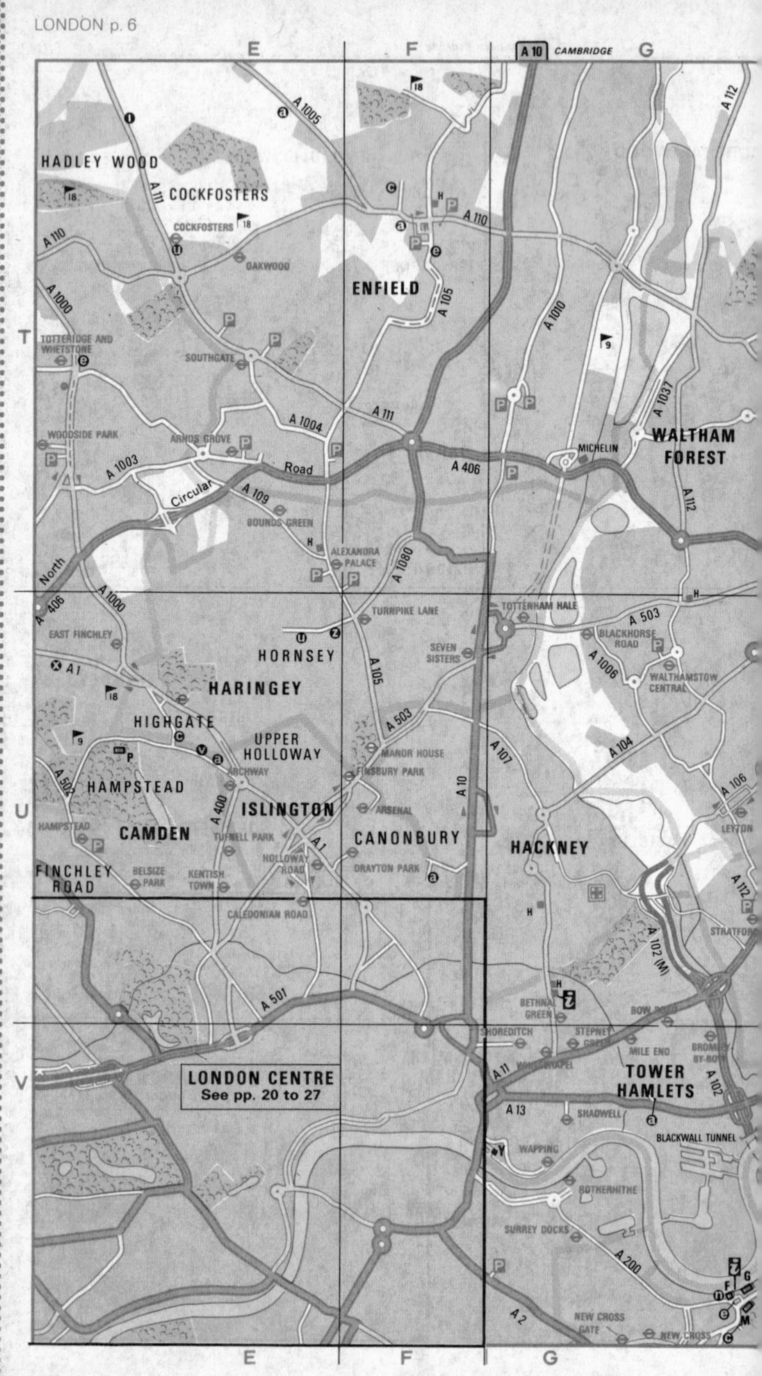

E
F
G
A 10 CAMBRIDGE
HADLEY WOOD
COCKFOSTERS
ENFIELD
WALTHAM FOREST
HORNSEY
HARINGEY
HIGHGATE
UPPER HOLLOWAY
HAMPSTEAD
ISLINGTON
CAMDEN
CANONBURY
HACKNEY
FINCHLEY ROAD
TOWER HAMLETS
LONDON CENTRE
See pp. 20 to 27
T
U
V

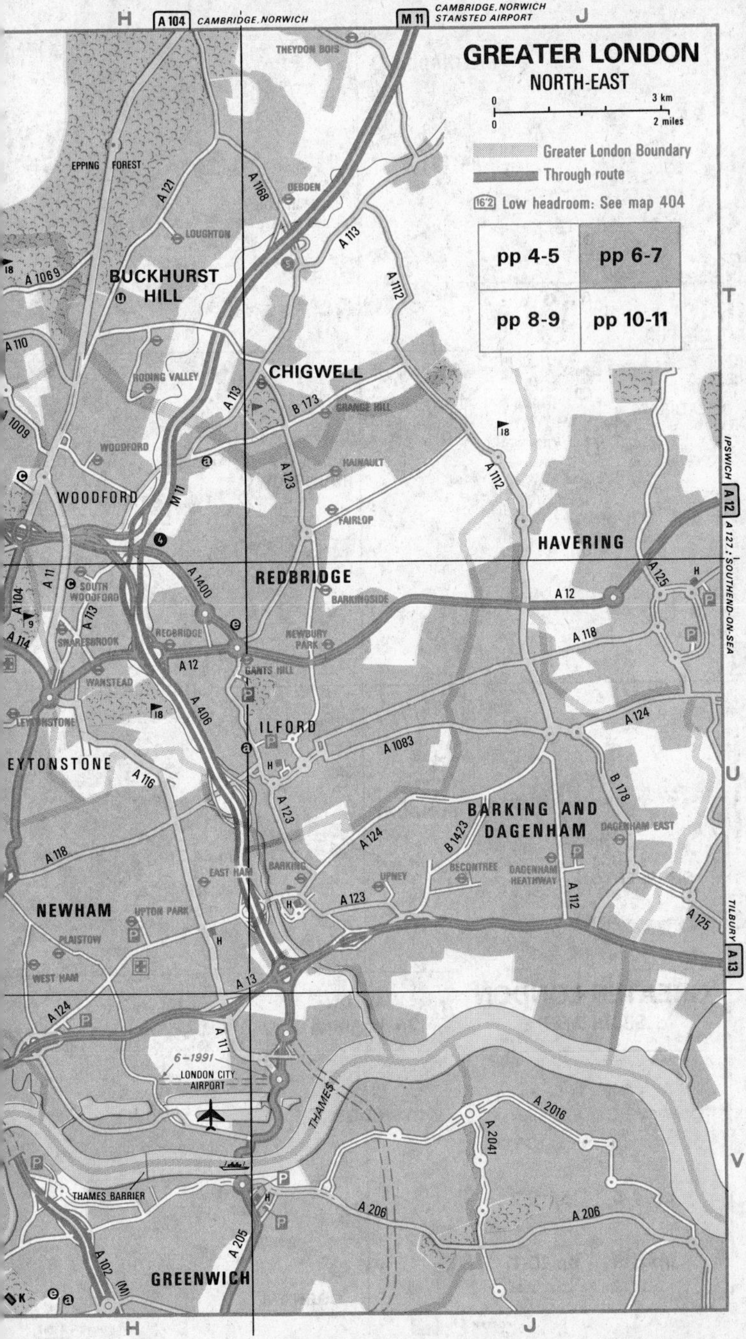

GREATER LONDON
NORTH-EAST

0 3 km
0 2 miles

Greater London Boundary
Through route
16'2 Low headroom: See map 404

pp 4-5	pp 6-7
pp 8-9	pp 10-11

H J
A 104 CAMBRIDGE, NORWICH
M 11 CAMBRIDGE, NORWICH STANSTED AIRPORT
THEYDON BOIS
EPPING FOREST
A 121
A 1168
DEBDEN
LOUGHTON
A 113
A 1069
BUCKHURST HILL
A 1112
T
A 110
RODING VALLEY
CHIGWELL
B 173
GRANGE HILL
A 1009
WOODFORD
HAINAULT
A 123
A 1112
IPSWICH A 12
WOODFORD
M 11
FAIRLOP
HAVERING
A 127 ; SOUTHEND-ON-SEA
A 11
SOUTH WOODFORD
REDBRIDGE
A 1400
BARKINGSIDE
A 12
A 125
A 104
A 113
A 114
SNARESBROOK
REDBRIDGE
NEWBURY PARK
A 118
A 12
GANTS HILL
WANSTEAD
A 406
LEYTONSTONE
ILFORD
A 124
A 1083
LEYTONSTONE
A 116
U
B 178
A 123
BARKING AND DAGENHAM
B 1423
A 124
DAGENHAM EAST
A 118
EAST HAM
BARKING
BECONTREE
DAGENHAM HEATHWAY
UPNEY
A 112
NEWHAM
UPTON PARK
A 123
A 125
TILBURY A 13
PLAISTOW
WEST HAM
A 13
A 124
A 117
6–1991
LONDON CITY AIRPORT
THAMES
A 2016
A 2041
V
THAMES BARRIER
A 206
A 206
A 205
A 102 (M)
GREENWICH
H J

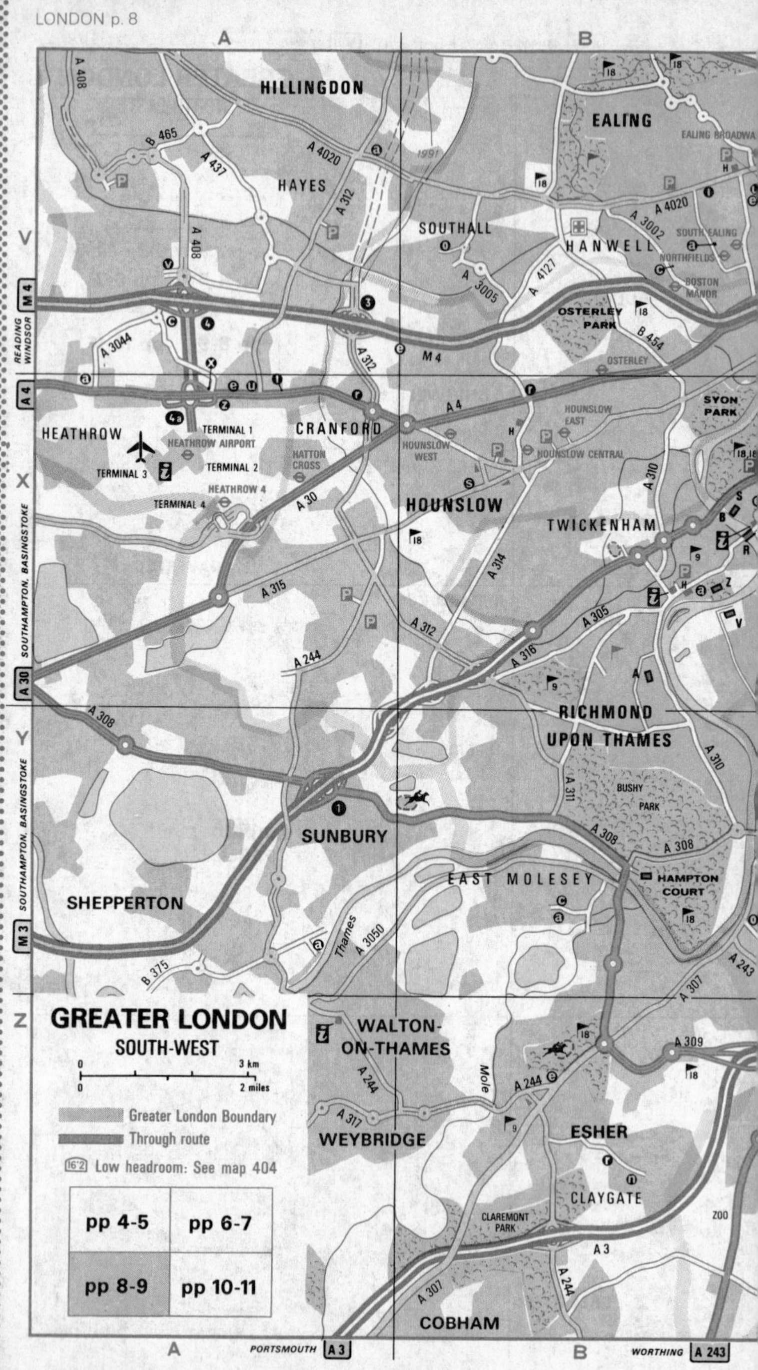
HILLINGDON
EALING
HAYES
SOUTHALL
HANWELL
EALING BROADWAY
SOUTH EALING
NORTHFIELDS
BOSTON MANOR
OSTERLEY PARK
OSTERLEY
SYON PARK
HEATHROW
TERMINAL 1
HEATHROW AIRPORT
TERMINAL 2
TERMINAL 3
HEATHROW 4
TERMINAL 4
CRANFORD
HATTON CROSS
HOUNSLOW WEST
HOUNSLOW EAST
HOUNSLOW CENTRAL
HOUNSLOW
TWICKENHAM
RICHMOND UPON THAMES
BUSHY PARK
SUNBURY
SHEPPERTON
EAST MOLESEY
HAMPTON COURT
WALTON-ON-THAMES
WEYBRIDGE
ESHER
CLAYGATE
CLAREMONT PARK
COBHAM
ZOO
Thames
Mole
READING WINDSOR
SOUTHAMPTON, BASINGSTOKE
PORTSMOUTH
WORTHING
M 4
A 4
A 30
M 3
A 3
A 243
GREATER LONDON
SOUTH-WEST
3 km
2 miles
Greater London Boundary
Through route
Low headroom: See map 404
pp 4-5
pp 6-7
pp 8-9
pp 10-11

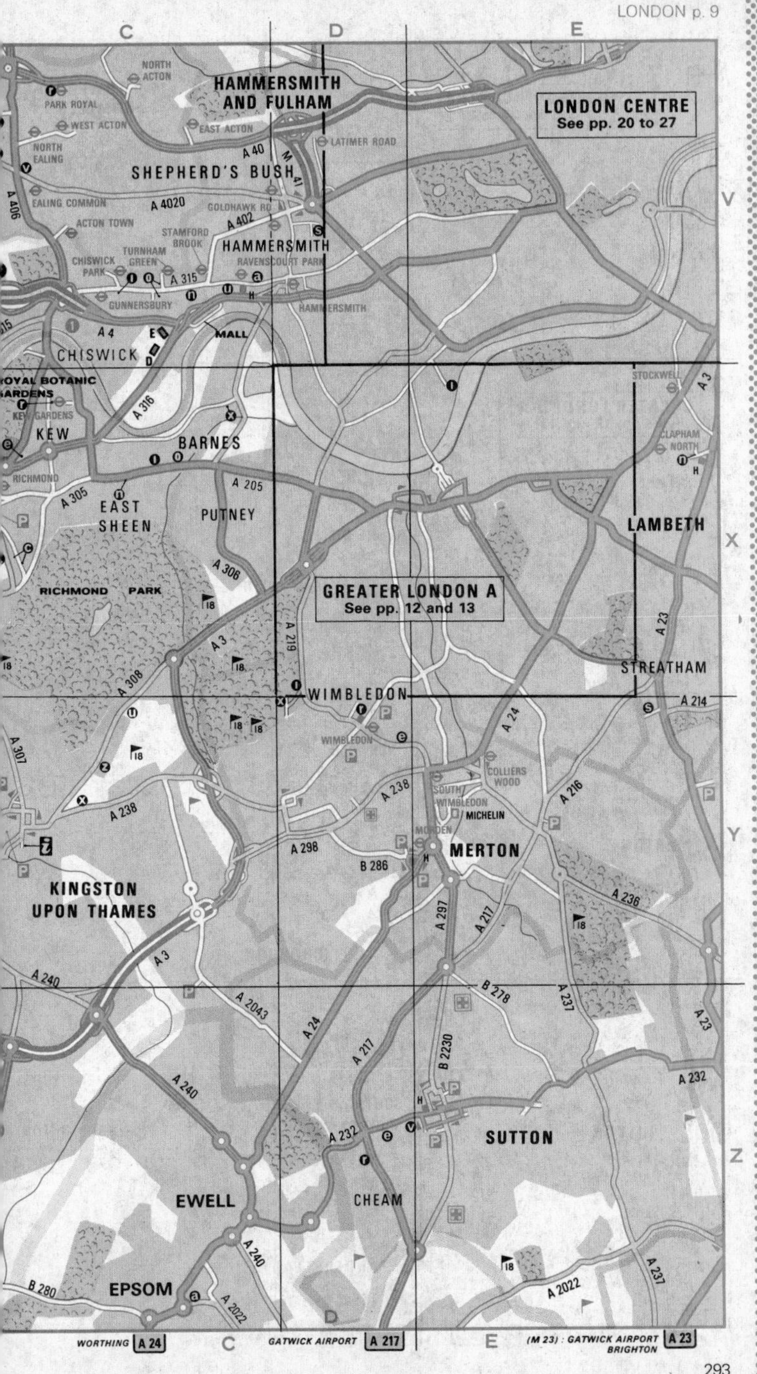

C
D
E
NORTH ACTON
HAMMERSMITH AND FULHAM
LONDON CENTRE
See pp. 20 to 27
PARK ROYAL
WEST ACTON
EAST ACTON
LATIMER ROAD
NORTH EALING
A 40
M 41
SHEPHERD'S BUSH
A 406
EALING COMMON
A 4020
GOLDHAWK RD
V
ACTON TOWN
A 402
STAMFORD BROOK
TURNHAM GREEN
HAMMERSMITH
CHISWICK PARK
RAVENSCOURT PARK
A 315
GUNNERSBURY
HAMMERSMITH
A 4
MALL
CHISWICK
ROYAL BOTANIC GARDENS
STOCKWELL
A 3
A 316
KEW GARDENS
KEW
BARNES
CLAPHAM NORTH
RICHMOND
A 205
A 305
EAST SHEEN
PUTNEY
LAMBETH
X
A 306
RICHMOND PARK
GREATER LONDON A
See pp. 12 and 13
A 219
A 23
A 3
A 308
STREATHAM
WIMBLEDON
A 214
A 307
A 24
WIMBLEDON
COLLIERS WOOD
A 238
SOUTH WIMBLEDON
A 216
A 238
MICHELIN
MORDEN
Y
A 298
MERTON
B 286
KINGSTON UPON THAMES
A 236
A 297
A 217
A 3
A 240
B 278
A 2043
A 237
A 23
A 24
A 217
B 2230
A 240
A 232
A 232
SUTTON
Z
EWELL
CHEAM
A 240
B 280
EPSOM
A 2022
A 2022
A 237
D
WORTHING A 24
C
GATWICK AIRPORT A 217
E
(M 23) : GATWICK AIRPORT A 23
BRIGHTON

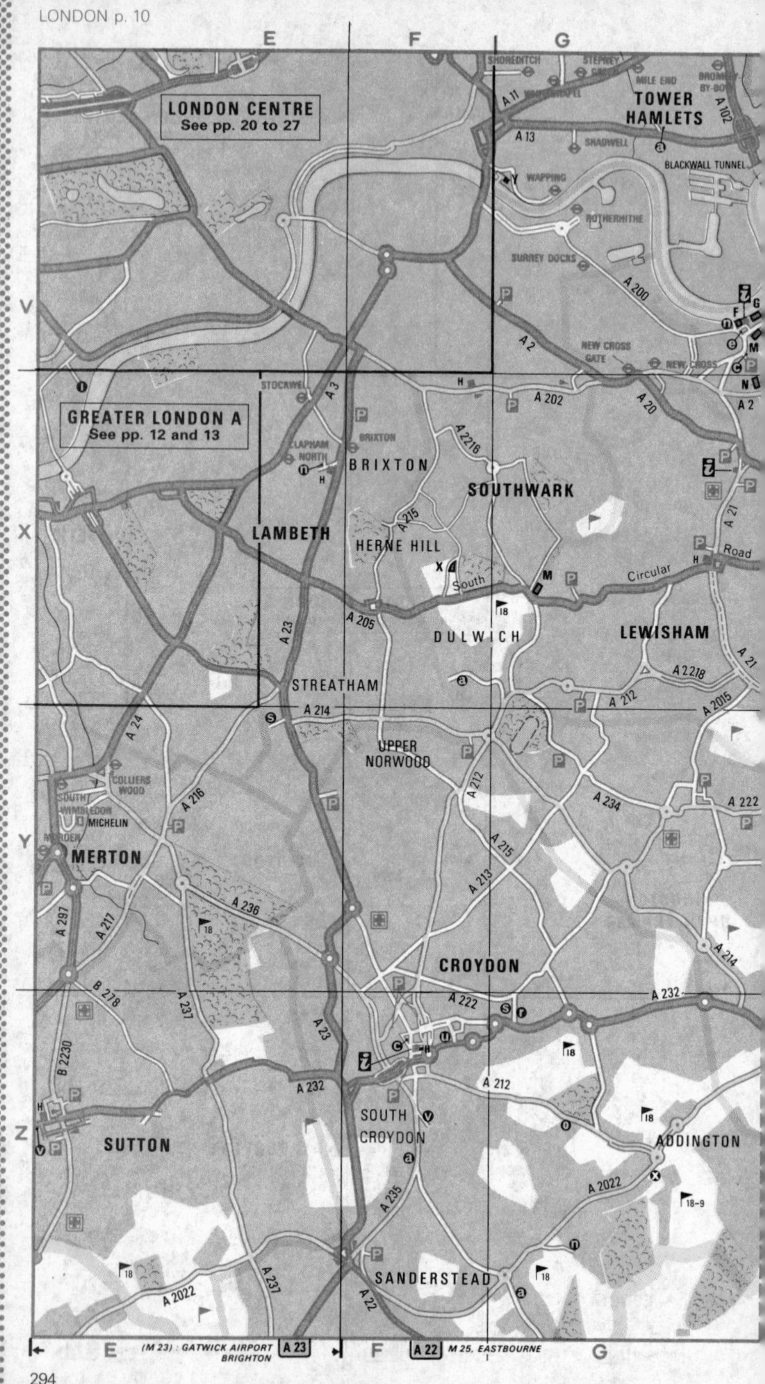
E
F
G
SHOREDITCH
STEPNEY
MILE END
A 11
TOWER
HAMLETS
A 102
LONDON CENTRE
See pp. 20 to 27
A 13
SHADWELL
BLACKWALL TUNNEL
WAPPING
ROTHERHITHE
SURREY DOCKS
A 200
V
A 2
NEW CROSS
GATE
NEW CROSS
A 202
A 20
A 2
STOCKWELL
A 3
GREATER LONDON A
See pp. 12 and 13
CLAPHAM
NORTH
BRIXTON
A 2216
BRIXTON
SOUTHWARK
X
LAMBETH
A 215
HERNE HILL
A 21
Road
South
Circular
A 205
A 23
DULWICH
LEWISHAM
A 2218
A 21
STREATHAM
A 212
A 214
A 2015
A 24
UPPER
NORWOOD
COLLIERS
WOOD
SOUTH
WIMBLEDON
MICHELIN
MORDEN
A 216
A 212
A 234
A 222
Y
MERTON
A 215
A 213
A 236
A 297
A 217
CROYDON
A 214
B 278
A 237
A 222
A 232
A 23
B 2230
A 232
A 212
SOUTH
CROYDON
ADDINGTON
Z
SUTTON
A 2022
A 235
SANDERSTEAD
A 2022
A 237
A 22
E
(M 23) : GATWICK AIRPORT
BRIGHTON
A 23
F
A 22
M 25, EASTBOURNE
G

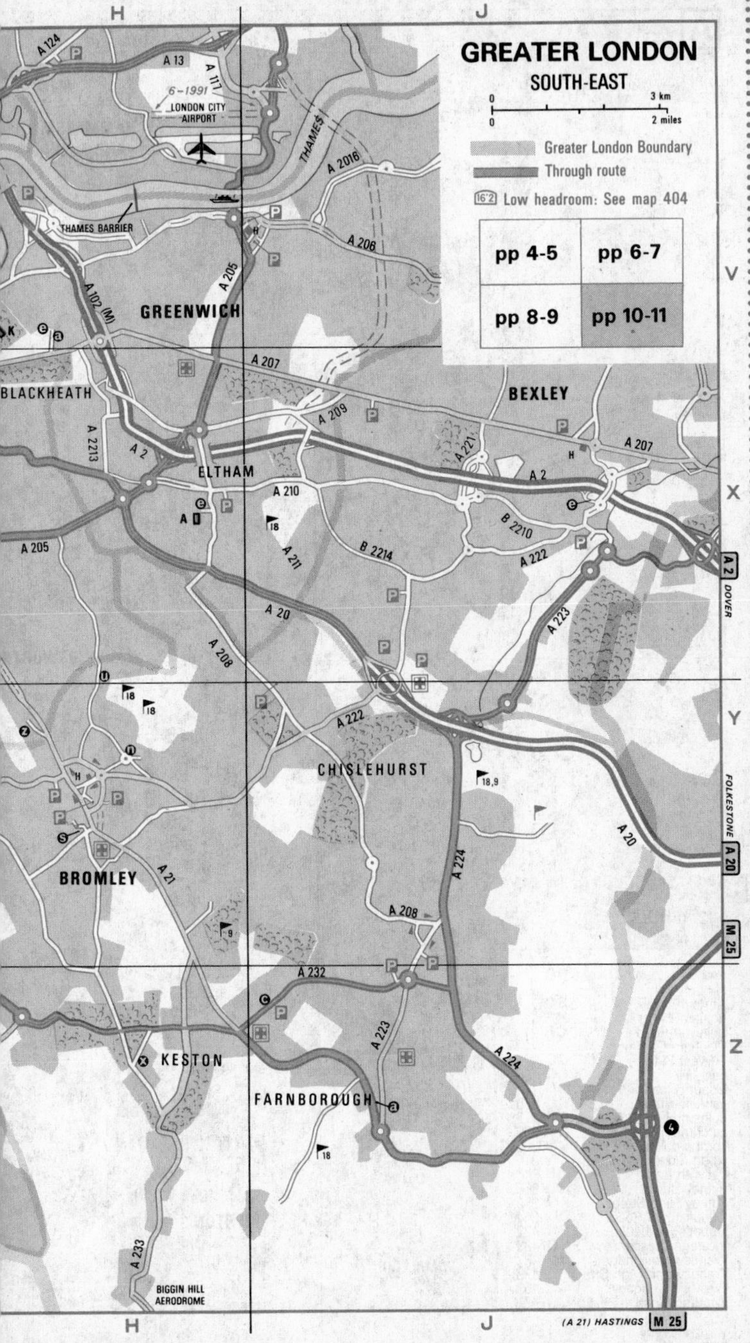

H
J
GREATER LONDON
SOUTH-EAST
0 3 km
0 2 miles
Greater London Boundary
Through route
16'2 Low headroom: See map 404
pp 4-5
pp 6-7
pp 8-9
pp 10-11
V
X
Y
Z
A 124
A 13
A 117
6-1991
LONDON CITY AIRPORT
THAMES
A 2016
THAMES BARRIER
A 206
A 205
A 102 (M)
GREENWICH
A 207
BLACKHEATH
BEXLEY
A 209
A 221
A 2213
A 2
ELTHAM
A 210
A 205
A 211
B 2214
B 2210
A 222
A 2
DOVER
A 223
A 20
A 208
A 222
CHISLEHURST
FOLKESTONE
A 20
A 224
BROMLEY
A 21
A 208
M 25
A 232
A 223
KESTON
A 224
FARNBOROUGH
A 233
BIGGIN HILL AERODROME
(A 21) HASTINGS
M 25

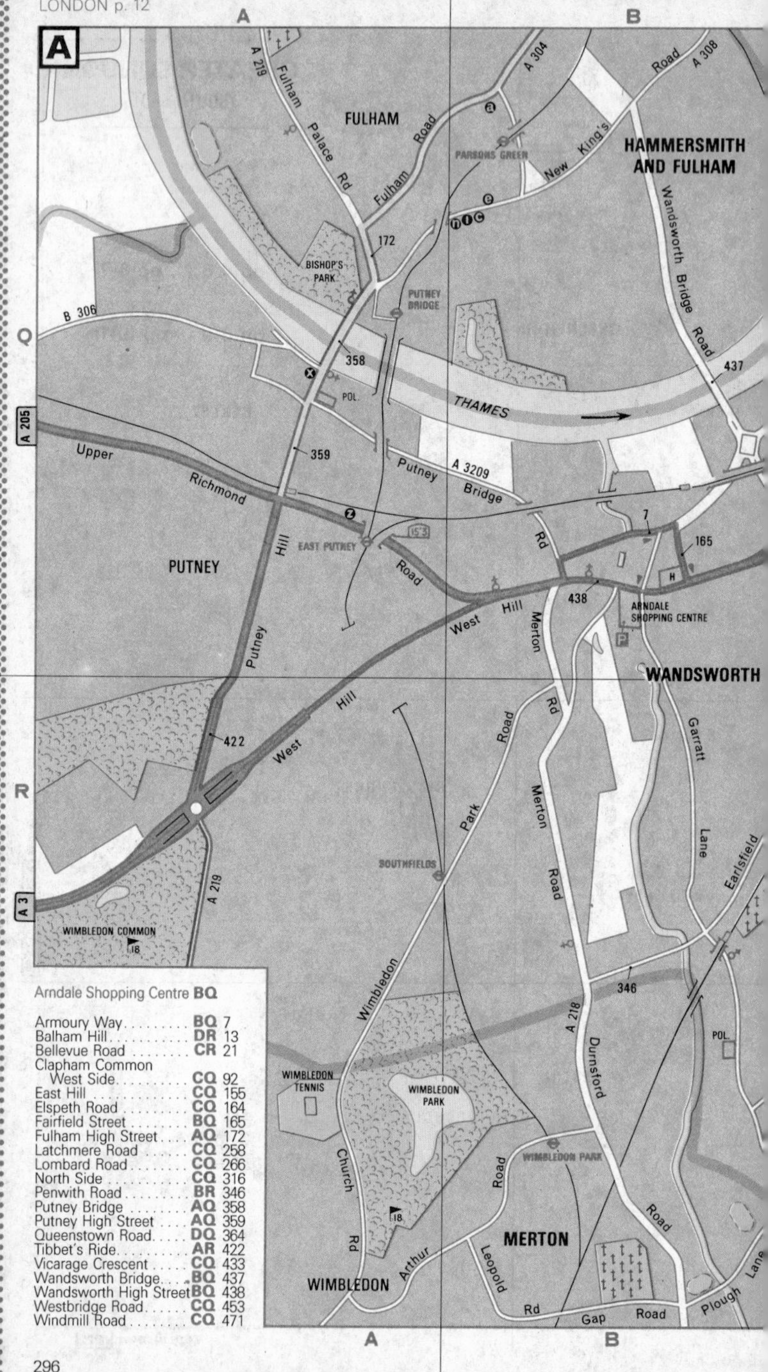

Arndale Shopping Centre **BQ**

C
D
BATTERSEA PARK
Battersea Bridge Road
A 3220
B 305
453
433
Park Road
BATTERSEA
Battersea
266
258
A 3205
Road
CLAPHAM JUNCTION
A 3216
364
Wandsworth Road
B 224
A 3036
Hill
Lavender
CLAPHAM
Cedars Rd
Q
A 3
CLAPHAM COMMON
Side
164
Clapham Common North
Long Rd
A 2217
South Side
155
St. John's Hill
Battersea Rise
92
CLAPHAM COMMON
The Avenue
316
Clapham Common
471
Clapham
CLAPHAM SOUTH
13
WANDSWORTH COMMON
Road
Lane
Nightingale
B 237
A 205
Trinity
Road
LAMBETH
21
BALHAM
15'6
R
Lane
High
B 229
Road
Balham
B 242
Burntwood
TOOTING BEC
Road
Tooting
TOOTING
TOOTING BEC COMMON
Garratt
Upper Tooting
Bec
Road
A 214
A 217
Lane
B 241
TOOTING BROADWAY
0
500 m
0
500 yards
C
A 24
D

LONDON CENTRE

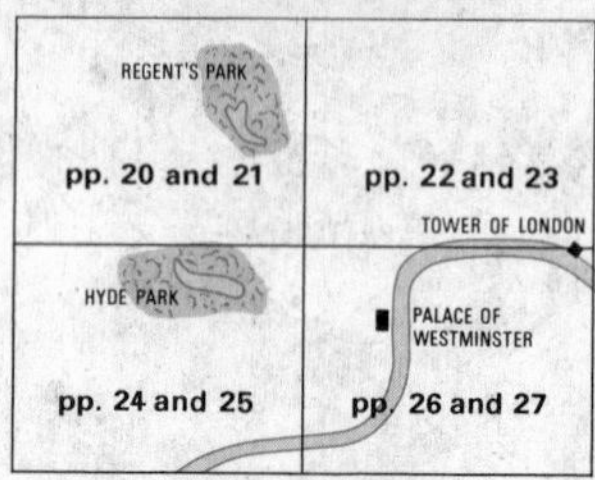

STREET INDEX TO LONDON CENTRE TOWN PLANS

Street	District	Page	Grid	No.
ruton Street	W1	p. 28	CM	
ryanston Square	W1	p. 21	HU	
ryanston Street	W1	p. 28	AK	
uckingham Gate	SW1	p. 32	CV	56
uckingham Palace Road	SW1	p. 32	AY	
unhill Row	EC1	p. 23	PU	
ury Street	SW1	p. 29	EN	
ute Street	SW7	p. 30	CS	59
yward Street	EC3	p. 23	PV	62
adogan Gardens	SW3	p. 31	FS	
adogan Place	SW1	p. 31	FR	
adogan Square	SW1	p. 31	FS	
adogan Street	SW3	p. 31	ET	
aledonian Road	N1, N7	p. 22	MS	
ale Street	SW3	p. 31	DT	
alshot Street	N1	p. 22	MT	
althorpe Street	WC1	p. 22	MT	65
amberwell New Road	SE5	p. 27	NZ	
amberwell Road	SE5	p. 27	OZ	
ambridge Circus	WC2	p. 29	GK	
ambridge Square	W2	p. 33	EZ	67
amden High Street	NW1	p. 22	JS	
amden Road	E11	p. 22	KS	
amden Street	NW1	p. 22	KS	
amomile Street	EC3	p. 23	PU	71
ampden Hill Road	W8	p. 24	EX	
annon Street	EC4	p. 23	OV	
anonbury Road	N1	p. 23	NS	
anonbury Square	N1	p. 23	NS	
arey Street	WC2	p. 33	EV	
arlisle Place	SW1	p. 32	BX	
arlos Place	W1	p. 28	BM	
arlton Gardens	SW1	p. 29	FP	74
arlton Hill	NW8	p. 20	FS	
arlton House Terrace	SW1	p. 29	FN	
arlton Vale	NW6	p. 20	ET	
arriage Drive East	SW11	p. 25	IZ	
arriage Drive North	SW11	p. 25	IZ	75
arriage Road (the)	SW7, SW11	p. 31	EQ	
astle Lane	SW1	p. 32	CX	
avendish Square	W1	p. 28	CJ	
entral Street	EC1	p. 23	OT	
halk Farm Road	NW1	p. 21	IS	
hancery Lane	WC2	p. 33	EV	
handos Place	WC2	p. 33	DY	
handos Street	W1	p. 28	CH	
hapel Market	N1	p. 23	NS	78
hapel Street	SW1	p. 32	AV	
hapter Road	SE17	p. 27	OZ	
harlbert Street	NW8	p. 21	HT	79
harles II Street	SW1	p. 29	FN	
harles Street	W1	p. 28	CN	
haring Cross	SW1	p. 33	DY	
haring Cross Road	WC2	p. 29	GJ	
harterhouse Square	EC1	p. 23	OU	81
harterhouse Street	EC1	p. 23	NU	83
Cheapside	EC2	p. 23	OV	
Chelsea Bridge	SW1, SW8	p. 25	IZ	
Chelsea Bridge Road	SW1	p. 25	IZ	
Chelsea Embankment	SW3	p. 25	HZ	
Chelsea Manor Street	SW3	p. 31	EU	
Chelsea Square	SW3	p. 31	DU	
Cheltenham Terrace	SW3	p. 31	FT	
Chepstow Crescent	W11	p. 32	AZ	84
Chepstow Place	W2	p. 32	AZ	
Chepstow Road	W2	p. 32	AZ	
Chesham Place	SW2	p. 31	FR	
Chesham Street	SW1	p. 31	FS	
Chester Road	NW1	p. 21	IT	
Chester Row	SW1	p. 32	AY	
Chester Square	SW1	p. 32	AX	88
Chester Street	SW1	p. 32	AV	
Cheval Place	SW7	p. 31	ER	
Cheyne Walk	SW3, SW10	p. 25	GZ	
Chilworth Street	W2	p. 32	CZ	90
Chippenham Road	W9	p. 20	EU	
Chiswell Street	EC1	p. 23	OU	
Church Row	NW3	p. 20	ES	
Church Street	NW8, NW2	p. 21	GU	
Churton Street	SW1	p. 26	KZ	91
Circus Road	NW8	p. 21	GT	
City Road	EC1	p. 23	NT	
Clapham Road	SW9	p. 26	MZ	
Clarendon Place	W2	p. 33	EZ	93
Clarendon Road	W11	p. 24	EX	
Claverton Street	SW1	p. 26	KZ	
Clayton Street	SE11	p. 26	MZ	
Clerkenwell Road	EC1	p. 23	NU	
Cleveland Gardens	W2	p. 32	CZ	94
Cleveland Square	W2	p. 32	CZ	
Cleveland Street	W1	p. 22	KU	
Cleveland Terrace	W2	p. 32	CZ	
Clifford Street	W1	p. 29	DM	

Street	District	Page	Grid	No.
Cliveden Place	SW1	p. 31	FS	
Cockspur Street	SW1	p. 29	GN	
Collingham Gardens	SW5	p. 30	AT	99
Collingham Road	SW5	p. 30	AT	101
Commercial Street	E1	p. 23	PU	
Conduit Street	W1	p. 29	DL	
Connaught Square	W2	p. 33	EZ	103
Connaught Street	W2	p. 33	EZ	
Constantine Road	NW3	p. 20	ES	106
Constitution Hill	SW1	p. 32	AV	
Copenhagen Street	N1	p. 22	LS	
Cork Street	W1	p. 29	DM	
Cornwall Crescent	W11	p. 20	EV	107
Cornwall Gardens	SW7	p. 30	AR	
Cornwall Road	SE1	p. 26	MX	108
Corporation Row	EC1	p. 23	NT	110
Courtfield Gardens	SW5	p. 30	AT	
Courtfield Road	SW7	p. 30	BS	
Coventry Street	W1	p. 29	FM	
Cowcross Street	EC1	p. 23	NU	113
Cranbourn Street	WC2	p. 33	DX	115
Cranley Gardens	SW7	p. 30	CT	
Craven Hill	W2	p. 32	CZ	
Craven Road	W2	p. 33	DZ	
Craven Street	WC2	p. 33	DY	
Craven Terrace	W2	p. 33	DZ	
Crawford Place	W1	p. 21	HU	116
Crawford Street	W1	p. 21	HU	
Cromwell Crescent	SW5	p. 24	EZ	119
Cromwell Place	SW7	p. 30	CS	120
Cromwell Road	SW7, SW5	p. 30	CS	
Crowndale Road	NW1	p. 22	KS	
Crucifix Lane	SE1	p. 27	PX	125
Culross Street	W1	p. 28	AM	
Curtain Road	EC2	p. 23	PT	126
Curzon Street	W1	p. 28	BN	
Cut (The)	SE1	p. 27	NX	
Dante Road	SE11	p. 27	NZ	129
D'Arblay Street	W1	p. 29	EK	
Davies Street	W1	p. 28	BK	
Dawes Road	SW6	p. 24	EZ	
Dawson Place	W2	p. 32	AZ	
Deanery Street	W1	p. 28	BN	132
Dean Street	W1	p. 29	FJ	
De Beauvoir Road	N1	p. 23	PS	
Delancey Street	NW1	p. 21	JS	
Delaware Road	W9	p. 20	FT	
Denbigh Street	SW1	p. 26	KZ	
Denman Street	W1	p. 29	FM	133
Denmark Street	WC2	p. 29	GJ	134
De Vere Gardens	W8	p. 30	BQ	
Devonshire Street	W1	p. 21	IU	
Devonshire Terrace	W2	p. 32	CZ	136
Dorset Road	SW8	p. 26	LZ	
Dorset Street	W1	p. 28	AH	
Dovehouse Street	SW3	p. 31	DU	
Dover Street	W1	p. 29	DM	
Downham Road	N1	p. 23	PS	
Downing Street	SW1	p. 26	LX	138
Downshire Hill	NW3	p. 20	ES	139
Draycott Avenue	SW3	p. 31	ET	
Draycott Place	SW3	p. 31	ET	
Drayton Gardens	SW10	p. 30	BT	
Druid Street	SE1	p. 27	PY	
Drury Lane	WC2	p. 33	DV	
Dufferin Street	EC1	p. 23	OT	141
Duke of Wellington Place	SW1	p. 32	AV	142
Duke of York Street	SW1	p. 29	EN	143
Duke's Place	EC3	p. 23	PV	145
Duke Street	W1	p. 28	BK	
Duke Street ST. JAMES	SW1	p. 29	EN	146
Duncannon Street	WC2	p. 33	DY	147
Dunraven Street	W1	p. 28	AL	149
Dunton Road	SE1	p. 27	PZ	
Durham Street	SE11	p. 26	MZ	150
Eagle Wharf Road	N1	p. 23	OS	
Eardley Crescent	SW5	p. 24	EZ	151
Earlham Street	WC2	p. 33	DV	153
Earl's Court Road	W8, SW5	p. 24	EY	
Eastbourne Terrace	W2	p. 33	DZ	
Eastcastle Street	W1	p. 29	EJ	
Eastcheap	EC3	p. 23	PV	154
East Heath Road	NW3	p. 20	ES	
East Road	N1	p. 23	PT	
East Street	SE17	p. 27	PZ	
Eaton Place	SW1	p. 32	AX	
Eaton Square	SW1	p. 32	AX	
Ebury Bridge	SW1	p. 25	IZ	156
Ebury Street	SW1	p. 32	AY	
Ebury Bridge Road	SW1	p. 25	IZ	
Eccleston Bridge	SW1	p. 32	BY	157
Eccleston Square	SW1	p. 32	BY	
Eccleston Street	SW1	p. 32	AY	

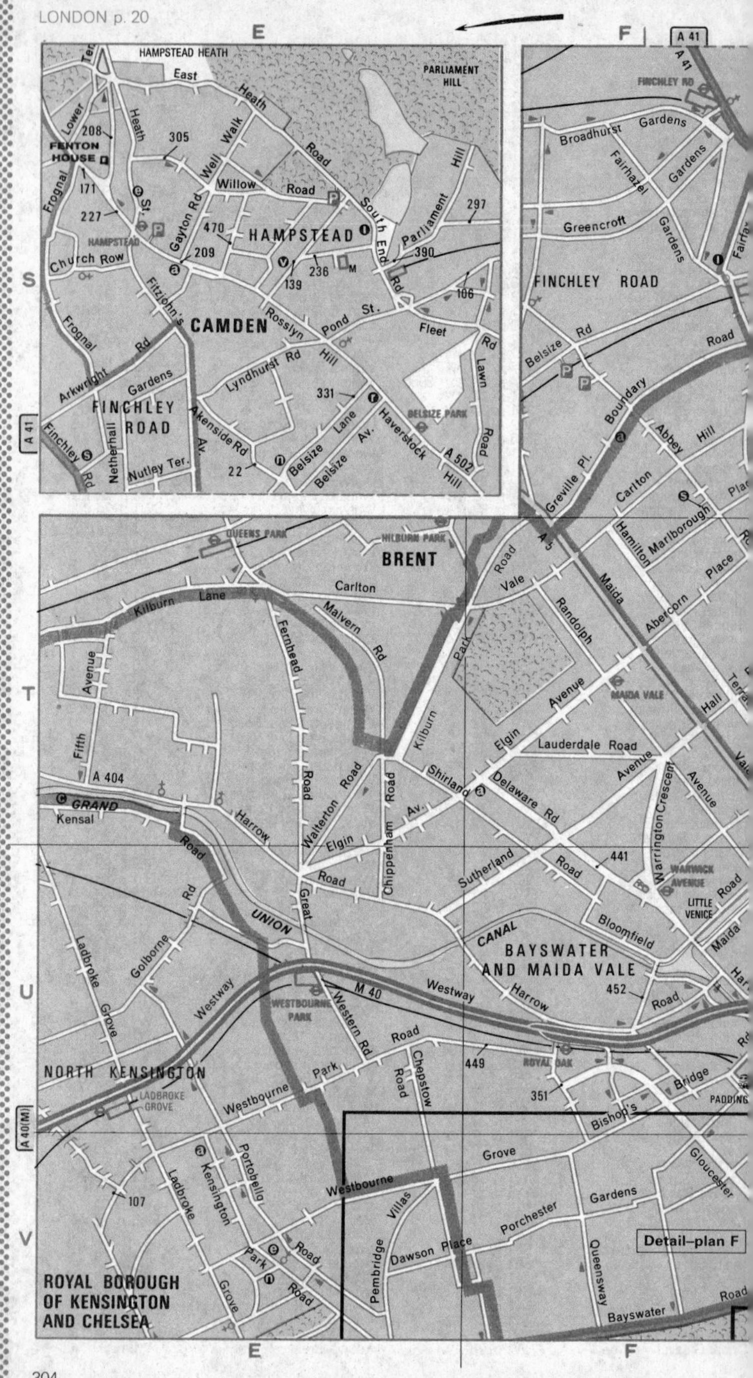
HAMPSTEAD HEATH
PARLIAMENT HILL
HAMPSTEAD
CAMDEN
FINCHLEY ROAD
FENTON HOUSE
BRENT
BAYSWATER AND MAIDA VALE
NORTH KENSINGTON
ROYAL BOROUGH OF KENSINGTON AND CHELSEA
GRAND UNION CANAL
LITTLE VENICE
Detail-plan F
A 41
A 502
A 5
A 404
A 40(M)
M 40

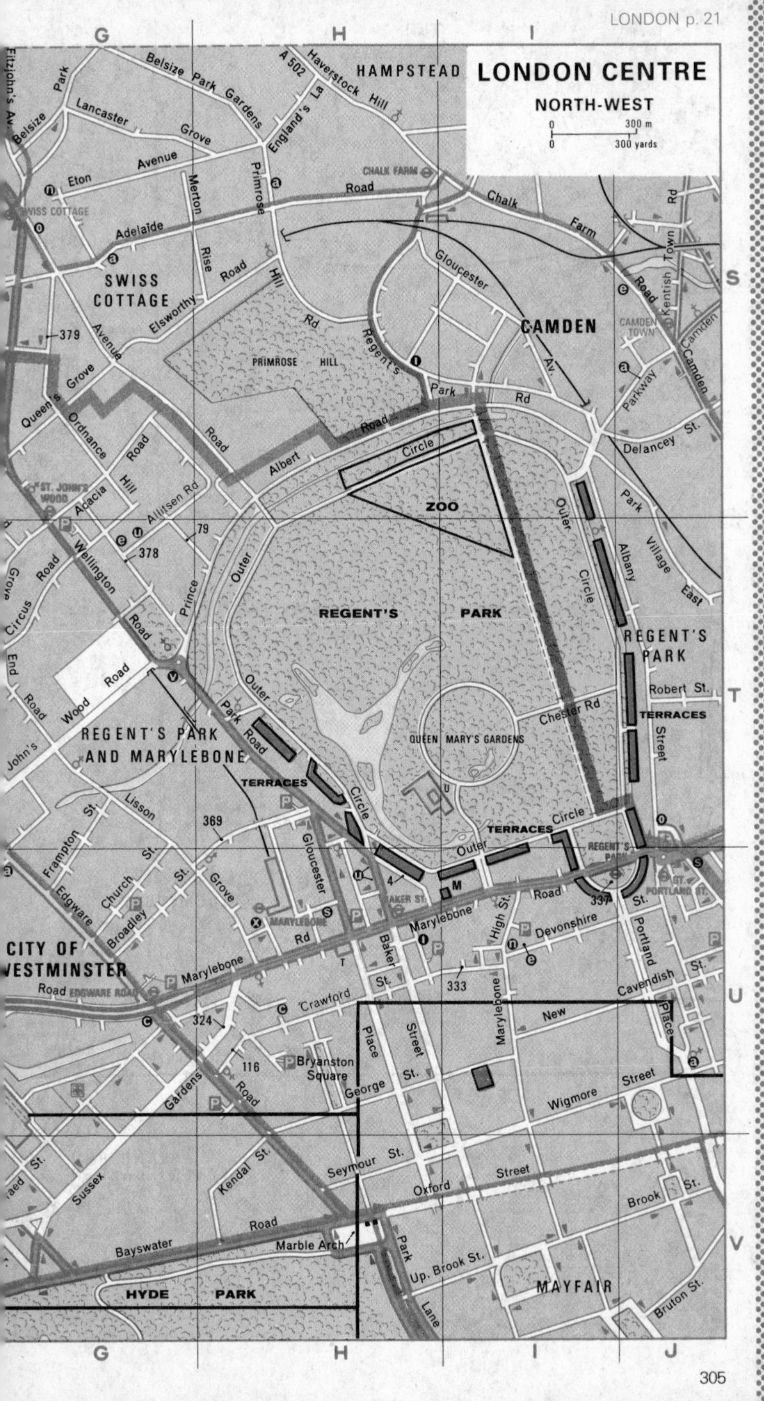
LONDON CENTRE
NORTH-WEST
0 300 m
0 300 yards
HAMPSTEAD
SWISS COTTAGE
CAMDEN
PRIMROSE HILL
ZOO
REGENT'S PARK
QUEEN MARY'S GARDENS
REGENT'S PARK AND MARYLEBONE
TERRACES
REGENT'S PARK TERRACES
CITY OF WESTMINSTER
HYDE PARK
MAYFAIR
Belsize Park Gardens
Haverstock Hill
England's La
Eton Avenue
Adelaide Road
Elsworthy Road
Primrose Hill Rd
Regent's Park Rd
Chalk Farm Road
Gloucester Av.
Parkway
Delancey St.
Albany Street
Park Village East
Outer Circle
Prince Albert Road
Wellington Road
Marylebone Road
Baker St.
Gloucester Place
Edgware Road
Oxford Street
Bayswater Road
Park Lane
Marble Arch
Wigmore Street
New Cavendish St.
Portland Place
Devonshire St.
Bryanston Square
George St.
Seymour St.
Up. Brook St.
Brook St.
Bruton St.
Crawford St.
Lisson Grove
Church St.
Frampton St.
Broadley St.
Kendal St.
Sussex Gardens
Robert St.
Chester Rd
Queen's Grove
Ordnance Hill
Acacia Road
Allitsen Rd
Circus Road
Grove End Road
St. John's Wood Road
Merton Rise
Lancaster Grove
Belsize Park
Fitzjohn's Av.
Kentish Town Rd
Camden
CHALK FARM
SWISS COTTAGE
ST. JOHN'S WOOD
CAMDEN TOWN
BAKER ST.
MARYLEBONE
EDGWARE ROAD
REGENT'S PARK
GT. PORTLAND ST.
379
378
79
369
4
337
333
324
116
G
H
I
J
S
T
U
V

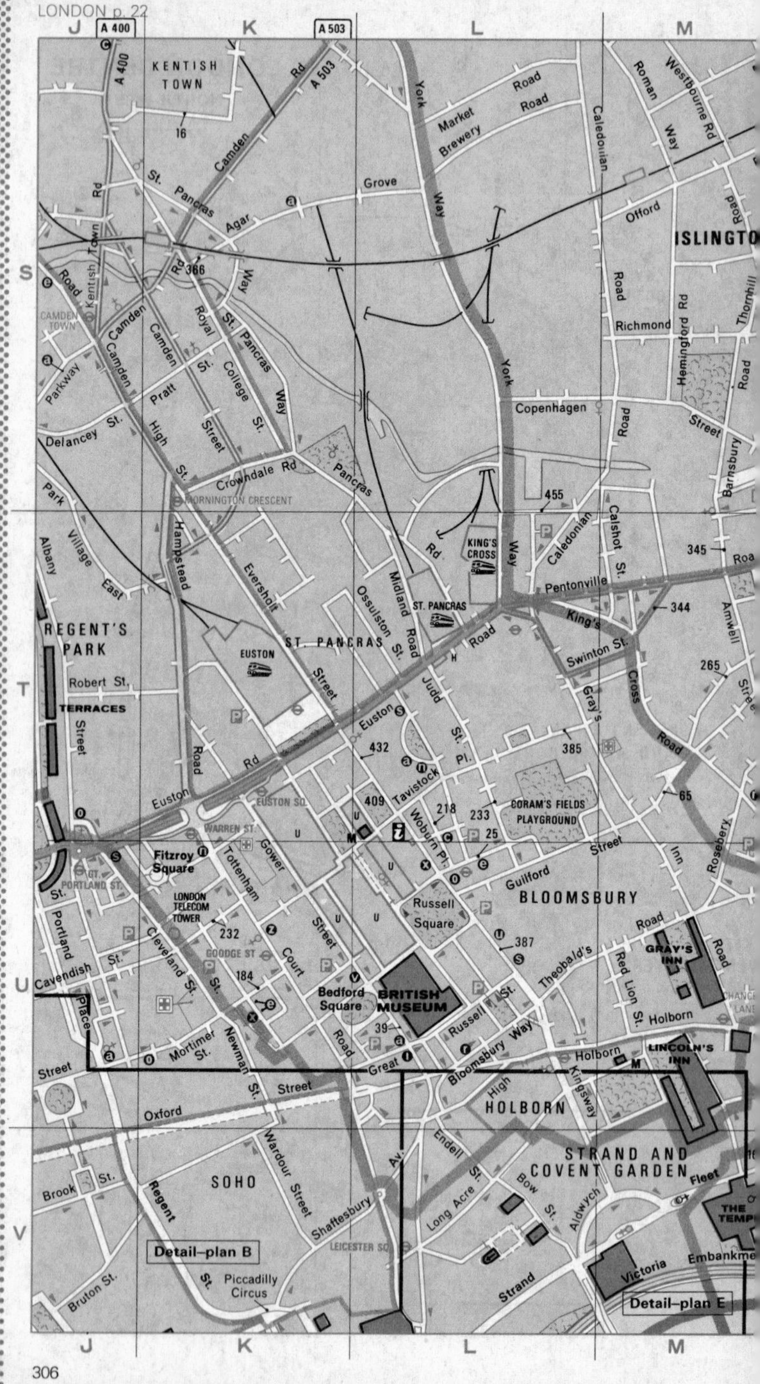
J
K
L
M
A 400
A 503
KENTISH TOWN
ISLINGTON
REGENT'S PARK
TERRACES
ST. PANCRAS
EUSTON
KING'S CROSS
ST. PANCRAS
BLOOMSBURY
CORAM'S FIELDS PLAYGROUND
BRITISH MUSEUM
Bedford Square
Russell Square
Fitzroy Square
LONDON TELECOM TOWER
GRAY'S INN
LINCOLN'S INN
HOLBORN
SOHO
STRAND AND COVENT GARDEN
THE TEMPLE
Piccadilly Circus
Detail-plan B
Detail-plan E
CAMDEN TOWN
MORNINGTON CRESCENT
EUSTON SQ.
WARREN ST.
GT. PORTLAND ST.
GOODGE ST
LEICESTER SQ
S
T
U
V

LONDON CENTRE
NORTH-EAST
0 300 m
0 300 yards
N
O
P
S
T
U
V
ISLINGTON
HACKNEY
TOWER HAMLETS
CITY OF LONDON
CHARTERHOUSE
BARBICAN CENTRE
BARBICAN
GUILDHALL
ST. PAUL'S CATHEDRAL
BANK OF ENGLAND
STOCK EXCHANGE
LIVERPOOL STREET
TOWER OF LONDON
THAMES
Canonbury Square

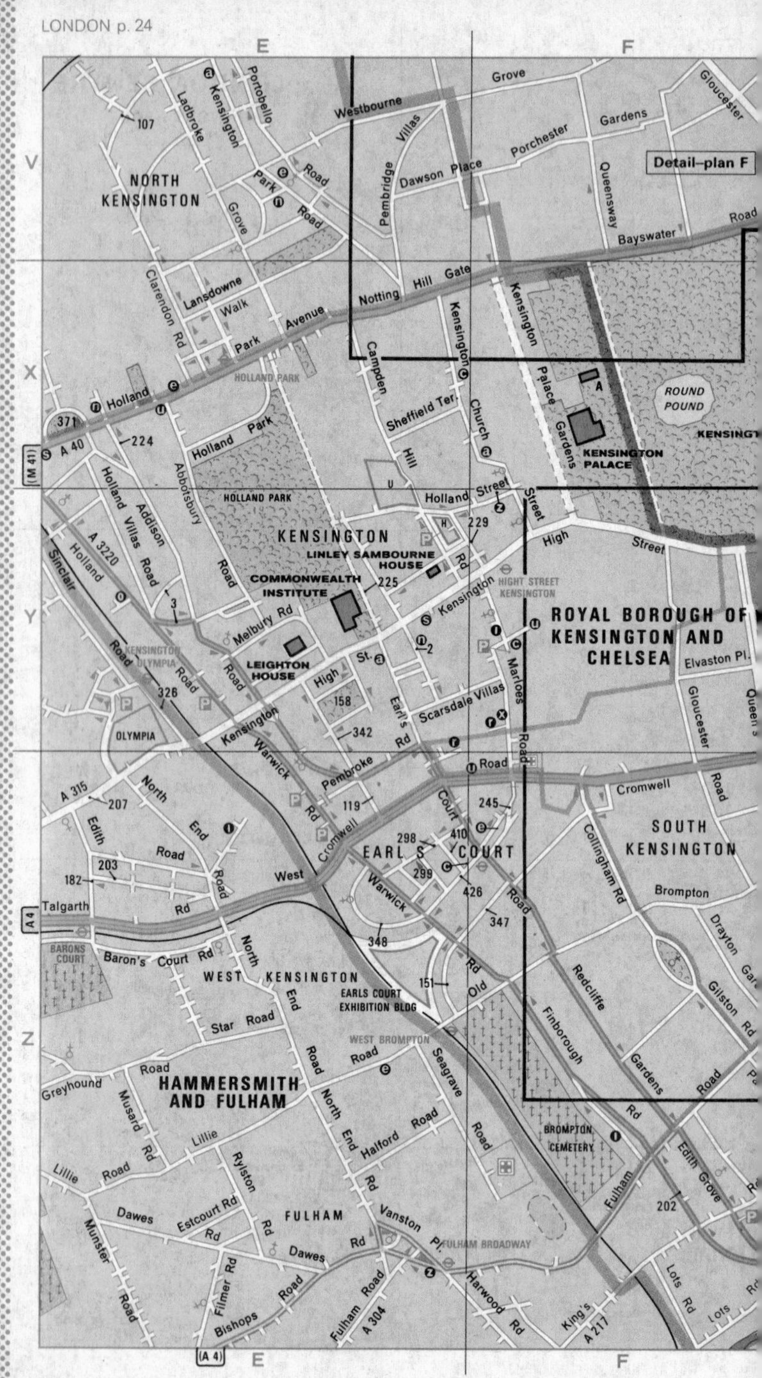
NORTH KENSINGTON
Detail-plan F
KENSINGTON PALACE
ROUND POUND
HOLLAND PARK
KENSINGTON
LINLEY SAMBOURNE HOUSE
COMMONWEALTH INSTITUTE
LEIGHTON HOUSE
ROYAL BOROUGH OF KENSINGTON AND CHELSEA
OLYMPIA
EARL'S COURT
SOUTH KENSINGTON
WEST KENSINGTON
EARLS COURT EXHIBITION BLDG
HAMMERSMITH AND FULHAM
BROMPTON CEMETERY
FULHAM
Westbourne
Grove
Gardens
Porchester
Bayswater
Road
Notting Hill Gate
Holland Park Avenue
Kensington High Street
Cromwell Road
West Cromwell
Talgarth Rd
Fulham Road
King's Road
A 40
A 4
A 3220
A 315
A 304
A 217
(M 41)

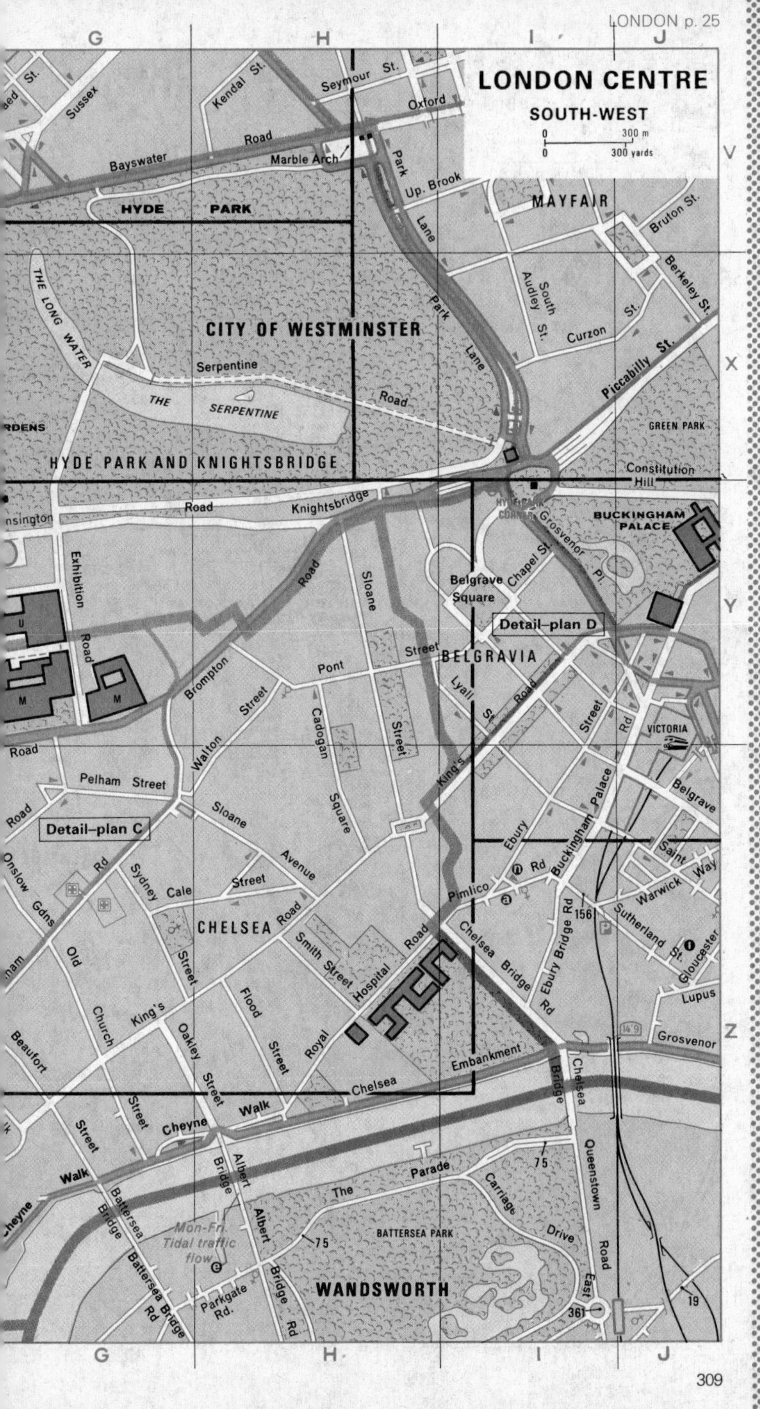
LONDON CENTRE
SOUTH-WEST
0 300 m
0 300 yards
HYDE PARK
CITY OF WESTMINSTER
THE SERPENTINE
THE LONG WATER
HYDE PARK AND KNIGHTSBRIDGE
MAYFAIR
GREEN PARK
BUCKINGHAM PALACE
BELGRAVIA
Belgrave Square
Detail-plan D
Detail-plan C
VICTORIA
CHELSEA
BATTERSEA PARK
WANDSWORTH
Mon-Fri. Tidal traffic flow
Bayswater Road
Oxford
Seymour St.
Kendal St.
Sussex
Marble Arch
Park Lane
Up. Brook
Bruton St.
Berkeley St.
South Audley St.
Curzon St.
Piccadilly St.
Serpentine Road
Constitution Hill
Knightsbridge
Grosvenor Pl.
Chapel St.
Exhibition Road
Brompton Road
Sloane Street
Pont Street
Lyall St.
Cadogan Square
Walton Street
Pelham Street
Sloane Avenue
King's Road
Ebury Street
Buckingham Palace Rd
Belgrave
Saint George's
Warwick Way
Sutherland St.
Gloucester
Lupus
Grosvenor
Pimlico Road
Ebury Bridge Rd
Chelsea Bridge Rd
Onslow Gdns
Sydney Street
Cale Street
Smith Street
Royal Hospital Road
Flood Street
Oakley Street
Old Church Street
Beaufort Street
Chelsea Embankment
Chelsea Bridge
Cheyne Walk
Albert Bridge
Albert Bridge Rd
Battersea Bridge
Battersea Bridge Rd
Parkgate Rd.
The Parade
Carriage Drive
Queenstown Road
East
G
H
I
J
V
X
Y
Z
75
156
149
19
361

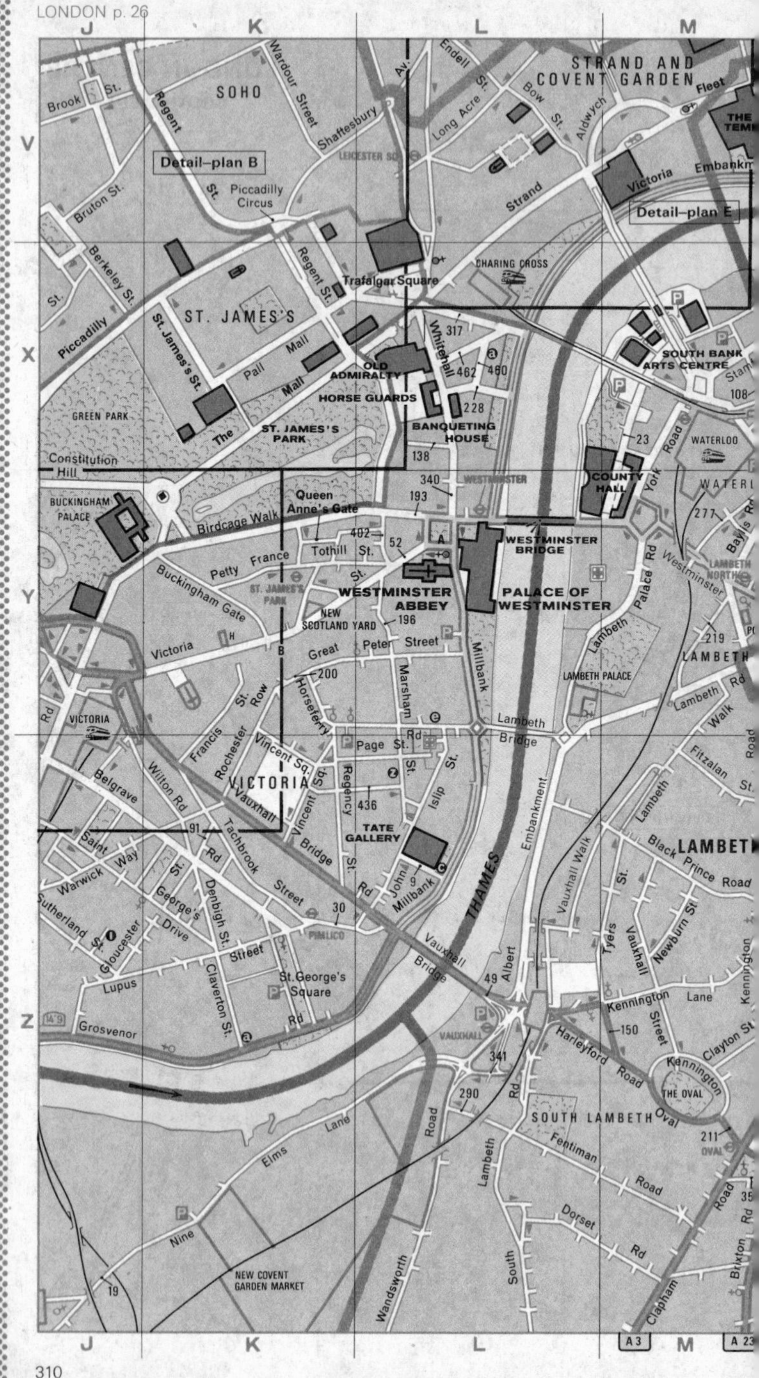
J
K
L
M
V
X
Y
Z
SOHO
STRAND AND COVENT GARDEN
Detail–plan B
Detail–plan E
Piccadilly Circus
Trafalgar Square
CHARING CROSS
ST. JAMES'S
OLD ADMIRALTY
HORSE GUARDS
BANQUETING HOUSE
SOUTH BANK ARTS CENTRE
GREEN PARK
ST. JAMES'S PARK
WATERLOO
COUNTY HALL
BUCKINGHAM PALACE
Queen Anne's Gate
WESTMINSTER BRIDGE
WESTMINSTER ABBEY
PALACE OF WESTMINSTER
NEW SCOTLAND YARD
LAMBETH PALACE
VICTORIA
TATE GALLERY
THAMES
THE OVAL
SOUTH LAMBETH
NEW COVENT GARDEN MARKET
A 3

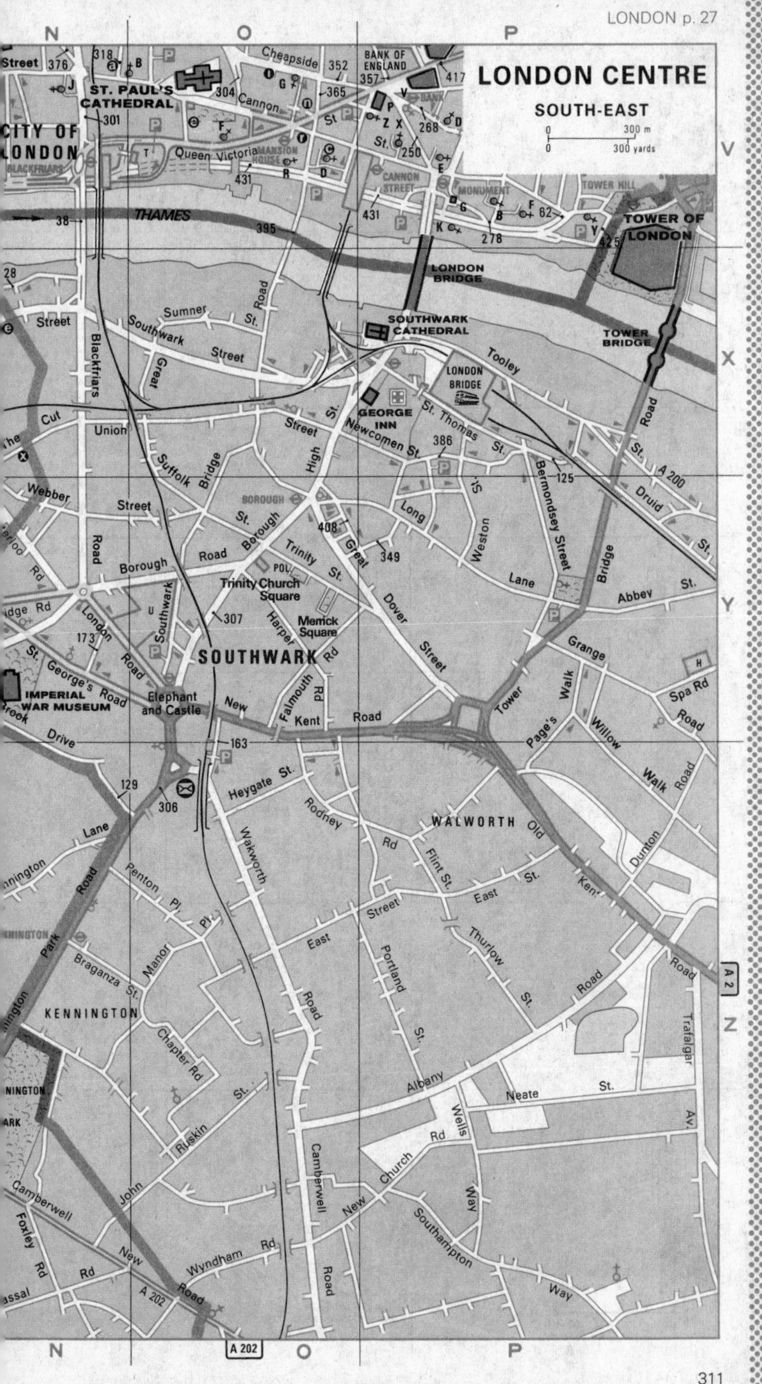
LONDON CENTRE
SOUTH-EAST
300 m
300 yards
ST. PAUL'S CATHEDRAL
CITY OF LONDON
BANK OF ENGLAND
Cheapside
Cannon St
Queen Victoria St
MANSION HOUSE
CANNON STREET
MONUMENT
TOWER HILL
TOWER OF LONDON
THAMES
LONDON BRIDGE
SOUTHWARK CATHEDRAL
TOWER BRIDGE
Tooley St.
Southwark Street
Sumner St.
Blackfriars Road
Great Suffolk St.
Union Street
Cut
GEORGE INN
St. Thomas St.
Newcomen St.
Borough High St.
BOROUGH
Long Lane
Weston St.
Bermondsey Street
Tower Bridge Road
Druid St.
A 200
Webber Street
Borough Road
Trinity St.
Trinity Church Square
Merrick Square
Harper Rd
Great Dover Street
Abbey St.
Grange
Spa Rd
SOUTHWARK
London Road
St. George's Road
IMPERIAL WAR MUSEUM
Elephant and Castle
New Kent Road
Falmouth Rd
Page's Walk
Willow Walk
Heygate St.
Rodney Rd
WALWORTH
Old Kent Road
Flint St.
East St.
East Street
Thurlow St.
Wakworth Road
Portland St.
Dunton Road
A 2
Kennington Park Road
Kennington Lane
Penton Pl.
Braganza St.
Manor Pl.
KENNINGTON
Chapter Rd
Ruskin St.
Albany Road
Neate St.
Trafalgar Av.
Wells Way
Camberwell Road
New Church Rd
Southampton Way
John Ruskin St.
Camberwell New Road
Wyndham Rd
Foxley Rd
A 202
N
O
P
V
X
Y
Z

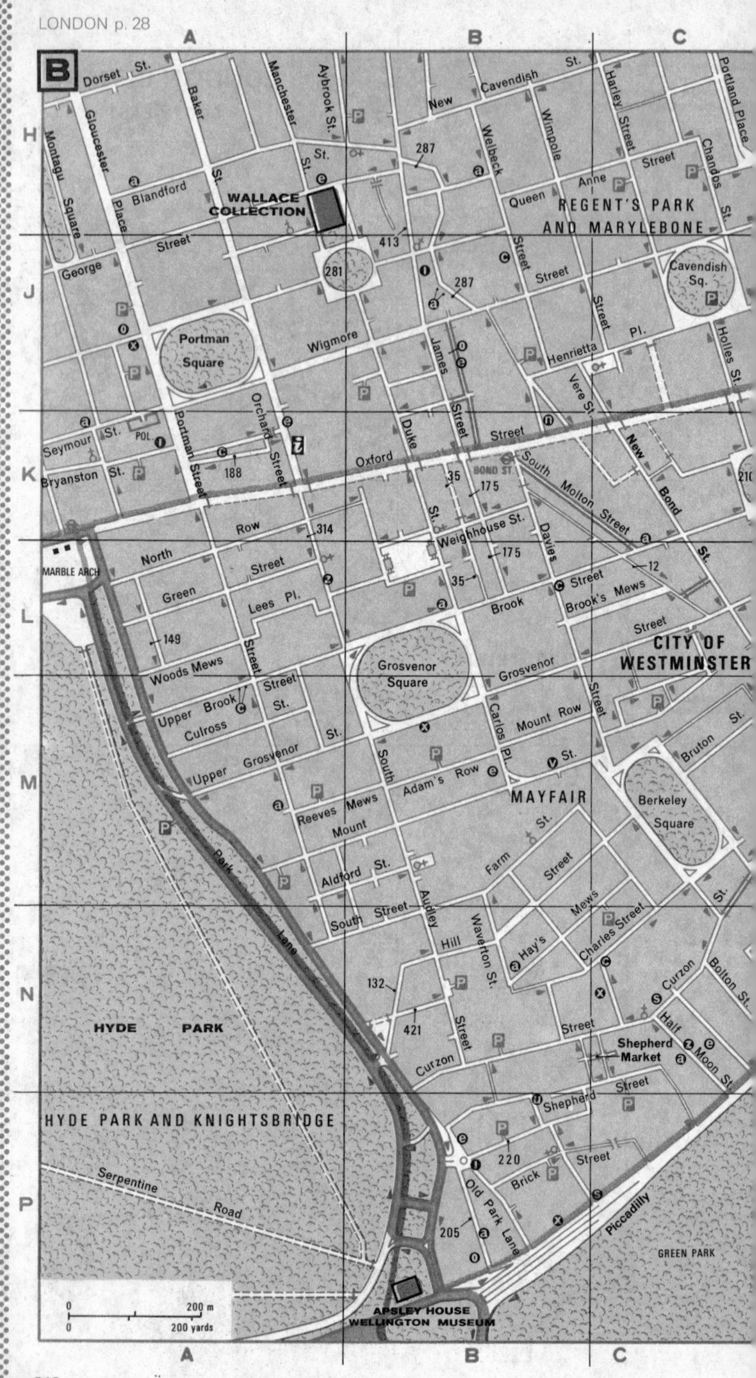
B
A
B
C
REGENT'S PARK AND MARYLEBONE
WALLACE COLLECTION
Portman Square
Cavendish Sq.
MARBLE ARCH
Grosvenor Square
CITY OF WESTMINSTER
MAYFAIR
Berkeley Square
HYDE PARK
HYDE PARK AND KNIGHTSBRIDGE
Shepherd Market
GREEN PARK
APSLEY HOUSE WELLINGTON MUSEUM
Oxford Street
Piccadilly
Park Lane
Serpentine Road
200 m
200 yards

Street	Grid	No.
Arlington Street	**DN**	6
Avery Row	**CL**	12
Bateman Street	**FK**	18
Berwick Street	**FK**	26
Binney Street	**BL**	35
Carlton Gardens	**FP**	74
Deanery Street	**BN**	132
Denman Street	**FM**	133
Denmark Street	**GJ**	134
Duke of York Street	**EN**	143
Duke Street ST. JAMES	**EN**	146
Dunraven Street	**AL**	149
Gerrard Street	**GL**	174
Gilbert Street	**BL**	175
Glasshouse Street	**EM**	179
Granville Place	**AK**	188
Great Castle Street	**DJ**	189
Greek Street	**GK**	198
Hamilton Place	**BP**	205
Hanover Square	**CK**	210
Hertford Street	**BP**	220
Leicester Square	**GM**	261
Manchester Square	**AJ**	281
Market Place	**DJ**	286
Marylebone Lane	**BJ**	287
North Audley Street	**AK**	314
Old Burlington Street	**DM**	322
Old Compton Street	**GK**	323
Panton Street	**FM**	336
Romilly Street	**GL**	368
Thayer Street	**BJ**	413
Tilney Street	**BN**	421
Warwick Street	**EM**	444

Oxford Street is closed to private traffic, Mondays to Saturdays : from 7 am to 7 pm between Portman Street and St. Giles Circus

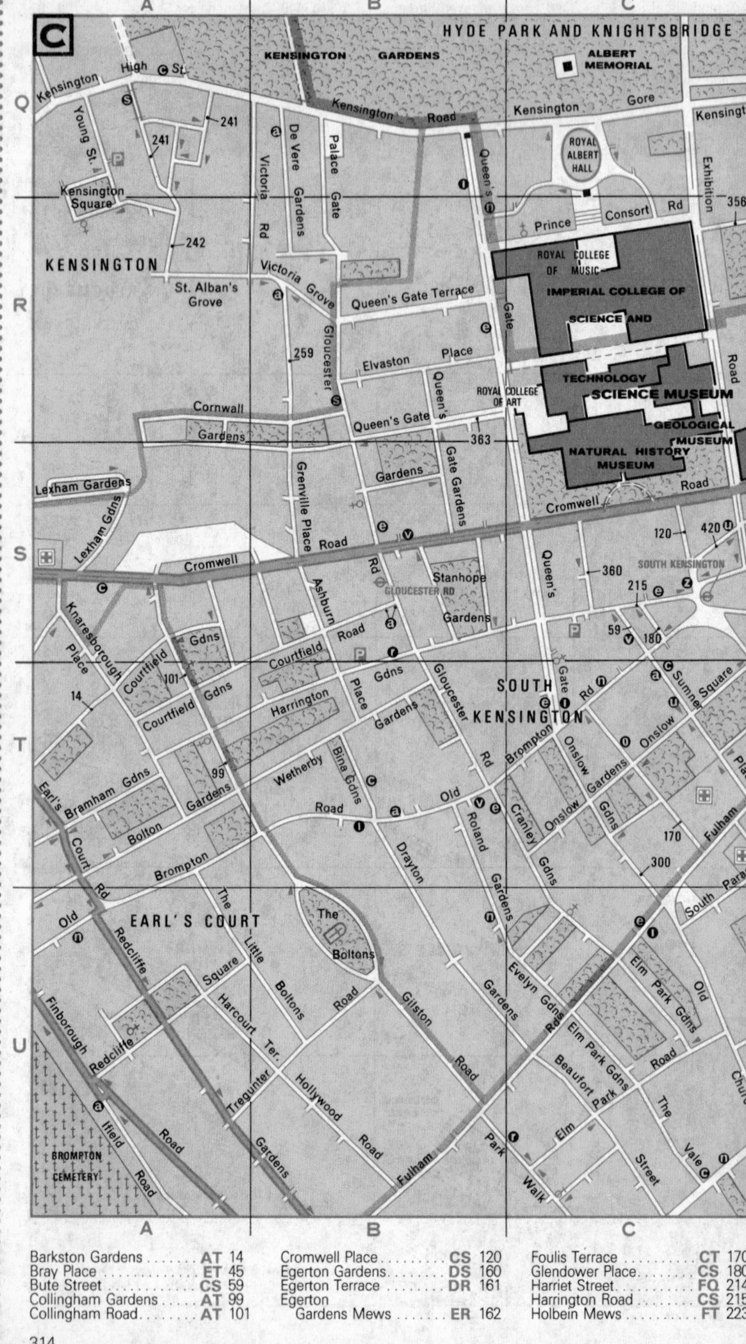

Barkston Gardens	AT 14	Cromwell Place	CS 120	Foulis Terrace	CT 170
Bray Place	ET 45	Egerton Gardens	DS 160	Glendower Place	CS 180
Bute Street	CS 59	Egerton Terrace	DR 161	Harriet Street	FQ 214
Collingham Gardens	AT 99	Egerton Gardens Mews	ER 162	Harrington Road	CS 215
Collingham Road	AT 101			Holbein Mews	FT 223

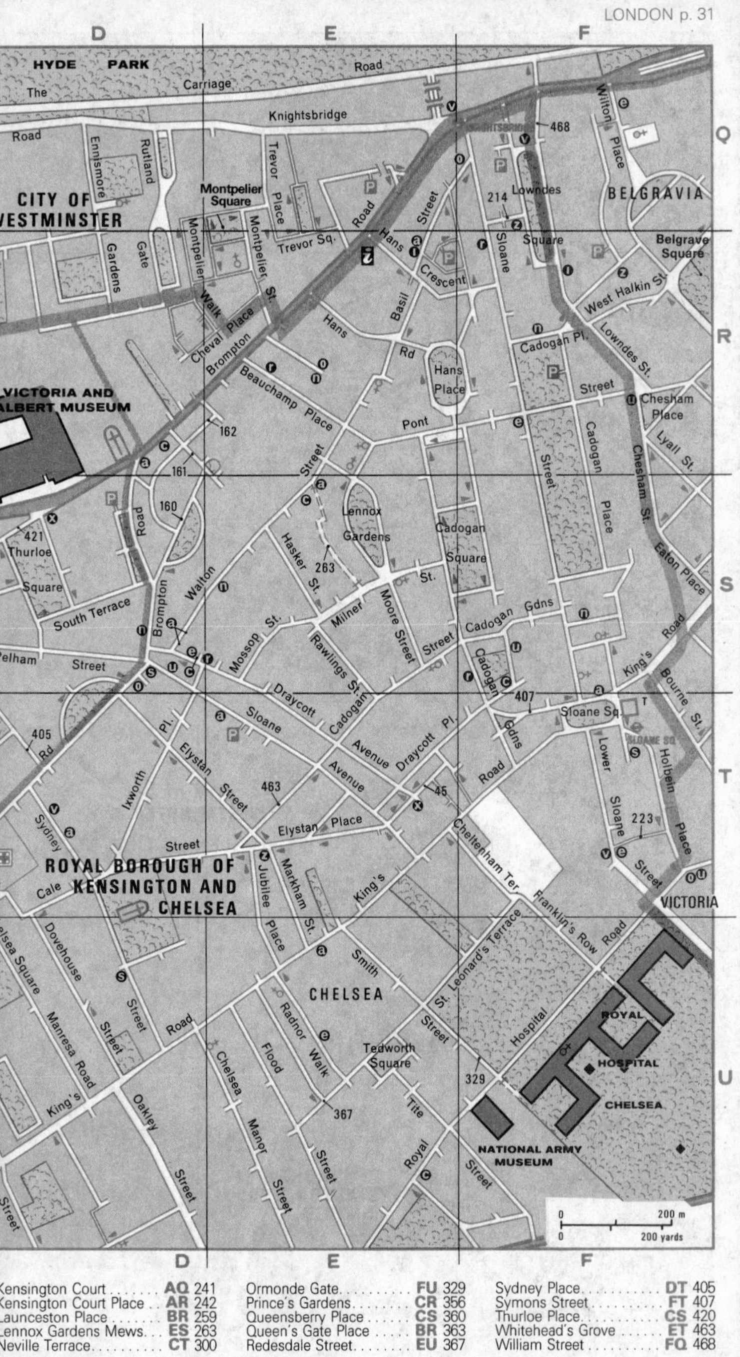

Kensington Court . . . . **AQ** 241	Ormonde Gate. . . . . **FU** 329	Sydney Place. . . . . **DT** 405
Kensington Court Place . . **AR** 242	Prince's Gardens. . . . . **CR** 356	Symons Street . . . . **FT** 407
Launceston Place . . . . **BR** 259	Queensberry Place . . . . . . **CS** 360	Thurloe Place. . . . . **CS** 420
Lennox Gardens Mews. . . **ES** 263	Queen's Gate Place . . . . . **BR** 363	Whitehead's Grove . . . . . . **ET** 463
Neville Terrace. . . . . **CT** 300	Redesdale Street. . . . . **EU** 367	William Street . . . . **FQ** 468

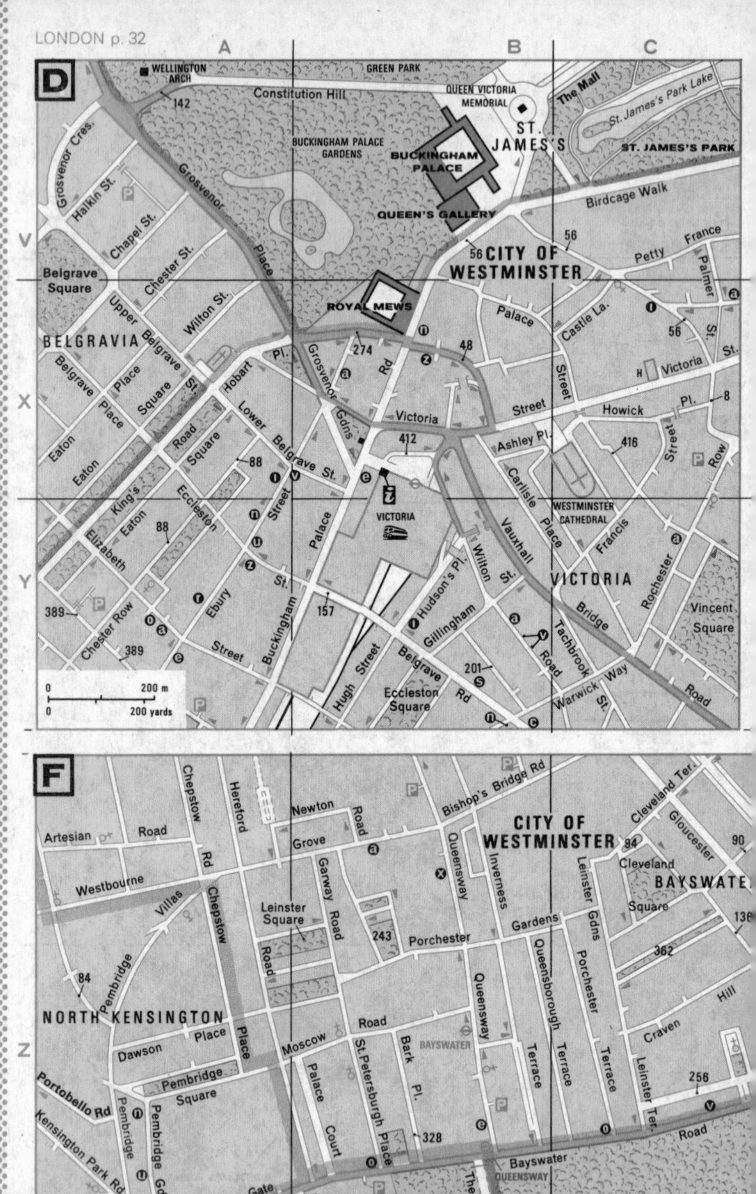
D
A
B
C
V
X
Y
WELLINGTON ARCH
GREEN PARK
Constitution Hill
QUEEN VICTORIA MEMORIAL
The Mall
St. James's Park Lake
ST. JAMES'S
ST. JAMES'S PARK
BUCKINGHAM PALACE GARDENS
BUCKINGHAM PALACE
QUEEN'S GALLERY
Birdcage Walk
CITY OF WESTMINSTER
Petty France
Palmer
Grosvenor Cres.
Halkin St.
Chapel St.
Chester St.
Grosvenor Place
Belgrave Square
Upper Belgrave St.
Wilton St.
ROYAL MEWS
Palace
Castle La.
BELGRAVIA
Belgrave Place
Eaton Square
Eaton Place
Hobart Pl.
Grosvenor Gdns
Grosvenor Rd
Victoria St.
Victoria Street
Street
Howick Pl.
Lower Belgrave St.
Ashley Pl.
Carlisle Place
WESTMINSTER CATHEDRAL
King's Road
Eaton Square
Eccleston
Street
Palace
VICTORIA
Vauxhall Bridge Road
Wilton St.
Hudson's Pl.
Francis
Rochester Row
Vincent Square
Elizabeth
Ebury Street
Buckingham Palace Rd
Gillingham
Tachbrook St.
Chester Row
Hugh Street
Belgrave Rd
Eccleston Square
Warwick Way
Road
142
56
48
274
412
88
416
8
157
389
201
0
200 m
200 yards
F
Z
Chepstow Rd
Hereford
Newton Road
Bishop's Bridge Rd
Cleveland Ter.
Gloucester
Artesian Road
Grove
CITY OF WESTMINSTER
Queensway
Inverness
Leinster Gdns
Cleveland Square
BAYSWATER
Westbourne
Villas
Chepstow Place
Leinster Square
Garway Road
Porchester
Gardens
Leinster Road
Queensway
Queensborough Terrace
Porchester Terrace
Pembridge Villas
Craven Hill
NORTH KENSINGTON
Dawson Place
Moscow Road
St.Petersburgh Place
Bark Pl.
BAYSWATER
Terrace
Leinster Ter.
Pembridge Square
Portobello Rd
Kensington Park Rd
Pembridge Rd
Pembridge Gdns
Palace Court
Bayswater Road
QUEENSWAY
Notting Hill Gate
ROYAL BOROUGH OF KENSINGTON AND CHELSEA
Kensington Palace Gardens
The Broad Walk
NOTTING HILL GATE
KENSINGTON GARDENS
Place
Kensington
KENSINGTON
94
90
136
243
362
84
256
328
238
335
0
200 m
200 yards

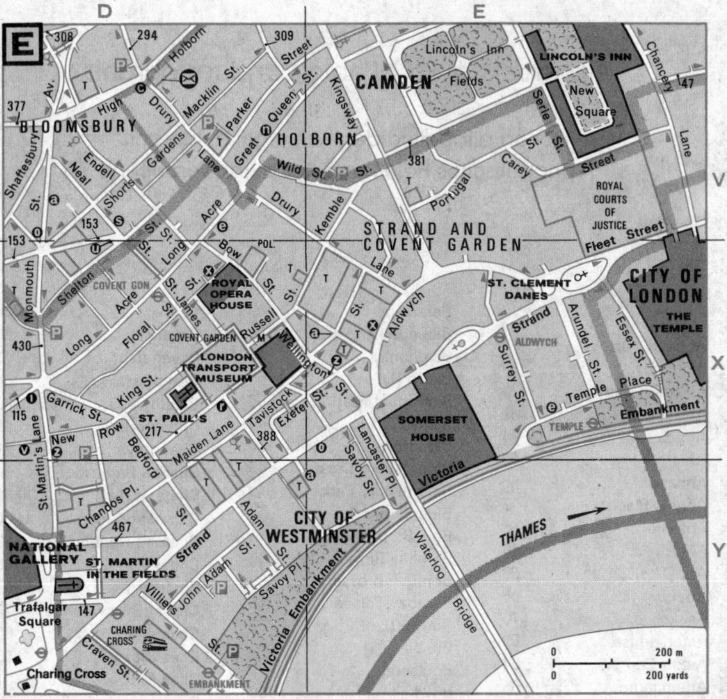

D E

E

308 294 309 Holborn Street St. Lincoln's Inn Fields CAMDEN LINCOLN'S INN Chancery 47 New Square 377 BLOOMSBURY High Drury Macklin St. Parker Queen Kingsway Serle St. Lane HOLBORN Shaftesbury Av. Endell Neal Gardens Lane Great Wild St. St. 381 St. Carey Street V Shorts Drury Portugal ROYAL COURTS OF JUSTICE St. 153 Acre Kemble 153 St. POL. STRAND AND COVENT GARDEN Fleet Street Long Bow Lane Monmouth Shelton COVENT GDN St. James St. ROYAL OPERA HOUSE St. St. ST. CLEMENT DANES CITY OF LONDON Acre Aldwych Strand Arundel Essex St. THE TEMPLE Long Floral St. Russell COVENT GARDEN M Wellington ALDWYCH Surrey St. 430 LONDON TRANSPORT MUSEUM X King St. Place Temple Garrick St. St. PAUL'S Tavistock Exeter St. St. SOMERSET HOUSE Embankment 115 Row TEMPLE 217 New Bedford Maiden Lane 388 Lancaster Pl. Savoy St. St. Martin's Lane Victoria Chandos Pl. St. Adam CITY OF WESTMINSTER THAMES 467 Waterloo St. Y NATIONAL GALLERY ST. MARTIN IN THE FIELDS Strand St. Savoy Pl. John Adam Embankment Bridge Trafalgar Square 147 Villiers CHARING CROSS Victoria Craven St. St. 0 200 m 0 200 yards Charing Cross EMBANKMENT

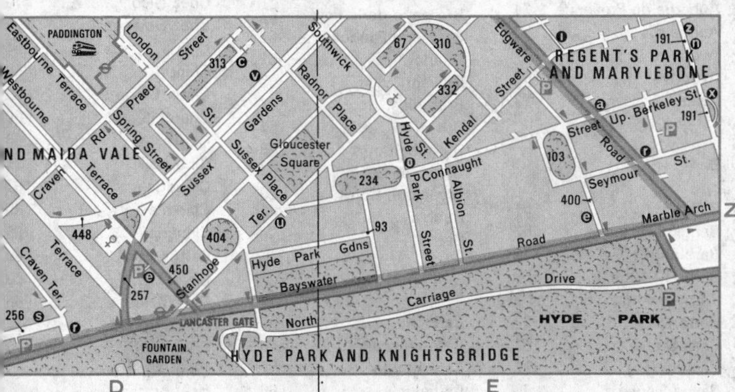

D E

Alphabetical list of hotels and restaurants
Liste alphabétique des hôtels et restaurants
Elenco alfabetico degli alberghi e ristoranti
Alphabetisches Hotel- und Restaurantverzeichnis

RESTAURANT
HOTEL

Alphabetical list of areas included
Liste alphabétique des quartiers cités
Elenco alfabetico dei quartieri citati
Liste der erwähnten Bezirke

Starred establishments in London

Les établissements à étoiles de Londres

Gli esercizi con stelle a Londra

Die Stern-Restaurants Londons

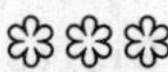

		Area	Page
XXXX	**Le Gavroche**	Mayfair	68

		Area	Page
XXXX	**La Tante Claire**	Chelsea	58
XXXX	**Chez Nico**	Regents Park and Marylebone	70
XXX	**Harvey's**	Wandsworth	66

		Area	Page
	Connaught	Mayfair	67
	Capital	Chelsea	57
XXXXX	**Oak Room**	Mayfair	68
XXXX	**Four Seasons**	Mayfair	68
XXX	**Suntory**	St. James's	71
XXX	**Arlequin (L')**	Battersea	65
XXX	**Cavaliers'**	Battersea	65
XX	**Sutherlands**	Soho	72

Further establishments which merit your attention

Autres tables qui méritent votre attention

Altre tavole particolarmente interessanti

Weitere empfehlenswerte Häuser

M

XXX	**Keat's**	Hampstead	50
XXX	**Red Fort**	Soho	72
XXX	**Bibendum**	Chelsea	58
XXX	**Dynasty II**	Chelsea	58
XXX	**Turner's**	Chelsea	58
XXX	**Zen Central**	Mayfair	68
XX	**Le Caprice**	St. James's	71
XX	**Hilaire**	South Kensington	62
X	**Vijay**	Kilburn	48
X	**Chinon**	Sheperd's Bush	54
X	**Kensington Place**	Kensington	60
X	**Al San Vincenzo**	Cheam	65

Restaurants classified according to type
Restaurants classés suivant leur genre
Ristoranti classificati secondo il loro genere
Restaurants nach Art und Einrichtung geordnet

Bistro

- X **Bougie (La)** (Camden - *Camden Town*) ... 50
- X **Langan's Bistro** (City of Westminster - *Regent's Park & Marylebone*) 71
- X **M'sieur Frog** (Islington - *Islington*) ... 57
- X **Thierry's** (Royal Borough of Kensington & Chelsea - *Chelsea*) ... 59

Seafood

- XX **Croisette (La)** (Royal Borough of Kensington & Chelsea) - *Earl's Court*) ... 59
- XX **Gravier** (Kingston-upon-Thames - *Kingston*) ... 63
- XX **Hippocampe (L')** (City of Westminster - *Soho*) ... 72
- XX **Hoizin** (City of Westminster - *Victoria*) ... 74
- XX **Poissonnerie de l'Avenue** (Royal Borough of Kensington & Chelsea - *Chelsea*) ... 59
- XX **Seppia (La)** (City of Westminster - *Mayfair*) ... 69
- XX **Sheekey's** (City of Westminster - *Strand & Covent Garden*) ... 73
- XX **Suquet (Le)** (Royal Borough of Kensington & Chelsea - *Chelsea*). 59
- XX **Tiger Lee** (Royal Borough of Kensington & Chelsea - *Chelsea*) ... 59
- X **Flounders** (City of Westminter - *Strand & Covent Garden*) ... 73
- X **Quai St. Pierre (Le)** (Royal Borough of Kensington & Chelsea - *Kensington*) ... 60
- X **34 Surrey Street** (Croydon - *Croydon*) ... 52

Californian

- XX **34 Surrey Street** (Croydon - *Croydon*) ... 52

Chinese

- XXX **Empress Garden** (City of Westminster - *Mayfair*) ... 68
- XXX **Inn of Happiness** (City of Westminster - *Victoria*) ... 74
- XXX **Princess Garden** (City of Westminster - *Mayfair*) ... 68
- XXX **Zen** (Royal Borough of Kensington & Chelsea - *Chelsea*) ... 58
- XXX **Zen Central** (City of Westminster - *Mayfair*) ... 68
- XX **Bayee House** (Wandsworth - *Rutney*) ... 66
- XX **Bayee Village** (Merton - *Wimbledon*) ... 63
- XX **Chin's** (Hammersmith - *Fulham*) .. 54
- XX **Chow Sings** (Enfield - *Enfield*) ... 53
- XX **Dragon City** (Redbridge - *Ilford*) .. 64
- XX **Evergreen** (Richmond-upon-Thames - *Richmond*) ... 64
- XX **Gallery Rendezvous** (City of Westminster - *Soho*) ... 72
- XX **Good Earth** (Barnet - *Mill Hill*) ... 48
- XX **Good Earth** (Royal Borough of Kensington & Chelsea - *Chelsea*). 59
- XX **Grove Park** (Hounslow - *Chiswick*) 56
- XX **Hee's** (Hounslow - *Hounslow*) ... 56
- XX **Ho-Ho** (City of Westminster - *Mayfair*) ... 69
- XX **Ho-Ho** (Redbridge - *South Woodford*) ... 64
- XX **Hoizin** (City of Westminster - *Victoria*) ... 74
- XX **Hsing** (City of Westminster - *Bayswater & Maida Vale*) ... 67

Chinese

English

French

French

XX **Croisette (La)** (Royal Borough of Kensington & Chelsea - *Earl's Court*) 59

XX **Gavvers** (Royal Borough of Kensington & Chelsea - *Chelsea*) 58

XX **Grafton (The)** (Lambeth - *Clapham Common*) 63

XX **Gravier** (Kingston-upon-Thames - *Kingston*) 63

XX **Jardin des Gourmets (Au)** (City of Westminster - *Soho*) 72

XX **Mon Plaisir** (Camden - *Bloomsbury*) 50

XX **Monsieur Thompson's** (Royal Borough of Kensington - *North Kensington*) 61

XX **Poissonnerie de l'Avenue** (Royal Borough of Kensington & Chelsea - *Chelsea*) 59

XX **Pomme d'Amour (La)** (Royal Borough of Kensington - *Kensington*) 60

XX **Poulbot (Le)** (basement) (City of London - *City of London*) 51

XX **P'tit Montmartre (Le)** (City of Westminster - *Regent Park & Marylebone*) 70

XX **St. Quentin** (Royal Borough of Kensington & Chelsea - *Chelsea*). 59

XX **Suquet (Le)** (Royal Borough of Kensington & Chelsea - *Chelsea*). 5

XX **Trois Plats (Les)** (Royal Borough of Kensington & Chelsea - *Chelsea*). 59

X **Ark (The)** (Royal Borough of Kensington & Chelsea - *Kensington*) . 60

X **Aventure (L')** (City of Westminster - *Regent Park & Marylebone*) 71

X **Bois St. Jean (Au)** (City of Westminster - *Regent Park & Marylebone*) 71

X **Bubb's** (City of London - *City of London*) 51

X **Dordogne (La)** (Hounslow - *Chiswick*) 56

X **Ma Cuisine** (Royal Borough of Kensington & Chelsea - *Chelsea*). 59

X **Magno's Brasserie** (City of Westminster - *Strand & Covent Garden*) 73

X **Poule au Pot (La)** (City of Westminster - *Victoria*) 74

X **Quai St. Pierre (Le)** (Royal Borough of Kensington & Chelsea - *Kensington*) 60

Hungarian

XX **Gay Hussar** (City of Westminster - *Soho*) 72

Indian & Pakistan

XXX **Bombay Brasserie** (Royal Borough of Kensington & Chelsea - *South Kensington*) 62

XXX **Bombay Palace** (City of Westminster - *Bayswater & Maida Vale*) .. 66

XXX **Red Fort** (City of Westminster - *Soho*) 72

XX **Bengal Lancer** (Camden - *Kentish Town*) 50

XX **Copper Chimney** (City of Westminster - *Mayfair*) 69

XX **Delhi Brasserie**(Royal Borough of Kensington & Chelsea - *South Kensington*) 62

XX **Gaylord** (City of Westminster - *Regent's Park & Marylebone*) 70

XX **Gopal's** (City of Westminster - *Soho*) 72

XX **Jamdani** (Camden - *Bloomsbury*) . 49

XX **Laguna Tandoori** (Ealing - *Ealing*) .. 52

XX **Memories of India** (Royal Borough of Kensington & Chelsea - *South Kensington*) 62

XX **Monsoon** (City of Westminster - *Bayswater and Maida Vale*) 67

XX **Nayab** (Hammersmith - *Fulham*) .. 54

XX **Tandoori Nights** (Enfield - *Cockfosters*) 53

XX **Tandoori Nights** (Hammersmith - *Hammersmith*) 54

XX **Zai'qa Tandoori** (Barnet - *High Barnet*) 48

X **Annapurna** (Hounslow - *Cheswick*) 56

X **Bombay Bicycle Club** (Wandsworth - *Wandsworth*) 66

X **Brilliant** (Ealing - *Southall*) 52

X **Jashan** (Haringey - *Hornsey*) 54

X **Malabar** (Royal Borough of Kensington & Chelsea - *Kensington*) . 60

X **Raj Vogue** (Islington - *Upper Holloway*) 57

X **Taste of India** (Greenwich - *Greenwich*) 53

X **Taste of Raj** (Richmond-upon-Thames - *East Sheen*) 64

X **Vijay** (Brent - *Kilburn*) 48

Italian

XX **L'Incontro** (City of Westminster - *Victoria*) 74

XX **Santini** (City of Westminster - *Victoria*) 74

XX **Amico (L')** (City of Westminster - *Victoria*) 74

XX **Antonio's** (Hounslow - *Chiswick*) .. 56

XX **Beccofino** (Royal Borough of Kensington & Chelsea - *Chelsea*) 59

XX **Bellini** (Richmond-upon-Thames - *Richmond*) 64

XX **Brivati's** (Islington - - *Finsbury*) ... 57

XX **Canaletto 2** (Harrow - *Hatch End*) . 55

XX **Capisano** (Bromley - *Bromley*) 40

XX **Eleven Park Walk** (Royal Borough of Kensington & Chelsea - *Chelsea*) 59

XX **Finezza (La)** (Royal Borough of Kensington & Chelsea - *Chelsea*). 58

XX **Fontana Amorosa** (City of Westminster - *Regent's Park & Marylebone*) 70

XX **Giannino's** (Bromley - *Keston*) 49

XX **Gran Paradiso** (City of Westminster - *Victoria*) 74

XX **Loggia (La)** (City of Westminster - *Regent's Park & Marylebone*) 70

XX **Luigi's** (Southwark - *Dulwich Village*) 65

XX **Mario** (Royal Borough of Kensington & Chelsea - *Chelsea*) 58

XX **Mezzaluna** (Barnet - - *Childs Hill*) . 48

XX **Orso** (City of Westminster - *Strand & Covent Garden*) 73

XX **Paesana (La)** (Royal Borough of Kensington & Chelsea - *Kensington*) 60

XX **Ponte Nuovo** (Royal Borough of Kensington & Chelsea - *Chelsea*). 59

XX **Primula (La)** (Royal Borough of Kensington & Chelsea - *Earl's Court*) 59

XX **Salotto** (Royal Borough of Kensington & Chelsea - *Chelsea*) 58

XX **San Carlo** (Haringey - *Highgate*) .. 54

XX **San Marino** (City of Westminster - *Bayswater & Maida Vale*) 66

XX **Seppia (La)** (City of Westminster - *Mayfair*) 69

XX **Topo d'Oro** (Royal Borough of Kensington & Chelsea - *Kensington*) 60

XX **Toto** (Royal Borough of Kensington & Chelsea - *Chelsea*) 59

XX **Waterfront** (Royal Borough of Kensington & Chelsea - *Chelsea*) 58

X **Barbino (Il)** (City of Westminster - *Regent's Park & Marylebone*) 71

X **Casale Franco** (Islington - *Islington*) 57

X **Cibo** (Royal Borough of Kensington & Chelsea - *Kensington*) 60

X **Elio** (Croydon - *Sanderstead*) 52

X **Fontana (La)** (City of Westminster - *Victoria*) 74

X **Gino's** (Ealing - *Ealing*) 52

X **Laguna** (City of Westminster - *Strand & Covent Garden*) 73

X **Mimmo d'Ischia** (City of Westminster - *Victoria*) 74

X **Ombrello (L')** (Bromley - *Farnborough*) 49

X **Paolo's** (Eling - *Ealing*) 52

X **Roberto's** (Hillingdon - *Ickenham*). 56

X **Sambuca** (Hillingdon - *Eastcote*) .. 55

X **San Vincenzo (Al)** (Sutton - *Cheam*) 65

X **Tagliatelle (Le)** (Richmond-upon-Thames - *East Sheen*) 64

X **Villa Medici** (City of Westminster - *Victoria*) 74

X **Ziani** (Royal Borough of Kensington & Chelsea - *Chelsea*) 59

Japanese

XXX ✿ **Suntory** (City of Westminster - *St. James's*) 71

XXX **Benihana** (Camden - *Hampstead*) . 50

XX **Asuka** (City of Westminster - *Regent's Park & Marylebone*) 70

XX **Hiroko** (Royal Borough of Kensington & Chelsea - *Kensington*) . 60

XX **Masako** (City of Westminster - *Regent's Park & Marylebone*) 70

XX **Miyama** (City of London - *City of London*) 51

XX **Miyama** (City of Westminster - *Mayfair*) 69

XX **Mon** (City of Westminster - *Regent's Park & Marylebone*) 70

XX **Nakano** (Royal Borough of Kensington & Chelsea - *Chelsea*) 59

XX **Shogun** (City of Westminster - *Mayfair*) 69

X **Azami** (City of Westminster - *Strand & Covent Garden*) 73

X **Ikeda** (City of Westminster - *Mayfair*) 69

X **Koto** (Camden - *Regents Park*) ... 51

X **Nakamura** (City of Westminster - *Regent's Park & Marylebone*) 71

Korean

XX **Kaya** (City of Westminster - *Soho*) 72

X **Garden** (Hammersmith - *Hammersmith*) 54

Lebanese

XX **Phoenicia** (Royal Borough of Kensington & Chelsea - *Kensington*) . 60

X **Beit Eddine** (Royal Borough of Kensington & Chelsea - *Chelsea*). 59

Oriental

XX **Dynasty II** (Royal Borough of Kensington & Chelsea - *Chelsea*) 58

X **Kelong** (Croydon - *South Croydon*) 52

Swedish

X **Anna's Place** (Islington - *Canonbury*) 57

Thai

XX **Blue Elephant** (Hammersmith - *Fulham*) 54

XX **Chada** (Wandsworth - *Battersea*) . 65

XX **Lena's** (Wandsworth - *Battersea*) . 65

XX **Tui** (Royal Borough of Kensington & Chelsea - *South Kensington*). . . 62

X **Ayudhya** (Kignston-upon-Thames - *Kingston*) 63

X **Bangkok** (Royal Borough of Kensington & Chelsea - *South Kensington*). 62

X **Chaopraya** (City of Westminter - *Regent Park & Marylebone*) 71

X **Lakorn** (Islington - *Finsbury*) 57

X **Oh Boy** (Croydon - *Croydon*) 52

X **Oh Boy** (Wandsworth - *Tooting*) . . 66

X **Taxin Thai** (City of Westminter - *Bayswater & Maida Vale*) 67

X **Taxin Thai Too** (City of Westminter - *Regent Park & Marylebone*) 71

X **Thai Castle** (Harrow - *North Harrow*) 55

X **Sri Sian** (City of Westminster - *Soho*) 72

Vietnamese

X **Nam Long at Le Shaker** (Royal Borough of Kensington & Chelsea - *South Kensington*). 62

X **Saigon** (City of Westminster - *Soho*) 72

X **Van Long** (City of Westminster - *Soho*) 72

Restaurants open on Sunday

L = lunch – **D** = dinner – ● = after 11.30 p.m.

Restaurants ouverts le dimanche

L = déjeuner – **D** = dîner – ● = après 23 h 30

Ristoranti aperti la domenica

L = colazione – **D** = pranzo – ● = dopo le 23.30

Restaurants, die sonntags geöffnet sind

L = Mittagessen – **D** = Abendessen – ● = nach 23.30

Berkeley (Restaurant) .... L D 67
(City of Westminster - *Belgravia*)

Claridge (Causerie) .... L D 67
(City of Westminster - *Mayfair*)

Hyatt Carlton Tower
(Chelsea Room) .... L D ● 57
(Rib Room) .... L D ●
(Royal Borough of Kensington & Chelsea - *Chelsea*)

Inn on the Park (lanes 12.00) .. L D ● 67
(City of Westminster - *Mayfair*)

Savoy (River) .... L D ● 72
(City of Westminster - *Strand & Covent Garden*)............ L D ●

Royal Garden (Royal Roof)....... ● 60
(Royal Borough of Kensington & Chelsea - *Kensington*)

Halcyon (Kingfisher) .... L D ● 60
(Royal Borough of Kensington & Chelsea - *Kensington*)

XXXX **Chateau (Le)**............ L D 68
(City of Westminster - *Mayfair*)

XXXX ✿ **Four Seasons**............ L D 68
(City of Westminster - *Mayfair*)

XXXX **Souffié (Le)**............ L D ● 68
(City of Westminster - *Mayfair*)

XXX **Bastide (La)**............ ● 72
(City of Westminster - *Soho*)

XXX **Benihana (12.00)** .... ● 50
(Camden - *Hampstead*)

XXX **Bibendum**............ L D ● 58
(Royal Borough of Kensington & Chelsea - *Chelsea*)

XXX **Bombay Palace**............ L D 66
(City of Westminster - *Bayswater & Maida Vale*)

XXX **Chateau Napoleon** .... L 52
(Croydon - *Croydon*)

XXX **Incontro (L')** .... D ● 74
(City of Westminster - *Victoria*)

XXX **Ivy (12.00)** .... L D ● 73
(City of Westminster - *Strand & Covent Garden*)

XXX **Leith's**............ D ● 61
(Royal Borough of Kensington & Chelsea - *Kensington*)

XXX **Lindsay House (12.00)** .... L D ● 72
(City of Westminster - *Soho*)

XXX **Odins**............ ● 70
(City of Westminster - *Regent's Park & Marylebone*)

XXX **Princess Garden**............ L D 68
(City of Westminster - *Mayfair*)

XXX **Turner's** .... L D 58
(Royal Borough of Kensington & Chelsea - *Chelsea*)

XXX **Waltons** .... L D ● 58
(Royal Borough of Kensington & Chelsea - *Chelsea*)

XXX **Zen Central**............ L D ● 68
(City of Westminster - *Mayfair*)

XX **Antonio's** .... L D 56
(Hounslow - *Chiswick*)

XX **Barton's**............ L 52
(Ealing - *Ealing*)

XX **Beccofino** .... ● 59
(Royal Borough of Kensington & Chelsea - *Chelsea*)

XX **Bengal Lancer (12.00)**........ L D ● 50
(Camden - *Kentish Town*)

XX **Blue Elephant (12.30)**........ L D ● 54
(Hammersmith - *Fulham*)

XX **Brasserie de la Paix**........ L D 62
(Royal Borough of Kensington & Chelsea - *South Kensington*)

XX **Burt's**............ ● 72
(City of Westminster - *Soho*)

XX **Caprice (Le) (12.00)**........ L D ● 71
(City of Westminster - *St. James's*)

XX **Chez Solange (12.15)**........ ● 73
(City of Westminster - *Strand & Covent Garden*)

XX **Chin's (11.40)** .... L D ● 54
(Hammersmith - *Fulham*)

XX **Chow Sings** .... L D ● 53
(Enfield - *Enfield*)

XX **Croisette (La)** .... L D 59
(Royal Borough of Kensington & Chelsea - *Earl's Court*)

XX **Daphne's (12.00)** .... ● 58
(Royal Borough of Kensington & Chelsea - *Chelsea*)

XX **Delhi Brasserie**........ L D 62
(Royal Borough of Kensington & Chelsea - *South Kensington*)

XX **Dynasty II**........ L D ● 58
(Royal Borough of Kensington & Chelsea - *Chelsea*)

XX **Eleven Park Walk (12.00)** ..... ● 59
(Royal Borough of Kensington & Chelsea - *Chelsea*)

XX **English Garden**........ L D ● 58
(Royal Borough of Kensington & Chelsea - *Chelsea*)

	Restaurant		Page
✗	**Aventure (L')** (City of Westminster - *Regent's Park & Marylebone*)	L D	71
✗	**Barbino II (11.45)** (City of Westminster - *Regent's Park & Marylebone*)	●	71
✗	**Bistroquet (Le)** (Camden - *Camden Town*)	L D	50
✗	**Bois St. Jean (Au)** (City of Westminster - *Regent's Park & Marylebone*)	L D ●	71
✗	**Bombay Bicycle Club** (Wandsworth - *Wandsworth*)	●	66
✗	**Bouffe (La)** (Wandsworth - *Clapham*)	L D	65
✗	**Bougie (La)** (Camden - *Camden Town*)	L D	50
✗	**Canal Brasserie** (Royal Borough of Kensington & Chelsea - *North Kensington*)	L	61
✗	**Chanterelle** (Kensington - *South Kensington*)	L D ●	62
✗	**Chateaubriand (12.00)** (Camden - *Hampstead*)	●	50
✗	**Fortune Cookie** (City of Westminster - *Bayswater & Maida Vale*)	L D	67
✗	**Garden** (Hammersmith & Fulham - *Hammersmith*)	L D	54
✗	**Good Friends** (Tower Hamlets - *Limehouse*)	L D	65
✗	**Jasmin** (Wandsworth - *Clapham*)	●	65
✗	**Kensington Place (11.45)** (Royal Borough of Kensington & Chelsea - *Kensington*)	L D ●	60
✗	**Langans Bistro** (City of Westminster - *Regent's Park & Marylebone*)	●	71
✗	**Malabar** (Royal Borough of Kensington & Chelsea - *Kensington*)	L D	60
✗	**Mandarin** (Royal Borough of Kensington & Chelsea - *Kensington*)	L D	60
✗	**Mr Tang's Mandarin** (Harrow - *Stanmore*)	L D	55
✗	**Nakamura** (City of Westminster - *Regent's Park & Marylebone*)	D	71
✗	**Nam Long at Le Shaker** (Royal Borough of Kensington & Chelsea - *South Kensington*)	●	62
✗	**Noughts 'N' Crosses** (Ealing - *Ealing*)	L	52
✗	**Peking Diner** (Bomley - *Bomley*)	●	49
✗	**Pollyanna's (12.00)** (Wandsworth - *Clapham*)	L ●	65
✗	**Quality Chop House** (Islington - *Finsbury*)	L ●	57
✗	**Raj Vogue (11.45)** (Ilsington - *Upper Holloway*)	L D ●	57
✗	**Sambuca** (Hillingdon - *Eastcole*)	L ●	55
✗	**Smith's** (Camden - *Bloomsbury*)	●	50
✗	**Spread Eagle** (Greenwich - *Greenwich*)	L	53
✗	**Sri Sian** (City of Westminster - *Soho*)	D ●	72
✗	**Swan** (Harrow - *Hatch End*)	L D ●	55
✗	**Taste of Raj (11.45)** (Richmond-upon-Thames - *East Sheen*)	L D ●	64
✗	**Thai Castle** (Harrow - *North Harrow*)	L D	55
✗	**Thierry's** (Royal Borough of Kensington & Chelsea - *Chelsea*)	●	59
✗	**Ziani** (Royal Borough of Kensington & Chelsea - *Chelsea*)	L D ●	59

Boroughs and areas

Greater London is divided, for administrative purposes, into 32 boroughs plus the City : thes sub-divide naturally into minor areas, usually grouped around former villages or quarter which often maintain a distinctive character.

BARNET pp. 4 and 5.

Child's Hill – ✉ NW2 – ☎ 071.

XX Mezzaluna, 424 Finchley Rd, NW2, ✆ 794 0455, Italian rest. DU

X **Quincy's,** 675 Finchley Rd, NW2 2JP, ✆ 794 8499 – ▤. AE VISA DU
closed Sunday, Monday, 2 weeks June and 2 weeks Christmas – **M** (booking essentia (dinner only) 21.00 **t.** 4.00.

Hendon – ✉ NW4 – ☎ 081. 18 off Sanders Lane ✆ 346 6023.

Hendon Hall (Mt. Charlotte Thistle), Ashley Lane, NW4 1HF, ✆ 203 3341, Telex 895608 Fax 203 9709, – TV ☎ P – 330. AE VISA. DU
M 15.00/16.95 **t.** and a la carte 4.25 – 7.25 – **51 rm** 75.50/93.00 **t.**, **1 suite** 135.50 – SB (weekends only) 106.00/116.00 **st.**

Peacehaven without rest., 94 Audley Rd, NW4 3HB, ✆ 202 9758, – TV. AE VISA – **14 rm** 38.00/65.00 **st.** CU

High Barnet – ✉ Herts – ☎ 081.

18 Old Fold Manor, Hadley Green ✆ 440 9185 – 9 Arkley, Rowley Green Rd ✆ 449 0394

XX **Zai'qa Tandoori,** 7d High St., EN5 5UE, ✆ 441 6375, Indian rest. – VISA
closed 25 December – **M** 6.95/8.50 **t.** and a la carte. DT

Mill Hill – ✉ NW7 – ☎ 081. 18 100 Barnet Way ✆ 959 2282.

XX Good Earth, 143-145 The Broadway, NW7 4RN, ✆ 959 7011, Chinese rest. – ▤ CT

Whestone – ✉ N20 – ☎ 081.

XX Ma and Pa, 1316 High Rd, N20 9HQ, ✆ 446 8237, Chinese rest. – ▤ ET

BEXLEY pp. 10 and 11.

Bexley – ✉ Kent – ☎ 0322 Crayford.

Crest (T.H.F.), Black Prince Interchange, Southwold Rd, DA5 1ND, on A 2 ✆ 526900 Telex 8956539, Fax 526113 – rm ▤ rest TV ☎ P – 70 JX
104 rm, 2 suites.

BRENT pp. 4 and 5.

Kilburn – ✉ NW6 – ☎ 071.

X **Vijay,** 49 Willesden Lane, NW6 7RF, ✆ 328 1087, South Indian rest. – ▤. AE VIS
M a la carte 7.50/8.00 **t.** DU

Wembley – ✉ Middx – ☎ 081. 18 Sudbury, Bridgwater Rd ✆ 902 0218.

Hilton National, Empire Way, HA9 8DS, ✆ 902 8839, Telex 24837, Fax 900 2201 – ▤ rest TV ☎ P – 300. AE VISA. CU

BROMLEY pp. 10 and 11. 18, 9 Cray Valley, Sandy Lane ✆ 0689 (Orpington) 31927, NE : by 224 – 18, 18 Sundridge Park, Garden Lane ✆ 460 1822.

Bromley – ✉ Kent – ☎ 081. 9 Magpie Hall Lane ✆ 462 7014.

Bromley Court, Bromley Hill, BR1 4JD, ✆ 464 5011, Telex 896310, Fax 460 0899, – TV ☎ P – 150. AE VISA. HY
M 11.00/12.50 **st.** and a la carte 3.95 – **122 rm** 64.00/86.00 **st.** – SB (weekend only) 40.00/50.00 **st.**

Grianan without rest., 23 Orchard Rd, BR1 2PR, ✆ 460 1795 – TV P. HY
12 rm 20.00/40.00 **st.**

Capisano, 9 Simpsons Rd, BR2 9AP, ℘ 464 8036, Italian rest. – VISA HY s
closed Sunday, Monday and 3 weeks August – **M** a la carte 20.00/30.00 **t.** 4.00.

Peking Diner, 71 Burnt Ash Lane, BR1 5AA, ℘ 464 7911, Chinese rest. – VISA HX u
closed Sunday and 25-26 December – **M** 13.50 **t.** and a la carte 4.50.

Farnborough – Kent – 0689 Farnborough.

High Elms, High Elms Rd, Orpington ℘ 58175, off A 21 via Shire Lane.

Xian, 324 High St., Orpington, ℘ 0689 (Orpington) 71881, Chinese (Peking, Szechuan) rest. – JZ a

L'Ombrello, 360 Crofton Rd, Locks Bottom, BR6 7XX, ℘ 52286, Italian rest. – VISA – *closed Sunday* – **M** 9.95 **t.** (lunch) and a la carte 11.30/18.30 **t.** 3.25. JZ c

Keston – Kent – 0689 Farnborough.

Giannino's, 6 Commonside, BR4 2TS, ℘ 56410, Italian rest. HZ x

CAMDEN Except where otherwise stated see pp. 20-23.

Bloomsbury – NW1/W1/WC1 – 071. 35-36 Woburn Pl., WC1 ℘ 580 4599.

Russell (T.H.F.), Russell Sq., WC1B 5BE, ℘ 837 6470, Telex 24615, Fax 837 2857 – rm – 450. VISA. LU o
M (carving rest.) 14.50 **t.** and a la carte 6.95 – 9.95 – **317 rm** 107.00/130.00 **st.**, **3 suites** 141.00/216.00 **st.** – SB (weekends only) 127.00/145.00 **st.**

Mountbatten, 20 Monmouth St., WC2H 9HD, ℘ 836 4300, Telex 298087, Fax 240 3540 – rm rest – 75. VISA. p.33 DV o
M *(closed Saturday lunch)* 18.50/22.50 **st.** and dinner a la carte 5.00 – 11.00 – **121 rm** 136.00/161.00 **st.**, **6 suites** 350.00 **st.** – SB (weekends only) 201.00 **st.**

Marlborough, Bloomsbury St., WC1B 3QD, ℘ 636 5601, Telex 298274, Fax 636 0532 – rest – 300 – **167 rm, 2 suites.** LU i

Grafton, 130 Tottenham Court Rd, W1P 9HP, ℘ 388 4131, Telex 297234, Fax 387 7394 – rest – 100. VISA KU n
M *(closed Saturday lunch)* 18.50 **st.** and a la carte 5.75 – 9.00 – **232 rm** 94.00/124.00 **st.**, **4 suites** 175.00/220.00 **st.**

Kenilworth, 97 Great Russell St., WC1B 3LB, ℘ 637 3477, Telex 25842, Fax 631 3133 – rest – 160. VISA. LU a
M 13.00 **st.** and a la carte – 9.00 – **192 rm** 99.00/135.00 **st.**

Kingsley (Mt. Charlotte Thistle), Bloomsbury Way, WC1A 2SD, ℘ 242 5881, Telex 21157, Fax 831 0225 – rm – 80. VISA LU r
M 13.00 **t.** and a la carte 3.95 – 7.75 – **143 rm** 77.50/97.50 **st.**, **2 suites** 200.00 **st.** – SB (weekends only) 107.00 **st.**

Bloomsbury Crest (T.H.F.), Coram St., WC1N 1HT, ℘ 837 1200, Telex 22113, Fax 837 5374 – rm rest . VISA LT c
M 16.50/18.50 **s.** and a la carte 5.95 – 9.25 – **282 rm** 104.00/119.00 **st.**, **2 suites** 215.00/275.00 **st.** – SB (weekends only) 101.00/113.00 **st.**

Bloomsbury Park (Mt. Charlotte Thistle), 126 Southampton Row, WC1B 5AD, ℘ 430 0434, Telex 25757, Fax 242 0665 – rm – 30. VISA
M *(closed Friday dinner, Saturday and Sunday)* 12.50 **st.** (dinner) and a la carte 14.25/20.80 **st.** 4.00 – 7.25 – **95 rm** 72.50/100.00 **st.** LU u

Academy, 17-21 Gower St., WC1E 6HG, ℘ 631 4115, Fax 636 3442 – rest . VISA. KLU v
M 15.50/22.50 **t.** and a la carte 4.50 – 8.50 – **32 rm** 45.00/145.00 **st.** – SB (weekends only November-May and August) 120.00/150.00 **st.**

Mentone without rest., 54-55 Cartwright Gdns, WC1H 9EL, ℘ 387 3927, – . VISA. – **27 rm** 28.00/52.00 **st.** LT a

Mabledon Court without rest., 10-11 Mabledon Pl., WC1H 9BA, ℘ 388 3866, Fax 387 5686 – – **32 rm.** LT s

Harlingford without rest., 61-63 Cartwright Gdns, WC1H 9EL, ℘ 387 1551, Fax 387 5686, – . VISA. LT n
43 rm 33.00/54.00 **st.**

Russell House without rest., 11 Bernard St., WC1N 1LN, ℘ 837 7686 – .
10 rm 40.00 **st.** LU e

L'Etoile, 30 Charlotte St., W1P 1HJ, ℘ 636 7189, French rest. – VISA
closed Saturday, Sunday and Bank Holidays – **M** 38.00 **t.** and a la carte approx. 26.50 **t.** 6.00. KU e

Jamdani, 34 Charlotte St., W1P 1HJ, ℘ 636 1178, Indian rest. – . VISA
closed Sunday and 25-26 December – **M** a la carte 15.50/20.00 **t.** KU e

Neal Street, 26 Neal Street, WC2 9PH, ℘ 836 8368 – VISA p. 33 DV s
closed Saturday, Sunday, Christmas-New Year and Bank Holidays – **M** a la carte 20.50/36.00 **t.** 6.50.

XX **Poons of Russell Square,** 50 Woburn Pl., WC1H 0JE, ✆ 580 1188, Chinese rest. – ▤ AE ⓓ VISA LU
closed 25-26 December and Bank Holidays – **M** a la carte 9.50/18.25 **t.**

XX **Heals,** First floor, Heal's Department Store, 196 Tottenham Court Rd, W1P 9LD ✆ 636 1666 (ext : 5513), Fax 631 3091 – ▤. AE ⓓ VISA KU
closed Sunday and Bank Holidays – **M** (lunch only) 25.75 **t.** 🌢 4.50.

XX **Mon Plaisir,** 21 Monmouth St., WC2H 9DD, ✆ 836 7243, French rest. – AE ⓓ VISA p. 33 DV
closed Saturday lunch and Sunday – **M** 12.95 **t.** and a la carte 14.00/19.10 **t.** 🌢 4.90.

X **Smith's,** 33 Shelton St., WC2 9HT, ✆ 379 0310, Fax 836 8395 – AE ⓓ VISA
closed Saturday lunch except September-23 December, Sunday, 23 December-1 January and Bank Holidays – **M** a la carte 12.35/24.20 **st.** 🌢 5.80. p. 33 DVX

X **Auntie's,** 126 Cleveland St., W1P 5DN, ✆ 387 1548 – AE ⓓ VISA JU
closed Saturday lunch, Sunday, 2 weeks August and Christmas – **M** approx. 18.50 **t.** 🌢 8.00

Camden Town – ✉ NW1 – ☎ 071.

X **Le Bistroquet,** 273-275 Camden High St., NW1 7BX, ✆ 485 9607 – AE VISA
closed 25 and 26 December – **M** a la carte 17.00/20.00 **t.** 🌢 4.00. JS

X **La Bougie,** 7 Murray St., NW1 9RE, ✆ 485 6400, Bistro KS
closed Saturday lunch, Monday, last 2 weeks August, 25 December-2 January and Bank Holidays – **M** a la carte 12.75/14.50 **t.** 🌢 3.00.

Finchley Road – ✉ NW3/NW6 – ☎ 071.

Charles Bernard, 5-7 Frognal, NW3 6AL, ✆ 794 0101, Telex 23560, Fax 794 0100 – |♦| TV ☎ P. AE ⓓ VISA. ES
M (bar lunch)/dinner a la carte 9.00/15.75 **st.** 🌢 3.50 – **57 rm** ☐ 52.00/88.00 **st.**

Hampstead – ✉ NW3 – ☎ 071.

Winnington Rd ✆ 455 0203.

Clive (Hilton), Primrose Hill Rd, NW3 3NA, ✆ 586 2233, Telex 22759, Fax 586 1659 – |♦| TV ☎ P – 350. AE ⓓ VISA HS
M *(closed lunch Saturday and Bank Holidays)* 15.50/17.50 **st.** 🌢 4.50 – ☐ 8.50 – **93 rm** 82.00/100.00 **st.**, **3 suites** 115.00/120.00 **st.** – SB (weekends only) 106.00/112.00 **st.**

Swiss Cottage, 4 Adamson Rd, NW3 3HP, ✆ 722 2281, Telex 297232, Fax 483 4588, « Antique furniture collection » – |♦| TV ☎ P – 40. AE ⓓ VISA. GS
M 12.80/20.65 **t.** and a la carte 🌢 4.95 – **62 rm** ☐ 65.00/105.00 **t.**, **3 suites** 115.00/125.00 **t.** – SB (weekends only) 75.00/90.00 **st.**

Post House (T.H.F.), 215 Haverstock Hill, NW3 4RB, ✆ 794 8121, Telex 262494, Fax 435 5586 – |♦| rm TV ☎ P – 30. AE ⓓ VISA ES
M 12.00/14.75 **st.** and a la carte – ☐ 6.25 – **140 rm** 83.00/100.00 **st.** – SB (weekends only) 98.00/110.00 **st.**

XXX **Keats,** 3a Downshire Hill, NW3 1NR, ✆ 435 3544 – AE VISA ES
closed Monday, Sunday, 3 weeks August and Bank Holidays – **M** 18.50/28.00 **st.** and a la carte 🌢 6.00.

XXX **Benihana,** 100 Avenue Rd, NW3 3HF, ✆ 586 9508, Fax 586 6740, Japanese Teppan-Yaki rest. – ▤. AE ⓓ VISA GS
M a la carte 16.40/46.95 **t.**

XX Carapace, 118 Heath St., NW3 1DR, ✆ 435 8000 ES

XX Zen W3, 83-84 Hampstead High St., NW3 1RE, ✆ 794 7863, Chinese rest. ES

XX Soong, 459 South End Rd, NW3, ✆ 794 2461, Chinese (Szechuan) rest. ES

X **Chateaubriand,** 48 Belsize Lane, NW3 5AR, ✆ 435 4882 – AE ⓓ VISA ES
closed Sunday, 24 to 26 December and 1 January – **M** (dinner only) a la carte 12.30/20.95 **t.** 🌢 3.20.

Holborn – ✉ WC2 – ☎ 071.

Drury Lane Moat House (Q.M.H.), 10 Drury Lane, High Holborn, WC2B 5RE, ✆ 836 6666, Telex 8811395, Fax 831 1548 – |♦| rm ▤ TV ☎ – 100. AE ⓓ VISA p. 33 DV
closed Christmas – **M** 15.00/20.00 **st.** and a la carte 🌢 5.00 – ☐ 8.95 – **151 rm** 109.00/153.50 **st.**, **2 suites** 175.00/250.00 **st.** – SB (weekends only) 104.00/115.00 **st.**

XXX L'Opera, 32 Great Queen St., WC2B 5AA, ✆ 405 9020 p. 33 DV

Kentish Town – ✉ NW5 – ☎ 071.

XX **Bengal Lancer,** 253 Kentish Town Rd, NW5 2JT, ✆ 485 6688, Fax 482 4523, Indian rest. – ▤. AE ⓓ VISA JS
closed Saturday lunch and 25-26 December – **M** 12.00 **t.** (dinner) and a la carte 10.50/23.50 **t.** 🌢 3.50.

Regent's Park – ✉ NW1 – ☎ 071.

White House (Rank), Albany St., NW1 3UP, ✆ 387 1200, Telex 24111, Fax 388 0091, – rm – 100. AE VISA. JT o
M 18.50 **st.** and a la carte 4.50 – ☕ 10.00 – **561 rm** 105.00/135.00 **st.**, **15 suites** 180.00/300.00 **st.**

XX **Odette's,** 130 Regent's Park Rd, NW1 8XL, ✆ 586 5486 – AE VISA HS i
closed Saturday lunch, Sunday, last 2 weeks August, and Bank Holidays – **M** a la carte 19.70/25.50 **t.** 5.95.

X **Koto,** 75 Parkway, NW1 7PP, ✆ 482 2036, Japanese rest. – AE VISA JS a
closed Sunday and Bank Holidays – **M** 12.80/22.00 **t.** and a la carte 4.30.

Swiss Cottage – ✉ NW3 – ☎ 071.

Holiday Inn, 128 King Henry's Rd, NW3 3ST, ✆ 722 7711, Telex 267396, Fax 586 5822, – rm – 400. AE VISA GS a
M 17.00/18.50 **t.** and a la carte 6.50 – ☕ 10.25 – **298 rm** 139.00/160.00 **t.**, **4 suites** 350.00/600.00 **t.**

XX **Peter's,** 65 Fairfax Rd, NW6 4EE, ✆ 624 5804 – AE VISA FS i
closed Saturday lunch and 26-27 December – **M** 13.95 **t.** (lunch) and a la carte 19.20/22.70 **t.** 4.50.

CITY OF LONDON – ☎ 071 Except where otherwise stated see p. 23.

XX **Candlewick Room,** 45 Old Broad St., EC2N 1HT, ✆ 628 7929 – AE VISA
closed Saturday, Sunday, 25 December and Bank Holidays – **M** (lunch only) 23.95 **t.** and a la carte 4.95. PU n

XX **Le Poulbot** (basement), 45 Cheapside, EC2V 6AR, ✆ 236 4379, French rest. – AE VISA OV i
closed Saturday, Sunday, Christmas and Bank Holidays – **M** (lunch only) 28.50 **st.** 5.20.

XX **Corney and Barrow,** 109 Old Broad St., EC2N 1AP, ✆ 638 9308 – AE VISA PU c
closed Saturday, Sunday and Bank Holidays – **M** (lunch only) 24.95 **t.** and a la carte 11.75.

XX **Corney and Barrow,** 118 Moorgate, EC2M 6UR, ✆ 628 2898 – AE VISA
closed Saturday, Sunday and Bank Holidays – **M** (lunch only) a la carte 23.85/27.85 **t.** 7.00. PU o

XX **Corney and Barrow,** 44 Cannon St., EC4N 6JJ, ✆ 248 1700 – AE VISA
closed Saturday, Sunday and Bank Holidays – **M** (lunch only) a la carte 19.85/24.40 **t.** 7.00. OV r

XX **Le Sous Sol,** 32 Old Bailey, EC4M 7HS, ✆ 236 7931 – AE VISA NV a
closed Saturday, Sunday and Bank Holidays – **M** (lunch only) 22.50 **st.** 4.95.

XX **Shares,** 12-13 Lime St., EC3M 7AA, ✆ 623 1843 – AE VISA PV s
closed Saturday, Sunday and Bank Holidays – **M** (lunch only) 28.50 **t.**

XX **Miyama,** 17 Godliman St., EC4V 5BD, ✆ 489 1937, Japanese rest. – AE VISA POV e
closed Saturday, Sunday and Bank Holidays – **M** 16.00/38.00 **t.** and a la carte 4.00.

X **Bubb's,** 329 Central Market, Farringdon St., EC1A 9NB, ✆ 236 2435, French rest.
closed Saturday, Sunday, 2 weeks August, 1 week Christmas and Bank Holidays – **M** (booking essential) (lunch only) a la carte 17.50/24.05 **t.** 4.50. NU a

X **Whittington's,** 21 College Hill, EC4R 2RP, ✆ 248 5855 – AE VISA OV c
closed Saturday, Sunday and Bank Holidays – **M** (lunch only) a la carte 15.95/22.20 **t.** 3.75.

CROYDON pp. 10 and 11.

18 Addigton Palace, Gravel Hill, Addington ✆ 654 3061.

Addington – ✉ Surrey – ☎ 081.

18, 18, 9 Addington Court, Featherbed Lane ✆ 657 0281 – 18 The Addington, Shirley Church Rd ✆ 777 1055.

XX **Willow,** 88 Selsdon Park Rd, CR2 8JT, ✆ 657 4656, Chinese (Peking, Szechuan) rest. – AE VISA GZ x
closed 25 and 26 December – **M** a la carte 14.85/21.00 **t.** 4.50.

Croydon – ✉ Surrey – ☎ 081.

18 Coulsdon Court Municipal ✆ 660 0468 – 18 Shirley Park, Addiscombe Rd ✆ 654 1143.

Central Library, Katherine St. ✆ 760 5630 ext 2984.

Holiday Inn, 7 Altyre Rd, CR9 5AA, ✆ 680 9200, Telex 8956268, Fax 760 0426, squash – rm – 300. AE VISA. FZ u
M 12.95/14.50 **st.** and a la carte 4.95 – ☕ 8.00 – **212 rm** 95.00/112.00 **t.**, **2 suites** 210.00/220.00 **t.**

Briarley, 8-10 Outram Rd, CR0 6XE, ℘ 654 1000, Fax 656 6084, – TV ☎ P. AE VISA. GZ
M *(closed Sunday dinner)* (dinner only and Sunday lunch)/dinner 10.50 **st.** 3.80 – **38 rm** 55.00/65.00 **st.**

Oakwood, 69-71 Outram Rd, CR0 6XJ, ℘ 654 2835, Fax 655 3948, – TV ☎ P. AE VISA GZ s
M *(closed Sunday)* (dinner only) 15.00 4.50 – **15 rm** 49.00/59.00 **st.**

XXX **Chateau Napoleon,** Coombe Lane, CR0 5RE, ℘ 680 6027, Fax 667 9023, – P. AE VISA GZ o
M *(closed Sunday dinner)* 12.95/16.75 **t.** and a la carte.

XX **Thirty Four Surrey Street,** 34 Surrey St., CR0 1RJ, ℘ 686 0586, Californian fish rest., Live jazz – AE VISA FZ c
closed Saturday lunch, Sunday dinner and Bank Holidays – **M** a la carte 13.65/23.65 **t.** 3.30.

X **Oh Boy,** 18 South End, CR0 1DN, ℘ 760 0278, Thai rest. – . AE VISA FZ a
closed Sunday – **M** approx. 17.65 **st.** and a la carte 3.40.

Sanderstead – ✉ Surrey – 081.

Selsdon Park Hotel, Addington Rd ℘ 657 8811.

Selsdon Park (Best Western), Addington Rd, CR2 8YA, ℘ 657 8811, Telex 945003, Fax 651 6171, ≤, heated, , park, squash – rest rest TV ☎ P – 150. AE VISA GZ n
M 21.00/28.50 **st.** and a la carte – **163 rm** 115.00/170.00 **st.**, **7 suites** 255.00/295.00 **st.** – SB (weekends only) 158.00/184.00 **st.**

X **Elio,** 17 Limpsfield Rd, CR2 9LA, ℘ 657 2953, Italian rest. – AE VISA GZ a
closed Saturday lunch, Sunday and 3 weeks August – **M** 9.00/15.00 **t.** and a la carte 3.50.

South Croydon – ✉ Surrey – 081.

X **Kelong,** 16 Selsdon Rd, CR2 6PU, ℘ 688 0726, Malaysian, Singaporean rest. – AE VISA FZ v
closed Sunday – **M** a la carte 14.00/26.00 **st.**

Upper Norwood – ✉ SE19 – 081.

Queens, 122 Church Rd, SE19 2UG, ℘ 653 6622, Telex 8951656, Fax 771 1506 – TV ☎ P – 600 – **149 rm.** FY n

EALING pp. 4 and 5.

Ealing – ✉ W5 – 081.

Perivale Lane, Greenford ℘ 997 2595 – Horsenden Hill, Woodland Rise ℘ 902 4555.

Carnarvon, Ealing Common, W5 3HN, ℘ 992 5399, Telex 935114, Fax 992 7082 – rm TV ☎ P – 200. AE VISA. CV v
M a la carte 16.45/20.20 **st.** – 7.95 – **145 rm** 79.50/105.50 **st.**

Kenton House, 5 Hillcrest Rd, Hanger Lane, W5 2JL, ℘ 997 8436, Telex 8812544, Fax 998 0037 – rest TV ☎ P. AE VISA. CV x
M (bar lunch)/dinner a la carte 10.75/14.20 **st.** 2.60 – **51 rm** 63.75/71.75 **st.** – SB (weekends only) 75.50 **st.**

XX **Barton's,** 7a The Green, High St., W5 5DA, ℘ 840 3297 – AE VISA BV e
M *(closed Sunday dinner)* 8.95 **t.** and a la carte 8.15/14.35 **t.**

XX **Laguna Tandoori,** 1-4 Culmington Par., Uxbridge Rd, W13, ℘ 579 9992, Indian rest. – . AE VISA BV i
closed 25 December – **M** a la carte 11.65/14.35 **t.** 3.05.

XX **Maxim,** 153-155 Northfield Av., W13 9QT, ℘ 567 1719, Chinese (Peking) rest. – . AE VISA BV a
closed Sunday lunch and 25 to 28 December – **M** 25.00 **t.** and a la carte.

X **Noughts 'N' Crosses,** 77 The Grove, W5 5LL, ℘ 840 7568 – AE VISA BV u
closed Sunday dinner, Monday, August and 25 December-3 January – **M** (dinner only and Sunday lunch)/dinner 16.90 **t.**

X **Gino's,** 4 The Mall, W5 2PJ, ℘ 567 3681, Italian rest. – AE VISA CV z
closed Saturday lunch, Sunday and Bank Holidays – **M** a la carte 15.00/22.90 **st.**

X Paolo's, 7 Hanger Green, W5 3EL, ℘ 997 8560, Italian rest. – CV r

Hanwell – ✉ W7 – 081.

Brent Valley, Church Rd, ℘ 567 1287.

X Happiness Garden, 22 Boston Par., Boston Rd, W7 2DG, ℘ 567 9314, Chinese rest. BV c

Southall – ✉ Middx – 081.

West Middlesex, Greenford Rd ℘ 574 3450.

X Brilliant, 72-74 Western Rd, UB2 5DZ, ℘ 574 1928, Indian rest. – BV o

ENFIELD pp. 6 and 7.

Leaside Picketts Lock Sports Centre, Edmonton 803 3611.

Cockfosters – Herts. – 081.

XX Tandoori Nights, 27 Station Par., Cockfosters Rd, EN4 0DW, 441 2131, Indian rest. – ET u

Enfield – Middx – 081.

Enfield Municipal, Beggars Hollow 363 2951, N : 1 m – Crews Hill, Cattlegate Rd 363 0787, N : 2½ m. – Old Park Road South 363 0083, NE : 1 m.

Royal Chase, 162 The Ridgeway, EN2 8AR, 366 6500, Telex 266628, Fax 367 7191, heated, – – 300. ET a
91 rm, 1 suite.

Holtwhites, 92 Chase Side, EN2 0QN, 363 0124, Fax 366 9089 – . VISA. FT c
closed 23 to 28 December – **M** *(closed dinner Friday to Sunday)* (bar lunch)/dinner a la carte 20.00 **t.** 2.95 – **30 rm** 70.00/98.00 **t.** – SB (weekends only) 98.00 **st.**

XXX **Norfolk,** 80 London Rd, EN2 6HU, 363 0979 – VISA FT e
closed Saturday lunch, Monday dinner, Sunday, first 3 weeks August and Bank Holidays – **M** a la carte 15.00/25.00 **t.**

XX **Chow Shings,** 2-4 Sarnesfield Rd, EN2 6AS, 363 5252, Chinese (Peking) rest. – VISA FT a
M 25.00/30.00 **st.** and a la carte 3.00.

Hadley Wood – Herts – 081.

Beech Hill, Hadley Wood 449 4486.

West Lodge Park, off Cockfosters Rd, Barnet, EN4 0PY, 440 8311, Telex 24734, Fax 449 3698, park – – 70 ET i
50 rm.

MICHELIN Distribution Centre, Eley's Estate, Angel Rd, N18 3DQ, 081 803 7341, Fax 081 807 0889

GREENWICH pp. 10 and 11.

Blackheath – SE3 – 081.

Bardon Lodge, 15-17 Stratheden Rd, SE3 7TH, 853 4051, Fax 858 7387, – . VISA. HV a
M *(closed Sunday dinner)* (bar lunch)/dinner 14.35 **t.** 3.75 – **37 rm** 45.00/75.00 **st.** – SB (weekends only) 90.00/112.00 **st.**

Vanbrugh, 21-23 St. John's Park, SE3 7TD, 853 5505 (reservations : 853 4051), – . VISA. HV e
M (see **Bardon Lodge Hotel** above) – **30 rm** 58.00/78.00 **st.**

Eltham – SE9 – 081.

Royal Blackheath, Court Rd 850 1795.

Yardley Court without rest., 18 Court Yard, SE9 5PZ, 850 1850, – . VISA. HX e
9 rm 30.00/49.50 **st.**

Greenwich – SE10 – 081.

46 Greenwich Church St. 858 6376.

XX **Treasure of China,** 10 Nelson Rd, SE10 9JB, 858 9884, Chinese (Peking, Szechuan) rest. – . VISA GV e
closed 25 and 26 December – **M** 18.00 **t.** and a la carte.

X **Spread Eagle,** 1-2 Stockwell St., SE10 9JN, 853 2333 – VISA GV c
closed Saturday lunch, Sunday dinner, last 2 weeks August and 26 to 30 December – **M** 11.75 **t.** (lunch) and a la carte 16.00/20.50 **t.**

X Taste of India, 7 Greenwich Church St., SE10 9BL, 858 2668, Indian rest. GV n

HACKNEY – p. 23.

Liverpool Street – EC2 – 071.

XX **Equities,** 1 Finsbury Av., EC2M 2PA, 247 1051 – . VISA PU a
closed Saturday, Sunday and Bank Holidays – **M** (lunch only) 29.00 **t.** 8.95.

***En saison,** surtout dans les stations fréquentées, il est prudent de retenir à l'avance.*
Cependant, si vous ne pouvez pas occuper la chambre que vous avez retenue, prévenez immédiatement l'hôtelier.
Si vous écrivez à un hôtel à l'étranger, joignez à votre lettre un coupon-réponse international (disponible dans les bureaux de poste).

HAMMERSMITH and FULHAM Except where otherwise stated see pp. 24-25.

Fulham – ✉ SW6 – ☎ 071.

XX **Hiders,** 755 Fulham Rd, SW6, ☎ 736 2331 – VISA p. 12 BQ
closed Saturday lunch, Sunday, 1 week Christmas and Bank Holidays – **M** 17.90/20.90 t. 3.75.

XX **Otters,** 271 New Kings Rd, SW6 4RD, ☎ 371 0434 – AE VISA
M a la carte 13.10/17.00 **t.** 3.50. p. 12 BQ

XX **Blue Elephant,** 4-6 Fulham Broadway, SW6 1AA, ☎ 385 6595, Fax 386 6595, Thai rest. – AE VISA EZ
closed Saturday lunch – **M** (booking essential) a la carte 14.45/27.20 **t.** 4.95.

XX **Chin's,** 311-313 New Kings Rd, SW6 4RF, ☎ 736 8833, Chinese rest. – AE VISA p. 12 BQ r
M 29.00 **t.** and a la carte 14.80/27.80 **t.** 4.00.

XX **Mao Tai,** 58 New Kings Rd., Parsons Green, SW6 4UG, ☎ 731 2520, Chinese (Szechuan) rest. – AE VISA p. 12 BQ e
M 15.60 **t.** and a la carte 12.90/19.40 **t.** 7.50.

XX **Nayab,** 309 New Kings Rd, SW6 4RF, ☎ 731 6993, Indian rest. – AE VISA
closed 24 to 26 December and 1 January – **M** a la carte 11.15/17.35 **t.** 3.80. p. 12 BQ

Hammersmith – ✉ W6/W12/W14 – ☎ 081.

XX **Tandoori Nights,** 319-321 King St., W6 9NH, ☎ 741 4328, Indian rest. – AE VISA p. 9 CV u
closed 25 and 26 December – **M** a la carte 5.90/12.15 **t.** 3.95.

X **Garden,** 210 King St., W6 0RA, ☎ 748 5058, Korean rest. p. 9 CV a
M 18.50 **t.** (dinner) and a la carte approx. 12.30 **t.**

Shepherd's Bush – ✉ W12/W14 – ☎ 071.

X **Chinon,** 25 Richmond Way, W14, ☎ 602 5968 – AE VISA p. 9 DV s
closed Saturday lunch, Sunday, Easter, 2 weeks August and Bank Holidays – **M** a la carte 23.00/30.50 **t.**

West Kensington – ✉ SW6/W14 – ☎ 071.

Ramada Inn West London, 44 Lillie Rd, SW6 1UQ, ☎ 385 1255, Telex 917728, Fax 381 4450 – rm – 2 000 p. 24 EZ e
497 rm, 4 suites.

Aston Court without rest., 25-27 Matheson Rd, W14 8SN, ☎ 602 9954, Telex 919208, Fax 371 1338 – p. 24 EZ
29 rm.

***Greater London** is divided, for administrative purposes, into 32 boroughs plus the City; these sub-divide naturally into minor areas, usually grouped around former villages or quarters, which often maintain a distinctive character.*

☎ *of Greater London:* ***071*** *or* ***081*** *except special cases.*

HARINGEY pp. 6 and 7.

Highgate – ✉ N6 – ☎ 081.

18 Denewood Rd ☎ 340 1906.

XX San Carlo, 2 High St., N6 5JL, ☎ 340 5823, Italian rest. EU v

Hornsey – ✉ N8 – ☎ 081.

X Jashan, 19a Turnpife Lane, N8 0EP, ☎ 340 9880, Indian rest. – EU z

X **Le Bistro,** 36 The High St., N8 7NX, ☎ 340 2116 – VISA EU u
closed Sunday, 2 weeks June and 2 weeks August – **M** (dinner only) 12.00/17.50 **st.** and a la carte 6.25.

HARROW pp. 4 and 5.

Central Harrow – ✉ Middx – ☎ 081.

Civic Centre, Station Rd ☎ 424 1103.

Cumberland, 1 St. John's Rd, HA1 2EF, ☎ 863 4111, Telex 917201, Fax 861 5668 – rm AE VISA. BU x
M 6.50/12.50 **st.** and a la carte 4.50 – **80 rm** 40.00/75.00 **st.**

Harrow, 12-22 Pinner Rd, HA1 4HZ, ☎ 427 3435, Telex 917898, Fax 861 1370 – rm – 100. AE VISA. BU a
M 16.95 **st.** and a la carte – **98 rm** 60.00/160.00 **st.** – SB (weekends only) 106.90/153.90 **st.**

Hatch End – ✉ Middx – ☎ 081.

Grimsdyke, Oxhey Lane ℘ 428 4093.

XX **Canaletto 2,** 302 Uxbridge Rd, HA5 4HR, ℘ 428 4232, Italian rest. – ▤. AE ⓓ VISA
closed Saturday lunch, Sunday and Bank Holidays – **M** a la carte 15.40/18.35 **t.** 4.95. BT **a**

X **Swan,** 322-326 Uxbridge Rd, HA5 4RH, ℘ 428 8821, Chinese (Peking) rest. – ▤. AE ⓓ BT **n**
M 13.00/22.00 **t.** and a la carte 4.00.

Kenton – ✉ Middx. – ☎ 081.

Travel Inn, Kenton Rd, HA3 8AT, ℘ 907 1671, Fax 909 1604 – rm TV & P
M (Beefeater grill) a la carte approx. 12.25 **t.** – 4.50 – **44 rm** -/27.50 **t.** BU **e**

North Harrow – ✉ Middx. – ☎ 081.

X **Thai Castle,** 28 The Broadwalk, Pinner Rd, HA2 6ED, ℘ 427 4732, Thai rest. – VISA
closed 25 and 26 December – **M** (dinner only and Sunday lunch)/dinner 20.00 **st.** and a la carte 3.75. BU **c**

Stanmore – ✉ Middx – ☎ 081.

Gordon Av. ℘ 954 4661.

X **Mr Tang's Mandarin** 28 The Broadway, ℘ 954 0339, Chinese rest. – AE ⓓ VISA BT **i**
closed 25 and 26 December – **M** 16.00 **t.** (dinner) and a la carte 12.00/16.00 **t.** 3.50.

If you find you cannot take up a hotel booking you have made, please let the hotel know immediately.

HAVERING pp. 6 and 7.

Hornchurch by A 12 – JT – on A 127 – ✉ Essex – ☎ 040 23 Ingrebourne.

Hilton National, Southend Arterial Rd (A 127), RM11 3UJ, ℘ 46789, Telex 897315, Fax 41719 – rm TV ☎ & P – 200. AE ⓓ VISA
M *(closed Saturday lunch)* 13.00/15.00 **t.** and a la carte 4.50 – 7.50 – **137 rm** 75.00/120.00 **t.**

Romford by A 118 – JU – ✉ Essex – ☎ 0708.

18, 9 Havering, Risebridge Chase ℘ 41429.

Coach House without rest., 48 Main Rd, RM1 3DB, on A 118 ℘ 751901, Fax 730290, – TV P.
32 rm 29.50/56.00 **st.**

HILLINGDON pp. 4 and 8.

18 Haste Hill, The Drive ℘ 092 74 (Northwood) 22877 – 18 Harefield Pl., The Drive ℘ 0895 (Uxbridge) 31169, by B 467 – 9 18 Dorset Way ℘ 0895 (Uxbridge) 39810.

Eastcote – ✉ Middx – ☎ 081.

18 Ruislip, Ickenham Rd ℘ 0895 (Ruislip) 632004.

X **Sambuca,** 113 Field End Rd, HA5 1QG, ℘ 866 7500, Italian rest. – AE ⓓ VISA
closed Monday, Sunday dinner, August, 25 December and Bank Holidays – **M** (dinner only and Sunday lunch)/dinner a la carte 8.50/15.00 **t.** 3.50. AU **s**

Hayes – ✉ Middx. – ☎ 081.

Travel Inn, 362 Uxbridge Rd, UB4 0HF, ℘ 573 7479, Fax 569 1204 – rm TV & P. AE VISA. AV **a**
M (Beefeater grill) a la carte approx. 12.25 **t.** – 4.50 – **40 rm** -/27.50 **t.**

Heathrow Airport – ✉ Middx – ☎ 081.

Heathrow Central Station, London Airport ℘ (071) 730 3488.

Sheraton Skyline, Bath Rd, Hayes, UB3 5BP, ℘ 759 2535, Telex 934254, Fax 750 9150, « Exotic indoor garden with », , – rm ▤ TV ☎ & P – 500. AE ⓓ VISA. AX **u**
M 21.50/34.00 **t.** and a la carte – 9.50 – **347 rm** 120.00/150.00 **s.**, **5 suites** 345.00/785.00 **t.**

Excelsior (T.H.F.), Bath Rd, West Drayton, UB7 0DU, ℘ 759 6611, Telex 24525, Fax 759 3421, , , – rm ▤ TV ☎ & P – 700. AE ⓓ VISA AX **x**
M *(closed Saturday lunch)* 13.95 **st.** and a la carte 4.35 – 8.75 – **830 rm** 200.00/225.00 **st.**, **7 suites** 180.00/200.00 **st.**

Holiday Inn, Stockley Rd, West Drayton, UB7 9NA, ☏ 0895 (West Drayton) 445555, Telex 934518, Fax 445122, squash – rm rm – 100. AE VISA AV v
M 15.00 **st.** and a la carte 5.00 – 8.50 – **374 rm** 104.00/124.00 **st.**, **6 suites** 450.00/510.00 **st.** – SB (weekends only) 150.00/300.00 **st.**

Post House (T.H.F.), Sipson Rd, West Drayton, UB7 0JU, ☏ 759 2323, Telex 934280, Fax 897 8659, – rm – 200. AE VISA AV c
M (carving rest.) 13.95/16.00 **st.** and a la carte 4.35 – 7.00 – **565 rm** 85.00/180.00 **st.** – SB (weekends only) 91.90 **st.**

Sheraton Heathrow, Colnbrook by-pass, West Drayton, UB7 0HJ, ☏ 759 2424, Telex 934331, Fax 759 2091, – rm – 70. AE VISA. AVX a
M 12.00/30.00 **t.** and a la carte 6.00 – 8.75 – **439 rm** 135.00/160.00 **s.**, **1 suite** 253.00 **s.**

Heathrow Penta, Bath Rd, Hounslow, TW6 2AQ, ☏ 897 6363, Telex 934660, Fax 897 1113, – – 600. AE VISA. AX z
M *(closed lunch Saturday and Sunday)* 14.50/15.70 **st.** and a la carte 5.30 – 8.80 – **629 rm** 95.00/107.00 **st.**, **6 suites** 167.00/385.00 **st.**

Skyway, 140 Bath Rd, Hayes, UB3 5AW, ☏ 759 6311, Telex 23935, Fax 759 4559, heated – rest – 250 AX e
444 rm, **2 suites.**

Heathrow Park (Mt. Charlotte Thistle), Bath Rd, Longford, West Drayton, UB7 0EQ, ☏ 759 2400, Telex 934093, Fax 759 5278 – rm – 700. AE VISA
M *(closed Sunday dinner)* (carving lunch)/dinner 13.50 **st.** and a la carte – **306 rm** 75.00/105.00 **st.** off A 4 AX

Ariel (T.H.F.), Bath Rd, Hayes, UB3 5AJ, ☏ 759 2552, Telex 21777, Fax 564 9265 – rm . AE VISA AX i
M *(closed Saturday lunch)* 13.50/14.50 **st.** and a la carte 3.60 – 7.75 – **177 rm** 90.00/100.00 **st.**

Ickenham – ✉ Middx. – ☏ 089 56 Ruislip

Roberto's, 15 Long Lane, UB10 8TB, ☏ 632519, Italian rest. – AE VISA AU i
closed Sunday and 5 to 20 August – **M** a la carte 8.95/25.00 **t.** 4.00.

HOUNSLOW pp. 8 and 9.

Wyke Green, Syon Lane, Isleworth ☏ (081) 560 8777, ½ m. from Gillettes Corner (A 4).

Chiswick – ✉ W4 – ☏ 081.

Antonio's, 6-8 Elliott Rd, W4 1PE, ☏ 742 1485, Italian rest. – AE VISA CV o
closed Christmas – **M** 25.00 **t.** and a la carte 3.50.

Grove Park, 313 Chiswick High Rd, W4 4HH, ☏ 995 3354, Chinese (Peking) rest. – CV i

La Dordogne, 5 Devonshire Rd, W4 2EU, ☏ 747 1836, Fax 994 9144, French rest. – AE VISA CV o
closed lunch Saturday and Sunday and Bank Holidays – **M** a la carte 16.15/23.65 **t.**

Annapurna, 101 Chiswick High Rd, W4 2ED, ☏ 995 4431, Indian rest. CV n

Cranford – ✉ Middx. – ☏ 081.

Berkeley Arms, Bath Rd, TW5 9QE, ☏ 897 2121, Telex 935728, Fax 759 7154, – – 70. AE VISA AX r
closed 24 to 27 December – **M** *(closed Saturday lunch)* (carving rest.) 14.50 **st.** and a la carte – 7.50 – **56 rm** 68.50/78.50 **st.** – SB (weekends only) 56.00/200.00 **st.**

Heston Service Area – ✉ Middx. – ☏ 081.

Granada Lodge without rest., on M 4 (westbound carriageway), TW5 9NA, ☏ 574 5875, Fax 574 1891 – . AE VISA ABV e
46 rm 36.00/39.00 **t.**

Hounslow – ✉ Middx. – ☏ 081.

Airlinks, Southall Lane ☏ 561 1418 – Hounslow Heath, Staines Rd ☏ 570 5271.

Shalimar, 219-221 Staines Rd, TW3 3JJ, ☏ 572 2816, – . BX s
31 rm.

Hee's, 476-478 Great West Rd, TW5 0TA, ☏ 577 3817, Chinese (Peking, szechuan) rest. – BX r

This Guide is not a comprehensive list of all hotels and restaurants, nor even of all good hotels and restaurants in Great Britain and Ireland.

Since our aim is to be of service to all motorists, we must show establishments in all categories and so we have made a selection of some in each.

ISLINGTON Except where otherwise stated see pp. 20-23.

Canonbury – ✉ N1 – ☎ 071.

Anna's Place, 90 Mildmay Park, N1 4PR, ☎ 249 9379, Swedish rest.
closed Sunday, Monday, 2 weeks Easter, August and 2 weeks Christmas – **M** (booking essential) a la carte 12.00/16.40 **t.** p. 6 FU **a**

Finsbury – ✉ WC1/EC1/EC2 – ☎ 071.

Brivati's, 71-73 St. John St., EC1, ☎ 253 4109, Italian rest.

Café Rouge, 2c Cherry Tree Walk, Whitecross St., EC1Y ONX, ☎ 588 0710 OU **e**

Le Mesurier, 113 Old St., EC1V 9JR, ☎ 251 8117 – AE VISA OT **e**
closed Saturday, Sunday, 3 weeks August and 1 week Christmas – **M** (lunch only) (booking essential) a la carte 17.00/24.00 **t.** 4.00.

Rouxl Britannia, Triton Court, 14 Finsbury Sq., EC2A 1RR, ☎ 256 6997 –
M Le Restaurant *(closed Saturday, Sunday, Christmas and Bank Holidays)* (lunch only) 18.00 **st.** 5.20 – **Le Café** *(closed Saturday, Sunday, Christmas and Bank Holidays)* (lunch only) a la carte 12.15/16.65 **st.** 5.20. PU **x**

Quality Chop House, 94 Farringdon Rd, EC1R 3EA, ☎ 837 5093 MT **n**
closed Saturday lunch, Sunday dinner and 2 weeks Christmas – **M** a la carte 7.00/16.00 **t.**

Lakorn, 197-199 Rosebery Av., EC1R 4TJ, ☎ 837 5048, Thai rest. – AE VISA NT **e**
closed Saturday lunch, Sunday and Bank Holidays – **M** a la carte 9.50/14.50 **t.** 3.50.

Islington – ✉ N1 – ☎ 071.

Frederick's, Camden Passage, N1 8EG, ☎ 359 2888, Fax 359 5173, « Conservatory and walled garden » – AE VISA NS **a**
closed Sunday, 29 March, 25 December and Bank Holidays – **M** 10.95 **st.** (lunch) and a la carte 15.60/18.80 **t.** 4.50.

M'sieur Frog, 31a Essex Rd, N1 2SE, ☎ 226 3495, Bistro NS **n**

Casale Franco, 134-137 Upper St. (behind the Citroen garage), ☎ 226 8994, Italian rest.

Upper Holloway – ✉ N19 – ☎ 071.

Raj Vogue, 34 Highgate Hill, N19 5NL, ☎ 272 9091, Indian rest. – AE VISA
closed 25 December – **M** 17.00/20.00 **st.** and a la carte. p.6 EU **a**

KENSINGTON and CHELSEA (Royal Borough of).

Chelsea – ✉ SW1/SW3/SW10 – ☎ 071 – Except where otherwise stated see pp. 30 and 31.

Hyatt Carlton Tower, 2 Cadogan Pl., SW1X 9PY, ☎ 235 5411, Telex 21944, Fax 245 6570, ≤, – rm – 250. AE VISA
M Chelsea Room 26.50/70.00 **st.** and a la carte 6.00 – **Rib Room** 23.50/50.00 **st.** and a la carte 6.75 – **194 rm** 210.00, **30 suites** 320.00/1 500.00. FR **n**

Conrad Chelsea Harbour, Chelsea Harbour, SW10 0XG, ☎ 823 3000, Telex 919222, Fax 351 6525, ≤, – rm – 180. AE VISA
M 15.00 **t.** (lunch) and a la carte 16.75/45.50 **t.** – 11.50 – **160 suites** 225.00/1 000.00. p. 9 EX **i**

Sheraton Park Tower, 101 Knightsbridge, SW1X 7RN, ☎ 235 8050, Telex 917222, Fax 235 8231 – rm – 80. AE VISA FQ **v**
M a la carte 28.00/35.25 **t.** 9.00 – 9.25 – **273 rm** 180.00/240.00 **s.**, **22 suites** 365.00/980.00 **s.**

✿ **Capital,** 22-24 Basil St., SW3 1AT, ☎ 589 5171, Telex 919042, Fax 225 0011 – AE VISA ER **a**
M 18.50/30.00 **st.** and a la carte 36.00/40.50 – 8.75 – **48 rm** 150.00/265.00 **st.**
Spec. Beignets of foie gras, endive salad, apple and Calvados coulis, Confit of veal sweetbreads cooked in goose fat with a garlic soubise, Tarte Tatin, Calvados sorbet, crème anglaise.

Draycott, 24-26 Cadogan Gdns, SW3 2RP, ☎ 730 6466, Telex 914947, Fax 730 0236 – AE VISA FS **c**
M (room service only) a la carte 13.95/25.50 **t.** – 8.50 – **26 rm** 65.00/210.00 **t.**

Basil Street, 8 Basil St., SW3 1AH, ☎ 581 3311, Telex 28379, Fax 581 3693 – – 55. AE VISA FQ **o**
M *(closed Saturday lunch)* 15.50 **t.** (lunch) and a la carte 22.00/26.00 **t.** 4.95 – 9.00 – **91 rm** 103.00/133.00 **st.**, **1 suite** 207.00 **st.**

Fenja without rest., 69 Cadogan Gdns, SW3 2RB, ☎ 589 7333, Telex 934272, Fax 581 4958 – VISA FS **r**
9.50 – **13 rm** 95.00/190.00 **t.**

Cadogan, 75 Sloane St., SW1X 9SG, ☎ 235 7141, Telex 267893, Fax 245 0994 – rm – 40 – **70 rm**, **5 suites.** FR **e**

Chelsea, 17-25 Sloane St., SW1X 9NU, ☎ 235 4377, Telex 919111, Fax 235 3705 – rm – 120. AE VISA FR **r**
M a la carte 14.10/31.20 **st.** 4.90 – 9.75 – **218 rm** 140.80/184.80 **st.**, **7 suites** 302.50 **st.**

Beaufort, 33 Beaufort Gdns, SW3 1PP, ✆ 584 5252, Telex 929200, Fax 589 2834, « English floral watercolour collection » – rm ☎. ER **n**
closed 23 December-2 January – **M** (room service only) – **28 rm** (room service included) 150.00/250.00 **st.** – SB (weekends only) 144.00/225.00 **st.**

Royal Court (Q.M.H.), Sloane Sq., SW1W 8EG, ✆ 730 9191, Telex 296818, Fax 824 8381 – rest ☎ – 40. FST **a**
M *(closed Saturday lunch)* 14.50/19.50 **st.** and a la carte – 8.50 – **102 rm** 120.00/150.00 **st.**

Eleven Cadogan Gardens without rest., 11 Cadogan Gardens, SW3 2RJ, ✆ 730 3426, Fax 730 5217 – ☎ FS **u**
56 rm, **5 suites.**

L'Hotel without rest., 28 Basil St., SW3 1AT, ✆ 589 6286, Telex 919042, Fax 225 0011 – ☎. ER **i**
12 rm 110.00/145.00 **t.**

Stone House in London without rest., 16 Sydney St., SW3, ✆ 0435 (Rushlake Green) 830553 – ☎. DT **a**
3 rm.

Claverley without rest., 13-14 Beaufort Gdns, SW3 1PS, ✆ 589 8541, Fax 584 3410 – ☎. ER **o**
32 rm 65.00/170.00 **t.**

Willett without rest., 32 Sloane Gdns, Sloane Sq., SW1W 8DJ, ✆ 824 8415, Telex 926678, Fax 824 8415 – ☎. FT **s**
18 rm 59.95/79.95.

Wilbraham, 1-5 Wilbraham Pl., Sloane St., SW1X 9AE, ✆ 730 8296 – ☎.
M *(closed Saturday lunch and Sunday)* (restricted menu) approx. 14.85 **t.** 2.95 – 5.50 – **53 rm** 36.50/72.00. FS **n**

XXXX ✿✿ **La Tante Claire** (Koffman), 68-69 Royal Hospital Rd, SW3 4HP, ✆ 352 6045, Fax 352 3257, French rest. – . EU **c**
closed Saturday, Sunday, 10 days Easter, 3 weeks August, and Christmas-New Year – **M** 21.50 **st.** (lunch) and a la carte 44.50/50.00 **st.**
Spec. Coquilles St. Jacques poêlées à l'encre de seiche, Confit de saumon sauvage à la graisse d'oie, Côte de veau poêlée à l'estragon.

XXX **Waltons,** 121 Walton St., SW3 2HP, ✆ 584 0204 – . DS **a**
closed 25 and 26 December – **M** 14.75/19.75 **t.** and a la carte 4.50.

XXX **Turner's,** 87-89 Walton St., SW3 2HP, ✆ 584 6711 – . ES **n**
closed Saturday lunch, 24 to 31 December and Bank Holidays – **M** 17.50/26.50 **st.** and a la carte 6.50.

XXX **Bibendum,** Michelin House, 81 Fulham Rd, SW3 6RD, ✆ 581 5817, Fax 823 7925 – . DS **s**
closed 24 to 28 December – **M** 24.50 **t.** (lunch) and dinner a la carte 34.00/45.00 **t.** 5.25.

XXX **Dynasty II,** Chelsea Wharf, 15 Lots Rd, SW10 0QJ, ✆ 351 1020, ≤, Oriental cuisine, « Riverside setting » – . p. 20 GZ **n**
closed Easter and 25-26 December – **M** 18.00/30.00 **t.** and a la carte 18.00/28.00 **t.**

XXX **Zen,** Chelsea Cloisters, Sloane Av., SW3 3DW, ✆ 589 1781, Chinese rest. – . ET **a**
M 13.50/38.00 **t.** and a la carte. EB **a**

XX **Daphne's,** 110-112 Draycott Av., SW3 3AE, ✆ 589 4257 – . DS **e**
closed Saturday lunch, Sunday and Bank Holidays – **M** a la carte 19.50/25.00 **t.** 4.50.

XX **Salotto,** 257-259 Fulham Rd, SW3 6HY, ✆ 351 1383, Italian rest. –
M a la carte approx. 18.25 **t.** 3.95. CU **i**

XX **La Finezza,** 62-64 Lower Sloane St., SW1N 8BP, ✆ 730 8639, Italian rest. – . FT **v**
closed Sunday and Bank Holidays – **M** a la carte 22.00/33.00 **t.** 4.00.

XX **English Garden,** 10 Lincoln St., SW3 2TS, ✆ 584 7272, English rest. – . ET **x**
closed 25 and 26 December – **M** 14.75 **t.** (lunch) and a la carte 21.00/28.50 **t.** 4.00.

XX **Gavvers,** 61-63 Lower Sloane St., SW1W 8DH, ✆ 730 5983, French rest. – . FT **e**
closed, Saturday lunch, Sunday and Bank Holidays – **M** 13.50/27.50 **st.** 5.20.

XX **Waterfront,** Harbour Yard, Chelsea Harbour, SW10 0QJ, ✆ 352 4562, Fax 351 6576, Italian rest. – . p. 9 EX **i**
closed Sunday dinner, Easter, 25-26 December, 1 January and Bank Holidays – **M** 16.50 **t.** and a la carte 3.75.

XX **Mario,** 260-262A Brompton Rd, SW3 2AS, ✆ 584 1724, Italian rest. –
closed Bank Holidays – **M** 16.50 **t.** (lunch) and a la carte 22.40/29.00 **t.** 4.75. DS **n**

XX **Poissonnerie de l'Avenue,** 82 Sloane Av., SW3 3DZ, ✆ 589 2457, Fax 581 3360, French Seafood rest. – DS **u**
closed Sunday, 23 December-3 January, 29 March-2 April and Bank Holidays – **M** a la carte 15.35/23.85 **t.** 4.50.

XX **Les Trois Plats,** 4 Sydney St., SW3 6PP, ✆ 352 3433, French rest. – ▤. AE VISA DT v
closed Sunday, Monday and Bank Holidays – **M** 12.00/22.00 **st.** and a la carte 5.20.

XX **St. Quentin,** 243 Brompton Rd, SW3 2EP, ✆ 589 8005, Fax 584 6064, French rest. – ▤. AE VISA DR a
M 11.90/14.90 **t.** and a la carte.

XX **Eleven Park Walk,** 11 Park Walk, SW10 0PZ, ✆ 352 3449, Italian rest. – ▤. AE VISA CU r
closed Sunday and Bank Holidays – **M** 13.50/20.50 **t.** and a la carte 3.50.

XX **Magic Dragon,** 99-103 Fulham Rd, SW3 6RH, ✆ 225 2244, Fax 929 5690, Chinese rest. – ▤. AE VISA DS o
closed Bank Holidays – **M** 9.50/34.00 **st.** and a la carte.

XX **Good Earth,** 233 Brompton Rd, SW3 2EP, ✆ 584 3658, Fax 823 8769, Chinese rest. – ▤. AE VISA DR c
closed 24 to 27 December – **M** 15.50/22.50 **t.** and a la carte 3.25.

XX Good Earth, 91 King's Rd, SW3 4PA, ✆ 352 9231, Chinese rest. – ▤ EU a

XX **Nakano,** 11 Beauchamp Pl., SW3 1NQ, ✆ 581 3837, Japanese rest. – ▤ AE VISA ER r
closed Sunday lunch, Monday, Easter, last 2 weeks August and Christmas-New Year – **M** 21.00/33.00 **t.**

XX **Toto,** Walton House, Walton St., SW3 2JH, ✆ 589 0075, Italian rest. – AE VISA ES a
closed 3 days at Easter and 4 days at Christmas – **M** a la carte 21.00/29.00 **st.** 4.50.

XX **Ponte Nuovo,** 126 Fulham Rd, SW3 6HU, ✆ 370 6656, Italian rest. – AE VISA CU e
closed Bank Holidays – **M** a la carte 17.50/26.00 **t.** 4.50.

XX **Beccofino,** 100 Draycott Av., SW3 3AD, ✆ 584 3600, Italian rest. – AE VISA ES r
closed Sunday and Bank Holidays – **M** a la carte 12.30/19.00 **t.** 3.50.

XX **Le Suquet,** 104 Draycott Av., SW3 3AE, ✆ 581 1785, French Seafood rest. – AE VISA DS c
M a la carte 18.50/26.50 **t.**

XX **Dan's,** 119 Sydney St., SW3 6NR, ✆ 352 2718, Fax 352 3265 – AE VISA DU s
closed Saturday lunch and Sunday – **M** 19.00 **t.** (dinner) and a la carte.

X **Ziani,** 45-47 Radnor Walk, SW3, ✆ 351 5297, Italian rest. – AE VISA EU e
closed Bank Holidays – **M** a la carte 12.45/15.55 **t.** 3.95.

X **Ma Cuisine,** 113 Walton St., SW3 2HP, ✆ 584 7585, French rest. – AE VISA DS a
closed Sunday, Easter, Christmas and Bank Holidays – **M** (booking essential) a la carte 20.00/28.25 **t.** 8.50.

X **Ming,** 338 Kings Rd, SW3 5ES, ✆ 351 0775, Chinese rest. – ▤. AE VISA CU n
M 5.90/22.50 **t.** and a la carte 3.40.

X Beit Eddine, 8 Harriet St., SW1 9JW, ✆ 235 3969, Lebanese rest. FQ z

X **Monkey's,** 1 Cale St., Chelsea Green, SW3 3QT, ✆ 352 4711 – ▤. VISA ET z
closed Saturday, Sunday, 2 weeks Easter and 3 weeks August – **M** 15.00/27.50 **t.** and a la carte 4.00.

X **Thierry's,** 342 King's Rd, SW3 5UR, ✆ 352 3365, Bistro – AE VISA CU c
closed Sunday, 18 August-1 September, 29 March, 1 April, 23 December-6 January and Bank Holidays – **M** 9.90 **t.** (lunch) and a la carte 16.95/29.20 **st.** 4.25.

Earl's Court – ⊠ SW5/SW10 – ☎ 071 – Except where otherwise stated see pp. 30 and 31.

Rushmore without rest., 11 Trebovir Rd, SW5 9LS, ✆ 370 3839, Fax 370 0274 – TV ☎ P. AE VISA. ✻ p. 24 EZ c
22 rm ☐ 42.00/78.00 **st.**

Amsterdam without rest., 7 Trebovir Rd, SW5 9LS, ✆ 370 2814, Fax 244 7608 – |‡| TV ☎. AE VISA. ✻ p. 24 EZ c
20 rm ☐ 38.00/65.00 **st.**

XX **Tiger Lee,** 251 Old Brompton Rd, SW5 9HP, ✆ 370 3176, Chinese Seafood rest. – ▤. AE VISA AU n
closed 25 and 26 December – **M** (dinner only) a la carte 19.00/31.50 **t.**

XX **La Croisette,** 168 Ifield Rd, SW10 9AF, ✆ 373 3694, French Seafood rest. – AE VISA AU a
closed Tuesday lunch, Monday and Christmas – **M** 25.00 **t.** and a la carte.

XX **La Primula,** 12 Kenway Rd, SW5 0RR, ✆ 370 5958, Italian rest. – AE VISA p. 24 FZ e
M 18.50 **t.** and a la carte 5.50.

X **Left Bank,** 88 Ifield Rd, SW10 9AD, ✆ 352 0970 – ▤. AE VISA p. 24 FZ i
closed Sunday dinner, 25-26 December and Bank Holidays – **M** (dinner only and Sunday lunch)/dinner 15.00 **t.** and a la carte 4.00.

***Le Grand Londres** (GREATER LONDON) est composé de la City et de 32 arrondissements administratifs (Borough) eux-mêmes divisés en quartiers ou en villages ayant conservé leur caractère propre (Area).*

Kensington – SW7/W8/W11/W14 – 071 – Except where otherwise stated see pp. 24-27.

Royal Garden (Rank), Kensington High St., W8 4PT, 937 8000, Telex 263151, Fax 938 4532, – rm – 900. p. 30 AQ c
M **Royal Roof** *(closed Saturday lunch and Sunday)* (Dancing Saturday night) 22.00/32.00 **st.** and a la carte – 10.75 – **381 rm** 135.00/185.00 **st.**, **17 suites** 400.00/950.00 **st.**

Halcyon, 81 Holland Park, W11 3RZ, 727 7288, Telex 266721, Fax 229 8516 – EX u
M **Kingfisher** *(closed Saturday lunch, Sunday and Bank Holidays except Christmas and New Year)* a la carte 19.25/29.50 **st.** 5.00 – 12.25 – **41 rm** 165.00/250.00 **st.**, **3 suites** 375.00/550.00 **st.** – SB (October-March) (weekends only) 375.00 **st.**

London Tara (Best Western), Scarsdale Pl., W8 5SR, 937 7211, Telex 918834, Fax 937 7100 – rm – 500. FY u
M 12.20 **t.** and a la carte 6.00 – 8.40 – **823 rm** 93.00/130.00 **st.**, **8 suites** 220.00/330.00 **st.** – SB (weekends only) 206.00 **st.**

London Kensington Hilton, 179-199 Holland Park Av., W11 4UL, 603 3355, Telex 919763, Fax 602 9397 – rm – 200. EX s
M 25.00/35.00 **st.** and a la carte 6.25 – (see also **Hiroko** below) – 12.50 – **606 rm** 110.00/350.00 **st.** – SB (weekends only) 252.00/300.00 **st.**

Kensington Palace Thistle (Mt. Charlotte Thistle), De Vere Gdns, W8 5AF, 937 8121, Telex 262422, Fax 937 2816 – rm rest – 160.
M 17.50 **st.** and a la carte – 8.25 – **297 rm** 90.00/140.00 **st.**, **1 suite.** p. 30 BQ a

Kensington Close (T.H.F.), Wrights Lane, W8 5SP, 937 8170, Telex 23914, Fax 937 8289, squash – rm rest – 200.
M a la carte 13.00/18.25 **st.** 4.50 – 8.50 – **524 rm** 90.00/105.00 **st.** FY c

London Lodge, 134-136 Lexham Gdns, W8 6JE, 244 8444, Telex 922921 – **27 rm.** EYZ r

La Ruelle, 14 Wright's Lane, W8 6TF, 937 8525, French rest. FY i

Clarke's, 124 Kensington Church St., W8 4BH, 221 9225, Fax 229 4564 – .
closed Saturday, Sunday, 4 days at Easter, 3 weeks August-September, 1 week Christmas and Bank Holidays – **M** 20.00/30.00 **st.** EX c

Shanghai, 38c Kensington Church St., W8 4BX, 938 2501, Chinese rest. – . FX a
M 15.50/21.50 **t.** and a la carte 3.95.

Launceston Place, la Launceston Pl., W8 5RL, 937 6912, Fax 376 0581 – .
closed Saturday lunch and Sunday dinner – **M** 13.75 **t.** and a la carte 3.95. p. 30 BR a

Boyd's, 135 Kensington Church St., W8 7LP, 727 5452 – p. 32 AZ r
closed Saturday, Sunday, 1 week Christmas and Bank Holidays – **M** 17.50/27.00 **t.**

La Pomme d'Amour, 128 Holland Park Av., W11 4UE, 229 8532, French rest. – EX e

Phoenicia, 11-13 Abingdon Rd, W8, 937 0120, Lebanese rest. – .
closed 25 and 26 December – **M** 12.70/23.70 **st.** and a la carte 4.00. EY n

Hiroko (at London Kensington Hilton H.), 179-199 Holland Park Av., W11 4UL, 603 5003, Japanese rest. – . EX s
closed Monday lunch – **M** 19.00/32.00 **t.** and a la carte 6.70.

Sailing Junk, 59 Marloes Rd, W8 6LE, 937 5833, Chinese rest. – FY x

La Paesana, 30 Uxbridge St., W8 7TA, 229 4332, Italian rest. – .
closed Sunday – **M** a la carte 11.55/13.30 **t.** p. 32 AZ i

Topo D'oro, 39 Uxbridge St., W8, 727 5813, Italian rest. – p. 32 AZ a

I Ching, 40 Earls Court Rd, W8 6EJ, 937 0409, Chinese rest. – EY a

Kensington Place, 201 Kensington Church St., W8 7LX, 727 3184, Fax 229 2025 – . p. 32 AZ z
closed 3 days August Bank Holidays and 24 to 27 December – **M** 12.50 **t.** (lunch) and a la carte 14.75/26.50 **t.** 3.75.

Cibo, 3 Russell Gdns, W14, 371 6271, Italian rest. EY o

The Ark, Kensington Court, 35 Kensington High St., W8 5BA, 937 4294, French rest. – p. 30 AQ s
closed Sunday lunch, 4 days at Easter and 4 days at Christmas – **M** a la carte 13.30/17.00 **t.** 2.95.

Malabar, 27 Uxbridge St., W8 7TQ, 727 8800, Indian rest. – p. 32 AZ e
closed 19 to 26 August and 23 to 26 December – **M** a la carte 11.00/19.15 **st.** 3.95.

Le Quai St. Pierre, 7 Stratford Rd, W8 3JS, 937 6388, French Seafood rest. – FY r
closed Monday lunch, Sunday and 2 weeks Christmas – **M** a la carte 18.50/27.50 **t.**

Mandarin, 197c Kensington High St., W8 6BA, 937 1551, Chinese rest. – . – **M** 9.50/16.00 **t.** and a la carte 3.50. EY s

Café Français, 6 Holland St., W8 4LT, 937 3367 – FY z
closed 25-26 December and 1-2 January – **M** 19.45 **t.** and a la carte.

North Kensington – ✉ W2/W10/W11 – ☎ 071 – Except where otherwise stated see pp. 20-23.

Abbey Court without rest., 20 Pembridge Gdns, W2 4DU, ✆ 221 7518, Telex 262167, Fax 792 0858, « Tastefully furnished Victorian town house » – TV ☎. AE VISA. ✻ ☕ 7.50 – **22 rm** 80.00/165.00 **t.** p. 32 AZ **u**

Portobello, 22 Stanley Gdns, W11 2NG, ✆ 727 2777, Telex 268349, Fax 792 9641, « Attractively furnished town house in Victorian terrace » – lift TV ☎. AE VISA. ✻ *closed 22 December-2 January* – **M** (residents only) 15.00/20.00 **st.** and a la carte 6.50 – ☕ 6.75 – **24 rm** 60.00/85.00 **st.**, **1 suite** 150.00 **st.** EV **n**

Pembridge Court, 34 Pembridge Gdns, W2 4DX, ✆ 229 9977, Telex 298363, Fax 727 4982 – lift rest rest TV ☎. AE VISA p. 32 AZ **n**
M *(closed Sunday and Bank Holidays)* (dinner only) a la carte 13.50/17.50 **t.** 3.60 – **25 rm** ☕ 69.00/130.00 **st.**

Leith's, 92 Kensington Park Rd, W11 2PN, ✆ 229 4481 – AE VISA EV **e**
closed 25-26 August and 24 to 27 December – **M** (dinner only) 21.50/42.50 **st.** 6.75.

Chez Moi, 1 Addison Av., Holland Park, W11 4QS, ✆ 603 8267, French rest. – AE VISA – *closed Saturday lunch, Sunday, Christmas-New Year and Bank Holidays* – **M** 13.50 **t.** (lunch) and a la carte 17.25/24.50 **t.** 3.50. p. 24 EX **n**

Monsieur Thompson's, 29 Kensington Park Rd, W11 2EU, ✆ 727 9957, French rest. – AE VISA EV **a**
closed Sunday and 25 December-3 January – **M** 18.50/20.00 **t.** (dinner) and a la carte 17.50/25.50 **t.** 3.50.

Canal Brasserie, Canalot Studios, 222 Kensal Rd, W10 5BN, ✆ 960 2732 – VISA
closed Sunday dinner – **M** a la carte approx. 18.20 **t.** ET **c**

South Kensington – ✉ SW5/SW7/W8 – ☎ 071 – Except where otherwise stated see pp. 30 and 31.

Blakes, 33 Roland Gdns, SW7 3PF, ✆ 370 6701, Telex 8813500, Fax 373 0442, « Oriental antique furnishings » – lift TV ☎. AE VISA BU **n**
M *(closed 25 and 26 December)* 28.50 **st.** (lunch) and a la carte 51.25/57.20 **t.** 7.00 – ☕ 14.00 – **42 rm** 125.00/185.00 **st.**, **10 suites** 220.00/600.00 **st.**

Pelham, 15 Cromwell Place, SW7 2LA, ✆ 589 8288, Telex 8814714, Fax 584 8444, « Tastefully furnished Victorian town house » – lift TV ☎. AE VISA. ✻ CS **z**
M 12.00/15.00 **t.** and a la carte 8.50 – **35 rm** 130.00/155.00 **t.**, **2 suites** 250.00 **t.**

Norfolk (Q.M.H.), 2-10 Harrington Rd, SW7 3ER, ✆ 589 8191, Telex 268852, Fax 581 1874, – lift rest TV ☎ – 60. AE VISA. ✻ CS **e**
M (see **Brasserie de la Paix** below) – ☕ 8.50 – **93 rm** 110.00/140.00 **st.**, **3 suites** 160.00/180.00 **st.** – SB 124.00/141.00 **st.**

Gloucester (Rank), 4-18 Harrington Gdns, SW7 4LH, ✆ 373 6030, Telex 917505, Fax 373 0409 – lift rm TV ☎ P – 400. AE VISA. ✻ BS **r**
M 18.25/19.25 **st.** and a la carte – ☕ 10.50 – **544 rm** 122.00/172.00 **st.**, **6 suites** 335.00/695.00 **st.**

Swallow International, Cromwell Rd, SW5 0TH, ✆ 973 1000, Telex 27260, Fax 244 8194, – lift rm rest TV ☎ P – 200. AE VISA. ✻
M 11.75/13.95 **st.** and a la carte 4.95 – ☕ 5.45 – **415 rm** 93.50/110.00 **st.**, **1 suite** 165.00/275.00 **st.** AS **c**

Rembrandt, 11 Thurloe Pl., SW7 2RS, ✆ 589 8100, Telex 295828, Fax 225 3363, – lift rm rest TV ☎ – 120. AE VISA. ✻ DS **x**
M 14.95 **st.** and a la carte – ☕ 8.75 – **200 rm** 90.00/110.00 **st.** – SB (weekends only) 106.90 **st.**

Gore (Best Western), 189-190 Queen's Gate, SW7 5EX, ✆ 584 6601, Telex 296244, Fax 589 8127 – lift TV ☎. AE VISA. ✻ BR **n**
M (see **One Ninety Queens Gate** below) – ☕ 9.00 – **54 rm** 83.00/155.00 **st.**

Regency, 100 Queen's Gate, SW7 5AG, ✆ 370 4595, Telex 267594, Fax 370 5555, – lift rm rest TV ☎ – 100. AE VISA. ✻ CT **e**
M 16.50/30.00 **st.** and a la carte 5.00 – ☕ 12.00 – **205 rm** 99.00/115.00 **st.**, **5 suites** 180.00/225.00 **st.** – SB (weekends only) 179.00/215.00 **st.**

John Howard (Best Western), 4 Queen's Gate, SW7 5EH, ✆ 581 3011, Telex 8813397, Fax 589 8403 – lift TV ☎. AE VISA. ✻ BQ **i**
M 16.50 **st.** and a la carte – ☕ 9.50 – **52 rm** 85.00/250.00 **st.** – SB (weekends only) 132.00 **st.**

Vanderbilt, 68-86 Cromwell Rd, SW7 5BT, ✆ 589 2424, Telex 946944, Fax 225 2293 – lift rest TV ☎ – 120. AE VISA BS **v**
M 11.50/12.50 **st.** and a la carte – ☕ 8.00 – **223 rm** 90.00/250.00 **st.** – SB (weekends only) 110.00/132.00 **st.**

Bailey's, 140 Gloucester Rd, SW7 4HQ, ✆ 373 6000, Telex 264221, Fax 370 3760 – lift TV ☎ – 70. AE VISA. ✻ BS **a**
M *(closed lunch Saturday and Sunday)* 14.25 **st.** and a la carte – ☕ 8.25 – **162 rm** 90.00/150.00 **st.**

Onslow, 109-113 Queen's Gate, SW7 5LR, ☎ 589 6300, Telex 262180, Fax 581 1492 – rest – 80. AE VISA. CT i
M 15.00 **st.** and a la carte 6.00 – 8.50 – **173 rm** 95.00/120.00 **st.** – SB (weekends only) 80.00/110.00 **st.**

Cranley Gardens without rest., 8 Cranley Gardens, SW7 3DB, ☎ 373 3232, Telex 894489, Fax 373 7944 – AE VISA BT e
4.50 – **85 rm** 63.00/109.00 **st.**

Embassy House, 31-33 Queen's Gate, SW7 5JA, ☎ 584 7222, Telex 914893, Fax 589 8193 – AE VISA. BR e
M *(closed lunch Saturday, Sunday and Bank Holidays)* (buffet lunch)/dinner 14.50 **st.** and a la carte 4.10 – 4.50 – **68 rm** 68.00/87.00 **st.**, **1 suite** 230.00/255.00 **st.**

Kensington Plaza, 61 Gloucester Rd, SW7 4PE, ☎ 584 8100, Telex 8950993, Fax 823 9175 – – 50. AE VISA BS e
M (Indian rest.) 20.00/25.00 **st.** and a la carte 6.00 – 7.00 – **51 rm** 60.00/110.00 **st.** – SB (weekends only) 94.00/116.00 **st.**

Cranley without rest., 10-12 Bina Gardens, SW5 0LA, ☎ 373 0123, Fax 373 9497, « Tasteful decor, antiques » – rm AE VISA. BT c
5.45 – **31 rm** 97.50/155.00 **st.**, **1 suite** 200.00/250.00 **st.**

Cranley Place without rest., 1 Cranley Pl., SW7 3AB, ☎ 589 7944, Fax 225 3931, « Tasteful decor » – AE VISA CT o
10 rm

Alexander without rest., 9 Sumner Pl., SW7 3EE, ☎ 581 1591, Telex 917133, Fax 581 0824, « Attractively furnished Victorian town houses », – AE VISA. CT a
37 rm 89.00/104.00, **1 suite** 182.00.

Number Sixteen without rest., 14-17 Sumner Pl., SW7 3EG, ☎ 589 5232, Telex 266638, Fax 584 8615, « Attractively furnished Victorian town houses », – AE VISA. CT c
36 rm 95.00/165.00 **t.**

Aster House without rest., 3 Sumner Pl., SW7 3EE, ☎ 581 5888, Fax 584 4925, – AE VISA. CT u
12 rm 50.00/95.00 **st.**

XXX **One Ninety Queen's Gate** (at Gore H.), 190 Queen's Gate, SW7 5EU, ☎ 581 5666, Fax 581 8261 – AE VISA
closed Saturday lunch and Sunday – **M** 22.50/32.50 **t** and a la carte 5.50.

XXX **Bombay Brasserie,** Courtfield Close, 140 Gloucester Rd, SW7 4QH, ☎ 370 4040, Indian rest., « Raj-style decor, conservatory garden » – VISA BS a
closed 26 and 27 December – **M** (buffet lunch) 12.95 **t.** and dinner a la carte approx. 15.25 **t.** 4.25.

XX **Hilaire,** 68 Old Brompton Rd, SW7 3LQ, ☎ 584 8993 – AE VISA CT n
closed Saturday lunch, Sunday dinner, 1 week Christmas, 1 week Easter, 2 weeks August and Bank Holidays – **M** (booking essential) 18.00/34.00 **t.** and a la carte.

XX **Brasserie de la Paix** (at Norfolk H.), 10 Harrington Rd, SW7 3ER, ☎ 589 8191, Telex 268852, Fax 581 1874 – AE VISA CS e
M *(closed Saturday lunch)* 14.50/16.75 **t.** and a la carte 5.75.

XX **Tui,** 19 Exhibition Rd, SW7 2HE, ☎ 584 8359, Fax 352 8343, Thai rest. – AE VISA
closed Bank Holidays – **M** a la carte 15.35/18.50 **t.** 3.75. CS u

XX **Delhi Brasserie,** 134 Cromwell Rd, SW7 4HA, ☎ 370 7617, Indian rest. – AE VISA p. 24 EFZ z
closed 25 and 26 December – **M** 12.95 **t.** and a la carte.

XX **Memories of India,** 18 Gloucester Rd, SW7 4RB, ☎ 589 6450, Telex 265196, Fax 581 5980, Indian rest. – AE VISA BR s
M 14.50 **st.** and a la carte.

X **Chanterelle,** 119 Old Brompton Rd, SW7 3RN, ☎ 373 5522 – AE VISA BT v
closed 4 days at Christmas – **M** 9.50/18.00 **t.** 4.40.

X **Nam Long at Le Shaker,** 159 Old Brompton Rd, SW5 0LJ, ☎ 373 1926, Vietnamese rest. – AE VISA BT i
closed Saturday lunch, Sunday and Bank Holidays – **M** 13.00/17.00 **t.** and a la carte 4.00.

X **Bangkok,** 9 Bute St., SW7 3EY, ☎ 584 8529, Thai bistro – AE VISA CS v
closed Sunday, 1 week August and Bank Holidays – **M** a la carte 14.00/21.50 **t.**

KINGSTON UPON THAMES pp. 9 and 10.

Hampton Wick ✆ (081) 977 6645, by A 308 – Coombe Wood, George Rd ✆ (081) 942 3828, NE : 1 1/4 m. on A 308.

Wheatfield Way ✆ (081) 546 5386.

Kingston – ✉ Surrey – ☎ 081. Malden, Traps Lane ✆ 942 0654.

Kingston Lodge (T.H.F.), Kingston Hill, KT2 7NP, ✆ 541 4481, Telex 936034, Fax 547 1013, – rm – 60. AE VISA CY **u**
M *(closed Saturday lunch and Bank Holidays)* 15.50/19.75 **st.** and a la carte 4.95 – 7.60 – **61 rm** 80.00/135.00 **st.** – SB (weekends only) 160.00 **st.**

XX **Gravier,** 9 Station Rd, Norbiton, KT2 7AA, ✆ 549 5557, French Seafood rest. – AE VISA CY **x**
closed Saturday lunch, Sunday, 1 week Easter, 2 last weeks August, 1 week January and Bank Holidays – **M** a la carte 19.25/27.30 **t.** 4.00.

X Ayudhya, 14 Kingston Hill, KT2 7NH, ✆ 549 5984, Thai rest. CY **z**

Surbiton – ✉ Surrey – ☎ 081.

Woodstock Lane, Chessington ✆ 398 3101, S : 3 1/2 m. by A 243.

XX **Chez Max,** 85 Maple Rd, KT6 4AW, ✆ 399 2365 – AE VISA BY **o**
closed Saturday lunch, Sunday, Monday, 2 weeks summer and 14 days at Christmas – **M** (booking essential) 17.00 **t.** (lunch) and a la carte 16.30/22.50 **t.** 5.90.

LAMBETH Except where otherwise stated see pp.10 and 11.

Brixton – ✉ SW9 – ☎ 071.

X **Twenty Trinity Gardens,** 20 Trinity Gdns, SW9 8DP, ✆ 733 8838 – VISA EX **n**
closed Saturday lunch, Sunday and 25 to 30 December – **M** 10.75/14.95 **t.** 3.75.

Clapham Common – ✉ SW4 – ☎ 071.

XX **The Grafton,** 45 Old Town, SW4 OJL, ✆ 627 1048, French rest. – AE VISA
closed Saturday lunch, Sunday dinner, Monday, last 3 weeks August and 1 week Christmas – **M** 25.00/36.00 **t.** and a la carte 5.50. p. 13 DQ **a**

Streatham – ✉ SW16 – ☎ 081.

Barrow House without rest., 45 Barrow Rd, SW16 5PE, ✆ 677 1925, – .
closed 1 to 7 January – **5 rm** 16.00/30.00 **st.** EY **s**

Waterloo – ✉ SE1 – ☎ 071.

XX **La Rive Gauche,** 61 The Cut, SE1 8LL, ✆ 928 8645, French rest. – AE VISA
closed Saturday lunch, Sunday, Christmas-New Year and Bank Holidays – **M** 16.50 **t.** and a la carte 5.00. p. 27 NX **x**

XX **RSJ,** 13a Coin St., SE1 8YQ, ✆ 928 4554 – . AE VISA p. 27 NX **e**
closed Saturday lunch and Sunday – **M** 14.75 **t.** and a la carte 5.25.

LONDON HEATHROW AIRPORT – see Hillingdon, London p. 61.

MERTON pp. 8 and 9.

Wimbledon – ✉ SW19 – ☎ 081.

London Scottish, Windmill Enclosure ✆ 788 0135 – Wimbledon Common, Camp Rd ✆ 946 0294 – Home Park Rd, Wimbledon Park ✆ 946 1002 – Royal Wimbledon, 20 Camp Rd ✆ 946 2125.

Cannizaro House (Mt. Charlotte Thistle), West Side, Wimbledon Common, SW19 4UF, ✆ 879 1464, Telex 9413837, Fax 879 7338, <, « 18C country house overlooking Cannizaro Park », – – 50. AE VISA. DXY **x**
M 16.50 **st.** and a la carte – 8.00 – **47 rm** 85.00/140.00 **st.**

Worcester House without rest., 38 Alwyne Rd, SW19 7AE, ✆ 946 1300 – . VISA. – **9 rm** 42.50/64.00 **st.** DY **r**

XX Bayee Village, 24 High St., SW19 5DX, ✆ 947 3533, Chinese (Peking, Szechuan) rest. – DX **i**

X **Wimbledon Palace,** 88 The Broadway, SW19 1RH, ✆ 540 4505, Chinese (Peking, Szechuan) rest. – . AE VISA DY **e**
closed Saturday lunch and 25-26 December – **M** 18.00 **t.** (dinner) and a la carte 8.30/15.50 **t.** 3.80.

MICHELIN Distribution Centre, Deer Park Rd, Merton, SW19 3UD, ✆ 081 540 9034/7, Fax 081 542 7448 South London Branch (Merton) p. 9

REDBRIDGE pp. 6 and 7.

Ilford – ✉ Essex – ☎ 081.

18 Wanstead Park Rd ✆ 554 5174, by A 12 – 18 Fairlop Waters, Forest Rd, Barkinside ✆ 500 9911.

XX **Mandarin Palace,** 559 Cranbrook Rd, Gants Hill, IG2 6JZ, ✆ 550 7661, Chinese (Peking, Canton) rest. – ▤. AE VISA HU e
M a la carte 17.50/25.30 **t.** 3.90.

XX **Dragon City,** 97 Cranbrook Rd, IG1 4PG, ✆ 553 0312, Chinese (Peking, Canton) rest. – ▤. AE VISA JHU a
closed Christmas – **M** a la carte approx. 14.00.

South Woodford – ✉ Essex – ☎ 081.

9 Sunset Av., Woodford Green ✆ 504 0553.

XX **Ho-Ho,** 20 High Rd, E18 2QL, ✆ 989 1041, Chinese rest. – ▤. AE VISA HU c
M 20.00 **t.** and a la carte.

Woodford – ✉ Essex – ☎ 081.

Prince Regent, Manor Rd, Woodford Bridge, IG8 8AE, E : ¾ m. ✆ 505 9966, Fax 506 0807, – ▤ rest TV ☎ – 400. AE VISA. HT a
M 15.80/20.95 **t.** and a la carte 3.95 – **61 rm** 75.00/125.00 **st.**

Woodford Moat House (Q.M.H.), 30 Oak Hill, Woodford Green, IG8 9NY, ✆ 505 4511, Telex 264428, Fax 506 0941, – TV ☎ – 150. AE VISA. HT c
M *(closed lunch Saturday and Bank Holidays)* 15.50 **t.** and a la carte 3.50 – **99 rm** 78.00/90.00 **st.** – SB (weekends only) 85.00/95.00 **st.**

RICHMOND-UPON-THAMES pp. 8 and 9.

Barnes – ✉ SW13 – ☎ 081.

XX **Sonny's,** 94 Church Rd, SW13 0DQ, ✆ 748 0393 – ▤. VISA CX x
closed Saturday lunch, and 25 to 31 December – **M** 10.50 **t.** and a la carte 3.25.

East Sheen – ✉ SW14 – ☎ 081.

XX **Crowther's,** 481 Upper Richmond Rd West, SW14 7PU, ✆ 876 6372 – ▤. AE VISA
closed lunch Monday and Saturday, Sunday, 1 week Christmas and 2 weeks summer –
M (booking essential) 15.00/21.00 **t.** 4.00. CX n

X Le Tagliatelle, 180 Upper Richmond Road West, SW14 8AW, ✆ 876 6559, Italian rest. CX i

X **Taste of Raj,** 130 Upper Richmond Road West, SW14 8DS, ✆ 876 8271, Indian rest. – AE VISA – **M** a la carte 11.25/13.75 **t.** CX o

Kew – ✉ Surrey – ☎ 081.

X **Le Mange Tout,** 3 Royal Par. (Station Approach), TW9 3QD, ✆ 940 9304 – AE VISA
closed Saturday lunch and Sunday – **M** 14.50/30.00 **t.** and a la carte 4.25. CX r

Richmond – ✉ Surrey – ☎ 081. 18, 18 Richmond Park ✆ 876 3205 – 18 Sudbrook Park ✆ 940 1463 – 18, 18 Old Deer Park ✆ 940 1894.

Old Town Hall, Whittaker Av. ✆ 940 9125.

Petersham , Nightingale Lane, Richmond Hill, TW10 6UZ, ✆ 940 7471, Group Telex 928556, Fax 940 9998, ≤, – TV ☎ – 50. AE VISA. CX c
M 16.50/19.50 **t.** and a la carte 5.00 – **54 rm** 90.00/130.00 **t.** – SB (weekends only) 105.00/130.00 **st.**

Richmond Gate (Best Western), Richmond Hill, TW10 6RP, ✆ 940 0061, Fax 332 0354, – TV ☎ – 40. AE VISA. CX c
closed Christmas-New Year – **M** (dinner only) 26.00 **t.** 4.75 – **51 rm** 75.00/95.00 **t.**

Richmond Park without rest., 3 Petersham Rd, TW10 6UH, ✆ 948 4666, Fax 940 7376 – TV ☎. AE VISA. CX v
24 rm 69.00/82.00 **st.**

Bingham, 61-63 Petersham Rd, TW10 6UT, ✆ 940 0902, Fax 948 8737, – TV ☎ – 50. AE VISA. CX z
M *(closed Sunday)* (dinner only) 15.00 **st.** – **29 rm** 59.50/100.00 **st.**

XX Evergreen, 102-104 Kew Rd, TW9 2PQ, ✆ 940 9044, Chinese rest. – ▤ CX e

XX **Bellini,** 12 The Quadrant, TW9 1DN, ✆ 940 0086, Italian rest. – VISA BX e
closed Saturday lunch, Sunday, 25-26 December and 1 January – **M** 20.00/30.00 **st.** and a la carte 3.60.

Twickenham – ✉ Middx. – ☎ 081. 9 Staines Rd ✆ 979 6946, W : 2 m. on A 305 – 9 Stawberry Hill, Wellesley Rd ✆ 894 1246.

Twickenham Library, Garfield Rd ✆ 940 9125.

XX **Cézanne,** 68 Richmond Rd, TW1 3BE, ✆ 892 3526 – AE VISA BX a
closed Saturday lunch, Sunday and Bank Holidays – **M** a la carte 14.00/18.00 **t.** 4.00.

SOUTHWARK Except where otherwise stated see pp. 10 and 11.

Dulwich – ✉ SE19 – ☎ 081.

Dulwich, Sydenham Hill, Grange Lane, College Rd ☎ 693 3961.

XX **Luigi's,** 129 Gipsy Hill, SE19 1QS, ☎ 670 1843, Italian rest. – ▤. AE VISA
closed Saturday lunch, Sunday, August and Bank Holidays – **M** a la carte 16.95/18.85 **t.** 4.00. FX **a**

SUTTON pp. 8 and 9.

Cheam – ✉ Surrey – ☎ 081.

X **Al San Vincenzo,** 52 Upper Mulgrave Rd, SM2 7AJ, ☎ 661 9763, Italian rest. – VISA
closed Saturday lunch, Sunday, Monday, 5 days at Easter, 2 weeks August and 1 week Christmas-New Year – **M** (booking essential) 23.00 **t.** 4.75. DZ **r**

Sutton – ✉ Surrey – ☎ 081.

18, 9 Oak Sports Centre, Woodmansterne Rd ☎ 643 8363, E : 1¼ m. on B 278.

Thatched House, 135 Cheam Rd, SM1 2BN, ☎ 642 3131, – TV ☎ P. VISA DZ **e**
M *(closed Saturday and Sunday)* (dinner only) 14.00 **st.** 3.50 – **29 rm** 35.00/57.50 **st.**

Dene without rest., 39 Cheam Rd, SM1 2AT, ☎ 642 3170, – TV ☎ P.
28 rm 20.70/59.80 **t.** DEZ **v**

Pas de publicité payée dans ce guide.

TOWER HAMLETS – pp. 6 and 7.

Limehouse – ✉ E14 – ☎ 071.

Mayfield House ☎ 980 4831.

X **Good Friends,** 139-141 Salmon Lane, E14 7PG, ☎ 987 5541, Chinese (Peking, Canton) rest. – AE VISA GV **a**
M 14.50 **st.** and a la carte 3.25.

WANDSWORTH Except where otherwise stated see pp. 12 and 13.

Battersea – ✉ SW8/SW11 – ☎ 071.

XXX ✿ **Cavaliers'** (Cavalier), 129 Queenstown Rd, SW8 3RH, ☎ 720 6960 – AE VISA
closed Sunday, Monday, 2 weeks August and 2 weeks Christmas – **M** 16.50/33.00 **t.** 4.50.
Spec. Terrine of foie gras, muscat jelly, Nage of shellfish with cabbage, "Miniatures". DQ **e**

XXX ✿ **L'Arlequin** (Delteil), 123 Queenstown Rd, SW8 3RH, ☎ 622 0555, Fax 498 0715, French rest. – ▤. AE VISA DQ **c**
closed Saturday, Sunday, 3 weeks August and 1 week at Christmas – **M** (booking essential) 19.50 **st.** (lunch) and a la carte approx. 50.00 **st.** 6.00.
Spec. Petits choux farcis à l'ancienne, Pistou aux coquilles St. Jacques, Assiette gourmande.

XX **Le Chausson,** Ransome's Dock, 35-37 Parkgate Rd, SW11 4NP, ☎ 223 1611, French rest. – ▤. AE VISA p. 25 HZ **e**
closed Saturday lunch, Sunday and August – **M** 18.00/29.00 **t.** 4.50.

XX **Chada,** 208-210 Battersea Park Rd, SW11 4ND, ☎ 622 2209, Thai rest. – ▤. AE VISA CQ **x**
closed Saturday lunch, Sunday and Bank Holidays – **M** a la carte 12.75/20.30 **t.**

XX **Lena's,** 196 Lavender Hill, SW11 1JA, ☎ 228 3735, Thai rest. – ▤. AE VISA
M *(closed Sunday lunch)* 15.00 **t.** (lunch) and a la carte approx. 20.75 **t.** 4.95. CQ **z**

XX **Sydney,** 12-14 Battersea High St., SW11 3JB, ☎ 978 5395, Fax 738 1460 – VISA
closed Saturday lunch, Sunday dinner and Bank Holidays – **M** 17.00/23.00 **t.** and a la carte 4.25. CQ **r**

X **Brasserie Faubourg,** 28 Queenstown Rd, SW8 3RX, ☎ 622 6245 – VISA DQ **n**
closed lunch Monday and Saturday, Sunday, 1 week Easter, 2 weeks August, 1 week Christmas and Bank Holidays – **M** 8.95/19.70 **t.** and a la carte 4.25.

Clapham – ✉ SW11 – ☎ 071.

XX **Pollyanna's,** 2 Battersea Rise, SW11 1ED, ☎ 228 0316 – VISA CQ **v**
closed Sunday dinner, 24 to 26 December and 1 January – **M** (dinner only and Sunday lunch)/dinner a la carte 15.95/26.00 **t.** 4.50.

X **Jasmin,** 50 Battersea Rise, SW11 1EG, ☎ 228 0336, Chinese (Peking, Canton) rest. – AE VISA CQ **u**
M *(closed Sunday)* 12.00/35.00 **st.** and a la carte 3.30.

X **La Bouffe,** 13 Battersea Rise, SW11 1HG, ☎ 228 3384 – ▤. VISA CQ **s**
closed 24 to 30 December – **M** (dinner only and Sunday lunch)/dinner 16.95 **t.** 5.00.

Putney – ✉ SW15 – ☎ 081.

XX Bayee House, 100 Upper Richmond Rd, SW15 2SP, ✆ 789 3161, Chinese (Peking, Szechuan) rest. – ▤ AQ z

X **Cassis,** 30 Putney High St., SW15, ✆ 788 8668 – AE VISA AQ x
closed Saturday lunch and Sunday – **M** 16.50 **t.** 4.15.

Tooting – ✉ SW17 – ☎ 081.

X **Oh Boy,** 843 Garratt Lane, SW17 0PG, ✆ 947 9760, Thai rest. – ▤. AE VISA CR c
closed Sunday – **M** (booking essential) (dinner only) 17.65 **t.** and a la carte 3.40.

Wandsworth – ✉ SW12/SW17/SW18 – ☎ 081.

XXX ✿✿ **Harvey's** (White), 2 Bellevue Rd, SW17 7EG, ✆ 672 0114 – ▤. VISA CR e
closed Sunday, Monday, first 2 weeks August, 2 weeks Christmas and Bank Holidays – **M** (booking essential) 22.00/42.00 **t.**
Spec. Vinaigrette de poireaux et homard aux truffes, Loup de mer au caviar, Feuillantine de framboise et sa crème légère.

X **Bombay Bicycle Club,** 95 Nightingale Lane, SW12, ✆ 673 6217, Indian rest. – VISA
closed Sunday, Christmas and Bank Holidays – **M** (dinner only) 15.00 **t.** and a la carte 3.50. DR o

***La Grande Londra** (GREATER LONDON) è composta dalla City e da 32 distretti amministrativi (Borough) divisi a loro volta in quartieri o villaggi che hanno conservato il loro proprio carattere (Area).*

WESTMINSTER (City of).

Bayswater and Maida Vale – ✉ W2/W9 – ☎ 071 – Except where otherwise stated see pp. 32 and 33.

Royal Lancaster (Rank), Lancaster Terr., W2 2TY, ✆ 262 6737, Telex 24822, Fax 724 3191, ← – ▤ rm ▤ TV ☎ P – 1 400. AE VISA. DZ e
M 18.50/21.50 **st.** and a la carte 6.50 – ☕ 11.00 – **398 rm** 140.00/190.00 **st.**, **20 suites** 395.00/1 050.00 **st.**

Whites (Mt. Charlotte Thistle), Bayswater Rd, 90-92 Lancaster Gate, W2 3NR, ✆ 262 2711, Telex 24771, Fax 262 2147 – ▤ TV ☎ P. AE VISA. CZ v
M 19.50/21.50 **t.** and a la carte 6.40 – ☕ 9.50 – **52 rm** 130.00/260.00 **st.**, **2 suites** 315.00 **st.**

London Metropole, Edgware Rd, W2 1JU, ✆ 402 4141, Telex 23711, Fax 724 8866, ← – rm ▤ TV ☎ – 220. p. 21 GU c
567 rm.

Plaza on Hyde Park (Hilton), Lancaster Gate, W2 3NA, ✆ 262 5022, Telex 8954372, Fax 724 8666 – rm TV ☎ – 50. AE VISA DZ r
M 13.75 **t.** (dinner) and a la carte 9.15/23.90 **t.** 4.20 – ☕ 8.75 – **402 rm** 73.00/140.00 **st.** – SB (weekends only) 108.00 **st.**

London Embassy, 150 Bayswater Rd, W2 4RT, ✆ 229 1212, Telex 27727, Fax 229 2623 – rm ▤ TV ☎ P – 70. AE VISA BZ o
M (carving rest.) 12.00 **st.** and a la carte 4.15 – ☕ 8.00 – **192 rm** 95.00/130.00 **st.**, **1 suite** 170.00 **st.** – SB (weekends only) 104.00/124.00 **st.**

Hospitality Inn (Mt. Charlotte Thistle), 104 Bayswater Rd, W2 3HL, ✆ 262 4461, Telex 22667, Fax 706 4560, ← – rm ▤ TV ☎ P – 40. AE VISA CZ o
M 8.50/16.00 **st.** and a la carte – ☕ 7.50 – **175 rm** 75.00/150.00 **st.**

Mornington (Best Western) without rest., 12 Lancaster Gate, W2 3LG, ✆ 262 7361, Telex 24281, Fax 706 1028, – TV ☎. AE VISA DZ s
closed 21 December-2 January – ☕ 3.50 – **68 rm** 71.00/92.00 **st.**

Delmere, 130 Sussex Gdns, W2 1UB, ✆ 706 3344, Telex 8953857, Fax 262 1863 – TV ☎. AE VISA DZ v
M *(closed Sunday)* (dinner only) 10.75 **t.** and a la carte 4.25 – ☕ 5.50 – **40 rm** 68.00/83.00 **st.**

Camelot without rest., 45-47 Norfolk Sq., W2 1RX, ✆ 262 1980 – TV. VISA. DZ c
44 rm ☕ 35.50/70.00 **st.**

Parkwood without rest., 4 Stanhope Pl., W2 2HB, ✆ 402 2241, Fax 402 1574 – TV ☎. VISA. EZ e
18 rm ☕ 42.50/69.75 **st.**

XXX **Bombay Palace,** 50 Connaught St., Hyde Park Sq., W2 2AA, ✆ 723 8855, North Indian rest. – AE VISA EZ o
M 18.00/25.00 **st.** and a la carte.

XX Poons, Whiteleys, Queensway, W21 4YN, ✆ 792 2884, Chinese rest. – ▤ p. 32 BZ x

XX **San Marino,** 26 Sussex Pl., W2 2TH, ✆ 723 8395, Italian rest. – AE VISA DZ u
closed Bank Holidays – **M** a la carte 15.60/19.80 **t.** 4.90.

XX **Hsing,** 451 Edgware Rd, W2 1TH, ✆ 402 0904, Chinese rest. – AE VISA GU **a**
M a la carte 12.50/18.00 **t.**

XX Monsoon, 57 Westbourne Grove, W2 4UA, ✆ 221 9396, Indian rest. – p. 32 BZ **a**

X Taxin Thai, 79 Castellain Rd, W9, ✆ 286 4801, Thai rest. FT **a**

X **Fortune Cookie,** 1 Queensway, W2 4QJ, ✆ 727 7260, Chinese rest. – VISA BZ **e**
M a la carte approx. 19.00 **t.**

Belgravia – ✉ SW1 – ☎ 071 – Except where otherwise stated see pp. 30 and 31.

Berkeley, Wilton Pl., SW1X 7RL, ✆ 235 6000, Telex 919252, Fax 235 4330, – AE VISA FQ **e**
M Restaurant *(closed Saturday)* a la carte 25.50/43.00 **st.** 4.80 – **Buttery** *(closed Sunday)* a la carte 17.25/32.75 **st.** 4.80 – **133 rm** 150.00/270.00 **st.**, **27 suites** 430.00/490.00 **st.**

Belgravia-Sheraton, 20 Chesham Pl., SW1X 8HQ, ✆ 235 6040, Telex 919020, Fax 259 6243 – rm FR **u**
82 rm, **7 suites.**

Lowndes, 21 Lowndes St., SW1X 9ES, ✆ 235 6020, Telex 919065, Fax 235 1154 – rm rest AE VISA FR **i**
M 21.50 **t.** and a la carte 5.20 – **74 rm** 135.00/155.00 **t.**, **5 suites** 200.00/225.00 **t.**

XX **Motcombs,** 26 Motcomb St., SW1X 8JU, ✆ 235 6382 – AE VISA FR **z**
closed Saturday lunch, Sunday and Bank Holidays – **M** a la carte 14.90/26.00 **t.**

Hyde Park and Knightsbridge – ✉ SW1/SW7 – ☎ 071 – pp. 30 and 31.

Harrods, Knightsbridge, SW1 ✆ 730 3488/824 8844.

Hyde Park (T.H.F.), 66 Knightsbridge, SW1Y 7LA, ✆ 235 2000, Telex 262057, Fax 235 4552, – rm – 230. AE VISA EQ **v**
M 26.00/45.00 **st.** and a la carte 8.00 – 14.50 – **167 rm** 199.00/265.00 **st.**, **19 suites** 475.00/1 250.00 **st.**

Mayfair – ✉ W1 – ☎ 071 – pp. 28 and 29.

Claridge's, Brook St., W1A 2JQ, ✆ 629 8860, Telex 21872, Fax 499 2210 – AE VISA BL **c**
M a la carte 28.00/58.00 **st.** and a la carte 4.10 – **Causerie** *(closed Saturday)* 14.50/26.00 **st.** and a la carte 20.50/39.50 **st.** – 13.50 – **133 rm** 185.00/285.00 **st.**, **57 suites** 475.00 **st.**

Inn on the Park, Hamilton Pl., Park Lane, W1A 1AZ, ✆ 499 0888, Telex 22771, Fax 493 1895 – rm – 250. AE VISA BP **a**
M – **Lanes** 29.20 **st.** (lunch) and dinner a la carte 29.50/35.00 **st.** – (see also **Four Seasons** rest. below) – 12.50 – **209 rm** 190.00/235.00 **s.**, **19 suites** 470.00/780.00 **s.**

Le Meridien Londres, Piccadilly, W1V 0BH, ✆ 734 8000, Telex 25795, Fax 437 3574, , squash – – 200. AE VISA EM **a**
M (see also **Oak Room** below) – 10.25 – **244 rm** 175.00/220.00 **s.**, **40 suites** 240.00/550.00 **s.**

Grosvenor House (T.H.F.), Park Lane, W1A 3AA, ✆ 499 6363, Telex 24871, Fax 493 3341, , – rm – 2 000. AE VISA
M 19.50/25.00 **st.** – (see also **90 Park Lane** below) – 12.00 – **381 rm** 205.00/225.00 **st.**, **73 suites** 357.00/700.00 **st.** AM **a**

✿ **Connaught,** 16 Carlos Pl., W1Y 6AL, ✆ 499 7070 – rest . BM **e**
M (booking essential) – **66 rm**, **24 suites.**
Spec. Pâté de turbot froid au homard, sauce pudeur, Rendez-vous du pêcheur, sauce légère au parfum d'Armorique, Salmis de canard strasbourgeoise en surprise.

Fortyseven Park Street, 47 Park St., W1Y 4EB, ✆ 491 7282, Telex 22116, Fax 491 7281 – AE VISA AM **c**
M (see **Le Gavroche** below) – **52 suites** 275.00/400.00 **s.**

Inter-Continental, 1 Hamilton Pl., Hyde Park Corner, W1V 0QY, ✆ 409 3131, Telex 25853, Fax 409 7460, , – rm – 700. AE VISA BP **o**
M (see **Le Soufflé** below) – 12.50 – **438 rm** 165.00/210.00, **29 suites** 270.00/1 300.00.

Park Lane, Piccadilly, W1Y 8BX, ✆ 499 6321, Telex 21533, Fax 499 1965, – rm – 600. AE VISA BP **x**
M 15.00/19.00 **st.** and a la carte 5.00 – 9.95 – **266 rm** 159.95/199.95 **st.**, **54 suites** 230.00/350.00 **st.**

Brown's (T.H.F.), 29-34 Albemarle St., W1A 4SW, ✆ 493 6020, Telex 28686, Fax 493 9381 – rm rest – 65. AE VISA DM **e**
M 25.75/29.95 **st.** and a la carte 7.00 – 11.75 – **127 rm** 155.00/195.00 **st.**, **6 suites** 230.00/390.00 **st.**

Londonderry, Park Lane, W1Y 8AP, ✆ 493 7292, Telex 263292, Fax 495 1395 – rm – 400. AE VISA BP **i**
120 rm 160.00/200.00 **st.**, **10 suites** 235.00/550.00 **st.**

Britannia (Inter-Con.), Grosvenor Sq., W1A 3AN, ✆ 629 9400, Telex 23941, Fax 629 7736 – rm – 80. AE VISA BM **x**
M *(closed Saturday lunch and Sunday)* 25.50 **t.** and a la carte 5.75 – (see also **Shogun** below) – 10.50 – **314 rm** 125.00/210.00 **s.**, **12 suites** 375.00 **s.**

London Hilton on Park Lane, 22 Park Lane, W1A 2HH, ✆ 493 8000, Telex 24873, Fax 493 4957, < London, – rm ☎ – 1 000. AE VISA BP e
M 11.50 **t.** and a la carte 6.50 – **394 rm** 165.00/260.00 **s.**, **54 suites** 300.00/1 500.00 **s.**

May Fair (Inter-Con.), Stratton St., W1A 2AN, ✆ 629 7777, Telex 262526, Fax 629 1459 – rm ☎ – 270. AE VISA. DN z
M (see **Le Chateau** below) – 12.00 – **251 rm** 195.00/240.00 **t.**, **24 suites** 300.00/1 400.00 **t.**

Westbury (T.H.F.), Conduit St., W1A 4UH, ✆ 629 7755, Telex 24378, Fax 495 1163 – rm ☎ – 110. AE VISA. DM a
M 20.00/24.00 **st.** and a la carte 7.50 – 11.50 – **228 rm** 160.00/190.00 **st.**, **15 suites** 250.00/550.00 **st.**

Marriott, Duke St., Grosvenor Sq., W1A 4AW, ✆ 493 1232, Telex 268101, Fax 491 3201 – ☎ – 375. AE VISA. BL a
M *(closed Saturday lunch)* 26.00 **t.** (lunch) and a la carte 12.25/19.25 **t.** 6.25 – 9.50 – **206 rm** 170.00/205.00, **17 suites** 260.00/460.00.

Athenaeum (Rank), 116 Piccadilly, W1V 0BJ, ✆ 499 3464, Telex 261589, Fax 493 1860 – rm ☎ – 50. AE VISA. CP s
M 21.50/28.00 **st.** and a la carte 7.75 – 11.00 – **106 rm** 160.00/188.00 **st.**, **6 suites** 230.00/270.00 **st.**

Washington, Curzon St., W1 8DT, ✆ 499 7000, Telex 24540, Fax 495 6172 – rm ☎ – 80. AE VISA. CN s
M 17.00 **st.** 6.25 – 10.25 – **169 rm** 138.00/168.00 **st.**, **4 suites** 178.00/375.00 **st.** – SB (weekends only) 296.00 **st.**

Chesterfield, 35 Charles St., W1X 8LX, ✆ 491 2622, Telex 269394, Fax 491 4793 – ☎ – 70. AE VISA. CN c
M 18.50/22.00 **t.** and a la carte 5.75 – 8.75 – **109 rm** 105.00/175.00 **t.**, **4 suites** 235.00/300.00 **t.**

Holiday Inn, 3 Berkeley St., W1X 6NE, ✆ 493 8282, Telex 24561, Fax 629 2827 – rm ☎ – 50. AE VISA. DN r
M 17.25/23.00 **t.** and a la carte 5.00 – 10.25 – **178 rm** 149.00/195.00 **st.**, **8 suites** 290.00/450.00 **st.** – SB (weekends only) 158.00/219.00 **st.**

Green Park, Half Moon St., W1Y 8BP, ✆ 629 7522, Telex 28856, Fax 491 8971 – rm rest ☎ – 70. AE VISA. CN a
M 17.00 **t.** and a la carte 5.00 – 9.00 – **160 rm** 102.00/140.00 **st.**

Hilton Mews at Park Lane without rest., 2 Stanhope Row, W1Y 7HE, ✆ 493 7222, Telex 24665, Fax 629 9423 – ☎ – 50. AE VISA BP u
70 rm 130.00/175.00 **st.**, **1 suite** 350.00/450.00 **st.**

Flemings, 7-12 Half Moon St., W1Y 7RA, ✆ 499 2964, Telex 27510, Fax 629 4063 – rest ☎ – 30 – **133 rm.** CN z

XXXXX ✿ **Oak Room** (at Le Meridien Londres H.), Piccadilly, W1V OBH, ✆ 734 8000, Telex 25795, Fax 437 3574, French rest. – . AE VISA EM a
closed Saturday lunch, Sunday and Bank Holidays – **M** 21.00/43.00 **t.** and a la carte 28.00/37.50 **t.** 6.50.
Spec. Gazpacho de langoustines à la crème de courgettes, Bar légèrement fumé à la crème de caviar, Dos de jeune lapin aux champignons et au romarin.

XXXXX **90 Park Lane** (T.H.F.), (at Grosvenor House H.), Park Lane, W1A 3AA, ✆ 499 6363, Telex 24871, Fax 493 3341 – . AE VISA AM a
closed Saturday lunch and Sunday – **M** 25.00/45.00 **st.** and a la carte.

XXXX ✿✿✿ **Le Gavroche** (Roux), 43 Upper Brook St., W1P 1PF, ✆ 408 0881, Fax 409 0939, French rest. – . AE VISA AM c
closed Saturday, Sunday, 22 December-2 January and Bank Holidays – **M** (booking essential) 30.00/60.00 **st.** and a la carte 41.10/77.20 **st.** 10.50.
Spec. Soufflé suissesse, Assiette du boucher, Sablé aux fraises.

XXXX **Le Soufflé** (at Inter-Continental H.), 1 Hamilton Pl., Hyde Park Corner, W1V 0QY, ✆ 409 3131, Telex 25853, Fax 493 3476 – . AE VISA BP o
M 24.00/40.00 **t.** and a la carte 35.50/42.50 **t.** 7.00.

XXXX ✿ **Four Seasons** (at Inn on the Park H.), Hamilton Pl., Park Lane, W1A 1AZ, ✆ 499 0888, Telex 22771, Fax 493 1895, French rest. – . AE VISA BP a
M 25.00/40.00 **st.** and a la carte 33.25/46.50 **st.**
Spec. Coquilles St. Jacques grillées et grecque de légumes, Poulet de Bresse rôti au jus, sa cuisse cuite à la vapeur, Nougat glacé, salade de fruits au gingembre.

XXXX **Le Chateau** (Inter-Con), (at Mayfair H.) Stratton St., W1A 2AN, ✆ 629 7777, Telex 262526, Fax 629 1459, French rest. – . AE VISA DN z
closed Sunday – **M** 21.50/32.50 **t.** and a la carte 9.00.

XXX **Princess Garden,** 8-10 North Audley St., W1Y 1WF, ✆ 493 3223, Fax 938 4694, Chinese (Peking) rest. – . AE VISA AL z
M 25.00 **t.** (lunch) and a la carte 20.00/30.00 **t.** 6.00.

XXX **Empress Garden,** 15-16 Berteley St., W1X 5AE, ✆ 493 1381, Chinese (Peking) rest. – . AE VISA – **M** 25.00/60.00 **t.** and a la carte 5.00. DN i

XXX **Zen Central,** 20 Queen St., W1X 7PJ, ✆ 629 8089, Chinese rest. – . AE VISA CN x
M a la carte approx. 15.50 **t.**

XX **Greenhouse,** 27a Hay's Mews, W1X 7RJ, ✆ 499 3331 BN **a**

XX Copper Chimney, 13 Heddon St., W1R 7LF, ✆ 439 2004, Indian rest. – ▤ EM **e**

XX **Ho-Ho,** 29 Maddox St., W1R 9LD, ✆ 493 1228, Oriental cuisine – ▤. AE VISA DL **x**
closed Sunday and Bank Holidays – **M** 22.00 **t.** (dinner) and a la carte 14.70/22.00 **t.**

XX **Langan's Brasserie,** Stratton St., W1X 5FD, ✆ 491 8822 – AE VISA DN **e**
closed Saturday lunch, Sunday, Easter, Christmas and Bank Holidays – **M** (booking essential) a la carte 16.90/28.95 **t.** 5.00.

XX **Shogun** (at Britannia H.), Adams Row, W1Y 5DE, ✆ 493 1255, Japanese rest. – AE VISA BM **x**
closed Monday – **M** (dinner only) 28.00 **t.** and a la carte.

XX **La Seppia,** 8a Mount St., ✆ 499 3385, Italian Seafood rest. – ▤. AE VISA
closed Saturday, Sunday, last 3 weeks August, 10 days at Christmas and Bank Holidays – **M** 18.50/24.50 **t.** and a la carte 5.00. BM **v**

XX **Miyama,** 38 Clarges St., W1Y 7PJ, ✆ 499 2443, Japanese rest. – ▤. AE VISA
closed Saturday dinner and Sunday – **M** 12.00/32.00 **t.** and a la carte 6.00. CN **e**

X **Ikeda,** 30 Brook St., W1Y 1AG, ✆ 629 2730, Japanese rest. – ▤. AE VISA
closed Saturday lunch and Sunday – **M** 13.00/35.00 **t.** and a la carte. CKL **a**

Regent's Park and Marylebone – ✉ NW1/NW6/NW8/W1 – ☎ 071 – Except where otherwise stated see pp. 28 and 29.

Selfridges, Oxford St., W1 ✆ 730 3488.

Churchill, 30 Portman Sq., W1A 4ZX, ✆ 486 5800, Telex 264831, Fax 486 1255, – rm ▤ – 200. AE VISA AJ **x**
M a la carte 30.00/50.00 **t.** 5.00 – 13.50 – **403 rm** 185.00/200.00, **49 suites** 300.00/995.00.

Portman Inter-Continental, 22 Portman Sq., W1H 9FL, ✆ 486 5844, Telex 261526, Fax 935 0537, – rm ▤ – 370. AE VISA. AJ **o**
M 19.50/28.50 **st.** and a la carte 7.50 – 11.50 – **262 rm** 144.90/166.75 **st.**, **10 suites** 402.50/690.00 **st.**

Selfridge (Mt. Charlotte Thistle), 400 Orchard St., W1H 0JS, ✆ 408 2080, Telex 22361, Fax 629 8849 – rm ▤ – 220. AE VISA. AK **e**
M 17.00 **t.** and a la carte – 9.25 – **294 rm** 124.00/170.00 **st.**, **2 suites.**

Berkshire, 350 Oxford St., W1N 0BY, ✆ 629 7474, Telex 22270, Fax 629 8156 – rm ▤ . AE VISA. BK **n**
M 19.75 **st.** (lunch) and a la carte 5.00 – 11.50 – **144 rm** 142.00/190.00 **st.**, **3 suites** 385.00 **st.**

Clifton Ford, 47 Welbeck St., W1M 8DN, ✆ 486 6600, Telex 22569, Fax 486 7492 – ▤ rest – 80. AE VISA BH **a**
M 13.00 **st.** (lunch) and dinner a la carte 13.00/23.00 **st.** 5.00 – 10.50 – **214 rm** 120.00/175.00, **4 suites** 350.00/750.00.

Holiday Inn, 134 George St., W1H 6DN, ✆ 723 1277, Telex 27983, Fax 402 0666, , – rm ▤ – 120. AE VISA p. 33 EZ **i**
M 14.50/25.00 **st.** and a la carte 6.00 – 10.25 – **239 rm** 136.00/152.00 **st.**, **2 suites** 395.00/495.00 **st.**

Ramada H. London, 10 Berners St., W1A 3BE, ✆ 636 1629, Telex 25759, Fax 580 3972 – ▤ rest – 300. AE VISA. EJ **r**
M 18.75/21.00 **st.** and a la carte 5.50 – 9.75 – **232 rm** 100.00/165.00 **st.**, **3 suites** 300.00 **st.**

London Regents Park Hilton, 18 Lodge Rd, NW8 7JT, ✆ 722 7722, Telex 23101, Fax 483 2408 – ▤ – 150. AE VISA p. 21 GT **v**
M *(closed Saturday lunch)* (carving rest.) 15.95 **t.** and a la carte 5.00 – 9.95 – **374 rm** 124.00/164.00 **st.**, **3 suites** 175.00/185.00 **st.**

Montcalm, Great Cumberland Pl., W1A 2LF, ✆ 402 4288, Telex 28710, Fax 724 9180 – ▤ rm p. 33 EZ **x**
101 rm, 12 suites.

St. George's (T.H.F.), Langham Pl., W1N 8QS, ✆ 580 0111, Telex 27274, Fax 436 7997, – rm ▤ rest – 40. AE VISA p. 21 JU **a**
M 18.50 **st.** and a la carte 6.60 – 10.50 – **83 rm** 110.00/140.00 **st.**, **3 suites** 250.00/275.00 **st.**

Regent Crest (T.H.F.), Carburton St., W1P 8EE, ✆ 388 2300, Telex 22453, Fax 387 2806 – rm ▤ rest – 500. AE VISA. p. 21 JU **i**
M 15.00 **st.** and a la carte 4.00 – 9.95 – **312 rm** 104.00/134.00 **st.**, **5 suites** 220.00/300.00 **st.**

Dorset Square, 39-40 Dorset Sq., NW1 6QN, ✆ 723 7874, Telex 263964, Fax 724 3328, « Attractively furnished Regency town houses » – ▤ . AE VISA.
M 16.50 **t.** and a la carte 4.50 – 9.00 – **37 rm** 80.00/155.00 **st.** p. 21 HU **s**

Durrants, 26-32 George St., W1H 6BJ, ✆ 935 8131, Telex 894919, Fax 487 3510, « Converted Georgian houses with Regency façade » – – 50. AE VISA.
M 24.00/34.00 **st.** and a la carte 4.50 – 8.00 – **93 rm** 55.00/110.00 **st.**, **3 suites** 140.00/180.00 **st.** AH **e**

Mostyn, Bryanston St., W1H 0DE, ☎ 935 2361, Telex 27656, Fax 487 2759 – 180 – **119 rm, 3 suites.** AK i

Londoner, Welbeck St., W1M 8HS, ☎ 935 4442, Telex 894 630, Fax 487 3782 – 90 – **144 rm.** BJ c

Rathbone, Rathbone St., W1P 1AJ, ☎ 636 2001, Telex 28728, Fax 636 3882 – rest. AE VISA. p. 22 KU x
M 12.50/38.00 **st.** and a la carte 5.60 – 8.50 – **72 rm** 105.00/180.00 **st.**

Savoy Court, 13-25 Granville Pl., W1H 0EH, ☎ 408 0130, Telex 8955515, Fax 493 2070 – AK c
97 rm.

Harewood (Best Western), Harewood Row, NW1 6SE, ☎ 262 2707, Telex 297225, Fax 262 2975 – rest – 60. AE VISA. p. 21 HU x
M *(closed lunch Saturday and Sunday)* 12.75/14.25 **st.** and a la carte 7.95 – **93 rm** 85.00/105.00 **st.** – SB (weekends only) 106.50/118.00 **st.**

Bryanston Court (Best Western) without rest., 56-60 Great Cumberland Pl., W1H 7FD, ☎ 262 3141, Group Telex 262076, Fax 262 7248 – AE VISA. 6.00 – **54 rm** 65.00/87.00 **st.** p. 33 EZ z

Blandford without rest., 80 Chiltern St., W1M 1PS, ☎ 486 3103, Telex 262594, Fax 487 2786 – AE VISA. p. 21 HU i
33 rm 60.00/95.00 **st.**

Concorde without rest., 50 Great Cumberland Pl., W1H 7FD, ☎ 402 6169, Group Telex 262076, Fax 262 7248 – AE VISA. p. 33 EZ n
closed 22 December-3 January – 6.00 – **28 rm** 65.00/75.00 **st.**

Edward Lear without rest., 28-30 Seymour St., W1H 5WD, ☎ 402 5401, Fax 706 3766 – VISA. AK a
31 rm 37.50/59.50 **st.**

XXXX ✿✿ **Chez Nico** (Ladenis), 35 Great Portland St., W1N 5DD, ☎ 436 8846, French rest. – VISA DJ c
closed Bank Holiday lunch, Saturday, Sunday, 4 days at Easter, 3 weeks August and 10 days at Christmas – **M** (booking essential) 46.00/61.00 **st.** 10.00.
Spec. Grillade coquille St. Jacques à l'ail confit et aux nouilles, Jarret de veau braisé "Jardinière", Tarte au citron.

XXX **Jason Court,** Jason Court, 76 Wigmore St., W1H 9DQ, ☎ 224 2992, English rest. – AE VISA BJ a
closed Saturday, Sunday, 10 to 27 August, 25 December-2 January and Bank Holidays – **M** 20.00 **t.** (lunch) and a la carte 23.00/31.00 **t.** 4.25.

XXX **Rue St. Jacques,** 5 Charlotte St., W1P 1HD, ☎ 637 0222, French rest. – AE VISA
closed Saturday lunch, Sunday, Easter, Christmas-New Year and Bank Holidays – **M** 23.00/33.00 **t.** p. 22 KU c

XXX **Odins,** 27 Devonshire St., W1N 1RJ, ☎ 935 7296 – AE VISA p. 21 IU n
closed Saturday lunch, Sunday, Easter, Christmas and Bank Holidays – **M** a la carte 24.45/31.50 **t.**

XXX **Martin's,** 239 Baker St., NW1 6XE, ☎ 935 3130 – AE VISA p. 21 HU u
closed Saturday lunch, Sunday, Easter, Christmas and Bank Holidays – **M** 17.50/21.00 **t.** 5.00.

XX Gaylord, 79-81 Mortimer St., W1N 7TB, ☎ 580 3615, Indian and Pakistani rest. – p. 22 KU o

XX **Masako,** 6-8 St. Christopher's Pl., W1M 5HB, ☎ 935 1579, Japanese rest. – AE VISA
closed Sunday – **M** 18.00/32.00 **t.** and a la carte. BJ e

XX **Mon,** (at Cumberland H.), Marble Arch, W1A 4RF, ☎ 262 6528, Japanese rest. – AE VISA AK n
M a la carte approx. 16.50 5.00.

XX **La Loggia,** 68 Edgware Rd, W2 2EG, ☎ 723 0554, Italian rest. – AE VISA
closed Sunday – **M** a la carte 15.20/26.20 **t.** 4.00. p. 33 EZ a

XX **Asuka,** Berkeley Arcade, 209a Baker St., NW1 6AB, ☎ 486 5026, Fax 262 1456, Japanese rest. – AE VISA p. 21 HU u
closed Saturday lunch, Sunday, 1 week Christmas and Bank Holidays – **M** a la carte 23.90/41.00 **st.**

XX **Le P'tit Montmartre,** 15 Marylebone Lane, W1M 5FE, ☎ 935 9226, French rest. – AE VISA BJ a
closed Saturday lunch, Sunday, 4 days Easter, 4 days Christmas and Bank Holidays – **M** a la carte 22.20/27.45 **t.** 4.50.

XX **Tino's,** 128 Allitsen Rd, NW8 7AU, ☎ 586 6264 – AE VISA p. 21 GT u
closed 29 March, 25 December and 1 January – **M** 20.00/32.00 **st.** and a la carte 4.50.

XX **Fontana Amorosa,** 1 Blenheim Terr., NW8 0EH, ☎ 328 5014, Italian rest. – AE VISA
closed Monday lunch, Sunday and mid August-mid September – **M** a la carte 15.00/26.00 **t.** p. 20 FS s

XX **Stephen Bull,** 5-7 Blandford St., W1H 3AA, ☎ 486 9696 – VISA AH a
closed Saturday lunch, Sunday, 23 December-3 January and Bank Holidays – **M** a la carte 17.75/25.00 **t.** 5.00.

X **L'Aventure,** 3 Blenheim Terr., NW8 0EH, ✆ 624 6232, French rest. – AE VISA
closed Saturday lunch, 4 days at Easter, 23 to 30 December and Bank Holidays – **M** 21.00 **t.** 4.25. p. 20 FS **s**

X **Au Bois St. Jean,** 122 St. John's Wood High St., NW8 7SG, ✆ 722 0400, French rest. – AE VISA – *closed Christmas* – **M** 20.25 **t.** and a la carte 3.95. p. 21 GT **e**

X **Langan's Bistro,** 26 Devonshire St., W1N 1RJ, ✆ 935 4531 – AE VISA
closed Saturday lunch, Sunday, Easter, Christmas and Bank Holidays – **M** a la carte 15.40/18.00 **t.** p. 21 IU **e**

X **Il Barbino,** 64 Seymour St., W1H 5AF, ✆ 402 6866, Italian rest. – AE VISA
closed Saturday lunch, Sunday and Bank Holidays – **M** a la carte 15.90/19.20 **t.** 3.50. p. 33 EZ **r**

X **Nakamura,** 31 Marylebone Lane, W1M 5FH, ✆ 935 2931, Japanese rest. – AE VISA BJ **i**
closed Sunday lunch, Saturday and Bank Holidays – **M** 10.50/35.00 **t.** and a la carte.

X **Chaopraya,** 22 St. Christopher's Pl., W1M 5HD, ✆ 486 0777, Thai rest. – AE VISA BJ **o**
closed Saturday lunch, Sunday and Bank Holidays – **M** 20.00 **st.** and a la carte 4.50.

X **Green Leaves,** 77 York St., W1H 1PQ, ✆ 262 8164, Chinese (Peking, Szechuan) rest. – AE VISA p. 21 HU **c**
closed Saturday lunch and Sunday – **M** 19.80 **t.** and a la carte 3.40.

X Taxin Thai Too, 103 Boundary Rd, NW8 0RG, ✆ 372 5497, Thai rest. FS **a**

St. James's – ✉ W1/SW1/WC2 – 071 – pp. 28 and 29.

Ritz, Piccadilly, W1V 9DG, ✆ 493 8181, Telex 267200, Fax 493 2687, « Elegant restaurant in Louis XV style » – TV ☎. AE VISA. DN **a**
M 23.50/39.50 **st.** and a la carte 5.75 – 12.50 – **111 rm** 185.00/255.00 **st.**, **17 suites** 490.00/880.00 **st.**

Dukes, 35 St. James's Pl., SW1A 1NY, ✆ 491 4840, Telex 28283, Fax 493 1264 – rest TV ☎. AE VISA. EP **x**
M *(closed Saturday lunch)* 25.00 **t.** (lunch) and a la carte 31.50/41.00 **t.** 5.50 – 11.00 – **36 rm** 165.00/194.00 **t.**, **26 suites** 310.00/590.00 **t.**

22 Jermyn St., 22 Jermyn St., SW1Y 6HL, ✆ 734 2353, Fax 734 0750 – rm TV ☎. AE VISA FM **e**
M (room service only) – 12.00 – **5 rm** -/150.00 **st.**, **13 suites** 210.00/260.00 **st.**

Stafford, 16-18 St. James's Pl., SW1A 1NJ, ✆ 493 0111, Telex 28602, Fax 493 7121 – rest TV ☎ – 40 – **56 rm, 6 suites.** DN **u**

Cavendish (T.H.F.), 81 Jermyn St., SW1Y 6JF, ✆ 930 2111, Telex 263187, Fax 839 2125 – rm rest TV ☎ P – 90. AE VISA EN **i**
M *(closed Saturday and Sunday)* a la carte 14.00/21.95 **st.** – **254 rm** 135.00/185.00 **st.** – SB (weekends only) 130.00/150.00 **st.**

Hospitality Inn Piccadilly (Mt. Charlotte Thistle), 31-39 Coventry St., W1V 8EL, ✆ 930 4033, Telex 8950058, Fax 925 2586 – TV ☎. AE VISA. FGM **a**
M (dinner only) 18.50 **t.** 4.25 – 8.75 – **92 rm** 102.50/112.50 **t.**

Royal Trafalgar Thistle (Mt. Charlotte Thistle), Whitcomb St., WC2H 7HG, ✆ 930 4477, Telex 298564, Fax 925 2149 – rm TV ☎. AE VISA GM **r**
M 12.50 **st.** and a la carte 5.00 – 8.95 – **108 rm** 87.00/115.00 **st.**

Pastoria, 3-6 St. Martin's St., WC2H 7HL, ✆ 930 8641, Telex 25538, Fax 925 0551 – rm TV ☎ – 50. AE VISA. GM **v**
M *(closed Saturday lunch, Sunday and Bank Holidays)* a la carte 17.80/22.50 **t.** – 7.75 – **58 rm** 95.00/115.00 **t.**

XXX ✲ **Suntory,** 72-73 St. James's St., SW1A 1PH, ✆ 409 0201, Fax 499 7993, Japanese rest. – . AE VISA EP **z**
closed Sunday, 27 December-4 January and Bank Holidays – **M** 54.00 **st.** and a la carte 28.00/54.50 **st.** 5.00.
Spec. Teppan-Yaki, Shabu-Shabu, Sashimi.

XX **Le Caprice,** Arlington House, Arlington St., SW1A 1RT, ✆ 629 2239, Fax 493 9040 – . AE VISA DN **c**
closed 24 December-2 January – **M** a la carte 18.25/23.25 **t.** 5.50.

XX **Green's,** 36 Duke St., St. James's, SW1Y 6DF, ✆ 930 4566, Fax 930 1383, English rest. – . AE VISA EN **n**
closed Sunday dinner, Christmas, New Year and Bank Holidays – **M** a la carte 19.00/24.00 **t.**

Soho – ✉ W1/WC2 – 071 – pp. 28 and 29.

Hampshire, Leicester Sq., WC2H 7LH, ✆ 839 9399, Telex 914848, Fax 930 8122 – TV ☎ – 90. AE VISA GM **s**
M 17.50/35.00 **st.** and a la carte 10.50 – 12.00 – **118 rm** 165.00/195.00 **st.**, **5 suites** 250.00/650.00 **st.**

Hazlitt's without rest., 6 Frith St., W1V 5TZ, ✆ 434 1771, Fax 439 1524 – TV ☎. AE VISA. FK **u**
closed 23 to 26 December – **22 rm** 85.00/95.00 **s.**, **1 suite** 145.00 **s.**

XXX **Lindsay House,** 21 Romilly St., WIV 5TG, ✆ 439 0450, English rest. – ▤. AE VISA GL
closed 25 and 26 December – **M** 14.75 **t.** (lunch) and a la carte 24.25/34.00 **t.** 4.50.

XXX **Red Fort,** 77 Dean St., W1V 5HA, ✆ 437 2525, Indian rest. – ▤. AE VISA FJK
closed 25 and 26 December – **M** a la carte 15.90/25.20 **st.**

XXX **La Bastide,** 50 Greek St., W1V 5LQ, ✆ 734 3300 – AE VISA GK
closed Saturday lunch, Sunday, Christmas-New Year and Bank Holidays – **M** 19.50/21.00 and a la carte 6.50.

XX **Au Jardin des Gourmets,** 5 Greek St., Soho Sq., W1V 5LA, ✆ 437 1816, Fax 437 0043 French rest. – ▤. AE VISA GJ
closed Saturday lunch, Sunday, Easter, Christmas and Bank Holidays – **M** 16.50 **t.** and a la carte 3.50.

XX **L'Escargot,** 48 Greek St., W1V 5LQ, ✆ 437 2679, Fax 437 0790 – AE VISA
closed Saturday lunch, Sunday, Easter, Christmas and Bank Holidays – **M** a la carte 21.20/27.95 **t.** 4.30. GK

XX **Burt's,** 42 Dean St., W1V 5AP, ✆ 734 3339 – AE VISA FK
closed Saturday lunch, Sunday and Bank Holidays – **M** a la carte 18.55/25.85 **t.** 5.00.

XX ✿ **Sutherlands,** 45 Lexington St., W1R 3LG, ✆ 434 3401, Fax 287 2997 – ▤. VISA EK
closed Saturday lunch, Sunday and Bank Holidays – **M** 27.50/29.50 **t.** 4.95.
Spec. Sutherlands shellfish terrine, Breast of duck in a rich Armagnac sauce with duck liver, apples and prunes, Chocolate tear filled with white chocolate and orange truffle.

XX **L'Hippocampe,** 63 Frith St., W1V 5TA, ✆ 734 4545, French Seafood rest. – ▤. AE VISA
closed Saturday lunch, Sunday, 24 December-4 January and Bank Holiday Saturdays – **M** a la carte 21.00/30.00 **t.** FK

XX **Gay Hussar,** 2 Greek St., W1V 6NB, ✆ 437 0973, Hungarian rest. – ▤. AE GJ
closed Sunday and Bank Holidays – **M** 14.00 **t.** (lunch) and a la carte 16.60/24.10 **st.** 5.60

XX **Ming,** 35-36 Greek St., W1V 5LN, ✆ 734 2721, Chinese rest. – AE VISA GK
closed Sunday and 25-26 December – **M** 12.00/20.00 **t.** and a la carte 6.00.

XX **Gopal's,** 12 Bateman St., W1V 5TD, ✆ 434 0840, Indian rest. – AE VISA
closed 25 and 26 December – **M** 8.50/9.50 **t.** and a la carte 3.90. GK

XX Chesa (Swiss Centre), 2 New Coventry St., W1V 3HG, ✆ 734 1291 – ▤ GM

XX Kaya, 22-25 Dean St., W1V 5AL, ✆ 437 6630, Korean rest. – ▤ FJ

XX **Gallery Rendezvous,** 53-55 Beak St., W1R 3LF, ✆ 734 0445, Chinese (Peking) rest. – ▤. AE VISA EL
M 16.50/32.00 **t.** and a la carte 4.45.

X **Sri Siam,** 14 Old Compton St., W1V 5PE, ✆ 434 3544, Thai rest. – AE VISA
closed Sunday lunch, 24 to 26 December and 1 January – **M** 9.50/14.50 **t.** and a la carte 3.85. GK

X **Alastair Little,** 49 Frith St., W1V 5TE, ✆ 734 5183 – ▤ FK
closed Saturday lunch and Sunday – **M** a la carte 25.00/40.00.

X **Frith's,** 14 Frith St., W1V 5TS, ✆ 439 3370 – ⅹ. VISA FGK
closed Saturday lunch, Sunday, Easter, Christmas-New Year and Bank Holidays – **M** a la carte 26.50/34.50 **t.**

X **Fung Shing,** 15 Lisle St., WC2H 7BE, ✆ 437 1539, Chinese (Canton) rest. – AE VISA GL
closed 25 and 26 December – **M** 10.50/11.50 **st.** and a la carte.

X **Saigon,** 45 Frith St., W1V 5TE, ✆ 437 7109, Vietnamese rest. – AE VISA
closed Sunday and Bank Holidays – **M** 13.70/16.70 **t.** and a la carte. FGK

X Van Long, 40 Frith St., W1, ✆ 439 1835, Vietnamese rest. GK

Strand and Covent Garden – ✉ WC2 – ☎ 071 – Except where stated see p. 33.

Savoy, Strand, WC2R 0EU, ✆ 836 4343, Telex 24234, Fax 240 6040 – ⅹ rm ▤ TV ☎ – 450. AE VISA. DEY
M Grill 29.00 **t.** (dinner) and a la carte 5.15 – **River** 26.00/43.25 **st.** and a la carte 5.15 – 16.50 – **152 rm** 170.00/260.00 **st.**, **48 suites** 280.00/600.00 **st.**

Howard, 12 Temple Pl., WC2R 2PR, ✆ 836 3555, Telex 268047, Fax 379 4547 – ▤ TV ☎ – 120. AE VISA. EX
M a la carte 26.25/59.50 **st.** 8.70 – 13.50 – **135 rm** 195.00/220.00 **st.**, **2 suites** 239.00/449.00 **st.**

Waldorf (T.H.F.), Aldwych, WC2B 4DD, ✆ 836 2400, Telex 24574, Fax 836 7244 – ⅹ rm ▤ rest TV ☎ – 300. AE VISA. EX
M 17.00/25.00 **st.** and a la carte 6.75 – 11.00 – **291 rm** 145.00/170.00 **st.**, **19 suites** 250.00/475.00 **st.**

XXXX **Boulestin,** 1a Henrietta St., WC2E 8PS, ✆ 836 7061, Fax 836 1283, French rest. – ▤. AE VISA DX r
closed Saturday lunch, Sunday, 1 week Christmas and Bank Holidays – **M** 22.50 **st.** (lunch) and a la carte 28.75/37.50 **st.** 6.00.

XXX **Ivy,** 1 West St., WC2H 9NE, ✆ 836 4751, Fax 497 3644 – AE VISA GK z
closed 25 and 26 December – **M** a la carte 18.75/28.00 **t.** 5.50.

XXX **Simpson's-in-the-Strand,** 100 Strand, WC2R 0EW, ✆ 836 9112, Fax 836 9112, English rest. – ▤. AE VISA EX o
closed Sunday and Bank Holidays – **M** 17.50 **t.** and a la carte 4.95.

XX **Orso,** 27 Wellington St., WC2E 7DA, ✆ 240 5269, Fax 497 2148, Italian rest. – ▤ EX z
closed 25 and 26 December – **M** (booking essential) a la carte 13.50/22.00 **t.** 4.25.

XX **Sheekey's,** 28-32 St. Martin's Court, WC2N 4AL, ✆ 240 2565, Seafood – ▤ DX v
closed Saturday lunch, Sunday and Bank Holidays – **M** a la carte 20.20/26.80 **t.** 4.50.

XX **Chez Solange,** 35 Cranbourn St., WC2H 7AD, ✆ 836 0542, French rest. – ▤. AE VISA DX i
closed Sunday and Bank Holidays – **M** 14.50 **t.** and a la carte 5.50.

X **Magno's Brasserie,** 65a Long Acre, WC2E 9JH, ✆ 836 6077, French rest. – AE VISA DV e
closed Saturday lunch, Sunday and Christmas-New Year – **M** 16.50 **st.** (dinner) and a la carte 18.85/24.85 **t.** 5.25.

X Azami, 13-15 West St., WC2H 9BL, ✆ 240 0634, Japanese rest.p. 29 GK z

X Flounders, 19 Tavistock St., WC2E 7PA, ✆ 836 3925, Seafood – ▤ EX a

X **Laguna,** 50 St. Martin's Lane, WC2N 4EA, ✆ 836 0960, Italian rest. – ▤. AE VISA DX z
closed Saturday lunch and Sunday – **M** a la carte 9.35/17.40 **t.** 3.75.

X **Happy Wok,** 52 Floral St., WC2E 9DA, ✆ 836 3696, Chinese (Peking) rest. – AE VISA DX x
closed Saturday lunch and Sunday – **M** 15.50/24.50 **t.** and a la carte.

Victoria – ✉ SW1 – 071 – Except where otherwise stated see p. 32.

Victoria Station Forecourt ✆ 730 3488.

St. James Court, Buckingham Gate, SW1E 6AF, ✆ 834 6655, Telex 938075, Fax 630 7587, – rm ▤ rest – 180. AE VISA. CX i
M (see **Auberge de Provence** and **Inn of Happiness** below) – 12.00 – **373 rm** 130.00/170.00, **18 suites** 200.00/500.00.

Royal Horseguards Thistle (Mt. Charlotte Thistle), 2 Whitehall Court, SW1A 2EJ, ✆ 839 3400, Telex 917096, Fax 925 2263 – rm ▤ rest – 60. AE VISA. p. 26 LX a
M 16.00/20.00 **t.** and a la carte 5.00 – 8.95 – **373 rm** 93.00/170.00 **st.**, **3 suites.**

Stakis St. Ermin's, 2 Caxton St., SW1H 0QW, ✆ 222 7888, Telex 917731, Fax 222 6914 – rm ▤ rest – 150. AE VISA CX a
M (carving rest.) 14.50/15.50 **t.** and a la carte – 7.50 – **282 rm** 108.00/163.00 **t.**, **8 suites** 240.00 **t.** – SB 84.00/185.00 **st.**

Goring, 15 Beeston Pl., Grosvenor Gdns, SW1W 0JW, ✆ 834 8211, Telex 919166, Fax 834 4393 – – 50. AE VISA. BX a
M 17.50/23.00 **t.** and a la carte 6.00 – 10.50 – **82 rm** 115.00/165.00 **st.**, **4 suites** 210.00 **st.**

Grosvenor (Mt. Charlotte Thistle), 101 Buckingham Palace Rd, SW1W 0SJ, ✆ 834 9494, Telex 916006, Fax 630 1978 – rm – 150. AE VISA. BX e
M (carving rest.) 14.95 **st.** and a la carte 4.15 – 8.50 – **363 rm** 89.50/110.00 **st.**, **3 suites** 215.00/295.00 **st.**

Royal Westminster Thistle (Mt. Charlotte Thistle), 49 Buckingham Palace Rd, SW1W 0QT, ✆ 834 1821, Telex 916821, Fax 931 7542 – rm ▤ – 150. AE VISA. BX z
M 16.00 **st.** and a la carte 5.00 – 9.25 – **134 rm** 105.00/155.00 **st.**

Rubens, 39-41 Buckingham Palace Rd, SW1W 0PS, ✆ 834 6600, Telex 916577, Fax 828 5401 – rm ▤ rest – 60. AE VISA. BX n
M 13.75/16.50 **st.** and a la carte 6.50 – 8.75 – **189 rm** 90.00/325.00 **t.**

Scandic Crown, 2 Bridge Pl., SW1V 1QA, ✆ 834 8123, Telex 914973, Fax 828 1099, – rm ▤ – 200. AE VISA. BY i
M *(closed Saturday lunch and Sunday)* 15.75 **t.** (lunch) and a la carte approx. 16.45 **t.** 4.75 – 9.00 – **205 rm** 105.00/135.00 **st.**, **5 suites** 215.00 **st.**

Winchester without rest., 17 Belgrave Rd, SW1V 1RB, ✆ 828 2972, Fax 828 5191 – . BY s
closed 23 to 30 December – **18 rm** 62.00 **st.**

Ebury Court, 26 Ebury St., SW1W 0LU, ✆ 730 8147 – . VISA AX i
closed 2 weeks Christmas-New Year – **M** 12.25/16.40 **st.** and a la carte 3.00 – **39 rm** 50.00/130.00 **st.**

Hamilton House, 60-64 Warwick Way, SW1V 1SA, ✆ 821 7113 – . VISA. **40 rm.** BY n

Collin House without rest., 104 Ebury St., SW1W 9QD, ✆ 730 8031 – AY **r**
13 rm 32.00/52.00 **t.**

Harcourt House without rest., 50 Ebury St., SW1W 0LU, ✆ 730 2722 – TV. AE.
closed 22 December-2 January – **9 rm** 40.00/55.00 **st.** AY **n**

XXX Inn of Happiness, (at St James Court H.) Buckingham Gate, SW1E 6AF, ✆ 834 6655, Telex 938075, Fax 630 7587, Chinese rest. – CX **i**

XXX **Auberge de Provence,** (at St. James Court H.) Buckingham Gate, SW1E 6AF, ✆ 834 6655, Telex 938075, Fax 630 7587, French rest. – AE VISA CX **i**
closed Saturday lunch, Sunday, Easter and Bank Holidays – **M** 19.50 **t.** (lunch) and a la carte 28.50/37.75 **t.**

XXX **Santini,** 29 Ebury St., SW1W 0NZ, ✆ 730 4094, Fax 730 0544, Italian rest. – AE VISA ABX **v**
closed Saturday and Sunday lunch and Bank Holidays – **M** 16.50 **t.** (lunch) and a la carte 28.20/40.50 **t.**

XXX **L'Incontro,** 87 Pimlico Rd, SW1W 8PH, ✆ 730 6327, Fax 730 5062, Italian rest. – AE VISA p. 31 FT **u**
closed Sunday lunch and Bank Holidays – **M** 14.50 **t.** (lunch) and a la carte 28.35/39.30 **t.**

XX **Green's,** Marsham Court, Marsham St., SW1P 4JY, ✆ 834 9552, English rest. – AE VISA p. 26 LZ **z**
closed Sunday lunch, Saturday, Christmas-New Year and Bank Holidays – **M** (booking essential) a la carte 19.00/24.00 **t.**

XX **Ken Lo's Memories of China,** 67-69 Ebury St., SW1W 0NZ, ✆ 730 7734, Chinese rest. – AE VISA AY **u**
closed Sunday and Bank Holidays – **M** a la carte 17.00/56.00 **t.** 4.00.

XX **Mijanou,** 143 Ebury St., SW1W 9QN, ✆ 730 4099, Fax 823 6402 – AE VISA
closed Saturday, Sunday, 1 week at Easter, 3 weeks August, 2 weeks at Christmas and Bank Holidays – **M** 16.50/36.00 **t.** 6.00. AY **e**

XX **Very Simply Nico,** 48a Rochester Row, SW1P 1JU, ✆ 630 8061 –. VISA CY **a**
closed lunch Saturday and Bank Holidays, Sunday, 4 days at Easter, 3 weeks August and 10 days at Christmas – **M** 21.00/25.00 **st.**

XX **Kym's,** 70-71 Wilton Rd, SW1V 1DE, ✆ 828 8931, Chinese (Szechuan, Hunan) rest. – AE VISA BY **v**
M a la carte 9.40/15.50 **t.** 3.50.

XX **Hoizin,** 72-73 Wilton Rd, SW1V 1DE, ✆ 630 5108, Chinese (Canton) Seafood rest. – AE VISA BY **v**
M 13.00/25.00 **t.** and a la carte 5.30.

XX **Pomegranates,** 94 Grosvenor Rd, SW1V 3LG, ✆ 828 6560 – AE VISA
closed Saturday lunch, Sunday, Easter, Christmas and New Year – **M** 16.00/28.00 **t.** 5.60. p. 26 KZ **a**

XX **Hunan,** 51 Pimlico Rd, SW1W 8NE, ✆ 730 5712, Chinese (Hunan) rest. – AE VISA
closed Bank Holidays – **M** a la carte 10.90/21.60 **t.** 4.00. p. 25 IZ **a**

XX **Eatons,** 49 Elizabeth St., SW1W 9PP, ✆ 730 0074 – AE VISA AY **a**
closed Saturday, Sunday and Bank Holidays – **M** a la carte 16.95/20.00 **s.** 4.20.

XX **Ciboure,** 21 Eccleston St., SW1W 9LX, ✆ 730 2505, French rest. – AE VISA
closed Saturday, Sunday, 10 August-4 September and Bank Holidays – **M** 15.00/19.50 **t.** and a la carte. AY **z**

XX **L'Amico,** 44 Horseferry Rd, SW1P 2AF, ✆ 222 4680, Italian rest. – AE VISA
closed Saturday, Sunday and 2 weeks August – **M** (booking essential) a la carte 16.30/25.90 **st.** 4.00. p. 26 LY **e**

XX **Gran Paradiso,** 52 Wilton Rd, SW1V 1DE, ✆ 828 5818, Italian rest. – AE VISA
closed Saturday lunch, Sunday and last 2 weeks August – **M** 16.00/20.00 **t.** and a la carte 2.80. BY **a**

X **Tate Gallery Rest.,** Tate Gallery, Millbank, SW1P 4RG, ✆ 834 6754, English rest., « Rex Whistler murals » – VISA p. 26 LZ **c**
closed Sunday, 29 March, 1 May, 24 to 26 December and 1 January – **M** (lunch only) (booking essential) a la carte 14.85/18.90 **t.** 4.75.

X La Poule au Pot, 231 Ebury St., SW1W 8UT, ✆ 730 7763, French rest. p. 25 IZ **n**

X **Mimmo d'Ischia,** 61 Elizabeth St., SW1W 9PP, ✆ 730 5406, Italian rest. – AE VISA
closed Sunday and Bank Holidays – **M** a la carte 20.00/35.50 **t.** 6.50. AY **o**

X **La Fontana,** 101 Pimlico Rd, SW1W 8PH, ✆ 730 6630, Italian rest. – AE VISA
closed Bank Holidays – **M** a la carte 21.00/28.00 **t.** 5.30. p. 31 FT **o**

X **Villa Medici,** 35 Belgrave Rd, SW1 5AX, ✆ 828 3613, Italian rest. – AE VISA
closed Saturday lunch, Sunday and Bank Holidays – **M** a la carte 15.90/19.20 **t.** 3.50. BY **c**

Car repairs in London
Réparation de voitures à Londres
Riparazione di vettura a Londra
KFZ - Reparatur in London

In the event of a breakdown in London, the location of the nearest dealer for your make of car can be obtained by calling the following numbers between 9am and 5pm.

En cas de panne à Londres, vous pouvez obtenir l'adresse du plus proche concessionnaire de votre marque d'automobile en appelant les numéros suivants entre 9 heures et 17 heures.

In caso di guasto a Londra, Vi sara' possibile ottenere l'indirizzo del concessionario della vostra marca di automobile, chiamando i seguenti numeri dalle ore 9.00 alle ore 17.00.

Im Pannenfall können sie die Adresse der nächstgelegenen Reparaturwerkstatt ihrer Automarke zwischen 9 Uhr und 17 Uhr unter folgenden Telefon-Nr. erfahren.

ALFA ROMEO — Alfa Romeo (GB) Ltd
P.O. Box 5
Poulton Close
Dover, Kent CT17 OHP
(0304) 212500

BMW — BMW (GB) Ltd
Ellesfielf Av.
Bracknell
Breks. RG12 4TA
(0344) 426565

CITROEN — Citroen (UK) Ltd
Mill St.
Slough
Berks. SL2 5DE
(0800) 282671

COLT-MITSUBISHI — Colt Car Co. Ltd
Watermore
Cirencester
Glos. GL7 1LS
(0285) 655777 ext 204/5

DATSUN-NISSAN — Nissan (UK) Ltd
Nissan House
Columbia Drive
Durrington
Worthing
West Sussex
(0903) 68561 ext 571

FIAT — Fiat Information Service
Telephone Operator
Services (100)
and ask for
Freephone Fiat

FORD — Ford Motor Co. Ltd
Central Office
Eagle Way
Brentwood
Essex CM13 3BW
(0277) 253000

HONDA — Honda (UK) Ltd
4 Power Rd
Chiswick
London W4 5YT
(081) 747 1400

JAGUAR — H.R. Owen Ltd
Lyttelton Rd
Hampstead
London N2 OEF
(081) 458 7111

LAND ROVER-RANGE ROVER — Land Rover Ltd
Lode Lane
Solihull
West Midlands B92 8NW
(021) 722 2424

MAZDA — Mazda Cars (UK) Ltd
77 Mount Ephraim
Tunbridge Wells
Kent TN4 8BS
(0892) 40123

MERCEDES Benz — Mercedes Benz (UK) Ltd
403 Edgware Rd
Colindale
London NW9 0HX
(081) 205 1212

PORSCHE — Porsche Cars (GB) Ltd
Bath Rd
Calcot
Reading
Berks. RG3 7SE
(0892) 511877

RELIANT — Reliant Motor PLC
Basin Lane
Kettlebrook Tamworth
Staffs. B77 2HH
(0827) 63521

RENAULT — Renault Ltd
Western Av.
Acton
London W3 ORZ
(081) 992 3481

ROVER — Rover Cars Commercial Division
Canley Rd
Canley
Coventry CVS 6QX
(0203) 70111

SAAB — Saab (GB) Ltd
Globe Park
Marlow
Bucks. SL7 1LY
(06284) 6977

SKODA — Skoda (GB) Ltd
150 Goswell Rd
London EC1V 7DS
(071) 253 7441

TALBOT PEUGEOT
Warwick Wright Motors Ltd
Chiswick Roundabout
Chiswick
London W4 5QD
(081) 995 1466

TOYOTA
Toyota (GB) Ltd
The Quadrangle
Station Rd
Redhill
Surrey RH1 1PS
(0737) 768585

VAUXHALL-OPEL
Dutton Forshaw
(West End)
466-480 Edgware Rd
London W2 1EL
(071) 723 0022

VOLKSWAGEN-AUDI
V.A.G. (UK) Ltd
Yeomans Drive
Blakelands
Milton Keynes
Bucks. MK14 5AN
(0908) 679121

VOLVO
Volvo Concessionaires Ltd
Raeburn Rd South
Ipswich
Suffolk IP3 OES
(0473) 270270 ext 3459

Tyre dealers
Spécialistes du pneu
Specialista in pneumatici
Reifenspezialisten

The address of the nearest ATS tyre dealer can be obtained by contacting the address below between 9am and 5pm.

Des renseignements sur le plus proche point de vente de pneus ATS pourront être obtenus en s'informant entre 9 h et 17 h à l'adresse indiquée ci-dessous.

Potrete avere informazioni sul più vicino punto vendita di pneumatici ATS presso l'indirizzo indicato qui di seguito, tra le ore 9 e le 17.

Die Anschrift der nächstegelegenen ATS-Verkaufsstelle erhalten Sie auf Anfrage (9-17 Uhr) bei nachstehender Adresse.

ATS HOUSE
180-188 Northolt Rd.
Harrow, Middlesex HA2 0ED
(081) 423 2000

LONGBRIDGE Warw. – see Warwick.

LONG EATON Derbs. 402 403 404 Q 25 – see Nottingham (Notts.).

LONGFORD West Midlands 403 404 P 26 – see Coventry.

LONGFRAMLINGTON Northumb. 401 402 O 18 – pop. 890 – ECD : Wednesday – ✉ Morpeth – ☎ 066 570.

◆London 304 – ◆Edinburgh 99 – ◆Newcastle-upon-Tyne 25.

- Embleton Hall, NE65 8DT, on A 697 ℘ 249, « Country house atmosphere », – TV ☎ P
10 rm.

LONG MARSTON Warw. – see Stratford-upon-Avon.

LONG MELFORD Suffolk 404 W 27 – pop. 2 739 – ECD : Thursday – ☎ 0787 Sudbury.

See : Holy Trinity Church★ (15C) – Melford Hall★.

◆ London 62 – ◆Cambridge 34 – Colchester 18 – ◆Ipswich 24.

- **Bull** (T.H.F.), Hall St., CO10 9JG, ℘ 78494, Fax 880307, « Part 15C coaching inn » – TV ☎ P – 60. AE VISA
M 11.25/18.00 **st.** and a la carte – 7.25 – **25 rm** 70.00/100.00 **st.**
- **Black Lion,** The Green, CO10 9DN, ℘ 312356, Fax 74557, – TV ☎ P. VISA
accommodation closed Christmas and New Year – **M** *(closed Monday lunch and Sunday dinner in winter)* 16.50/27.50 **t.** and a la carte 5.00 – **9 rm** 45.00/70.00 **t.**, **1 suite** 60.00/80.00 **t.** – SB (weekends only) 90.00/110.00 **st.**
- Crown Inn, Hall St., CO10 9JL, ℘ 77666 – TV ☎ P
11 rm.
- XXX **Chimneys,** Hall St., CO10 9JR, ℘ 79806, « Part 16C cottage », – VISA
closed Sunday dinner – **M** 12.50 **t.** (lunch) and a la carte 23.75/28.05 **t.** 4.25.

Prices	For full details of the prices quoted in the guide, consult the introduction.

LONGNOR Staffs. 402 403 404 O 24 – pop. 381 – ✉ Buxton – ☎ 029 883.

◆London 161 – Derby 29 – ◆Manchester 31 – ◆Stoke-on-Trent 22.

- Ye Old Cheshire Cheese, High St., SK17 0NS, ℘ 218 – TV P
3 rm.

LOOE Cornwall 403 G 32 **The West Country G.** – pop. 4 279 – ECD : Thursday – ☎ 050 36.

See : Site★ – Monkey Sanctuary★ *AC.*

18 Looe, Bin Down ℘ 050 34 (Widegates) 239, E : 3 m.

The Guildhall, Fore St. ℘ 2072/2409 (summer only).

◆London 264 – ◆Plymouth 21 – Truro 39.

- **Klymiarven**, Barbican Hill, East Looe, PL13 1BH, E : 2 m. by A 387 off B 3253 or access from town by foot ℘ 2333, ← Looe and harbour, heated, – TV P. VISA
closed January – **M** (bar lunch)/dinner 12.00 **st.** and a la carte 3.00 – **14 rm** 30.00/68.00 **st.** – SB (except August) 52.00/83.00 **st.**
- **Harescombe Lodge**, Watergate, PL13 2NE, NW : 2 m. by A 387 and turn right opposite Waylands farm onto single track rd ℘ 3158, P.
M 8.50 **s.** – **3 rm** 17.50/35.00 **s.**

at Sandplace N : 2¼ m. on A 387 – ✉ ☎ 050 36 Looe :

- Polraen Country House, PL13 1PJ, ℘ 3956, – TV P
5 rm.

at Widegates NE : 3½ m. on B 3253 – ✉ Looe – ☎ 050 34 Widegates :

- **Coombe Farm**, PL13 1QN, on B 3253 ℘ 223, ← countryside, heated, , park – P.
March-October – **M** 10.00 **st.** 2.25 – **8 rm** 18.50/37.00 **st.** – SB 47.00/54.00 **st.**

at Talland Bay SW : 4 m. by A 387 – ✉ Looe – ☎ 0503 Polperro :

- **Talland Bay**, PL13 2JB, ℘ 72667, Fax 72940, ←, « Country house atmosphere », heated, – TV ☎ P. AE VISA
closed 2 January-8 February – **M** (bar lunch in winter) (buffet lunch in summer)/dinner 17.00 **t.** and a la carte 3.70 – **22 rm** 38.00/145.00 **t.**, **1 suite** – SB (except May-23 October) 76.00/82.00 **st.**
- **Allhays Country House**, PL13 2JB, ℘ 72434, Fax 72929, ←, – TV ☎ P. VISA
closed 24 December-4 January – **M** *(closed Sunday to non-residents)* (bar lunch, residents only)/dinner 11.00 **st.** and a la carte 3.80 – **7 rm** 19.00/66.00 **st.**

LOSTWITHIEL Cornwall 403 G 32 The West Country G. – pop. 1 972 – ECD : Wednesday – 0208 Bodmin.

Envir. : Restormel Castle★ *AC* (✻★), N : 1½ m.

Community Centre, Liddicoat Rd ✆ 872207.

◆London 273 – ◆Plymouth 30 – Truro 23.

- **Restormel Lodge,** 17 Castle Hill, PL22 0DD, on A 390 ✆ 872223, Fax 873568, heated – TV ☎ P. VISA
  M (bar lunch)/dinner 16.00 **t.** and a la carte 3.50 – **34 rm** 38.00/54.00 **t.** – SB 70.00/80.00 **st.**

LOUGHBOROUGH Leics. 402 403 404 Q 25 – pop. 44 895 – ECD : Wednesday – 0509.

18 Longcliffe, Nanpantan ✆ 216321, SW : 3 m. by B 5350 – 9 Lingdale, Joe Moores Lane, Woodhouse Eaves ✆ 890035 – 9 Charnwood Forest, Breakback Rd ✆ 890259.

John Storer House, Wards End ✆ 230131.

◆London 117 – ◆Birmingham 41 – ◆Leicester 11 – ◆Nottingham 15.

- King's Head, High St., LE11 2QL, ✆ 233222, Fax 262911 – TV ☎ P – 100 **78 rm.**
- **Cedars,** Cedar Rd, LE11 2AB, SE : 1 m. by Leicester Rd ✆ 214459, Fax 233573, heated, – TV ☎ P. VISA
  closed 26 to 29 December – **M** *closed Saturday lunch, Sunday dinner and Bank Holidays)* a la carte 10.90/15.70 **st.** 3.50 – **37 rm** 45.00/55.00 **st.** – SB (weekends only) 50.00 **st.**
- **Garendon Park,** 92 Leicester Rd., LE11 2AQ, on A 6 ✆ 236557 – TV. VISA
  M 8.50 **st.** – **9rm** 15.00/35.00 **st.**
- XXX **Roger Burdell,** The Manor House, 11-12 Sparrow Hill, LE11 1BT, ✆ 231813 – VISA
  closed Monday lunch and Sunday – **M** 17.50/21.50 **t.** 5.00.
- X **Waffles,** 11 Sparrow Hill, LE11 1BT, ✆ 210583, Bristro – . VISA
  closed Monday lunch and Sunday – a la carte 11.35/13.45 **t.**

at Quorn SE : 3 m. on A 6 – ✉ 0509 Loughborough :

- **Quorn Country,** 66 Leicester Rd, LE12 8BB, ✆ 415050, Telex 347166, Fax 415557 – rm TV ☎ P – 50. VISA
  M *(closed Saturday lunch)* 12.95/17.95 **t.** and a la carte – 7.50 – **16 rm** 48.00/82.00 **t.**, **3 suites** 90.00/110.00 **t.** – SB (weekends only) 95.00/115.00 **st.**
- XXX **Quorn Grange** with rm, 88 Wood Lane, LE12 8DB, ✆ 412167, Fax 415621, – TV ☎ P – 120. VISA
  M *(closed Sunday and Bank Holidays to non-residents)* (lunch by arrangement)/dinner 30.00 **st.** and a la carte 3.00 – **17 rm** 45.00/70.00 **st.** – SB (except Christmas) (weekends only) 90.00/146.00 **st.**

CITROEN Nottingham Rd ✆ 267657
FIAT Station Rd ✆ 672523
MAZDA Clarence St. ✆ 266901
PEUGEOT Nottingham Rd ✆ 212949
ROVER Woodgate ✆ 611211
SEAT Southfield Rd ✆ 212330
TOYOTA Pinfold Gate ✆ 215731
VAUXHALL-OPEL Woodgate ✆ 213030
VOLVO Derby Rd ✆ 611777
VW-AUDI 28 Market St. ✆ 217080
ATS Bridge St. ✆ 218447/218472

LOUTH Lincs. 402 404 U 23 – pop. 13 019 – ECD : Thursday – 0507.

See : St. James' Church★ (15C).

18 Crowtree Lane ✆ 602554.

◆London 155 – Boston 33 – Great Grimsby 17 – Lincoln 26.

- **Abbey Farm** , North Ormsby, LN11 0TJ, NW : 6½ m. by A 16 ✆ 0472 (Great Grimsby) 840272, , , park – P.
  closed November, Christmas and New Year – **M** (by arrangement) 9.00 **s.** – **4 rm** 14.00/25.00 **s.**

FORD Northolme Rd ✆ 600911
PEUGEOT-TALBOT Newbridge Hill ✆ 600422
ROVER 155 Newmarket ✆ 605661
VOLVO Grimsby Rd ✆ 603451
VW-AUDI Tattershall Way ✆ 600929
ATS 179 Newmarket ✆ 601975

LOWER BEEDING West Sussex 404 T 30 – see Horsham.

LOWER BRAILES Warw. 403 404 P 27 – see Shipston-on-Stour.

LOWER SLAUGHTER Glos. 403 404 O 28 – see Bourton-on-the-Water.

LOWER SWELL Glos. 403 404 O 28 – see Stow-on-the-Wold.

Bitte beachten Sie die Geschwindigkeitsbeschränkungen in Großbritannien
- 60 mph (= 96 km/h) außerhalb geschlossener Ortschaften
- 70 mph (= 112 km/h) auf Straßen mit getrennten Fahrbahnen und Autobahnen.

LOWESTOFT Suffolk 404 Z 26 – pop. 59 430 – ECD : Thursday – ☎ 0502.

Carlton Colville ☎ 560380.

The Esplanade ☎ 565989/514274.

London 116 – Ipswich 43 – Norwich 30.

Rockville, 6 Pakefield Rd, NR33 0HS, ☎ 581011 – rest. **M** 9.50 **st.** 3.00 – **8 rm** 18.00/38.50 **st.**

Shanghai Coolie, 215 London Rd South, NR33 0DS, ☎ 514573, Chinese (Peking, Szechuan) rest. – AE VISA
closed Sunday lunch and 25-26 December – **M** 15.00 **st.** and a la carte 12.60/19.50 **st.** 3.30.

at Oulton NW : 2 m. by B 1074 – ✉ ☎ 0502 Lowestoft :

Parkhill, Parkhill, NR32 5DQ, N : ½ m. on A 1117 ☎ 730322, Telex 975391, Fax 731695, – 80. AE VISA
closed Christmas and New Year – **M** *(closed Saturday lunch and Sunday)* 15.00/25.00 **t.** and a la carte 3.75 – **14 rm** 45.00/55.00 **st.** – SB (weekends only) 42.00/80.00 **st.**

FORD Whapload Rd ☎ 565353
ROVER 97-101 London Rd South ☎ 561711
VW-AUDI Cooke Rd, South Lowestoft Industrial Estate ☎ 572583
ATS 263 Whapload Rd ☎ 561581

LOWESWATER Cumbria 402 K 20 – pop. 231 – ECD : Thursday – ✉ Cockermouth – ☎ 090 085 Lorton.

London 305 – Carlisle 33 – Keswick 12.

Scale Hill, CA13 9UX, ☎ 232, ≤, –
closed December-February except Christmas – **M** (bar lunch residents only)/dinner 16.00 **st.** 4.00 – **14 rm** 36.00/84.00 **st.**

LOWICK GREEN Cumbria 402 K 21 – see Ulverston.

LOW LAITHE North Yorks. – see Pateley Bridge.

Per spostarvi più rapidamente utilizzate le **carte Michelin "Grandi Strade" :**
n° 970 Europa, n° 980 Grecia, n° 984 Germania, n° 985 Scandinavia-Finlanda,
n° 986 Gran Bretagna-Irlanda, n° 987 Germania-Austria-Benelux, n° 988 Italia,
n° 989 Francia, n° 990 Spagna-Portogallo, n° 991 Jugoslavia.

LUDLOW Shropshire 403 L 26 – pop. 7 496 – ECD : Thursday – ☎ 0584.

See : Site★ – Castle★ (ruins 11C-16C) *AC* – Feathers Hotel★ (early 17C) – Broad Street★ (17C) – St. Lawrences Parish Church★ (13C).

Envir. : Stokesay Castle★ (13C) *AC*, NW : 6½ m.

Bromfield ☎ 058 477 (Bromfield) 285, N : 2 m. on A 49.

Castle St. ☎ 875053.

London 162 – Birmingham 39 – Hereford 24 – Shrewsbury 29.

Feathers, Bull Ring, SY8 1AA, ☎ 875261, Telex 35637, Fax 876030, « Part Elizabethan house » – rest – 90. AE VISA.
M 13.50 **st.** (lunch) and a la carte 4.00 – **40 rm** 60.00/102.00 **st.** – SB 98.00/114.00 **st.**

Dinham Hall, ☎ 876464, Fax 876019, –
14 rm.

Overton Grange, Overton Rd, SY8 4AD, S : 1¾ m. on old A 49 ☎ 873500, Fax 873524, – 100. AE VISA.
M 12.95/19.50 **t.** and a la carte 4.25 – **16 rm** 31.00/80.00 **t.** – SB (except Christmas) 65.00/90.00 **st.**

Angel, 8 Broad St., SY8 1NG, ☎ 872581 – AE VISA
M (bar lunch)/dinner 12.00 **st.** and a la carte 3.25 – **17 rm** 40.00/60.00 **st.**

Cecil, Sheet Rd, SY8 1LR, ☎ 872442, – rm. AE VISA
M (by arrangement) 8.50 **st.** 3.00 – **10 rm** 15.50/36.00 **st.** – SB (November-April) (except Bank Holidays) 18.00/20.50 **st.**

FORD Temeside Ind Est. ☎ 875553
NISSAN Sheet Rd Ind. Est. ☎ 876911
ROVER Corve St. ☎ 872301
VOLVO, SUBARU, ISUZU Bromfield Rd ☎ 874666
ATS Weeping Cross Lane ☎ 872401

LUDWELL Wilts. – see Shaftesbury (Dorset).

LUNDY (Isle of) Devon 403 FG 30 **The West Country G.** – pop. 52 – ☎ 062 882 Littlewick Green.

See : Site★★.

Helicopter service to Ilfracombe (Hartland Point) ☎ 3431.

to Bideford (Lundy Co.) 1-2 weekly (2 h) (summer only) – to Ilfracombe (Lundy Co.) 2-3 weekly (summer only).

LUPTON Cumbria 402 L 21 – see Kirkby Lonsdale.

LUTON Beds. 404 S 28 – pop. 163 209 – ECD : Wednesday – ☎ 0582.

See : Luton Hoo★ (Wernher Collection★★) and park★ *AC* X.

18 Stockwood Park, London Rd ℘ 413704, S : 1 m. on A 6 X.
9 Griffin, 3 Hillcrest Av. ℘ 415573, W : 3 m. X.
9 South Beds, Narden Hill ℘ 575201, N : 3 m. V.

✈ Luton International Airport : X – ℘ 405100, Telex 826409, E : 1 ½ m. – **Terminal :** Luton Bu Station.

ℹ Grosvenor House, 45-47a Alma St. ℘ 401579.

◆London 35 – ◆Cambridge 36 – ◆Ipswich 93 – ◆Oxford 45 – Southend-on-Sea 63.

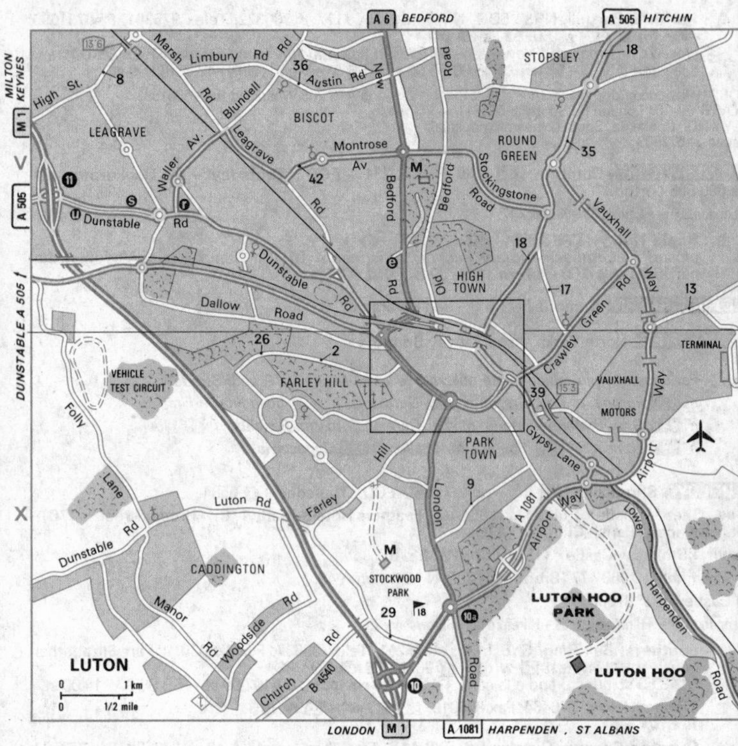

Ashburnham Road	X 2	Hart Lane	V 17	Stopsley Way	V 3
Compton Avenue	V 8	Hitchin Road	V 18	Trinity Road	V 3
Cutenhoe Road	X 9	Long Croft Road	X 26	Windmill Road	X 3
Eaton Green Road	V 13	Newlands Road	X 29	Woodland Avenue	V 4

Strathmore Thistle (Mt. Charlotte Thistle), Arndale Centre, LU1 2TR, ℘ 34199, Tele 825763, Fax 402528 – rest – 200. AE VISA. Y
M 13.00/16.00 **st.** and a la carte – 7.75 – **147 rm** 70.00/94.00 **st.**, **3 suites** – SB 84.00 st

Chiltern Crest (T.H.F.), Waller Av., Dunstable Rd, LU4 9RU, NW : 2 m. on A 50 ℘ 575911, Telex 825048, Fax 581859 – rm rest – 250. AE VISA V
M *(closed lunch Saturday and Bank Holidays)* 16.50/18.50 **st.** and a la carte 4.15 – 7.9 – **93 rm** 81.00/106.00 **st.** – SB (weekends only) 84.00/94.00 **st.**

Crest (T.H.F.), 641 Dunstable Rd, LU4 8RQ, NW : 2 ¾ m. on A 505 ℘ 575955, Tele 826283, Fax 490065 – rm – 80. AE VISA V
M *(closed lunch Saturday and Bank Holidays and 25 December)* 12.95/18.95 **t.** and la carte 5.00 – 7.95 – **117 rm** 73.00/85.00 **t.**

Red Lion (Lansbury), Castle St., LU1 3AA, ℘ 413881, Telex 826856, Fax 23864 – rr – 40. AE VISA. Z
M *(closed Saturday lunch)* 8.25/14.50 **t.** and a la carte 4.50 – **38 rm** 72.00/84.00 **t.**

LUTON

eorge St. .... Z
rndale Centre .... YZ
ute Street .... Y 3
Chapel Viaduct .... Z 5
Church Street .... Y 6
Dunstable Road .... Y 12
Hastings Street .... Z 16
King Street .... Z 19
Latimer Road .... Z 23
Liverpool Road .... Y 24
Mill Street .... Y 27
Park St West .... Z 30
Park Viaduct .... Z 32
Silver Street .... Y 33
Upper George Street .... Z 37
Windmill Road .... Z 39
Winsdon Road .... Z 40

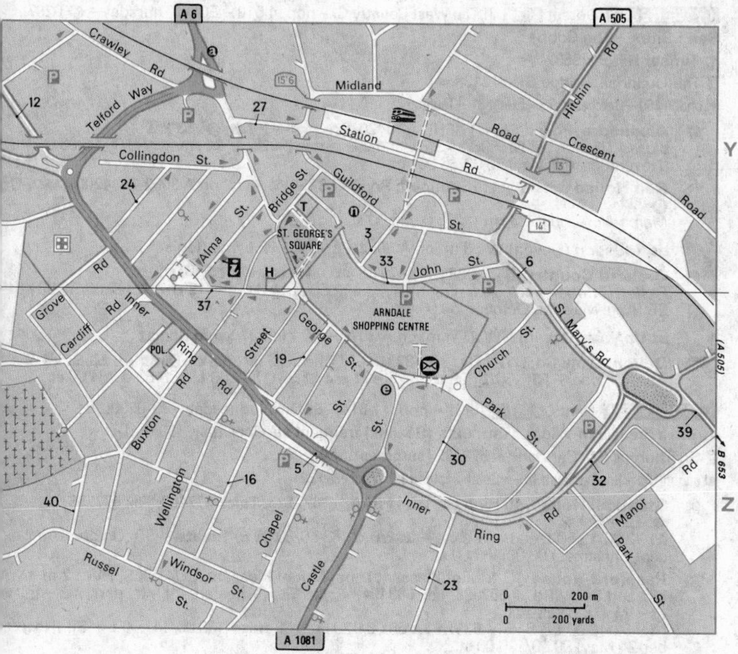

Leaside, 72 New Bedford Rd, LU3 1BT, ☎ 417643, Fax 598646 – TV ☎ P. AE VISA. Y **a**
closed 25-26 December and 1 January – **M** *(closed Saturday lunch and Sunday dinner)* 17.00 **t.** and a la carte 2.85 – **13 rm** 40.00/60.00 **t.**

Ambassador, 31 Lansdowne rd., off New Bedford rd, LU3 1EE, ☎ 451656, – TV ☎ P. VISA V **e**
closed Christmas and New Year – **M** (dinner only) 12.95 **s.** 2.95 – **14 rm** 49.00/63.00 **s.**

Humberstone, 616-618 Dunstable Rd, LU4 8RT, NW : 2 ½ m. on A 505 ☎ 574399, Fax 491424 – TV ☎ P. AE VISA. V **s**
M (by arrangement) 11.55 **t.** 2.50 – **21 rm** 32.00/48.00.

MW 76-88 Marsh Rd ☎ 576622
ORD 326-340 Dunstable Rd ☎ 31133
AND-ROVER, JAGUAR Latimer Rd ☎ 411311
IAZDA High St. Markgate ☎ 840474
ISSAN Leagrave Rd ☎ 571221
ENAULT 619 Hitchin Rd ☎ 35332
AUXHALL-OPEL 15 Hitchin Rd ☎ 454666
AUXHALL-OPEL 540-550 Dunstable Rd ☎ 575944
VAUXHALL Memorial Rd ☎ 572577
VW-AUDI Castle St. ☎ 417505

ATS 67 Kingsway ☎ 597519
ATS High St., Oakley Rd, Leagrave ☎ 507020/592381

UTTERWORTH Leics. 403 404 Q 26 – pop. 6 673 – ECD : Wednesday – ☎ 0455 (6 fig.) or 45 55 (5 fig.).

Rugby Rd ☎ 2532, on A 426 – 18 Ullesthorpe Court, Frolesworth Rd ☎ 209023.

London 93 – Birmingham 34 – Coventry 14 – Leicester 16.

Denbigh Arms, 24 High St., LE17 4AD, ☎ 553537, Telex 342545, Fax 556627 – TV ☎ P – 60. AE VISA.
M *(closed Saturday lunch and Sunday dinner)* a la carte 18.50/23.70 **st.** – **34 rm** 70.00/85.00 **st.**

AAB Ashby Parva ☎ 209191

YDDINGTON Leics. – see Uppingham.

LYDFORD Devon 403 H 32 The West Country G. – pop. 1 762 – ✉ Okehampton – ☎ 082 282.
◆London 234 – Exeter 33 – ◆Plymouth 24.

Castle Inn, EX20 4BH, ✆ 242, « 16C inn », – TV P. VISA
closed 25 December – **M** (bar lunch)/dinner 11.50 **t.** and a la carte 4.25 – **10 rm** 25.00/45.00 **t.** – SB (November-March) 49.50/69.50 **st.**

LYME REGIS Dorset 403 L 31 The West Country G. – pop. 4 510 – ECD : Thursday – ☎ 0297.
See : Site★ – The Cobb★.
Timber Hill ✆ 2963.
The Guildhall, Bridge St. ✆ 2138.
◆London 160 – Dorchester 25 – Exeter 31 – Taunton 27.

Alexandra, Pound St., DT7 3HZ, ✆ 442010, ←, – TV ☎ P. VISA
closed January – **M** 7.95/14.95 **t.** and a la carte 4.25 – **24 rm** 39.00/86.00 **t.** – SB (November-mid May) 76.00/86.00 **st.**

Red House without rest., Sidmouth Rd, DT7 3ES, W : ¾ m. on A 3052 ✆ 442055, – TV P.
March-November – **3 rm** 35.00/40.00 **s.**

at Rousdon (Devon) W : 3 m. on A 3052 – ✉ ☎ 0297 Lyme Regis :

Orchard Country, DT7 3XW, ✆ 442972, – rest P. VISA
Easter-October – **M** (bar lunch)/dinner 12.50 **st.** 3.00 – **12 rm** 27.00/59.00 **st.** – SB (April,May and October) 58.00 **st.**

at Uplyme (Devon) NW : 1 ¼ m. on A 3070 – ✉ ☎ 0297 Lyme Regis :

Devon, Lyme Rd, DT7 3TQ, ✆ 443231, ←, heated, , park – TV ☎ P. AE VISA
April-October – **M** 6.50/11.95 **t.** 4.25 – **21 rm** 33.00/70.00 **t.** – SB 80.00/84.00 **st.**

LYMINGTON Hants. 403 404 P 31 – pop. 11 614 – ECD : Wednesday – ☎ 0590.
to the Isle of Wight : Yarmouth (Sealink) frequent services daily (30 mn).
St. Thomas St., Car Park ✆ 672422 (summer only).
◆London 104 – Bournemouth 18 – ◆Southampton 19 – Winchester 32.

Stanwell House, 15 High St., SO41 9AA, ✆ 677123, Telex 477463, Fax 677756, – TV ☎. VISA.
M 12.00/19.50 **t.** and a la carte – **34 rm** 62.50/80.00 **t.**, **1 suite** – SB (October-April except Christmas) 98.00/183.00 **st.**

Passford House , Mount Pleasant Lane, Mount Pleasant, SO41 8LS, NW : 2 m. by A 337 and Sway Rd ✆ 682398, Fax 683494, ←, , , heated, , , park, – TV ☎ P – 60. AE VISA
M 9.90/18.50 **t.** 5.75 – **53 rm** 65.00/120.00 **t.**, **1 suite** 130.00/147.00 **t.** – SB (November-24 May) 99.00/130.00 **st.**

Albany House, Highfield, SO41 9GB, ✆ 671900, – TV P.
M 10.50 **st.** 3.00 – **5 rm** 18.50/48.00 **st.** – SB (November-April) (except Bank Holidays) 48.00/60.00 **st.**

Limpets, 9 Gosport St., SO41 9BG, ✆ 675595 – VISA
closed Sunday, Monday and December – **M** (dinner only) a la carte 13.50/19.75 **t.** 3.60.

SEAT Sway ✆ 059 068 (Sway) 2212 — ATS Marsh Lane ✆ 675938/9

LYMM Cheshire 402 403 404 M 23 – pop. 10 036 – ECD : Wednesday – ☎ 092 575.
Whitbarrow Rd ✆ 2177.
◆London 193 – Chester 24 – ◆Liverpool 23 – ◆Manchester 15.

Lymm (De Vere), Whitbarrow Rd, WA13 9AQ, ✆ 2233, Telex 629455, Fax 6035, – TV ☎ P – 120 – **69 rm.**

LYMPSTONE Devon 403 J 32 – see Exmouth.

YNDHURST Hants. 403 404 P 31 – pop. 2 828 – ECD : Wednesday – 0703.

ee : New Forest★ (Rhinefield Ornamental Drive★★★ – Bolderwood Ornamental Drive★★★ – berwater Walk★★).

New Forest, Southampton Rd ℘ 282450 – 18, 18 Bramshaw, Brook ℘ 0703 (Southampton) 13433.

Main Car Park ℘ 282269 (summer only).

London 95 – Bournemouth 20 – ◆Southampton 10 – Winchester 23.

Parkhill, Beaulieu Rd, SO43 7FZ, SE : 1 ¼ m. by B 3056 ℘ 282944, Fax 283268, <, heated, park – TV ☎ P – 45. AE VISA
M 12.50/20.00 **t.** and a la carte – **20 rm** 67.00/100.00 **t.** – SB (weekends only) 95.00/110.00 **st.**

Crown (Best Western), 9 High St., SO43 7NF, ℘ 282922, Fax 282751 – TV ☎ P – 70. AE VISA
M *(closed Saturday lunch)* 15.00 **st.** and a la carte 4.50 – **39 rm** 54.00/95.00 **st.**, **1 suite** 112.00 **st.** – SB 86.00/112.00 **st.**

Beaulieu, Beaulieu Rd, SO4 7YQ, SE : 3 ½ m. on B 3056 ℘ 293344, – TV ☎ P
12 rm, **1 suite.**

Whitemoor House without rest., Southampton Rd, SO43 7BU, ℘ 282186 – TV P. VISA
5 rm 25.00/40.00 **st.**

AUXHALL-OPEL Romsey Rd ℘ 2609

YNMOUTH Devon 403 I 30 – see Lynton.

La guida cambia, cambiate la guida ogni anno.

YNTON Devon 403 I 30 **The West Country G.** – pop. 2 075 (inc. Lynmouth) – ECD : Thursday – 0598.

ee : Site★ (<★★).

nvir. : Valley of the Rocks★, W : 1 m. – Watersmeet★, E : 1 ½ m.

Town Hall, Lee Rd ℘ 52225.

London 206 – Exeter 59 – Taunton 44.

Lynton Cottage, North Walk, EX35 6ED, ℘ 52342, Fax 52597, < bay and Countisbury hill, – TV ☎ P. AE VISA
closed January – **M** *(closed Sunday lunch)* 18.50/23.50 **t.** 5.75 – **17 rm** 54.00/120.00 **t.**

Hewitt's, North Walk, EX35 6HJ, ℘ 52293, Fax 52489, < bay and Countisbury hill, « Country house atmosphere » – rest TV ☎ P. AE VISA
closed January – **M** (bar lunch)/dinner 21.00 **st.** and a la carte 4.50 – **10 rm** 40.00/84.00 **st.** – SB 78.00/110.00 **st.**

Chough's Nest, North Walk, EX35 6HJ, ℘ 53315, < bay and Countisbury hill – TV P.
Easter-October – **M** (bar lunch)/dinner 8.50 **t.** 3.20 – **12 rm** 22.00/44.00 **st.** – SB 60.00 **st.**

Neubia House, Lydiate Lane, EX35 6AH, ℘ 52309 – rest TV ☎ P. VISA
March-25 November – **M** (dinner only) 12.00 **t.** 4.00 – **12 rm** 24.25/53.50 **t.** – SB (except Bank Holidays) 61.00/68.50 **st.**

Seawood, North Walk, EX35 6HJ, ℘ 52272, < – rest TV P
March-October – **M** (bar lunch)/dinner 12.00 **st.** – **12 rm** 25.00/48.00 **st.**

Crown, Sinai Hill, EX35 6AG, ℘ 52253 – TV ☎ P. AE VISA
closed December and January – **M** (bar lunch)/dinner 16.95 **t.** and a la carte 5.00 – **13 rm** 34.50/68.00 **t.**, **3 suites** 72.00/79.00 **t.** – SB 71.00/75.00 **st.**

Rockvale, Lee Rd, EX35 6HW, off Lee Rd ℘ 52279 – TV ☎ P. VISA
2 March-14 November – **M** 11.00 **t.** 4.25 – **8 rm** 18.00/36.00 **t.** – SB 54.00/60.00 **st.**

at Lynmouth – ✉ Lynmouth – 0598 Lynton :

Tors, EX35 6NA, ℘ 53236, < Lynmouth and bay, heated, – TV ☎ P. AE VISA
closed 4 December-February – **M** 20.00 **st.** (dinner) and a la carte 4.00 – **34 rm** 35.00/82.00 **st.** – SB (except April-late September) 64.00/76.00 **st.**

Rising Sun, The Harbour, EX35 6EQ, ℘ 53223, Fax 53480, « Part 14C inn », – TV ☎. AE VISA
M (bar lunch)/dinner 16.50 **t.** and a la carte 4.60 – **15 rm** 39.00/90.00 **t.**, **1 suite** 100.00 **t.** – SB (except summer and Bank Holidays) 88.00/96.00 **st.**

Beacon, Countisbury Hill, EX35 6ND, E : ½ m. on A 39 ℘ 53268, <, – TV P.
mid March-mid October – **M** (lunch residents only)/dinner 16.50 **st.** and a la carte 2.95 – **7 rm** 27.50/55.00 **st.** – SB 75.00 **st.**

Countisbury Lodge, Tors Park, EX35 6NB, ℘ 52388, < – rest P. VISA
M 6.50 **st.** – **8 rm** 17.00/42.00 **st.** – SB (April-October) 50.00/51.00 **st.**

Heatherville, Tors Park, EX35 6NB, by Tors Rd ℘ 52327 – rest P.
Easter-mid October – **M** 8.00 **st.** – **8 rm** 17.00/37.00 **st.** – SB 49.00 **st.**

at Countisbury E : 2 ¼ m. on A 39 – ✉ Lynton – ☎ 059 87 Brendon :

Exmoor Sandpiper Inn, Countisbury Hill, EX35 6NE, ☎ 263, Fax 358 – TV P
M (bar lunch Monday to Saturday)/dinner 17.00 **s.** and a la carte 2.99 – **16 rm** 35.00 56.00.

at Hillsford Bridges S : 4 ½ m. by A 39 – ✉ 0598 Lynton :

Combe Park, EX35 6LE, ☎ 52356, – rest P
Mid March-October and Christmas – **M** (dinner only) 14.50 **t.** 4.00 – **9 rm** 40.00 52.00 **t.**

at Woody Bay W : 3 ¼ m. on Coast road – ✉ ☎ 059 83 Parracombe :

Woody Bay, EX31 4QX, ☎ 264, ← Woody Bay – P. VISA
closed 2 January-mid February – **M** (bar lunch)/dinner 15.00 **t.** and a la carte 3.50 – **14 rm** 31.00/78.00 **t.** – SB 68.00/93.00 **st.**

at Martinhoe W : 4 ¼ m. via Coast road – ✉ ☎ 059 83 Parracombe :

Old Rectory, EX31 4QT, ☎ 368, – rest TV P
March-mid November – **M** (dinner only) 14.50 **t.** 3.40 – **9 rm** 33.00/66.00 **t.** – S 73.75 **st.**

LYONSHALL Heref. and Worc. 403 L 27 – see Kington.

LYTHAM ST ANNE'S Lancs. 402 L 22 – pop. 39 599 – ECD : Wednesday – ☎ 0253 St. Anne's

See : Site★.

Lytham Green Drive, Ballam Rd ☎ 737390 – Fairhaven, Lytham Hall Park ☎ 736741 – S Annes Old Links, Highbury Rd ☎ 723597 – Royal Lytham StAnnes, Links Gate ☎ 724206.

The Square, St. Anne's ☎ 725610.

London 237 – Blackpool 7 – Liverpool 44 – Preston 13.

Dalmeny, 19-33 South Promenade, FY8 1LX, ☎ 712236, Fax 724447, squash – TV ☎ P – 200. VISA.
closed 24 to 26 December – **M** 17.50 **t.** and a la carte 3.25 – 5.00 – **104 rm** 40.00 99.00 **t.**

at Lytham SE : 3 m. – ✉ ☎ 0253 Lytham :

Clifton Arms (Lansbury), West Beach, FY8 5QJ, ☎ 739898, Telex 677463, Fax 73065 – TV ☎ P – 150. AE VISA
M 8.95/14.00 **t.** and a la carte – **40 rm** 79.00/100.00 **t.**, **1 suite** – SB (weekend only) 88.00/96.00 **st.**

FORD Preston Rd ☎ 733261
VAUXHALL Heeley Rd ☎ 726714

MACCLESFIELD Cheshire 402 403 404 N 24 – pop. 47 525 – ECD : Wednesday – ☎ 0625.

The Hollins ☎ 23227, SE : by A 523 – The Tytherington ☎ 617622.

Town Hall, Market Pl. ☎ 21955 ext 114/5.

London 186 – Chester 38 – Manchester 18 – Stoke-on-Trent 21.

Fourways Diner Motel, Cleulow Cross, Wincle, on A 54, SK11 0QL, SE : 4 ½ m. on A 523 ☎ 0260 (Congleton) 227228, ← – TV P. VISA
M (by arrangement) 9.00 **st.** 3.25 – **12 rm** 26.00/40.00 **st.**

at Bollington N : 3 ½ m. by A 523 on B 5090 – ☎ 0625 Bollington :

Mauro's, 88 Palmerston St., SK10 5LF, ☎ 573898, Italian rest. – AE VISA
closed Sunday, Monday and 25-26 December – **M** a la carte 10.50/17.75 **t.** 3.50.

Randall's, 22 High St., Old Market Pl., SK10 5PH, ☎ 75058 – AE VISA
closed Sunday dinner and Monday – **M** (dinner only and Sunday lunch)/dinner 25.00 and a la carte.

at Chelford W : 7 m. on A 537 – ✉ Macclesfield – ☎ 0625 Chelford :

Dixon Arms, Knutsford Rd, SK11 9AZ, on A 537 ☎ 861313, Fax 861443 – TV ☎ P. VISA
closed 24 December-1 January – **M** *(closed Monday lunch and Sunday dinner)* 7.50 10.50 **st.** and a la carte 3.00 – 5.00 – **11 rm** 38.00/46.00 **st.**

FIAT, AUDI-VW, VAUXHALL London Rd ☎ 28866
FORD Sence Av. ☎ 27766
HONDA Beech Lane ☎ 23592
MERCEDES-BENZ Crossall St. ☎ 23036
PEUGEOT-TALBOT Waters Green ☎ 22226
VAUXHALL, OPEL 98 Chestergate ☎ 22909
ATS 115 Hurdsfield Rd ☎ 25481/25233/24237

Dieser Führer ist kein vollständiges Hotel- und Restaurantverzeichnis.
Um den Ansprüchen aller Touristen gerecht zu werden,
haben wir uns auf eine Auswahl in jeder Kategorie beschränkt.

MACHYNLLETH Powys 402 403 I 26 – pop. 1 952 – ECD : Thursday – ☎ 0654.

Envir. : NW : Cader Idris (road★★ to Cader Idris : Cregenneu lakes) – Aberangell Clipiau (site★) NE : 10 m. – SE : Llyfnant Valley★ via Glaspwll.

Newtown Rd ☎ 2000.

Canolfan Owain Glyndwr ☎ 2401/702401.

♦London 220 – Shrewsbury 56 – Welshpool 37.

Dolguog Hall, SY20 8UJ, E : 1 ½ m. by A 489 ☎ 2244 (from February : 702244), ←, « 17C country house », – rest ☎
9 rm.

White Lion, Heol Pentrerhedyn, SY20 8ND, ☎ 703455, Fax 703746 – AE VISA
M a la carte 7.55/14.15 **st.** – **9 rm** 20.00/52.00 **st.** – SB 55.95/65.95 **st.**

Bacheiddon Farm without rest., Aberhosan, SY20 8SG, SE : 5 ¼ m. on Dylife rd ☎ 702229, « Working farm » –
3 rm -/40.00.

at Corris (Gwynedd) N : 5 ¼ m. on A 487 – ✉ Machynlleth (Powys) – ☎ 065 473 Corris :

Braich Goch, SY20 9RD, on A 487 ☎ 229, ←, – rest VISA
M 8.00 **st.** (dinner) and a la carte 6.20/13.00 **t.** 4.00 – **7 rm** 17.00/38.00 **t.** – SB (October-April) 47.00/53.00 **st.**

at Eglwysfach (Dyfed) SW : 6 m. on A 487 – ✉ Machynlleth (Powys) – ☎ 0654 Glandyfi :

Ynyshir Hall, SY20 8TA, ☎ 781209, ←, « Georgian country house, gardens », park – rest ☎ AE VISA
M *(closed Sunday dinner to non-residents)* 18.50/19.00 **t.** 4.00 – **9 rm** 40.00/120.00 **t.** – SB (October-March) 120.00/150.00 **st.**

FORD ☎ 065 04 (Dinas Mawddwy) 326 ROVER Station Garage ☎ 2108

"Short Breaks"

Many hotels now offer a special rate for a stay of 2 nights which includes dinner, bed and breakfast.

MADINGLEY Cambs. 404 U 27 – see Cambridge.

MAENORBYR = Manorbier.

MAGHAM DOWN East Sussex – see Hailsham.

MAIDENCOMBE Devon 403 J 32 – see Torquay.

MAIDENHEAD Berks. 404 R 29 – pop. 59 809 – ECD : Thursday – ☎ 0628.

Hawthorn Hill, Drift Rd ☎ 771030.

Central Library, St. Ives Rd ☎ 781110.

♦London 33 – ♦Oxford 32 – Reading 13.

Plan on next page

Holiday Inn, Manor Lane A, SL6 2RA, ☎ 23444, Telex 847502, Fax 770035, squash – rm ☎ – 500 X a
M (rest. see also **Shoppenhangers Manor below**) – **Promenade rest.** – **187 rm**, **2 suites.**

Fredrick's, Shoppenhangers Rd – A –, SL6 2PZ, ☎ 35934, Telex 849966, Fax 771054, – rest ☎ – 150. AE VISA X c
closed 24 to 30 December – **M** (rest. see **Fredrick's** below) – **37 rm** 79.50/145.00 **st.**, **1 suite** 210.00 **st.**

Thames Riviera, at the bridge, Bridge Rd – B –, SL6 8DW, ☎ 74057, Telex 846687, Fax 776586, ← – ☎ – 80. AE VISA V e
closed 25 to 31 December – **M** 16.50/25.00 **st.** and a la carte 4.00 – 6.25 – **51 rm** 82.50/93.50 **st.** – SB (weekends only) 98.50 **st.**

XXX **Fredrick's** (at Fredrick's H.), Shoppenhangers Rd – A –, SL6 2PZ, ☎ 24737, Telex 849966, Fax 771054, – AE VISA X c
closed Saturday lunch and 24 to 30 December – **M** 33.50/46.50 **st.** 5.50.

XXX Shoppenhangers Manor (at Crest H.), Manor Lane – A –, SL6 2RA, ☎ 25660, Telex 847502, Fax 770035, – X n

XX **Jasmine Peking,** 29 High St., SL6 1JG, ☎ 20334, Chinese rest. – AE VISA Y o
M 13.50 **st.** and a la carte 6.70.

at Cliveden NE : 4 ½ m. by Berry Hill-V – ✉ Taplow – ☎ 0628 Burnham :

Cliveden, SL6 0JF, ☎ 668561, Telex 846562, Fax 661837, « Mid-Victorian stately home – ← National Trust Gardens and parterre », heated, park, squash – ☎ – 25. VISA
M 27.00/39.80 **st.** and a la carte 37.50/46.50 **st.** 8.00 – **28 rm** 150.00/265.00 **st.**, **3 suites** 310.00/425.00 **st.**

MAIDENHEAD

High Street	Y	
Bad Godesberg Way	Y	2
Belmont Park Avenue	V	3
Blackamoor Lane	V	5
Boyn Hill Avenue	Z	6
Braywick Road	Z	7
Bridge Street	Y	9
Cannon Hill	X	10
College Road	V	13
Cookham Road	Y	14
Crescent (The)	Y	15
Ferry Road	X	17
Frascati Way	YZ	18
Furze Platt Road	V	20
Grenfell Place	Z	21
Gringer Hill	V	22
Harrow Lane	V	24
High Street BRAY-ON-THAMES	X	25
King's Grove	Z	27
Linden Avenue	V	28
Lower Cookham Road	V	29
Manor Lane	X	31
Market Street	Y	32
Nicholson's Walk	Y	34
Norreys Drive	X	35
Oldfield Road	X	36
Ray Street	V	38
Ray Mill Rd West	V	39
St. Ives Road	Y	41
St. Mark's Road	V	42
Upper Bray Road	X	43
Victoria Street	Z	45

For business or tourist interest : MICHELIN Red Guide Main Cities EUROPE.

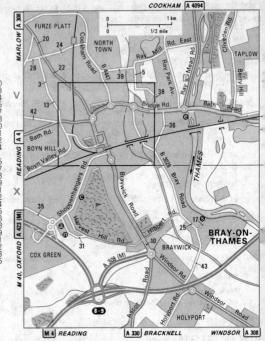

COOKHAM A 4094
MARLOW A 308
FURZE PLATT
NORTH TOWN
Cookham Road
B 4447
Ray Mill Rd. East
Ray Park Av.
Ray Mead Rd.
Cliveden Rd
TAPLOW
Berry Hill
Bridge Rd.
Bath Road
Bath Rd.
BOYN HILL
Boyn Valley Rd.
READING A 4
Shoppenhangers Rd.
Braywick Road
B 3028 Bray Road
THAMES
Harvest Hill Rd.
Hibbert Rd.
BRAY-ON-THAMES
BRAYWICK
COX GREEN
M 40, OXFORD A 423 (M)
A 308 (M)
Windsor Rd.
Windsor Road
Ascot Road
Holyport Rd.
HOLYPORT
8-9
M 4 READING
A 330 BRACKNELL
WINDSOR A 308
0 1 km
0 1/2 mile

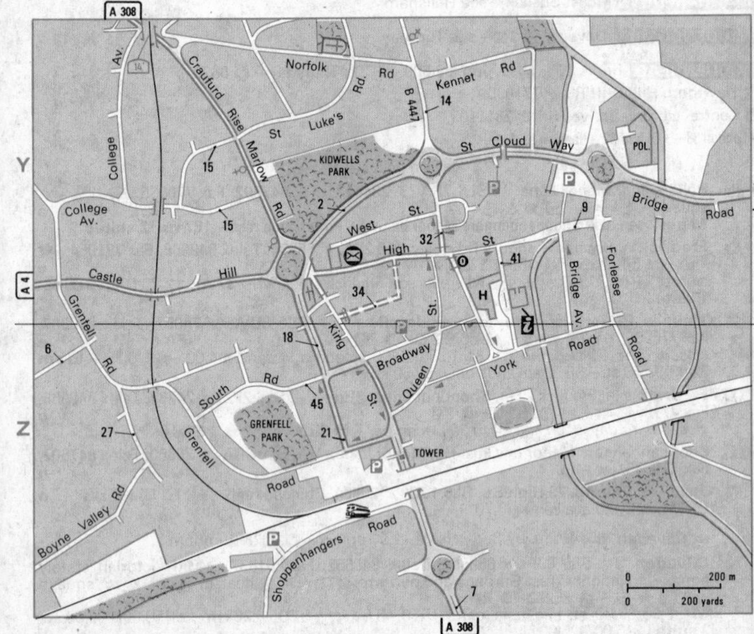

BMW 84 Altwood Rd ✆ 37611
FORD Bath Rd, Taplow ✆ 29711
HONDA 14-20 Bath Rd ✆ 21331
MAZDA 7 Bath Rd ✆ 32339
ROLLS-ROYCE Burnham ✆ 06286 (Burnham) 68361

ROVER 128 Bridge Rd ✆ 33188
VAUXHALL Braywick Rd ✆ 75461 27575

ATS Denmark St., Cordwallis Est. ✆ 20161

MAIDEN NEWTON Dorset 403 404 M 31 – pop. 777 – ECD : Thursday – 0300.

◆London 143 – Bournemouth 35 – ◆Bristol 55 – Taunton 34 – Weymouth 16.

Maiden Newton House ⑤, ✉ Dorchester, DT2 OAA, ✆ 20336, « Attractively converted 19C medieval style manor house », ⑤, ⑤, park – ⑤ Ⓟ. ⑤ VISA
closed January-mid February – **M** (communal dining) (booking essential) (dinner only) 25.00 **st.** ⑤ 5.00 – **6 rm** ⑤ 45.00/138.00 **st.** – SB (except Christmas) 138.00/180.00 **st.**

Le Petit Canard, Dorchester Rd, DT2 0BE, ✆ 20536 – ⑤ VISA
closed first 2 weeks November – **M** *(closed Sunday and Monday)* (dinner only) 17.95 **t.** ⑤ 5.00.

MAIDSTONE Kent 404 V 30 – pop. 86 067 – ECD : Wednesday – 0622.

See : All Saints' Church★ – Carriage Museum★ *AC* – Chillington Manor (Museum and Art Gallery★).

Envir. : Leeds Castle★ *AC*, SE : 4 ½ m. – Aylesford (The Friars carmelite priory : great courtyard★) NW : 3 ½ m. – Coldrum Long Barrow (prehistoric stones) site★ : NE : 1 m. from Trottiscliffe plus 5 mn walk, NW : 12 m.

18 Cobtree Manor Park, Chatham Park, Boxley ✆ 53276, N : ¼ m.

The Gatehouse, Old Palace Gardens, Mill St. ✆ 673581.

◆London 36 – ◆Brighton 64 – ◆Cambridge 84 – Colchester 72 – Croydon 36 – ◆Dover 45 – Southend-on-Sea 49.

Grange Moor, 4-8 St. Michael's Rd (off Tonbridge Rd), ME16 8BS, ✆ 677623, Fax 678246, ⑤ – TV ☎ Ⓟ – ⑤ 100. ⑤ VISA
M 11.50 **st.** and a la carte ⑤ 3.50 – **36 rm** ⑤ 45.00/60.20 **st.** – SB (weekends only) 60.50/69.50 **st.**

Rock House without rest., 102 Tonbridge Rd, ME16 8SL, ✆ 751616 – TV Ⓟ. ⑤ VISA. ⑤
closed 24 December-2 January – **12 rm** ⑤ 27.00/45.00 **st.**

at Bearsted E : 3 m. by A 249 on A 20 – ✉ 0622 Maidstone :

Tudor Park H. Golf & Country Club, Ashford Rd, ME14 4NQ, E : 1 m. on A 20 ✆ 34334, Telex 966655, Fax 35360, ⑤, ⑤, 18, ⑤, park, squash – ⑤ rm TV ☎ ⑤ Ⓟ – ⑤ 250. ⑤ AE ⑤ VISA
M *(closed Saturday lunch)* 16.50 **st.** (dinner) and a la carte ⑤ 6.75 – **120 rm** ⑤ 90.00/120.00 **st.** – SB (weekends only) 110.00/125.00 **st.**

Sueffle, The Green, ME14 4DN, ✆ 37065 – Ⓟ. ⑤ AE ⑤ VISA
closed Saturday lunch, Sunday, Monday and Bank Holidays – **M** 28.50 **t.**

at Boughton Monchelsea S : 4 ½ m. by A 229 on B 2163 – ✉ 0622 Maidstone :

Tanyard ⑤, Wierton Hill, ME17 4JT, S : 1 ½ m. by Park Lane ✆ 744705, ⑤, « 14C Tannery standing in orchards », ⑤ – TV ☎ Ⓟ. ⑤ VISA. ⑤
closed mid December-early March – **M** (dinner only) 18.40 **t.** ⑤ 4.50 – **5 rm** ⑤ 55.20/115.00 **t.**

at Wateringbury SW : 4 ½ m. on A 26 – ✉ 0622 Maidstone :

Wateringbury (Lansbury), Tonbridge Rd, ME18 5NS, ✆ 812632, Telex 96265, Fax 812720, ⑤ – TV ☎ Ⓟ – ⑤ 80. ⑤ AE ⑤ VISA. ⑤
M 9.95/15.00 **t.** and a la carte – **28 rm** ⑤ 70.00/82.00 **t.** – SB (weekends only) 68.00 **st.**

at Larkfield W : 3 ¼ m. on A 20 – ✉ Larkfield – 0732 West Malling :

Larkfield (T.H.F.), 812 London Rd, ME20 6HJ, ✆ 846858, Telex 957420, Fax 846786 – ⑤ rm ⑤ rest TV ☎ Ⓟ – ⑤ 70. ⑤ AE ⑤ VISA
M *(closed Saturday lunch)* 12.00/16.00 **st.** and a la carte ⑤ 4.35 – ⑤ 7.00 – **52 rm** 65.00/100.00 **st.**

ALFA-ROMEO, CITROEN Bow Rd, Wateringbury ✆ 812358
BMW Broadway ✆ 686666
COLT Forstal Rd, Aylesford ✆ 76421
FORD Ashford Rd ✆ 56781
LADA Loose Rd ✆ 52584
NISSAN Ashford Rd, Harrietsham ✆ 859363
PEUGEOT-TALBOT Mill St. ✆ 53333
PORSCHE Broadway ✆ 686666
RENAULT Ashford Rd ✆ 54744
ROLLS-ROYCE, LAND-ROVER Bucholt Rd ✆ 65461

ROVER, DAIMLER-JAGUAR Bircholt Rd ✆ 65461
SAAB Linton Rd, Loose ✆ 46629
VAUXHALL-OPEL, MERCEDES-BENZ Park Wood, Sutton Rd ✆ 55531
VAUXHALL London Rd, Ditton ✆ 0732 (West Malling) 844922
VOLVO Cavendish Way ✆ 3953
VW-AUDI Upper Stone St. ✆ 50821

ATS 165 Upper Stone St. ✆ 58738/58664

MALDON Essex 404 V 28 – pop. 14 638 – ECD : Wednesday – ☏ 0621.

Forrester Park, Beckingham Rd ✆ 891406 – Beeleigh Langford ✆ 53212 – Three Rivers, Stow Rd, Purleigh ✆ 0621 (Purleigh) 828631, S : 5 m.

Maritime Centre, The Hythe ✆ 856503.

◆London 42 – Chelmsford 9 – Colchester 17.

Blue Boar (T.H.F.), Silver St., CM9 7QE, ✆ 852681 – rm TV ☎ P – 40. AE VISA
M 10.50/13.50 **st.** and a la carte 4.35 – **28 rm** 55.00/70.00 **st.** – SB (weekends only) 72.00/84.00 **st.**

Benbridge, The Square, Heybridge, CM9 7LT, ✆ 857666 – TV ☎ P. AE VISA
M *(closed Sunday dinner)* a la carte 12.00/20.00 **t.** 4.00 – **13 rm** 35.00/49.50 **t.**

BMW Spital Rd ✆ 852131
FORD 1 Spital Rd ✆ 852345
ROVER Heybridge ✆ 852468
VAUXHALL-OPEL 127-131 High St. ✆ 852424
ATS 143-147 High St. ✆ 856541

MALMESBURY Wilts. 403 404 N 29 – pop. 4 220 – ECD : Thursday – ☏ 0666.

See : Site★ – Market Cross★★ – Abbey★.

Town Hall, Cross Hayes ✆ 823748.

◆London 108 – ◆Bristol 28 – Gloucester 24 – Swindon 19.

Old Bell, Abbey Row, SN16 0BW, ✆ 822344, Fax 825145, « Part 13C building », – TV ☎ P. VISA
M 12.00/19.50 **t.** and a la carte – **35 rm** 65.00/80.00 **t.**, **1 suite** – SB (October-April except Christmas and New Year) 98.00/100.50 **st.**

at Crudwell N : 4 m. on A 429 – ✉ ☏ 066 67 Crudwell :

Crudwell Court, SN16 9EP, ✆ 7194, Fax 7853, « Former 17C vicarage », heated, – TV ☎ P. AE VISA
M 17.00 **t.** 3.75 – **15 rm** 40.00/100.00 **t.** – SB (except Christmas-New Year and Bank Holidays) 104.00/125.00 **st.**

Mayfield House, SN16 9EW, ✆ 7198, Fax 7977, – TV ☎ P. AE VISA
M (dinner only and Sunday lunch)/dinner 19.95 **t.** and a la carte 3.50 – **20 rm** 40.00/53.00 **t.** – SB 74.00/80.00 **st.**

at Stanton St. Quintin SW : 6¼ m. by A 429 – ✉ Chippenham – ☏ 0666 Malmesbury :

Stanton Manor, SN14 6DQ, ✆ 837552, Fax 837022, – TV ☎ P
5 rm.

at Easton Grey W : 2 m. on B 4040 – ✉ ☏ 0666 Malmesbury :

Whatley Manor, SN16 0RB, E : ½ m. on B 4040 ✆ 822888, Telex 449380, Fax 826120, ←, « 18C Manor house », heated, , , park, – TV ☎ P – 40. AE VISA
M 14.50/26.00 **t.** 5.00 – **29 rm** 70.00/116.00 **t.** – SB (weekends only) 118.00/130.00 **st.**

FORD Corston ✆ 3317
PEUGEOT-TALBOT Gloucester Rd ✆ 823434
RENAULT 26 High St. ✆ 822787

MALPAS Cheshire 402 403 L 24 – pop. 1 522 – ☏ 0948.

◆London 177 – ◆Birmingham 60 – Chester 15 – Shrewsbury 26 – ◆Stoke-on-Trent 30.

XX **Market House,** Church St., SY14 8NU, ✆ 860400, – VISA
closed Sunday dinner, Monday, last 2 weeks August, 4 days in October and 2-6 January – **M** (dinner only and Sunday lunch)/dinner a la carte 9.00/16.75 **t.** 4.95.

MALTON North Yorks. 402 R 21 – pop. 4 033 – ECD : Thursday – ☏ 0653.

Envir. : Castle Howard★★ (18C) *AC*, SW : 6 m. – Flamingo Park Zoo★ *AC*, N : 4½ m.

Malton and Norton, Welham Park ✆ 692959.

Old Town Hall, Market Pl. ✆ 600048 (summer only).

◆London 229 – ◆Kingston-upon-Hull 36 – Scarborough 24 – York 17.

Greenacres Country, Amotherby, YO17 0TG, W : 2½ m. on B 1257 ✆ 693623, , – TV P. VISA
closed December and January – **M** *(closed Sunday)* (dinner only) 8.50 **st.** 2.00 – **9 rm** 20.00/40.00 **st.**

Oakdene, 29 Middlecave Rd, YO17 0NE, ✆ 693363, – rest TV P.
M (by arrangement) 11.00 **st.** 3.20 – **6 rm** 28.00/39.00 **st.**

at Norton E : ½ m. on B 1248 – ✉ ☏ 0653 Malton :

Auburn Hill, Langton Road, YO17 9PZ, S : 1 m. on Langton Rd ✆ 695335, – rest TV ☎ P. VISA
closed Christmas and New Year – **M** (dinner only) a la carte 12.05/15.25 **t.** 3.95 – **5 rm** 43.00/65.00 **t.** – SB 77.00/89.00 **st.**

at Wharram-Le-Street SE : 6 m. on B 1248 – ✉ Malton – ☎ 094 46 North Grimston :

Red House, YO17 9TL, ☎ 455, – rm ▣ Ⓟ
closed 24 to 27 December – **M** 13.00 **s.** 2.50 – **4 rm** 20.00/40.00 **s.**

VER Wintringham ☎ 09442 (Rillington) 242 — ATS 27 Commercial St., Norton ☎ 692567/693525

ALVERN Heref. and Worc. 403 404 N 27 – see Great Malvern.

ALVERN WELLS Heref. and Worc. 403 404 N 27 – see Great Malvern.

ANCHESTER Greater Manchester 402 403 404 N 23 – pop. 437 612 – ECD : Wednesday – 061.

ee : Site★ – Town Hall★ (19C) DYZ**H** – City Art Gallery★ DZ**M2** – Whitworth Art Gallery★ BX**M**
Cathedral 15C (chancel★) DY**B** – John Ryland's Library (manuscripts★) CY**A**.

vir. : Heaton Hall★ (18C) *AC*, N : 5 m. AV**M**.

Heaton Park, ☎ 798 0295, N : by A 576 ABV – Fairfield Golf and Sailing, Booth Rd, denshaw, ☎ 370 1641, E : by A 635 BX – Houldsworth, Wingate House, Higher Levshulme ☎ 224 5055 BX – Disbury, Ford Lane, Northenden ☎ 998 9278 BX – Hopwood ttage, Rochdale Rd, Middleton ☎ 643 2718, N : 7 m. BV – Northenden, Palatine Rd ☎ 998 38, S : 5 m. BX – Strand, The Dales, Ashbourne Grove, Whitefield ☎ 766 2388, N : 5 m. AV.

Manchester International Airport ☎ (061) 489 3000(British Airways) Telex – **Terminal** : ach service from Victoria Station.

Town Hall Extension, Lloyd St. ☎ 234 3157/8 – Manchester International Airport, International Arrivals Hall ☎ 436 3344.

ondon 202 – ◆Birmingham 86 – ◆Glasgow 221 – ◆Leeds 43 – ◆Liverpool 35 – ◆Nottingham 72.

Plans on following pages

Holiday Inn Crowne Plaza Midland, 16 Peter St., M60 2DS, ☎ 236 3333, Telex 667550, Fax 228 2241, squash – rm ▣ ☎ – 300. AE VISA. DZ **x**
M French rest. 14.95/27.50 **st.** and a la carte – **Trafford Room** (carving rest.) 14.95 **st.** – 8.95 – **296 rm** 95.00/112.00 **st.**, **7 suites** 185.00/375.00 **st.** – SB (weekends only) 113.90/138.00 **st.**

Ramada Renaissance, Blackfriars St., Deansgate, M3 2EQ, ☎ 835 2555, Telex 669699, Fax 835 3077 – rm rest ▣ ☎ Ⓟ – 400. AE VISA CY **v**
M 14.50/27.00 **st.** and a la carte **200 rm** 95.00/110.00 **t.**, **5 suites** 145.00/250.00 **t.** – SB (weekends only) 138.50/142.50 **st.**

Piccadilly, Piccadilly Plaza, M60 1QR, ☎ 236 8414, Telex 668765, Fax 228 1568, ≤, – rm rest ▣ ☎ Ⓟ – 700. AE VISA. DY **s**
M 11.50/17.50 **t.** and a la carte 4.00 – 8.75 – **264 rm** 95.00/115.00 **st.**, **9 suites** 210.00/220.00 **st.** – SB (weekends only) 99.00/105.00 **st.**

Copthorne Manchester (Best Western), Clippers Quay, Salford Quays, M5 3DL, ☎ 873 7321, Telex 669090, Fax 873 7318, – rm rest ▣ ☎ Ⓟ – 75. AE VISA. AX **n**
M 13.50/28.25 **st.** and a la carte 4.75 – 8.25 – **166 rm** 75.00/100.00 **st.**

Portland Thistle (Mt. Charlotte Thistle), Portland St., Piccadilly Gdns., M1 6DP, ☎ 228 3400, Telex 669157, Fax 228 6347, – rm rest ▣ ☎ Ⓟ – 300. AE VISA
M 12.00/14.00 **st.** – **205 rm** 79.00/105.00 **st.**, **3 suites** – SB 85.00 **st.** DY **a**

Hazledean, 467 Bury New Rd, M7 ONX, ☎ 792 6667, Fax 792 6668 – ▣ ☎ Ⓟ. AE VISA. AV **a**
closed 5 days at Christmas – **M** *(closed Bank Holidays)* (bar lunch)/dinner a la carte 11.50/15.40 **t.** 3.70 **24 rm** 40.25/59.80 **t.**

New Central, 144-146 Heywood St., M8 7PD, ☎ 205 2169 – Ⓟ BV **e**
M 8.20 **t.** 3.80 – **10 rm** 20.50/35.00.

Sabre D'or, 392 Wilbraham Rd, Chorlton-cum-Hardy, M21 1UH, S : 5 m. by A 5103 on A 6010 ☎ 881 5055 – ▣ Ⓟ AX **c**
M 6.50 **st.** 3.00 – **17 rm** 21.50/35.00 **st.**

Isola Bella, Dolefield, Crown Sq., M3 3EN, ☎ 831 7099, Italian rest. – AE VISA
closed Sunday and Bank Holidays – **M** a la carte 14.20/30.20 **st.** 5.00. CY **e**

Giulio's Terrazza, 14 Nicholas St., M1 4FE, ☎ 236 4033, Italian rest. – AE VISA
closed Sunday and Bank Holidays – **M** 9.50 **t.** and a la carte 19.35/28.35 **t.** 4.50. DZ **r**

Gaylord, Amethyst House, Marriott's Court, Spring Gdns, M2 1EA, ☎ 832 6037, Indian rest. – . AE VISA DY **c**
closed 25 December and 1 January – **M** a la carte 6.85/9.50 **t.** 4.25.

Yang Sing, 34 Princess St., M1 4JY, ☎ 236 2200, Fax 236 5934, Chinese (Canton) rest. – AE VISA DZ **a**
closed 25 December – **M** (booking essential) a la carte approx. 12.00 **t.**

Market, 104 High St., M4 1HQ, ☎ 834 3743, Bistro – AE VISA
closed Monday, Sunday, 1 week Easter, August, 1 week Christmas and Bank Holidays – **M** (dinner only) a la carte 10.95/17.85 **t.** 3.75. DY **o**

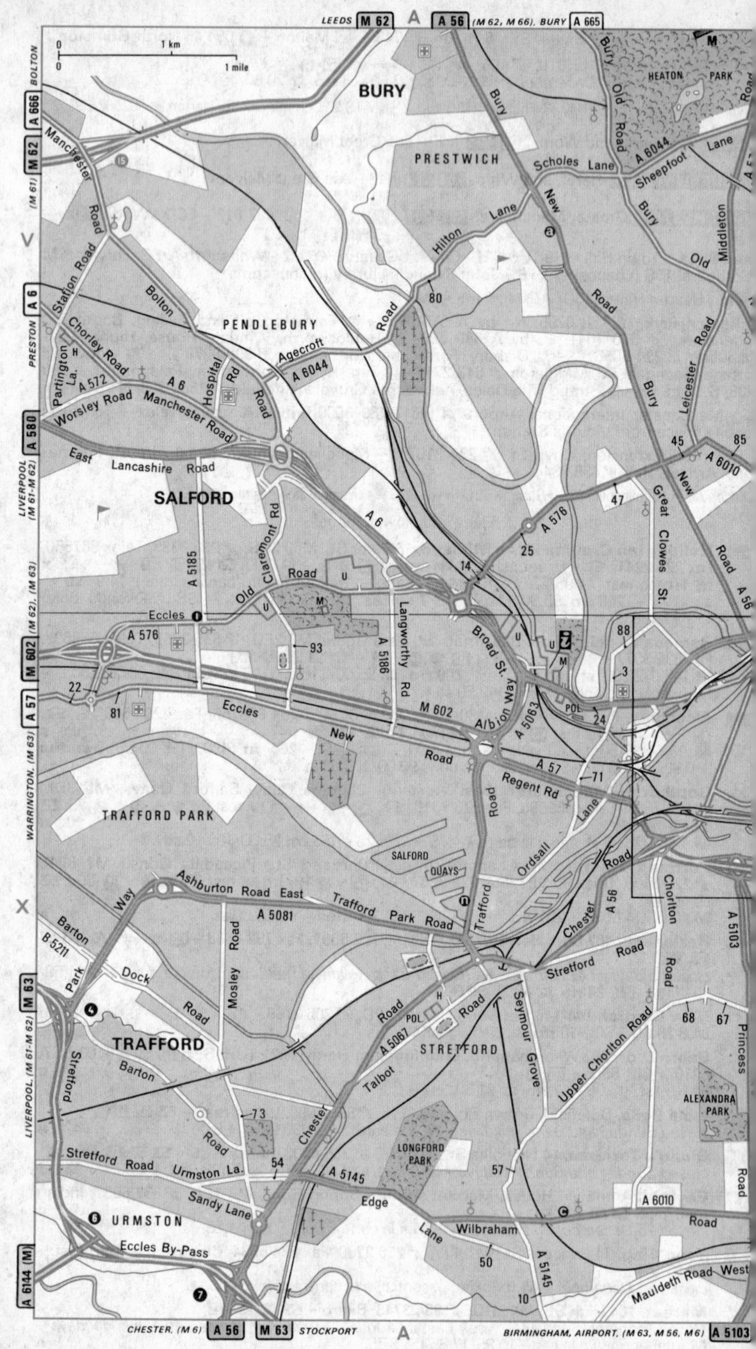
LEEDS M 62
A
A 56 (M 62, M 66), BURY A 665
BOLTON A 666
M 62 (M 61)
V
PRESTON A 6
LIVERPOOL (M 61-M 62) A 580
WARRINGTON, (M 62), (M 63) M 602
WARRINGTON, (M 63) A 57
X
LIVERPOOL (M 61-M 62) M 63
A 6144 (M)
CHESTER, (M 6) A 56
M 63 STOCKPORT
BIRMINGHAM, AIRPORT, (M 63, M 56, M 6) A 5103
0 1 km
0 1 mile
BURY
PRESTWICH
PENDLEBURY
SALFORD
TRAFFORD PARK
SALFORD QUAYS
TRAFFORD
STRETFORD
URMSTON
HEATON PARK
ALEXANDRA PARK
LONGFORD PARK
Bury Old Road
Scholes Lane
Sheepfoot Lane
A 6044
Bury New Road
Bury Old Road
Middleton Road
Hilton Lane
Manchester Road
Station Road
Bolton Road
Chorley Road
Partington La.
A 572
A 6
Worsley Road
Manchester Road
Hospital Rd
Agecroft Road
A 6044
East Lancashire Road
Leicester Road
A 6010
A 576
Great Clowes St.
A 56
Claremont Rd
Old Road
A 5185
Eccles
A 576
Langworthy Rd
A 5186
Broad St.
Albion Way
A 5063
M 602
Eccles New Road
A 57
Regent Rd
Ordsall Lane
Trafford Road
Chester Road
A 56
Chorlton Road
A 5103
Ashburton Road East
A 5081
Trafford Park Road
Barton Way
B 5211
Barton Dock Road
Park
Mosley Road
Stretford Road
Seymour Grove
Upper Chorlton Road
Princess Road
Talbot Road
A 5067
POL.
Stretford
Barton Road
Chester Road
Stretford Road
Urmston La.
Sandy Lane
A 5145
Edge Lane
Wilbraham Road
A 6010
A 5145
Eccles By-Pass
Mauldeth Road West
80
45
85
47
25
14
88
3
24
71
93
22
81
73
54
57
68
67
50
10

MANCHESTER

BUILT UP AREA

Adelphi Street .... AX 3
Albert Road .... BX 4
Ardwick Green South BX 6
Ashton Road......... BV 7

Barlow Moor Rd . AX 10
Bellevue Street . . BX 12
Broughton Road . AV 14
Chancellor Lane. . BX 17
Church Street .... AX 22
Clive Road .... BV 23
Crescent......... AX 24
Cromwell Road .. AV 25
Delaunay's Road . BV 29
Devonshire Street BX 31
Devonshire Street North. . . BX 32
Edge Lane .... BX 35
Fairfield Street . . . BX 39
Great Ancoats St. BX 40
Great Cheetham Street East . . . . AV 45
Great Cheetham Street West . . . AV 47
Harpurhey Road . BV 49
High Lane .... AX 50
Kingsway .... AX 54
Lansdowne Road. BV 55
Manchester Road AX 57
Manchester New Road . . . . BV 58
Mancunian Way . BX 59
Merrill Street . . . . BX 63
Millstream Lane. . BV 64
Moss Bank....... BV 65
Moss Lane East. . BX 67
Moss Lane West. AX 68
Moston Lane . . . . BV 69
Northampton Rd . BV 70
Oldfield Road. . . . AX 71
Old Market Street BV 72
Park Road. . . . . . AX 73
Pottery Lane. . . . . BX 77
Pollard Street . . . . BX 79
Rainsough Brow . AV 80
Regent Street . . . AX 81
Rose Hey Lane . . BV 83
St. James's Road AV 85
Silk Street . . . . . . AX 88
Thorp Road . . . . BV 91
Weaste Lane . . . . AX 93

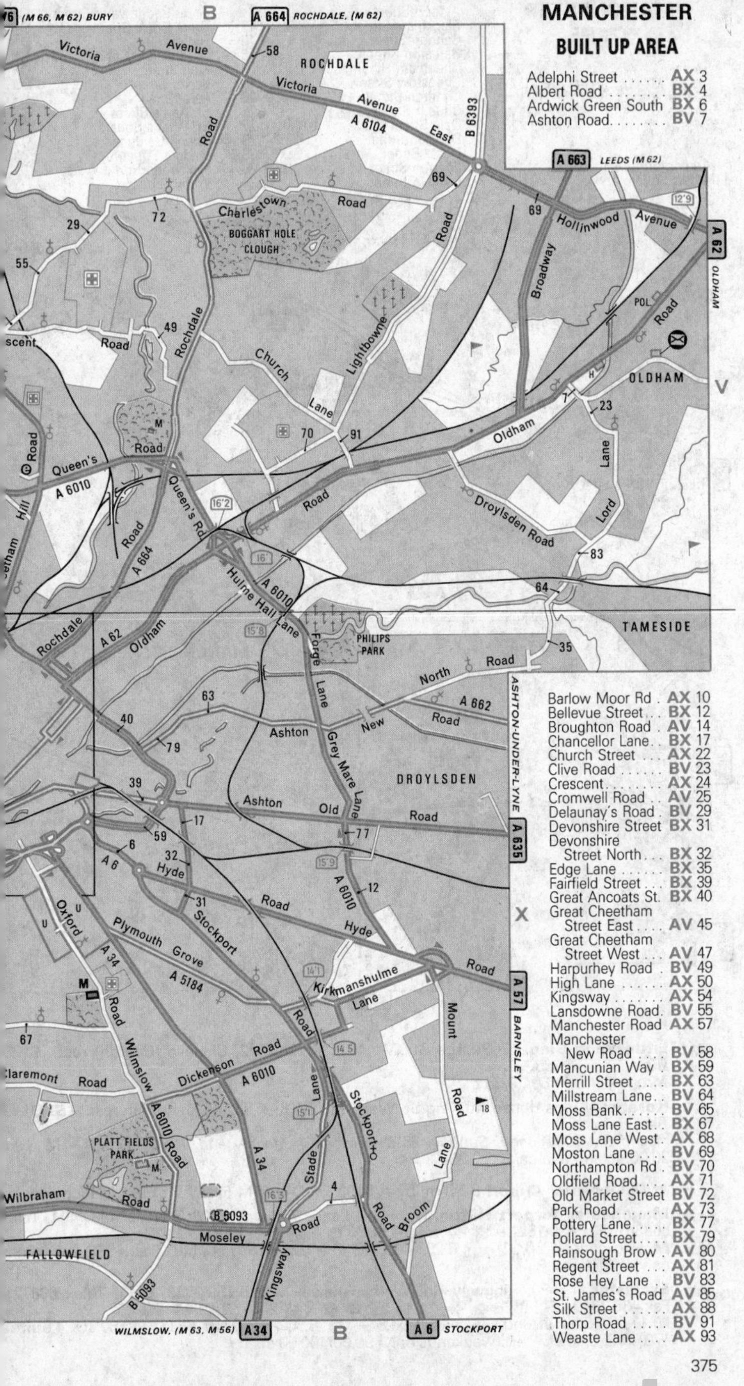

MANCHESTER
CENTRE

Deansgate .... CYZ
Lower Mosley Street ..... DZ 56
Market Place .... CDY
Market Street .... DY
Mosley Street .... DYZ
Princess Street .... DZ

Addington Street .... DY 2
Albert Square .... CDYZ 5
Aytoun Street .... DZ 8
Blackfriars Street .... CY 13
Cannon Street .... DY 15
Cateaton Street .... DY 16
Cheetham Hill Road .... DY 18
Chepstow Street .... DZ 19
Chorlton Street .... DZ 20
Church Street .... DY 21
Dale Street .... DY 27
Dawson Street .... CZ 28
Ducie Street .... DYZ 33
Egerton Street .... CZ 36
Fairfield Street .... DZ 39
Great Bridgewater Street .. CZ [illegible]
Great Ducie Street .... CY [illegible]
High Street .... DY [illegible]
John Dalton Street .... CY [illegible]
King Street .... DY [illegible]
Parker Street .... DY [illegible]
Peter Street .... CZ [illegible]
St. Ann's Street .... CY [illegible]
St. Peter's Square .... DZ [illegible]
Spring Gardens .... DY [illegible]
Viaduct Street .... CY [illegible]
Whitworth Street West .... CZ [illegible]
Withy Grove .... DY [illegible]

X **Little Yang Sing,** 17 George St., M1 4HE, ☎ 228 7722, Chinese (Canton) rest.. [illegible] AE VISA DZ e
M a la carte 11.60/16.25 **t.**

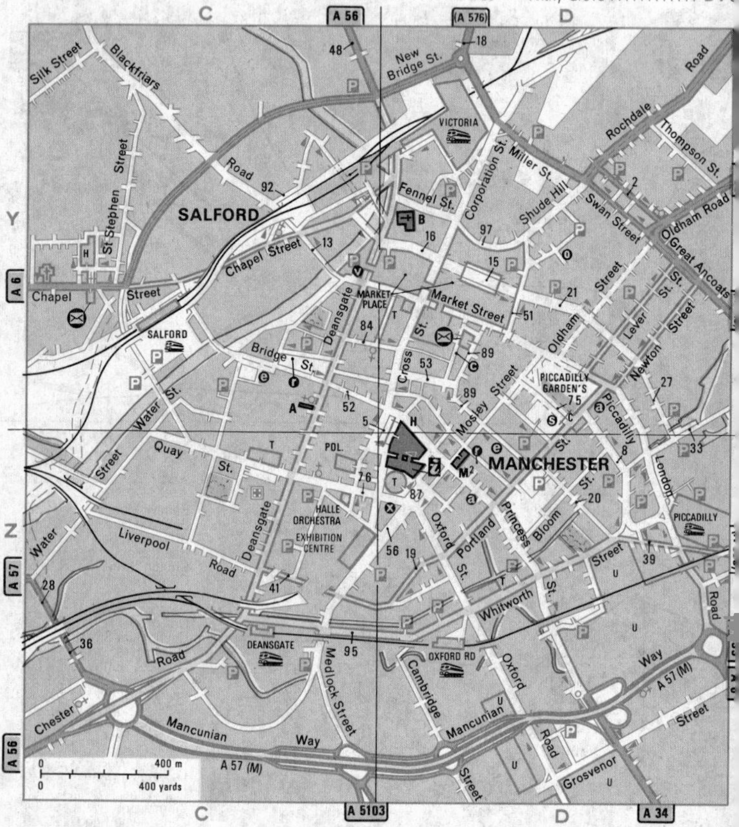

X **Koreana,** Kings House, 40 King St. West, M3 2WY, ☎ 832 4330, Korean rest. – [illegible] AE ① VISA CY [illegible]
closed Saturday lunch, Sunday, 25 December, 1 January and Bank Holidays – **M** 6.95/20.00 **st.** and a la carte 🍷 3.95.

at Manchester Airport S : 9 m. by A 5103 – AX– off M 56 – ✉ ⚙ 061 Manchester :

Manchester Airport Hilton, Outwood Lane, Ringway, M22 5WP, ☎ 436 4404, Telex 668361, Fax 436 1521 – 🛗 ⇆ rm 📺 ☎ ♿ 🅟 – 🏛 130. [illegible] AE ① VISA
M a la carte 15.50/31.75 🍷 6.25 – ☕ 10.25 – **223 rm** 97.50/140.00 **st.** – SB (weekends only) 245.00 **st.**

Excelsior (T.H.F.), Ringway Rd, Wythenshawe, M22 5NS, ☎ 437 5811, Telex 668721, Fax 436 2340, ≘s, [illegible] – 🛗 ⇆ rm ▤ 📺 ☎ 🅟 – 🏛 200. [illegible] AE ① VISA
M 11.50/16.50 **st.** and a la carte 🍷 5.25 – ☕ 8.50 – **300 rm** 95.00/110.00 **st.**, **4 suites** 170.00/270.00 **st.** – SB (weekends only) 90.00/100.00 **st.**

XXX **Moss Nook,** Ringway Rd, Moss Nook, M22 5NA, ☎ 437 4778 – P. AE VISA
closed Saturday lunch, Sunday, Monday, 25 December-10 January and Bank Holidays – **M** 16.50/24.00 **st.** and a la carte 6.50.

at Worsley W : 7¼ m. by M 602 – AX – off M 62 East – ✉ 061 Manchester :

Novotel Manchester West, Worsley Brow, at junction 13 of M 62, M28 4YA, ☎ 799 3535, Telex 669586, Fax 703 8207, heated – rm TV ☎ P – 200. AE VISA
M 11.50/12.50 **st.** and a la carte 3.85 – 6.50 – **119 rm** 58.00/116.00 **st.**

ALFA-ROMEO 123a/b Jersey St. ☎ 205 2213
BMW 325-327 Deansgate ☎ 832 8781
BMW 45 Upper Brook St. ☎ 273 1571
CITROEN, FIAT, LANCIA Ashton Old Rd ☎ 273 4411
FIAT Ashton Old Rd ☎ 273 4411
FORD 271 Bury New Rd ☎ 792 6161
FORD 391 Palatine Rd ☎ 998 3427
FORD Oxford Rd ☎ 224 7301
FORD 660 Chester Rd ☎ 872 2201
FORD 3-5 New Wakefield St. ☎ 236 4168
HONDA Liverpool St. ☎ 737 3540
MAZDA Oldham Rd, Ashton ☎ 330 8135
MERCEDES-BENZ Upper Brook St. ☎ 273 8123
MORGAN, RENAULT Ashley Rd, Hale ☎ 941 1916
NISSAN Victoria Rd ☎ 330 3840
NISSAN Windsor St, Salford ☎ 745 7737
NISSAN Chancellor Lane, Ardwick ☎ 273 8198
PEUGEOT-TALBOT Chester Rd ☎ 834 6677
PEUGEOT Waterloo Rd ☎ 792 4220
PORSCHE Bury New Rd at Whitefield ☎ 796 7414
RENAULT Blackfriars Rd ☎ 832 6121
ROVER 208 Bury New Rd ☎ 792 4343
SAAB Water St. ☎ 832 6566
SUBARU, ISUZU, HYUNDAI Greenside Lane ☎ 370 2145
TOYOTA Moseley Rd ☎ 224 6265
VAUXHALL-OPEL 292 Bury New Rd ☎ 792 4321
VAUXHALL-OPEL Blackfriars Rd ☎ 834 8200
VAUXHALL-OPEL 799 Chester Rd ☎ 872 2141
VAUXHALL-OPEL Ashton Old Rd ☎ 273 4361
VOLVO Rowsley St. ☎ 223 7272
VW-AUDI Stamford Rd ☎ 320 5454

ATS Chester St. ☎ 236 5505
ATS 98 Wilmslow Rd, Rusholme ☎ 224 6296
ATS Warren Rd, Trafford Park ☎ 872 7631
ATS 122 Higher Rd, Urmston ☎ 748 6990/5923
ATS 20-28 Waterloo Rd ☎ 832 7752

MANORBIER **(MAENORBYR)** Dyfed 403 F 29 – pop. 1 136 – ECD : Saturday – ☎ 0834 (6 fig.) or 0834 871 (3 fig.).

♦London 253 – Carmarthen 33 – Fishguard 33.

Castlemead, SA70 7TA, ☎ 871358, – TV P. AE VISA
April-September – **M** (dinner only) 2.75 **t.** 2.50 – **8 rm** 25.00/50.00 **t.** – SB 60.00 **st.**

MARAZION Cornwall 403 D 33 **The West Country G.** – pop. 1 366 – ECD : Wednesday – ✉ ☎ 0736 Penzance.

♦London 318 – Penzance 3 – Truro 26.

Mount Haven, Turnpike Rd, TR17 0DQ, ☎ 710249, ≤ St. Michael's Mount and Mount's Bay – rest TV ☎ P. AE VISA
M 13.00 **st.** (dinner) and a la carte 3.75 – **17 rm** 26.00/58.00 **st.** – SB (October-May) 56.00/64.00 **st.**

at St. Hilary E : 2½ m. by Turnpike Rd, on B 3280 – ✉ ☎ 0736 Penzance :

Enny's Trewhelln Lane, TR20 9BZ, ☎ 740262, – rm TV P.
M 11.00 **t.** – **5 rm** 25.00/55.00 **t.** – SB (December-March) (weekends only) 75.00 **st.**

at Perranuthnoe SE : 1¾ m. by A 394 – ✉ ☎ 0736 Penzance :

Ednovean House TR20 9LZ, ☎ 711071, ≤ St. Michael's Mount and Mount's Bay, – rest P. AE VISA
M 11.00 **st.** 3.55 – **9 rm** 15.00/40.00 **st.**

MARKET DRAYTON Shropshire 402 403 404 M 25 – pop. 9 003 – ECD : Thursday – ☎ 0630.

9 Sutton ☎ 2266, S : 1 m.

♦London 161 – ♦Birmingham 44 – Chester 33 – Shrewsbury 19 – ♦Stoke-on-Trent 16.

Corbet Arms, 8 High St., TF9 1PY, ☎ 2037, Fax 2961 – TV ☎ P. AE VISA
M (carving lunch)/dinner 11.95 **t.** – **12 rm** 32.00/55.00 **t.** – SB 65.00/70.00 **st.**

FORD Shrewsbury Rd ☎ 2027
RENAULT Shrewsbury Rd ☎ 4257
VAUXHALL, VOLVO Cheshire St. ☎ 652444

ATS 71-73 Shrewsbury Rd ☎ 58446

When looking for a quiet hotel
use the maps found in the introductory pages
or look for establishments with the sign or

Si vous cherchez un hôtel tranquille,
consultez d'abord les cartes de l'introduction
ou repérez dans le texte les établissements indiqués avec le signe ou

Wenn Sie ein ruhiges Hotel suchen,
benutzen Sie zuerst die Karte in der Einleitung
oder wählen Sie im Text ein Hotel mit dem Zeichen oder

MARKET HARBOROUGH Leics. 404 R 26 – pop. 15 852 – ECD : Wednesday – ☎ 0858.

Oxendon Rd ✆ 63684.

Pen Lloyd Library, Adam and Eve St. ✆ 62649.

◆London 88 – ◆Birmingham 47 – ◆Leicester 15 – Northampton 17.

Three Swans (Best Western), 21 High St., LE16 7NJ, ✆ 466644, Telex 342375, Fax 433101 – rm – 50. VISA.
M 10.95/15.95 **t.** 3.50 – **37 rm** 45.00/81.00 **t.** – SB (weekends only) 79.00/95.00 **st.**

at Glooston NE : 7½ m. by A 6 and B 6047 off Hallaton Rd – ✉ Market Harborough – ☎ 0858 84 East Langton :

Old Barn Inn with rm, LE16 7ST, ✆ 215 – . VISA.
M *(closed Monday lunch and Sunday dinner)* (bar lunch)/dinner 17.50 **t.** and a la carte 3.25 – **3 rm** 32.50/39.50 **t.** – SB (weekends only) 50.00 **st.**

at Marston Trussell (Northants.) W : 3½ m. by A 427 – ✉ ☎ 0858 Market Harborough :

Sun Inn, Main St., LE16 9TY, ✆ 65531 – – 50
20 rm.

FIAT Main St. ✆ 66984
VAUXHALL-OPEL Springfield St. ✆ 67177
VW-AUDI Northampton Rd ✆ 65511
ATS 47-49 Kettering Rd ✆ 64535

MARKFIELD Leics. 402 403 404 Q 25 – pop. 4 140 – ☎ 0530.

◆London 113 – ◆Birmingham 45 – ◆Leicester 6 – ◆Nottingham 24.

Granada Lodge without rest., Little Shaw Lane, LE6 0PP, on A 50 ✆ 244237, Fax 244580 – . VISA.
39 rm 27.50/29.50 **t.**

MARKHAM MOOR Notts. – ✉ ☎ 0777 Retford.

◆London 143 – Lincoln 18 – ◆Nottingham 28 – ◆Sheffield 27.

Travelodge without rest., A 1 North Bound, DN22 0QH, ✆ 838091, Reservations (Toll free) 0800 850950 – . VISA.
40 rm 24.00/29.50 **t.**

MARKINGTON North Yorks. 402 P 21 – see Harrogate.

MARLBOROUGH Wilts. 403 404 O 29 **The West Country G.** – pop. 5 330 – ECD : Wednesday – ☎ 0672.

See : Site★.

Envir. : Savernake Forest★★ (Grand Avenue★★★), SE : 2 m. by A 346 – The Ridgeway Path★★, 85 miles starting from Overton Hill near Avebury including White Horse ≤★ – West Kennett Long Barrow★, W : 4½ m. – Silbury Hill★, W : 6 m. – Pewsey : Vale of Pewsey★, S : 7 m. on A 3455 – at Avebury★★, The Stones★, Church★, W : 7 m. – Wilton Windmill★*AC*, S : 9 m. by A 346 on A 338 – at Great Bedwyn, Crofton Beam Engines★*AC*, on Kennet and Avon Canal, SE : 10 m.

The Common ✆ 52147, N : 1 m – Ogbourne St George ✆ 067 284 (Ogbourne) 217.

St. Peter's Church, High St. ✆ 53989 (summer only).

◆London 84 – ◆Bristol 47 – ◆Southampton 40 – Swindon 12.

Ivy House (Best Western), High St., SN8 1HJ, ✆ 515333, Fax 515338 – – 50. VISA.
closed Christmas and New Year – **M** (see **Garden** below) – 7.50 – **33 rm** 49.50/81.00 **t.** – SB 84.00 **st.**

Castle and Ball (T.H.F.), High St., SN8 1LZ, ✆ 515201, Fax 515895 – rm – 40. VISA
M 11.50/17.95 **st.** and a la carte 4.00 – 7.00 – **36 rm** 75.00/100.00 **st.** – SB 84.00/110.00 **st.**

Garden (at Ivy House H.), High St., SN8 1HJ, ✆ 515333, Fax 515338 – VISA
closed Christmas and New Year – **M** 12.00/18.00 **t.** and a la carte 4.50.

at Burbage SE : 5¾ m. on A 346 – ✉ ☎ 0672 Marlborough :

Old Vicarage, Eastcourt, via Taskers Lane, SN8 3AG, ✆ 810495, – . VISA.
M (by arrangement) (communal dining) 25.00 **st.** – **3 rm** 30.00/50.00 **st.**

CITROEN Granham Hill ✆ 54461
PORSCHE London Rd ✆ 52001
ROVER 80-83 High St. ✆ 52076
ATS 120-121 London Rd ✆ 512274

Si vous écrivez à un hôtel à l'étranger,
joignez à votre lettre un coupon-réponse international.
(disponible dans les bureaux de poste).

MARLOW Bucks. 404 R 29 – pop. 18 584 – ECD : Wednesday – ☎ 0628 (6 fig.) or 062 84 (4 fig.).

Court Garden, Leisure Complex, Pound Lane ☎ 3597 (summer only).

London 35 – Aylesbury 22 – ♦Oxford 29 – Reading 14.

Compleat Angler (T.H.F.), Marlow Bridge, Bisham Rd, SL7 1RG, ☎ 484444, Telex 848644, Fax 486388, ≤ River Thames, « Riverside setting and grounds », – rm 120.
M 27.50 **st.** (lunch) and a la carte 25.25/42.20 **st.** 6.75 – 9.65 – **42 rm** 110.00/145.00 **st.**, **4 suites** 250.00/275.00 **st.** – SB (December-March) (weekends only) 150.00/160.00 **st.**

Country House without rest., Bisham Rd, SL7 1RP, ☎ 890606, Fax 890983, –
8 rm 55.00/73.00 **st.**

Hare and Hounds, Henley Rd, SL7 2DF, SW : ¾ m. on A 4155 ☎ 3343 –
closed Sunday – **M** a la carte 18.45/21.85 **t.** 4.50.

FORD Oxford Rd ☎ 890909

MARPLE Gtr Manchester 402 403 404 N 23 – pop. 18 708 – ECD : Wednesday – ☎ 061 Manchester.

London 190 – Chesterfield 35 – ♦Manchester 11.

Springfield, 99 Station Rd, SK6 6PA, ☎ 449 0721, –
M (restricted lunch) 9.00/12.50 **st.** and a la carte 4.00 – **6 rm** 38.00/48.00 **st.**

MARSTON MORETAINE Beds. 404 S 27 – see Bedford.

MARSTON TRUSSELL Northants. – see Market Harborough (Leics.).

MARTINHOE Devon – see Lynton.

MASHAM North Yorks. 402 P 21 – pop. 976 – ECD : Thursday – ✉ Ripon – ☎ 0765 Ripon.

Burnholme, Swinton Rd ☎ 0765 (Ripon) 89379.

London 231 – ♦Leeds 38 – ♦Middlesbrough 37 – York 32.

King's Head, Market Pl., HG4 4EF, ☎ 0765 (Ripon) 89295 –
10 rm.

Bank Villa, HG4 4DB, on A 6108 ☎ 0765 (Ripon) 89605, (from spring : 689605), – rest
April-October – **M** 12.00 **st.** 5.00 – **7 rm** 17.00/29.00 **st.**

Floodlite, 7 Silver St., HG4 4DX, ☎ 0765 (Ripon) 89000.

at Healey W : 3 m. by A 6018 – ✉ ☎ 0765 Ripon :

Pasture House, Colsterdale, HG4 4LJ, W : 1½ m. ☎ 0765 (Ripon) 89149, ≤, , park – – **4 rm.**

at Jervaulx Abbey NW : 5½ m. on A 6108 – ✉ Ripon – ☎ 0677 Bedale :

Jervaulx Hall, HG4 4PH, ☎ 60235, ≤, « Converted manor house, country house atmosphere », , park –
Mid March-mid November – **M** (dinner only) 15.00 **t.** 4.00 – **10 rm** 65.00/85.00 **t.** – SB (mid March-Easter) 90.00 **st.**

Old Hall, HG4 4PH, ☎ 60313 –
M (dinner only)(residents only)(communal dining) 16.00 **st.** – **3 rm** 30.00/40.00 **st.**

MATLOCK Derbs. 402 403 404 P 24 – pop. 13 706 – ECD : Thursday – ☎ 0629.

See : Site★.

Envir. : Riber Castle (ruins) ≤★ (Fauna Reserve and Wildlife Park *AC*) SE : 2½ m.

Chesterfield Rd ☎ 582191, NE : 1½m..

The Pavilion ☎ 55082.

London 153 – Derby 17 – ♦Manchester 46 – ♦Nottingham 24 – ♦Sheffield 24.

Riber Hall, Riber, DE4 5JU, SE : 3 m. by A 615 ☎ 582795, Fax 580475, ≤, « Elizabethan manor house », , –
M 12.50 **t.** (lunch) and a la carte 4.50 – 6.50 – **11 rm** 63.00/78.00 **t.** – SB (mid October-April) 115.00/139.00 **st.**

at Dethick SE : 4 m. by A 615 – ✉ ☎ 0629 Matlock :

Manor Farm, DE4 5GG, ☎ 534246, ≤, , park –
M 8.50 **st.** – **4 rm** 15.00/32.00 **st.**

at Matlock Bath S : 1½ m. on A 6 – ✉ ☎ 0629 Matlock :

New Bath (T.H.F.), New Bath Rd, DE4 3PX, ☎ 583275, Fax 580268, , heated, , , – rm – 100.
M 9.35/14.85 **st.** and a la carte 4.55 – **55 rm** 71.50/104.50 **st.** – SB (except Christmas) 84.00/114.00 **st.**

FORD 41 Causeway Lane ☎ 582231

MATLOCK BATH Derbs. 402 403 404 P 24 – see Matlock.

MAWGAN PORTH Cornwall 403 E 32 – ECD : Wednesday – ✉ Newquay – ☎ 0637 St. Mawgan.

♦London 293 – Newquay 7 – Truro 20.

- **Tredragon**, Tredragon Rd, TR8 4DQ, ☎ 860213, Telex 860269, ≤ Mawgan Porth, 🏊, 🌳 – 📺 ☎ 🅿
29 rm.

MAWNAN SMITH Cornwall 403 E 33 – see Falmouth.

MAYFIELD East Sussex 404 U 30 – pop. 1 784 – ECD : Wednesday – ☎ 0435.

♦London 46 – ♦Brighton 25 – Eastbourne 22 – Lewes 17 – Royal Tunbridge Wells 9.

- **Rose and Crown**, Fletching St., TN20 6TE, ☎ 872200 – 📺. 🐕
M 9.00/13.00 **st.** and a la carte 🍷 3.25 – ☕ 6.50 – **5 rm** 30.00/45.00 **st.**

MEADOW HEAD South Yorks. – see Sheffield.

MELBOURN Cambs. 404 U 27 – pop. 3 846 – ✉ ☎ 0763 Royston (Herts.).

♦London 44 – ♦Cambridge 10.

- **Melbourn Bury** 🐦, SG8 6DE, SW : ¾ m. on London rd ☎ 261151, Fax 262375, ≤, « Tastefully furnished country house of Tudor origin », 🌳, park – 📺 🅿. AE VISA. 🐕
closed Easter and Christmas-New Year – **M** *(closed Sunday)* (communal dining) (dinner only) 13.50 **st.** 🍷 3.00 – **3 rm** ☕ 45.00/75.00 **st.**

- XX **Pink Geranium**, 25 Station Rd, SG8 6DX, ☎ 260215, 🌳 – 🚭 🅿. VISA
closed Sunday dinner and Monday – **M** 12.95/26.00 **t.** and a la carte 🍷 4.50.

- XX **Sheen Mill** with rm, Station Rd, SG8 6DX, ☎ 261393, ≤, 🌳 – 📺 ☎ 🅿. AE ⓓ VISA. 🐕
M *(closed Sunday dinner and Bank Holidays)* (dancing Saturday) 12.50 **t.** (lunch) and a la carte 16.60/26.95 **t.** 🍷 3.50 – **7 rm** ☕ 40.00/75.00 **st.**

MELKSHAM Wilts. 403 404 N 29 – pop. 13 248 – ECD : Wednesday – ☎ 0225.

ℹ Roundhouse, Church St. ☎ 707424.

♦London 113 – ♦Bristol 25 – Salisbury 35 – Swindon 28.

- **Beechfield House**, Beanacre, SN12 7PU, N : 1 m. on A 350 ☎ 703700, Fax 790118, ≤, « Country house and gardens », 🏊 heated, 🎣, park, 🎾 – 🚭 rest 📺 ☎ 🅿. AE ⓓ VISA. 🐕
M 16.50/27.50 **st.** and a la carte 🍷 5.95 – ☕ 8.50 – **24 rm** 80.00/99.00 **t.** – SB (except Christmas and New Year) 105.00 **st.**

- **Shurnhold House** without rest., Shurnhold, SN12 8DG, NW : 1 m. on A 365 ☎ 790555, « Jacobean Manor House », 🌳 – 🚭 📺 ☎ 🅿. AE VISA. 🐕
☕ 2.50 – **8 rm** ☕ 38.00/68.00 **st.**

at Westbrook E : 3½ m. on A 3102 – ✉ Chippenham – ☎ 0380 Devizes :

- **Cottage** without rest., on A 3102, SN15 2EE, ☎ 850255, 🌳 – 📺 🅿. 🐕
March-October – **3 rm** ☕ 25.00/40.00 **s.**

at Shaw NW : 1½ m. on A 365 – ✉ Melksham – ☎ 0225 Shaw :

- **Shaw Country**, Bath Rd, SN12 8EF, on A 365 ☎ 702836, Fax 790275, 🏊 heated, 🌳 – 🚭 rest 📺 ☎ 🅿. AE VISA. 🐕
M *(closed Sunday dinner to non-residents)* 8.50/12.50 **t.** 🍷 3.95 – **13 rm** ☕ 38.00/75.00 **t.** – SB 130.00/172.00 **st.**

FORD Beanacre Rd ☎ 702230
RENAULT Semington Rd ☎ 702182
ROVER Lancaster Rd ☎ 702256

MELLOR Lancs. – see Blackburn.

MELTHAM West Yorks. 402 404 O 23 – pop. 7 098 – ✉ ☎ 0484 Huddersfield.

⛳18 Thick Hollins Hall ☎ 850227, E : 1 m.

♦London 192 – ♦Leeds 21 – ♦Manchester 23 – ♦Sheffield 26.

- **Durker Roods**, Bishops Way, HD7 3AG, ☎ 851413, Fax 851843, 🌳 – 📺 ☎ 🅿 – 🏛 80. AE ⓓ VISA
M *(closed Saturday lunch and Sunday dinner)* 8.50/12.50 **st.** and a la carte 🍷 4.00 – **31 rm** ☕ 35.00/50.00 **st.** – SB (weekends only) 60.00 **st.**

Gli alberghi o ristoranti ameni sono indicati nella guida
con un simbolo rosso.
Contribuite a mantenere
la guida aggiornata segnalandoci
gli alberghi ed i ristoranti dove avete soggiornato piacevolmente.

🏨🏨🏨🏨🏨 ... 🏠
XXXXX ... X

MELTON MOWBRAY Leics. 402 404 R 25 – pop. 23 379 – ECD : Thursday – ☎ 0664.

Thorpe Arnold ✆ 62118, NE : 2 m – Waltham Rd, Thorpe Arnold ✆ 62118.

Melton Carnegie Museum, Thorpe End, ✆ 69946.

♦London 113 – ♦Leicester 15 – Northampton 45 – ♦Nottingham 18.

- **Stapleford Park** , LE14 2EF, E : 5 m. by B 676 on Stapleford rd ✆ 057 284 (Wymondham) 522, Telex 342319, Fax 651, ≤, « Part 16C and 19C mansion in park », , , – rest TV ☎ P – 300. AE VISA
  M 22.50/27.50 **st.** and a la carte 20.50/28.00 **st.** 5.95 – 8.00 – **33 rm** 115.00/225.00 **st.**, **2 suites** 225.00 **st.**
- Harboro (T.H.F.), Burton St., LE13 1AF, ✆ 60121 – rm P. AE VISA.
  closed Christmas Day – 5.95 – **26 rm** -/39.50 **st.**
- **Westbourne House,** Nottingham Rd, LE13 0NP, ✆ 69456, – TV P.
  closed Christmas – **M** (by arrangement) 10.00 **t.** 4.00 – **16 rm** 19.00/29.00 **t.**

FIAT Mill St. ✆ 60141
RENAULT Victoria St. ✆ 62235
ROVER ✆ 60266
VOLVO Leicester Rd ✆ 410595
ATS Leicester Rd ✆ 62072

MENTMORE Bucks. 404 R 28 – pop. 196 – ✉ Leighton Buzzard – ☎ 0296 Cheddington.

♦London 46 – Aylesbury 10 – Luton 15.

- **The Stable Yard** without rest., LU7 0QG, ✆ 661488, « Attractive 19C stable and coach yard » – TV P.
  4 rm 35.00/60.00 **s.**
- XX **Stag Inn,** The Green, LU7 0QF, ✆ 668423, – P. VISA
  M 13.95 **t.** (lunch) and a la carte 17.85/26.45 **t.** 3.95.

MERE Wilts. 403 404 N 30 **The West Country G.** – pop. 2 201 – ECD : Wednesday – ☎ 0747.

Envir. : Stourhead House★★★ *AC*, NW : 3 m.

The Square, ✆ 860341.

♦ London 113 – Exeter 65 – Salisbury 26 – Taunton 40.

- **Chetcombe House,** Chetcombe Rd, BA12 6AZ, ✆ 860219, – TV P. VISA
  M (lunch by arrangement)/dinner 9.75 **st.** 2.20 – **5 rm** 25.00/45.00 **st.**

Citroen Castle St. ✆ 860404

MERE BROW Lancs. 402 L 23 – ✉ Preston – ☎ 077 473 (4 fig.) and 0772 (6 fig.) Hesketh Bank.

♦London 221 – ♦Liverpool 22 – Preston 11 – Southport 6.

- X **Crab and Lobster,** behind the Leigh Arms, Tarleton, PR4 6LA, ✆ 812734, Seafood – P. VISA
  closed Sunday, Monday and Christmas-end January – **M** (dinner only) a la carte 14.00/21.00 **t.**

MERIDEN West Midlands 403 404 P 26 – see Coventry.

MERTHYR TYDFIL Mid Glam. 403 J 28 – pop. 52 870 – ECD : Thursday – ☎ 0685.

Pant Dowlais ✆ 722822 – Cilsanws Mountain, Cefn Coed ✆ 723308.

14a Glebeland St. ✆ 79884.

♦London 179 – ♦Cardiff 25 – Gloucester 59 – ♦Swansea 33.

- **Tregenna,** Park Terr., CF47 8RF, ✆ 723627, Fax 721951 – TV ☎ P. AE VISA
  M 7.75/9.00 **t.** and a la carte 3.75 – **21 rm** 35.00/52.00 **st.** – SB 56.00/59.00 **st.**

ATS Dowlouis Top, Merthr Tydfil ✆ 82903

MEVAGISSEY Cornwall 403 F 33 **The West Country G.** – pop. 1 896 – ECD : Thursday – ☎ 0726.

See : Site★★.

♦London 287 – Newquay 21 – ♦Plymouth 44 – Truro 20.

- **Mevagissey House** , Vicarage Hill, PL26 6SZ, ✆ 842427, – rest TV P. VISA.
  March-October – **M** 14.00 **t.** 3.30 – **6 rm** 23.00/50.00 **t.**

MICKLETON Glos. 403 404 O 27 – see Chipping Campden.

MICKLE TRAFFORD Cheshire – see Chester.

MIDDLECOMBE Somerset – see Minehead.

MIDDLEHAM North Yorks. 402 O 21 – pop. 737 – ECD : Thursday – ☎ 0969 Wensleydale.

♦London 233 – Kendal 45 – ♦Leeds 47 – York 45.

- **Miller's House,** Market Pl., DL8 4NR, ✆ 22630, – rest TV ☎ P. VISA.
  closed January – **M** (bar lunch residents only)/dinner 16.00 **t.** 3.30 – **7 rm** 32.50/68.00 **t.** – SB 80.00/95.00 **st.**

at West Scrafton SW : 6 m. by Coverdale Rd – ✉ Leyburn – ☎ 0969 Wensleydale :

Coverdale Country, Swineside, DL8 4RX, ☎ 40601, ←, – rest TV P. VISA.
closed January – **M** 12.00 **t.** 3.90 – **11 rm** 27.00/60.00 **t.** – SB (October-May) 49.00/66.00 **st.**

Remember the speed limits that apply in the United Kingdom, unless otherwise signposted.

– 60 mph on single carriageway roads

– 70 mph on dual carriageway roads and motorways

MIDDLESBROUGH

Cleveland Centre ABY
Corporation Road BY 8
Dundas Street ABY 12
Grange Road ABY
Hill Street Centre AY
Linthorpe Road AY
Newport Road AY

Albert Road BY 2
Ayresome Green Lane AZ 3
Bridge Street West AY 4
Bright Street BY 5
Clairville Road BZ 6
Cleveland Street BY 7
Devonshire Road AZ 10
Eastbourne Road AZ 14
Ferry Road BY 15
Finsbury Street AZ 16
Gresham Road AZ 18
Hartington Road AY 19
Longford Street AZ 22
Ormesby Road BZ 24
Princes Road AZ 26
St. Barnabas Road AZ 27
Saltersgill Avenue BZ 28
Smeaton Street BY 30
Tees Bridge Approach Road AZ 34
West Terrace BZ 35
Westbourne Grove BZ 36
Wilson Street AY 38
Woodlands Road BZ 39
Zetland Street ABY 41

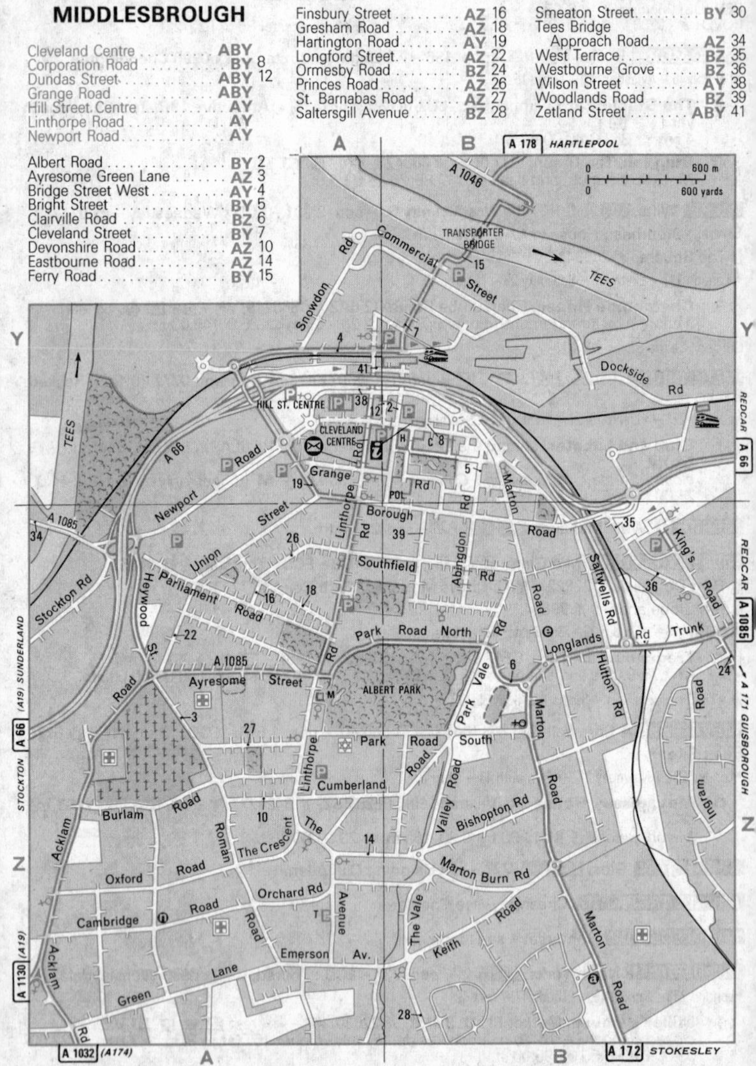

MIDDLESBROUGH Cleveland 402 Q 20 – pop. 158 516 – ECD : Wednesday – ☎ 0642.

⛳ Middlesbrough Municipal, Ladgate Lane ✆ 315533, S : by Acklam Rd AZ – ⛳ Brass Castle Lane ✆ 316430, by A 172 BZ.

✈ Teesside Airport : ✆ 0325 (Darlington) 332811, SW : 13 m. by A 66 AZ and A 19 on A 67.

ℹ 51 Corporation Rd ✆ 243425.

♦London 246 – ♦Kingston-upon-Hull 89 – ♦Leeds 66 – ♦Newcastle-upon-Tyne 41.

Plan opposite

- **Baltimore,** 250 Marton Rd, TS4 2EZ, ✆ 224111, Fax 226156 – TV ☎ P. AE VISA
  M 9.50/15.00 **st.** and a la carte 🍷 4.95 – ☕ 6.45 – **30 rm** 50.00/65.00 **st.**, **1 suite** 85.00/125.00 **st.** BZ **e**
- **Highfield** (B.C.B.), 358 Martan Rd, T54 2PA, ✆ 817638, Fax 821219 – TV ☎ P – 75. AE VISA.
  M (grill rest.) 8.00/15.00 **st.** – **23 rm** ☕ 41.00/54.00 **st.**
- **Marton Way Motel,** Marton Rd, TS4 3BS, ✆ 817651, Fax 829409 – rm TV ☎ P – 80. AE VISA BZ **a**
  M (carving rest.) 6.95 **t.** and a la carte – **53 rm** ☕ 24.50/44.50 **st.** – SB (weekends only) 27.00/33.50 **st.**
- **Grey House,** 79 Cambridge Rd, TS5 5NL, ✆ 817485, – TV P AZ **n**
  closed Christmas and New Year – **M** 7.00 **st.** – **7 rm** ☕ 28.00/38.00 **st.**

CITROEN Linthorpe Rd ✆ 822884
FORD Ormesby ✆ 242451
NISSAN Trunk Rd ✆ 461451
RENAULT Newport Rd ✆ 249346
ROVER 336 Stokesley Rd, Marton ✆ 317171
ROVER 237 Acklam Rd ✆ 817741
SKODA Eston Grange ✆ 452436
TALBOT, PEUGEOT Marton Rd ✆ 242873
TOYOTA Eastbourne Rd ✆ 816658
VAUXHALL Stokesley ✆ 710566
VAUXHALL-OPEL Marton Rd ✆ 243415
VW-AUDI Park End ✆ 317971

ATS Murdock Rd (off Sotherby Rd), Cargo Fleet ✆ 249245/6

☛ ***Michelin n'accroche pas de panonceau aux hôtels et restaurants qu'il signale.***

MIDDLETON STONEY Oxon. 403 404 Q 28 – pop. 238 – ECD : Saturday – ✉ Bicester – ☎ 086 989.

♦London 66 – Northampton 30 – ♦Oxford 12.

- **Jersey Arms,** OX6 8SE, ✆ 234, Fax 565 – TV ☎ P. AE VISA.
  M *(closed Sunday dinner)* a la carte 15.95/24.15 **t.** 🍷 4.95 – **13 rm** ☕ 55.00/69.50 **t.**, **3 suites** 85.00/100.00 **t.** – SB (except Christmas and New Year) 89.50/95.00 **st.**

MIDDLE WALLOP Hants. 403 404 P 30 – ✉ Stockbridge – ☎ 0264 Andover.

♦London 80 – Salisbury 11 – ♦Southampton 21.

- **Fifehead Manor,** SO20 8EG, on A 343 ✆ 781565, Fax 781400, « Converted 16C manor house », – TV ☎ ♿ P. AE VISA
  closed 2 weeks Christmas – **M** 16.00/30.00 **t.** and a la carte – **16 rm** ☕ 45.00/90.00 **st.** – SB (November-Easter) 100.00 **st.**

MIDHURST West Sussex 404 R 31 – pop. 5 991 – ECD : Wednesday – ☎ 0730.

See : Cowdray House (Tudor ruins)★ *AC*.

Envir. : Uppark★ (17C-18C) *AC*, SW : 12 m.

⛳ Cowdray Park ✆ 2088, NE : 1 m. on A 272.

♦London 57 – ♦Brighton 38 – Chichester 12 – ♦Southampton 41.

- **Spread Eagle** (Best Western), South St., GU29 9NH, ✆ 816911, Telex 86853, Fax 815668, « 15C hostelry, antique furnishings » – TV ☎ P – 40. AE VISA
  M 25.50/30.00 **st.** 🍷 5.75 – **41 rm** ☕ 73.00/195.00 **st.** – SB 120.00/180.00 **st.**
- **Mida,** Wool Lane, GU29 9BY, ✆ 813284
  closed Sunday, Monday last week May and last week October – **M** (booking essential) a la carte approx. 35.00 **t.**
- **Hindle Wakes,** 1 Church Hill, GU29 9NX, ✆ 813371 – VISA
  closed Tuesday lunch, Sunday and Monday – **M** a la carte 9.85/23.95 **t.** 🍷 3.75.
- **Maxine's,** Red Lion St., GU29 9PB, ✆ 816271 – AE VISA
  closed Monday lunch, Tuesday, 6 to 16 January and 9 to 22 March – **M** 9.95 **st.** and a la carte 🍷 4.25.

at Bepton SW : 2½ m. by A 286 – ✉ ☎ 073 081 Midhurst :

- **Park House**, South Bepton, GU29 0JB, ✆ 812880, Fax 815643, heated, , – TV ☎ P. VISA
  M (by arrangement) 12.50/18.00 🍷 3.20 – **11 rm** ☕ 46.00/126.50 **t.**

at Trotton W : 3¼ m. on A 272 – ✉ Petersfield (Hants.) – ☎ 073 080 Rogate :

- **Southdowns**, GU31 5JN, S : 1 m. ✆ 821521, Telex 86658, Fax 821790, , , – rm rest TV ☎ ♿ P – 150. AE VISA.
  M 12.95/17.50 **t.** and a la carte 🍷 3.75 – **21 rm** ☕ 45.00/100.00 **t.** – SB 75.00/95.00 **st.**

RENAULT Rumbolds Hill ✆ 2162

MILDENHALL Suffolk 404 V 26 – pop. 9 794 – ECD : Thursday – ☎ 0638.

London 73 – Cambridge 22 – Ipswich 38 – Norwich 41.

Bell (Best Western), High St., IP28 7EA, ☎ 717272, Telex 94011647, Fax 717057 – 100 – **17 rm.**

ATS Southgate Av. ☎ 713841/713891

MILFORD HAVEN (ABERDAUGLEDDAU) Dyfed 403 E 28 – pop. 13 927 – ECD : Thursday – ☎ 0646.

Woodbine House, Hubberstone ☎ 2368.

London 258 – Carmarthen 39 – Fishguard 23.

Lord Nelson, Hamilton Terr., SA73 3AL, ☎ 695341, Fax 693265, – rm. VISA.
M (bar lunch)/dinner 10.35 **t.** and a la carte 3.10 – **30 rm** 41.00/65.00 **t.**, **1 suite** 85.00/125.00 **t.** – SB (weekends only) 85.00/105.00 **st.**

MILFORD-ON-SEA Hants. 403 404 P 31 – pop. 3 953 – ECD : Wednesday – ✉ Lymington – ☎ 0590.

London 109 – Bournemouth 15 – Southampton 24 – Winchester 37.

South Lawn, Lymington Rd, SO41 0RF, ☎ 643911, Fax 644820, – rest. VISA.
closed mid-December-mid January – **M** *(closed dinner Sunday and Monday to non-residents)* (dinner only and Sunday lunch)/dinner 17.00 **t.** 5.00 – **24 rm** 45.00/91.00 **t.** – SB (November-May) 90.00/95.00 **st.**

Westover Hall, Park Lane, SO41 0PT, ☎ 643044, Fax 644490, ≤ – . VISA
M 16.95 **st.** and a la carte 4.95 – **13 rm** 35.00/49.000 **st.** – SB (except Easter, Christmas, New Year and Bank Holidays) 45.00/67.00 **st.**

MILTON ABBAS Dorset 403 404 N 31 **The West Country G.** – pop. 433 – ✉ Blandford – ☎ 0258.

See : Village★.

London 127 – Bournemouth 23 – Weymouth 19.

Milton Manor, DT11 0AZ, ☎ 880254, ≤, , park – rest. VISA.
M 18.00 4.50 – **12 rm** 42.00/72.00 – SB 98.00/108.00 **st.**

Old Bakery without rest., DT11 0BW, ☎ 880327, « Late 18C bakehouse in attractive conservation village », , park –
2 rm 12.00/35.00 **st.**, **1 suite** 35.00/40.00 **st.**

MILTON DAMEREL Devon 403 H 31 – ✉ ☎ 040 926.

Woodford Bridge, EX22 7LL, N : 1 m. on A 388 ☎ 481, Fax 585, , , , squash – rest. VISA
M (carving lunch)/dinner 20.95 **t.** and a la carte 4.90 – **12 rm** 45.00/90.00 **t.** – SB (September-June) 75.00/91.00 **st.**

MILTON KEYNES Bucks. 404 R 27 – pop. 93 305 – ☎ 0908.

Abbey Hill, Two Mile Ash ☎ 563845, W : 2 m. by A 5 – Windmill Hill, Tattenhoe Lane, Bletchley ☎ 648149 – , Woburn Bow Brickhill ☎ 370756.

Saxon Court, 502 Avebury Boulevard ☎ 691995.

London 56 – Birmingham 72 – Bedford 16 – Northampton 18 – Oxford 37.

Post House (T.H.F.), 500 Saxon Gate West, Milton Keynes Central, MK9 2HQ, ☎ 667722, Telex 826842, Fax 674714, , , – rm – 150. VISA
M 10.95/14.50 **st.** and a la carte 4.75 – 7.60 – **161 rm** 85.00/95.00 **st.**, **2 suites** 160.00 **st.**

Broughton, Broughton Village, MK10 9AA, E : 4 m. by A 509 and A 5130 ☎ 667726, Fax 604844, – . VISA.
M (bar lunch Monday to Saturday)/dinner 9.95 **t.** and a la carte – **30 rm** 56.00/72.00 **t.**

Moorings Toby, Milton Keynes Marina, Waterside, Peartree Bridge, MK6 3PE, SE : 1 ¾ m. by A 509 off A 4146 (Marlborough St.) ☎ 691515, Telex 826244, Fax 690274, « Marina setting alongside the Grand Union Canal » – rm. VISA.
M (grill rest.) a la carte 8.15/14.15 **t.** – **40 rm** 65.00/75.00 **t.**

Friendly H., Monks Way, Two Mile Ash, MK8 8LY, NW : 2 m. by A 509 and A5 at junction with A 422 ☎ 561666, Telex 826152, Fax 568303 – – 120. VISA.
M (carving rest.) 16.00 **st.** and a la carte 4.00 – 5.00 – **50 rm** 52.00/73.00 **st.** – SB (weekends only) 70.00/75.00 **st.**

WayFarer, Willen Lake, MK15 0DS, E : 2 m. by A 509 off Brickhill St. ☎ 675222, Fax 674679, ≤, « Lakeside setting » – – 50. VISA.
M *(bar lunch Saturday)* 7.95 **st.** (lunch) and a la carte 3.85 – **41 rm** 59.50/69.50 **st.** – SB (weekends only) 70.00 **st.**

XX **Jaipur,** Elder House, 502 Eldergate, Station Sq., MK9 1LR, ☎ 669796, Indian rest. – AE VISA
M a la carte 8.50/18.20 **t.**

AUDI, VW 3 Denbigh Rd ☎ 641535
FIAT Unit 15, Erica Rd ☎ 320355
FORD Bilton Rd ☎ 374011
FORD Stratford Rd ☎ 313117
LADA, PROTON 9 London Rd ☎ 562361
MAZDA 14 London Rd, Old Stratford ☎ 502194
NISSAN Tavistock St. ☎ 375388
PEUGEOT-TALBOT 125 Buckingham Rd ☎ 643322
ROVER 32 Aylesbury St. ☎ 643636
SAAB,MAZDA London Rd, Old Stratford ☎ 562194
TOYOTA 84 Newport Rd ☎ 313383

ATS 38 Victoria Rd ☎ 640420/640445

MILTON ON STOUR Dorset 403 404 N 30 – see Gillingham.

MILTON-UNDER-WYCHWOOD Oxon – pop. 1 471 – ☎ 0993 Shipton-under-Wychwood.
♦London 83 – ♦Birmingham 52 – Gloucester 35 – ♦Oxford 27.

Hillborough, The Green, OX7 6JH, ☎ 830501 – TV P. AE VISA
closed January – **M** *(closed Sunday dinner)* 13.50 **t.** and a la carte 3.25 – **10 rm** 35.00/48.00 **t.** – SB (except Bank Holidays) 60.00/68.00 **st.**

MINEHEAD Somerset 403 J 30 **The West Country G.** – pop. 8 449 – ECD : Wednesday – ☎ 0643.

See : Site★ – Higher Town : Church Steps★ – St. Michael's Church★ – West Somerset Railway★.

Envir. : Selworthy★ : Church★★ (≤★★★ from Church of Dunkery Beacon), W : 4 ½ m. – Timberscombe Church★, S : 5 m.

18 Warren Rd ☎ 2057.

Market House, The Parade ☎ 702624.

♦London 187 – ♦Bristol 64 – Exeter 43 – Taunton 25.

Benares ⑤, Northfield Rd, TA24 5PT, ☎ 704911, ≤, « Gardens » – ⇔ rest TV ☎ P. AE VISA
22 March-3 November – **M** (bar lunch)/dinner 15.00 **st.** 3.90 – **20 rm** 45.00/74.00 **st.** – SB (March-November) 80.00/86.00 **st.**

Northfield (Best Western) ⑤, Northfield Rd, TA24 5PU, ☎ 705155, ≤ bay, « Gardens », – TV ☎ P – 80. AE VISA
M 6.00/11.95 **t.** 3.50 – **26 rm** 48.00/96.00 **t.** – SB (except Christmas and New Year) 102.00/112.00 **st.**

Beacon Country House ⑤, Beacon Rd, TA24 5SD, ☎ 703476, , park – TV ☎ P. VISA
M a la carte 16.50/22.00 **t.** 7.45 – **7 rm** 60.00/75.00 **st.** – SB (weekdays only) 133.00/144.00 **st.**

Beaconwood ⑤, Church Rd, North Hill, TA24 5SB, ☎ 702032, ≤ sea and Minehead, heated, – ⇔ rest TV ☎ P. VISA
March-October – **M** (bar lunch)/dinner 11.00 **st.** 3.00 – **15 rm** 30.00/55.00 **t.** – SB (October, March and April) 63.00/67.50 **st.**

Remuera ⑤, Northfield Rd, TA24 5QH, ☎ 702611, – ⇔ rest TV P. VISA
May-September – **M** 15.00 (dinner) and a la carte 4.00 – **8 rm** 25.00/50.00 – SB 34.00 **st.**

York House Inn, 48 The Avenue, TA24 5AN, ☎ 705151 – TV ☎ P. AE VISA
closed 24 to 31 December – **M** a la carte 6.45/13.55 **st.** – **15 rm** 21.00/42.00 **st.** – SB (October-May) 46.00 **st.**

Woodbridge, 12-14 The Parks, TA24 8BS, ☎ 704860 – P. AE VISA
M (by arrangement) 7.50 **t.** 2.00 – **9 rm** 14.00/30.00 **t.** – SB 31.45/38.60 **st.**

at Middlecombe W : 1 ½ m. by A 39 – ✉ ☎ 0643 Minehead:

Periton Park ⑤, TA24 8SW, ☎ 706885, ≤, , park – ⇔ rest TV ☎ P. AE VISA
closed first 2 weeks January – **M** *(closed lunch Tuesday to Saturday, Sunday dinner and Monday to non-residents and Sunday lunch)* (restricted lunch)/dinner 16.50 **st.** and a la carte 3.95 – **7 rm** 52.50/75.00 **t.** – SB (November-August) 82.00/96.00 **st.**

FIAT Alcombe Rd ☎ 703379

ATS Bampton St. ☎ 704808/9

MINSTER-IN-THANET Kent 404 Y 29 – see Ramsgate.

MINSTER LOVELL Oxon. 403 404 P 28 – pop. 1 364 – ✉ ☎ 0993 Witney.
♦London 72 – Gloucester 36 – ♦Oxford 16.

Old Swan ⑤, Main St., Old Minster, OX8 5RN, ☎ 775614, Fax 702002, « 14C inn », – TV ☎ P. AE VISA
M 9.50 **t.** (lunch) and a la carte 4.50 – **10 rm** 95.00/121.00 **st.** – SB (weekends only) 143.00/158.00 **st.**

MISKIN Mid Glam. – ✉ Cardiff – ☎ 0443 Pontypridd.

◆London 169 – ◆Cardiff 22 – ◆Swansea 31.

Miskin Manor, CF7 8ND, E : 1¾ m. by A 4119 (Groes Faen rd) ℘ 224204, Fax 237606, ≤, « Local stone building in attractive formal grounds », ▣, ≉, park, squash – TV ☎ P – 150. AE VISA. ✻
M 30.00 **t.** and a la carte 5.75 – ☕ 7.00 – **34 rm** 70.00/90.00 **t.**, **1 suite** 95.00/125.00 **t.** – SB (weekends only) 200.00 **st.**

MITHIAN Cornwall 403 E 33 – see St. Agnes.

MOLD (YR WYDDGRUG) Clwyd 402 403 K 24 – pop. 8 487 – ECD : Thursday – ☎ 0352.

Pantmywyn ℘ 740318, W : 4 m. – Old Padeswood, Station Rd ℘ 0244 (Buckley) 547401, E : 2 m. on A 5118.

Town Hall, Earl St. ℘ 59331 (summer only).

◆London 211 – Chester 12 – ◆Liverpool 29 – Shrewsbury 45.

Soughton Hall ⛰, CH7 6AB, N : 2 ½ m. by A 494 and A 5119 on Alltami rd ℘ 035 286 (Northop) 811, Telex 61267, Fax 382, ≤, « Early 18C Italianate mansion », ≉ – TV ☎ P. AE VISA. ✻
closed first 2 weeks January – **M** (lunch by arrangement Monday and Saturday)/dinner 26.50 **t.** – **11 rm** ☕ 90.00/133.40 **t.**

Beaufort Palace, Alltami Rd, New Brighton, CH7 6RQ, ℘ 58646, Fax 57132 – TV ☎ P – 300. AE VISA
M 7.50/11.95 **st.** and a la carte – **102 rm** ☕ 58.00/95.00 **st.** – SB (weekends only and August) 75.00 **st.**

Bryn Awel, Denbigh Rd, CH7 1BL, on A 541 ℘ 58622, Fax 58625 – TV ☎ P. VISA. ✻
M *(closed Saturday lunch and Sunday dinner)* 7.50 **t.** and a la carte 3.60 – **17 rm** ☕ 30.00/44.00 **t.**

ATS Wrexham Rd ℘ 3682

There is no paid publicity in this Guide.

MONK FRYSTON North Yorks. 402 Q 22 – pop. 737 – ✉ Lumby – ☎ 0977 South Milford.

Envir. : Selby Abbey Church★★ (12C-16C) E : 8½ m. – Carlton Towers★ (19C) *AC*, SE : 14½ m.

◆London 190 – ◆Kingston-upon-Hull 42 – ◆Leeds 13 – York 20.

Monk Fryston Hall, LS25 5DU, ℘ 682369, Telex 556634, Fax 683544, « Italian garden », park – ⇎ rest TV ☎ P – 50. AE VISA
M 10.50/16.00 **t.** and a la carte 5.80 – **29 rm** ☕ 54.00/95.00 **t.** – SB (except Christmas and NewYear) (weekends only) 82.00/102.00 **st.**

Selby Fork Post House (T.H.F.), South Milford, LS25 5LF, W : 2¼ m. by A 63 on A 1 ℘ 682711, Telex 557074, Fax 685462, ≘, ▣, ✻ – ⇎ rm ▤ rest TV ☎ P – 300. AE VISA
M 11.20/14.20 **st.** and a la carte 4.35 – ☕ 7.50 – **103 rm** 69.00/110.00 **st.** – SB (weekends only) (except Christmas and New Year) 74.00/86.00 **st.**

MONKTON COMBE Avon – see Bath.

MONMOUTH (TREFYNWY) Gwent 403 L 28 – pop. 7 379 – ECD : Thursday – ☎ 0600.

Envir. : SE : Wye Valley★ – Raglan (castle★ 15C) SW : 7 m. – Skenfrith (castle and church★) NW : 6 m.

Rolls of Monmouth, The Hendre ℘ 5353, W : 4 m. on B 4233 – Leasebrook Lane ℘ 2212.

Shire Hall ℘ 3899.

◆London 147 – Gloucester 26 – Newport 24 – ◆Swansea 64.

King's Head, Agincourt Sq., NP5 3DY, ℘ 2177, Telex 497294, Fax 3545 – TV ☎ P – 80. AE VISA
M 14.00/20.00 **t.** 3.70 – ☕ 6.00 – **29 rm** 50.00/68.00 **t.** – SB 95.00/105.00 **st.**

at Whitebrook SE : 8½ m. by A 466 – ✉ ☎ 0600 Monmouth :

XX **Crown at Whitebrook** ⛰ with rm, NP5 4TX, ℘ 860254, Fax 860607, ≉ – TV ☎ P. AE VISA
closed 25-26 December and 3 weeks January – **M** *(closed Sunday dinner and Monday lunch to non-residents)* 12.50/24.00 **t.** 3.50 – **12 rm** ☕ 43.00/76.00 **t.** – SB (except Bank Holidays) 96.00/106.00 **st.**

at Trelleck S : 5½ m. on B 4293 – ✉ ☎ 0600 Monmouth :

XX **Village Green,** NP5 4DA, ℘ 860119 – P. VISA
closed Sunday dinner and Monday – **M** 11.00 **t.** (lunch) and a la carte 16.25/22.00 **t.** 3.50.

FORD Redbrook Rd ℘ 2366
MERCEDES-BENZ 8 Wonastow Rd ℘ 3118
ROVER St. James Sq. ℘ 2773
SUZUKI Wonastow Rd ℘ 2896
ATS Wonastow Rd, Ind. Est. ℘ 6832

MONTACUTE Somerset 403 L 31 – see Yeovil.

MONTGOMERY **(TREFALDWYN)** Powys 403 K 26 – pop. 1 035 – ☎ 068 681.

◆London 194 – ◆Birmingham 71 – Chester 53 – Shrewsbury 30.

Dragon, Town Square, SY15 6AA, ☎ 668359 – TV ☎ P. VISA. **M** 10.75/12.50 **t.** and a la carte 3.25 – **15 rm** 35.00/52.50 **t.** – SB (except Christmas and New Year) 72.50 **st.**

MORCOTT SERVICE AREA Leics. – see Uppingham.

MORECAMBE Lancs. 402 L 21 – pop. 41 432 – ECD : Wednesday – ☎ 0524.

See : Marineland★ *AC.*

Bare ☎ 418050, on sea front.

Marine Rd Central ☎ 414110.

◆London 248 – ◆Blackpool 29 – ◆Carlisle 66 – Lancaster 4.

Strathmore (Best Western), Marine Rd, East Promenade, LA4 5AP, ☎ 421234, Telex 65452, Fax 414242, ← – rest TV ☎ P – 100. AE VISA. **M** 9.00/15.00 **t.** – **51 rm** 46.00/80.00 **t.** – SB 76.00/90.00 **st.**

Prospect, 363 Marine Rd, East Promenade, LA4 5AQ, ☎ 417819 – TV. AE VISA *Easter-October* – **M** 5.00 **st.** 3.00 – **14 rm** 18.00/34.00 **st.** – SB (except Bank Holidays) 30.00 **st.**

CITROEN-LADA West Gate ☎ 413891
ROVER Marine Drive Central ☎ 414078
VAUXHALL-OPEL Bare Lane ☎ 410205
VOLVO Marlborough Rd ☎ 417437
VW, AUDI Heysham Rd ☎ 415833
ATS Westgate ☎ 68075/62011

MORETONHAMPSTEAD Devon 403 I 32 – ✉ Newton Abbot – ☎ 0647.

◆London 213 – Exeter 13 – ◆Plymouth 28.

Moorcote without rest., TQ13 8LS, on A 382 ☎ 40966, – TV P. **6 rm** 15.00/32.00 **st.**

Hocks with rm, 11A Cross St., TQ13 8NL, ☎ 40691 – TV. VISA. *closed November* – **M** *(closed Tuesday and Wednesday December-June, Monday and Sunday)* (dinner only) a la carte 11.70/16.80 **st.** – **3 rm** 15.00/25.00 **st.**

MORETON-IN-MARSH Glos. 403 404 O 28 – pop. 2 545 – ECD : Wednesday – ☎ 0608.

Envir. : Chastleton House★★ (Elizabethan) *AC,* SE : 3½ m.

◆London 86 – ◆Birmingham 40 – Gloucester 31 – ◆Oxford 29.

Manor House, High St., GL56 0LJ, ☎ 50501, Telex 837151, Fax 51481, « 16C manor house, gardens », , , – TV ☎ P – 75. AE VISA. **M** 10.95/25.00 **t.** and a la carte – **38 rm** 55.00/79.50 **t.**

Redesdale Arms, High St., GL56 0AW, ☎ 50308, Fax 51843 – TV ☎ P. AE VISA **M** 16.95 **t.** (dinner) and a la carte 17.95/26.65 **t.** 3.75 – **15 rm** 44.50/65.00 **t.**, **2 suites** 85.00/115.00 **t.** – SB (except Christmas) 85.00 **st.**

White Hart Royal (T.H.F.), High St., GL56 0BA, ☎ 50731, Fax 50880 – rm TV ☎ P – 65. AE VISA **M** *(closed lunch Monday to Saturday)/dinner* 13.95 **st.** and a la carte 4.25 – **18 rm** 40.00/65.00 **st.**

Annies, 3 Oxford St., GL56 0LA, ☎ 51981 – AE VISA *closed 28 January-10 February* – **M** *(closed Sunday dinner)* (dinner only Monday to Saturday and Sunday lunch)/dinner a la carte 17.70/23.85 **st.** 3.75.

at Evenlode SE: 3m. by A 44 – ✉ ☎ 0608 Moreton-in Marsh :

Twostones without rest., GL56 0NY, ☎ 51104, ←, – rm P. *April-October* – **3 rm** 15.00/27.00 **st.**

PEUGEOT-TALBOT London Rd ☎ 50585
RENAULT Little Compton ☎ 74202

MORPETH Northumb. 401 402 O 18 – pop. 14 301 – ECD : Thursday – ☎ 0670.

Envir. : Brinkburn Priory (site★, church★ : Gothic) *AC,* NW : 10 m – Wallington House★ W : 11 m.

Newbiggin-by-the-Sea ☎ 817344, E : 9 m – The Common ☎ 519980, S : 1 m. on A 197.

The Chantry, Bridge St. ☎ 511323.

◆London 301 – ◆Edinburgh 93 – ◆Newcastle-upon-Tyne 15.

Linden Hall , Longhorsley Rd, NE65 8XF, NW : 7½ m. by A 192 on A 697 ☎ 516611, Telex 538224, Fax 88544, ←, « Country house in extensive grounds », , , park, – TV ☎ P – 180. AE VISA. **M** 14.50/19.50 **st.** and a la carte 3.65 – **45 rm** 85.00/250.00 **st.** – SB 119.00/130.00 **st.**

CITROEN Pegswood ☎ 512189
FORD 53-55 Bridge St. ☎ 519611
PEUGEOT, TALBOT Ellington ☎ 860327
PEUGEOT Hillgate ☎ 517441
VAUXHALL Bridge End ☎ 512115
VW 12 Castle Sq. ☎ 519011
ATS Coopies Lane Ind Est. ☎ 514627

MORSTON Norfolk – see Blakeney.

MORTEHOE Devon 403 H 30 – see Woolacombe.

MORWENSTOW Cornwall 403 G 31 – ✉ Bude – ☎ 028 883.

◆London 259 – Exeter 58 – ◆Plymouth 51 – Truro 60.

Old Vicarage 🐎, EX23 9SR, ☎ 369, ⚘ – ⚟ rm 🅟. ✻
March-November – **M** 10.00 – **3 rm** ☐ 19.00/38.00 **s.**

MOULSFORD Oxon. 403 404 Q 29 – pop. 494 – ☎ 0491 Cholsey.

◆London 58 – ◆Oxford 17 – Reading 13 – Swindon 37.

Beetle and Wedge 🐎, Ferry Lane, OX10 9JF ☎ 651381, Fax 651376, ←, ⚘ – 📺 ☎ 🅟. 🅢 AE VISA. ✻
closed Christmas Day – **M** *(closed Sunday dinner)* 35.00 **t.** and a la carte – **13 rm** ☐ 60.00/75.00 **t.** – SB (weekends only) (except Christmas and New Year) 110.00 **t.**

MOULTON Northants. 404 R 27 – see Northampton.

MOULTON North Yorks. 402 P 20 – ✉ Richmond – ☎ 0325 Darlington.

◆London 243 – ◆Leeds 53 – ◆Middlesbrough 25 – ◆Newcastle-upon-Tyne 43.

XX **Black Bull Inn,** DL10 6QJ, ☎ 377289, Fax 377422, « Brighton Belle Pullman coach » – 🅟. 🅢 AE VISA
closed Sunday and 24 December-1 January – **M** 9.75 **t.** (lunch) and a la carte 13.00/18.25 **t.**

MOUSEHOLE Cornwall 403 D 33 **The West Country G.** – ECD : Wednesday except summer – ✉ ☎ 0736 Penzance.

See : Site★.

◆London 321 – Penzance 3 – Truro 29.

Carn Du 🐎, Raginnis Hill, TR19 6SS, ☎ 731233, ← Mounts Bay, ⚘ – ⚟ rest 🅟. 🅢 AE VISA. ✻
closed February – **M** (bar lunch)/dinner 12.00 **t.** 🍷 3.95 – **7 rm** ☐ 25.00/50.00 **t.**

Tavis Vor, The Parade, TR19 6PR, ☎ 731306, ← Mounts Bay, ⚘ – 🅟. ✻
M 9.50 **t.** 🍷 4.00 – **7 rm** ☐ 18.60/41.20 **t.**

MUDEFORD Dorset 403 404 O 31 – see Christchurch.

MUCH BIRCH Heref. and Worc. – see Hereford.

MUKER North Yorks. 402 N 21 – ✉ ☎ 0748 Richmond.

◆London 262 – ◆Carlisle 63 – Kendal 38.

Old Vicarage 🐎, DL11 6QH, ☎ 86498, ←, ⚘ – ⚟ 📺 ☎ 🅟. ✻
March-October – **4 rm** ☐ (dinner included) 34.25/56.50 **st.** – SB 131.00 **st.**

MULLION Cornwall 403 E 33 **The West Country G.** – pop. 1 958 – ECD : Wednesday – ✉ Helston – ☎ 0326.

See : Mullion Cove★★★ (Church★).

⛳18 Cury Helston ☎ 240276.

◆London 323 – Falmouth 21 – Penzance 21 – Truro 26.

Polurrian, TR12 7EN, SW : ½ m. ☎ 240421, Fax 240083, ← Mounts Bay, ⚹, ≘, ⛱ heated, ⛱, ⚘, ⚔, squash – 📺 ☎ 🅟. 🅢 AE ⓞ VISA
closed mid December-mid March – **M** (bar lunch)/dinner 14.50 **st.** and a la carte 🍷 3.50 – **40 rm** ☐ (dinner included) 68.00/78.00 **st.**, **1 suite** 83.00 **st.** – SB 96.00/123.00 **st.**

MUMBLES West Glam. 403 I 29 – ECD : Wednesday – ✉ ☎ 0792 Swansea.

See : Mumbles Head★.

Envir. : Cefn Bryn (✻★★★ from the reservoir) W : 12 m. – Rhosili (site and ←★★★) W : 18 m. – W : Oxwich Bay★.

◆London 202 – ◆Swansea 6.

Langland Court (Best Western), 31 Langland Court Rd, Langland Bay, SA3 4TD, W : 1 m. ☎ 361545, Telex 498627, Fax 362302, ⚘ – ⚟ rm 📺 ☎ 🚗 🅟 – 🏛 150. 🅢 AE ⓞ VISA. ✻
closed 25 and 26 December – **M** (bar lunch Monday to Saturday)/dinner 18.50 **st.** and a la carte 🍷 4.75 – **21 rm** ☐ 46.00/72.00 **st.** – SB 84.00/92.00 **st.**

Osborne, Rotherslade Rd, Langland Bay, SA3 4QL, W : ¾ m. ☎ 366274, Fax 363100, ← – 🛗 📺 ☎ 🅟 – 🏛 50
36 rm.

Norton House, 17 Norton Rd, SA3 5TQ, ☎ 404891, Fax 403210 – 📺 ☎ 🅟. 🅢 AE ⓞ VISA. ✻
M (dinner only) 17.50 **t.** and a la carte 🍷 3.95 – ☐ 6.00 – **15 rm** 45.00/70.00 **t.** – SB (weekends only) (except Christmas and New Year) 90.00/100.00 **st.**

Old School House, 37 Nottage Rd, Newton, SA3 4TF, W : 1 m. ✆ 361541 – TV ☎ P. AE VISA.
M *(closed Saturday)* 8.00 **t.** (dinner) and a la carte 4.00 – **7 rm** 40.00/50.00 **t**

Wittemberg, 2 Rotherslade Rd, Langland, SA3 4QN, W : ¾ m. ✆ 369696 – rm TV P. VISA.
closed Christmas – **M** 10.00 **st.** – **11 rm** 30.00/45.00 **st.** – SB 58.00/62.00 **st.**

MUNGRISDALE Cumbria 401 402 L 19 20 – pop. 336 – ✉ Penrith – 059 683 Threlkeld.

♦London 301 – ♦Carlisle 33 – Keswick 8.5 – Penrith 13.

Mill, CA11 0XR, ✆ 79659, – rest TV P
closed November-February – **M** (dinner only) 16.00 **st.** 3.40 – **7 rm** 32.00/60.00 **st.**

NAILSWORTH Glos. 403 404 N 28 – ✉ 045 383.

Flynns, 3 Fountain St., GL6 0BL, ✆ 5567 – P. VISA
closed Monday lunch and Sunday – **M** 14.50/25.50 **t.** and a la carte.

NANTGAREDIG Dyfed 403 H 28 – see Carmarthen.

NANTWICH Cheshire 402 403 404 M 24 – pop. 11 867 – ECD : Wednesday – 0270.

Beam St. ✆ 623914.

♦London 176 – Chester 20 – ♦Liverpool 45 – ♦Stoke-on-Trent 17.

Rookery Hall, Worleston, CW5 6DQ, N : 2 ½ m. by A 51 on B 5074 ✆ 626866, Fax 626027, ≤, « Late 18C country house with an unusual Continental character », , park, – rest TV ☎ P – 60. AE VISA.
M (booking essential) 16.50/27.50 **t.** – **40 rm** 92.50/140.00 **t.**, **5 suites** 260.00/300.00 **t.** – SB (weekends only) 180.00 **st.**

Crown, High St., CW5 5AS, ✆ 625283, Fax 628047, « 16C inn » – TV ☎ P – 100. AE VISA
closed Christmas Day – **M** (bar lunch)/dinner 15.00 **t.** 4.00 – **18 rm** 49.00/65.00 **t.** – SB (weekends only) 62.00/82.00 **st.**

FORD Crewe Rd ✆ 623739
HONDA Whitchurch Rd ✆ 780300
LANCIA Welsh Row ✆ 627678
ROVER London Rd ✆ 623151
VAUXHALL-OPEL Station Rd ✆ 0270 (Crewe) 258822

NARBOROUGH Leics. 403 404 Q 26 – see Leicester.

NATIONAL EXHIBITION CENTRE West Midlands 403 404 O 26 – see Birmingham.

NAWTON North Yorks. – see Helmsley.

NEAR SAWREY Cumbria 402 L 20 – see Hawkshead.

NEASHAM Durham 402 P 20 – see Darlington.

NEATH (CASTELL-NED) West Glam. 403 I 29 – 0639.

Swansea Bay, Jersey Marine ✆ 0792 (Swansea) 814153 – Cadoxton ✆ 643615.

♦London 188 – ♦Cardiff 40 – ♦Swansea 8.

Castle (Lansbury), The Parade, SA11 1RB, ✆ 643581, Telex 48119, Fax 641624, – rm TV ☎ P – 150. AE VISA
M 8.95/14.00 **t.** and a la carte – **28 rm** 56.00/69.00 **t.** – SB (weekends only) 56.00/66.00 **st.**

NEATISHEAD Norfolk 404 Y 25 – pop. 524 – 0692 Horning.

♦London 122 – North Walsham 8.5 – ♦Norwich 11.

Regency without rest., Neatishead Post Office, NR12 8AD, ✆ 630233 – TV
5 rm 18.00/40.00 **s.**

NEEDHAM MARKET Suffolk 404 X 27 – pop. 3 420 – ECD : Tuesday – ✉ 0449.

♦London 77 – ♦Cambridge 47 – ♦Ipswich 8.5 – ♦Norwich 38.

Pipps Ford, Norwich Rd Roundabout, IP6 8LJ, SE : 1 ¾ m. by B 1078 at junction of A 45 and A 140 ✆ 044 979 (Coddenham) 208, « Elizabethan farmhouse », , , – rm P.
closed Christmas and New Year – **M** (by arrangement) 15.00 **st.** 2.50 – **6 rm** 30.00/50.00 **st.**

NEFYN Gwynedd 402 403 G 25 – pop. 2 236 – ECD : Wednesday – ☎ 0758.

See : Site★.

Nefyn District ℘ 720218.

◆London 265 – Caernarfon 20.

Caeau Capel , Rhodfar Mor, LL53 6EB, ℘ 720240, – . VISA
Easter-October – **M** (bar lunch)/dinner 11.00 **t.** 1.95 – **19 rm** 20.50/49.70 **t.**

ROVER Church St. ℘ 720206

NETTLETON Wilts. 403 404 N 29 – see Castle Combe.

NEW ALRESFORD Hants. 403 404 Q 30 – pop. 4 117 – ☎ 0962.

◆London 63 – ◆Portsmouth 40 – Reading 33 – ◆Southampton 20.

Old School House, 60 West St., SO24 9AU, ℘ 732134 – . VISA
closed lunch Monday to Friday – **M** 17.00/19.00 **t.** and a la carte 4.00.

NEWARK-ON-TRENT Notts. 402 404 R 24 – pop. 33 143 – ECD : Thursday – ☎ 0636.

See : St. Mary Magdalene Church★.

Coddington ℘ 84241, E : 4 m. on A 17.

The Ossington, Beast Market Hill, Castlegate ℘ 78962.

◆London 127 – Lincoln 16 – ◆Nottingham 20 – ◆Sheffield 42.

Grange, 73 London Rd, at corner of Charles St., NG24 1RZ, ℘ 703399, Fax 702328, –
. VISA
closed 24 December-2 January – **M** (bar lunch)/dinner a la carte approx. 15.50 **t.** 3.00 –
9 rm 40.00/65.00 **t.** – SB (September-March) (weekends only) 60.00/70.00 **st.**

at North Muskham N : 4 m. by A 6065 – ☎ 0636 Newark-on-Trent :

Travelodge without rest., NG23 6HT, N : ½ m. on A1 (Southbound carriageway)
℘ 703635, Reservations (Toll free) 0800 850950 – . VISA.
30 rm 24.00/29.50 **t.**

FORD Farndon Rd ℘ 704131
RENAULT Clinton St. ℘ 704619
ROVER 69 Northgate ℘ 703413
SKODA London Rd ℘ 705845

VAUXHALL 116 Farndon Rd ℘ 705431
VW, AUDI Northern Rd ℘ 704484

ATS 70 William St. ℘ 77531

NEWBURY Berks. 403 404 Q 29 – pop. 31 488 – ECD : Wednesday – ☎ 0635.

Newbury Crookham, Bury7s Bank Rd ℘ 40035 – DonningtonValley, Oxford Rd ℘ 32488 –
West Berkshire, Chaddleworth ℘ 048 82 (Chaddleworth) 574.

The Wharf ℘ 30267.

◆London 67 – ◆Bristol 66 – ◆Oxford 28 – Reading 17 – ◆Southampton 38.

Foley Lodge, Stockcross, RG16 8JU, NW : 2 m. by A 4 on B 4000 ℘ 528770, Fax 528398,
, – – 180. VISA.
M 12.50/22.50 **t.** and a la carte 6.00 – **68 rm** 89.00/110.00 **t.**, **2 suites** 130.00/180.00 **t.**
– SB (weekends only) 115.00 **st.**

Hilton National, Pinchington Lane, RG14 7HL, S : 2 m. by A 34 ℘ 529000, Telex 848247,
Fax 529337, , , – rm – 190. VISA
M 23.50/29.50 **t.** and a la carte – 8.50 – **112 rm** 79.00/115.00 **st.** – SB (weekends only)
150/224.00 **st.**

Elcot Park Resort, RG16 8NJ, W : 5 m. by A 4 ℘ 58100, Telex 846448, Fax 58288, <, ,
park, – – 50
34 rm, **2 suites.**

Stakis Newbury, Oxford Rd, RG16 8XY, N : 3 ¼ m. on A 34 ℘ 247010, Telex 848694,
Fax 247077, , , – rm – 40. VISA
M (carving lunch) 8.50/13.00 and a la carte – 7.50 – **110 rm** 70.00/96.00 **t.**, **2 suites**
115.00 **t.** – SB 70.00/122.00 **st.**

Chequers (T.H.F.), 7-8 Oxford St., RG13 1JB, ℘ 38000, Telex 849205, Fax 37170, –
rm – 50. VISA
M *(closed Saturday lunch)* 9.50/16.95 **st.** and a la carte 4.35 – 7.00 – **56 rm** 70.00/
105.00 **st.** – SB (weekends only) 168.00/200.00 **st.**

Enborne Grange, Enborne St., Wash Common, RG14 6RP, SW : 2 ½ m. by A 343 via
Essex St. ℘ 40046, Fax 580246, – – 60. VISA.
M *(closed Sunday dinner)* 13.95 **t.** and a la carte 3.75 – **25 rm** 45.00/60.00 **t.** –
SB (weekends only) 72.00/80.00 **st.**

Blue Boar Inn, North Heath, RG16 8UE, N : 4 m. on A 4494 ℘ 248236 – .
VISA.
M 12.95 **t.** and a la carte 2.95 – **13 rm** 28.00/58.00 **t.**

Starwood without rest., 1 Rectory Close, off Pound St., RG14 6DF, SW : ¼ m. by
Enborne rd ℘ 49125 – .
4 rm 16.00/32.00 **st.**

at Hamstead Marshall SW : 5 ½ m. by A 4 – ✉ Newbury – ☎ 0488 Kintbury :

White Hart Inn, RJ15 0HW, ☎ 58201, 🐦 – TV ☎ P. AE VISA. ⚔
closed 4 to 27 August – **M** *(closed Sunday and 25-26 December)* a la carte 15.00/23.00 **st.** 3.50 – **6 rm** 40.00/60.00 **st.**

at Speen W : 1 ¾ m. on A 4 – ✉ ☎ 0635 Newbury :

Hare & Hounds, Bath Rd, RG13 1QY, ☎ 521152, Telex 847662, Fax 47708 – TV ☎ P **30 rm**, **1 suite.**

RENAULT London Rd ☎ 41020
ROVER London Rd ☎ 41100
VW-AUDI 22 Newtown Rd ☎ 41911

ATS 30 Queens Rd ☎ 42250

NEWBY BRIDGE Cumbria 402 L 21 – ECD : Saturday – ✉ Ulverston – ☎ 05395.

♦London 270 – Kendal 16 – Lancaster 27.

Lakeside H. on Lake Windermere, Lakeside, LA12 8AT, NE : 1 m. on Hawkshead rd ☎ 31207, Telex 65149, Fax 31699, ≤, « Lakeside setting », 🐦 – lift, rest TV ☎ P – 120. AE VISA
closed 4 to 11 January – **M** (bar lunch Monday to Saturday)/dinner 20.00 **st.** – **78 rm** 60.00/120.00 **st.**, **2 suites** 160.00 **st.**

Whitewater, The Lakeland Village, LA12 8PX, SW : 1 ½ m. by A 590 ☎ 31133, Fax 31881, squash – lift TV ☎ P – 70. AE VISA. ⚔
M (bar lunch Monday to Saturday)/dinner 9.50/16.00 **t.** and a la carte 3.50 – **35 rm.**

Swan, LA12 8NB, ☎ 31681, Telex 65108, Fax 31917, ≤, 🐦 – TV ☎ P – 65. AE VISA. ⚔
closed 2 to 12 January – **M** (bar lunch Monday to Saturday)/dinner 16.50 **t.** and a la carte 5.00 – **35 rm** 46.00/100.00 **t.**, **1 suite** 105.00/120.00 **t.** – SB (November-April) (weekends only) 78.00/100.00 **st.**

During the season, particularly in resorts, it is wise to book in advance.

NEWBY WISKE North Yorks. – see Northallerton.

NEWCASTLE EMLYN Dyfed 403 G 27 – ☎ 0239.

♦London 240 – Carmarthen 21 – Fishguard 30.

Felin Geri, Cwm Con, SA38 9PA, N : 2 ¾ m. by A 475 and B 4333, on Felin Geri rd ☎ 710810, Japanese rest., « Restored 16C water mill », park – P.

NEWCASTLE-UNDER-LYME Staffs. 402 403 404 N 24 – pop. 73 208 – ECD : Thursday – ☎ 0782.

Envir. : Wedgewood Visitor's Centre S : 4 ½ m. by A 519.

Newcastle Municipal, Keele Rd ☎ 627596, NW : 2 m. on A 525 V.

Area Reference Library, Ironmarket ☎ 711964.

♦London 161 – ♦Birmingham 46 – ♦Liverpool 56 – ♦Manchester 43.

Plan of Built up Area : see Stoke-on-Trent

NEWCASTLE-UNDER-LYME CENTRE

High Street . . . . . YZ

Albert Street . . . . . Y
Barracks Road . . . . . YZ
Blackfriars Road . . . . . Z 9
Brook Lane . . . . . Z
Brunswick Street . . . . . Y
Church Street . . . . . Y 20
Friarswood Road . . . . . Z
George Street . . . . . Y
Hassell Street . . . . . Y
Higherland . . . . . Z 37
Iron Market . . . . . Y 38
King Street . . . . . Y
Lancaster Road . . . . . Z
Liverpool Road . . . . . Y 41
Lower Street . . . . . YZ
Merrial Street . . . . . Y 47
North Street . . . . . Y 51
Parkstone Avenue . . . . . Z
Pool Dam . . . . . Z
Queen Street . . . . . Y
Ryecroft . . . . . Y
Vessey Terrace . . . . . Z 73
Victoria Road . . . . . Z

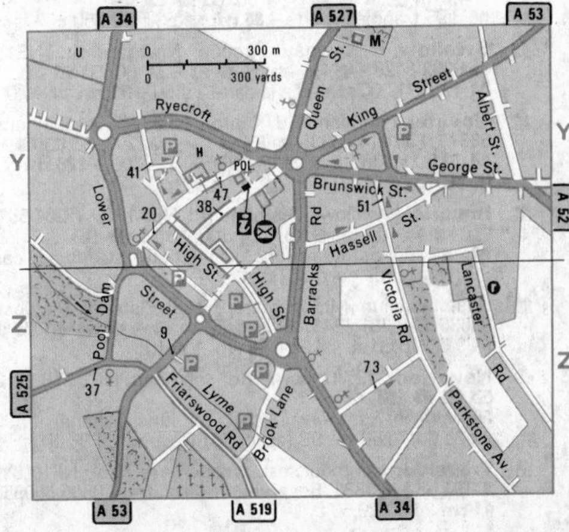

Post House (T.H.F.), Clayton Rd, Clayton, ST5 4DL, S : 2 m. on A 519 ℰ 717171, Telex 36531, Fax 717138, – rm – 70. VISA V n
M *(closed Saturday lunch)* 11.95/18.75 **st.** and a la carte 3.95 – 7.50 – **126 rm** 69.00/83.00 **st.** – SB (weekends only) 76.00 **st.**

Clayton Lodge, Clayton Rd, Clayton, ST5 4AF, S : 1 ¼ m. on A 519 ℰ 613093, Telex 36547, Fax 711896 – rm – 300. VISA V e
M *(closed Saturday lunch)* 10.30/11.30 **st.** and a la carte 4.75 – 7.00 – **50 rm** 67.00/87.00 **st.** – SB (weekends only) 64.00 **st.**

Deansfield, 98 Lancaster Rd, ST5 1DS, ℰ 619040 – . VISA Z r
M 20.00 **st.** 3.00 – **11 rm** 28.00/35.00 **st.**

BMW Pool Dam ℰ 711000
FIAT Higherland ℰ 622141
FORD London Rd ℰ 717799
PEUGEOT Hassell St. ℰ 614621
RENAULT High St., Wolstanton ℰ 626284
ROVER Brook Lane ℰ 618461
VAUXHALL-OPEL Higherland ℰ 610941
VW, AUDI Brunswick St. ℰ 617321
ATS Lower St. ℰ 622431

NEWCASTLE-UPON-TYNE Tyne and Wear 401 402 0 19 – pop. 199 064 – ECD : Monday and Wednesday – 091 Tyneside.

See : Site★★ – Quayside★ CZ – All Saints Church★ CZ – Castle Keep★ CZ – City Centre★ – Grey Street★ CZ – Laing Art Gallery and Museum★ CY M1 – Museum of Antiquities★*AC* CY M2.

Envir. : North of England Open Air Museum, Beamish★★*AC*, S : 10 m. by A 692 – Seaton Delaval Hall★*AC*, NE : 11 m. by A 6125 – Wallington House★*AC*, NW : 20 m. by A 696.

High Gosforth Park ℰ 236 4480 AV – Broadway East, Gosforth ℰ 285 6710, N : 3 m. AV – Whorlton Grange, Westerhope, ℰ 286 9125, W : 5 m. by B 6324 AV – City of Newcastle, Three Mile Bridge, Great North Rd ℰ 285 1775, N : 3 m. AV.

Newcastle Airport : ℰ 2860966, Telex 537831 NW : 5 m. by A 696 AV – **Terminal** : Bus Assembly : Central Station Forecourt.

ℰ 261 1234 ext 2621.

Shipping connections with the Continent : to Norway (Bergen, Stavanger) (Norway Line) March-December – to Denmark (Esbjerg) (Scandinavian Seaways) summer only – to Sweden (Götenborg) (Scandinavian Seaways) summer only – to Norway (Kristiansand) (Fred Olsen Lines KDS) – to Norway (Oslo) via Denmark (Hirtshals) (Fred Olsen Lines KDS).

Central Library, Princess Sq. ℰ 261 0691 – Newcastle Airport, Woolsington ℰ 271 1929.

♦London 276 – ♦Edinburgh 105 – ♦Leeds 95.

Plans on following pages

County Thistle (Mt. Charlotte Thistle), Neville St., NE99 1AH, ℰ 232 2471, Telex 537873, Fax 232 1285 – rm – 120. VISA CZ a
M 8.50/14.00 **st.** and a la carte – 7.75 – **115 rm** 60.00/90.00 **st.** – SB 80.00 **st.**

Crest (T.H.F.), New Bridge St., NE1 8BS, ℰ 232 6191, Telex 53467, Fax 261 8529 – rm rest – 400. VISA CY n
M 12.00/14.50 **st.** and a la carte 5.95 – 7.95 – **165 rm** 75.00/87.00 **st.**, **1 suite** 160.00 **st.** – SB (weekends only) 79.00 **st.**

Bank Top Toby, Kenton, NE3 3TY, A1 (M) junction with A 696 ℰ 214 0877, Fax 214 0095 – rm – 30. VISA AV a
M 6.95 **t.** and a la carte – **30 rm** 53.50/63.50 **t.**

Swallow, 1 Newgate Arcade, Newgate St., NE1 5SX, ℰ 232 5025, Telex 538230, Fax 232 8428 – rm – 80. VISA CZ o
M 12.00/17.00 **st.** and a la carte 4.50 – **93 rm** 70.00/90.00 **st.** – SB 85.00 **st.**

Novotel, Ponteland Rd, Kenton, NE3 3H2, A1 (M) junction with A 696 ℰ 214 0303, Telex 53675, Fax 214 0633 – – 200. VISA AV a
M 12.50 **st.** and a la carte 3.95 – 7.00 – **126 rm** 59.00/64.00 **st.** – SB (weekends only) 65.00/75.00 **st.**

Imperial (Swallow), Jesmond Rd, NE2 1PR, ℰ 281 5511, Telex 537972, Fax 281 8472, , – rm – 100. VISA CY c
M *(closed Saturday lunch)* 7.50/12.50 **st.** and a la carte – **129 rm** 25.00/80.00 **st.** – SB (weekends only) 85.00 **st.**

Hospitality Inn (Mt. Charlotte Thistle), Osborne Rd, Jesmond, NE2 2AT, ℰ 281 7881, Telex 53636, Fax 281 6241, – – 80. VISA. BV a
M 9.50/16.50 **st.** 3.95 – **86 rm, 1 suite.**

New Kent, 127 Osborne Rd, Jesmond, NE2 2TB, ℰ 281 1083, Fax 281 3369 – . VISA. BV c
M *(closed Saturday lunch)* (bar lunch)/dinner 11.90 **t.** and a la carte 4.75 – **32 rm** 35.00/76.50 **t.** – SB (except 31 December) 88.00 **st.**

Travelodge without rest., Whitemare Pool, NE10 8YB, at junction of A 1 (M) BX and A 194 ℰ 438 3333, Reservations (Toll free) 0800 850950 – . VISA.
41 rm 24.00/29.50 **t.**

Whites, 38-40 Osborne Rd, Jesmond, NE2 2AL, ℘ 281 5126 – TV. AE VISA. **M** *(closed Sunday dinner and Bank Holidays)* (bar lunch)/dinner 12.00 **st.** and a la carte 5.50 – **25 rm** 28.00/47.00 **st.** BV **u**

Avenue without rest., 2 Manor House Rd, Jesmond, NE2 2LU, ℘ 281 1396 – rest TV. AE VISA BV **x**
8 rm 19.50/40.00 **st.**

Westland, 27 Osborne Av., Jesmond, NE2 1JR, ℘ 281 0412 – rest TV. VISA. **M** (by arrangement) 7.00 **st.** – **14 rm** 22.00/44.00 **st.** BV **z**

21 Queen Street, 21 Queen St., Prices Wharf, Quayside, NE1 3UG, ℘ 222 0755 – AE VISA CZ **c**
closed Saturday lunch, Sunday and Bank Holidays – **M** 13.00 **t.** (lunch) and a la carte 21.10/27.00 **t.** 4.50.

Vujon, 29 Queen St., Princes Wharf, Quayside, NE1 3UG, ℘ 221 0601, Fax 221 0602, Indian rest. – AE VISA CZ **i**
closed saturday lunch and Christmas Day – **M** 12.00/20.00 **t.** and a la carte 6.90.

Fisherman's Wharf, 15 The Side, NE1 3JE, ℘ 232 1057, Seafood – AE VISA
closed Saturday lunch, Sunday, and Bank Holidays – **M** 22.00/50.00 **t.** and a la carte 4.20. CZ **v**

Fisherman's Lodge, Jesmond Dene, Jesmond, NE7 7BQ, ℘ 281 3281, Fax 2816410, Seafood – AE VISA BV **e**
closed Saturday lunch, Sunday, 25 to 28 December, 1-2 January and Bank Holidays – **M** 14.00 **t.** (lunch) and a la carte 24.00/36.00 **t.** 4.40.

Le Roussillon, 52-54 St. Andrew's St., NE1 5SF, ℘ 261 1341 – AE VISA CZ **e**
closed Saturday lunch, Sunday and Bank Holidays – **M** 7.00/9.00 **st.** and a la carte 3.75.

at Gosforth N : 4 ¾ m. on A 6125 – AV – ✉ 091 Tyneside:

Gosforth Park Thistle (Mt. Charlotte Thistle), High Gosforth Park, NE3 5HN, on B 1318 ℘ 236 4111, Telex 53655, Fax 236 8192, park, squash – rm TV – 200
173 rm, **5 suites.**

at Seaton Burn N : 8 m. by A 6125 – AV – ✉ Newcastle-upon-Tyne – 091 Tyneside:

Holiday Inn, Great North Rd, NE13 6BP, N : ¾ m. at junction with A 1 ℘ 236 5432, Telex 53271, Fax 236 8091, – rm TV – 200. AE VISA
M (carving lunch)/dinner 17.50 **st.** and a la carte 6.00 – 8.95 – **149 rm** 82.50/92.50 **t.**, **1 suite** 192.50/199.50 **t.** – SB 115.30/150.40 **st.**

Horton Grange, NE13 6BU, NW : 3 ½ m. by Airport rd on Porteland rd ℘ 860686 – rest TV. VISA.
closed 1 and 2 January – **M** *(closed Sunday dinner)* (dinner only and Sunday lunch)/dinner 26.50 **st.** – **5 rm** 75.00/90.00 **st.**

at Wallsend NE : 6 m. on A 1058 – BV – ✉ Newcastle-upon-Tyne – 091 Tyneside :

Newcastle Moat House (Q.M.H.), Coast Rd, NE28 9HP, at junction with A 1 ℘ 262 8989, Telex 53583, Fax 263 4172, – TV – 400. AE VISA
M 13.25 **st.** and a la carte 4.50 – **146 rm** 65.00/80.00 **st.** – SB (weekends only) 72.00/80.00 **st.**

at Newcastle Airport NW : 6 m. on A 696 – AV – ✉ Woolsington – 0661 Ponteland :

Stakis Airport, Woolsington, NE13 8DJ, ℘ 24911, Telex 537121, Fax 860157 – TV – 200 – **98 rm**, **2 suites.**

ALFA-ROMEO Diana St. ℘ 273 0700
BMW Fenham Barracks ℘ 261 7366
CITROEN Westgate Rd ℘ 273 7821
FIAT Railway St. ℘ 273 2131
FORD Scotswood Rd ℘ 273 0747
FORD Melbourn St. ℘ 261 1471
HONDA Warwick St. ℘ 261 1519
LAND-ROVER Comington ℘ 267 6271
MAZDA, DAIHATSU Jesmond ℘ 237 0658
MERCEDES-BENZ Swalwell ℘ 414 2882
MITSUBISHI, SEAT Longbenton ℘ 266 8223
NISSAN Benfield Rd ℘ 226 0333
NISSAN Stoddart St. ℘ 232 3838
PEUGEOT-TALBOT Benton Rd ℘ 266 6361
PORSCHE Melbourne St. ℘ 261 2591
RENAULT Scotswood Rd ℘ 273 0101
ROVER Etherstone Av. ℘ 266 3311
ROVER Westgate Rd ℘ 273 7901
SAAB Whitley Rd ℘ 266 8223
TOYOTA Brunton Lane ℘ 286 8611
VAUXHALL Two Ball Lonnen ℘ 274 1000
VAUXHALL Great North Rd ℘ 236 3176
VOLVO Brunton Lane ℘ 286 7111
VW, AUDI Byker ℘ 265 7121

ATS 80-90 Blenheim St. ℘ 2323921/2325031
ATS Newton Park Garage, Newton Rd ℘ 2812243
ATS White St, Walker ℘ 2620811

When travelling for business or pleasure
in England, Wales, Scotland and Ireland:

- use the series of five maps (nos 401, 402, 403, 404 and 405) at a scale of 1:400 000
- they are the perfect complement to this Guide as towns underlined in red on the maps will be found in this Guide.

NEWCASTLE-UPON-TYNE

Street	Grid	No.
Adelaide Terrace	AX	2
Atkinson Road	AX	3
Bath Street	BX	4
Bensham Road	AX	6
Benton Bank	BV	8
Buddle Street	BV	13
Byker Bridge	BV	15
Church Avenue	AV	16
Church Road	AV	18
Clayton Road	BV	21
Coldwell Lane	BX	22
Coldwell Street	BX	24
Condercum Road	AX	26
Fossway	BV	31
Haddrick's Mill Road	BV	36
High Street West	BV	37
Jesmond Dene Road	BV	39
Killingworth Road	BV	42
Lobley Hill Road	AX	45
Matthew Bank	BV	49
Neptune Road	BV	51
Red Hall Drive	BV	61
Redheugh Bridge	AX	62
Saltwell Road	BX	69
Shipdon Road	AX	71
Springfield Road	AV	72
Station Road	BX	73
Stephenson Road	BV	74
Sunderland Road	BX	76
Sutton Street	BV	77
Swalwell Bank	AX	79
Waverdale Avenue	BV	83
West Farm Avenue	BV	87
Whickham Bank	AX	88
Windy Nook Road	BX	89

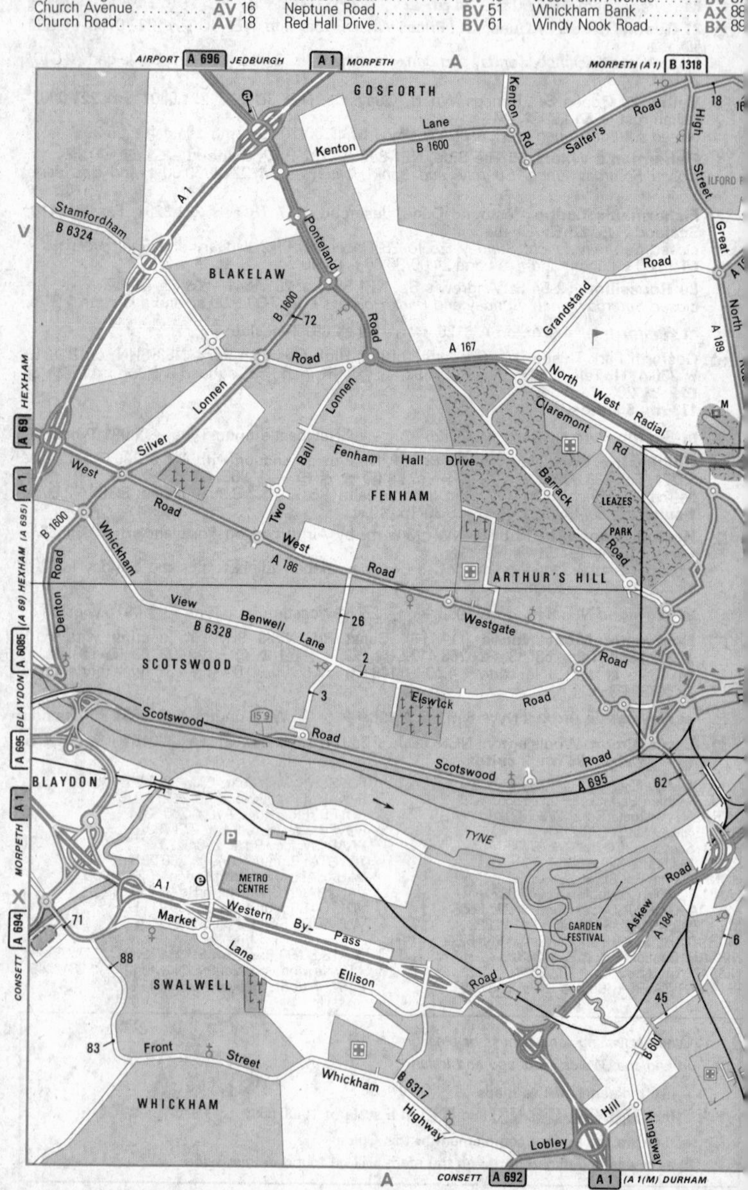

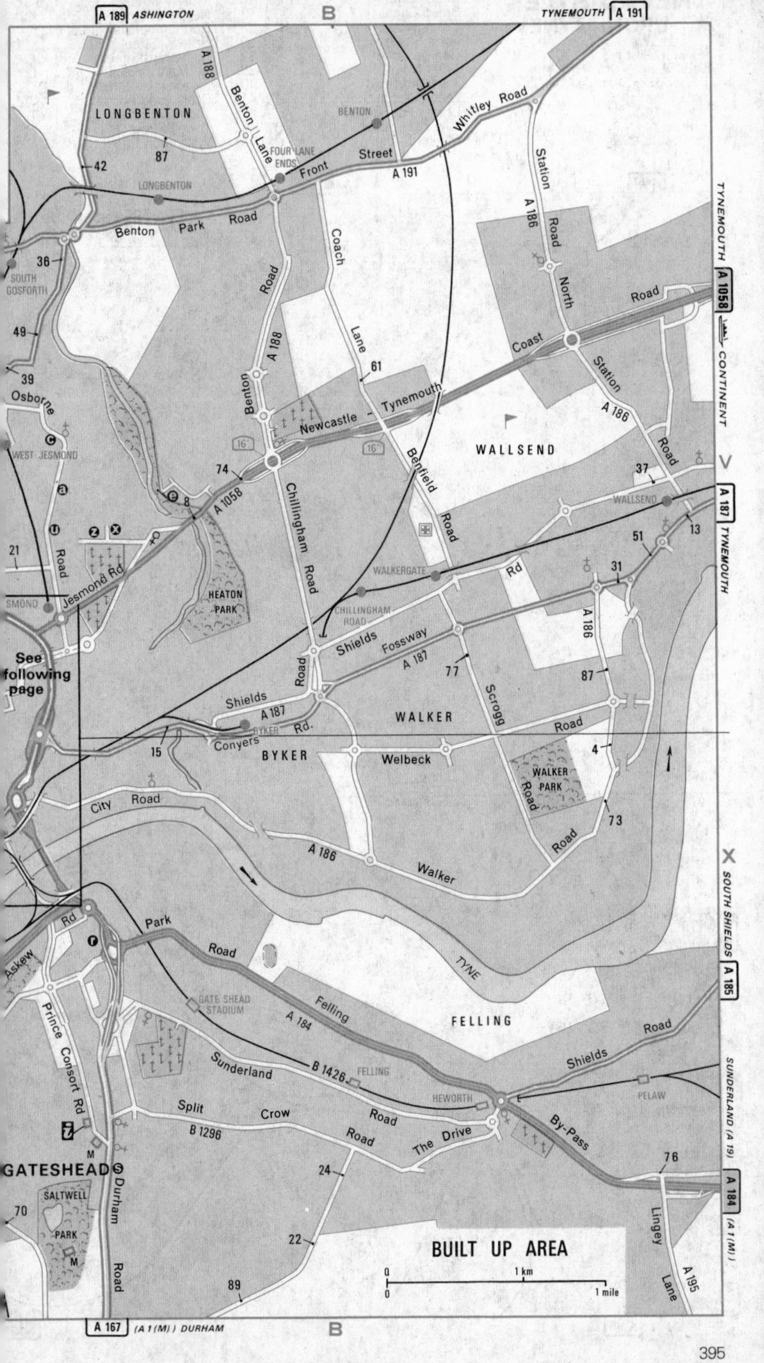
A 189 ASHINGTON
B
TYNEMOUTH A 191
LONGBENTON
BENTON
FOUR LANE ENDS
Benton Lane
A 188
Whitley Road
Front Street
A 191
Station Road
A 186
North
Benton Park Road
Coach Lane
Benton Road
A 188
Road
Coast
Newcastle - Tynemouth
Station
A 186
Road
TYNEMOUTH A 1058 CONTINENT
SOUTH GOSFORTH
Osborne
WEST JESMOND
WALLSEND
Benfield Road
Chillingham Road
A 1058
Jesmond Rd
Road
HEATON PARK
WALKERGATE
CHILLINGHAM ROAD
Rd
A 187 TYNEMOUTH
Shields
Fossway
A 187
A 186
Scrogg
Road
WALKER
Shields
A 187
BYKER
Rd.
Conyers
BYKER
Welbeck
Road
WALKER PARK
Road
See following page
City Road
A 186
Walker
Road
X
SOUTH SHIELDS A 185
Park
Road
Rd
Askew
TYNE
Felling
A 184
GATE SHEAD STADIUM
FELLING
Prince Consort Rd
Sunderland
B 1426
FELLING
Road
Shields
HEWORTH
PELAW
SUNDERLAND (A 19)
Split
Crow
Road
B 1296
Road
The Drive
By-Pass
GATESHEAD
Durham Road
SALTWELL PARK
A 184 (A 1(M))
Lingey Lane
A 195
BUILT UP AREA
1 km
1 mile
A 167 (A 1(M)) DURHAM
B

NEWCASTLE - UPON - TYNE

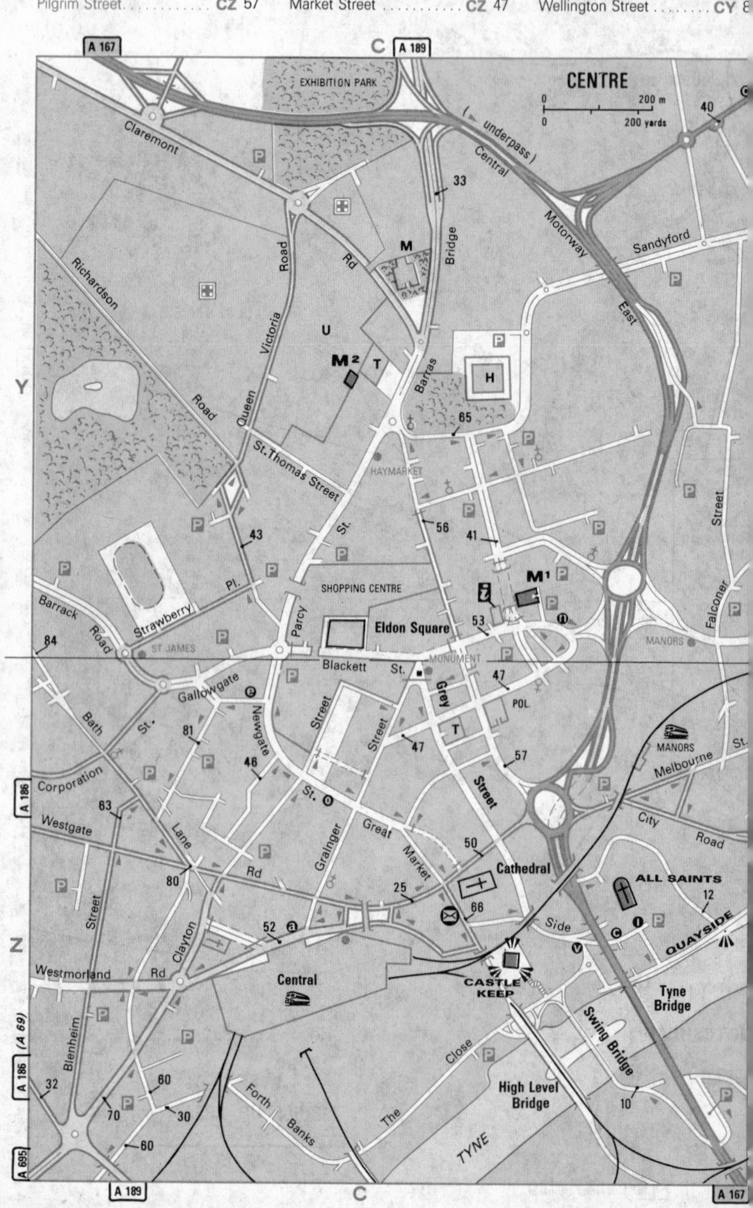

EWHAVEN East Sussex 404 U 31 – pop. 10 697 – ECD : Wednesday – ☎ 0273.

Peacehaven, Brighton Rd ✆ 514049.

Shipping connections with the Continent : to France (Dieppe) (Sealink) (4 h).

London 63 – ♦Brighton 9 – Eastbourne 14 – Lewes 7.

EWLYN Cornwall 403 D 33 – see Penzance.

EWMARKET Suffolk 404 V 27 – pop. 15 861 – ECD : Wednesday – ☎ 0638.

Links, Cambridge Rd ✆ 662708, SW : 1 m.

London 64 – ♦Cambridge 13 – ♦Ipswich 40 – ♦Norwich 48.

Newmarket Moat House (Q.M.H.), Moulton Rd, CB8 8DY, ✆ 667171, Fax 666533 – 60. VISA
closed Christmas – **M** *(closed Saturday lunch)* 14.95 **t.** and a la carte 4.00 – **47 rm** 60.00/150.00 **t.** – SB (weekends only) 62.00 **st.**

White Hart, High St., CB8 8JP, ✆ 663051, Fax 667284 – 80
23 rm.

at Six Mile Bottom (Cambs.) SW : 6 m. on A 1304 – ✉ Newmarket – ☎ 063 870 Six Mile Bottom :

Swynford Paddocks, CB8 0UE, ✆ 234, Group Telex 817438, Fax 283, ≤, « Country house », park, – 30. VISA
closed 1 to 3 January – **M** *(closed Saturday lunch)* 13.50/18.50 **t.** and a la carte 4.50 – **15 rm** 60.00/130.00 **t.** – SB (weekends only) 110.00/120.00 **st.**

EUGEOT-TALBOT Dullingham ✆ 063 876 (Stetchworth) 244
OYOTA Bury Rd ✆ 662130
ATS 2 Exeter Rd ✆ 662088/662521

NEW MILTON Hants. 403 404 P 31 – ECD : Wednesday – ☎ 0425.

London 106 – Bournemouth 12 – ♦Southampton 21 – Winchester 34.

❀ **Chewton Glen**, Christchurch Rd, BH25 6QS, W : 2 m. by A 337 and Ringwood Rd on Chewton Farm Rd ✆ 275341, Telex 41456, Fax 272310, ≤, « Gardens », heated, park, – 40. VISA
M 22.00/42.00 **st.** and a la carte 42.00/70.00 **st.** 7.50 – 14.00 – **45 rm** -/225.00 **st.**, **13 suites** 320.00/400.00 **st.** – SB (weekdays only) 202.00/368.00 **st.**
Spec. Terrine de foie gras au vin de noix verte, Suprême de bar braisé aux lentilles, Piccata de ris de veau au vinaigre de Xérès.

OLT Christchurch Rd ✆ 611198
ISSAN 25 Station Rd ✆ 620660
RENAULT 53 Lymington Rd ✆ 612296
ROVER Old Milton Rd ✆ 614665

NEWPORT Essex 404 U 28 – ✉ ☎ 0799 Saffron Walden.

London 38 – ♦Cambridge 21 – Colchester 41.

Village House, High St., CB11 3PF, ✆ 41560 – VISA
closed Sunday, Monday and 1 to 23 January – **M** (dinner only) a la carte 19.00/24.00 **t.** 3.50.

NEWPORT I.O.W. 403 404 Q 31 – see Wight (Isle of).

NEWPORT **(CASNEWYDD-AR-WYSG)** Gwent 403 L 29 – pop. 115 896 – ECD : Thursday – ☎ 0633.

Envir. : Caerleon : Roman Amphitheatre★ *AC*, NE : 3 m.

Tredegar Park, Bassaleg Rd ✆ 895219, SW : 2 m. by A 467 – 18 Great Oak, Rogerstone ✆ 892683, 3 m. on B 4591.

Museum and Art Gallery, John Frost Sq. ✆ 842962.

London 145 – ♦Bristol 31 – ♦Cardiff 12 – Gloucester 48.

Celtic Manor, Coldra Woods, NP6 2YA, E : 3 m. on A 48 ✆ 413000, Telex 497557, Fax 412910, park – rm – 200. VISA
M (see also **Hedley's** below) 17.60/22.00 **t.** and a la carte – 8.50 – **72 rm** 82.50/99.00 **t.**, **2 suites** 150.00 **t.** – SB (weekends only) 175.00/200.00 **st.**

Hilton National, The Coldra, NP6 2YG, E : 3 m. on A 48 ✆ 412777, Telex 497205, Fax 413087 – rm – 350
119 rm.

Kings, High St., NP9 1QU, ✆ 842020, Telex 497330, Fax 244667 – 200. VISA
M *(closed Saturday lunch)* 8.95/11.45 **st.** and a la carte 3.95 – 7.00 – **47 rm** 44.00/61.00 **st.**

Newport Lodge, 147 Bryn Bevan, Brynglas Rd, NP9 5QN, via Malpas Rd ✆ 821818, Fax 856360 – VISA
M 12.50/18.95 and a la carte – **27 rm** 29.50/58.00 **t.**

Anderley Lodge, 216 Stow Hill, NP9 4HA, ✆ 266781 – VISA
M 10.50 **st.** – 3.00 – **4 rm** 19.00/30.00 **st.** – SB 52.00/56.00 **st.**

XXX **Hedley's,** (at Celtic Manor H.) Coldra Woods, NP6 2YA, E : 3 m. on A 48 ℘ 41300(Fax 412910, – Ⓟ. AE VISA
M a la carte 22.35/32.00 **t.**

X **Fratelli,** 173b Caerleon Rd, NP9 7FX, E : 1 m. on B 4596 ℘ 264602, Italian rest. – VISA
closed Saturday lunch, 3 weeks August, 1 week Christmas and Bank Holiday Mondays – **M** a la carte 10.50/21.75 **t.**

at Caerleon N : 3½ m. on B 4596 – ✉ Newport – ✆ 0633 Caerleon

X **Bagan Tandoori,** 2 Cross St., NP6 1AF, ℘ 430086, Indian rest. – AE VISA **M** 10.5C 15.50 **t.** and a la carte 5.50.

at Langstone E : 4½ m. on A 48 – ✉ Newport – ✆ 0633 Llanwern :

Country Court, Chepstow Rd, NP6 2LX, ℘ 413737, Telex 497147, Fax 413713, – rm rest TV ☎ Ⓟ – 70
131 rm, 10 suites.

New Inn, Chepstow Rd, NP6 2JN, ℘ 412426, Fax 413679 – TV ☎ Ⓟ. AE VISA.
M (grill rest.) 16.70 **t.** and a la carte 3.95 – **34 rm** 52.00/66.00 **t.**

NISSAN Spytty Rd ℘ 273414
PEUGEOT-TALBOT Bassaleg Rd ℘ 265488
ATS 101 Corporation Rd ℘ 216115/216117

NEWPORT (TREFDRAETH) Dyfed 403 F 27 – pop. 1 224 – ECD : Wednesday – ✆ 0239.

See : Site★.
Envir. : Pentre Ifan (burial chamber★) SE : 4½ m.
Newport ℘ 820244, NW : 2½ m.
East St. ℘ 820912.
♦London 258 – Fishguard 7.

X **Cnapan** with rm, East St., on A 487, SA42 0WF, ℘ 820575, – rest TV Ⓟ. VISA.
closed Tuesday April-October, February and 25-26 December (restricted service November-March) – **M** (wholefood lunch only) (booking essential) 7.60/19.00 **t.** and a la carte 4.50 – **5 rm** 26.00/42.00 **t.**

at Velindre (Felindre Farchog) E : 2¾ m. on A 487 – ✉ Cardigan – ✆ 0239 Newport :

Salutation Inn, Felindre Farchog, SA41 3UY, ℘ 820564, – rest TV Ⓟ. VISA
M (bar lunch)/dinner 18.00 **t.** and a la carte – **9 rm** 28.00/44.00 **st.** – SB (October-June) 64.00/77.00 **st.**

Europe — If the name of the hotel is not in bold type, on arrival ask the hotelier his prices.

NEWPORT Shropshire 402 403 404 M 25 – pop. 10 339 – ECD : Thursday – ✆ 0952.

Envir. : Weston Park★★ SE : 6½ m.
Abbey Rd, Litlleshall ℘ 603840.
9 St. Mary's St. ℘ 814109.
♦London 150 – ♦Birmingham 33 – Shrewsbury 18 – ♦Stoke-on-Trent 21.

Royal Victoria, St. Mary's St., TF10 7AB, ℘ 820331, Fax 820209 – TV ☎ Ⓟ – **24 rm.**

FORD Browns Garage ℘ 811076

NEWPORT PAGNELL Bucks. 404 R 27 – pop. 10 733 – ECD : Thursday – ✆ 0908.

♦London 57 – Bedford 13 – Luton 21 – Northampton 15.

Coach House (Lansbury), London Rd, Moulsoe, SE : 1½ m. by B 526 on A 509 ℘ 613688, Telex 825341, Fax 617335, – rm TV ☎ Ⓟ – 220. AE VISA.
M *(closed lunch Saturday and Bank Holidays)* 11.50/17.50 **t.** and a la carte 4.50 – **48 rm** 82.00/95.00 **t.**, **1 suite** 100.00/120.00 **t.**

Swan Revived, High St., MK16 8AR, ℘ 610565, Telex 826801, Fax 210995 – TV ☎ Ⓟ – 50. AE VISA
M a la carte 10.30/12.10 **t.** 3.75 – **40 rm** 54.00/60.00 **st.**

PEUGEOT High St. ℘ 611484

NEWQUAY Cornwall 403 E 32 The West Country G. – pop. 13 905 – ECD : Wednesday – ✆ 063 73 (4 and 5 fig.) or 0637 (6 fig.).

Envir. : Pentire Points and Kelsey Head★ (≤★★) SW : 5 m. by A 3075 Y – Trerice Manor★ AC 3½ m. by A 392 Y.
Cliff Rd ℘ 871345.
♦London 291 – Exeter 83 – Penzance 34 – ♦Plymouth 48 – Truro 14.

Plan on next page

Bristol, Narrowcliff, TR7 2PQ, ℘ 875181, Fax 879347, ≤, – TV ☎ Ⓟ – 80. AE VISA
M 9.50/15.00 **st.** and a la carte – **83 rm** 47.00/85.00 **st.** – SB (October-April) (weekends only) 80.00 **st.**

NEWQUAY

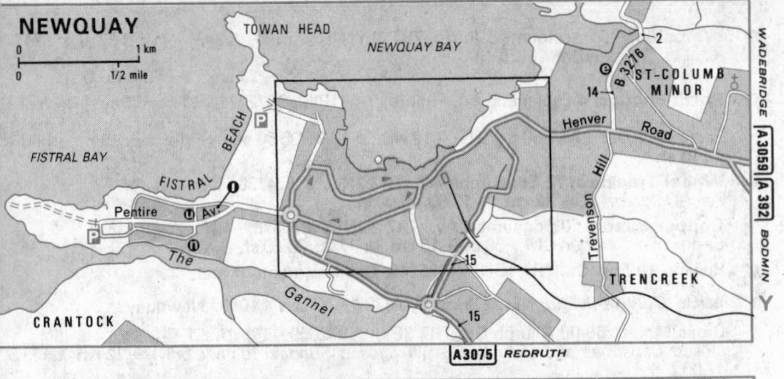

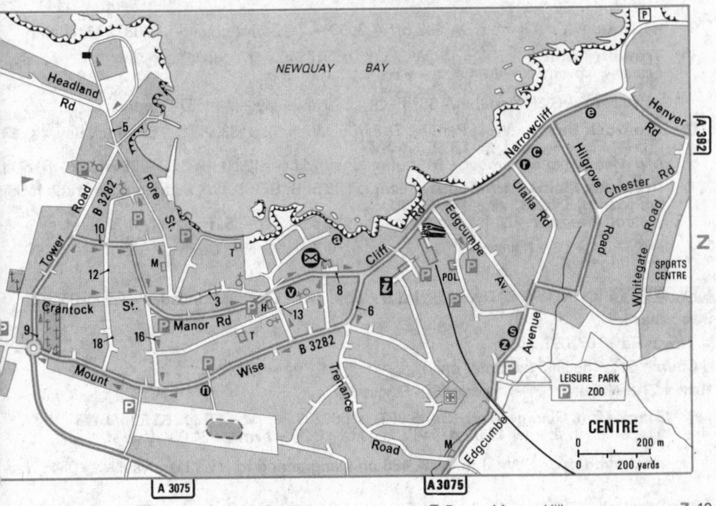

ank Street	Z 3	Beacon Road	Z 5	Marcus Hill	Z 13
ast Street	Z 8	Berry Road	Z 6	Porth Way	Y 14
ore Street	Z	Higher Tower Road	Z 9	Trevemper Road	Y 15
		Hope Terrace	Z 10	St. Georges Road	Z 16
Alexander Road	Y 2	Jubilee Street	Z 12	St. John's Road	Z 18

Trebarwith, Trebarwith Cres., TR7 1BZ, ℘ 872288, ≤ bay and coast, ⌂s, ☐, ⌐ – TV ☎ ⓟ. AE VISA. ✂ Z a
April-October – **M** (bar lunch)/dinner 12.00 – **42 rm** ▭ 40.00/80.00 **st.**

Kilbirnie, Narrowcliff, TR7 2RS, ℘ 875155, Fax 850769, ⌂s, heated, ☐ – |ǂ| TV ☎ ⓟ. AE VISA Z e
M (bar lunch)/dinner 10.50 **st.** 2.95 – **70 rm** ▭ 34.00/71.00 **st.**

Windsor, Mount Wise, TR7 2AY, ℘ 875188, ⌂s, heated, ☐, ⌐, squash – ⇸ rest TV ☎ ⓟ. AE VISA. ✂ Z n
closed 3 January-February – **M** (bar lunch)/dinner 16.00 **st.** – **44 rm** ▭ 25.00/47.00 **st.**

New Garth, Narrowcliff, TR7 2PG, ℘ 873250, ≤ – |ǂ| TV ☎ ⓟ – 100. AE VISA. ✂
closed January – **M** (bar lunch Monday to Saturday)/dinner 10.95 **t.** and a la carte 3.75 – **50 rm** ▭ 23.00/55.00 **t.** Z c

Water's Edge, Esplanade Rd, Pentire, TR7 1QA, ℘ 872048, ≤ Fistral Bay, ⌐ – TV ☎ ⓟ. AE VISA. ✂ Y u
May-October – **M** (bar lunch)/dinner 11.95 **st.** 3.50 – **20 rm** ▭ 32.00/64.00 **t.** – SB (weekends only) 54.00/74.00 **st.**

Corisande Manor, Riverside Av., Pentire, TR7 1PL, ℘ 872042, ≤ Gannel Estuary, ⌐ – TV ⓟ Y n
19 rm.

Porth Veor Manor, 56 Porth Way, TR7 3LW, ℘ 873274, ⌐, ✕ – ⇸ rest TV ⓟ. AE VISA
closed November – **M** (bar lunch Monday to Saturday)/dinner 7.25/18.25 **t.** and a la carte 3.75 – **16 rm** ▭ 26.00/84.00 **t.** – SB (except summer) 54.00 **st.** Y e

Whipsiderry, Trevelgue Rd, Porth, TR7 3LY, NE : 2 m. by A 392 - Y- off B 3276 ℰ 874777, ≤, heated, – TV P
Easter-October – **M** (bar lunch)/dinner 11.00 **st.** 4.90 – **23 rm** 17.50/45.00 **st.**

Porth Enodoc, 4 Esplanade Rd, Pentire, TR7 1PY, ℰ 872372, ≤ Fistral Bay – rest P Y
Easter-October – **M** 7.50 **t.** 2.50 – **16 rm** 17.75/35.50 **st.** – SB (except summer) 40.15/42.15 **st.**

Wheal Treasure, 72 Edgcumbe Av., TR7 2NN, ℰ 874136 – rest P. Z
April-October 4.50 – **12 rm** 12.00/40.00 **st.**

Copper Beech, 70 Edgcumbe Av., TR7 2NN, ℰ 873376 – rest P. Z
Easter-mid October – **M** 7.50 **st.** – **15 rm** 17.25/36.80 **st.**

XX Riviera, 10 East St., TR7 1BH, ℰ 875246, Chinese (canton) rest. Z

at St. Columb Minor NE : 2 ¼ m. by A 392 – Y – ✉ 0637 Newquay :

Cross Mount, 58-60 Church St., TR7 3EX, ℰ 872669 – TV P. VISA.
closed Christmas and New Year – **M** *(closed Sunday)* (dinner only) – **12 rm** 23.50/47.00 **t.**

at Trerice SE : 4 ¾ m. by A 392 off A 3058 – Y – ✉ Newquay – 0872 Mitchell :

Trewerry Mill, TR8 5HS, W : ½ m. ℰ 510345, – P.
Easter-1 Novemebr – **M** 4.50 **t.** – **6 rm** 13.00/26.00 **t.**

at Crantock SW : 4 m. by A 3075 – Y – ✉ Newquay – 0637 Crantock :

Crantock Bay, West Pentire, TR8 5SE, W : ¾ m. ℰ 830229, ≤ Crantock Bay, , , – rest P. AE VISA
Mid March-mid November – **M** (buffet lunch)/dinner 12.50 **t.** 3.00 – **36 rm** -/61.50 **t.**

Crantock Plains Farmhouse, Cubent, TR8 5PH, SE : 1 ½ m. bearing right at the fork in the road ℰ 830253, – P.
March-November – **M** (by arrangement) 6.50 **st.** 2.75 – **6 rm** 14.00/32.00 **st.**

DAF Newlyn East ℰ 0872 (Mitchell) 510347
FIAT Tower Rd ℰ 872378
ROVER Quintrell Downs ℰ 872410

NEW QUAY (CEINEWYDD) Dyfed 403 G 27 – pop. 775 – ECD : Wednesday – ✉ 0545.

See : site★.

Tower Rd ℰ 872091.

Church St. ℰ 580865 (summer only).

◆London 234 – Aberystwyth 24 – Carmarthen 31 – Fishguard 39.

Black Lion, Glanmor Terr., SA45 9PT, ℰ 560209, ≤, – TV P. AE VISA
M (bar lunch)/dinner 15.00 **st.** and a la carte 3.25 – **7 rm** 24.00/50.00 **st.**

at Llwyndafydd SW : 3 m. by A 486 on Llangrannog rd – ✉ Llandysul – 0545 New-quay :

Park Hall, Cwmtydu, SA44 6LG, NW : 1 ¾ m. ℰ ≤, – rest TV P
5 rm.

NEW ROMNEY Kent 404 W 31 – pop. 4 547 – ECD : Wednesday – 0679.

Envir. : Lydd (All Saints' Church tower : groined vaulting★) SW : 3 ½ m. – Brookland (St Augustine's Church : belfry★ 15C, Norman font★) W : 6 m.

18, 9 Littlestone ℰ 62310.

Light Railway Car Park, 2 Littlestone Rd ℰ 64044 (summer only).

◆London 71 – Folkestone 14 – Hastings 23 – Maidstone 33.

Blue Dolphins, Dymchurch Rd, TN28 8BE, ℰ 63224 – TV P. VISA.
M (dinner only) 15.95 **st.** 3.65 – **8 rm** 19.00/36.00 **st.**

NEWTON FERRERS Devon 403 H 33 **The West Country G.** – pop. 1 609 – 0752 Plymouth.

◆London 242 – Exeter 42 – ◆Plymouth 11.

at Alston Cross E : 3 ¼ m. by Stoke Beach rd, Membland rd and Holbeton rd – ✉ 075 530 Holbeton :

Alston Hall, PL8 1HN, ℰ 259, Fax 494, ≤, , , , , – TV P – 100. AE VISA
M 23.50 **t.** 3.50 – **11 rm** 85.00/125.00 **t.** – SB (weekends only) 110.00/150.00 **st.**

NEWTON POPPLEFORD Devon 403 K 31 – ✉ Ottery St. Mary – 0395 Colaton Rayleigh.

◆London 208 – Exeter 10 – Sidmouth 4.

Coach House ; Southerton, EX11 1SE, N : ½ by Venn Ottery Rd ℰ 68577, Fax 68946, – rest TV P. VISA. *closed January* – **M** (dinner only and Sunday lunch) 7.50/18.00 **t.** and a la carte 3.50 – **5 rm** 33.00/66.00 **t.**, **1 suite** 66.00 **t.**

NEWTON SOLNEY Derbs. 402 403 404 P 25 – see Burton-upon-Trent (Staffs.).

NEWTOWN **(DRENEWYDD)** Powys 403 K 26 – pop. 8 906 – ECD : Thursday – 0686.

St. Giles, Pool Rd 625844 NE : ½ m.

Central Car Park 625580 (summer only).

London 196 – Aberystwyth 44 – Chester 56 – Shrewsbury 32.

Highgate Farm, Highgate, SY16 3LF, N : 2 ¾ m. by B 4568 on Llanfair rd 625981, «Working farm », – .
March to November – **M** (by arrangement) 7.00 **st.** – **3 rm** 20.00/34.00 **st.**

at Abermule (Aber-Miwl) NE : 4 ½ m. on A 483 – 0686 Abermule :

Dolforwyn Hall, Dolforwyn, SY15 6JG, N : ½ m. on A 483 630221 – . AE VISA.
M a la carte 12.00/20.00 **st.** 3.00 – **7 rm** 29.50/47.00 **st.**

AUDI, VW Abermule 068 686 (Abermule) 615
FORD Pool Rd 625514
ATS Dulas Garage, Llanidloes Rd 626069/627532

NITON I.O.W. 403 404 Q 32 – see Wight (Isle of).

NORMAN CROSS Cambs. 404 T 26 – see Peterborough.

NORMANTON PARK Leics. - see Stamford.

NORTHALLERTON North Yorks. 402 P 20 – pop. 13 566 – ECD : Thursday – 0609.

Envir. : Bedale, Leyburn Rd (Parish church★ 13C-14C) SW : 7 ½ m.

at Bedale, Leyburn Rd 0677 (Bedale) 22568, SW : 7 ½ m.

Applegarth Car Park 776864.

London 238 – Leeds 48 – Middlesbrough 24 – York 33.

Golden Lion (T.H.F.), 114 High St., DL7 8PP, 777411, Fax 773250 – rm – 100. AE VISA
M 11.50/19.00 **st.** and a la carte 4.50 – 7.50 – **26 rm** 65.00/80.00 **st.** – SB 86.00/90.00 **st.**

Romanby Court, High St., DL7 8PG, 774918.

at Staddlebridge NE : 7 ½ m. by A 684 on A 19 at junction with A 172 – Northallerton – 060 982 East Harlsey :

McCoys at the Tontine with rm, DL6 3JB, 671, «1930's decor » – . AE VISA
closed 25 to 26 December and 1 January – **M** *(closed Sunday and Monday)* (dinner only) a la carte 25.00/36.00 **t.** 5.00 – **6 rm** 69.00/89.00 **t.**

at Newby Wiske S : 2 ½ m. by A 167 – 0609 Northallerton :

Solberge Hall (Best Western), DL7 9ER, 779191, Fax 780472, park – – 80
24 rm, 1 suite.

AUDI-VW Darlington Rd 771011
FORD South Par. 780820
PEUGEOT-TALBOT 2-3 Tannery Lane 780888
RENAULT Leeming Bar 0677 (Bedale) 22388
ROVER Brompton Rd 773891

NORTHAMPTON Northants. 404 R 27 – pop. 154 172 – 0604.

See : Church of the Holy Sepulchre★ 12C XA – Central Museum and Art Gallery (collection of footwear★) XM.

Envir. : Boughton House★★ N : 3 ½ m. – Earls Barton (All Saints Church : 10C Saxontower★) NE : 5 m. by A 45 Y – Castle Ashby★ (16C-17C) *AC*, NE : 8 m. by A 428 Z – Brixworth (All Saints Church★ 7C Saxon) N : 7 m. by A 508 Y.

Delapre, Eagle Drive 764036 Z – Kettering Rd 711054, E : 2 m. on A 43 Y – Kingthorpe, Kinsley Rd 711173 Y – Church Brampton 842170, NW : 5 m. by A 50 Y – Cold Asby 740548 Z.

21 St. Giles St. 22677/34881 ext 404.

London 69 – Cambridge 53 – Coventry 34 – Leicester 42 – Luton 35 – Oxford 41.

Plan on next page

Swallow, Eagle Drive, NN4 0HW, SE : 2 m. by A 428 on A 45 768700, Telex 31562, Fax 769011, – rm rest – 150. AE VISA Z **a**
M 11.25/17.00 **st.** and a la carte 4.75 – **122 rm** 80.00/130.00 **st.** – SB (weekends only) 90.00/115.00 **st.**

Northampton Moat House (Q.M.H.), Silver St., NN1 2TA, 22441, Telex 311142, Fax 230614, – – 600. AE VISA X **n**
closed 25 and 26 December – **M** 12.00/13.00 **st.** and a la carte 7.50 – **136 rm** 69.50/85.00 **st.**, **4 suites** 98.00 **st.** – SB (weekends only) 68.00 **st.**

NORTHAMPTON

Abington Street X
Drapery .... X 18
Gold Street X
Grosvenor Centre X
Weston
  Favell Centre .... Y

Abington Square .... X 2
Ashley Way .... Y 3
Bewick Road .... Y 4
Billing Road .... X 7
Bridge Street .... X 8
Campbell Street .... X 9
Charnwood Avenue .... Y 10
Church Lane .... X 13
College Street .... X 14
Derngate .... X 15
Earl Street .... X 19
Greyfriars .... X 23
Guildhall Road .... X 24
Horse
  Shoe Street .... X 28
Kenmuir Avenue .... Y 29
Kettering Road .... X 30
Kingsthorpe Grove .... Y 34
Lower Mounts .... X 35
Mare Fair .... X 37
Oaklands Drive .... Y 38
Overstone Road .... X 39
Park Avenue North .... Y 40
Park Avenue South .... Z 43
Rushmere Road .... Z 44
St. Andrew's Road .... Y 45
St. Edmund's Road .... X 48
St. James's Road .... X 49
St. John's Street .... X 50
St. Leonard's Road .... Z 52
St. Michael's Road .... X 53
Sheep Street .... X 54
Silver Street .... X 55
Spencer Bridge Road .... X, Z 57
Towcester Road .... Z 58
Upper Mounts .... X 59
Waveney Way .... Y 60
West Bridge .... X 62
Windrush Way .... Y 63

B 5347 (A 508)
A 508
A 45
A 43
A 4500
A 428
(A 45)
(A 43)
X
Grafton St.
St. Andrew's Rd
Broad St.
Horse Market
Robert St.
POL
Lady's Lane
GROSVENOR CENTRE
Abington St.
York Rd
St. Giles' St.
Cheyne Walk
Gold St.
Peter's Way
Victoria Promenade
Bedford Rd
0 200 m
0 200 yards

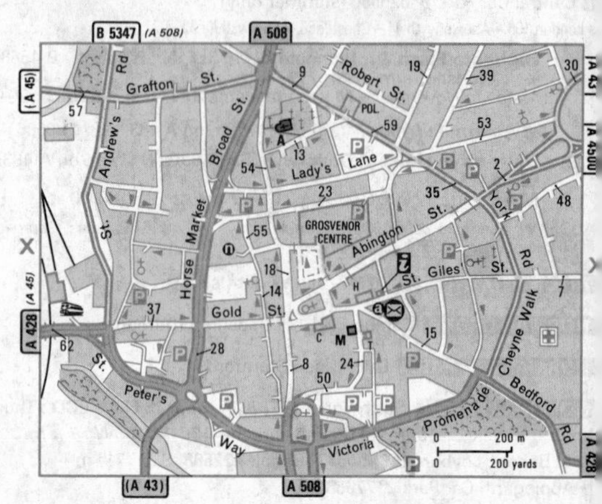

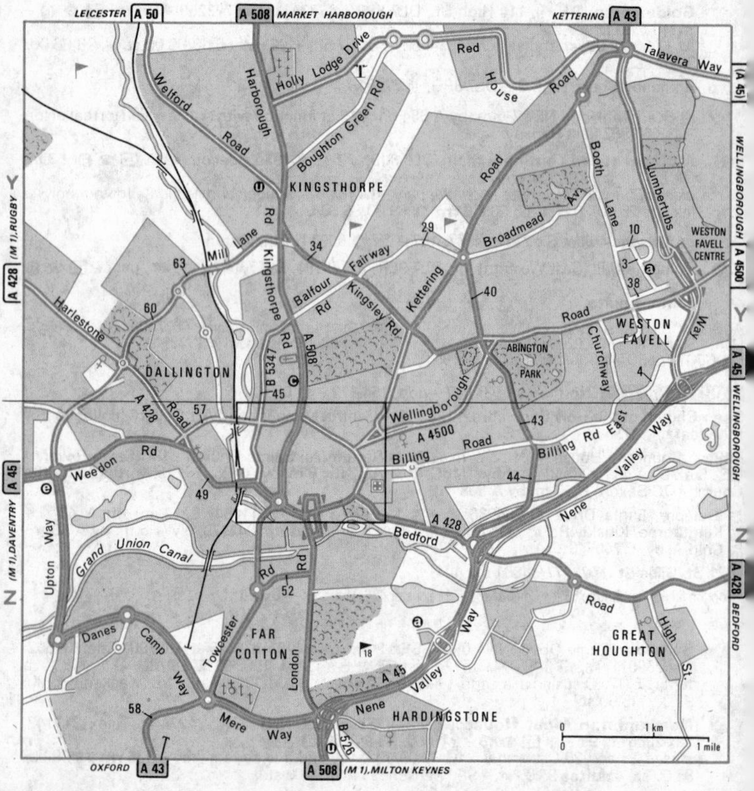

LEICESTER A 50
A 508 MARKET HARBOROUGH
KETTERING A 43
(A 45)
WELLINGBOROUGH A 4500
A 45 WELLINGBOROUGH
A 428 BEDFORD
A 428 (M 1), RUGBY
A 45 (M 1), DAVENTRY
OXFORD A 43
A 508 (M 1), MILTON KEYNES
Y
Z
Welford Road
Harborough Rd
Holly Lodge Drive
Boughton Green Rd
Red House Road
Talavera Way
KINGSTHORPE
Booth Lane
Lumbertubs Way
WESTON FAVELL CENTRE
Broadmead Av.
Kettering Road
Mill Lane
Kingsthorpe Rd
Fairway
Balfour Rd
Kingsley Rd
Harlestone Road
DALLINGTON
ABINGTON PARK
WESTON FAVELL
Churchway
Wellingborough Rd
A 4500
Billing Road
Billing Rd East
Valley Way
Weedon Rd
A 428
Bedford Rd
Nene Valley Way
Grand Union Canal
Upton Way
Danes Camp Way
Towcester Rd
FAR COTTON
London Rd
A 45
Nene Valley Way
HARDINGSTONE
Mere Way
B 526
GREAT HOUGHTON
High St.
0 1 km
0 1 mile

Midway Toby, London Rd, Wootton, NN4 0TG, S : 2 ½ m. on A 508 Z ℘ 769676, Fax 769523 – rest – 60. – **M** (grill rest.) a la carte 8.60/14.85 **t.** – **29 rm** 55.00/68.00 **t.**

Northampton, 4 Leicester Parade, NN2 6AQ, on A 508 ℘ 38795, Fax 24763 – – 50. Y c
M 10.00/30.00 **t.** and a la carte – **11 rm** 55.00/70.00 **t.** – SB (weekends only) 75.00 **st.**

Queen Eleanor (B.C.B), Newport Pagnell Rd, Wootton, NN4 0JJ, S : 1 ¾ m. by A 508 on B 526 ℘ 762468, – – 60. Z u
M (carving rest.) 8.00/15.00 **st.** – **19 rm** 53.00/60.50 **st.**

Travel Inn, Harpole Turn, Weedon Rd, NN7 4DD, W : 3 ¾ m. on A 45 ℘ 832340, Fax 831807 – rm . Z
M (Beefeater grill) a la carte approx. 12.25 **t.** – 4.50 – **51 rm** -/27.50 **t.**

Travelodge without rest., Upton Way (Ring Rd), NN5 6EG, SW : 1 ¾ m. by A 45 ℘ 758395, Reservations (Toll free) 0800 850950 – . Z e
40 rm 24.00/29.50 **t.**

Vineyard, 7 Derngate, NN1 1TU, ℘ 33978. X a
closed Sunday – **M** 8.50 **t.** (lunch) and a la carte approx. 17.95 **t.**

Bombay Palace, 9-11 Welford Rd, Kingsthorpe, NN2 8AE, N : 1 ¾ m. by A 508 on A 50 ℘ 713899, Indian rest. Y u

at Spratton N : 7 m. by A 508 off A 50 – Y – ✉ 0604 Northampton :

Broomhill, Holdenby Rd, NN6 8LD, SW : 1 m. by A 50 ℘ 845959, Fax 845834, ≤, heated, , park, – .
M 13.45 **t.** and a la carte 4.75 – **12 rm** 56.00/66.00 **t.**

at Weston Favell NE : 3 ½ m. by A 4500 – ✉ 0604 Northampton :

Westone Moat House (Q.M.H.), Ashley Way, NN3 3EA, ℘ 406262, Telex 312587, Fax 415023, , – rest – 120. Y a
closed Christmas-New Year – **M** *(closed Saturday lunch)* 10.50/11.50 **st.** and a la carte 3.95 – **65 rm** 65.00/75.00 **st.**, **1 suite** 95.00 **st.** – SB (weekends only) 74.00 **st.**

at Moulton NE : 4 ½ m. by A 43 – Y – ✉ 0604 Northampton :

Poplars, 33 Cross St., NN3 1RZ, ℘ 643983, – .
closed 1 week at Christmas – **M** 10.50 **t.** 3.00 – **21 rm** 20.00/50.00 **t.** – SB (weekends only) 50.00/75.00 **st.**

at Holdenby NW : 6 ½ m. by A 508 – Y – off A 50 – ✉ 0604 Northampton :

Lynton House with rm, NN6 8DJ, ℘ 770777, Italian rest., – .
closed 1 week March, 2 weeks August and Christmas – **M** *(closed Monday lunch, Sunday dinner and Bank Holidays)* 15.20/25.00 **st.** 6.00 – **5 rm** 58.00/70.00 **st.**

FIAT 74 Kingsthorpe Rd ℘ 714555
FORD Weston Favell Centre ℘ 404211
MERCEDES-BENZ Bedford Rd ℘ 250151
PEUGEOT, SAAB 590 Wellingborough Rd ℘ 401141
RENAULT Bedford Rd ℘ 39645
ROVER Weedon Rd ℘ 754041
TOYOTA 348 Wellingborough Rd ℘ 31086
VOLVO Bedford Rd ℘ 21363

ATS Kingsthorpe Rd ℘ 713303

NORTH BOVEY Devon 403 I 32 – pop. 368 – ✉ Newton Abbot – 0647 Moretonhampstead.

London 214 – Exeter 13 – Plymouth 31 – Torquay 21.

Glebe House, TQ13 8RA, ℘ 40544, ≤, , park – .
closed January and February – **M** (bar lunch residents only)/dinner 15.80 **t.** and a la carte 4.00 – **9 rm** 25.00/38.00 **t.**

Blackaller House without rest., TQ13 8QY, ℘ 40322, ≤, – .
April-October – **5 rm** 17.25/45.00 **s.**

NORTH DALTON Humberside 402 S 22 – see Great Driffield.

NORTH FERRIBY Humberside 402 S 22 – see Kingston-upon-Hull.

NORTHFIELD West Midlands 403 ㉒ 404 ⑳ – see Birmingham.

NORTH HUISH Devon – see South Brent.

NORTHIAM East Sussex 404 V 31 – pop. 1 657 – ECD : Wednesday – ✉ Rye – 0797.

London 55 – Folkestone 36 – Hastings 12 – Maidstone 27.

Hayes Arms, Village Green, TN31 6NN, ℘ 253142, « Part Tudor and Georgian country house », – .
M a la carte 9.50/13.30 **st.** 4.00 – **7 rm** 40.00/66.00 **st.** – SB (except Christmas) 78.00/82.00 **st.**

NORTHLEACH Glos. 403 404 O 28 – pop. 1 043 – ECD : Thursday – ☎ 0451 Cotswold.
ℹ Cotswold Countryside Collection ☎ 60715 (summer only).
♦London 84 – ♦Birmingham 63 – Gloucester 21 – ♦Oxford 28 – Swindon 24.

XX Wickens, Market Pl., GL54 3EJ, ☎ 60421 – ⅀.

NORTH MUSKHAM Notts. 402 404 R 24 – see Newark-on-Trent.

NORTH NEWINGTON Oxon – see Banbury.

NORTH NIBLEY Glos. 403 404 M 29 – ✉ ☎ 0453 Dursley.
♦London 115 – ♦Bristol 21 – Gloucester 20 – Swindon 32.

Burrows Court ⅀, Nibley Green, GL11 6AZ, NW : 1 m. via The Street ☎ 546230, ⅀, ⅀, ⅀ – TV P. AE VISA. ⅀
closed January – **M** (dinner only) (residents only) 12.50 **st.** 4.25 – **10 rm** 33.00/45.00 **st.** – SB 58.00/65.00 **st.**

NORTH PETHERTON Somerset 403 K 30 – see Bridgwater.

NORTH STIFFORD Essex 404 ㊹ – ✉ Grays – ☎ 0375 Grays Thurrock.
♦London 22 – Chelmsford 24 – Southend-on-Sea 20.

Stifford Moat House (Q.M.H), High Rd, RM16 1UE, ☎ 390909, Telex 995126, Fax 390426, ⅀, ⅀ – TV ☎ P – ⅀ 100. AE ⅀ VISA
closed 27 and 28 December – **M** *(closed Saturday lunch)* 16.00 **st.** and a la carte 4.95– 7.95 – **98 rm** 66.00/135.00 **st.** – SB (weekends only) 75.00 **st.**

When visiting the West Country,
use the Michelin Green Guide **"England: The West Country".**
– *Detailed descriptions of places of interest*
– *Touring programmes by county*
– *Maps and street plans*
– *The history of the region*
– *Photographs and drawings of monuments, beauty spots, houses...*

NORTH STOKE Oxon. – see Wallingford.

NORTH WALSHAM Norfolk 403 404 Y 25 – pop. 7 929 – ECD : Wednesday – ☎ 0692.
♦London 125 – ♦Norwich 16.

Beechwood, 20 Cromer Rd, NR28 0HD, ☎ 403231, ⅀ – ⅀ rest P
closed 24 December-1 January – **M** 9.00 **t.** – **11 rm** 17.00/40.00 **t.** – SB 38.00/46.00 **st.**

at Knapton NE : 3½ m. on B 1145 – ✉ North Walsham – ☎ 0263 Mundesley :

Knapton Hall, The Street, NR28 0SB, ☎ 720405, Fax 721692, ⅀, ⅀, ⅀ – TV ☎ P. AE VISA. ⅀
M a la carte 7.45/18.45 **t.** 4.00 – **9 rm** 40.00/70.00 **t.** – SB (weekends only) 62.00/ 98.50 **st.**

at Felmingham S : 1 ½ m. on B 1145 – ✉ North Walsham – ☎ 069 269 Swanton Abbott :

Felmingham Hall ⅀, NR28 0LP, S : 1½ m. by Skeyton Rd ☎ 631, Fax 320, ⅀, ⅀ heated, ⅀, park – TV ☎ P. AE VISA. ⅀
M (lunch by arrangement)/dinner 22.95 **t.** and a la carte 4.90 – **12 rm** (dinner included) 70.00/143.00 **t.** – SB (except weekends and Bank Holidays) 108.90/129.00 **st.**

ROVER Bacton Rd ☎ 403401

NORTH WALTHAM Hants. 403 404 Q 30 – pop. 692 – ✉ ☎ 0256 Basingstoke.
♦London 59 – Reading 24 – Southampton 24 – Swindon 52.

Wheatsheaf (Lansbury), RG25 2BB, S : ¾ m. on A 30 ☎ 398282, Telex 859775, Fax 398253 – ⅀ rm TV ☎ P – ⅀ 80. AE ⅀ VISA. ⅀
M a la carte 10.10/18.05 **t.** and a la carte – **28 rm** 67.00/79.00 **t.** – SB (weekends only) 68.00 **st.**

NORTON Shropshire – see Telford.

NORTON North Yorks. 402 R 21 – see Malton.

NORTON ST PHILIP Somerset 403 404 N 30 – see Bath (Avon).

NORWICH Norfolk 404 Y 26 – pop. 169 814 – ☎ 0603.

ee : Site★★ – Cathedral★★ Y – Castle (Museum and Art Gallery★) Z – Market Place★ Z – ainsbury Centre for Visual Arts★ (University of East Anglia) *AC* by B 1108 X.

nvir. : Blickling Hall★★*AC* (Jacobean) N : 15 m. by A 140 V – The Broads★ (East : from orwich).

Royal Norwich, Hellesdon ☎ 45712 V – 18 Wroxham Rd, Sprowston Park ☎ 410657, NE : 2 m. – 18 Costessy Park ☎ 746333, W : 3m. V – 18, 18 Barnham Broom ☎ 0605 45 (Barnham Broom) 93, SW : 8 m. X.

✈ ☎ 411923, Telex 97209, N : 3½ m. by A 140 V.

Guildhall, Gaol Hill ☎ 666071/761082.

London 109 – ◆Kingston-upon-Hull 148 – ◆Leicester 117 – ◆Nottingham 120.

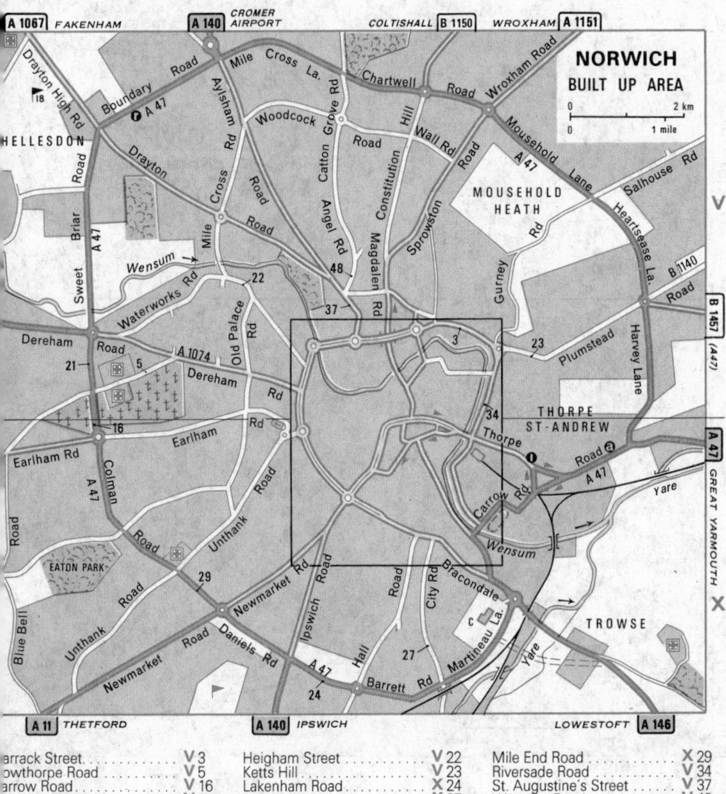

arrack Street . . . . V 3	Heigham Street . . . . V 22	Mile End Road . . . . X 29
owthorpe Road . . . . V 5	Ketts Hill . . . . V 23	Riversade Road . . . . V 34
arrow Road . . . . V 16	Lakenham Road . . . . X 24	St. Augustine's Street . . . . V 37
uardian Road . . . . V 21	Long John Hill . . . . X 27	Waterloo Road . . . . V 48

🏨 **Friendly H.,** 2 Barnard Rd, Bowthorpe, NR5 9JB, W : 3½ m. by A 1074 on A 47 – X – ☎ 741161, Telex 975557, Fax 741500, 🏋, ≘s, 🏊 – TV ☎ P – 🏛 180. AE ⓪ VISA. ✂
M 16.00 **st.** and a la carte 🍷 4.00 – ☕ 5.00 – **80 rm** 52.00/73.00 **st.** – SB (weekends only) 70.00/75.00 **st.**

🏨 Maid's Head (Q.M.H.), Tombland, NR3 1LB, ☎ 761111, Telex 975080, Fax 613688 – 🛗 TV ☎ P – 🏛 60 Y **u**
80 rm, 1 suite.

🏨 **Nelson,** Prince of Wales Rd, NR1 1DX, ☎ 760260, Telex 975203, Fax 620008, ≤ – 🛗 ▤ rest TV ☎ ♿ P – 🏛 90. AE ⓪ VISA. ✂ Z **a**
M *(closed lunch Saturday and Bank Holidays)* 11.50/14.00 **st.** and a la carte 🍷 4.50 – **118 rm** ☕ 69.50/90.50 **st.**, **3 suites** 95.00/125.00 **st.** – SB (except Christmas) 82.00/90.00 **st.**

P.T.O. →

NORWICH

Elm Hill	Y	
Gentleman's Walk	Z	17
London Street	YZ	26
St. Andrew's Street	Y	36
St. Stephen's Street	Z	
Bank Plain	Y	2
Bethel Street	Z	4
Castle Meadow	Z	6
Cattle Market Street	Z	7
Chapel Field North	Z	9
Charing Cross	Y	10
Colegate	Y	14
Exchange Street	YZ	15
Grapes Hill	Y	19
Market Avenue	Z	28
Rampant Horse Street	Z	32
Red Lion Street	Z	33
St. George's Street	Z	38
St. Giles Street	Y	40
Thorn Lane	Z	42
Timber Hill	Z	43
Tombland	Y	45
Upper King Street	Y	46
Wensum Street	Y	49
Westlegate	Z	50
Whitefriars	Y	51

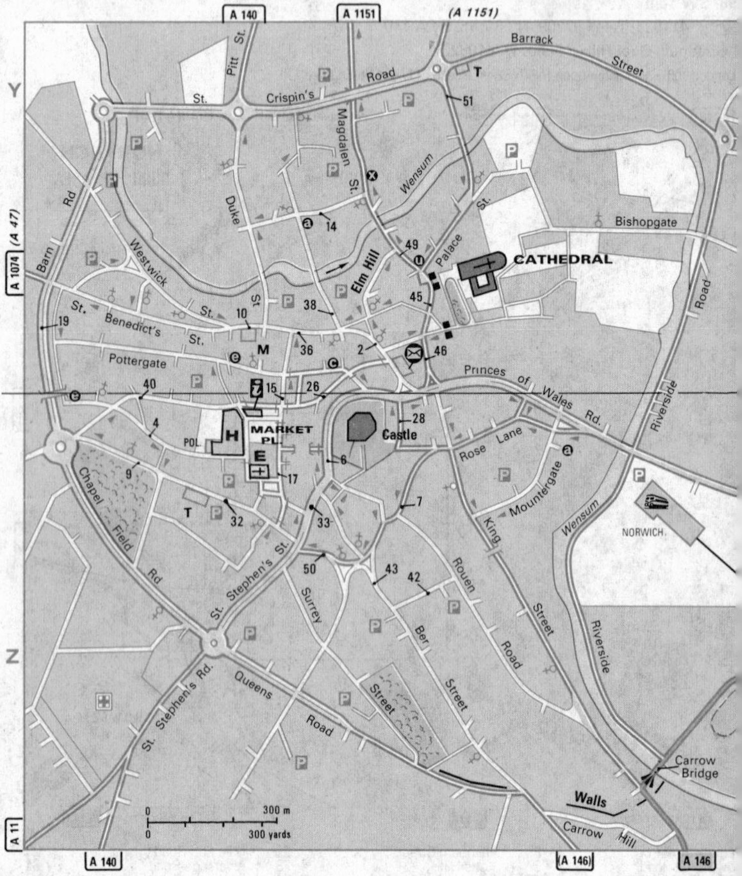

Post House (T.H.F.), Ipswich Rd, NR4 6EP, S : 2 ¼ m. on A 140 ☎ 56431, Telex 975106 Fax 506400, ≘, 🏊 – ⇔ rm 📺 ☎ 🅟 – 🎪 100. AE ⓓ VISA — on A 140 X
M *(closed lunch Saturday and Bank Holiday Mondays)* 7.50/13.95 **st.** and a la carte 🍷 4.35 – ☕ 7.50 – **116 rm** 69.00/79.00 **st.** – SB (weekends only) 76.00/90.00 **st.**

Norwich (Best Western), 121-131 Boundary Rd, NR3 2BA, on A 47 ☎ 787260, Telex 975337, Fax 400466 – ⇔ rm 📺 ☎ ♿ 🅟 – 🎪 300. AE ⓓ VISA. ✻ — V
M *(closed Saturday lunch)* (carving lunch)/dinner a la carte 14.75/20.50 **st.** – **99 rm** ☕ 57.00/67.00 **st.**, **3 suites** 70.00 **st.**

Sprowston Manor, Wroxham Rd, Sprowston, NR7 8RP, NE : 3 ¼ m. on A 1151 – V – ☎ 410871, Telex 975356, Fax 423911, ⛳ – 📺 ☎ 🅟 – 🎪 200 – **38 rm.**

Lansdowne, 116 Thorpe Rd, NR1 1RU, ☎ 620302, Fax 761706 – 🛗 ⇔ rm 📺 ☎ 🅟 – 🎪 120 — X
44 rm.

Cumberland, 212-216 Thorpe Rd, NR1 1TJ, ☎ 34550, Fax 33355 – ⇔ rm 📺 ☎ 🅟. AE VISA. ✻ — X
M 13.95 **t.** 🍷 3.60 – **28 rm** ☕ 34.00/60.00 **st.** – SB (weekends only) 55.00/63.00 **st.**

XX ꕥ **Adlard's** (Adlard), 79 Upper St. Giles St., NR2 1AB, ☏ 633522 – VISA Z e
closed Saturday lunch, Sunday and Monday – **M** 16.50/27.50 **t.** 4.00.
Spec. Chartreuse of duck confit with savoy cabbage and a spiced sauce, Loin of wild venison with a package of spinach, pine kernels and raisins, Rack of English lamb with pancake of celeriac, ginger and vegetables.

XX **By Appointment,** 27 St. Georges St., NR3 1AB, ☏ 630730 – VISA Y a
closed Sunday – **M** 16.50 **t.** and a la carte.

XX **Brasted's,** 8-10 St. Andrew's Hill, NR2 1AD, ☏ 625949 – AE VISA Y c
closed Saturday lunch, Sunday and Bank Holidays – **M** 16.00 **t.** (lunch) and a la carte 5.25.

XX **Marco's,** 17 Pottergate, NR2 1DS, ☏ 624044, Italian rest. – AE VISA Y e
closed Sunday and Monday – **M** 18.00 **t.** (lunch) and a la carte 3.70.

X **Bombay,** 9-11 Magdalen st., NR3 1LE, ☏ 666618, Indian rest. – AE VISA Y x
closed 25 December – **M** a la carte 9.15/10.95 **t.**

at Horsham St. Faith N : 4 ½ m. by A 140 – V – ✉ 0603 Norwich :

Elm Farm Chalet, 55 Norwich Rd, NR10 3HH, ☏ 898366, Fax 897129, – rest TV ☎ P. AE VISA.
M (by arrangement) 13.50 **t.** 3.00 – **25 rm** 25.00/49.50 **t.** – SB (November-March) (except Bank Holidays) 60.35/67.55 **st.**

at Thorpe St. Andrew E : 2 ½ m. on A 47 – X – ✉ 0603 Norwich :

Oaklands, 89 Yarmouth Rd, NR7 0HH, ☏ 34471, Fax 700318, – TV ☎ P – 60
41 rm.

at Hethersett SW : 6 m. by A 11 – X – ✉ 0603 Norwich :

Park Farm, on B 1172, NR9 3DL, ☏ 810264, Fax 812104, ←, , , , – TV ☎ P – 80. AE VISA.
closed 1 week Christmas – **M** 9.50/11.50 **t.** and a la carte 4.35 – **35 rm** 52.00/105.00 **st.** – SB (except Bank Holiday weekends) 82.00/120.00 **st.**

STON-MARTIN,ROVER Ipswich Rd, Long Stratton ☏ 0508 (Long Stratton) 30491
MW 26-29 Cattlemarket St. ☏ 621471
ITROEN Earlham Rd ☏ 621393
ORD 39 Palace St. ☏ 624144
IERCEDES-BENZ, VW, AUDI Heigham Causeway, Heigham St. ☏ 612111
EUGEOT-TALBOT 79 Mile Cross Lane ☏ 410661
ORSCHE Hall Rd ☏ 616716
ENAULT 22 Heigham St. ☏ 628911
OVER Norwich Rd, Stoke Holy Cross ☏ 05086 (Framingham Earl) 2218
ROVER Mile Cross Lane ☏ 483001
ROVER, DAIMLER-JAGUAR, ROLLS-ROYCE 5 Prince of Wales Rd ☏ 628383
TALBOT, PEUGEOT 3 Recorder Rd ☏ 628811
TOYOTA Rouen Rd ☏ 629655
VAUXHALL-OPEL Aylsham Rd, Mile Cross ☏ 414321
VAUXHALL-OPEL Mountergate ☏ 623111
VOLVO Westwick St. ☏ 626192

ATS Mason Rd, Mile Cross Lane ☏ 423471
ATS Aylsham Rd, Aylsham Way ☏ 426316

Si vous écrivez à un hôtel à l'étranger,
joignez à votre lettre un coupon-réponse international.
(disponible dans les bureaux de poste).

NOTTAGE (DRENEWYDD YN NOTAIS) Mid Glam. 403 I 29 – see Porthcawl.

NOTTINGHAM Notts. 402 403 404 Q 25 – pop. 273 300 – ECD : Thursday – 0602.
See : Castle★ (Renaissance) and Art Gallery★ *AC* CZ **M.**
Envir. : Newstead Abbey★ (16C) and gardens★★ *AC*, N : 9 m. by B 683 AY – Wollaton Hall★ (16C) *AC*, W : 3 ½ m. AZ **M.**

Bulwell Forest ☏ 770576, NW : 4 m. AY – Wollaton Park ☏ 787574, 2 m. AZ – Mapperley, Central Av. ☏ 265611 BY – Nottingham City, Lawton Drive ☏ 278021 AY – Beeston Fields, Beeston ☏ 257062, W : 4 m. AZ – , Chilwell Manor, Meadow Lane, Chilwell ☏ 257050, W : m. AZ – Edwalton ☏ 234775, S : 2 m. BZ.

East Midlands Airport : Castle Donington ☏ 0332 (Derby) 810621, SW : 15 m. by A 453 AZ.

14-16 Wheeler Gate ☏ 470661 – at West Bridgford: County Hall ☏ 823823.

London 135 – ♦Birmingham 50 – ♦Leeds 74 – ♦Manchester 72.

Plans on following pages

Albany (T.H.F.), St. James St., NG1 6BN, ☏ 470131, Telex 37211, Fax 484366 – rm TV ☎ – 500. AE VISA CYZ a
M 12.50 **st.** and a la carte – 8.60 – **138 rm** 80.00/95.00 **st.**, **1 suite** 190.00 **st.** – SB (weekends only) 74.00/84.00 **st.**

Royal Moat House International (Q.M.H.), Wollaton St., NG1 5RH, ☏ 414444, Telex 37101, Fax 475667, , squash – rm TV ☎ P – 450. AE VISA.
closed 25 and 26 December – **M** a la carte 8.95/25.00 **st.** 6.50 – 8.00 – **201 rm** 59.00/175.00 **st.** CY e

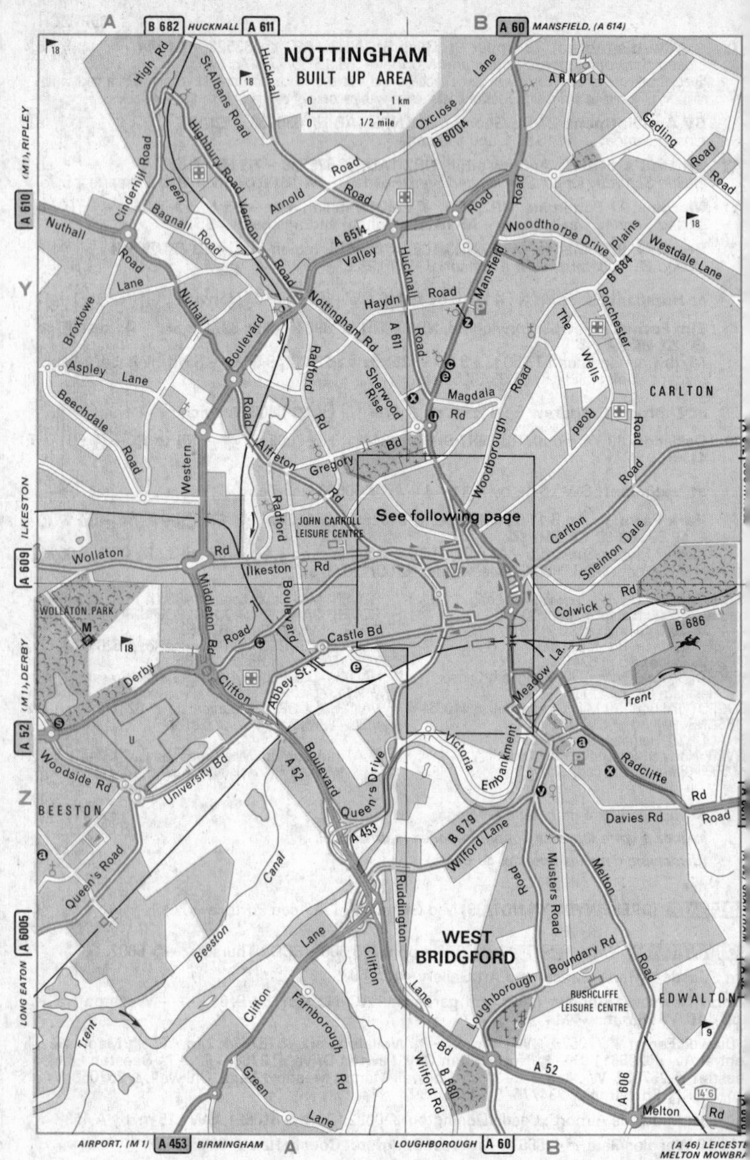

When looking for a quiet hotel use the maps found in the introductory pages or look for establishments with the sign or .

We suggest:

For a successful tour, that you prepare it in advance. Michelin maps and guides will give you much useful information on route planning, places of interest, accommodation, prices etc.

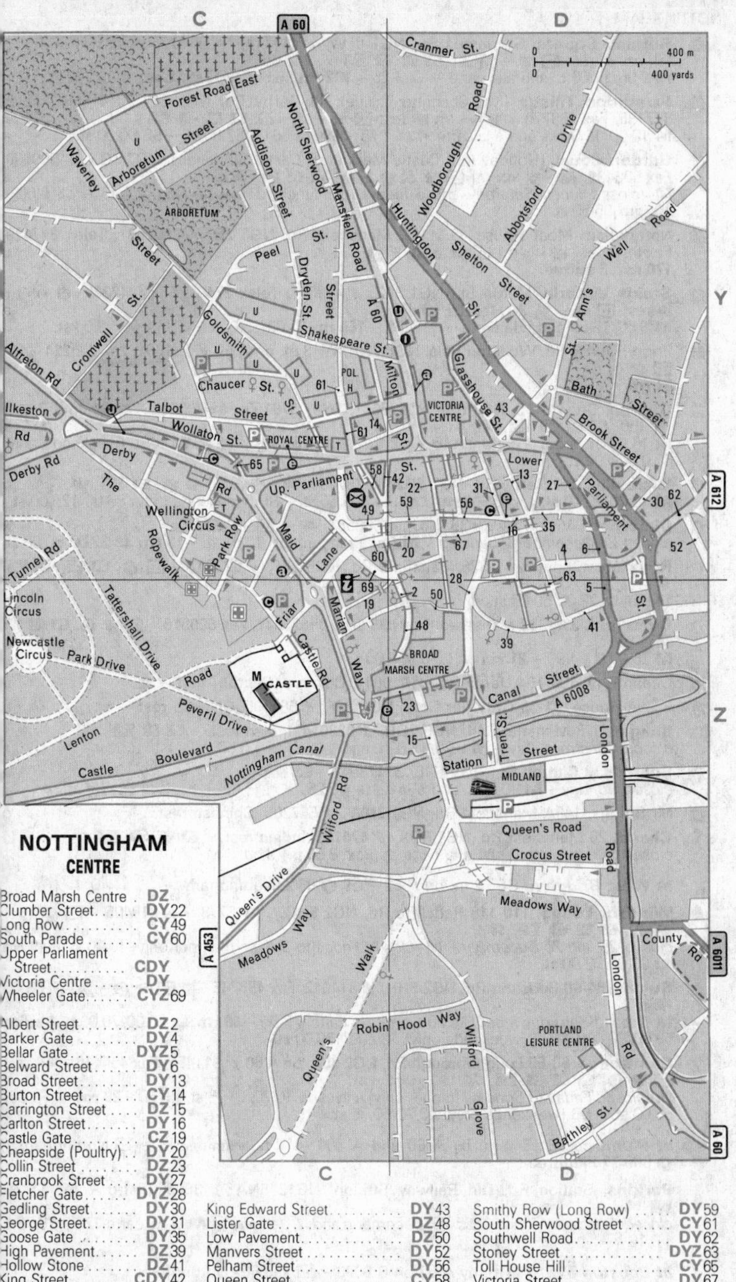

NOTTINGHAM
CENTRE

Broad Marsh Centre . DZ
Clumber Street . . . . DY 22
Long Row . . . . CY 49
South Parade . . . . . . CY 60
Upper Parliament Street . . . . CDY
Victoria Centre . . . . . DY
Wheeler Gate . . . . . CYZ 69

Albert Street . . . . . . DZ 2
Barker Gate . . . . DY 4
Bellar Gate . . . . DYZ 5
Belward Street . . . . . DY 6
Broad Street . . . . DY 13
Burton Street . . . . . . CY 14
Carrington Street . . . . DZ 15
Carlton Street . . . . . . DY 16
Castle Gate . . . . CZ 19
Cheapside (Poultry) . . DY 20
Collin Street . . . . DZ 23
Cranbrook Street . . . . DY 27
Fletcher Gate . . . . . . DYZ 28
Gedling Street . . . . . . DY 30
George Street . . . . . . DY 31
Goose Gate . . . . DY 35
High Pavement . . . . . DZ 39
Hollow Stone . . . . . . DZ 41
King Street . . . . CDY 42

King Edward Street . . . . DY 43
Lister Gate . . . . DZ 48
Low Pavement . . . . DZ 50
Manvers Street . . . . DY 52
Pelham Street . . . . DY 56
Queen Street . . . . CY 58

Smithy Row (Long Row) . . . . DY 59
South Sherwood Street . . . . . CY 61
Southwell Road . . . . DY 62
Stoney Street . . . . DYZ 63
Toll House Hill . . . . CY 65
Victoria Street . . . . DY 67

If you find you cannot take up a hotel booking you have made, please let the hotel know immediately.

Rutland Square, St. James St., NG1 6FW, ✆ 411114, Telex 378504, Fax 410014 – |‡| ⇔ rm ▤ rest TV ☎ – 🏛 30. AE VISA CZ **c**
M 8.95/11.00 **t.** and a la carte – ☐ 4.25 – **102 rm** 55.00/65.00 **st.**, **1 suite** 195.00 **st.**

Strathdon Thistle (Mt. Charlotte Thistle), 44 Derby Rd, NG1 5FT, ✆ 418501, Telex 377185, Fax 483725 – |‡| ⇔ rm ▤ rest TV ☎ – 🏛 120. AE VISA CY **c**
M 10.00/11.00 **st.** and a la carte – ☐ 7.75 – **69 rm** 56.00/82.00 **st.** – SB 90.00 **st.**

Garden Court, (Holiday Inn) Castle Marina off Castle Boulevard, NG7 1GX, ✆ 500600, Fax 500433, – |‡| ⇔ rm TV ☎ ♿ P – 🏛 40. AE VISA AZ **e**
M *(closed lunch Saturday and Sunday)* (bar lunch)/dinner 12.00 **st.** 4.45 – ☐ 6.00 – **100 rm** 35.50 **st.**

Nottingham Moat House (Q.M.H.), Mansfield Rd, NG5 2BT, ✆ 602621, Telex 377429, Fax 691506 – |‡| ⇔ rm TV ☎ ♿ P – 🏛 180 BY **u**
170 rm, **3 suites.**

Stakis Victoria, Milton St., NG1 3PZ, ✆ 419561, Telex 37401, Fax 484736 – |‡| ⇔ rm ▤ rest TV ☎ – 🏛 200. AE VISA DY **a**
M 8.50/12.50 and a la carte – ☐ 7.50 – **166 rm** 62.00/85.00 **t.** – SB 72.00/90.00 **st.**

Priory, Derby Rd, Wollaton Vale, NG8 2NR, W: 3 m. on A 52 ✆ 221691, Fax 256224 – ⇔ TV ☎ ♿ P AZ **s**
31 rm.

George, George St., NG1 3BP, ✆ 475641, Telex 378150, Fax 483292 – |‡| ⇔ rm TV ☎ – 🏛 150. AE VISA. DY **e**
M 16.00 **st.** and a la carte 4.00 – ☐ 5.00 – **69 rm** 49.00/66.00 **st.** – SB (weekends only) 68.00/70.00 **st.**

Lucieville, 349 Derby Rd, NG7 2DZ, ✆ 787389, – ⇔ TV ☎ P. VISA. AZ **c**
M 18.00/22.00 **st.** 4.95 – **8 rm** ☐ 49.50/69.50 **st.** – SB (weekends only) 86.00/125.00 **st.**

Claremont, Vivian Av., NG5 1AU, ✆ 608587, – TV P. VISA BY **x**
closed 24 December-2 January – **M** (by arrangement) 10.00 **st.** – **13 rm** ☐ 32.00/50.00 **st.**

Royston without rest., 326 Mansfield Rd, NG5 2EF, ✆ 622947 – TV P. AE VISA.
14 rm ☐ 28.00/50.00 **st.** BY **e**

Cotswold, 330-332 Mansfield Rd, NG5 2EF, ✆ 623547, Fax 609910 – TV ☎ P. AE VISA BY **c**
M 25.00 **t.** 4.90 – **21 rm** ☐ 20.00/48.00 **t.**

Ocean City, 100-104 Derby Rd, ✆ 410041, Chinese (Canton) rest. – ▤ CY **u**

Noble House, 31-33 Greyfriar Gate, NG1 7EF, ✆ 501105, Chinese rest. – ▤ CDZ **e**

Saagar, 973 Mansfield Rd, NG5 2DR, ✆ 622014, Indian rest. – AE VISA BY **z**
closed Christmas Day – **M** 6.95/12.00 **t.** and a la carte 3.50.

Sonny's, 3 Carlton St., NG1 1NL, ✆ 473041 – VISA DY **u**
closed Sunday – **M** 10.50 **t.** and a la carte 3.25.

Mr Shings, 148A Mansfield Rd, NG1 3HW, ✆ 587209, Chinese rest. DY **c**

Chand, 26 Mansfield Rd, NG1 3GX, ✆ 474103, Indian rest. – AE VISA DY **i**
closed Sunday lunch – **M** a la carte approx. 8.50 **t.** 3.50.

at West Bridgford SE : 2 m. on A 52 – ✉ ☎ 0602 Nottingham :

Windsor Lodge, 110-118 Radcliffe Rd, NG2 5HG, ✆ 813773, Fax 819405 – TV ☎ P – 🏛 30. AE VISA. BZ **x**
closed 25 and 26 December – **M** *(closed Friday to Sunday)* (dinner only) 10.00 **st.** – **49 rm** ☐ 33.00/52.00 **st.**

Swans, 84-90 Radcliffe Rd, NG2 5HH, ✆ 814042, Fax 455745 – |‡| TV ☎ P – 🏛 50. AE VISA BZ **a**
M *(closed Saturday lunch)* 15.00 **t.** and a la carte 3.95 – **30 rm** ☐ 20.00/70.00 **t.**, **1 suite** 59.00/80.00 **t.** – SB (weekends only) 130.00/178.00 **st.**

Cambridge, 63-65 Loughborough Rd, NG2 7LA, on A 60 ✆ 811455, Fax 455416 – ⇔ rest TV ☎ P. AE VISA. BZ **v**
M *(closed Friday to Sunday)* (dinner only) a la carte 10.70/14.75 **st.** 3.50 – **20 rm** ☐ 30.00/58.00 **st.** – SB (weekends only) 40.70/60.75 **st.**

at Plumtree SE : 5 ¾ m. by A 60 and A 606 – BZ off Plumtree rd – ✉ Nottingham – ☎ 060 77 Plumtree :

Perkins, Station Rd, Old Railway Station, NG12 5NA, ✆ 3695, Bistro – P. AE VISA
closed Sunday, Monday, 25-26 December and 1 January – **M** a la carte 12.70/15.70 **t.** 3.10.

at Beeston SW : 4 ½ m. by A 52 on B 6006 – ✉ ☎ 0602 Nottingham :

Les Artistes Gourmands, 61 Wollaton Rd, NG9 2NG, ✆ 228288, French rest. – AE VISA AZ **a**
closed lunch Monday and Saturday, Sunday and 2 weeks August – **M** 18.00/22.00 **t.** and a la carte 4.00.

at Toton SW : 6 ½ m. on A 6005 – AZ – ✉ ☎ 0602 Nottingham :

Manor, 350 Nottingham Rd, NG9 6EF, junction with B 6003 ☎ 733487 – TV P. VISA
M 10.95 **t.** 3.45 – **11 rm** 27.50/48.50 **t.**

at Long Eaton (Derbs.) SW : 8 m. by A 52 on B 6002 – AZ – ✉ ☎ 0602 Nottingham :

Novotel Nottingham, Bostock Lane, NG10 4EP, ☎ 720106, Telex 377585, Fax 720106 (ext : 106), heated, – rest TV ☎ P – 100. AE VISA
M 10.50 **st.** and a la carte – 6.00 – **110 rm** 52.00/57.00 **st.** – SB (weekend only) 32.50 **st.**

at Sandiacre (Derbs.) SW : 8 m. on A 52 – AZ – ✉ ☎ 0602 Nottingham :

Post House (T.H.F.), Bostocks Lane, NG10 5NJ, ☎ 397800, Telex 377378, Fax 490469 – rm TV ☎ P – 75. AE VISA
M 9.50/16.95 **st.** and a la carte 2.50 – 7.50 – **107 rm** 65.00/75.00 **st.** – SB (weekends only) 60.00/76.00 **st.**

Talbot (T.H.F.), NewSt., PE8 4EA, ☎ 273621, Telex 32364, Fax 274545, – rm TV ☎ P – 120. AE VISA
M 9.50/14.00 **st.** and a la carte 3.95 – 7.00 – **35 rm** 59.00/82.00 **st.**, **3 suites.**

AUDI Vernon Rd, Basford ☎ 789291
BMW 165 Huntingdon St. ☎ 582831
CITROEN, FIAT 333 Mansfield Rd ☎ 621000
COLT 61a Mansfield Rd ☎ 475635
DAIMLER, ROLLS-ROYCE, BENTLEY Derby Rd ☎ 780730
FIAT Wilford Rd, Ruddington ☎ 844114
FORD Derby Rd ☎ 476111
FORD Nottingham Rd, Stapleford ☎ 395000
FORD 201 Lower Parliament St. ☎ 506282
HYUNDAI Greasley St., Bulwell ☎ 272228
LADA Woodborough Rd ☎ 623324
MAZDA Station Rd, Plumtree ☎ Plumtree (060 77) 5111
MERCEDES-BENZ Loughborough Rd ☎ 822333
PEUGEOT-TALBOT Pasture Rd, Stapleford ☎ 394444
PEUGEOT-TALBOT Clifton Lane, Clifton ☎ 211228
RENAULT Ilkeston Rd ☎ 781938
RENAULT Sawley, Long Eaton ☎ 0602 (Long Eaton) 733121
ROVER 136 Burton Rd, Carlton ☎ 617111
ROVER Derby Rd ☎ 787701
ROVER 199 Mansfield Rd, Arnold ☎ 204141
SAAB 152 Beechdale Rd ☎ 293023
SKODA 134-138 Loughborough Rd ☎ 814320
TOYOTA 431 Nottingham Rd, Basford ☎ 422242
VAUXHALL-OPEL 5 Haywood Rd, Mapperley ☎ 603231
VAUXHALL-OPEL Main St., Bulwell ☎ 770777
VOLVO 50 Plains Rd ☎ 266336
VOLVO 131 Alfreton Rd ☎ 708181
VW, AUDI 180 Loughborough Rd ☎ 813813

ATS 116 Highbury Rd, Bulwell ☎ 278824
ATS 66 Castle Boulevard ☎ 476678
ATS 126-132 Derby Rd, Stapleford ☎ 392986

NUNEATON Warw. 403 404 P 26 – pop. 60 377 – ECD : Thursday – ☎ 0203.

Envir. : Arbury Hall★ (Gothic house 18C) *AC*, SW : 4 m.

Nuneaton Library, Church St. ☎ 384027.

London 107 – Birmingham 25 – Coventry 10 – Leicester 18.

at Sibson (Leics.) N : 7 m. on A 444 – ✉ Nuneaton – ☎ 0827 Tamworth :

Millers', Main Rd, CV13 6LB, ☎ 880223, Fax 880223 (ext : 222), « Reconstructed early 19C bakery and water-mill » – TV ☎ P – 30. AE VISA
M 12.95/15.95 **st.** and a la carte 3.75 – **40 rm** 49.50/59.50 **st.** – SB (weekends only) 43.00/51.00 **st.**

FIAT Haunchwood Rd ☎ 382807
HYUNDAI, LADA, PROTON Midland Rd ☎ 346351
PEUGEOT-TALBOT 208-214 Edward St. ☎ 383339
RENAULT Nuneaton Rd, Bulkington ☎ 374777
ROVER Weddington Rd ☎ 383471
SEAT 45 Attleborough Rd ☎ 382241

ATS Weddington Rd ☎ 341130/341139

NUNNINGTON North Yorks. 402 R 21 – see Helmsley.

OADBY Leics. 402 403 404 R 26 – see Leicester.

OAKFORDBRIDE Devon – see Tiverton.

OAKHAM Leics. 402 404 R 25 – pop. 7 914 – ECD : Thursday – ☎ 0572.

Oakham Library, Catmos St. ☎ 724329.

London 103 – Leicester 26 – Northampton 35 – Nottingham 28.

Whipper-In, Market Pl., LE15 6DT, ☎ 756971, Fax 757759, « Attractively decorated part 17C inn » – TV ☎ – 45. AE VISA
M (dinner only and Sunday lunch)/dinner 25.00 **t.** and a la carte – **24 rm** 68.00/80.00 **st.** – SB (weekends only) 85.00 **st.**

Boultons, 4 Catmose St., LE15 6HW, ☎ 722844, Fax 724473 – rm TV ☎ P – 150. AE VISA
M 8.95/15.00 **st.** and a la carte 3.50 – **25 rm** 45.00/120.00 **st.** – SB (weekends only) 70.00/80.00 **st.**

Crown, Crown Walk, High St., LE15 6AP, ☎ 723631, Fax 724635 – TV ☎ P. AE VISA
M a la carte approx. 17.70 **t.** 6.00 – **16 rm** 50.00/59.00 **t.**

at Hambleton E : 3 m. by A 606 – ✉ ☎ 0572 Oakham :

🏨 ✿ **Hambleton Hall** 🐦, LE15 8TH, ✆ 756991, Telex 342888, Fax 724721, ≤ Rutland water, 🎣, 🌳, park, 🎾 – 🛗 📺 ☎ 🅿. 💳 VISA. 🚫
M 28.00/40.00 **st.** and a la carte 31.00/40.00 **st.** 🍷 6.50 – ☕ 4.50 – **15 rm** 105.00/205.00 **st.**
Spec. Steamed fillet of sea bass on an aubergine terrine, Grilled pavé steak with a potato and horseradish galette, Toasted marshmallow flavoured with rose petals.

ROVER Burley Rd ✆ 722657

OAKLEY Hants. 403 404 Q 30 – see Basingstoke.

OBORNE Dorset 403 404 M 31 – see Sherborne.

OCKHAM Surrey 404 ㊷ – ✉ Ripley – ☎ 0483 Guildford.

◆London 27 – Guildford 9.

XXX **Hautboy** with rm, Ockham Lane, GU23 6NP, ✆ 225355, 🌳 – 📺 ☎ 🅿. 💳 AE ⓓ VISA. 🚫
M *(closed 26 December)* 11.50 **t.** (lunch) and a la carte 16.80/20.45 **t.** 🍷 3.95 – ☕ 5.95 – **5 rm** 78.00/98.00 **st.**

ODIHAM Hants. 404 R 30 – pop. 3 002 – ECD : Wednesday – ☎ 0256 Basingstoke.

◆London 51 – Reading 16 – Winchester 25.

🏨 **George,** 100 High St., RG25 1LP, ✆ 702081, Fax 704213 – 📺 ☎ 🅿. 💳 AE ⓓ VISA
M *(closed dinner Monday and Sunday)* (bar lunch Monday to Saturday)/dinner a la carte 16.75/22.00 **t.** – **15 rm** ☕ 55.00/65.00 **t.**

X King's, 65 High St., RG25 1LF, ✆ 703811, Chinese rest. –.

OKEHAMPTON Devon. 403 H 31 – pop. 4 113 – ECD : Wednesday – ✉ ☎ 0837.

⛳18 ✆ 52113.
ℹ 3 West St. ✆ 53020 (summer only).

◆London 226 – Exeter 25 – ◆Plymouth 30.

🏨 **Travelodge** without rest., Sourton Cross, EX20 4LY, SW : 4 m. by A 30 on A 386 ✆ 52124, Reservations (Toll free) 0800 850950 – 📺 ♿ 🅿. 💳 AE VISA. 🚫
32 rm 24.00/29.50 **t.**

at Sourton SW : 5 m. by A 30 on A 386 – ✉ Okehampton – ☎ 083 766 Bridestowe :

🏨 **Collaven Manor** 🐦, EX20 4HH, S : ¾ m. on A 386 ✆ 522, Fax 570, « 15C manor house, gardens » – 📺 ☎ 🅿. 💳 VISA. 🚫
closed 2 weeks January – **M** 13.95/27.95 **t.** 🍷 3.75 – **9 rm** ☕ 50.00/95.00 **t.** – SB 80.00/90.00 **st.**

FIAT Exeter Rd ✆ 2255
FORD East St. ✆ 2776
⊛ ATS Crediton Rd ✆ 53277/52799

OLD Northants. – ☎ 0604.

◆London 77 – ◆Birmingham 58 – ◆Leicester 26 – Northampton 6.

⌂ **Wold Farm** 🐦, Harrington Rd, NN6 9RJ, ✆ 781258, 🌳, park – 🅿
M (meals by arrangement)(communal dining) 10.00 – **6 rm** ☕ 17.00/38.00.

OLD BROWNSOVER Warw. – see Rugby.

OLD BURGHCLERE Berks. – ✉ Reading – ☎ 063 527.

◆London 77 – ◆Bristol 76 – Newbury 10 – Reading 27 – ◆Southampton 28.

XX **Dew Pond,** RG15 9LH, ✆ 408 – 🅿. 💳 VISA
closed Saturday lunch, Sunday, Monday, first 2 weeks January, 2 weeks August and 26 December – **M** 16.50/31.00 **t.** 🍷 4.50.

OLDBURY West Midlands – see Birmingham.

OLDHAM Greater Manchester 402 404 N 23 – pop. 107 095 – ECD : Tuesday – ☎ 061 Manchester. ⛳18 Crompton and Royton, High Barn ✆ 624 2154 – ⛳18 Saddleworth, Uppermill ✆ 045 77 (Saddleworth) 3653 E : 5 m – ⛳18 Lees New Rd ✆ 624 4986 – ⛳18 Wermeth, Green Lane Garden Surbub ✆ 624 1190.

ℹ 84 Union St. ✆ 678 4654.

◆London 212 – ◆Leeds 36 – ◆Manchester 7 – ◆Sheffield 38.

🏨 **Bower** (De Vere), Hollinwood Av., Chadderton, OL9 8DE, SW : 3¼ m. by A 62 on A 6104 ✆ 682 7254, Telex 666883, Fax 683 4605, 🌳 – 📺 ☎ ♿ 🅿 – 🎤 200. 💳 AE ⓓ VISA
M *(closed Saturday lunch)* 10.75/22.00 **st.** – **66 rm** ☕ 65.00/72.00 **st.** – SB (weekends only) 60.00/70.00 **st.**

FIAT Lees Rd ✆ 624 8046
MAZDA Oldham Rd, Springhead ✆ 624 3620
NISSAN Huddersfield Rd ✆ 624 6042
⊛ ATS 169-171 Huddersfield Rd ✆ 633 1551
ATS 179-185 Hollins Rd ✆ 627 0180/665 1958

OLD SODBURY Avon 403 404 M 29 – ✉ Bristol – ☎ 0454 Chipping Sodbury.

♦London 110 – Bristol 14 – Gloucester 30 – Swindon 29.

- **Dornden** ⛰, Church Lane, BS17 6NB, ☎ 313325, ≤, 🌳 – 📺 🅿
 closed 3 weeks October, Christmas and New Year – **M** 7.00 **t.** – **9 rm** ☕ 23.00/45.00 **t.**

OLLERTON Notts. 402 403 404 Q 24 – pop. 11 303 (inc. Boughton) – ECD : Thursday – ✉ Newark – ☎ 0623 Mansfield.

⛳ Woodhouse ☎ 0623 (Mansfield) 23521, SW : 7 m.

ℹ Sherwood Heath, Ollerton Roundabout, Newark ☎ 824545.

♦London 151 – ♦Leeds 53 – Lincoln 25 – ♦Nottingham 19 – ♦Sheffield 27.

- **Old Rectory,** Main St., Kirton, NG22 9LP, NE : 3 m. on A 6075 ☎ 861540, Fax 860751, 🌳 – 🅿. VISA. ✗
 closed Christmas and New Year – **M** 13.50 **st.** – **10 rm** ☕ 21.50/47.50 **st.**

OLNEY Bucks. 404 R 27 – ☎ 0234 Bedford.

♦London 63 – Bedford 14 – Northampton 13.

- XX Dhaka Dynasty, 2-3 Stanley Court, Weston Rd, MK46 5NH, ☎ 713179, Indian rest.
- XX **Old Shanghai,** 17a High St., MK46 4ED, ☎ 240260, Chinese rest. – AE VISA
 M 13.00/16.00 **t.** and a la carte.

ORMESBY ST. MARGARET Norfolk 404 Z 25 – pop. 2 961 – ✉ ☎ 0493 Great Yarmouth.

♦London 146 – ♦Cambridge 81 – ♦Ipswich 63 – ♦Norwich 20.

- **Ormesby Lodge,** Decoy Rd., NR29 3LG, ☎ 730910, Fax 730910 – 📺 ☎ 🅿. AE ⓓ VISA
 M *(closed Sunday dinner)* (restricted lunch) 12.85/27.40 **st.** and a la carte 🍷 4.50 – **8 rm** ☕ 34.50/46.00 **st.** – SB 60.00 **st.**

☞ *Keine bezahlte Reklame im Michelin-Führer.*

ORMSKIRK Lancs. 402 L 23 – ☎ 0704.

- **Beaufort,** High Lane, Burscough, L40 7SN, NE : 1 ¾ m. by B 5319 on A 59 ☎ 892655, Fax 895135 – 📺 ☎ ♿ 🅿 – 🏛 50. AE ⓓ VISA. ✗
 M (carving lunch)/dinner 19.95 **t.** and a la carte – **21 rm** ☕ 54.00/80.00 **st.**

OSWESTRY Shropshire 402 403 K 25 – pop. 13 200 – ECD : Thursday – ☎ 0691.

⛳ Aston Park ☎ 069 188 (Queen's Head) 221.

ℹ Mile End Service Area A 5 ☎ 662488/657876 – Library, Arthur St. ☎ 662753.

♦London 182 – Chester 28 – Shrewsbury 18.

- **Wynnstay,** Church St., SY11 2SZ, ☎ 655261, Fax 670606, 🌳 – 🚭 rm 📺 ☎ 🅿 – 🏛 180. AE ⓓ VISA
 M 11.00/30.00 **t.** and a la carte – ☕ 7.50 – **25 rm** 40.00/110.00 **t.**, **1 suite** 110.00 **t.** – SB (weekends only) 82.00/134.00 **st.**
- **Ashfield,** Llwyn-y-Maen, Trefonen Rd, SY10 9DD, SW : 1 ½ m. ☎ 655200, ≤, 🌳 – 🚭 rest 📺 ☎ 🅿. VISA
 M 12.00/15.00 **st.** and a la carte – **12 rm** ☕ 46.00/60.00 **st.** – SB 80.00 **st.**
- **Travelodge** without rest., Mile End service area, SY11 4JA, SE : 1 ¼ m. at junction of A 5 and A 483 ☎ 658178, Reservations (Toll free) 0800 850950 – 📺 ♿ 🅿. AE VISA. ✗
 40 rm 24.00/29.50 **t.**
- XX **Starlings Castle** ⛰ with rm, Bron Y Garth, SY10 7NU, ☎ 72464, ≤, 🌳 – 📺 🅿. VISA
 M (lunch by arrangement)/dinner a la carte approx. 16.50 **t.** – ☕ 2.50 – **8 rm** 12.00/24.00 **t.**

BMW Victoria Rd ☎ 652413
FORD Salop Rd ☎ 654141
HONDA ☎ 653491
PEUGEOT-TALBOT Willow St. ☎ 652301
VAUXHALL-OPEL Smithfield St. ☎ 652235
VOLVO West Felton ☎ 069 188 (Queens Head) 451
ATS Oswald Rd ☎ 653540/653256

OTLEY Suffolk 404 X 27 – pop. 627 – ✉ Ipswich – ☎ 0473 Helmingham.

⛳ West Bucks Lane ☎ 461015.

♦London 83 – ♦Ipswich 7.5 – ♦Norwich 43.

- **Otley House** ⛰, IP6 9NR, ☎ 890253, ≤, « Part 17C manor house », 🌳 – 🚭 📺 🅿. ✗
 March-October – **M** (communal dining) (dinner only Monday to Saturday) 14.00 **st.** 🍷 3.20 – **4 rm** ☕ 30.00/46.00 **st.**

OTLEY West Yorks. 402 O 22 – pop. 14 136 – ☎ 0943.

ℹ Council Office, 8 Boroughgate ☎ 465151.

London 216 – Harrogate 14 – ♦Leeds 12 – York 28.

- **Chevin Lodge** ⛰, Yorkgate, LS21 3NU, S : 2 m. by East Chevin Rd ☎ 467818, Telex 51538, Fax 850335, « Pine log cabin village », 🌳, park – ▤ rest 📺 ☎ ♿ 🅿 – 🏛 40. AE VISA. ✗
 M *(closed Saturday lunch)* 9.50/14.50 **st.** and a la carte 🍷 3.95 – **40 rm** ☕ 49.00/92.50 **st.** – SB (weekends only) 85.00/95.00 **st.**

OTTERBURN Northumb. 401 402 N18 – pop. 1506 – ECD : Thursday – 0830.
◆London 314 – ◆Carlisle 54 – ◆Edinburgh 74 – ◆Newcastle-upon-Tyne 31.

Percy Arms, Main St., NE19 1NR, 20261, – – 50. AE VISA
M (bar lunch Monday to Saturday)/dinner 16.50 **t.** 3.50 – **28 rm** 41.50/90.00 **t.** – SB 70.00/100.00 **st.**

OTTERY ST MARY Devon 403 K 31 **The West Country G.** – pop. 3 957 – ECD : Wednesday – 040 481.
See : Site★ – St. Mary's Church★★.
The Flexton 813964 (summer only).
◆London 167 – Exeter 12 – Bournemouth 71 – ◆Plymouth 53 – Taunton 23.

Hotels : see Exeter W : 12 m.

FORD Brook St. 2007 — ATS Alansway, Station Yard 3444

OULTON Suffolk – see Lowestoft.

OUNDLE Northants. 404 S 26 – pop. 3 225 – ECD : Wednesday – Peterborough – 0832.
Benefield Rd 273267.
Market Pl. 274333.
◆London 89 – ◆Leicester 37 – Northampton 30.

Talbot (T.H.F.), New St., PE8 4EA, 273621, Fax 274545, – rm – 100. AE VISA
M 9.25/16.95 **st.** and a la carte 4.35 – 7.00 – **35 rm** 65.00/80.00 **st.**, **3 suites** 90.00 **st.** – SB (weekends only) 80.00/94.00 **st.**

FORD 1 Station Rd 273542 — ROVER 1 Benefield Rd 273519

Great Britain and Ireland is now covered
by a series of Atlases at a scale of 1 inch to 4.75 miles.
Three easy to use versions:
Paperback, Spiralbound, Hardback.

OUTLANE West Yorks. – see Huddersfield.

OWER Hants 403 404 P 31 – see Romsey.

OWERMOIGNE Dorset 403 404 N 32 – see Dorchester.

OXFORD Oxon. 403 404 Q 28 – pop. 113 847 – ECD : Thursday – 0865.
See : Site★★★ – Colleges : Trinity★★ BY **S** – Queens★★ BZ **R** – New★★ (Cloister★, Chapel★) BZ – Magdalene★★ (Cloister★★, Chapel★) BZ – Lincoln★ BZ **J** – Jesus★ BZ **X** – Merton★ (Old Library★★★, Hall★, Quadrangle★, Chapel windows and glass★) BZ – St. John's★ BY **Q** – Bodleian Library★★ (Painted Ceiling★★) BZ **M2** – Ashmolean Museum★★ **M1** – Churches : St. Mary the Virgin★★ BZ **D** – Christ Church★★ (Tom Quad Tower★) BZ – St. Michael at Northgate★ BZ **K** – Sheldonian Theatre★ BZ **M3** – University Museum★ BY **M4** – Pitt Rivers Museum★ BY **M5**.
Banbury Rd 54415, N : by A 423 AY – Southfield, Hill Top Rd 242158 and B 480 AZ.
St. Aldates Chambers, St. Aldates 726871.
◆London 59 – ◆Birmingham 63 – ◆Brighton 105 – ◆Bristol 73 – ◆Cardiff 107 – ◆Coventry 54 – ◆Southampton 64.

Plans on following pages

Randolph (T.H.F.), Beaumont St., OX1 2LN, 247481, Telex 83446, Fax 791678 – rm – – 300. AE VISA BZ
M 16.00/20.00 **st.** and a la carte 4.75 – 9.25 – **104 rm** 95.00/125.00 **st.**, **5 suites** 140.00/225.00 **st.**

Linton Lodge (Hilton), 9-13 Linton Rd, off Banbury Rd, OX2 6UJ, 53461, Telex 837093 Fax 310365, – rm – 100. AE VISA AY
M *(closed Saturday lunch)* (carving lunch) 9.75/16.00 **t.** and a la carte 4.20 – 8.50 – **71 rm** 78.00/130.00 **st.** – SB (weekends only) 100.00/140.00 **st.**

Cotswold House without rest., 363 Banbury Rd, OX2 7PL, 310558, – . **5 rm** 24.00/50.00 **st.** AY

Dial House without rest., 25 London Rd, Headington, OX3 7RE, 69944, – *closed Christmas and New Year* – **8 rm** 42.00/46.00 **st.** AY

Chestnuts without rest., 45 Davenant Rd, OX2 8BU, 53375 – . BY
4 rm 24.00/50.00.

Tilbury Lodge without rest., 5 Tilbury Lane, Botley, OX2 9NB, W : 2 m. by A 420 off B 4044 (Eynsham Rd) 862138, – . VISA. AZ
8 rm 30.00/60.00 **st.**

Mount Pleasant, 76 London Rd., Headington, OX3 9AJ, 62749 – rm . AE VISA. AY
M (by arrangement) 15.00 **st.** 4.00 – **8 rm** 35.00/60.00 **st.**

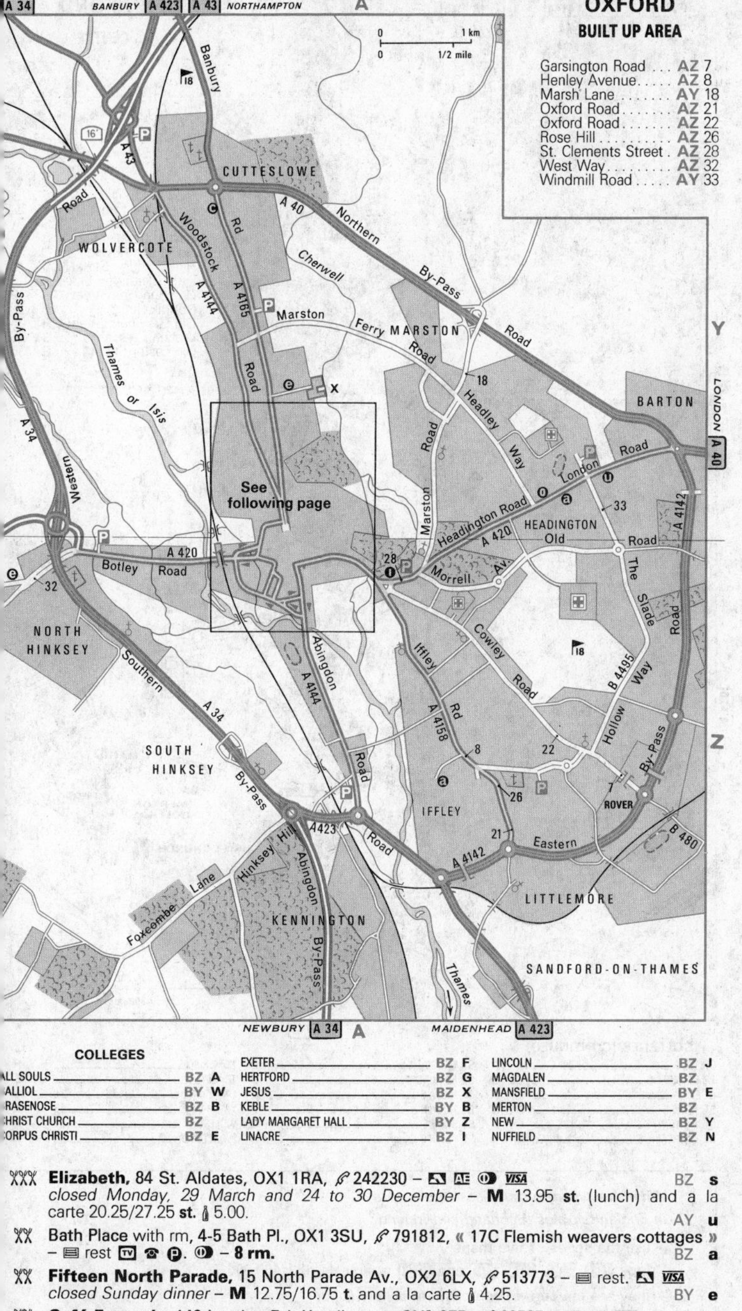

COLLEGES

LL SOULS	BZ	A	EXETER	BZ	F	LINCOLN	BZ	J
ALLIOL	BY	W	HERTFORD	BZ	G	MAGDALEN	BZ	
RASENOSE	BZ	B	JESUS	BZ	X	MANSFIELD	BY	E
HRIST CHURCH	BZ		KEBLE	BY	B	MERTON	BZ	
ORPUS CHRISTI	BZ	E	LADY MARGARET HALL	BY	Z	NEW	BZ	Y
			LINACRE	BZ	I	NUFFIELD	BZ	N

XXX **Elizabeth,** 84 St. Aldates, OX1 1RA, ☎ 242230 – AE VISA BZ **s**
closed Monday, 29 March and 24 to 30 December – **M** 13.95 **st.** (lunch) and a la carte 20.25/27.25 **st.** 5.00.
AY **u**

XX Bath Place with rm, 4-5 Bath Pl., OX1 3SU, ☎ 791812, « 17C Flemish weavers cottages » – rest TV ☎ P. – **8 rm.** BZ **a**

XX **Fifteen North Parade,** 15 North Parade Av., OX2 6LX, ☎ 513773 – rest. VISA
closed Sunday dinner – **M** 12.75/16.75 **t.** and a la carte 4.25. BY **e**

XX **Café Francais,** 146 London Rd, Headington, OX3 9ED, ☎ 62587 – AE VISA AY **u**
M 10.95/17.45 **t.**

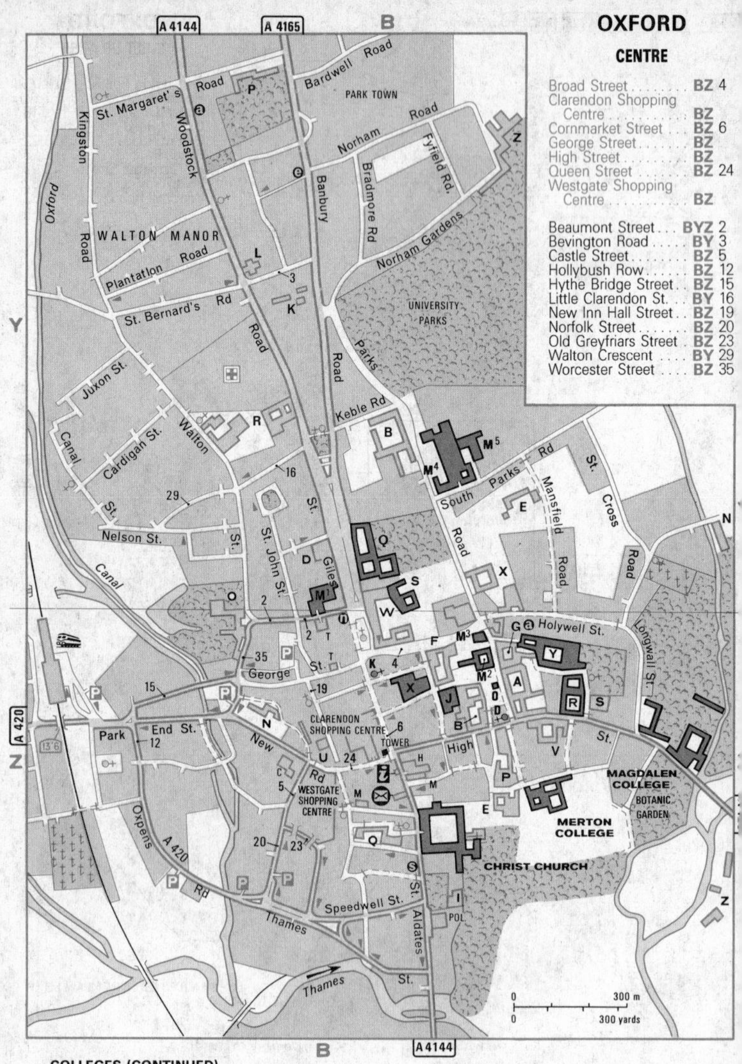

COLLEGES (CONTINUED)

ORIEL	BZ	P	ST. CROSS	BY	D	SOMERVILLE	BY	R
PEMBROKE	BZ	Q	ST. EDMUND'S	BZ	S	TRINITY	BY	S
QUEEN'S	BZ	R	ST. HILDA'S	BZ	Z	UNIVERSITY	BZ	V
ST. ANNE'S	BY	K	ST. HUGH'S	BY	P	WADHAM	BY	X
ST. ANTHONY'S	BY	L	ST. JOHN'S	BY	Q	WOLFSON	AY	X
ST. CATHERINE'S	BY	N	ST. PETER'S	BZ	U	WORCESTER	BY	O

When travelling for business or pleasure in England, Wales, Scotland and Ireland:

- use the series of five maps (nos **401**, **402**, **403**, **404** and **405**) at a scale of 1:400 000
- they are the perfect complement to this Guide as towns underlined in red on the maps will be found in this Guide.

at Kidlington N : 4 ½ m. on A 423 – AY – ✉ Oxford – ☎ 0865 Oxford :

Bowood House, 238 Oxford Rd, OX5 1EB, ☎ 842288, Fax 841858 – ⇔ rest TV ☎ ♿ P. VISA. ✻
closed 24 December-1 January – **M** *(closed Sunday)* (bar lunch)/dinner 12.50 **st.** and a la carte – **22 rm** ☐ 35.00/65.00 **st.** – SB (except summer) (weekends only) 70.00/85.00 **st.**

at Wheatley E : 7 m. by A 40 – ✉ Oxford – ☎ 086 77 Wheatley :

Travelodge without rest., London Rd, Reservations (toll free) 0800 850950 – TV ♿ P. AE VISA. ✻
24 rm 24.00/29.50 **t.**

at Iffley SE : 2 m. by A 4158 – ✉ ☎ 0865 Oxford

Tree, Church Way, OX4 4EY, ☎ 775974, Fax 747554, – TV ☎ P AZ **a**
7 rm.

at Great Milton SE : 12 m. by A 40 off A 329 – AY – ✉ Oxford – ☎ 0844 Great Milton :

✿✿ **Le Manoir aux Quat' Saisons** (Blanc) ⛰, Church St., OX9 7PD, ☎ 278881, Telex 837552, Fax 278847, ←, « 15C and 16C manor house », heated, , park, – rest TV ☎ ♿ P – 40. AE VISA. ✻
closed 23 December-18 January – **M** 56.00 **st.** and a la carte 59.50/68.00 **st.** – ☐ 12.00 – **14 rm** -/250.00 **st.**, **5 suites** 300.00/350.00 **st.**
Spec. Tiân d'aubergines et tomates au vinaigre balsamique, Croustillant de rouget de roche et son jus parfumé aux langues d'oursins, Le café crème.

at Cumnor SW : 4 ½ m. by A 420 – AY – – ✉ ☎ 0865 Oxford :

XX **Bear and Ragged Staff,** Appleton Rd, OX2 9QH, ☎ 862329, Fax 865134 – P. AE VISA
closed Saturday lunch – **M** 12.95/15.95 **t.** and a la carte.

CITROEN 281 Banbury Rd ☎ 512277
MERCEDES-BENZ Banbury Rd, Shipton-on-Cherwell ☎ 086 75 (Kidlington) 71011
NISSAN 72 Rose Hill ☎ 774696/748000
ROVER Oxford Rd, Kidlington ☎ 086 75 (Kidlington) 4363/78187
SAAB 75 Woodstock Rd ☎ 57028
VAUXHALL-OPEL Woodstock Rd ☎ 59955/722455
VW Abingdon Rd ☎ 242241
ATS Pony Rd, Horspath Trading Est, Cowley ☎ 777188
ATS 2 Stephen Rd, Headington ☎ 61732

Se cercate un albergo tranquillo,
oltre a consultare le carte dell'introduzione,
rintracciate nell'elenco degli esercizi quelli con il simbolo ⛰ o ⛰.

PADSTOW Cornwall 403 F 32 **The West Country G.** – pop. 2 256 – ECD : Wednesday – ☎ 0841.
See : Site★.
Envir. : Trevone (Cornwall Coast Path★★), W : 3 m. – Bedruthan Steps★*AC*, SW : 8 m. – Trevose Head★ (←★★), W : 6 m.
18, 9 Trevose Constantine Bay ☎ 520208.
London 288 – Exeter 78 – Plymouth 45 – Truro 23.

Metropole (T.H.F.), Station Rd, PL28 8DB, ☎ 532486, Fax 532867, ← Camel Estuary, heated, – |‡| ⇔ rm TV ☎ ♿ P – 50. AE VISA
M (dinner only and Sunday lunch) 14.00/22.50 **st.** 4.35 – ☐ 7.00 – **44 rm** 60.00/120.00 **st.**

Woodlands, Treator, PL28 8RU, W : 1 ¼ m. by A 389 on B 3276 ☎ 532426, – ⇔ TV P
March-October – **M** 8.00 2.50 – **9 rm** ☐ 21.50/59.00 **st.**

XX **Seafood** with rm, Riverside, PL28 8BY, ☎ 532485, ←, Seafood, « Attractively converted granary on quayside » – TV ☎. VISA
closed 15 December-31 January – **M** *(closed Sunday)* (booking essential) (dinner only) 23.75 **t.** and a la carte 7.00 – **10 rm** 26.00/94.60 **t.** – SB (except April-October) 84.00 **st.**

at Little Petherick S : 3 m. on A 389 – ✉ Wadebridge – ☎ 0841 Rumford :

Old Mill Country House, PL27 7QT, ☎ 540388, « Part 16C corn mill », – P. ✻
Easter-October – **M** 10.00 2.80 – **6 rm** ☐ 32.50/46.00 **t.**

at Constantine Bay SW : 4 m. by B 3276 – ✉ ☎ 0841 Padstow :

Treglos ⛰, PL28 8JH, ☎ 520727, Fax 521163, ←, , – |‡| ⇔ rest rest TV ☎ P
7 March-2 November – **M** 10.25/17.50 **t.** and a la carte 4.50 – **41 rm** ☐ (dinner included) 63.00/121.00 **t.**, **3 suites** 161.00 **t.**

at Treyarnon Bay SW : 4 ¾ m. by B 3276 – ✉ ☎ 0841 Padstow :

Waterbeach ⛰, PL28 8JW, ☎ 520292, ←, , – TV ☎ P. AE VISA. ✻
March-October – **M** (bar lunch)/dinner 12.50 **t.** – **16 rm** ☐ 28.00/72.00 **st.**, **5 suites** 62.00/72.00 **st.**

PAIGNTON Devon 403 J 32 **The West Country G.** – pop. 39 565 – ECD : Wednesday – 0803.

See : Paignton Zoo★★ *AC*, by A 385 Z – Kirkham House★ *AC* Y **B.** Esplanade Rd ✆ 558383.

◆London 226 – Exeter 26 – ◆Plymouth 29.

Plan of Built up Area : see Torbay

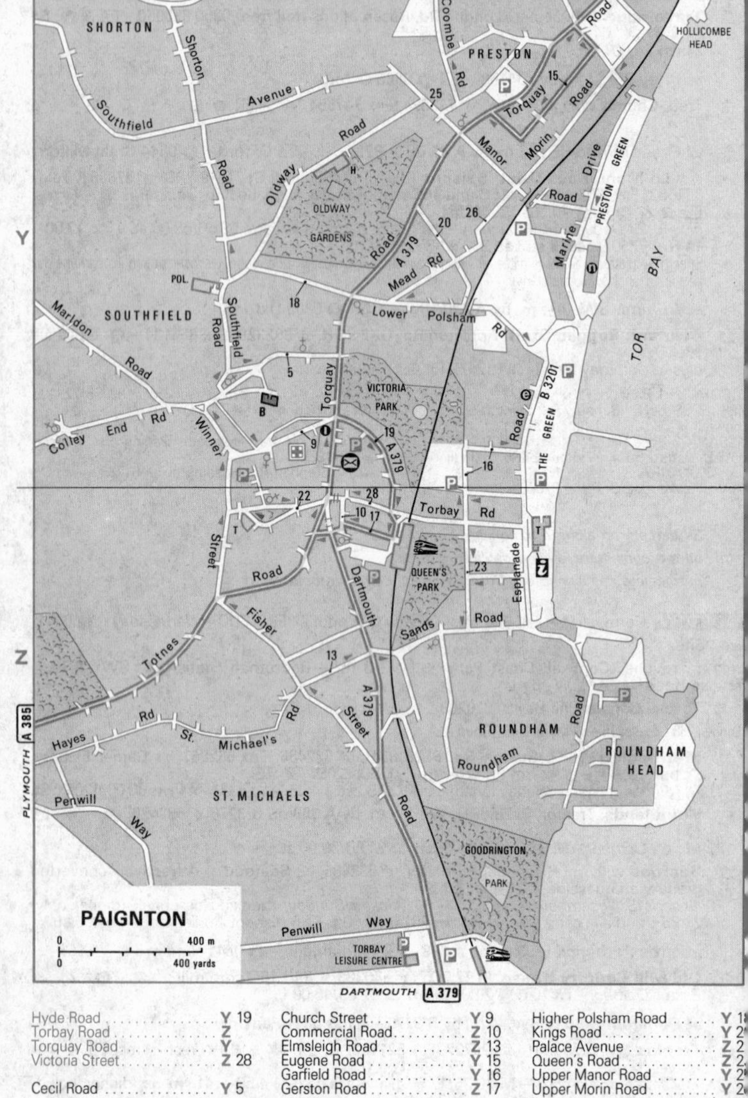

Hyde Road . . . . Y 19	Church Street . . . . Y 9	Higher Polsham Road . . . . . . Y 1
Torbay Road . . . . Z	Commercial Road . . . . Z 10	Kings Road . . . . Y 2
Torquay Road . . . . Y	Elmsleigh Road . . . . Z 13	Palace Avenue . . . . Z 2
Victoria Street . . . . Z 28	Eugene Road . . . . Y 15	Queen's Road . . . . Z 2
	Garfield Road . . . . Y 16	Upper Manor Road . . . . . . Y 2
Cecil Road . . . . Y 5	Gerston Road . . . . Z 17	Upper Morin Road . . . . Y 2

Palace (T.H.F.), Esplanade Rd, TQ4 6BJ, ✆ 555121, Fax 527974, heated, – . VISA
M (buffet lunch Monday to Saturday)/dinner 20.00 **st.** and a la carte 4.50 – 7.00
52 rm 60.00/88.00 **st.** Y

Redcliffe, 4 Marine Drive, TQ3 2NL, ✆ 526397, Fax 528030, ≤ Torbay, heated, – TV ☎ P. VISA.
M (bar lunch Monday to Saturday)/dinner 12.75 **t.** and a la carte 3.75 – **60 rm** 32.00/90.00 **t.** – SB (October-March) 70.00/80.00 **st.**

Luigi, 59 Torquay Rd, TQ3 3DT, ✆ 556185, Italian rest. – VISA Y i
closed Monday lunch and Sunday – **M** 14.95 **st.** (dinner) and a la carte 17.90/22.15 **st.** 4.25.

BMW 349 Totnes Rd ✆ 558567
HONDA 45 Totnes Rd ✆ 554484
MERCEDES-BENZ 59 Totnes Rd ✆ 559362
SEAT Bishop's Pl. ✆ 556234
TOYOTA 288-290 Torquay Rd ✆ 553415
ATS Orient Rd ✆ 556888/558975

PAINSWICK Glos. 403 404 N 28 – pop. 1 757 – ECD : Saturday – ✉ Stroud – ✆ 0452.

18 Painswick ✆ 812180.

Painswick Library, Stroud Rd ✆ 813552.

London 107 – Bristol 35 – Cheltenham 10 – Gloucester 7.

Painswick ⛰, Kemps Lane, Tibiwell, GL6 6YB, ✆ 812160, Telex 43605, Fax 812160, – TV ☎ P. AE VISA
M *(closed Sunday dinner)* (dinner only and Sunday lunch)/dinner 25.00 **t.** and a la carte – **15 rm** 60.00/80.00 **t.**

Damsell's Lodge ⛰ without rest., The Park, GL6 6SR, N : 1 m. by A 46 on Sheepscombe rd ✆ 813777, ≤, – TV P.
3 rm 20.00/36.00 **st.**

Country Elephant, New St., GL6 6XH, ✆ 813564 – VISA
closed Sunday and Monday – **M** (dinner only) 23.60 **t.** and a la carte 3.60.

PANGBOURNE Berks. 403 404 Q 29 – pop. 3 445 (inc. Whitchurch) – ECD : Thursday – ✆ 0734.

London 56 – Oxford 22 – Reading 6.

Copper Inn, 2 Church Rd, RG8 7AR, ✆ 842244, Fax 845542, – TV ☎ & P – 45. AE VISA.
M 15.50/17.95 **t.** and a la carte 7.20 – 6.50 – **22 rm** 65.00/95.00 **t.** – SB (weekends only) 84.00/94.00 **st.**

ROVER 23-25 Reading Rd ✆ 842376

PANT MAWR Powys 403 I 26 – ✉ ✆ 055 15 Llangurig.

London 219 – Aberystwyth 21 – Shrewsbury 55.

Glansevern Arms, SY18 6SY, on A 44 ✆ 240, ≤, – TV P
closed 1 week Christmas – **M** *(closed Sunday dinner)* (booking essential) (dinner only and Sunday lunch)/dinner 17.00 **t.** 3.30 – **8 rm** 33.00/55.00 **t.** – SB 78.00/85.00 **st.**

PARKGATE Cheshire 402 403 K 24 – pop. 3 480 – ECD : Wednesday – ✉ Wirral – ✆ 051 Liverpool.

London 206 – Birkenhead 10 – Chester 11 – Liverpool 12.

Ship (T.H.F.), The Parade, L64 6SA, ✆ 336 3931 – TV ☎ P

Parkgate (Lansbury), Boat House Lane, L64 6RD, N : ½ m. on B 5135 ✆ 336 5001, Telex 629469, Fax 336 8504, – rm TV ☎ P – 100. AE VISA
M 8.95/14.00 **t.** and a la carte – **27 rm** 63.00/76.00 **t.** – SB (weekends only) 60.00/72.00 **st.**

PARKHAM Devon 403 H 31 – see Horns Cross.

PATCHWAY Avon 403 404 M 29 – see Bristol.

PATELEY BRIDGE North Yorks. 402 O 21 – ✉ ✆ 0423 Harrogate.

Envir. : Brimham Rocks★ E : 4½ m.

Southlands Car Park, off High St. ✆ 711147 (summer only).

London 225 – Leeds 28 – Middlesbrough 46 – York 32.

Grassfields Country House ⛰, Ramsgill Rd, HG3 5HL, ✆ 711412, – P
April-November – **M** (dinner only) (residents only) 10.50 **t.** 2.50 – **9 rm** 22.00/42.00 **t.**

at Low Laithe SE : 2¾ m. on B 6165 – ✉ ✆ 0423 Harrogate :

Dusty Miller, Main Rd, HG3 4BU, ✆ 780837 – P. AE VISA
closed Sunday, first 2 weeks August, 25-26 December and 1 January – **M** (dinner only) a la carte 15.30/24.30 **t.** 4.15.

at Wath-in-Nidderdale NW : 2¼ m. – ✉ ✆ 0423 Harrogate :

Sportsman's Arms ⛰ with rm, HG3 5PP, ✆ 711306, – rm TV P. AE VISA
closed Christmas and New Year – **M** *(closed Sunday dinner)* (bar lunch Monday to Saturday)/dinner a la carte 14.75/28.50 **t.** 3.75 – **7 rm** 28.00/50.00 **t.** – SB (December-February) 62.00/82.00 **st.**

PATRICK BROMPTON North Yorks. 402 P 21 – pop. 145 – ✉ ☎ 0677 Bedale.
♦London 228 – ♦Leeds 48 – ♦Newcastle 33 – York 41.

Elmfield House ⛰, Arrathorne, DL8 1NE, NW : 2 ¼ m. by A 684 on Richmond rd ✆ 50558 – 📺 ☎ ♿ 🅟. ✗
M 9.00 **st.** 🍷 2.50 – **9 rm** ☕ 25.00/38.00 **st.** – SB (winter only) 48.00 **st.**

PATTINGHAM Staffs. 402 403 404 N 26 – see Wolverhampton (W. Midlands).

PEASMARSH East Sussex 404 W 31 – see Rye.

PEMBROKE **(PENFRO)** Dyfed 403 F 28 – pop. 15 284 – ECD : Wednesday – ☎ 0646.
See : Site★ – Castle★★.
Envir. : Lamphey (Bishop's palace★) *AC*, E : 2 m. – Carew (castle★ 13C) *AC*, NE : 4 ½ m.
⛳ Defensible Barracks, Pembroke Dock ✆ 683817.
⛴ to Rosslare (B & I Line) 1 daily.
ℹ Drill Hall ✆ 682148.
♦London 252 – Carmarthen 32 – Fishguard 26.

Underdown Country House ⛰, Grove Hill, SA71 5PR, ✆ 683350, Fax 621229, « Antiques and gardens » – 📺 ☎ 🅟. 🅂 ⓓ VISA. ✗
M (booking essential) (dinner only) a la carte 13.95/18.50 **t.** 🍷 4.00 – **6 rm** ☕ 37.50/57.50 **t.**

Coach House, 116 Main St., SA71 4HN, ✆ 684602, 🌳 – 📺 ☎ 🅟. 🅂 AE ⓓ VISA. ✗
closed 24 to 26 December – **M** (bar lunch)/dinner 12.50 **st.** and a la carte 🍷 4.75 – **14 rm** ☕ 35.00/49.00 **st.** – SB 55.00/60.00 **st.**

High Noon, Lower Lamphey Rd, SA71 4AB, ✆ 683736 – 📺 🅟
M 6.00 **st.** 🍷 2.20 – **9 rm** ☕ 11.50/30.00 **st.**

at Lamphey E : 1 ¾ m. on A 4139 – ✉ Pembroke – ☎ 0646 Lamphey :

Court (Best Western) ⛰, SA71 5NT, ✆ 672273, Telex 48587, Fax 672480, 🏋, ≘s, 🏊, 🌳 – 📺 ☎ 🅟 – 🎪 80. 🅂 AE ⓓ VISA. ✗
M (bar lunch)/dinner 13.50 **st.** and a la carte 🍷 3.90 – **23 rm** ☕ 48.00/95.00 **st.**, **7 suites** 84.00/100.00 **st.** – SB 84.00/102.00 **st.**

Bethwaite's Lamphey Hall, SA71 5NR, ✆ 672394, Fax 672369, 🌳 – 📺 ☎ 🅟. 🅂 AE VISA. ✗
closed 25 and 26 December – **M** *(closed Sunday dinner to non-residents)* (bar lunch Monday to Saturday)/dinner 12.50 **t.** and a la carte 🍷 3.50 – **10 rm** ☕ 35.00/67.00 **t.**

at Pembroke Dock NW : 2 m. on A 4139 – ✉ ☎ 0646 Pembroke :

Cleddau Bridge, Essex Rd, SA72 6UT, NE : 1 m. by A 4139 on A 477 (at Toll Bridge) ✆ 685961, Fax 685746, 🏊 heated – 📺 ☎ 🅟 – 🎪 175. 🅂 AE ⓓ VISA
M 16.00 **t.** and a la carte – **21 rm** ☕ 50.00/80.00 **t.**, **3 suites** 85.00 **t.** – SB (weekends only) 80.00/134.00 **st.**

ROVER London Rd, Pembroke Dock ✆ 683143 | ATS Well Hill Garage ✆ 683217

PEMBROKESHIRE (Coast) ★★ Dyfed 403 E 27 28.
See : From Cemaes Head to Strumble Head★★ : Newport (site★) – Bryn Henllan (site★) – Goodwick ≤★★ – Strumble Head (≤★★ from the lighthouse). From Strumble Head to Solva★★ : Trevine ≤★★ – Porthgain (cliffs ✻★★★) – Abereiddy (site★) – St. David's Head★★ – Whitesand Bay★★ – Solva (site★). From Solva to Dale★★ : Newgale ≤★★ – Martin's Haven ✻★★ – St. Ann's Head ≤★★ – Dale ≤★. From Dale to Freshwater West★ : Freshwater West (site★). From Freshwater West to Pendine Sands★★ (Stack Rocks★★) – St. Govan's Chapel (site★) – Freshwater East (site★) – Manorbier (castle★) – Tenby (site★★) – Amroth (site★) – Pendine Sands★.

PENALLY **(PENALUN)** Dyfed 403 F 29 – see Tenby.

PENALUN **(PENALLY)** Dyfed 403 F 29 – see Tenby.

PENCOED Mid Glam. 403 J 29 – pop. 8 182 – ☎ 0656.
♦London 173 – ♦Cardiff 16 – ♦Swansea 27.

Travelodge without rest., CF35 5HU, E : 1 ¼ m. on Felindre rd ✆ 864404, Reservations (Toll free) 0800 850950 – 📺 ♿ 🅟. 🅂 AE VISA. ✗
40 rm 24.00/29.50 **t.**

PENCRAIG Heref. and Worc. – see Ross-on-Wye.

PENDOGGETT Cornwall 403 F 32 – ✉ – ☎ 0208 Bodmin.
♦London 264 – Newquay 22 – Truro 30.

Cornish Arms, PL30 3HH, on B 3314 ✆ 880263, « Retaining 16C features » – 🅟. 🅂 AE ⓓ VISA. ✗
M 10.00/15.00 **t.** and a la carte 🍷 3.00 – **7 rm** ☕ 34.00/54.00 **st.**

PENFRO = Pembroke.

PENMAENHEAD Clwyd – see Colwyn Bay.

PENMAENPOOL Gwynedd 402 403 I 25 – see Dolgellau.

PENN STREET Bucks. 404 S 29 – see Amersham.

PENRITH Cumbria 401 402 L 19 – pop. 12 086 – ECD : Wednesday – 0768.

Salked Rd 62217.

Robinson's School, Middlegate 67466.

London 290 – ♦Carlisle 24 – Kendal 31 – Lancaster 48.

- **North Lakes Gateway,** Ullswater Rd, CA11 8QT, S : 1 m. at M 6 junction 40 68111, Telex 64257, Fax 68291, , , squash – rm – 200. AE VISA
  M *(closed Saturday lunch)* 9.50/14.00 **st.** and a la carte 4.50 – **85 rm** 74.00/130.00 **st.**
- **Travelodge** without rest., Redhills, CA11 0DT, SW : 1 ½ m. by A 592 on A 66 66958, Reservations (Toll free) 0800 850950 – . AE VISA.
  32 rm 24.00/29.50 **t.**
- **Passepartout,** 51 Castlegate, CA11 7HY, 65852 – . VISA
  M *(closed Sunday)* (dinner only) 7.00 **t.** and a la carte 14.60/20.10 **t.** 3.00.

FORD Old London Rd 64571
PEUGEOT-TALBOT Gilwilly Estate 890870
RENAULT 11 King St. 62371
ROVER Victoria Rd 63666
TOYOTA 15 Victoria Rd 64555
ATS Gilwilly Ind Est. 65656/7

*Es ist empfehlenswert, **in der Hauptsaison** und vor allem in Urlaubsorten, Hotelzimmer im voraus zu bestellen. Benachrichtigen Sie sofort das Hotel, wenn Sie ein bestelltes Zimmer nicht belegen können.*
Wenn Sie an ein Hotel im Ausland schreiben, fügen Sie Ihrem Brief einen internationalen Antwortschein bei (im Postamt erhältlich).

PENSHURST Kent 404 U 30 – pop. 1 749 – 0892 Tunbridge Wells.

See : Penshurst Place★ (and Tudor gardens★★ 14C) *AC*.

Envir. : Chiddingstone (castle : Egyptian and Japanese collections★ *AC*) NW : 5 m. – Hever Castle★ (13C) *AC*, W : 6 m.

London 38 – Maidstone 19 – Royal Tunbridge Wells 6.

- **Leicester Arms,** High St., TN11 8BT, 870551 – . AE VISA
  M *(closed Sunday dinner and Monday)* 10.50 **t.** and a la carte 4.00 – **7 rm** 40.00/65.00 **t.**
- Swale Cottage without rest., Old Swaylands, Tonbridge, TN11 8AH, SE : 1 m. by B 2176 off Poundsbridge Lane 870738, ←, –
  3 rm.

PENYBONT Powys 403 K 27 – ✉ Llandrindod Wells – 059 787.

London 170 – ♦Birmingham 79 – Hereford 37 – Shrewsbury 58.

- **Ffaldau Country House** with rm Llandegley, LD1 5UD, E : 1 ¼ m. on A 44 421, –
  closed first 2 weeks January – **M** *(closed Sunday and Monday dinner to non-residents)* (bar lunch)/dinner 16.00 **t.** – **3 rm** 22.00/35.00 **t.**

PEN-Y-BONT = Bridgend.

PENZANCE Cornwall 403 D 33 **The West Country G.** – pop. 18 501 – ECD : Wednesday – 0736.

See : Site★ – Outlook★★★ – Western Promenade (←★★★) YZ – Chapel St.★ Y – Museum of Nautical Art★ *AC* Y **M1**.

Envir. : St. Michael's Mount★★, (←★★) E : 5 m. by A 30 Y – Sancreed Church★★, Celtic Crosses★★, W : 4 m. by A 30 Z – St. Buryan★★ (Church Tower★★), SW : 4 ½ m. by A 30 Z – Chysauster★ *AC*, N : 4½ m. by B 3311 Y – Morvah, North Cornwall Coast Path (←★★), NW : 6½ m. by B 3312 Y – Trengwainton Garden★★ *AC*, NW : 2 m. by B 3312 Y – Prussia Cove★, SE : 9 m. by A 30 and A 394 Y – Land's End★ (cliff scenery★★★), SW : 10 m. by A 30 Z.

Praa Sands, Germoe Cross Roads 763445, E : 7 m. on A 394 Y.

Access to the Isles of Scilly by helicopter 63871.

0345 090700.

to the Isles of Scilly : Hugh Town, St.Mary's (Isles of Scilly Steamship Co.) (summer only) (2 h 30 mn).

Station Rd 62207.

London 319 – Exeter 113 – ♦Plymouth 77 – Taunton 155.

Abbey, Abbey St., TR18 4AR, ☎ 66906, « Attractively furnished 17C house », – P. AE VISA Y
M (dinner only) 16.50 **t.** 3.90 – **6 rm** 50.60/85.00 **t.**, **1 suite** 95.00/125.00 **t.**

Tarbert, 11 Clarence St., TR18 2NU, ☎ 63758 – TV ☎. AE VISA. Y
closed 1 December-14 January – **M** (bar lunch)/dinner 12.00 **st.** and a la carte 3.30 **12 rm** 23.50/53.00 **st.** – SB (October-mid May) 55.00/63.50 **st.**

Sea and Horses, 6 Alexandra Terr., TR18 4NX, ☎ 61961 – TV ☎ P. VISA. Z
mid February-mid November – **M** (bar lunch)/dinner 8.95 **st.** 2.80 – **11 rm** 17.50/37.00 **st.**

Estoril, 46 Morrab Rd, TR18 4EX, ☎ 62468 – rest TV ☎ P. VISA. Y
closed December – **M** 10.00 **st.** 3.00 – **10 rm** 23.00/64.00 **st.** – SB (except summer and January) 55.00 **st.**

Dunedin, Alexandra Rd, TR18 4LZ, ☎ 62652 – TV Y
closed Christmas – **M** 6.50 **t.** 3.00 – **9 rm** 13.00/28.00 **t.**

Woodstock, 29 Morrab Rd, TR18 4EZ, ☎ 69049 – rest TV. AE VISA. Y
M (by arrangement) – **5 rm** 9.50/27.00 **st.**

Harris's, 46 New St., TR18 2LZ, ☎ 64408 – AE VISA Y
closed Monday lunch, Monday dinner October-May, Sunday, 1 week February, 2 weeks November – **M** (restricted lunch)/dinner a la carte 16.75/28.50 **t.** 3.50.

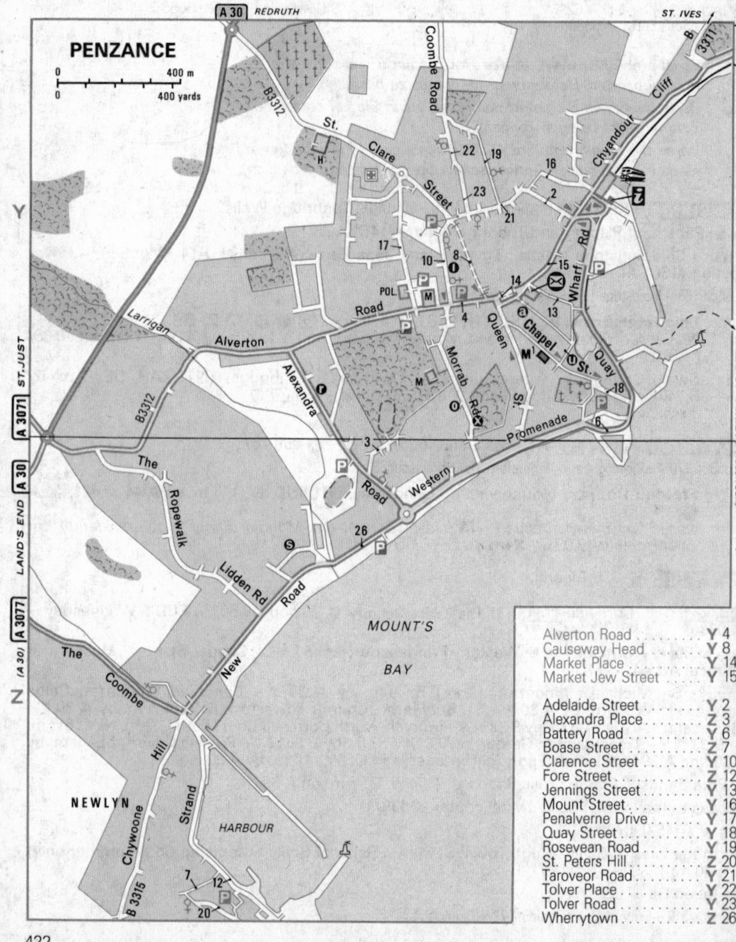

at Newlyn SW : 1 ½ m. on B 3315 – Z – ✉ ☎ 0736 Penzance :

Higher Faugan ⛰, TR18 5NS, SW : ¾ m. on B 3315 ☎ 62076, Fax 62076, heated, park, – rest TV ☎ P. AE VISA.
M (bar lunch residents only)/dinner 16.00 **st.** 3.60 – **11 rm** 42.00/86.00 **st.** – SB (October-April) 65.00/80.00 **st.**

at Drift SW : 2 ½ m. on A 30 – Z – ✉ ☎ 0736 Penzance :

Rose Farm ⛰ without rest., Chyanhal, Buryas Bridge, TR19 6AN, SW : ¾ m. on Chyanhal rd ☎ 731808, « Working farm », – TV P.
closed Christmas and New Year – **3 rm** 21.00/35.00 **t.**

ORD Coinage Hall St. ☎ 69169
OVER Newlyn ☎ 61998/62038
ATS Jelbert Way, Eastern Green ☎ 62768

PERRANUTHNOE Cornwall 403 D 33 – see Marazion.

PERSHORE Heref. and Worc. 403 404 N 27 – pop. 6 850 – ECD : Thursday – ☎ 0386.
19 High St. ☎ 554262.
London 106 – ◆Birmingham 32 – Cheltenham 22 – Stratford-on-Avon 21 – Worcester 9.

Avonside, Main Rd, Wyne Piddle, WR10 2JB, NE : 2 m. by B 4082 and B 4083 on B 4084 ☎ 552654, ←, heated, – TV ☎ P. VISA.
M (bar lunch)/dinner 14.95 **t.** 4.00 – **7 rm** 40.00/52.00 **t.** – SB (except Christmas) 70.00 **st.**

ORD Pinvin ☎ 552691
OVER Three Springs Rd ☎ 552817
ATS Cherry Orchard ☎ 554494

☛ *Use this year's Guide.*

PETERBOROUGH Cambs. 402 404 T 26 – pop. 113 404 – ECD : Monday and Thursday – ☎ 0733.
See : Cathedral★★ 12C-13C (nave : painted roof★★★) Y.
Envir. : Crowland : Abbey Church★ (8C ruins), Triangular Bridge★ 13C, NE : 8 m.
18 Thorpe Wood, Nene Parkway ☎ 267701, W : 3 m. by B 1095 BX – 18 Ramsey ☎ 0487 (Ramsey) 813573, SE : 12 m. BX – 18 Orton Meadows, Ham Lane ☎ 237478, SW : 2 m. by A 605 BX – 18 Milton Ferry ☎ 380204 BX.
45 Bridge St. ☎ 317336.
London 85 – ◆Cambridge 35 – ◆Leicester 41 – Lincoln 51.

Plan on next page

Peterborough Moat House (Q.M.H.), Thorpe Wood, PE3 6SG, SW : 2 ¼ m. at Roundabout 33 ☎ 260000, Telex 32708, Fax 262737, – rm TV ☎ P – 300. AE VISA — BX **s**
M 11.95/13.95 **st.** and a la carte – 7.40 – **121 rm** 70.00/79.00 **st.**, **4 suites** 80.00/105.00 **st.** – SB 74.00 **st.**

Butterfly, Thorpe Meadows, PE3 6GA, W : 1 m. by Thorpe Rd ☎ 64240, Fax 65538 – rest TV ☎ P – 80. AE VISA. — BX **e**
M 10.00 **t.** and a la carte 3.25 – 5.00 – **66 rm** 57.00/114.00, **4 suites** 75.00/95.00 **t.**

Bull, Westgate, PE1 1RP, ☎ 61364, Group Telex 329265 – TV ☎ P – 100 — Y **z**
112 rm, 1 suite.

Thorpe Lodge, 83 Thorpe Rd, PE3 6JQ, ☎ 48759 – TV P. VISA. — BX **c**
M *(closed Friday dinner, Saturday and Sunday)* (bar lunch)/dinner 11.50 **t.** 4.00 – 4.50 – **22 rm** 32.00/58.00 **t.** – SB (weekends only) 68.00/70.00 **st.**

Grain Barge, The Quayside, Embankment Rd, PE1 1EG, ☎ 311967, Chinese (Peking) rest. – AE VISA — Z **v**
M 5.00/10.00 **t.** and a la carte 3.75.

at Norman Cross S : 5 ¾ m. on A 15 at junction with A 1 – BX – ✉ ☎ 0733 Peterborough :

Crest (T.H.F.), Great North Rd, PZ7 3XH, ☎ 240209, Telex 32576, Fax 244455, – rm TV ☎ P – 35. AE VISA — BX **r**
M 15.00/20.00 **st.** and a la carte – 7.95 – **93 rm** 68.00/80.00 **st.** – SB (weekends only) 82.00/92.00 **st.**

at Alwalton SW : 5 ¾ m. on A 605 – AX – ✉ ☎ 0733 Peterborough :

Swallow, Lynch Wood (opposite East of England Showground), PE2 0GB, on A 605 ☎ 371111, Telex 32422, Fax 236725, – rm rest TV ☎ P – 275. AE VISA — AX **u**
M 12.75/16.95 **st.** and a la carte – **160 rm** 74.00/92.00 **st.**, **3 suites** 140.00 **st.** – SB (weekends only) 90.00/92.00 **st.**

Travelodge without rest., A 1 Great North Rd (Southbound), PE7 3UR, ☎ 231109, Reservations (Toll free) 0800 850950 – TV P. AE VISA. — AX **x**
32 rm 24.00/29.50 **t.**

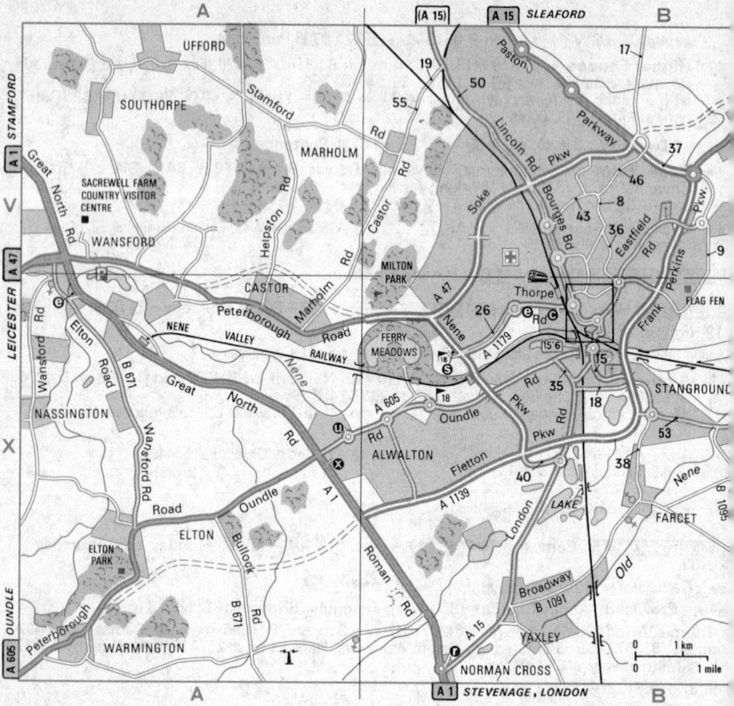

PETERBOROUGH

Bridge Street . . . . Z
Church Street . . . . YZ
Long Causeway . . . . Y 25
Queensgate
Shopping Centre . . . . Y

Cattle Market
Road . . . . Y 2
City Road . . . . Y 3
Cowgate . . . . Y 5
Cross Street . . . . Z 6
Dogsthorpe Road . . . . BV 8
Edgerley Drain
Road . . . . BV 9
Embankment Road . . . . Z 12
Exchange Street . . . . Y 13
Fletton Avenue . . . . BX 15
Geneva Street . . . . Y 16
Guntons Road . . . . BV 17
High Street . . . . BX 18
Hurn Road . . . . BV 19
Longthorpe Parkway . . . . . BX 26
Market Way . . . . Y 28
Midgate . . . . Y 29
New Road . . . . Y 34
New Road . . . . BX 35
Park Road . . . . BV 36
Paston Parkway . . . . BV 37
Peterborough Road . . . . . . BX 38
Phorpres Way . . . . BX 40
Rivergate . . . . Z 42
St Paul's Road . . . . BV 43
Thorpe Road . . . . Y 45
Welland Road . . . . BV 46
Wentworth Street . . . . Z 48
Werrington
Parkway . . . . BV 50
Wheelyard . . . . Y 52
Whittlesey Road . . . . BX 53
Woodcroft Road . . . . BV 55

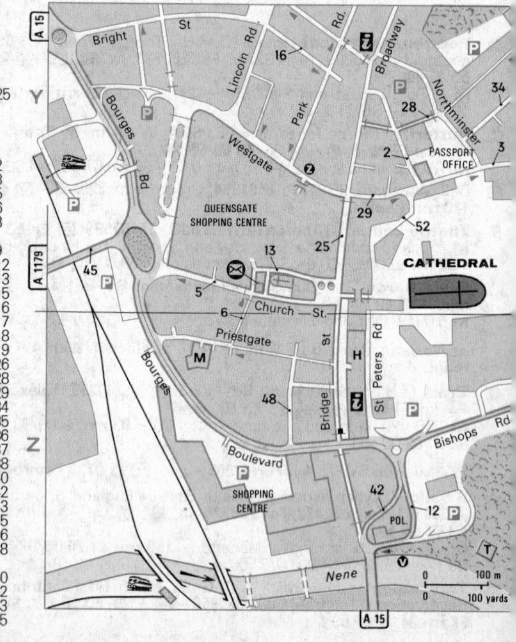

at Wansford W : 8 ½ m. by A 47 – AX – ✉ Peterborough – ☎ 0780 Stamford :

Haycock, PE8 6JA, ℰ 782223, Telex 32710, Fax 783031, – TV ☎ ♿ P – 150. AE ⓓ VISA AX e
M a la carte 17.80/26.30 **st.** 5.75 – **50 rm** 63.00/120.00 **st.**, **1 suite** 85.00/135.00 **st.** – SB (weekends only) 85.00/105.00 **st.**

MW Helpston Rd, Glinton ℰ 253333
AT Midland Rd ℰ 314431
ORD 27-53 New Rd ℰ 40104
ANCIA, SUZUKI 659 Lincoln Rd ℰ 52141
MAZDA 50-64 Burghley Rd ℰ 65787
MERCEDES-BENZ High St., Eye ℰ 222363
EUGEOT-TALBOT 343 Eastfield Rd ℰ 310900
RENAULT Bretton Way ℰ 330030
ROVER, FREIGHT-ROVER 7 Oundle Rd ℰ 66011
VAUXHALL-OPEL, BEDFORD Sturrock Way ℰ 264981
VW-AUDI Newark Rd ℰ 312213
ATS Wareley Rd (off George St.) ℰ 67112/3

PETERSFIELD Hants. 404 R 30 – pop. 10 078 – ECD : Thursday – ☎ 0730.

Heath Rd ℰ 63725, E : ½ m.

Country Library, 27 The Square ℰ 68829.

London 59 – Brighton 45 – Guildford 25 – Portsmouth 19 – Southampton 32 – Winchester 19.

Langrish House , Langrish, GU32 1RN, W : 3 ½ m. by A 272 ℰ 66941, Fax 60543, ←, , park – TV ☎ P – 50. AE ⓓ VISA
M *(closed Sunday and Bank Holidays)* (dinner only) 18.00 **t.** and 3.60 – 3.65 – **18 rm** 35.00/59.00 **t.** – SB (winter only) (weekends only) 74.00 **st.**

UDI-VW Station Rd ℰ 62992
ONDA Alton Rd, Steep ℰ 66341
EUGEOT-TALBOT 38 Collace St. ℰ 62266
KODA Alton Rd, Froxfield ℰ 073 084 (Hawkley) 01
VOLVO 23 London Rd ℰ 64541
ATS 15-31 Dragon St. ℰ 65151

PETERSTOW Heref. and Worc. 403 404 M 28 – see Ross-on-Wye.

PETWORTH West Sussex 404 S 31 – pop. 2 003 – ECD : Wednesday – ☎ 0798.

See : Petworth House★★★, 17C (paintings★★★ and carved room★★★) *AC.*

London 54 – Brighton 31 – Portsmouth 33.

Soanes, Grove Lane, GU28 0HY, S : ½ m. by High St. ℰ 43659, ← – P. VISA
closed 1 week February, 1 week October and 25 to 29 December – **M** *(closed Sunday dinner, Monday and Tuesday)* (dinner only and Sunday lunch)/dinner a la carte approx. 26.00 **st.** 4.25.

PICKERING North Yorks. 402 R 21 – pop. 5 316 – ECD : Wednesday – ☎ 0751.

See : SS. Peter and Paul's Church (wall paintings★ 15C) – Norman castle★ (ruins) : ←★ *AC.*

Eastgate Car Park ℰ 73791 (summer only).

London 237 – Middlesbrough 43 – Scarborough 19 – York 25.

Forest and Vale, Malton Rd, YO18 7DL, ℰ 72722, – TV ☎ P – 100. AE ⓓ VISA
M 9.50/14.50 **t.** and a la carte 4.15 – **17 rm** 45.00/82.00 **t.** – SB 74.00/98.00 **st.**

White Swan, Market Pl., YO18 7AA, ℰ 72288 – rm TV ☎ P. ⓓ
M (bar lunch Monday to Saturday)/dinner 15.00/25.00 **t.** 3.75 – **12 rm** 41.00/84.00 **t.**, **1 suite** 100.00/110.00 **t.** – SB (except Christmas) 70.00/80.00 **st.**

The Lodge, Middleton Rd, YO18 8NQ, ℰ 72976, – TV ☎ P. AE VISA
M *(closed Sunday dinner and Monday)* 9.75 **st.** (lunch) and a la carte 12.40/16.95 **st.** – **9 rm** 30.00/60.00 **st.** – SB (except Christmas) 66.00/80.00 **st.**

at Aislaby NW : 1 ¾ m. on A 170 – ✉ ☎ 0751 Pickering :

Blacksmiths Arms with rm, YO18 8PE, ℰ 72182 – rest TV P. VISA
M *(closed Sunday dinner and Monday except summer)* (bar lunch)/dinner a la carte 10.05/14.75 **t.** 3.15 – **5 rm** 19.00/38.00 **t.**

ORD, MERCEDES-BENZ Eastgate ℰ 72251
FORD Middleton ℰ 72331

PICKHILL North Yorks. 402 P 21 – pop. 300 (inc. Roxby) – ✉ ☎ 0845 Thirsk.

London 229 – Leeds 41 – Middlesbrough 30 – York 34.

Nags Head, YO7 4JG, ℰ 567391, Fax 567212 – rest TV ☎ P. VISA
M (bar lunch Monday to Saturday)/dinner a la carte 9.95/22.45 **t.** 3.25 – **15 rm** 27.00/40.00 **st.**

PIMPERNE Dorset. 403 404 N 31 – see Blandford Forum.

PINHOE Devon 403 J 31 – see Exeter.

PITTON Wilts. – see Salisbury.

PLAYDEN East Sussex – see Rye.

PLUCKLEY Kent 404 W 30 – pop. 1 109 – ☎ 023 384.

♦London 53 – Folkestone 25 – Maidstone 18.

⌂ **Elvey Farm** ⛰, TN27 0SU, W : 3 m. by B 2077 off Mundy Bois Rd ✆ 442, ≤, 🌳 – 📺 🅟 VISA
restricted service October-April – **M** 14.95 **t.** – **10 rm** ☕ 35.50/49.50 **t.**

PLUMTREE Notts. – see Nottingham.

PLYMOUTH Devon 403 H 32 **The West Country G.** – pop. 238 583 – ECD : Wednesday ☎ 0752.

See : Site★★ – Smeaton's Tower (≤★★) *AC* BZ – Royal Citadel★ *AC* (The Ramparts ≤★★) BZ City Museum and Art Gallery★*AC* BZ **M.**

Envir. : Buckland Abbey★★*AC*, N : 7 m. by A 386 ABY – Saltram House★★ *AC*, E : 3½ m. BY A Antony House★*AC*, W : 5 m. by A 374 AY – Yelverton Paperweight Centre★*AC*, N : 9 m. c A 386 ABY – Mount Edgcumbe (≤★) *AC*, W : 9 m. by car ferry from Cremyll or passenger ferr from Stonehouse.

⛳18 Plymstock, Staddon Heights ✆ 402475 BY – ⛳9 Elfordleigh, Plympton, ✆ 336428, E : 6 m. b A 374 BY.

✈ Roborough Airport : ✆ 772752/3, N : 3½ m. by A 386 ABY.

⛴ Shipping connections with the Continent : to France (Roscoff) (Brittany Ferries) (6 h t 7 h) – to Spain (Santander)(Brittany Ferries)(24 h).

ℹ Civic Centre, Royal Parade ✆ 264849 – 12 The Barbican ✆ 223806.

♦London 242 – ♦Bristol 124 – ♦Southampton 161.

Plans on following pages

🏨 **Copthorne Plymouth** (Best Western), Armada Centre, Armada Way, PL1 1AR, (vi Western Approach) Southbound ✆ 224161, Telex 45756, Fax 670688, ≘s, 🏊 – 🛗 ⇔ r 📺 ☎ ♿ 🅟 – 🏛 70. AE ⓓ VISA. ✂ BZ
M 17.45/18.45 **t.** and a la carte – ☕ 6.50 – **131 rm** 72.00/85.00 **t.**, **4 suites** 140.00/145.00 – SB (weekends only) 42.50/44.50 **st.**

🏨 **Plymouth Moat House** (Q.M.H.), Armada Way, PL1 2HJ, ✆ 662866, Telex 4563 Fax 673816, ≤ city and Sound, ≘s, 🏊 – 🛗 ⇔ rm 📺 ☎ ♿ 🅟 – 🏛 250. AE ⓓ VISA
M 12.50 **st.** and a la carte 🍷 4.75 – ☕ 8.75 – **213 rm** 75.00/86.00 **t.**, **2 suites** 165.0 195.00 **t.** – SB (weekends only) 85.00/105.00 **st.** BZ

🏨 **Grand,** Elliott St., The Hoe, PL1 2PT, ✆ 661195, Telex 45359, Fax 600653, ≤, 🏋, ≘s – 📺 ☎ 🅟 – 🏛 70. AE ⓓ VISA. ✂ BZ
M 10.50/14.95 **st.** and a la carte – **76 rm** ☕ 55.00/85.00 **st.**, **1 suite** 85.00/120.00 **st.** SB (weekends only) 69.00/90.00 **st.**

🏨 **Mayflower Post House** (T.H.F.), Cliff Rd, The Hoe, PL1 3DL, ✆ 662828, Telex 4544 Fax 660974, ≤ Plymouth Sound, 🏊 heated – 🛗 ⇔ rm 📺 ☎ 🅟 – 🏛 85. AE ⓓ VISA
M 10.50/16.95 **st.** and a la carte 🍷 4.35 – ☕ 7.50 – **102 rm** 65.00/75.00 **st.**, **4 suites** 90.0 110.00 **st.** AZ

🏨 **New Continental,** Millbay Rd, PL1 3LD, ✆ 220782, Telex 45193, Fax 227013, 🏋, ≘s, – 🛗 📺 ☎ 🅟 – 🏛 350. AE ⓓ VISA. ✂ AZ
closed 23 December-3 January – **M** *(closed Saturday lunch)* 10.00/14.50 **t.** and a la cart 🍷 4.50 – **84 rm** ☕ 55.00/70.00 **t.** – SB (weekends only) 70.00/77.00 **st.**

🏨 Astor (Mt. Charlotte Thistle), 14-22 Elliott St., The Hoe, PL1 2PS, ✆ 225511, Telex 45652 🛗 ⇔ rm 📺 ☎ – 🏛 120 BZ
56 rm.

🏨 **Novotel Plymouth,** 270 Plymouth Rd., Marsh Mills Roundabout, PL6 8NH, ✆ 22142 Telex 45711, Fax 221422, 🏊 – 🛗 ⇔ rm ▤ rest 📺 ☎ ♿ 🅟 – 🏛 200. AE ⓓ VISA
M 12.50 **st.** and a la carte 🍷 2.15 – ☕ 7.00 – **100 rm** 52.00/55.00 **st.** BY

🏠 **Georgian House,** 51 Citadel Rd, The Hoe, PL1 3AU, ✆ 663237 – 📺 ☎. AE ⓓ VISA. ✂
closed end December-mid January – **M** *(closed Sunday)* (dinner only) 16.00 **t.** and a la cart – **12 rm** ☕ 29.00/39.00 **t.** AZ

🏠 **Campanile**, Longbridge Rd, Marsh Mills, PL6 8LD, ✆ 601087, Telex 44544, Fax 223213 📺 ☎ ♿ 🅟 – 🏛 30. VISA BY
M 9.40 **st.** and a la carte – ☕ 3.95 – **51 rm** 33.00 **st.**

⌂ **Cranbourne** without rest., 282 Citadel Rd, The Hoe, PL1 2PZ, ✆ 263858 – 📺. AE VISA
12 rm ☕ 18.00/46.00 **st.** BZ

⌂ **Berkeley's of St James** without rest., 4 St. James Place East, The Hoe, PL1 3AS ✆ 221654 – 🛗 ⇔ rm 📺. VISA. ✂ AZ
closed Christmas – **5 rm** ☕ 15.00/32.00 **st.**

⌂ **Athenaen Lodge** without rest., 4 Athenaeun St., The Hoe, PL1 2RH, ✆ 665005 – 📺 🅟 ✂ BZ
8 rm ☕ 14.00/32.00 **st.**

⌂ **Sea Breezes,** 28 Grand Par., West Hoe, PL1 3DJ, ✆ 667205 – 📺 AZ
M (by arrangement) 8.50 **st.** 🍷 2.50 – **7 rm** ☕ 11.00/27.00 **st.**

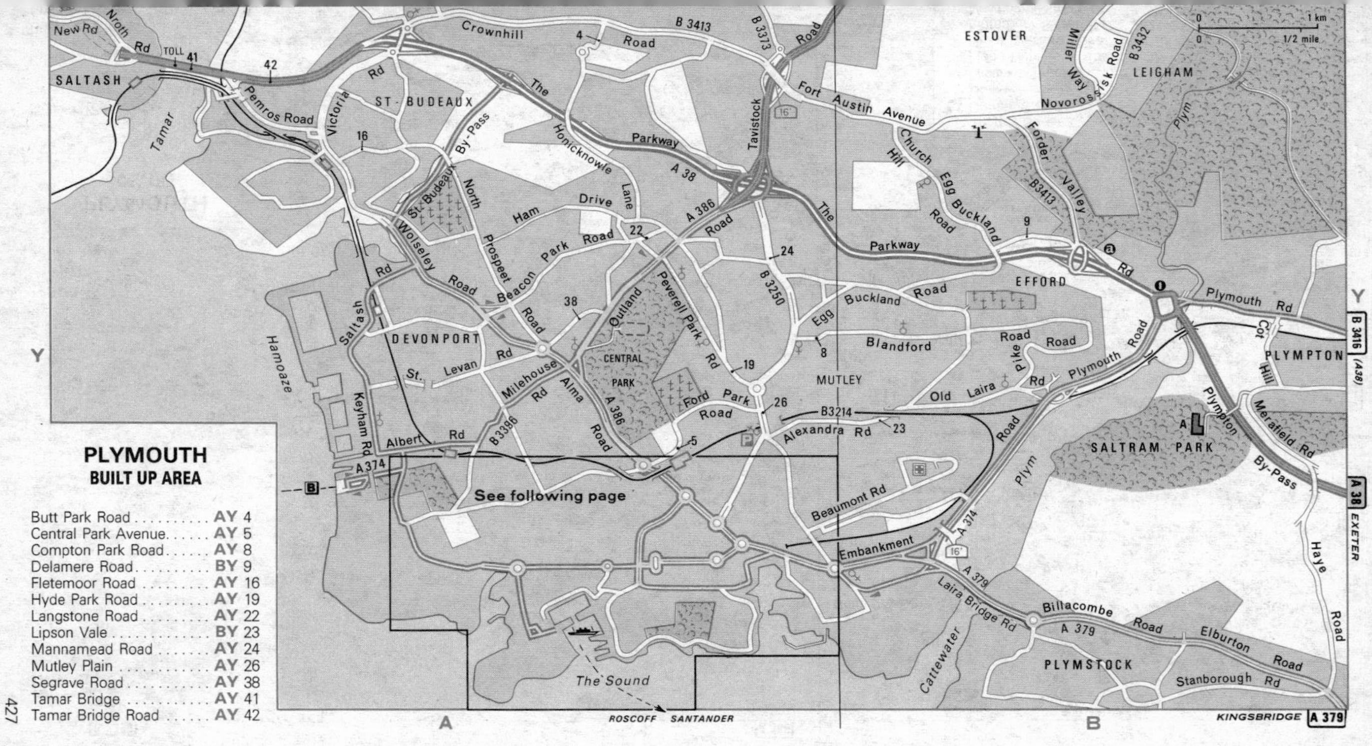

PLYMOUTH
BUILT UP AREA

Butt Park Road	AY 4
Central Park Avenue	AY 5
Compton Park Road	AY 8
Delamere Road	BY 9
Fletemoor Road	AY 16
Hyde Park Road	AY 19
Langstone Road	AY 22
Lipson Vale	BY 23
Mannamead Road	AY 24
Mutley Plain	AY 26
Segrave Road	AY 38
Tamar Bridge	AY 41
Tamar Bridge Road	AY 42

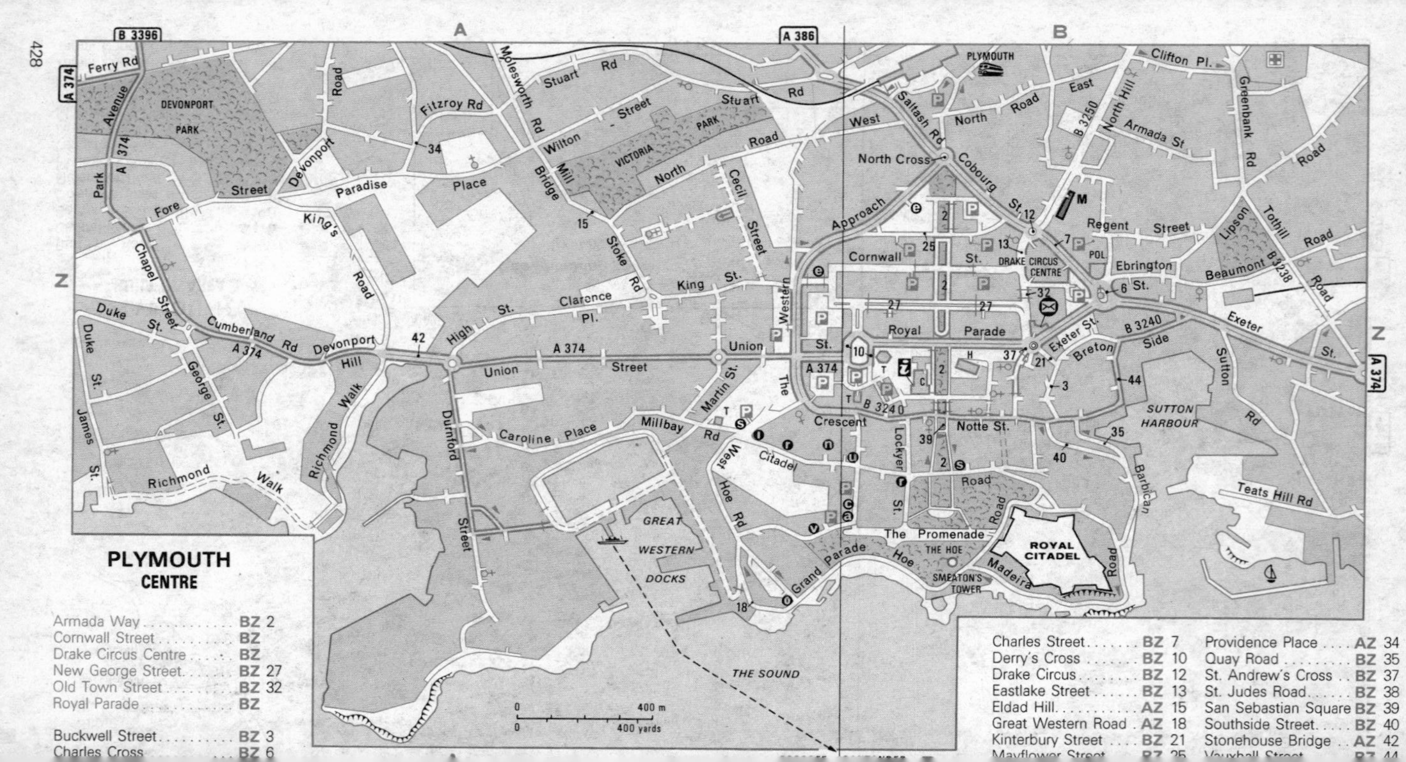

PLYMOUTH
CENTRE

Armada Way .... BZ 2
Cornwall Street .... BZ
Drake Circus Centre .... BZ
New George Street .... BZ 27
Old Town Street .... BZ 32
Royal Parade .... BZ

Buckwell Street .... BZ 3
Charles Cross .... BZ 6
Charles Street .... BZ 7
Derry's Cross .... BZ 10
Drake Circus .... BZ 12
Eastlake Street .... BZ 13
Eldad Hill .... AZ 15
Great Western Road .... AZ 18
Kinterbury Street .... BZ 21
Mayflower Street .... BZ 25
Providence Place .... AZ 34
Quay Road .... BZ 35
St. Andrew's Cross .... BZ 37
St. Judes Road .... BZ 38
San Sebastian Square .... BZ 39
Southside Street .... BZ 40
Stonehouse Bridge .... AZ 42
Vauxhall Street .... BZ 44

XX ✿ **Chez Nous** (Marchal), 13 Frankfort Gate, PL1 1QA, ✆ 266793, French rest. – AE VISA AZ **e**
closed Sunday, Monday, first 3 weeks February, first 3 weeks September and Bank Holidays – **M** (booking essential) 24.00 **t.** and a la carte 29.00/41.00 **t.** 4.00.
Spec. Escalopes de saumon aux fines herbes, Mignons de veau aux shi'itake, Gâteau marbré noir et blanc.

BMW Union St. ✆ 669202
CITROEN Colebrook Rd ✆ 336606
FORD Millbay Rd ✆ 668040
HONDA, SEAT Albert Rd ✆ 564171/561810
MERCEDES-BENZ Crown Hill ✆ 785611
PEUGEOT-TALBOT 241 Union St. ✆ 673553
ROVER, LAND-ROVER Union St. ✆ 263355
VAUXHALL-OPEL Normandy Way ✆ 361251
VAUXHALL-OPEL Bretonside ✆ 667111
VAUXHALL, BEDFORD 24 Middlebridge St. ✆ 513806
VOLVO Valley Rd, Plympton ✆ 338306
ATS Teats Hill Rd ✆ 266217/227964
ATS Miller Way, Novorossisk rd, Estover ✆ 769123
ATS 3 Market rd, Plympton ✆ 330250

POCKLINGTON Humberside 402 R 22 – pop. 5 051 – ECD : Wednesday – ✉ York – ☎ 075 92 (4 fig.) or 0759 (6 fig.).
◆London 213 – ◆Kingston-upon-Hull 25 – York 13.

Feathers, 56 Market Pl., YO4 2AH, ✆ 303155 – TV ☎ P. AE VISA.
M 9.50 **t.** and a la carte 3.50 – **12 rm** 31.50/50.00 **t.** – SB (October-March) (weekends only) 65.00 **st.**

at Barmby Moor W : 2 m. on B 1246 – ✉ York – ☎ 0759 Pocklington :

Barmby Moor, Hull Rd, YO4 5EZ, on A 1079 ✆ 302700, heated, – TV ☎ P. AE VISA.
M *(closed Sunday dinner)* (dinner only and Sunday lunch)/dinner 16.00 **st.** 3.50 – **10 rm** 42.00/50.00 **st.** – SB (except Sunday and Christmas) 68.00 **st.**

FORD Hallgate ✆ 302768
VAUXHALL Kilnwick Rd ✆ 303221

Great Britain and Ireland is now covered
by a series of Atlases at a scale of 1 inch to 4.75 miles.
Three easy to use versions:
Paperback, Spiralbound, Hardback.

POLPERRO Cornwall 403 G 33 **The West Country G.** – pop. 1 192 – ✉ Looe – ☎ 0503.
See : Site★.
◆London 271 – ◆Plymouth 28.

Lanhael House without rest., Langreek Rd, PL13 2PW, ✆ 72428, – rm P. VISA.
April-October – **6 rm** 19.00/34.00 **s.**

Claremont, Fore St., PL13 2RG, ✆ 72241 – TV ☎ P. VISA
M *(closed October-March)* 16.50 **st.** – **9 rm** 23.50/48.00 **st.** – SB (April-September) 50.00/60.00 **st.**

X **Kitchen,** Fish Na Bridge, The Coombes, PL13 2RQ, ✆ 72780 – VISA
closed Sunday to Thursday in winter and Tuesday – **M** (dinner only) 15.00/25.00 **t.** 3.50.

PONTARFYNACH = Devil's Bridge.

PONTFAEN Dyfed - see Fishguard.

PONTSHAEN (Pontsian) Dyfed – ✉ Llandyssul – ☎ 054 555.
◆London 239 – Carmarthen 19 – Fishguard 37.

X **Farmhouse,** Castell Howell, SA44 4UA, N : 1 ½ m. by B 4459 ✆ 209, , park, squash – P. VISA
M *(closed dinner Sunday, Monday and Wednesday)* (bar lunch)/dinner a la carte 11.30/14.50 **st.** 2.75.

PONT-Y-PANT Gwynedd – see Betws-y-Coed.

POOLE Dorset 403 404 O 31 **The West Country G.** – pop. 122 815 – ECD : Wednesday – ☎ 0202.
See : Site★ – The Three Museums★ *AC* by A 35 AX.
Envir. : Compton Acres Gardens★★, (≤★★★) *AC*, SE : 3 m. AX – Brownsea Island★, Baden Powell Stone (≤★★) *AC*, by boat from Poole Quay or Sandbanks *AC*.
18 Parkstone, Links Rd ✆ 708025.
Shipping connections with the continent : to France (Cherbourg) (Truckline Ferries) summer only (4 h 30 mn) – to The Channel Islands : Jersey (St. Helier) and Guernsey (St. Peter Port) (British Channel Island Ferries) summer : 2 daily, winter : 4 weekly (except Monday).
The Quay ✆ 673322.
◆London 116 – Bournemouth 4 – Dorchester 23 – Weymouth 28.

Plan : see Bournemouth

Haven, Banks Rd, Sandbanks, BH13 7QL, SE : 4¼ m. on B 3369 ℘ 707333, Telex 41338, Fax 708796, ≤ Ferry, Old Harry Rocks and Poole Bay, squash – 100. VISA. by B 3369 AX
M (buffet lunch)/dinner 28.00 **t.** 6.00 – **95 rm** 50.00/150.00 **t.**

Mansion House, 11 Thames St., BH15 1JN, ℘ 685666, Telex 41495, Fax 665709, « 18C town house, staircase » – rest – 25. VISA
closed 26 to 31 December – **M** *(closed Saturday lunch)* 21.50/30.00 **st.** 5.10 – **28 rm** 75.00/115.00 **st.** – SB 117.00 **st.** by A 35 AX

Salterns (Best Western), 38 Salterns Way, Lilliput, BH14 8JR, ℘ 707321, Telex 41259, Fax 707488, ≤, squash – – 50. VISA. by B 3369 AX
M 20.00/27.50 **t.** and a la carte 3.75 – 6.50 – **16 rm** 60.00/102.00 **t.** – SB 95.00/125.00 **st.**

Hospitality Inn - The Quay (Mt. Charlotte Thistle), The Quay, BH15 1HD, ℘ 666800, Telex 418374, Fax 684470, ≤ – – 60. VISA by A 35 AX
M 14.00/15.00 **t.** and a la carte 4.25 – 8.00 – **68 rm** 72.50/87.50 **st.**

Antelope, 8 High St., BH15 1BP, ℘ 672029, Telex 418387, Fax 678286 –
21 rm. by A 35 AX

Sea Witch, 47 Haven Rd, Canford Cliffs, BH13 7LH, ℘ 707697 – . VISA.
M *(closed Monday lunch)* 8.50/10.00 **st.** and a la carte 4.00 – **8 rm** 40.00/56.00 **st.** AX **o**

Warehouse, Poole Quay, BH15 1HJ, ℘ 677238, ≤ – VISA
closed 23 to 30 December – **M** 17.50 **t.** and a la carte 4.00. by A 35 AX

Le Chateau, 13 Haven Rd, Canford Cliffs, BH13 7LE, ℘ 707400 – VISA AX **r**
closed Sunday and Monday – **M** 21.00 **t.** and a la carte 4.25.

Isabel's, 32 Station Rd, Lower Parkstone, BH14 8UD, ℘ 747885 – VISA
closed dinner Monday and Sunday, 25-26 December and 1 to 4 January – **M** (lunch by arrangement)/dinner a la carte 16.00/23.50 **t.** AX **a**

John B's, 20 Old High St., BH15 1BP, ℘ 672440 – VISA by A 35 AX
M *(closed Sunday)* (dinner only) 15.50 **t.**

AUDI-VW Cabot Lane ℘ 745000
CITROEN Blandford Rd ℘ 623636
RENAULT The Quay ℘ 674187
VAUXHALL-OPEL Poole Rd, Branksome ℘ 763361
ATS 1 Fernside Rd ℘ 733301/733326

POOLEY BRIDGE Cumbria 401 402 L 20 – see Ullswater.

POOL IN WHARFEDALE West Yorks. 402 P 22 – pop. 1 706 – ✉ Otley – 0532 Leeds.

♦London 204 – Bradford 10 – Harrogate 8 – ♦Leeds 10.

Pool Court with rm, Pool Bank, LS21 1EH, ℘ 842288, Fax 843115, – rest . VISA.
closed Sunday, Monday, 2 weeks July-August and 2 weeks Christmas-New Year – **M** (dinner only)(booking essential) 10.00 **t.** and a la carte 21.50/29.75 **t.** – 6.75 – **6 rm** 70.00/120.00 **t.** – SB (weekends only) 105.00/145.00 **st.**

PORLOCK Somerset 403 J 30 **The West Country G.** – pop. 1 453 (inc. Oare) – ECD : Wednesday – 0643.

See : Site★ – St. Dubricius Church★.

Envir. : St. Culbone★, NW : 5 m. including 3 m. return on foot.

♦London 190 – ♦Bristol 67 – Exeter 46 – Taunton 28.

Oaks, TA24 8ES, ℘ 862265, ≤, – rest .
M (dinner only) 14.50 **st.** 3.95 – **11 rm** 35.00/56.00 **st.** – SB 80.00/95.00 **st.**

at Porlock Weir NW : 1½ m. – ✉ Minehead – 0643 Porlock :

Anchor and Ship Inn, TA24 8PB, ℘ 862636, Fax 862843, ≤, – . VISA
M (bar lunch)/dinner 14.75 **st.** and a la carte 4.25 – **25 rm** 34.00/99.00 **st.** – SB 85.00/120.00 **st.**

PORT DINORWIC (FELINHELI) Gwynedd 402 403 H 24 – 0248.

♦London 249 – Caernarfon 4 – Holyhead 23.

Ty'n Rhos Farm , Seion, Llanddeiniolen, LL55 3AE, E : 2½ m. by A 487 off B 4547 ℘ 670489, ≤, – rest
closed 20 December-8 January – **M** (by arrangement) 12.50 3.50 – **11 rm** 25.00/56.00 **st.** – SB 58.00/76.00 **st.**

PORTHAETHWY = Menai Bridge.

***En saison,** surtout dans les stations fréquentées, il est prudent de retenir à l'avance.*
Cependant, si vous ne pouvez pas occuper la chambre que vous avez retenue, prévenez immédiatement l'hôtelier.
Si vous écrivez à un hôtel à l'étranger, joignez à votre lettre un coupon-réponse international (disponible dans les bureaux de poste).

PORTHCAWL Mid Glam. 403 I 29 – pop. 15 162 – ECD : Wednesday – ☎ 065 671.
The Old Police Station, John St. ℘ 6639 (summer only).
London 183 – Cardiff 28 – Swansea 18.

Seabank (Lansbury), The Promenade, CF36 3LU, ℘ 2261, Telex 497797, Fax 5363, ← – rm – 200. – **M** 8.95/14.00 **t.** and a la carte – **64 rm** 63.00/76.00 **t.** – SB (weekends only) 64.00/76.00 **st.**

Atlantic, West Drive, CF36 3LT, ℘ 5011, ← – **M** *(closed Sunday dinner)* (bar lunch)/dinner 10.75 **t.** and a la carte 3.90 – **20 rm** 46.75/61.60 **t.** – SB (weekends only) 70.40 **st.**

Minerva, 52 Esplanade Av., CF36 3YU, ℘ 2428 – rest. **M** 7.50 **s.** 3.00 – **8 rm** 13.00/38.00 **s.**

at Nottage (Drenewydd yn Notais) N : 1 m. by A 4229 – ✉ ☎ 065 671 Porthcawl :

Rose and Crown (B.C.B.), Heol-y-Capel, CF36 3ST, ℘ 4850 – **M** 15.00 **st.** – **8 rm** 42.00/54.00 **st.**

PORTHMADOG Gwynedd 402 403 H 25 – pop. 2 865 – ECD : Wednesday – ☎ 0766.
Morfa Bychan ℘ 512037, W : 2 m. High St. ℘ 512981.
London 245 – Caernarfon 20 – Chester 70 – Shrewsbury 81.

Bwlch-y-Fedwen Country House, Penmorfa, LL49 9RY, NW : 2 m. on A 487 ℘ 512975, « Tastefully renovated 17C inn » – rest. *April-October* – **5 rm** (dinner included) 43.00/70.00 **t.**

VOLVO Penamser Rd ℘ 513717 — ATS Madoc Hill, Smith St. ℘ 512588

PORTINSCALE Cumbria – see Keswick.

PORT ISAAC Cornwall 403 F 32 **The West Country G.** – ECD : Wednesday – ☎ 0208 Bodmin.
London 266 – Newquay 24 – Tintagel 14 – Truro 32.

Port Gaverne, Port Gaverne, PL29 3SQ, S : ½ m. ℘ 880244, Fax 880151, « Retaining 17C features » – *closed 13 January-15 February* – **M** (bar lunch)/dinner a la carte 12.75/24.25 **t.** 3.00 – **18 rm** 39.00/82.00 **t.** – SB (except summer and Christmas-New Year) 85.00/89.00 **st.**

Slipway, PL29 3RH, ℘ 880264, « 16C inn » – *closed February* – *(closed Wednesday lunch, Sunday dinner, Monday, Tuesday and Thursday in winter)* (bar lunch)/dinner a la carte 13.15/19.50 **t.** 3.75 – **10 rm** 20.00/32.00 **t.**

Archer Farm, Trewetha, PL29 3RU, SE : ½ m. by B 3276 ℘ 880522, ← – *April-October* – **M** 12.50 **t.** 3.75 – **9 rm** 21.00/48.00 – SB 60.00 **st.**

PORTLAND Dorset 403 404 M 32 **The West Country G.** – pop. 12405 – ECD : Wednesday – ☎ 0305. **See:** Site★ (vantage point★★).
London 149 – Dorchester 14 – Weymouth 6.

Portland Heights (Best Western), Yeates Corner, DT5 2EN, ℘ 821361, Fax 860081, ←, heated, squash – rm – 165. **M** 9.00/15.00 **t.** and a la carte 3.75 – **66 rm** 49.00/74.00 **t.** – SB (weekends only) 70.00/88.00 **st.**

FORD Easton Lane ℘ 820483

PORTLOE Cornwall 403 F 33 – ✉ ☎ 0872 Truro.
London 296 – St. Austell 15 – Truro 15.

Lugger, TR2 5RD, ℘ 501322, Fax 501691, ← – rest. *February-November* – **M** (bar lunch Monday to Saturday)/dinner 15.00 **t.** and a la carte 2.25 – **19 rm** 33.00/88.00 **t.**

PORTMEIRION Gwynedd 402 403 H 25 – ☎ 0766 Porthmadog. **See :** Site★.
London 245 – Caernarfon 23 – Colwyn Bay 40 – Dolgellau 24.

Portmeirion, LL48 6ER, ℘ 770228, Telex 61540, Fax 771331, ← village and estuary, « Private Italianate village, antiques », heated, park – rest – 100. *closed 14 January-8 February* – **M** *(closed Monday lunch except Bank Holidays)* (buffet lunch)/dinner 22.50 **t.** 5.00 – 7.50 – **28 rm** 50.00/105.00 **t.**, **6 suites** 70.00/125.00 **t.** – SB (weekdays only) 106.00/172.00 **st.**

PORTSCATHO Cornwall 403 F 33 – ECD : Wednesday and Saturday – ✉ Truro – ☎ 087 258.
London 298 – Plymouth 55 – Truro 16.

Gerrans Bay, Tregassick Rd, TR2 5ED, ℘ 338. *April-October and Christmas* – **M** (bar lunch Monday to Saturday)/dinner 15.75 **t.** 3.75 – **14 rm** 23.00/49.50 **st.**

Roseland House, Rosevine, TR2 5EW, N : 2 m. by A 3078 ℘ 644, ← Gerrans Bay – rest. *March-October and Christmas* – **M** (bar lunch Monday to Saturday)/dinner 15.00 **t.** 3.20 – **13 rm** (dinner included) 31.00/80.00 **t.** – SB 62.00/70.00 **st.**

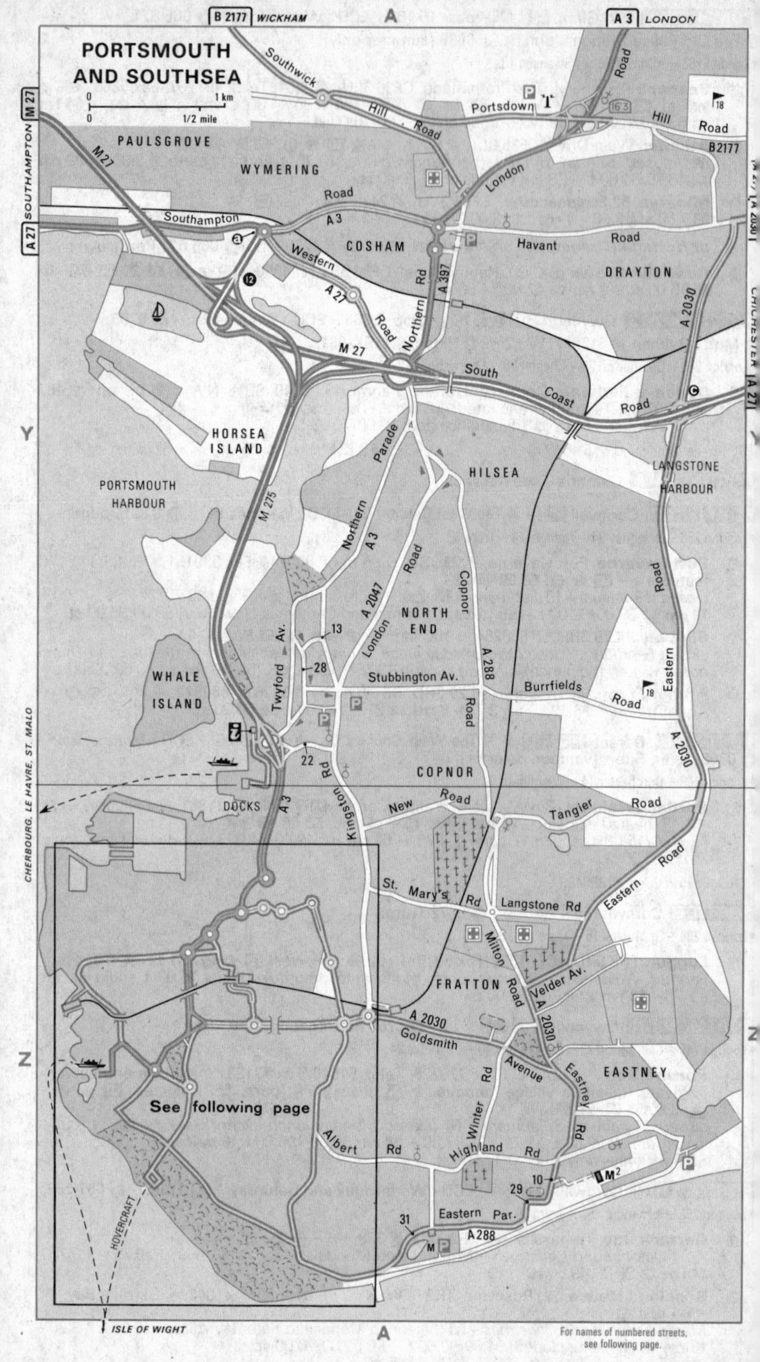
PORTSMOUTH AND SOUTHSEA
0 1 km
0 1/2 mile
B 2177 WICKHAM
A 3 LONDON
M 27 SOUTHAMPTON
A 27
CHICHESTER A 27
CHERBOURG, LE HAVRE, ST. MALO
ISLE OF WIGHT
HOVERCRAFT
PAULSGROVE
WYMERING
COSHAM
DRAYTON
HORSEA ISLAND
PORTSMOUTH HARBOUR
HILSEA
LANGSTONE HARBOUR
NORTH END
WHALE ISLAND
COPNOR
DOCKS
FRATTON
EASTNEY
Southwick
Portsdown Hill Road
London Road
Southampton Road
Havant Road
Western Road
Northern Rd
South Coast Road
Northern Parade
London Road
Copnor Road
Twyford Av.
Stubbington Av.
Burrfields Road
Eastern Road
Kingston Rd
New Road
Tangier Road
St. Mary's Rd
Langstone Rd
Milton Road
Velder Av.
Goldsmith Avenue
Winter Rd
Eastney Rd
Albert Rd
Highland Rd
Eastern Par.
See following page
For names of numbered streets, see following page.

PORTSMOUTH AND SOUTHSEA

Arundel Street . . . . BY
Cascade Centre . . . . BY
Charlotte Street . . . . BY 9
Commercial Road . . . . BY
Palmerston Road . . . . BZ
Tricorn Centre . . . . BY

Alec Rose Lane . . . . BY 2
Alfred Road . . . . BY 5
Bellevue Terrace . . . . BZ 7
Bradford Road . . . . BY 8
Cromwell Road . . . . AZ 10
Edinburgh Road . . . . BY 12
Gladys Avenue . . . . AY 13
Gordon Road . . . . BZ 14
Grove Road South . . . . BZ 15
Guildhall Walk . . . . BY 16
Gunwharf Road . . . . BZ 17
Hampshire Terrace . . . . BY 18
Hard (The) . . . . BY 19
Isambard Brunel Road . . . . . . BY 20
King's Terrace . . . . BZ 21
Kingston Crescent . . . . AY 22
Landport Terrace . . . . BZ 23
Lennox Road South . . . . BZ 24
Ordnance Row . . . . BY 26
Stamshaw Road . . . . AY 28
St. George's Road . . . . AZ 29
St. Helen's Parade . . . . AZ 31
St. Michael's Road . . . . BY 33
Southsea Terrace . . . . BZ 36
Stanhope Road . . . . BY 37

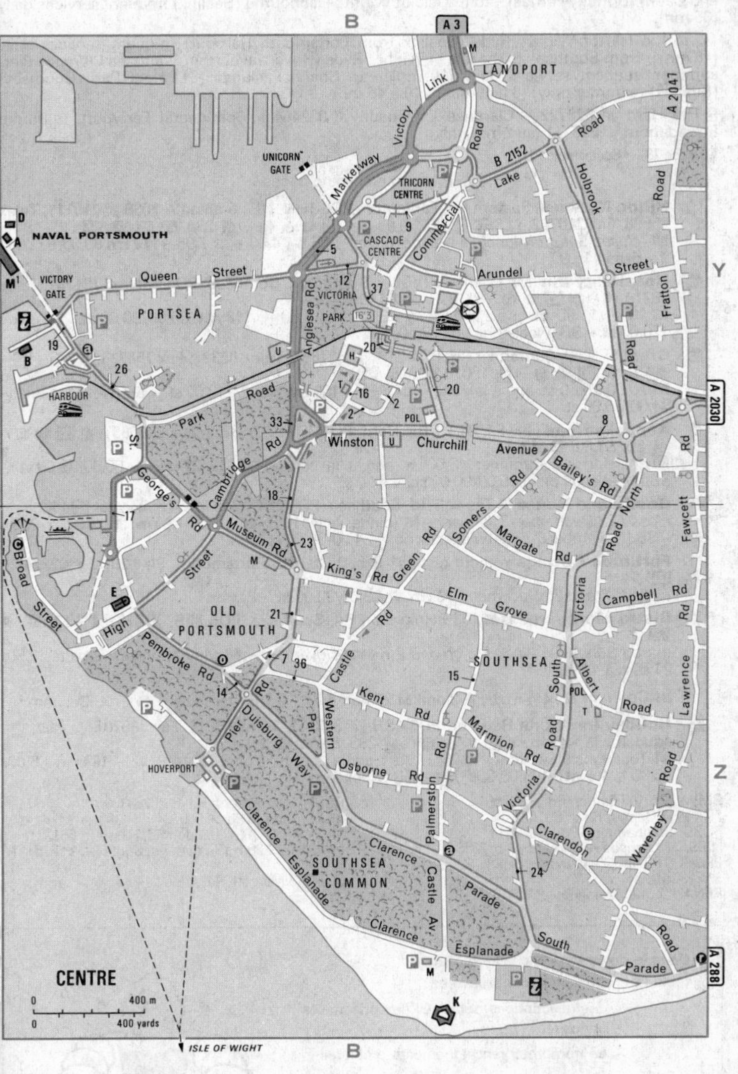

Town plans: *roads most used by traffic and those on which guide listed hotels and restaurants stand are fully drawn; the beginning only of lesser roads is indicated.*

PORTSMOUTH and SOUTHSEA Hants. 403 404 Q 31 – pop. 174 218 – ECD : Monday, Wednesday and Thursday – ☎ 0705.

See : Site★ – Naval Portsmouth★★★ BY : H.M.S. Victory★★ **A**, The Mary Rose★★ **D**, H.M.S Warrior★ **B**, Royal Naval Museum★ **M1***AC* – Royal Marines' Museum★, at Eastney AZ **M2** – Old Town★ BZ – St. Thomas Cathedral★ BZ **E**.

Envir. : Southsea Castle★ SE : ½ m. BZ **K** – Portchester Castle★ NW : 6 m. by A 27 AY.

Great Salterns ☎ 664549. AY – Crookhorn Lane, Widley ☎ 372210 AY.

Shipping connections with the Continent : to France (Cherbourg) (P & O European Ferries) (summer only) – to France (Le Havre) (P & O European Ferries) – to France (Saint-Malo and Caen) (Brittany Ferries) – to the Isle of Wight : Fishbourne (Sealink) frequent services daily (35 mn).

to the Isle of Wight : Ryde (Sealink from Portsmouth Harbour) frequent services daily (15 mn) – from Southsea to the Isle of Wight : Ryde (Hovertravel from Southsea Clarence Pier) summer frequent services daily (10 mn) – to Channel Islands (St.Peters Port, Guernsey) (Sealink) (summer only) (8 h 45 mn to 10 h 45 mn).

The Hard ☎ 826722 – Clarence Esplanade ☎ 832464 – Continental Ferryport, Rudmore Roundabout ☎ 698111 (summer only).

◆London 78 – ◆Southampton 21.

Plans on preceding pages

Hilton National, Eastern Rd, Farlington, PO6 1UN, NE : 5 m. on A 2030 ☎ 219111, Telex 86598, Fax 210762, – rest – 230. AE VISA
M *(closed Saturday lunch)* a la carte 12.75/21.65 **t.** 4.50 – 7.95 – **119 rm** 80.00/92.00 **t.**, **2 suites** 115.00 **t.** AY **c**

Hospitality Inn (Mt. Charlotte Thistle), South Par., Southsea, PO4 0RN, ☎ 731281, Telex 86719, – – 300. AE VISA BZ **r**
M 10.50/11.95 **st.** and a la carte 3.80 – 6.50 – **113 rm** 60.00/90.00 **st.**, **2 suites** 120.00 **st.** – SB (weekends only) 73.00 **st.**

Crest (T.H.F.), Pembroke Rd, PO1 2TA, ☎ 827651, Telex 86397, Fax 756715, – rm – 150. AE VISA BZ **o**
M 20.00/25.00 **st.** and a la carte – 7.95 – **163 rm** 80.00/110.00 **st.** – SB (weekends only) 84.00/96.00 **st.**

Keppel's Head (T.H.F.), 24-26 The Hard, PO1 3DT, ☎ 833231, Fax 838688 – – 60. AE VISA BY **a**
M (carving lunch)/dinner 18.00 **st.** and a la carte 4.50 – **27 rm** 60.00/75.00 **st.** – SB (weekends only) 80.00/90.00 **st.**

Goodwood House, 1 Taswell Rd, Southsea, PO5 2RG, ☎ 824734 – rest.
closed 23 December-2 January – **M** (dinner only) 10.00 **st.** 3.00 – **8 rm** 12.00/26.00 **st.** – SB (November-April) (weekends only) 34.00/38.00 **st.** BZ **e**

Fortitude Cottage without rest., 51 Broad St., Old Portsmouth, PO1 2JD, ☎ 823748 – . BZ **c**
closed 25 and 26 December – **3 rm** 28.00/32.00 **st.**

Bistro Montparnasse, 103 Palmerston Rd, Southsea, PO5 3PS, ☎ 816754 – AE VISA BZ **a**
closed Sunday, 1 week March and 2 weeks November – **M** (dinner only) a la carte 13.50/21.50 **t.** 4.90.

at Cosham N : 4½ m. by A 3 and M 275 on A 27 – ✉ Portsmouth – ☎ 0705 Cosham :

Holiday Inn, North Harbour, PO6 4SH, ☎ 383151, Telex 86611, Fax 388701, squash – rm – 280. AE VISA AY **a**
M (bar lunch Saturday) 15.25/17.75 **t.** and a la carte 6.50 – 9.95 – **169 rm** 85.00/95.00 **t.**, **1 suite** 175.00/200.00 **t.** – SB (weekends only) 148.00 **st.**

BMW 135-153 Fratton Rd ☎ 827551
FIAT 117 Copnor Rd ☎ 691621
FORD Southampton Rd ☎ 370944
NISSAN Granada Rd, Southsea ☎ 735311
PEUGEOT-TALBOT Grove Rd South, Southsea ☎ 823261
RENAULT 128 Milton Rd ☎ 815151
ROVER Hambledon Rd ☎ 262641
SEAT Gamble Rd ☎ 660734
VAUXHALL-OPEL London Rd, Hilsea ☎ 661321
VW-AUDI 226 Haslemere Rd, Southsea ☎ 815111

ATS 3 Margate Rd ☎ 827544

POWBURN Northumb. 401 402 O 17 – ✉ Alnwick – ☏ 066 578.
♦London 312 – ♦Edinburgh 73 – ♦Newcastle-upon-Tyne 36.

Breamish House ⑤, NE66 4LL, ☏ 266, Fax 500, ←, ⌂ – ⅏ rest ☐ ☎ Ⓟ
closed January and first 2 weeks February – **M** (dinner only and Sunday lunch)/dinner 18.50 **t.** ⅃ 4.75 – **10 rm** ⊐ 46.00/95.00 **t.** – SB (October-March) (except Bank Holidays) 90.00/115.00 **st.**

POWERSTOCK Dorset 403 L 31 – see Bridport.

PRESTBURY Cheshire 402 403 404 N 24 – pop. 2 970 – ☏ 0625.
Envir. : Adlington Hall★ (15C) *AC*, N : 3½ m.
♦London 184 – ♦Liverpool 43 – ♦Manchester 17 – ♦Stoke-on-Trent 25.

Mottram Hall (De Vere) ⑤, Wilmslow Rd, Mottram St. Andrew, SK10 4QT, NW : 2¼ m. on A 538 ☏ 828135, Telex 668181, Fax 829284, ←, « Part 18C mansion in park », ⌂, ☐, ⌂, ✗, squash – ⅏ rm ☐ ☎ ♿ Ⓟ – 🏛 100. ☐ AE ⓘ VISA
M *(closed Saturday lunch)* 14.50/20.50 **st.** and a la carte ⅃ 5.00 – **92 rm** ⊐ 95.00/120.00 **st.**, **3 suites** 170.00 **st.**

White House, The Village, SK10 4DG, ☏ 829376 – Ⓟ. ☐ AE ⓘ VISA. ⅏
closed Sunday dinner and Monday – **M** 9.95 **t.** (lunch) and a la carte 20.70/26.40 **t.** ⅃ 4.00.

Legh Arms and Black Boy, The Village, SK10 4DG, ☏ 829130 – Ⓟ. ☐ AE ⓘ VISA
closed dinner 25 December and 1 January – **M** 10.50/14.00 **t.** and a la carte ⅃ 4.30.

PRESTEIGNE Powys 403 K 27 – pop. 1 490 – ECD : Thursday – ☏ 0544.
See : Church (Flemish Tapestry★).
Envir. : Old Radnor (church★) SW : 7½ m.
ℹ Old Market Hall ☏ 260193.
♦London 159 – Llandrindod Wells 20 – Shrewsbury 39.

Radnorshire Arms (T.H.F.), High St., LD8 2BE, ☏ 267406, Fax 260415, ⌂ – ⅏ rm ☐ ☎ Ⓟ – 🏛 25. ☐ AE ⓘ VISA
M 12.00/14.75 **st.** and a la carte ⅃ 4.35 – ⊐ 7.00 – **16 rm** 58.00/74.00 **st.** – SB 94.00/104.00 **st.**

Die Preise — Einzelheiten über die in diesem Führer angegebenen Preise finden Sie in der Einleitung.

PRESTON Lancs. 402 L 22 – pop. 166 675 – ECD : Thursday – ☏ 0772.
Envir. : Samlesbury Old Hall★ (14C) *AC*, E : 2½ m.
⛳ Fulwood Hall Lane, Fulwood ☏ 700011 – ⛳ Longridge, Fell Barn, Jeffrey Hill ☏ 783291, NE : 8 m. by B 6243 – ⛳ Fishwick Hall, Glenluce Drive, Farringdon Park ☏ 798300 – ⛳ Ingol, Tanterton Hall Rd ☏ 734556 – ⛳ Aston Lea, Tudor Av. ☏ 726480 – ⛳ Penwortham, Blundell Lane ☏ 743207.
ℹ Guildhall, Lancaster Rd ☏ 53731.
♦London 226 – ♦Blackpool 18 – Burnley 22 – ♦Liverpool 30 – ♦Manchester 34 – ♦Stoke-on-Trent 65.

Crest (T.H.F.), The Ring Way, PR1 3AU, ☏ 59411, Telex 677147, Fax 201923 – |♦| ⅏ ☐ ☎ Ⓟ – 🏛 100. ☐ AE ⓘ VISA
M 9.95/15.95 **st.** and a la carte ⅃ 5.25 – ⊐ 7.95 – **126 rm** 66.00/130.00 **t.** – SB (weekends only) 80.00 **st.**

at Fulwood N : 1½ m. on A 6 – ✉ ☏ 0772 Preston :

Briarfield without rest., 147 Watling Street Rd, off Garstang Rd, PR2 4AE, ☏ 700917 – ☐ Ⓟ. ⅏
closed Christmas – **9 rm** ⊐ 20.00/40.00 **t.**

at Broughton N : 3 m. on A 6 – ✉ ☏ 0772 Preston :

Broughton Park, 418 Garstang Rd, PR3 5JB, ☏ 864087, Group Telex 67180, Fax 861728, ⌂, ☐, ⌂, squash – |♦| ⅏ rm ☐ ☎ ♿ Ⓟ – 🏛 150. ☐ AE ⓘ VISA. ⅏
M (see **Courtyard** below) – **98 rm** ⊐ 78.00/98.00 **st.** – SB (weekends only) 90.00 **st.**

Courtyard (at Broughton Park H.), 418 Garstang Rd, PR3 5JB, ☏ 864087, Group Telex 67180, Fax 861728 – Ⓟ. ☐ AE ⓘ VISA
M (booking essential) 25.00/30.00 **st.** and a la carte.

at Samlesbury E : 2½ m. at junction M 6 and A 59 – ✉ Preston – ☏ 0772 Preston :

Swallow Trafalgar, Preston New Rd, PR5 0UL, E : 1 m. at junction A 59 and A 677 ☏ 877351, Telex 677362, Fax 877424, ☐, squash – |♦| ⅏ rm ☐ ☎ Ⓟ – 🏛 150. ☐ AE ⓘ VISA
M *(closed Saturday lunch and Bank Holidays)* 8.25/12.50 **st.** and a la carte ⅃ 5.00 – **78 rm** ⊐ 65.00/78.00 **st.** – SB (weekends only July and August) 84.00 **st.**

Tickled Trout, Preston New Rd, PR5 0UJ, ☏ 877671, Telex 677625, Fax 877463, ←, ⌂, ⌂ – ☐ ☎ Ⓟ – 🏛 100. ☐ AE ⓘ VISA
M 10.85/17.00 **t.** and a la carte ⅃ 4.95 – **66 rm** ⊐ 70.00/85.00 **st.** – SB (January-October) (weekends only) 80.00/85.00 **st.**

at Bamber Bridge S : 5 m. on A 6 – ✉ ☎ 0772 Preston :

🏨 Novotel, Reedfield Place, Walton Summit, PR5 6AB, SE : ¾ m. by A 6 at junction with M 6 ☎ 313331, Telex 677164, heated, – 🛗 📺 ☎ ♿ 🅿 –
100 rm.

at Lea W : 3 ½ m. on A 583 – ✉ ☎ 0772 Preston :

🏨 **Travel Inn,** Blackpool Rd, PR4 0XL, on A 583 ☎ 720476, Fax 729971 – rm 📺 ♿ 🅿. AE VISA.
M (Beefeater grill) a la carte approx. 12.25 **t.** – 4.50 – **38 rm** -/27.50 **t.**

MICHELIN Distribution Centre, Unit 20, Roman Way, Longbridge Rd, Ribbleton, PR2 5BB ☎ 651411, Fax 655108

BMW Blackpool Rd, Ashton ☎ 724391
COLT, YUGO Preston Rd ☎ 652323
FIAT 306-310 Ribbleton Lane ☎ 792823
FORD Penwortham ☎ 744471
HONDA Corporation St. ☎ 58862
LADA Watling Street Rd ☎ 717262
NISSAN Ribbleton Lane ☎ 704704
PEUGEOT-TALBOT. Blackpool Rd ☎ 735811
RELIANT Blackpool Rd ☎ 726066
SKODA New Hall Lane ☎ 794491
TOYOTA 350 Blackpool Rd ☎ 719841
VAUXHALL Blackpool Rd ☎ 793054
VOLVO Strand Rd ☎ 50501
VW-AUDI ☎ 702288

ATS 296-298 Aqueduct St. ☎ 57688

PRIORS HARDWICK Warw. 403 404 Q 27 – pop. 167 – ✉ Rugby – ☎ 0327 Byfield.

◆London 94 – ◆Coventry 17 – Northampton 26 – Warwick 15.

XX **Butchers Arms,** CV23 8SN, ☎ 60504, Fax 60502, – 🅿
closed Saturday lunch and Sunday dinner – **M** 11.00 **s.** (lunch) and a la carte 13.65/21.95 **s.** 3.20.

I prezzi — Per ogni chiarimento sui prezzi qui riportati, consultate le spiegazioni alle pagine dell'introduzione.

PUCKRUP Glos. – see Tewkesbury.

PUDDINGTON Cheshire 402 403 K 24 – pop. 318 – ✉ South Wirral – ☎ 051 Liverpool.

◆London 204 – Birkenhead 12 – Chester 8.

XXX **Craxton Wood** with rm, Parkgate Rd, L66 9PB, on A 540 ☎ 339 4717, Fax 339 1740 ←, « Gardens », park – 📺 ☎ ♿ 🅿. AE VISA.
closed Sunday, last 2 weeks August and Bank Holidays – **M** a la carte 15.50/21.35 **s.** 4.95 – **13 rm** 42.50/85.00 **s.**, **1 suite** 65.00/85.00 **s.**

PUDSEY West Yorks. 402 P 22 – see Leeds.

PULBOROUGH West Sussex 404 S 31 – pop. 3 197 – ECD : Wednesday – ☎ 079 82.

Envir. : Hardham (church : wall paintings★ 12C) S : 1 m.

West Sussex, Hurston Lane ☎ 2563, E : 1 ½ m. on A 283.

◆London 49 – ◆Brighton 25 – Guildford 25 – ◆Portsmouth 35.

🏨 **Chequers,** Church Pl., RH20 1AD, NE : ¼ m. on A 29 ☎ 2486, Fax 2715, – rest 📺 ☎ 🅿. AE VISA
M (bar lunch)/dinner 14.50 **st.** 3.00 – **11 rm** 44.50/55.00 **st.** – SB (except Christmas) 65.00/70.00 **st.**

XX **Stane Street Hollow,** Codmore Hill, RH20 1BG, NE : 1 m. on A 29 ☎ 2819, Swiss rest. – 🅿
closed last 2 weeks May, last 2 weeks October, 24 to 26 December and 1 January – **M** *(closed Saturday lunch and Sunday to Tuesday)* (booking essential) 7.50 **t.** (lunch) and a la carte 15.00/21.00 **t.** 4.00.

HONDA London Rd ☎ 0798 (Petworth) 831691
ROLLS-ROYCE, JAGUAR, DAIMLER, RANGE-ROVER, LAND-ROVER London Rd ☎ 2407

PURTON Wilts. 403 404 O 29 – ✉ ☎ 0793 Swindon.

◆London 94 – ◆Bristol 41 – Gloucester 31 – ◆Oxford 38 – Swindon 10.

🏨 **The Pear Tree at Purton,** Church End, SN5 9ED, S : ½ m. on Lydiard Millicent rd ☎ 772100, Fax 772369, ←, « Conservatory restaurant », – 📺 ☎ 🅿. AE VISA
M *(closed Saturday lunch)* 14.50/20.50 **t.** 5.00 – **16 rm** 75.00/95.00 **t.**, **2 suites** 120.00 **t.**

PWLLHELI Gwynedd 402 403 G 25 – ☎ 0758.

Golf Rd ☎ 612520.

Y Maes ☎ 3000 (summer only).

◆London 261 – Aberystwyth 73 – Caernarfon 21.

XX ❀ **Plas Bodegroes** (Chown) with rm, LL53 5TH, NW : 1¾ m. on A 497 ✆ 612363, Fax 701247, « Georgian country house », park – rest. VISA.
closed January – **M** *(closed lunch, Monday and Sunday to non-residents)* 23.00 **st.** (dinner) and a la carte 4.00 – **5 rm** 40.00/80.00 **st.** – SB (November-May except Bank Holidays) 80.00/100.00 **st.**
Spec. Tartare of wild salmon with potato and dill salad, Chargrilled loin of spring lamb with a chanterelle and fresh garlic sauce, Strawberry lemon mousse with strawberry sauce.

at Bodfuan NW : 3¾ m. on A 497 – ✉ 0758 Pwllheli :

Old Rectory, LL53 6DT, ✆ 720923, – . VISA
M (dinner only) a la carte 13.00/18.50 **st.** 4.00 – **4 rm** 18.00/32.00 **st.**

FORD The Garage ✆ 0766 (Chwilog) 810240

QUEDGELEY Glos. 403 404 N 28 – see Gloucester.

QUORN Leics. – see Loughborough.

RADLETT Herts. 404 T 28 – pop. 7 749 – ECD : Wednesday – 0923.

at Aldenham, Radlett Rd ✆ 853929, SW : 3 m. by B462 BT – Potters Park, Shenley Hill ✆ 854127.

♦London 21 – Luton 15.

Plan : see Greater London (North-West)

XX **Tim's Table,** 335 Watling St., WD7 7LB, ✆ 854388, Chinese (Peking, Szechuan) rest. – . AE VISA BT **o**
M 8.50/15.50 **t.** and a la carte 3.50.

BMW 74-76 Watling St. ✆ 854802
FORD 203-205 Watling St. ✆ 854851
VAUXHALL 411 Watling St. ✆ 855681

RAMSBOTTOM Greater Manchester 402 N 23 – pop. 16 334 – 0706.

♦London 223 – ♦Blackpool 39 – Burnley 12 – ♦Leeds 46 – ♦Manchester 13 – ♦Liverpool 39.

Old Mill, Springwood St., off Carr St., BL0 9DS, ✆ 822991, Fax 822291, – . AE VISA.
M 6.95/11.95 **t.** and a la carte 3.75 – **36 rm** 28.50/59.50 **t.** – SB (weekends only) 63.50 **st.**

X **Village,** 16 Market Pl., BL0 9HT, ✆ 825070 – . VISA
closed Sunday and Monday – **M** (booking essential) (dinner only) 25.00 **st.**

RAMSGATE Kent 404 Y 30 – pop. 36 678 – ECD : Thursday – 0843 Thanet.

See : St. Augustine's Abbey Church (interior★).

Envir. : Minster-in-Thanet (abbey : remains★ 7C-12C) W : 4 ½ m. – Birchington-on-Sea : in Quex Park (Powell-Cotton Museum★ of African and Asian natural history and ethnology, *AC*) NW : 9 m.

St Augustines, Cottington Rd ✆ 590333.

Shipping connections with the Continent : to France (Dunkerque) (Sally Line) (2 h 30 mn).

Argyle Centre, Queen St. ✆ 591086 – Ferry Terminal ✆ 589830 (summer only).

♦London 77 – ♦Dover 19 – Maidstone 45 – Margate 4.5.

Marina Resort, Harbour Par., CT11 9DS, ✆ 588276, Fax 586866, ≤, – rest – 100. AE VISA
M (bar lunch Monday to Saturday)/dinner 14.50 **t.** and a la carte – **59 rm** 65.00/85.00 **t.** – SB (weekends only) 76.00 **st.**

Savoy, 43 Grange Rd, CT11 9NA, ✆ 592637, Fax 851420 – . AE VISA.
M 7.50 **st.** (lunch) and a la carte 9.00/17.00 **st.** 3.90 – **26 rm** 25.00/48.00 **st.**

Abbeygail without rest., 17 Penshurst Rd, East Cliff, CT11 8EG, ✆ 594154 –
11 rm 11.00/22.00 **s.**

at Minster-in-Thanet W : 5½ m. by A 253 on B 2048 – ✉ Ramsgate – 0843 Thanet :

XX Old Oak Cottage, 53 High St., CT12 4BT, ✆ 821229, – .

FIAT Wilson Rd ✆ 593465
FORD Boundary Rd ✆ 593784
RENAULT Margate Rd ✆ 592629
ROVER Grange Rd ✆ 583541
VAUXHALL West Cliff Rd ✆ 593877
ATS 82-84 Bellevue Rd ✆ 595829

RASKELF North Yorks. – see Easingwold.

En saison, *surtout dans les stations fréquentées, il est prudent de retenir à l'avance.*
Cependant, si vous ne pouvez pas occuper la chambre que vous avez retenue, prévenez immédiatement l'hôtelier.
Si vous écrivez à un hôtel à l'étranger, joignez à votre lettre un coupon-réponse international (disponible dans les bureaux de poste).

RAVENSTONEDALE Cumbria 402 M 20 – pop. 501 – ECD : Thursday – ✉ Kirkby Stephen – ☎ 058 73 Newbiggin-on-Lune.

♦London 280 – ♦Carlisle 43 – Kendal 19 – Kirkby Stephen 5.

- **Black Swan,** CA17 4NG, ☎ 204, « Attractive country inn », – rest ☎ P. AE VISA
  M 16.00 **t.** (dinner) and a la carte 4.50 – **14 rm** 36.50/60.00 **t.** – SB (October-May) (weekends only) 82.00 **st.**
- **Fat Lamb,** Crossbank, Fell End, CA17 4LL, SE : 1¾ m. on A 683 ☎ 242, <, – P
  M 13.50 **t.** and a la carte 2.60 – **12 rm** 29.50/46.00 **t.** – SB 67.00/73.00 **st.**

READING Berks. 403 404 Q 29 – pop. 194 727 – ☎ 0734.

Envir. : Stratfield Saye Park★ *AC*, S : 7 m. by A 33 X – Mapledurham House★ *AC*, NW : 3½ m. by A 329 X.

18 Calcot Park, Calcot ☎ 427124.

Old Town Hall, ☎ 566226.

♦London 43 – ♦Brighton 79 – ♦Bristol 78 – Croydon 47 – Luton 62 – ♦Oxford 28 – ♦Portsmouth 67 – ♦Southampton 46.

Plan opposite

- **Ramada,** Oxford Rd, RG1 7RH, ☎ 586222, Telex 847785, Fax 597842, – rm ☎ P – 220. AE VISA. Z i
  M 12.75/27.50 **t.** and a la carte – 7.95 – **195 rm** 82.00/102.00 **t.**, **1 suite** 180.00 **t.** – SB (weekends only) 90.00/100.00 **st.**
- **Caversham** (Q.M.H.), Caversham Bridge, Richfield Av., RG1 8BD, ☎ 391818, Telex 846933, Fax 391665, <, « Thames-side setting », – rm ☎ P – 120. AE VISA X e
  M 25.00/35.00 **st.** and a la carte 5.65 – 8.25 – **110 rm** -/103.00 **st.**, **4 suites** 190.00/195.00 **st.** – SB (weekends only) 116.00 **st.**
- **Post House** (T.H.F), 500 Basingstoke Rd, RG2 0SL, S : 2½ m. on A 33 ☎ 875485, Telex 849160, Fax 311958, – rm ☎ P – 100. AE VISA X a
  M *(closed Saturday lunch)* 11.95/16.50 **st.** and a la carte 3.95 – 7.60 – **143 rm** 85.00/95.00 **st.**
- **Ship,** 4-8 Duke St., RG1 4RY, ☎ 583455, Fax 504450 – ☎ P – 40. AE VISA.
  M *(closed Saturday lunch and Bank Holidays)* 14.00 **t.** and a la carte 4.50 – **31 rm** 82.00/95.00 **t.** – SB (weekends only) 105.00/120.00 **st.** Z e
- **Rainbow Corner,** 132-138 Cavoisham Rd, RG1 8AY, ☎ 588140, Fax 586500 – ☎ P. AE VISA. X u
  M *(closed Sunday)* (dinner only) 19.50 **t.** and a la carte 5.95 – **22 rm** 59.00/74.00 **t.** – SB (weekends only) 84.70/95.70 **st.**
- **Travelodge** without rest, 387 Basingstoke Rd, RG2 0JE, S : 2 m. on A 33 ☎ 750618, Reservations (Toll free) 0800 850950 – P. AE VISA. X c
  36 rm 24.00/29.50 **t.**
- **George** (B.C.B.), King St., RG1 2HE, ☎ 573445 – ☎. AE VISA. Z c
  M 8.00/15.00 **st.** – **68 rm** 59.50/70.00 **st.**

at Sindlesham SE : 5 m. by A 329 on B 3030 – X – ✉ Wokingham – ☎ 0734 Reading :

- **Reading Moat House** (Q.M.H.), Mill Lane, RG11 5DF, NW : ½ m. via Mole Rd ☎ 351035, Telex 846360, Fax 666530, – rest ☎ P – 70. AE VISA
  M 16.00/17.00 **st.** and a la carte 4.50 – 7.00 – **92 rm** 97.00/104.00 **st.**, **4 suites** 120.00/150.00 **st.** – SB (weekends only) 84.00/90.00 **st.**

at Shinfield S : 4¼ m. on A 327 – X – ✉ ☎ 0734 Reading :

- XXX ✿✿ **L'Ortolan** (Burton-Race), The Old Vicarage, Church Lane, RG2 9BY, ☎ 883783, Fax 885391, French rest., – P. AE VISA
  closed Sunday dinner, Monday, last 2 weeks February and last 2 weeks August – **M** 27.00/50.00 **t.**
  Spec. Lasagne de homard à l'huile de truffe, Pigeonneau soubise au coulis de cresson, Assiette chocolatière.

at Burghfield SW : 5 m. by A 4 – X – ✉ ☎ 0734 Reading :

- XX **Knight's Farm,** Berrys Lane, RG3 3XE, NE : 2 m. ☎ 572366, Fax 566726, – P. AE VISA
  closed Saturday lunch and Sunday – **M** 15.50/22.50 **t.**

BMW Kings Meadow Rd ☎ 500100
CITROEN 9 Eaton Pl., Chatham St. ☎ 582521
FORD Bath Rd ☎ 412021
FORD 160 Basingstoke Rd ☎ 312550
JAGUAR 38 Portman Rd ☎ 585011/875151
PEUGEOT-TALBOT Christchurch Rd ☎ 875242
RENAULT Chatham St. ☎ 583322
RENAULT Wokingham Rd ☎ 669456
ROVER, FREIGHT-ROVER, LEYLAND, RENAULT Station Rd, Theale ☎ 323383
TOYOTA 569-575 Basingstoke Rd ☎ 871278
VOLVO 406-412 London Rd ☎ 67321
VW-AUDI Erleigh Rd ☎ 666111/861176
VW-AUDI Oxford Rd ☎ 418181

ATS Basingstoke Rd ☎ 580651/2

Europe

Si le nom d'un hôtel figure en petits caractères,
demandez à l'arrivée
les conditions à l'hôtelier.

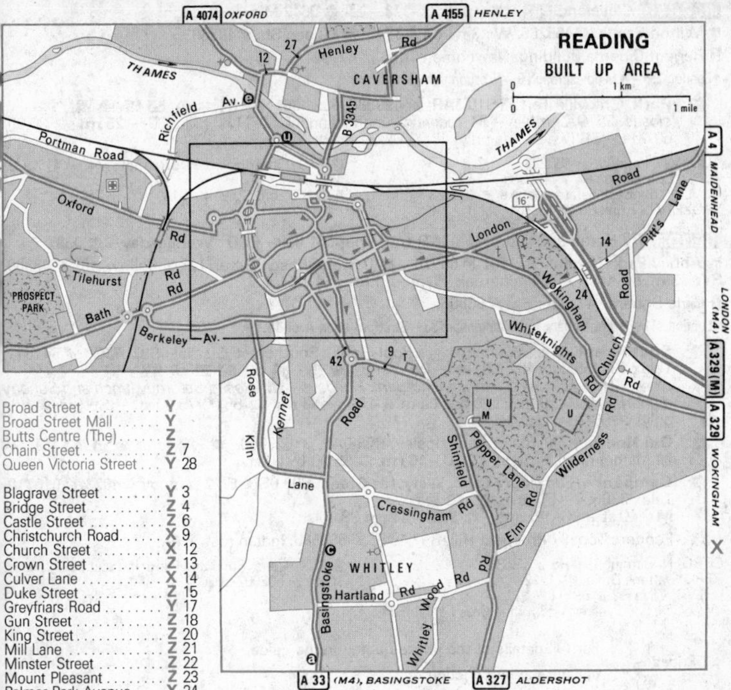

READING
BUILT UP AREA

Broad Street . . . . Y
Broad Street Mall . . . . . . Y
Butts Centre (The) . . . . . . Z
Chain Street . . . . Z 7
Queen Victoria Street . . . Y 28

Blagrave Street . . . . Y 3
Bridge Street . . . . Z 4
Castle Street . . . . Z 6
Christchurch Road . . . . . . X 9
Church Street . . . . X 12
Crown Street . . . . Z 13
Culver Lane . . . . X 14
Duke Street . . . . Z 15
Greyfriars Road . . . . Y 17
Gun Street . . . . Z 18
King Street . . . . Z 20
Mill Lane . . . . Z 21
Minster Street . . . . Z 22
Mount Pleasant . . . . Z 23
Palmer Park Avenue . . . . X 24
Prospect Street . . . . X 27
St. Mary's Butts . . . . Z 29
Station Hill . . . . Y 30
Station Road . . . . Y 31
Tilehurst Road . . . . Z 33
Tudor Road . . . . Y 34
Valpy Street . . . . Y 37
Watlington Street . . . . Z 40
West Street . . . . Y 41
Whitley Street . . . . X 42

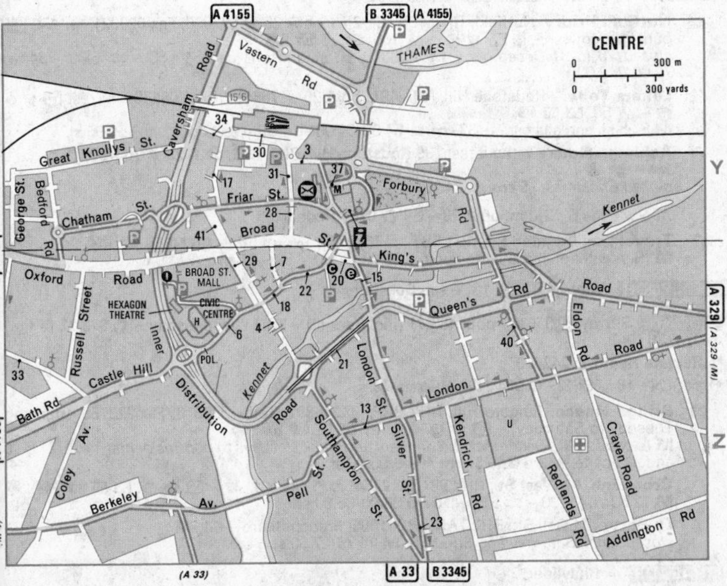

CENTRE

REDCAR Cleveland 402 Q 20 – pop. 35 373 – ✉ ☎ 0642 Middlesbrough.

Wilton Castle ☏ 465265, W : 3 m. on A 174 – Queen St. ☏ 483693.

Regent Cinema Building, Newcomen Terr. ☏ 471921.

♦London 255 – ♦Middlesbrough 9 – Scarborough 43.

- **Park,** Granville Terr., TS10 3AR, ☏ 490888, Fax 486147 – TV ☎ P. AE VISA.
  closed 25 December – **M** (carving lunch)/dinner 6.50/11.60 **t.** 3.30 – **25 rm** 30.00/60.00 **t.** – SB (weekends only) 48.00/62.00 **st.**

AUDI-VW Park Av. ☏ 488222
FORD Corporation Rd ☏ 490909
ROVER Longbeck Estate, Marske ☏ 480823
VAUXHALL Trunk Rd ☏ 486161
ATS Limerick rd, Dormanstown ☏ 477100/477163
ATS 162 Lord St. ☏ 484013

REDDITCH Heref. and Worc. 403 404 O 27 – pop. 61 639 – ECD : Wednesday – ☎ 0527.

Abbey Park, Dagnell End Rd ☏ 63918 – Lower Grinsty, Green Lane, Callow Hill ☏ 43309 SW : 3 m. by A 441 – Pitcheroak, Plymouth Rd ☏ 41054.

Civic Square, Alcester St. ☏ 60806.

♦London 111 – ♦Birmingham 15 – Cheltenham 33 – Stratford-upon-Avon 15.

- **Southcrest** (Best Western) , Pool Bank, Southcrest District, B97 4JG, ☏ 541511, Telex 338455, Fax 402600, – rest TV ☎ P – 60. AE VISA
  closed 24 December-2 January and Bank Holidays – **M** *(closed Saturday lunch and Sunday dinner)* 10.50/13.00 **st.** and a la carte 4.50 – **58 rm** 65.00/75.00 **st.** – SB (weekends only) 68.00/78.00 **st.**
- **Old Rectory** , Ipsley Lane, Ipsley, B98 0AP, ☏ 523000, – rest ☎ P. VISA.
  M (dinner only) 14.50 **st.** 3.80 – **10 rm** 35.00/69.00 **st.**
- **Campanile,** Far Moore Lane, Winyates Green, B98 0SD, E : 2½ m. by A 4023 ☏ 510710, Telex 339608 – TV ☎ P. VISA
  M 9.40 **st.** and a la carte – 3.95 – **47 rm** 33.00 **st.**
- Peppers Too, 37 Prospect Hill, B97 4BS, ☏ 584580, Indian rest. – P.

CITROEN Birmingham Rd ☏ 63636
FORD Battens Drive ☏ 21212
VOLVO Clive Rd ☏ 69111
VW-AUDI 530 Evesham Rd, Crabe Cross ☏ 544554
ATS Pipers Rd, Park Farm Ind Est., Park Farm South ☏ 502002/502027

Prices	For full details of the prices quoted in the guide, consult the introduction.

REDHILL Surrey 404 T 30 – pop. 48 241 (inc. Reigate) – ECD : Wednesday – ☎ 0737.

Pendleton Rd ☏ 244626.

♦London 22 – ♦Brighton 31 – Guildford 20 – Maidstone 34.

- **Nutfield Priory,** Nutfield, RH1 4EN, E : 2 m. on A 25 ☏ 822066, Fax 823321, ←, , , park, , squash – TV ☎ P – 100. AE VISA.
  closed 26 to 31 December – **M** 15.50/16.50 **st.** and a la carte 4.50 – 5.00 – **34 rm** 72.00/242.00.
- **Lakers Toby,** 2 Redstone Hill, RH1 4BL, on A 25 ☏ 768434, Fax 768828 – rest TV ☎ P – 50. AE VISA.
  M 6.95 **st.** and a la carte – **37 rm** 54.00/64.00 **st.** – SB (weekends only) 50.90 **st.**
- **Ashleigh House** without rest., 39 Redstone Hill, RH1 4BG, on A 25 ☏ 764763, heated, – P.
  closed Christmas – **9 rm** 24.25/48.50 **t.**

at Salfords S : 2½ m. on A 23 – ✉ ☎ 0737 Redhill :

- **Travel Inn,** Brighton Rd, RH1 5BT, ☏ 767277 – rm TV P. AE VISA.
  M (Beefeater grill) a la carte approx. 12.25 **t.** – 4.50 – **21 rm** -/27.50 **t.**

REDLYNCH Wilts. 403 404 O 31 – see Salisbury.

REIGATE Surrey 404 T 30 – pop. 48 241 (inc. Redhill) – ECD : Wednesday – ☎ 073 72 (5 fig.) or 0737 (6 fig.).

Reigate Heath ☏ 242610.

♦London 26 – ♦Brighton 33 – Guildford 20 – Maidstone 38.

- **Bridge House,** Reigate Hill, RH2 9RP, ☏ 246801, Telex 268810, Fax 223756, (dancing Tuesday to Saturday) – TV ☎ P – 40. AE VISA.
  M *(closed 26-27 December, 1-2 January and Bank Holidays to non-residents)* 14.75/21.50 **t.** and a la carte – 6.50 – **37 rm** 40.00/95.00 **st.**
- **Cranleigh,** 41 West St., RH2 9BL, ☏ 223417, heated, – TV ☎ P. AE VISA.
  M 12.50 **st.** 4.00 – 3.50 – **10 rm** 38.00/65.00 **st.**
- **La Barbe,** 71 Bell St., RH2 7AN, ☏ 241966, French Bistro – VISA
  closed lunch Saturday and Sunday – **M** 14.75/27.50 **st.** 5.00.

RHAEADR = Rhayader.

RHAYADER **(RHAEADR)** Powys 403 J 27 – pop. 1 411 – ☎ 0597.

ℹ The Old Swan, West St. ✆ 810591.

◆London 180 – Brecon 34 – Hereford 46 – Shrewsbury 60.

- **Elan Valley,** Elan Valley, LD6 5HN, SW : 2½ m. on B 4518 ✆ 810448, – Ⓟ. VISA
  M *(closed Christmas Day)* (bar lunch)/dinner 15.00 **st.** and a la carte 3.00 – **10 rm** 25.00/45.00 **st.** – SB (October-April) 48.00/55.00 **st.**
- **Elan,** West St., LD6 5AF, ✆ 810373 – TV Ⓟ. VISA
  M *(closed dinner Monday and Sunday to non-residents)* (bar lunch Monday to Saturday)/ dinner 17.00 **t.** 4.50 – **11 rm** 17.50/46.00 **t.** – SB 58.00/60.00 **st.**

RHOSCOLYN Gwynedd 402 403 G 24 – pop. 543 – ✉ Holyhead – ☎ 0407 Trearddur Bay.

◆London 269 – Bangor 25 – Caernarfon 30 – Holyhead 5.5.

- **Old Rectory** ⛰, LL65 2DQ, ✆ 860214, ≤ – rest TV Ⓟ. VISA
  closed January and December – **M** 11.00 **st.** 3.95 – **5 rm** 21.50/41.00 **st.** – SB 60.00/ 63.00 **st.**

RHOSMAEN Dyfed 403 I 28 – see Llandeilo.

RHOS-ON-SEA **(LLANDRILLO-YN-RHOS)** Clwyd 402 403 I 24 – see Colwyn Bay.

RHUTHUN = Ruthin.

RHYDAMAN = Ammanford.

RHYDGALED **(CHANCERY)** Clwyd 403 H 26 – see Aberystwyth (Dyfed).

RICHMOND North Yorks. 402 O 20 – pop. 7 596 – ECD : Wednesday – ☎ 0748.

See : Castle★ (Norman ruins) *AC* – Georgian Theatre★.

Envir. : Bolton Castle★ (15C) *AC*, ≤★, SW : 13 m.

⛳18 Bend Hagg ✆ 2457 – ⛳18 Catterick Garrison, Leyburn Rd ✆ 833268, S : 3 m.

ℹ Friary Gardens, Victoria Rd ✆ 850252.

◆London 243 – ◆Leeds 53 – ◆Middlesbrough 26 – ◆Newcastle-upon-Tyne 44.

- **Howe Villa** ⛰, Whitcliffe Mill, DL10 4TJ, W : ½ m. by A 6108 ✆ 850055, ≤, – rest TV Ⓟ.
  Mid March-November – **M** (dinner only) 18.00 **t.** – **4 rm** 40.00/55.00 **t.**
- **Frenchgate,** 59-61 Frenchgate, DL10 7AE, ✆ 2087, – TV ☎ Ⓟ. AE VISA
  closed mid December-mid February – **M** *(closed Sunday)* (bar lunch)/dinner 10.00 **t.** and a la carte 1.60 – **13 rm** 24.50/52.00 **t.** – SB (except mid May-September) 56.00/62.00 **st.**
- **Whashton Springs Farm** ⛰, DL11 7JS, NW : 3½ m. by Ravensworth rd ✆ 2884, « Working farm », – TV ☎ Ⓟ.
  closed Christmas-New Year – **M** (by arrangement) 10.00 **st.** 3.80 – **8 rm** 25.00/ 36.00 **st.**

at Kirby Hill NW : 4½ m. by Ravensworth rd – ✉ ☎ 0748 Richmond :

- **Shoulder of Mutton Inn,** DL11 7JH, ✆ 2772 – TV Ⓟ
  M *(closed Sunday and Monday)* (dinner only) a la carte 9.30/10.30 **t.** 4.00 – **5 rm** 15.50/37.00 **t.**

ATS Reeth Rd ✆ 4182/3

RIDGEWAY Derbs. – see Sheffield (South Yorks.).

RINGWOOD Hants. 403 404 O 31 – pop. 10 941 – ECD : Monday and Thursday – ☎ 042 54 (4 and 5 fig.) or 0425 (6 fig.).

⛳9 Ringwood ✆ 042 53 (Burley) 2431, NE : 4 m.

ℹ The Furlong ✆ 470896 (summer only).

◆London 102 – Bournemouth 11 – Salisbury 17 – ◆Southampton 20.

- **Moortown Lodge,** 244 Christchurch Rd, BH24 3AS, ✆ 471404 – TV ☎ Ⓟ. VISA.
  closed 24 December-14 January – **M** *(closed Sunday)* (dinner only) 15.00 **t.** and a la carte 3.95 – **6 rm** 29.00/50.00 **t.** – SB 70.00/100.00 **st.**

at Avon S : 4 m. on B 3347 – ✉ Christchurch – ☎ 0425 Bransgore :

- **Tyrrells Ford** ⛰, BH23 7BH, ✆ 72646, Fax 72262, , park – TV ☎ Ⓟ – 25. VISA.
  M 14.95/16.95 **t.** and a la carte 4.50 – **16 rm** 45.00/90.00 **t.** – SB 80.00/100.00 **st.**

at St Leonards (Dorset) SW : 3 m. on A 31 – ✉ ☎ 0425 Ringwood :

- **St. Leonards** (Lansbury), 185 Ringwood Rd, BH24 2NP, ✆ 471220, Telex 418215, Fax 480274, – rm TV ☎ Ⓟ. AE VISA.
  M a la carte 11.90/17.10 **t.** – **33 rm** 63.00/75.00 **t.** – SB (weekends only) 72.00 **st.**

FIAT Salisbury Rd ✆ 476111 FORD Christchurch Rd ✆ 470707

RIPLEY Surrey 404 S 30 – pop. 1 903 – ECD : Wednesday – 0483 Guildford.

♦London 28 – Guildford 6.

XXX **Michels',** 13 High St., GU23 6AQ, 224777, – VISA
closed Saturday lunch, Sunday dinner, Monday and 25 December – **M** 20.00/30.00 **t** 4.00.

ATS Meadow Rd 747478

RIPON North Yorks. 402 P 21 – pop. 13 036 – ECD : Wednesday – 0765.

See : Cathedral★ (12C-15C).

Envir. : Fountains Abbey★★★ (ruins 12C-13C, floodlit in summer) – Studley Royal Gardens★★ and Fountains Hall★ (17C) *AC*, SW : 3 m. – Newby Hall★ (18C) *AC* (the tapestry room★★ and gardens★ *AC*) SE : 3½ m.

Palace Rd 3640, N : 1 m. on A 6108.

Minster Rd 4625 (summer only).

♦London 222 – ♦Leeds 26 – ♦Middlesbrough 35 – York 23.

Ripon Spa (Best Western), Park St., HG4 2BU, 2172, Telex 57780, Fax 690770, – VISA
M 14.00/20.00 **t.** – **40 rm** 53.00/80.00 **t.** – SB 88.00/104.00 **st.**

Crescent Lodge without rest., 42 North St., HG4 1EN, 2331 – .
closed Christmas and New Year – **12 rm** 14.00/34.00 **t.**

FORD 30 North St. 2324
ROVER Blossom Gate 707074
VOLVO Palace Rd 2461
ATS Dallamires Lane 701579/701570

RIVENHALL END Essex 404 V-W 28 – see Witham.

ROADE Northants. – pop. 2 703 – 0604.

♦London 66 – ♦Coventry 36 – Northampton 5.5.

X **Roadhouse,** 16 High St., NN7 2NW, 863372 – . VISA
closed Saturday lunch, Sunday and Monday – **M** 12.00 **st.** (lunch) and a la carte 14.75/19.00 **st.** 4.00.

ROBERTSBRIDGE East Sussex 404 V 31 – 0580.

♦London 49 – ♦Brighton 39 – Folkestone 44 – Maidstone 24.

X Bough House, 43 High St., TN32 5AL, 880440 –.

ROCHESTER Kent 404 V 29 – pop. 23 840 – ECD : Wednesday – ✉ Chatham – 0634 Medway.

See : Castle★, ★★ (142 steps) *AC* – Cathedral★ (interior★★) – Eastgate House★ (1590) – Fort Pitt Hill ★.

Envir. : Cobham Hall (Gilt Hall★) *AC*, W : 4 m.

Deangate Ridge Hoo 251180.

Eastgate Cottage, High St. 43666.

♦London 30 – ♦Dover 45 – Maidstone 8 – Margate 46.

Bridgewood Manor, Maidstone Rd, ME5 9AX, SE : 3 m. by A 2 on A 229 201333, Telex 965864, Fax 201330, , – rest – 150. VISA
M 14.00/17.50 **t.** and a la carte 4.00 – **94 rm** 70.00/135.00 **t.**, **4 suites** 120.00 **t.**

Crest (T.H.F.), Maidstone Rd, ME5 9SF, SE : 2 ½ m. by A 2 on A 229 687111, Telex 965933, Fax 684512, , – rm rest – 110. VISA.
M 13.50/16.50 **t.** and a la carte 5.50 – 7.95 – **105 rm** 79.00/92.00 **st.** – SB (weekends only) 96.00/108.00 **st.**

FIAT, LANCIA Pier Rd, Gillingham 52333
PEUGEOT-TALBOT High St. 42231
RELIANT Gundulph Rd, Chatham 41279
RENAULT Hoath Lane, Wigmore 31688
ROVER, JAGUAR 16 Medway St., Chatham 41122
TOYOTA High St. 407788
VAUXHALL Station Rd, Strood 721021
VOLVO Wood St., Gillingham 402777

ROCHFORD Essex 404 W 29 – pop. 13 426 – ECD : Wednesday – ✉ 0702 Southend-on-Sea.

♦London 43 – Southend-on-Sea 4.

Hotel Renouf, Bradley Way, SS4 1BU, 541334, Telex 995158, Fax 549563, – rest . VISA
closed 27 to 30 December – **M** *(closed lunch Tuesday to Friday)* 19.50 **st.** and a la carte 4.40 – **24 rm** 56.00/90.00 **st.**

XX **Renouf's,** 1 South St., SS4 1BL, 544393 – VISA
closed Saturday lunch, Sunday, Monday, first 3 weeks January and last week June-first week July – **M** 19.50 **st.** (dinner) and a la carte 16.15/24.80 **st.** 4.60.

ROCK Cornwall 403 F 32 – ECD : Wednesday – ✉ Wadebridge – ☎ 0208 Bodmin.

18, 18 St. Enodoc ☎ 3216.

◆London 288 – Newquay 22 – ◆Plymouth 45 – Truro 30.

St. Enodoc ⑤, PL27 6LA, ☎ 863394, Fax 863394, ←, squash – ⇔ rest TV ☎ P. AE VISA
M (bar lunch Monday to Saturday)/dinner 17.05 **t.** and a la carte – **13 rm** 40.80/81.60 **t.** – SB 91.85/98.50 **st.**

ROCKBOURNE Hants. 403 404 O 31 – see Fordingbridge.

ROCK FERRY Merseyside – ✉ Wirral – ☎ 051 Liverpool.

◆London 212 – Chester 15 – ◆Liverpool 5.

Yew Tree, 58 Rock Lane West, L42 4PA, ☎ 645 4112 – TV P. VISA.
M 8.50 **st.** 2.50 – **14 rm** 19.50/40.00 **st.**

RODBOROUGH Glos. – see Stroud.

ROEWEN Gwynedd – see Conwy.

ROGATE West Sussex 404 R 30 – pop. 1 459 – ✉ Petersfield (Hants.) – ☎ 073 080 (from May : 0730).

◆London 63 – ◆Brighton 42 – Guildford 29 – ◆Portsmouth 23 – ◆Southampton 36.

Mizzards Farm ⑤ without rest., GU31 5HS, SW : 1 m. by Harting Rd ☎ 821656, ←, « 17C farmhouse », heated, – ⇔ TV P.
closed Christmas – **3 rm** 30.00/40.00 **st.**

We suggest:
For a successful tour, that you prepare it in advance.
Michelin maps and guides will give you much useful information on route planning, places of interest, accommodation, prices etc.

ROLLESTON-ON-DOVE Staffs. 402 403 404 P 25 – see Burton-upon-Trent.

ROMALDKIRK Durham 402 N 20 – see Barnard Castle.

ROMSEY Hants. 403 404 P 31 – pop. 14 818 – ECD : Wednesday – ☎ 0794.

See : Abbey Church★ (12C-13C).

Envir. : Broadlands House★ S : 1 m.

18 Dunwood Manor, Shootash Hill ☎ 0794 (Lockerley) 40549, SE : 4 m. on A 27 – 18 Nursling ☎ 0703 (Southampton) 732218.

ℹ Bus Station car park, Broadwater Rd ☎ 512987 (summer only).

◆London 82 – Bournemouth 28 – Salisbury 16 – ◆Southampton 8 – Winchester 10.

White Horse (T.H.F.), Market Pl., SO51 8ZJ, ☎ 512431, Fax 517485 – ⇔ rm TV ☎ P. AE ① VISA
M 9.00/14.50 **st.** and a la carte 4.35 – 7.00 – **33 rm** 65.00/80.00 **st.**

XXX **Old Manor House,** 21 Palmerston St., SO51 8GF, ☎ 517353, « Timbered 16C house » – ⇔ P. VISA
closed Sunday dinner, Monday, last 3 weeks August and 24 to 31 December – **M** 21.50/33.00 **t.** 4.00.

at Ower SW : 3¼ m. on A 31 – ✉ Romsey – ☎ 0703 Southampton :

New Forest Heathlands, Romsey Rd, SO51 6ZJ, on A 31 ☎ 814333, Fax 812123, – TV ☎ P – 200. AE ① VISA
M *(closed Saturday lunch)* 8.50/15.25 **t.** and a la carte 4.50 – **50 rm** 40.00/92.00 **t.** – SB 80.00/98.00 **st.**

CITROEN Industrial Est., Greatbridge ☎ 830100
PEUGEOT 45-55 Winchester Hill ☎ 513185
ROVER Winchester Rd ☎ 512850
VAUXHALL,BEDFORD 24 Middlebridge St. ☎ 513806

ROSEDALE ABBEY North Yorks. 402 R 20 – ✉ Pickering – ☎ 075 15 Lastingham.

◆London 247 – ◆Middlesbrough 27 – Scarborough 25 – York 36.

Milburn Arms, YO18 8RA, ☎ 312, Fax 312, – ⇔ rest TV ☎ P. VISA
closed Christmas Day – **M** (bar lunch)/dinner 18.00 **t.** and a la carte 3.00 – **11 rm** 42.00/70.00 **t.** – SB (except Bank Holidays) 76.00/95.00 **st.**

White Horse Farm, YO18 8SE, ☎ 239 – TV P. AE ① VISA
closed 24 and 25 December – **M** (dinner only and Sunday lunch)/dinner 16.00/17.00 **t.** 4.10 – **15 rm** 45.00/74.00 **t.** – SB 79.00/93.00 **t.**

Sevenford House ⑤ without rest., Thorgill, YO18 8SE, NW : ¾ m. ☎ 283, – ⇔ TV P.
4 rm 20.00/28.00 **st.**

ROSSETT (YR ORSEDD) Clwyd 402 403 L 24 – pop. 2 323 – ☎ 0244.

◆London 203 – Chester 8 – Shrewsbury 39.

Llyndir Hall ⛰, Llyndir Lane, LL12 0AY, NE : ¾ m. by B 5445 ☏ 571648, « Strawberry Gothic country house », ▣, ⛰ – ⇹ rest ▣ ☎ Ⓟ – 🏰 160. ▣ AE ⓓ VISA. ⚡
M 11.50/14.75 **t.** and a la carte – ☐ 4.60 – **37 rm** 65.00/120.00 **t.** – SB (weekends only) 98.00 **st.**

ROSSINGTON South Yorks. 402 403 404 Q 23 – see Doncaster.

ROSS-ON-WYE Heref. and Worc. 403 404 M 28 – pop. 8 281 – ECD : Wednesday – ☎ 0989.

Envir. : Goodrich (Castle★ : ruins 12C-14C) *AC*, SW : 3½ m.

⛳ Ross-on-Wye, Two Park, Gorsley ☏ 098 982 (Gorsley) 267.

ℹ 20 Broad St. ☏ 62768.

◆London 118 – Gloucester 15 – Hereford 15 – Newport 35.

Royal (T.H.F.), Palace Pound, Royal Par., HR9 5HZ, ☏ 65105, Fax 768058, ≤, ⛰ – ⇹ rm ▣ ☎ Ⓟ – 🏰 80. ▣ AE ⓓ VISA
M (dinner only and Sunday lunch)/dinner 16.95 **st.** and a la carte ⅟ 4.35 – ☐ 7.00 – **40 rm** 69.00/89.00 **st.** – SB 94.00/110.00 **st.**

Chasedale, Walford Rd, HR9 5PQ, ☏ 62423, ⛰ – ▣ ☎ Ⓟ. ▣ ⓓ VISA
M (dinner only and Sunday lunch)/dinner 9.75/10.75 **st.** and a la carte ⅟ 3.30 – **11 rm** ☐ 31.50/50.00 **st.** – SB (except Christmas) 63.00/70.00 **st.**

Woodlands ⛰ without rest., HR9 6QJ, W : 2 m. by A 49 on Hoarwithy Rd ☏ 62972, ≤, ⛰, park, ✂ – ⇹ ▣ Ⓟ. ⚡
closed January and December – **3 rm** ☐ 25.00/36.00 **st.**

Sunnymount ⛰, Ryefield Rd, off Gloucester Rd (A 40), HR9 5LU, ☏ 63880 – Ⓟ. ▣ VISA ⚡
closed 20 December-1 January – **M** 10.50 **st.** ⅟ 3.00 – **7 rm** ☐ 16.00/44.00 **st.** – SB (November-May) (except Bank Holidays) 54.00 **st.**

at Weston-Under-Penyard SE : 2 m. on A 40 – ✉ Ross-On-Wye – ☎ 098 981 Weston-Under-Penyard :

Wharton Lodge, HR9 7JX, SE : 1½ m. on A 40 ☏ 795, Fax 700, ⛰, park – ▣ ☎ Ⓟ. ▣ AE ⓓ VISA. ⚡
closed 27 December-12 January – **M** 16.00/21.50 **t.** and a la carte – **8 rm** ☐ 80.00/120.00 **t.**

at Glewstone SW : 3¼ m. by A 40 – ✉ Ross-on-Wye – ☎ 098 984 Llangarron:

Glewstone Court ⛰, HR9 6AW, ☏ 367, Fax 282, ≤, ⛰ – Ⓟ. ▣ AE VISA
closed 25 and 26 December – **M** (bar lunch Monday to Saturday)/dinner 18.00 **t.** ⅟ 2.50 – **9 rm** ☐ 43.00/68.00 **t.** – SB (except Bank Holidays) 88.00/98.00 **st.**

at Pencraig SW : 3¾ m. on A 40 – ✉ Ross-on-Wye – ☎ 098 984 Llangarron :

Pencraig Court, HR9 6HR, ☏ 84306, ⛰ – Ⓟ. ▣ AE ⓓ VISA. ⚡
April-October – **M** (dinner only) 13.00 ⅟ 3.75 – **11 rm** ☐ 35.00/52.00 **st.** – SB 70.00/80.00 **st.**

at Peterstow W : 2½ m. on A 49 – ✉ Ross-on-Wye – ☎ 098 987 Harewood End :

Pengethley Manor (Best Western) ⛰, HR9 6LL, NW : 1½ m. on A 49 ☏ 211, Fax 238, ≤, « Georgian country manor », ⛱ heated, ⛰, park – ▣ ☎ Ⓟ – 🏰 35. ▣ AE ⓓ VISA
closed Christmas – **M** 13.75/18.50 **st.** and a la carte ⅟ 5.95 – **19 rm** ☐ 60.00/110.00 **st.** **3 suites** 150.00 **st.** – SB 120.00/170.00 **st.**

PEUGEOT-TALBOT High St. ☏ 62447
RENAULT Overross St. ☏ 63666
ROVER Cantilupe Rd ☏ 62400
VW-AUDI Whitchurch ☏ 0600 (Monmouth) 890235
Ⓜ ATS Ind Est., Alton Rd ☏ 64638

ROSTHWAITE Cumbria 402 K 20 – see Keswick.

ROTHAY BRIDGE Cumbria – see Ambleside.

ROTHBURY Northumb. 401 402 O 18 – pop. 1 694 – ECD : Wednesday – ✉ Morpeth – ☎ 0669.

⛳ Old Race Course, S : off B 6342 ☏ 20718.

ℹ National Park Information Centre, Church St. ☏ 20887.

◆London 311 – ◆Edinburgh 84 – ◆Newcastle-upon-Tyne 29.

Orchard, High St., NE65 7TL, ☏ 20684, ⛰ – ▣. ⚡
March and November – **M** (residents only) 11.00 **t.** ⅟ 3.50 – **6 rm** ☐ 19.00/38.00 **t.**

ROTHERHAM South Yorks. 402 403 404 P 23 – pop. 122 374 – ECD : Thursday – ☎ 0709.

⛳ Thrybergh Park ☏ 850466, E : 3 m. – ⛳ Sitwell Park, Shrogs Wood Rd ☏ 541046, E : 2½ m. – ⛳ Grange Park, Upper Wortley Rd ☏ 558884, NW : 3 m. by A 629 – ⛳ Phoenix, Pavilion Lane, Brinsworth ☏ 382624 – ⛳ Abdy Rawmarsh ☏ 872149.

ℹ Central Library, Walker Pl. ☏ 367343.

◆London 166 – ◆Kingston-upon-Hull 61 – ◆Leeds 36 – ◆Sheffield 6.

Rotherham Moat House (Q.M.H.), 102-104 Moorgate Rd, S60 2BG, ℘ 364902, Telex 547810, Fax 368960, – rm rest – 100. **M** (bar lunch Saturday and Bank Holiday Mondays) 6.25/22.20 **t.** and a la carte 4.95 – 5.95 – **81 rm** 58.00/122.00 **st.** – SB (weekends only) 65.00 **st.**

UDI Brampton Rd ℘ 873366
TROEN 106 Barnsley Rd, Goldthorpe ℘ 893864
AT 126 Fitzwilliam Rd ℘ 361666
ORD Sheffield Rd ℘ 860151
ANCIA Wortley Rd ℘ 551155
AZDA West Bawtry Rd, Brinsworth ℘ 364204
EUGEOT-TALBOT 132-138 Fitzwilliam Rd
℘ 382213
OVER Doncaster Rd ℘ 373991

TOYOTA 7-9 Canklow Rd ℘ 820681
VAUXHALL-OPEL 128 Wellgate ℘ 828484
VW Bawtry Rd, Wickersley ℘ 0709 (Wickersley) 543462
VW-AUDI Brampton Rd, Wath ℘ 873366

ATS Eastwood Works, Fitzwilliam Rd ℘ 371556/372391

ROTHERWICK Hants – see Basingstoke.

ROTHLEY Leics. 402 403 404 Q 25 – see Leicester.

ROTTINGDEAN East Sussex 404 T 31 – pop. 10 888 (inc. Saltdean) – ECD : Wednesday – ✉ 0273 Brighton.

London 58 – ◆Brighton 4 – Lewes 9 – Newhaven 5.

Rottingdean Olde Place, High St., BN2 7HE, ℘ 301051 – **M** *(closed Sunday dinner)* 9.95/15.75 **t.** and a la carte 3.50 – **21 rm** 25.00/49.00 **st.** – SB 55.00/65.00 **st.**

Braemar without rest., Steyning Rd, BN2 7GA, ℘ 304263, **15 rm** 13.00/26.00 **t.**

ROUGHAM GREEN Suffolk – see Bury St. Edmunds.

ROUSDON Devon 403 L 31 – see Lyme Regis.

ROWSLEY Derbs. 402 403 404 P 24 – pop. 200 – ECD : Thursday – ✉ Matlock – 0629 Matlock.

London 157 – Derby 23 – ◆Manchester 40 – ◆Nottingham 30.

Peacock, Bakewell Rd, DE4 2EB, ℘ 733518, Fax 732671, « 17C stone house with antiques », – rm **M** 12.30/28.50 **st.** 5.95 – 8.00 – **20 rm** 67.50/80.00 **st.** – SB (weekends only) 79.00/110.00 **st.**

ROWTON Cheshire 402 403 L 24 – see Chester.

ROYAL LEAMINGTON SPA

Parade UV
Regent Street UV
Royal Priors Shopping Centre U
Warwick Street U

Adelaïde Road V
Avenue Road V 2
Bath Street V 3
Beauchamp Avenue U
Beauchamp Hill U 4
Binswood Street U 6
Brandon Parade U 10
Church Hill UV 16
Clarendon Avenue U
Clarendon Place U 18
Dale Street UV
Hamilton Terrace V 21
High Street V 22
Holly Walk U
Kenilworth Road U
Leam Terrace V
Leicester Street U
Lillington Avenue U
Lillington Road U
Lower Avenue V 28
Newbold Terrace V 30
Northumberland Road U 33
Old Warwick Road V
Priory Terrace V 37
Radford Road V
Regent Grove UV 40
Rugby Road U
Russell Terrace V
Spencer Street V 44
Tachbrook Road V 47
Victoria Terrace V 49
Willes Road UV

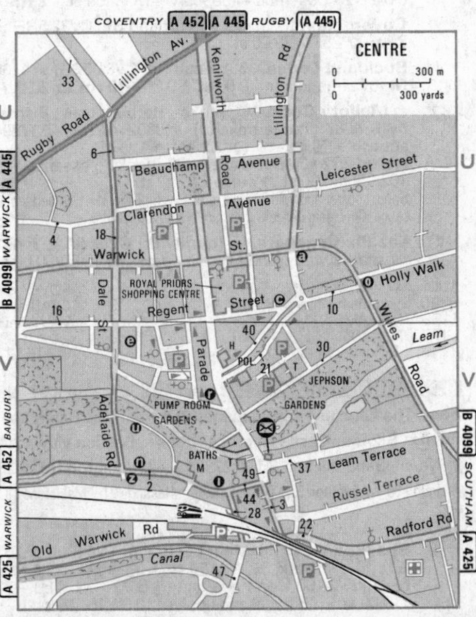

ROYAL LEAMINGTON SPA Warw. 403 404 P 27 – pop. 56552 – ECD : Monday and Thursda – ☎ 0926.

Newbold-Comyn, Newbold Terrace East ☎ 421157, plan of Warwick – Z – Leamington ar Country, Golf Lane, Whitnash ☎ 420298 by A 452 V.

London 99 – Birmingham 23 – Coventry 9 – Warwick 3.

Plan on preceding page

Tuscany, 34 Warwick Pl., CV32 5DE, ☎ 332233, Fax 332232 – rm TV ☎ P. AE VISA
M (lunch by arrangement)/dinner 24.95 **t.** and a la carte 4.95 – 6.00 – **8 rm** 85.00 95.00 **st.** Z

Manor House (T.H.F.), Avenue Rd, CV31 3NJ, ☎ 423251, Fax 425933 – rm TV P – 100. AE VISA V
M *(closed Saturday lunch)* 10.50/15.50 **st.** and a la carte 4.75 – 7.50 – **53 rm** 65.00 80.00 **st.** – SB (except Christmas and New Year) 80.00/100.00 **st.**

Inchfield, 64 Upper Holly Walk, CV32 4JL, ☎ 883777, Fax 330467, – TV ☎ P – 40 AE VISA. U
M 10.25/18.50 **t.** and a la carte 3.75 – 6.50 – **22 rm** 55.00/90.00 **t.**

Garden Court Holiday Inn, Olympus Ave, Tachbrook Park, CV34 6RJ, SW : 1 ½ m. by A 452 ☎ 425522, Fax 881322, – rm rest TV ☎ P – 50. AE VISA
M 10.50/15.50 **st.** and a la carte 5.25 – 6.95 – **98 rm** 52.00/72.00 **st.** Z

Angel, 143 Regent St., CV32 4NZ, ☎ 881296, Fax 881296 – TV ☎ P – 30. U

Lansdowne, 87 Clarendon St., CV32 4PF, ☎ 450505 – TV ☎ P. VISA. U
M (dinner only) 15.95 **t.** 3.85 – **15 rm** 28.95/55.90 **t.** – SB (except Christmas and New Year) 59.90/73.90 **st.**

Eaton Court, 1-3 St. Marks Rd, CV32 6DL, ☎ 885848, Fax 885848, – TV ☎ P
21 rm. plan of Warwick Z

Adams, 22 Avenue Rd, CV31 3PQ, ☎ 450742, Fax 313110, – rm TV ☎ P. AE VISA. V
M *(closed Saturday, Sunday and Bank Holidays)* (bar lunch)/dinner 18.00 **st.** and a la carte 4.80 – **11 rm** 34.00/52.00 **t.**

Abbacourt, 40 Kenilworth Rd, CV32 6JF, ☎ 451755, Fax 311188, – TV ☎ P. AE VISA plan of Warwick Z
M 15.50/18.00 **st.** and a la carte 4.00 – **26 rm** 25.00/65.00 **st.** – SB (weekends only) 55.00 **st.**

Flowerdale House without rest., 58 Warwick New Rd, CV32 6AA, ☎ 426002, – TV P. VISA. plan of Warwick Z
6 rm 21.00/40.00 **s.**

York House, 9 York Rd, CV31 3PR, ☎ 424671 – TV ☎. AE VISA V
closed 23 December-1 January – **M** 12.50 **st.** – **8 rm** 18.00/45.00 **st.**

Coverdale without rest., 8 Portland St., CV32 5HE, ☎ 330400, Fax 833388 – TV ☎. VISA
8 rm 25.00/38.00 **st.** V

Buckland Lodge, 35 Avenue Rd, CV31 3PG, ☎ 423843 – rest TV ☎ P. AE VISA
M (by arrangement) 8.00 **st.** 3.00 – **10 rm** 20.00/40.00 **st.** V

XXX ✿ **Mallory Court** with rm, Harbury Lane, Bishop's Tachbrook, CV33 9QB, S : 2 ¼ m by B 4087 (Tachbrook Rd) ☎ 330214, Telex 317294, Fax 451714, <, , park, squash – TV ☎ P. VISA. plan of Warwick Z
closed 25 to 30 December – **M** (booking essential) 21.00/38.50 **st.** 5.00 – 9.75 – **9 rm** 102.00/180.00 **st.**, **1 suite** 276.00 **st.**
Spec. Lobster and wild salmon terrine with pistachios, Sautéed breast and crisply roasted leg of duckling, Armagnac sauce, Chocolate delice with a mint crème anglaise.

XX **Les Plantagenets,** 15 Dormer Pl., CV32 5AA, ☎ 451792, French rest. – V
closed Saturday lunch and Sunday – **M** 12.50/30.00 **st.** and a la carte 9.85.

AUDI-VW Dormer Pl. ☎ 336511
FORD Sydenham Drive ☎ 314466
JAGUAR Rugby Rd ☎ 833181
MITSUBISHI Wood St. ☎ 424681
RENAULT Russell St. ☎ 421171
ROVER Station Approach ☎ 427156
SAAB Lime Av. ☎ 423221
VAUXHALL-OPEL Old Warwick Rd ☎ 420861

ATS 52-54 Morton St. ☎ 339643/4

ROYAL TUNBRIDGE WELLS Kent 404 U 30 – pop. 57 699 – ECD : Wednesday – ☎ 0892.

See : The Pantiles★ (promenade 18C) B – Town Hall Museum (wood-mosaic articles★) B **M.**

Envir. : Scotney Castle Gardens (trees★, Bastion view★) *AC*, SE : 8 m. by B 2169 A.

Nevill, Bendhall Mill Rd ☎ 27820 A – Langton Rd ☎ 23034 A.

London 36 – Brighton 33 – Folkestone 46 – Hastings 27 – Maidstone 18.

Plan opposite

Spa (Best Western), Mount Ephraim, TN4 8XJ, ☎ 20331, Telex 957188, Fax 510575, <, , , , park, – TV ☎ P – 300. AE VISA A
M 20.00/24.00 **t.** and a la carte 5.00 – 4.50 – **72 rm** 65.00/85.00 **st.**, **4 suites** 95.00 110.00 **st.** – SB (weekends only) 110.00/150.00 **st.**

ROYAL TUNBRIDGE WELLS

:alverley Road	B		Clarence Road	B 8		Mount Ephraim	A 23
ligh Street	B 14		Crescent Road	B 9		Mount Ephraim Road	B 24
/lount Pleasant Road	B 25		Fir Tree Road	A 10		Prospect Road	A 27
'antiles (The)	B 26		Grosvenor Road	B 12		Rusthall Road	A 28
			Hall's Hole Road	A 13		St. John's Road	B 29
;enhall Mill Road	A 3		High Rocks Lane	A 16		Tea Garden Lane	A 30
;ishop's Down	A 4		Hungershall Park Road	A 17		Upper Grosvenor Road	B 31
:alverley Park Gardens	B 7		Lansdowne Road	B 18		Vale Road	B 33
			Lower Green Road	A 20		Victoria Road	B 34
			Major York's Road	A 22		Warwick Park	B 35

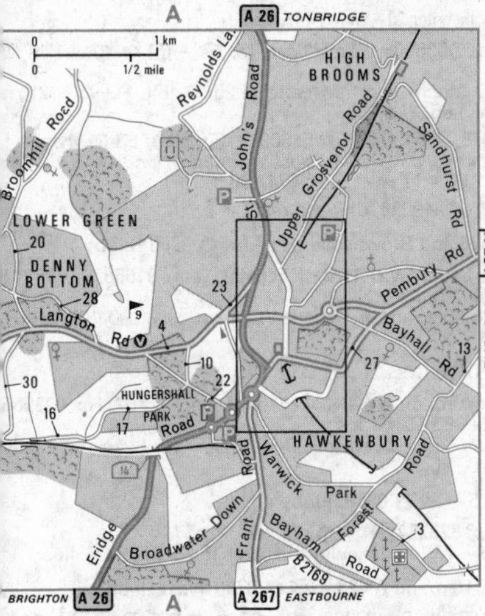

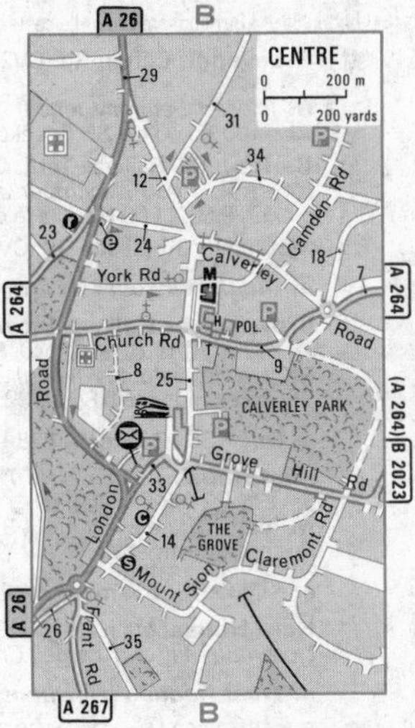

Royal Wells Inn, Mount Ephraim, TN4 8BE, ✆ 511188, Fax 511908 – AE VISA B r
closed 25-26 December and Bank Holiday Mondays – **M** 21.00 **st.** and a la carte 3.80 – **22 rm** 55.00/75.00 **st.** – SB 90.00/95.00 **st.**

Russell, 80 London Rd, TN1 1DZ, ✆ 544833, Telex 95177, Fax 515846 – rm AE VISA B a
M (bar lunch)/dinner 20.00 **t.** 5.50 – 7.00 – **26 rm** 55.00/130.00 **t.**

Cheevers, 56 High St., TN1 1XF, ✆ 545524 – VISA B c
closed Sunday, Monday, 2 weeks Easter, 2 weeks September and 2 weeks Christmas – **M** 21.00 **t.** (dinner) and a la carte 14.85/17.90 **t.** 3.35.

Eglantine, 65 High St., TN1 1XX, ✆ 24957 – AE VISA B s
closed Sunday dinner, Monday and 24 to 30 December – **M** 12.00/18.00 **t.**

Xian, 54 High St., TN1 1XF, ✆ 22930, Chinese rest. – AE VISA B c
closed Sunday, 25 to 27 December and Bank Holidays – **M** 9.50/18.00 **t.** and a la carte 3.50.

at Frant S : 2 ½ m. on A 267 – A – ✉ 0892 Royal Tunbridge Wells :

Old Parsonage without rest., Church Lane, TN3 9DX, ✆ 75773, ≤, –
closed 16 to 30 December – **3 rm** 29.00/39.00 **s.**

at Speldhurst NW : 3 ½ m. by A 26 – A – ✉ Royal Tunbridge Wells – 089 286 Langton :

George and Dragon Inn, Barden Rd, TN3 0NN, ✆ 3125, « 13C inn » – AE VISA
closed Saturday lunch, Sunday dinner and Monday – **M** 9.50/20.75 **t.** and a la carte 3.25.

BMW St. John's Rd ✆ 39355
COLT, RELIANT Grosvenor Rd ✆ 27174
FORD Commercial Rd, Paddock Wood ✆ (089 283) Paddock Wood 6388
LANCIA 319 St. Johns Rd ✆ 511522
RENAULT Langton Rd ✆ 39466

ROYSTON Herts. 404 T 27 – 0763.

◆London 41 – Bedfort 30 – ◆Cambridge 14 – Luton 22.

Chiswick House without rest., Chiswick End, off Whitecroft Rd, Meldreth (Cambs.), SG8 6LZ, N : 4 m. by A 10 ✆ 260242, –
6 rm 32.00/36.00 **t.**

RUAN-HIGH-LANES Cornwall 403 F 33 – see Veryan.

RUCKHALL Heref. and Worc. – see Hereford.

RUGBY Warw. 403 404 Q 26 – pop. 59 039 – ECD : Wednesday – 0788.

Envir. : Stanford-on-Avon (castle 17C : park★ *AC*) NE : 5 m.

Clifton Rd 542306.

Public Library, St. Matthew's St. 71813/53.

◆London 88 – ◆Birmingham 33 – ◆Leicester 21 – Northampton 20 – Warwick 17.

Grosvenor, Clifton Rd, CV21 3QQ, 535686, Fax 541297, – . VISA.
M *(closed Saturday lunch)* 11.95 **t.** (lunch) and a la carte 14.25/31.45 **t.** 3.95 – **21 rm** 55.00/85.00 **t.** – SB (weekends only) 65.00 **st.**

Carlton, 130 Railway Terr., CV21 3HE, 543076, Fax 546091 – . VISA
closed 26 to 30 December and Bank Holidays – **M** *(closed Saturday lunch and Sunday dinner)* 9.00/11.00 **t.** and a la carte 3.80 – **17 rm** 28.00/47.00 **t.**

Mr Chan's, 3-5 Castle St., CV21 2TP, 542326, Chinese rest.

at Old Brownsover N : 2 m. by A 426 and Brownsover Rd – 0788 Rugby :

Brownsover Hall , Brownsover Lane, CV21 1HV, 546100, Telex 31658, Fax 79241 , – – 120. VISA.
M *(closed Saturday lunch)* 10.50/16.50 **t.** and a la carte – **31 rm** 30.00/100.00 **st.** – SB (weekends only) 84.00/92.00 **st.**

at Crick SE : 6 m. on A 428 – 0788 Crick :

Post House (T.H.F.), NN6 7XR, W : ½ m. on A 428 822101, Telex 311107, Fax 823955 , , – rm – 150. VISA
M 16.95 **st.** and a la carte 3.95 – 7.50 – **96 rm** 69.00/89.00 **st.** – SB (weekends only) (except Christmas and New Year) 76.00 **st.**

at Kilsby SE : 6¼ m. by A 428 on A 5 – 0788 Rugby :

Hunt House, Main Rd, CV23 8XR, 823282, – . VISA.
closed Sunday and 1 week Christmas – **M** (dinner only) a la carte 15.75/19.75 **t.** 4.45.

at West Haddon (Northants.) SE : 10 m. on A 428 – 0788 West Haddon :

Pytchley, 23 High St., NN6 7AP, 87426, Fax 87209, – . VISA.
M *(closed Sunday dinner)* 10.95/17.50 **t.** and a la carte 4.50 – **17 rm** 48.00/60.00 **t.**

at Stretton Under Fosse NW : 7 ½ m. by A 426 and B 4112 on A 427 – 0788 Rugby :

Ashton Lodge , CV23 0PJ, N : 1 m. by A 427 on B 4112 832278, – . VISA
M *(closed Sunday dinner, Christmas-New Year and Bank Holidays)* (bar lunch)/dinner a la carte approx. 18.00 **t.** 3.00 – **11 rm** 26.50/60.50 **t.**

CITROEN 50 Albert St. 73671
HONDA Leicester Rd 60333
PEUGEOT-TALBOT Leicester Rd 62731
ATS 73 Bath St. 74705

RUGELEY Staffs. 402 403 404 O 25 – pop. 23 751 – ECD : Wednesday – 0889.

◆London 134 – ◆Birmingham 31 – Derby 29 – ◆Stoke-on-Trent 22.

Travelodge without rest., Western Springs Rd, WS15 2AS, at junction A 51 and A 460 570096, Reservations (Toll free) 0800 850950 – . VISA.
32 rm 24.00/29.50 **t.**

RUNCORN Cheshire 402 403 L 23 – pop. 63 995 – ECD : Wednesday – 092 85 (5 fig.) or 0928 (6 fig.).

Dundalk Rd, Widnes 051 (Liverpool) 424 6230, N : 1 ½ m. – Clifton Rd 574214.

57-61 Church St. 576776 and 569656.

◆London 202 – ◆Liverpool 14 – ◆Manchester 29.

Crest (T.H.F.), Wood Lane, Beechwood, WA7 3HA, SE : ½ m. off junction 12 of M 56 714000, Telex 627426, Fax 714611, , – rm – 450. VISA.
M *(closed Saturday lunch)* 13.50/17.95 **t.** and a la carte – 8.50 – **127 rm** 79.00/104.00 **st** – SB (weekends only) 84.00/98.00 **st.**

FORD Victoria Rd 74333
MAZDA Picow Farm Rd 63099
ROVER Balfour St. 72271
ATS Sandy Lane, Weston Point 567715/6

Europe

Wenn der Name eines Hotels dünn gedruckt ist,
hat uns der Hotelier Preise
und Öffnungszeiten nicht angegeben.

RUSHLAKE GREEN East Sussex 404 U 31 – ✉ Heathfield – ☎ 0435.

London 54 – ◆Brighton 26 – Eastbourne 13.

Stone House ⛰, TN21 9QJ, ☎ 830553, « Part 14C and part Georgian country house, antiques », ⛵, 🌳, park – TV ☎ P
closed 19 December-19 January and last week August – **M** (lunch by arrangement) (residents only)/dinner 23.95 **t.** 🍷 4.00 – **8 rm** ☕ 60.00/160.00 **t.** – SB (weekdays only) (September-June) 118.00 **st.**

RUSPER West Sussex 404 T 30 – pop. 2 678 – ☎ 029 384.

London 30 – ◆Brighton 35 – Horsham 6.

Ghyll Manor (T.H.F.), High St., RH12 4PX, ☎ 871571, Telex 877557, Fax 871419, « Part Elizabethan house », 🏊, heated, 🌳, park, 🎾 – TV ☎ P – 🏢 80. AE VISA
M 17.50/22.00 **st.** and a la carte 🍷 7.65 – ☕ 8.50 – **25 rm** 88.00/130.00 **st.**, **3 suites** 130.00/140.00 **st.**

RUTHIN (RHUTHUN) Clwyd 402 403 K 24 – pop. 4 417 – ECD : Thursday – ☎ 082 42.

See : Church★.

Pwllglas ☎ 2296, S : 2½ m.

Ruthin Craft Centre ☎ 3992.

London 210 – Birkenhead 31 – Chester 23 – Shrewsbury 46.

Ruthin Castle (Best Western) ⛰, Corwen Rd, LL15 2NU, ☎ 2664, Telex 61169, Fax 5978, ≤, « Reconstructed medieval castle », ⛵, 🌳, park – lift TV ☎ P. AE VISA.
M (bar lunch Monday to Saturday)/dinner 13.95 **st.** and a la carte 🍷 4.50 – **58 rm** ☕ 45.00/94.00 **t.** – SB 78.00/98.00 **st.**

Castle, St. Peters Sq., LL15 1AA, ☎ 2479, Fax 4924 – TV ☎ P – 🏢 40. AE VISA
closed 24 December-15 January – **M** *(closed Sunday dinner)* (bar lunch)/dinner 15.50 **t.** 🍷 2.75 – **24 rm** ☕ 30.00/60.00 **t.** – SB 62.50/67.50 **st.**

Llanbedr Hall, Llanbedr Hall Estate, LL15 1YA, NE : 1½ m. by A 494 off B 5429 ☎ 4204 – P. VISA
closed Sunday dinner, Monday and January – **M** 8.25/16.75 **st.** 🍷 3.00.

CITROEN Well St. ☎ 2645 ROVER Llarhaedr ☎ 227/543

Les prix — Pour toutes précisions sur les prix indiqués dans ce guide, reportez-vous à l'introduction.

RYARSH Kent – see Wrotham Heath.

RYDAL Cumbria 402 L 20 – see Ambleside.

RYE East Sussex 404 W 31 – pop. 4 127 – ECD : Tuesday – ☎ 0797.

See : Old Town★★ (chiefly : Mermaid Street) – Ypres Tower ≤★.

Envir. : Winchelsea★ (Church of St. Thomas the Martyr★ 1283 : Tombs★★ 12C) SW : 3 m. – Small Hythe (Ellen Terry's House★ *AC*) N : 7½ m.

Camber ☎ 225241.

48 Cinque Ports St. ☎ 222293.

◆London 61 – ◆Brighton 49 – Folkestone 27 – Maidstone 33.

George (T.H.F.), High St., TN31 7JP, ☎ 222114, Fax 224065 – ⊁ rm TV ☎ P – 🏢 70. AE VISA
M 8.95/12.25 **st.** and a la carte 🍷 4.35 – ☕ 7.00 – **22 rm** 60.00/100.00 **st.** – SB 94.00/104.00 **st.**

Mermaid, Mermaid St., TN31 7EU, ☎ 223065, Group Telex 957141, Fax 226995, « 15C inn » – TV ☎ P. AE VISA.
M 12.50/16.50 **t.** and a la carte 🍷 4.00 – **28 rm** ☕ 48.00/84.00 **t.** – SB 94.00/100.00 **st.**

Old Vicarage without rest., 66 Church Sq., TN31 7HF, ☎ 222119, 🌳 – ⊁ TV.
closed Christmas – **5 rm** ☕ 28.00/56.00 **st.**

Jeake's House without rest., Mermaid St., TN31 7ET, ☎ 222828 – TV. AE VISA
9 rm ☕ 18.00/96.00 **st.**

Flushing Inn, Market St., TN31 7LA, ☎ 223292, Seafood, « 15C inn with 16C mural » – ⊁. AE VISA
closed Monday dinner, Tuesday, first 2 weeks January and 2 weeks June – **M** 11.80/20.00 **t.** and a la carte 🍷 4.60.

Landgate Bistro, 5-6 Landgate, TN31 7LH, ☎ 222829 – AE VISA
closed Sunday, Monday, 1 week June, 2 weeks October and 1 week Christmas – **M** (dinner only) a la carte 12.90/18.90 **st.** 🍷 3.50.

at Playden N : 1 m. on A 268 – ✉ ☎ 0797 Rye :

Playden Oasts, Peasmarsh Rd, TN31 7UL, on A 268 ☎ 223502, 🌳 – TV ☎ P. AE VISA
M a la carte 11.40/15.25 **st.** – **8 rm** ☕ 30.00/46.00 **st.** – SB 60.00/76.00 **st.**

at Stone-in-Oxney (Kent) N : 6½ m. by A 268 off B 2082 – ✉ Tenterden ☎ 023 383 Appledore :

Tighe Farm ⛰, without rest., Military Canal Rd, TN30 7JU, S : ¾ m. ✆ 251, ≤, « 17 farmhouse », 🌳, park – Ⓟ. ✻
March-November – **3 rm** ☐ 15.00/30.00 **s.**

at Rye Foreign NW : 2 m. on A 268 – ✉ Rye – ☎ 079 78 Iden :

Broomhill Lodge, TN31 7UN, on A 268 ✆ 421, ≘s, 🌳 – TV ☎ Ⓟ. VISA. ✻
M *(closed Tuesday lunch, Sunday dinner and Monday)* 11.50 **t.** (dinner) and a carte 14.75/21.30 **t.** 🍷 2.95 – **12 rm** ☐ 37.00/69.00 **t.** – SB (except Easter and Christmas) 75.00/84.00 **st.**

at Peasmarsh NW : 4 m. on A 268 – ✉ Rye – ☎ 079 721 Peasmarsh :

Flackley Ash (Best Western), London Rd, TN31 6YH, ✆ 651, Telex 957210, Fax 510, ≘s, ◻, 🌳 – TV ☎ Ⓟ. AE ◑ VISA
M 11.95 **t.** (lunch) and a la carte 🍷 3.95 – **30 rm** ☐ 54.50/82.50 **st.**, **2 suites** 114.50 117.50 **st.** – SB (except Christmas, New Year and Bank Holidays) 90.00/98.00 **st.**

ROVER, LAND-ROVER, RANGE-ROVER Fishmarket Rd ✆ 223334

RYE FOREIGN East Sussex – see Rye.

SAFFRON WALDEN Essex 404 U 27 – pop. 11 879 – ECD : Thursday – ☎ 0799.

See : Parish Church★ (Perpendicular) – Audley End House★ (Jacobean : interior★★) *AC.*

18 Windmill Hill ✆ 22786.

ℹ 1 Market Pl., Market Sq ✆ 24282/26637.

♦London 46 – ♦Cambridge 15 – Chelmsford 25.

Saffron, 10-18 High St., CB10 1AY, ✆ 22676, Fax 513979 – TV ☎ Ⓟ – 🏛 80. VISA
M *(closed Saturday lunch and Sunday)* 10.50/15.95 **t.** and a la carte 🍷 3.25 – ☐ 3.00 **21 rm** 25.00/60.00 **t.** – SB (weekends only) 43.20/55.45 **st.**

RENAULT High St. ✆ 27909
ROVER 66 High St. ✆ 23597
ATS Station Rd ✆ 21426/21001

ST. AGNES Cornwall 403 E 33 The West Country G. – pop. 2 421 – ECD : Wednesday ☎ 087 255.

See : St. Agnes Beacon★★ (✻★★).

♦London 302 – Newquay 12 – Penzance 26 – Truro 9.

Trevaunance Point ⛰, Quay Rd, Trevaunance Cove, TR5 0RZ; ✆ 3235, ≤ bay and cliffs, 🌳 – TV ☎ Ⓟ. AE ◑ VISA
M 9.50/14.25 **st.** and a la carte 🍷 5.25 – **8 rm** ☐ 49.50/72.00 **st.** – SB (November-March except Bank Holidays) (weekends only) 82.00 **st.**

at Mithian E : 2 m. by B 3285 – ✉ ☎ 087 255 St. Agnes :

Rose-in-Vale ⛰, TR5 0QD, ✆ 2202, ⛱ heated, 🌳 – ⇎ rest TV ☎ Ⓟ. VISA
March-October – **M** (bar lunch)/dinner 13.95 **st.** and a la carte 🍷 3.05 – **17 rm** ☐ (dinner included) 29.95/64.90 **st.** – SB (except summer) 50.00/60.00 **st.**

FORD Trevellas Garage, Trevellas ✆ 2372

ST. ALBANS Herts. 404 T 28 – pop. 76 709 – ECD : Thursday – ☎ 0727.

See : Site★ – Cathedral and Abbey Church★ (Norman Tower★).

Envir. : Hatfield House★★★ *AC* (gardens★ and Old Palace★) E : 6 m. – Verulamium Park★ (Roman remains and Museum★)*AC*, W : 2 m.

18 Batchwood Hall ✆ 33349 – 18 Verulam, London Rd ✆ 53327.

ℹ Town Hall, Market Pl. ✆ 64511.

♦London 27 – ♦Cambridge 41 – Luton 10.

Noke Thistle (Mt. Charlotte Thistle) Watford Rd, AL2 3DS, SW : 2½ m. at junction A 405 and B 4630 ✆ 54252, Telex 893834, Fax 41906 – ⇎ rm TV ☎ ♿ Ⓟ – 🏛 70. AE ◑ VISA
M 15.50/17.50 **st.** and a la carte – ☐ 7.25 – **57 rm** 70.00/85.00 **st.**

Sopwell House (Best Western) ⛰, Cottonmill Lane, AL1 2HQ, SE : 1½ m. by A 1081 and Mile House Lane ✆ 64477, Telex 927823, Fax 44741, 🌳, park – |♦| TV ☎ Ⓟ – 🏛 400. AE ◑ VISA
M *(closed Saturday lunch)* 15.50/18.50 **t.** and a la carte 🍷 6.95 – ☐ 4.95 – **65 rm** 77.00 99.00 **t.** – SB (except Christmas) 80.00/120.00 **st.**

St. Michael's Manor, Fishpool St., AL3 4RY, ✆ 864444, Telex 917647, Fax 48909 « Manor house, lake, ≤ garden », park – TV ☎ Ⓟ – 🏛 30. AE ◑ VISA. ✻
closed 28 to 30 December – **M** 17.00/19.50 **t.** and a la carte – **26 rm** ☐ 70.00/96.00 **st.**

Black Lion Inn, 198 Fishpool St., AL3 4SB, ✆ 51786 – TV ☎ Ⓟ
8 rm.

- **Ardmore House** without rest., 54 Lemsford Rd, AL1 3PR, ✆ 59313 – TV P. VISA
14 rm 28.75/49.45 **st.**
- **Melford House** without rest., 24 Woodstock Rd North, AL1 4QQ, ✆ 53642, – P
12 rm 24.15/46.00 **st.**
- XX **Cinta,** 20-26 High St., AL3 4EN, ✆ 37606, Chinese rest. – AE VISA
M 26.00 **st.** and a la carte 5.00.
- X **Koh-I-Noor,** 8 George St., AL3 4ER, ✆ 53602, Indian rest – AE VISA
M a la carte 9.10/14.10 **t.** 3.30.

CITROEN, VAUXHALL-OPEL 68-70 High St., Potters Bar ✆ 0707 (Potters Bar) 42391
CITROEN Campfield Rd ✆ 46767
FIAT Beech Rd ✆ 50871
FORD Ashley Rd ✆ 59155
HONDA Catherine St. ✆ 54342
RENAULT 220 London Rd ✆ 63377
ROVER Acrewood Way, Hatfield Rd ✆ 66522
ROVER Park St., Frogmore ✆ 72626
TOYOTA Watford Rd ✆ 34376
VAUXHALL-OPEL 100 London Rd ✆ 50601
ATS Grimston Rd ✆ 35174
ATS Lyon Way, Hatfield Rd ✆ 52314/5

ST. ASAPH (LLANELWY) Clwyd 402 403 J 24 – pop. 3 156 – ECD : Thursday – 0745.

Envir. : Rhuddlan (castle★★ 13C) *AC*, NW : 3 m – Denbigh Castle★ S : 5 m.

♦London 225 – Chester 29 – Shrewsbury 59.

- **Oriel House,** Upper Denbigh Rd, LL17 0LW, S : ¾ m. on A 525 ✆ 582716, Fax 582716, – TV ☎ P – 200. AE VISA
closed 26 December – **M** 8.50/11.25 **t.** and a la carte 3.00 – **19 rm** 35.00/65.00 **t.** – SB (weekends only) 70.40 **st.**
- **Plas Elwy,** The Roe, LL17 0LT, N : ½ m. at junction of A 525 and A 55 ✆ 582263 – TV ☎ P. AE VISA.
closed 26 to 31 December – **M** *(closed Sunday dinner)* (dinner only and Sunday lunch)/ dinner 12.00 **t.** and a la carte 3.80 – **13 rm** 34.50/55.00 **t.** – SB (weekends only) 65.00/ 70.00 **st.**

FORD Bod Ewr Corner ✆ 582345
RENAULT The Roe ✆ 582233

Europe

Se il nome di un albergo è stampato in carattere magro, chiedete arrivando le condizioni che vi saranno praticate.

ST. AUSTELL Cornwall 403 F 32 The West Country G. – pop. 20 267 – ECD : Thursday – 0726.

See : Holy Trinity★★.

Envir. : St. Austell Bay★★ (Gribbin Head★★), E : 3 m. by A 3601 – Wheal Martyn Museum★★ *AC*, N : 2 m. on A 391 – Polkerris★, E : 9 m. by A 3082.

18 Tregongeeves Lane ✆ 74756 SW : 1 m – 18 Carlyon Bay ✆ 072 681 (Carlyon Bay) 4250.

✆ 071 (London) 723 7000 ext. 3148.

♦London 281 – Newquay 16 – ♦Plymouth 38 – Truro 14.

- **White Hart,** Church St., PL25 4AT, ✆ 72100 – TV ☎ – 50. AE VISA
closed 25 and 26 December – **M** 7.50/11.50 **st.** 3.50 – **18 rm** 37.00/58.00 **st.** – SB (October-May) (weekends only) 55.00/65.00 **st.**

at Tregrehan E : 2½ m. by A 390 – ✉ St. Austell – 072 681 Par :

- XX **Boscundle Manor** with rm, PL25 3RL, ✆ 3557, Fax 4997, « Tastefully converted 18C manor », heated, , park – TV ☎ P. VISA
Mid April-mid October – **M** *(closed Sunday dinner to non-residents)* (dinner only) 20.00 **st.** 3.75 – **10 rm** 52.50/95.00 **st.**, **1 suite** 140.00 **st.**

at Carlyon Bay E : 2½ m. by A 3601 – ✉ St. Austell – 072 681 Par :

- **Carlyon Bay,** PL25 3RD, ✆ 2304, Fax 4938, ≤ Carlyon Bay, « Extensive gardens », , heated, , 18, – TV ☎ P – 50. AE VISA.
M 11.00/16.00 **t.** and a la carte – **69 rm** 62.00/180.00 **t.**
- **Porth Avallen** , Sea Rd, PL25 3SG, ✆ 2802, Fax 7097, ≤ Carlyon Bay, – TV ☎ P – 100.
closed 23 December-2 January – **M** (booking essential) 11.80/18.30 **t.** 6.00 – **22 rm** 40.00/125.00 **t.** – SB (weekends only) 70.00/90.00 **st.**
- **Wheal Lodge,** 91 Sea Rd, PL25 3SH, ✆ 5543, – TV P.
M approx. 12.00 **t.** – **6 rm** 45.00/65.00 **t.**

CITROEN 77 Fore St. ✆ 850 241
PEUGEOT-TALBOT Gwendra Rd, St. Stephen ✆ 822566
ROVER Carlyon Bay ✆ 072 681 (Par) 4081
ATS Gover Rd ✆ 65685/6

ST. BLAZEY Cornwall 403 F 32 – ✉ Par – 072 681 St. Blazey.

♦London 276 – Newquay 21 – ♦Plymouth 33 – Truro 19.

- **Nanscawen House** , Prideaux Rd, PL24 2SR, W : ¾ m. ✆ 4488, heated, –
TV ☎ P. VISA.
closed Christmas – **M** (communal dining) 15.00 **st.** – **3 rm** 45.00/55.00 **st.**

ST.BRIDES-SUPER-ELY South Glam. – pop. 85 – ☎ 0446 Peterston-Super-Ely.

♦London 155 – ♦Bristol 51 – ♦Cardiff 9 – Newport 22.

- **St.-Y-Nyll House** without rest., CF5 6EZ, ☎ 760209, <, park – TV P
  5 rm 20.00/30.00 **s.**

ST. CLEARS **(SANCLER)** Dyfed 403 G 28 – pop. 2 159 – ECD : Wednesday – ☎ 0994.

♦London 229 – Carmarthen 9 – Fishguard 37.

- **Forge Motel,** E : ½ m. on A 40, SA33 4NA, ☎ 230300, Fax 230300, – TV ☎ P VISA
  closed 25 and 26 December – **M** (grill rest.) a la carte 5.05/14.50 **t.** 3.00 – **18 rm** 30.00/50.00 **t.**

  at Llandowror SW : 2½ m. on A 477 – ✉ ☎ 0994 St. Clears :

- XX **Old Rectory,** SA33 4HH, ☎ 230030, – P. AE VISA
  closed Monday dinner – **M** 15.00/25.00 **st.** and a la carte.

ST. COLUMB MINOR Cornwall – see Newquay.

During the season, particularly in resorts, it is wise to book in advance.

ST. DAVIDS **(TYDDEWI)** Dyfed 403 E 28 – pop. 1 428 – ECD : Wednesday – ☎ 0437.

See : Cathedral★★ 12C (site★) – Bishops Palace★ *AC.*

Envir. : Porthgain (cliffs ★★★) NE : 7 m. – Whitesand Bay★★ and St. David's Head★★ NW 2 m. – Newgale (<★★) by Solva (site★) E : 7 m. – Abereiddy (site★) NE : 5 m.

9 St. Davids City, Whitesands Bay ☎ 034 83 (Croesgoch) 607, NW : 2 m. on B 4583.

City Hall ☎ 720392 (summer only).

♦London 266 – Carmarthen 46 – Fishguard 16.

- **Warpool Court**, SA62 6BN, ☎ 720300, Fax 720300, < St. Brides bay and countryside, – TV ☎ P. AE VISA
  M 17.50/28.00 **st.** and a la carte 4.25 – **25 rm** 45.00/130.00 **st.** – SB (except Christmas and New Year) 90.00/158.00 **st.**
- **St. Non's,** Catherine St., SA62 6RJ, ☎ 720239, Fax 721839, – TV ☎ P. AE VISA
  M (bar lunch Monday to Saturday)/dinner 14.85 **t.** and a la carte 3.30 – **24 rm** 26.00/68.00 **t.** – SB 65.00/90.00 **st.**
- **Old Cross,** Cross Sq., SA62 6SP, ☎ 720387, – TV ☎ P. VISA
  March-October – **M** (bar lunch)/dinner 16.00 **t.** and a la carte 1.95 – **17 rm** 23.00/56.00 **t.** – SB 58.00/67.00 **st.**
- **Alandale,** 43 Nun St., SA62 6NU, ☎ 720333 – TV.
  M 7.00 **st.** – **6 rm** 12.50/27.00 **st.** – SB (except August) 36.00 **st.**

  at Beara NE : 4½ m. by A 487, B 4583 and Llanrian rd – ✉ St. Davids – ☎ 034 83 Croesgoch :

- Cwmwdig Water, SA62 6DW, NE : ½ m. ☎ 434, <, – P
  10 rm.

  at Llandeloy E : 9 m. by A 487 and B 4330 via Treffynnon – ✉ Haverfordwest – ☎ 034 83 Croesgoch :

- Upper Vanley Farm, SA62 6LT, E : ¼ m. ☎ 418, <, – TV P
  8 rm.

ST.DOGMAELS Dyfed 403 G 27 – see Cardigan.

ST. HILARY Cornwall – see Marazion.

ST. IVES Cornwall 403 D 33 **The West Country G.** – pop. 9 439 – ECD : Thursday – ☎ 0736 Penzance.

See : Site★★ – Barbara Hepworth Museum★★ *AC* Y **M1** – St. Ia Church★ Y **A.**

18 Trezenna Castle Hotel ☎ 795254 ext: 121 – 18 West Cornwall, Lelant ☎ 753319.

The Guildhall, Street-an-Pol ☎ 796297/797600.

♦London 319 – Penzance 10 – Truro 25.

Plan opposite

- **Porthminster** (Best Western), The Terrace, TR26 2BN, ☎ 795221, Fax 797043, <, heated, – TV ☎ P. AE VISA Y s
  M (buffet lunch)/dinner 13.50 and a la carte 4.25 – **50 rm** 41.00/90.00 **st.** – SB (October-May) (except Easter, Christmas and New Year) 74.00/83.00 **st.**

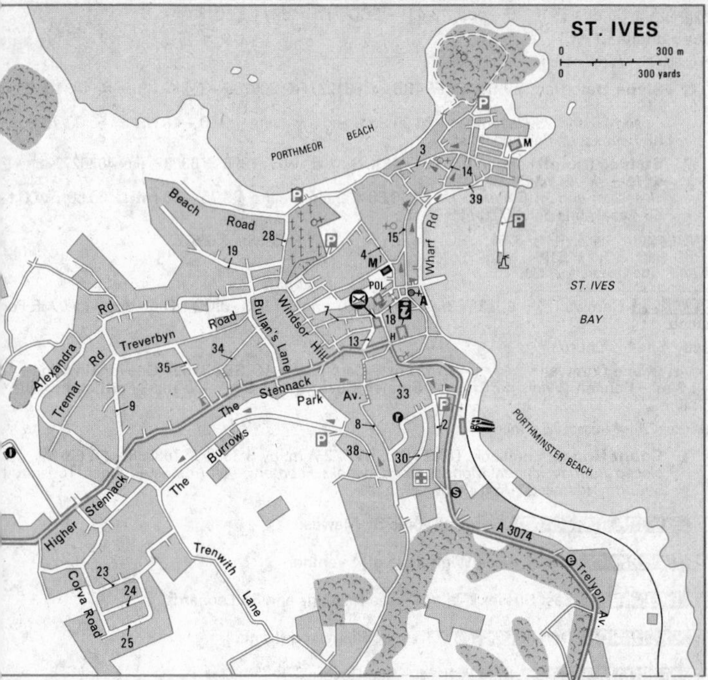

ore Street	Y 15	Penwith Road	Y 23
ligh Street	Y 18	Porthia Crescent	Y 24
lbert Road	Y 2	Porthia Road	Y 25
ack Road West	Y 3	Porthmeor Hill	Y 28
arnoon Hill	Y 4	Porthrepta Road	Z 29
edford Road	Y 7	Talland Road	Y 30
ishop's Road	Y 8	Tregenna Terrace	Y 33
arnellis Road	Y 9	Trelawney Road	Y 34
hapel Street	Y 13	Trerice Road	Y 35
ish Street	Y 14	Trewidden Road	Y 38
range Lane	Y 19	Wharf (The)	Y 39
arc Owles	Z 20	Wheal Whidden	Z 40

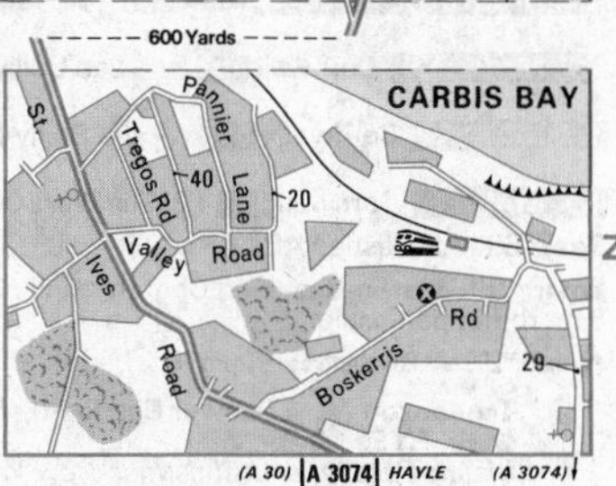

Pedn-Olva, The Warren, Porthminster Beach, TR26 2EA, ☎ 796222, < coastline – TV ☎ P. VISA
M a la carte 8.30/17.50 **t.** 4.60 – **35 rm.** Y **n**

Countryman, Old Coach Rd, TR26 3JQ, S : 2 ½ m. by B 3306 and B 3311 on Hayle rd ☎ 797571, – rm TV P. AE VISA Y
M (bar lunch)/dinner a la carte 10.25/12.95 **t.** 3.50 – **8 rm** 26.00/44.00 **t.** – SB (October-April) 62.00 **st.**

Dean Court, Trelyon Av., TR26 2AD, ☎ 796023, < St. Ives and bay – rest TV P.
April-October – **12 rm.** Y **e**

Old Vicarage, Parc-an-Creet, TR26 2ET, ☎ 796124, – TV P. AE VISA Y **i**
March-October – **M** (by arrangement) 10.00 **t.** 2.90 – **8 rm** 16.50/36.00 **t.**

Pondarosa, 10 Porthminster Terr., TR26 2DQ, ☎ 795875 – TV P. Y **r**
M 8.00 **s.** – **9 rm** 15.00/38.00 **s.**

at Carbis Bay S : 1 ¾ m. on A 3074 – ✉ St. Ives – ☎ 0736 Penzance :

Boskerris, Boskerris Rd, TR26 2NQ, ☎ 795295, Fax 798632, <, heated, – TV ☎ P. VISA Z **x**
Easter-October and Christmas – **M** (bar lunch)/dinner 16.00 **st.** 3.35 – **18 rm** 27.00/95.50 **st.**

OVER Long Stone Hill, Carbis Bay ☎ 795188

ST. IVES Cambs. 404 T 27 – pop. 13 431 – ECD : Thursday – ☎ 0480.

See : Bridge★ (15C).

◆London 75 – ◆Cambridge 14 – Huntingdon 6.

- **Slepe Hall**, Ramsey Rd, PE17 4RB, ✆ 63122, Fax 300706 – TV ☎ P – 🏛 40. AE VISA
  closed 25 and 26 December – **M** 11.95 **t.** and a la carte 🍷 3.50 – **16 rm** 55.00/70.00 **t.** SB (weekends only) 60.00 **st.**
- **St. Ives Motel**, London Rd, PE17 4EX, S : ¾ m. on A 1096 ✆ 63857, Fax 492027, – TV ☎ P – 🏛 75. AE VISA
  closed 25 and 26 December – **M** 10.50 **t.** and a la carte 🍷 3.75 – **16 rm** 39.50/55.00 **t.** SB (weekends only) 60.00/65.00 **st.**

FIAT, LANCIA Station Rd ✆ 62641
FORD Ramsey Rd ✆ 63184
ROVER The Quadrant ✆ 62871
ATS East St. ✆ 65572

ST. JUST Cornwall 403 C 33 **The West Country G.** – pop. 1 903 – ECD : Thursday – ☎ 0736 Penzance.

See : Site★ – Church★.

Envir. : Cape Cornwall★ (<★★), W : 1½ m. – Carn Euny★ *AC*, SE : 3 m. – Geevor Tin Mine★ *AC* N : 3 m – Sennen (Wayside Cross★, Sennen Cove★ (<★) SW : 4½ m. – Porthcurno (site★) S : 8 m.

◆London 325 – Penzance 7.5 – Truro 35.

- **Count House**, Botallack, TR19 7QQ, NW : 2¼ m. by B 3306 ✆ 788588 – P. VISA
  closed Sunday dinner, Monday and 3 weeks February – **M** (restricted lunch Tuesday to Saturday)/dinner 21.75 **t.** 🍷 4.65.

ST. JUST IN ROSELAND Cornwall – see St. Mawes.

ST. LAWRENCE I.O.W. – see Wight (Isle of) : Ventnor.

ST. LEONARDS East Sussex 404 V 31 – see Hastings and St. Leonards.

ST. LEONARDS Dorset 403 404 O 31 – see Ringwood (Hants.).

ST. MARGARET'S BAY Kent 404 Y 30 – see Dover.

ST. MARTINS Cornwall 403 ㉚ – see Scilly (Isles of).

ST. MARY'S Cornwall 403 ㉚ – see Scilly (Isles of).

ST. MAWES Cornwall 403 E 33 **The West Country G.** – ✉ Truro – ☎ 0326.

See : Site★ – Castle★ *AC* (<★).

Envir. : St. Just-in-Roseland Church★★, N : 2½ m. by A 3078 – St. Anthony-in-Roseland (<★★) 8 m. round peninsula.

◆London 299 – ◆Plymouth 56 – Truro 18.

- **Tresanton** 🐦, 27 Lower Castle Rd, TR2 5DR, ✆ 270544, Fax 270002, < estuary, – TV ☎ P. AE VISA
  March-October and Christmas-New Year – **M** (buffet lunch)/dinner 17.50 **t.** 🍷 4.25 – **20 rm** 43.50/97.00 **t.**, **1 suite** 145.00 **t.** – SB (March, April and October) 102.00/122.00 **st.**
- Rising Sun, The Square, TR2 5DJ, ✆ 270233 – TV ☎ P
  12 rm.
- **Idle Rocks**, Tredenham Rd, TR2 5AN, ✆ 270771, < harbour and estuary – rest TV ☎ AE VISA
  M (bar lunch)/dinner 19.00 **t.** 🍷 3.75 – **19 rm** 25.00/108.00 **t.**
- **St. Mawes**, The Seafront, TR2 5DW, ✆ 270266, < – TV. VISA
  mid-February-mid November – **M** 17.50/23.00 **st.** 🍷 3.50 – **7 rm** (dinner included) 40.00/80.00 **t.**

at St. Just in Roseland N : 2½ m. on A 3078 – ✉ Truro – ☎ 0326 St. Mawes :

- **Rose da Mar** 🐦, TR2 5JB, N : ¼ m. on B 3289 ✆ 270450, <, – P.
  April-October – **M** (dinner only) 13.00 **t.** 🍷 3.00 – **8 rm** 21.00/48.00 **t.**

This Guide is not a comprehensive list of all hotels and restaurants, nor even of all good hotels and restaurants in Great Britain and Ireland.

Since our aim is to be of service to all motorists, we must show establishments in all categories and so we have made a selection of some in each.

ST. MICHAELS-ON-WYRE Lancs. 402 L 22 – ☎ 099 58.

◆London 235 – ◆Blackpool 24 – Burnley 35 – ◆Manchester 43.

XX **Mallards,** Garstang Rd, PR3 0TE, ☎ 661 – Ⓟ. VISA
closed Sunday dinner, 1 week January and 2 weeks August – **M** (dinner only and Sunday lunch)/dinner a la carte 15.40/19.75 **t.** 3.75.

ST. NEOTS Cambs. 404 T 27 – pop. 12 468 – ☎ 0480 Huntingdon.

See : St. Mary's Church★ 15C.

Eynesbury Hardwicke, St. Neots Leisure Centre ☎ 215153, SE : 2 m – Crosshall Rd ☎ 74311, W : 1 m. on A 45 – Wyboston Lakes ☎ 21900.

◆London 60 – Bedford 11 – ◆Cambridge 17 – Huntingdon 9.

Stephenson's Rocket Motel, Crosshall Rd, PE19 4AG, NW : 1 m. on A 45 ☎ 72773, Fax 407520 – TV ☎ Ⓟ.
9 rm.

XX **Chequers Inn,** St. Mary's St., Eynesbury, PE19 2TA, S : ½ m. on B 1043 ☎ 72116 – Ⓟ. AE VISA
closed Christmas Night – **M** a la carte 18.15/29.70 **t.** 3.55.

at Wyboston (Beds.) SW : 2 ½ m. by B 1428 on A 1 – ✉ St. Neots (Cambs.) – ☎ 0480 Huntingdon :

Wyboston Lakes Motel without rest., Great North Rd, MK44 3AL, N : ½ m. at junction of A 45 and A 1 ☎ 219949, Fax 407349 – TV Ⓟ. AE VISA
closed 1 week Christmas – ☕ 4.00 – **38 rm** 33.90/43.00 **st.**

FORD Cambridge St. ☎ 73321 | ATS Brook St. ☎ 72920
ROVER 42 Huntingdon St. ☎ 73237

Utilisez le guide de l'année.

SALCOMBE Devon 403 I 33 **The West Country G.** – pop. 1 968 – ECD : Thursday – ☎ 054 884.

Envir. : Kingsbridge★, N : 5 m. by A 381 Y – Prawle Point (≤★★★), E : 16 m. around coast by A 381 Y – Sharpitor Overbecks Museum and garden (≤★★) *AC*, SW : 2 m. by South Sands Z.

66 Fore St. ☎ 3927 (summer only).

◆London 243 – Exeter 43 – ◆Plymouth 27 – Torquay 28.

SALCOMBE

Fore Street	Y
Allenhayes Road	Y 2
Bonaventure Road	Y 3
Buckley Street	Y 4
Camperdown Road	Y 7
Church Street	Y 8
Coronation Road	Y 9
Devon Road	Y 13
Fortescue Road	Z 14
Grenville Road	Y 15
Herbert Road	Z 18
Knowle Road	Y 19
Moult Road	Z 20
Newton Road	Y 23
Sandhills Road	Z 24
Shadycombe Road	Y 25

Town plans
roads most used by traffic and those on which guide listed hotels and restaurants stand are fully drawn; the beginning only of lesser roads is indicated.

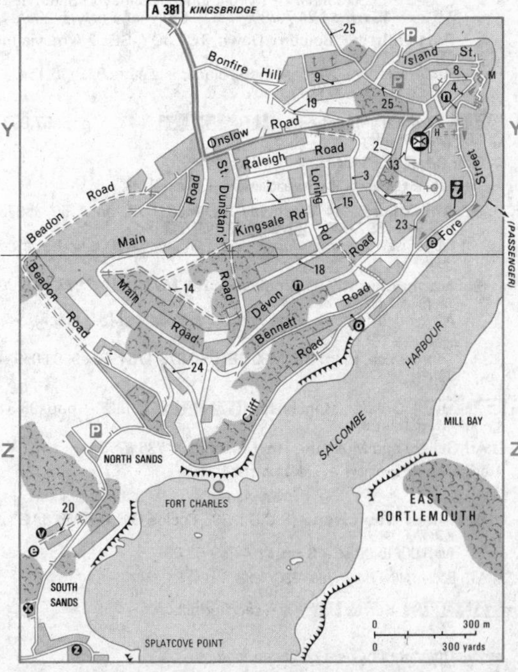

Tides Reach, South Sands, TQ8 8LJ, ℘ 3466, Fax 3954, ≤ estuary, squash – TV ☎ P Z
41 rm.

Marine, Cliff Rd, TQ8 8JH, ℘ 2251, Fax 3109, ≤ estuary, – TV ☎ P. AE VISA. Y
M 10.50/29.50 **st.** and a la carte 5.00 – **50 rm** 77.00/154.00 **t.**, **1 suite** 88.00/95.00 **st.** – SB (November-March) 105.00/125.00 **st.**

Bolt Head (Best Western), South Sands, TQ8 8LL, ℘ 3751, Fax 3060, ≤ estuary heated – rest TV ☎ P. AE VISA Z
23 March-2 November – **M** (buffet lunch)/dinner 32.00 **t.** – **28 rm** 69.00/138.00 **t.** – SB (except Easter and Bank Holidays) 96.00/138.00 **st.**

Grafton Towers, Moult Rd, TQ8 8LG, ℘ 2882, ≤ estuary, – rest TV P. VISA
April-September – **M** (dinner only) 15.50 **t.** 3.70 – **13 rm** 29.50/65.00 **t.** Z

The Wood, De Courcy Rd, Moult Hill, TQ8 8LQ, via Moult Rd ℘ 2778, ≤ estuary, – rest TV P Z
closed December and January – **M** 14.00 **t.** 4.00 – **6 rm** 23.00/58.00 **t.**

Bay View without rest., Bennett Rd, TQ8 8JJ, ℘ 2238, ≤ estuary – P. VISA.
March-September – **4 rm** 30.00/50.00. Z

Woodgrange, Devon Rd, TQ8 8HJ, ℘ 2439, – TV ☎ P. AE VISA Z
April-September – **M** (bar lunch)/dinner 15.00 **st.** – **9 rm** 24.00/48.00 **st.** – SB 68.00/70.00 **st.**

Wellingtons, 84 Fore St., TQ8 8BY, ℘ 3385 – VISA Y
early March-mid November – **M** (dinner only) 10.95 **t.** and a la carte 4.75.

at Soar Mill Cove SW : 4 ¼ m. by A 381 via Marlborough village – Y – ✉ Malborough – ☎ 0548 Kingsbridge :

Soar Mill Cove, TQ7 3DS, ℘ 561566, Fax 561223, ≤, – rest TV ☎ P VISA.
closed 29 December-7 February – **M** 22.00/32.00 16.00 **t.** – **16 rm** 60.00/250.00 **t.**

at Hope Cove W : 4 m. by A 381 – via Marlborough village Y – ✉ ☎ 0548 Kingsbridge

Lantern Lodge, TQ7 3HE, via Grand View Rd ℘ 561280, ≤, – rest TV P. VISA.
March-November – **M** (bar lunch)/dinner – **14 rm** 34.40/68.00 **t.**

Cottage, TQ7 3HJ, ℘ 561555, ≤ Bolt Tail and Bigbury Bay, – TV ☎ P
closed 2 to 30 January – **M** (bar lunch Monday to Saturday)/dinner 15.15 **st.** and a la carte 5.35 – **35 rm** 24.70/80.00 **st.** – SB (winter only) 54.00/64.00 **st.**

Port Light, Bolberry Down, TQ7 3DY, SE : 2 ¼ m. via Inner Hope ℘ 561384, ≤, – TV P. VISA
April-October – **M** (bar lunch)/dinner a la carte 8.25/16.15 **t.** 4.00 – **5 rm** 20.00/60.00 **t.** – SB 44.00/50.00 **st.**

SALE

Greater Manchester 402 403 404 N 23 – pop. 57 993 – ECD : Wednesday – ✉ ☎ 061 Manchester.

Golf Rd ℘ 973 3404.

London 212 – Liverpool 36 – Manchester 6 – Sheffield 43.

Amblehurst, 44 Washway Rd, M33 1QZ, on A 56 ℘ 973 8800, Group Telex 668871, Fax 905 1697, – TV ☎ P. AE VISA.
M *(closed Saturday lunch and Sunday)* 25.00 **t.** and a la carte 4.00 – **40 rm** 25.00/65.00 **t.**

Normanhurst, 195 Brooklands Rd, M33 1PJ, ℘ 973 1982, Group Telex 668871, – TV ☎ P. AE VISA.
M *(closed Sunday lunch and Bank Holidays)* (bar lunch)/dinner 9.95 **st.** – **50 rm** 39.50/50.00 **st.**

Lennox Lea, Irlam Rd, M33 2BH, ℘ 973 1764, Fax 969 6059, – TV ☎ P
30 rm.

SALFORD

Greater Manchester 402 403 404 N 23 – pop. 98 343 – ECD : Wednesday – ✉ ☎ 061 Manchester.

Art Gallery and Museum, The Crescent ℘ 736 8773.

London 206 – Liverpool 31 – Manchester 4.

Town plans : see Manchester built up area.

Inn of Good Hope (B.C.B.), 226 Eccles Old Rd, M6 8AG, ℘ 707 6178 – TV ☎ P. AE VISA. AX
M 8.00/15.00 **st.** – **8 rm** 41.50/53.00.

ATS Eccles New Rd ℘ 789 4360/3988

SALFORDS

Surrey 404 T 30 – see Redhill.

Utilizzate la Guida dell'anno in corso.

SALISBURY Wilts. 403 404 O 30 **The West Country G.** – pop. 36 890 – ECD : Wednesday – ☎ 0722.

See : Site★★ – Cathedral★★★*AC* Z – The Close★ Z : Mompesson House★*AC* Z **A**, Military Museum★★*AC* Z **M1** – Salisbury and South Wiltshire Museum★*AC* Z **M2** – Sarum St. Thomas Church★ Y **B**.

Envir. : Stonehenge★★★*AC*, NW : 10 m. by A 345 Y – Wilton House★★*AC*, W : 2½ m. by A 30 Y – Old Sarum★*AC* N : 2 m. by A 345 Y – at Wilton Village, Royal Wilton Carpet Factory★*AC*, W : 2½ m. by A 30 Y – Heale House★*AC* N : 7 m. by Stratford Rd Y – Wardour Castle★*AC*, W : 10 m. by A 30. Y.

18, 9 Salisbury and South Wilts., Netherhampton ☎ 742131, by A 3094 Z – 18 High Post, Great Durnford ☎ 73231, N : 4 m. by A 345 Y.

Fish Row ☎ 334956/27269.

London 91 – Bournemouth 28 – ◆Bristol 53 – ◆Southampton 23.

Plan on next page

White Hart (T.H.F.), 1 St. John St., SP1 2SD, ☎ 27476, Fax 412761 – rm TV ☎ P – 80. AE VISA Z **s**
M 9.50/13.95 **st.** and a la carte 4.35 – 7.50 – **68 rm** 69.00/105.00 **st.** – SB 90.00/110.00 **st.**

Country (B.C.B.), Bridge St., SP1 2ND, ☎ 20229 – TV ☎ P – 100. AE VISA. Z **n**
M 8.00/15.00 **st.** – **31 rm** 53.00/70.00 **st.**

Kings Arms (B.C.B.), 9 St. John's St., SP1 2SB, ☎ 27629, Fax 414246, « Part 13C and part 15C inn » – TV ☎ Z **r**
15 rm.

Stratford Lodge, 4 Park Lane, Castle Rd Y, SP1 3NP, ☎ 325177, – TV P. Y
closed Christmas and New Year – **M** (by arrangement) 15.00 **t.** 2.50 – **7 rm** 25.00/50.00 **st.**

Byways House, 31 Fowlers Rd, off Milford Hill, SP1 2QP, ☎ 328364, Fax 322146, – rm TV P. VISA Z **e**
M 10.50 **st.** 2.50 – **17 rm** 19.00/40.00 **st.** – SB (except Bank Holidays) 50.00/71.00 **st.**

Cricketfield Cottage without rest., Wilton Rd, SP2 7NS, W : 1¼ m. on A 30 Y ☎ 22595, – TV P
5 rm.

Glen Lyn without rest., 6 Bellamy Lane, Milford Hill, SP1 2SP, ☎ 327880 – TV P. YZ **x**
9 rm 16.00/36.00 **st.**

Old Bell Inn without rest., 2 St. Ann St., SP1 2DN, ☎ 327958, Fax 411485, « Converted 14C inn » – AE VISA. Z **v**
2.50 – **7 rm** 50.00/55.00 **st.**

Shah-Jahan, 111-113 South Western Rd, ☎ 335992, Indian rest. Y **a**

Chef Peking, 39 Catherine St., SP1 2HD, ☎ 326063, Chinese rest. – . AE VISA Z **c**
closed Sunday lunch except Bank Holidays – **M** 10.00/17.00 **st.**

at Pitton E : 6 m. by A 30 – Y – ✉ Salisbury – ☎ 072 272 Farley :

Silver Plough, White Hill, SP5 1DZ, ☎ 266 – P. AE VISA
M (bar meals Sunday and Monday dinner) 11.25 **t.** (lunch) and dinner a la carte 17.40/24.65 **t.**

at Redlynch SE : 8½ m. by A 338 – Z – off B 3080 – ✉ Salisbury – ☎ 0794 Romsey :

Langley Wood with rm, Hamptworth Rd, SP5 2PB, SE : 1½ m. ☎ 390348, – P. AE VISA
closed 3 weeks January-February – **M** *(closed dinner Sunday, Monday and Tuesday to non-residents)* (lunch by arrangement) a la carte 16.00/20.20 **t.** 2.50 – **3 rm** 15.00/30.00 **t.**

at Downton S : 6 m. by A 338 – Z – on B 3080 – ✉ ☎ 0725 Downton :

Warren without rest., 15 High St., SP5 3PG, ☎ 20263, – P
6 rm 25.00/38.50 **s.**

at Harnham SW : 1½ m. by A 3094 – ✉ ☎ 0722 Salisbury :

Rose and Crown (Q.M.H.), Harnham Rd, SP2 8JQ, ☎ 327908, Telex 47224, Fax 339816, <, « 13C inn, riverside setting », – TV ☎ P – 85. AE VISA. Z **u**
M 12.50 **st.** and a la carte 4.50 – **28 rm** 65.50/145.00 **st.** – SB (weekends only) 98.00/105.00 **st.**

Grasmere without rest., 70 Harnham Rd, SP2 8JN, ☎ 338388, <, – TV ☎ P. Z **a**
5 rm 39.00/50.00 **st.**

at Broad Chalke SW : 8 m. by A 354 and Broad Chalke Valley Rd Z – ✉ ☎ 0722 Salisbury :

Stoke Farm, SP5 5EF, E : ¾ m. ☎ 780209, « Working farm », – P
M 11.00 **s.** – **3 rm** 17.00/34.00 **s.**

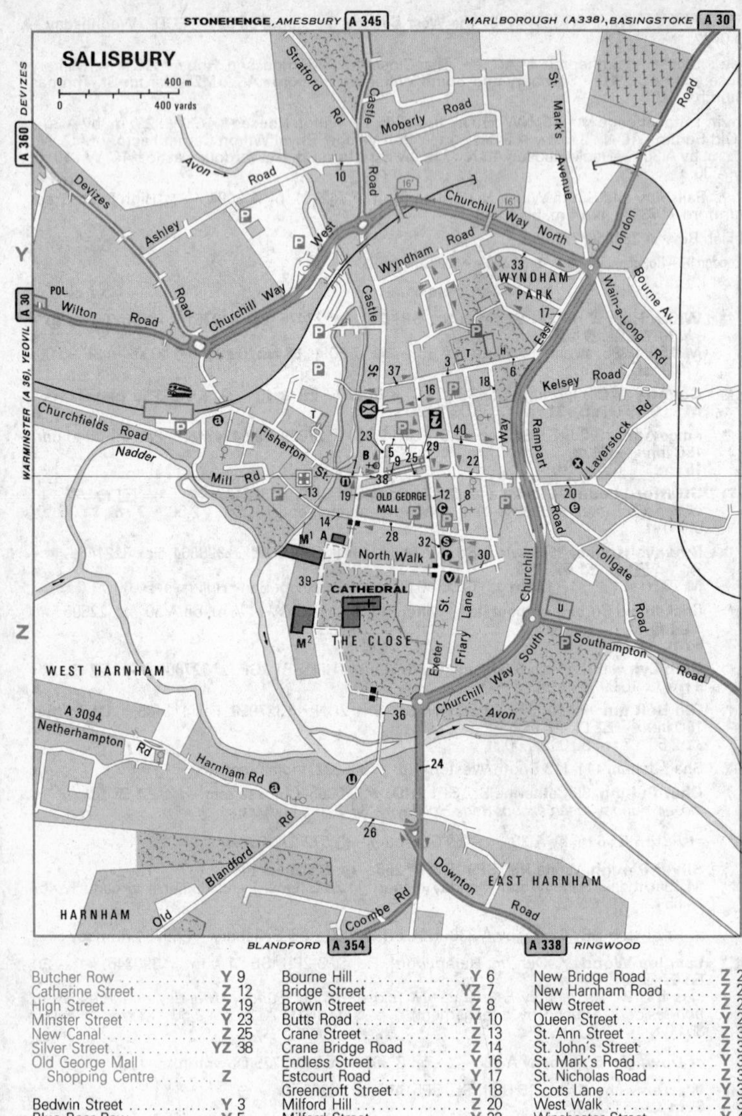

Butcher Row ... Y 9	Bourne Hill ... Y 6	New Bridge Road ... Z 2
Catherine Street ... Z 12	Bridge Street ... YZ 7	New Harnham Road ... Z 2
High Street ... Z 19	Brown Street ... Z 8	New Street ... Z 2
Minster Street ... Y 23	Butts Road ... Y 10	Queen Street ... Y 2
New Canal ... Z 25	Crane Street ... Z 13	St. Ann Street ... Z 3
Silver Street ... YZ 38	Crane Bridge Road ... Z 14	St. John's Street ... Z 3
Old George Mall Shopping Centre ... Z	Endless Street ... Y 16	St. Mark's Road ... Y 3
	Estcourt Road ... Y 17	St. Nicholas Road ... Z 3
	Greencroft Street ... Y 18	Scots Lane ... Y 3
Bedwin Street ... Y 3	Milford Hill ... Z 20	West Walk ... Z 3
Blue Boar Row ... Y 5	Milford Street ... Y 22	Winchester Street ... Y 4

at Teffont W : 10 1/4 m. by A 36 and A 30 on B 3089 – ✉ ☎ 0722 Salisbury :

XX **Howard's House** with rm Teffont Evias, SP3 5Dr, on lane opposite Black Horse ✆ 716392, ←, « Part 17C former dower house », – TV ☎ P. VISA
closed 2 weeks February and 24 to 30 December – **M** (dinner only and Sunday lunch)/ dinner 25.00 **t.** and a la carte 4.50 – **9 rm** 65.00/80.00 **t.** – SB 125.00/145.00 **st.**

BMW Harnham ✆ 24933
CITROEN Stephenson Rd ✆ 413141
FIAT Lower Rd, Churchfield Ind Est. ✆ 336681
FORD Castle St. ✆ 28443
NISSAN 114-120 Wilton Rd ✆ 28328
PEUGEOT-TALBOT Southampton Rd ✆ 335268
ROVER Southampton Rd ✆ 335251
VAUXHALL-OPEL Brunell Rd ✆ 23522
VOLVO Telford Rd, Churchfields ✆ 333650
VW-AUDI 16 Lower Rd, Churchfields ✆ 27162
ATS 155 Wilton Rd ✆ 336789
ATS 28 St. Edmunds Church St. ✆ 22390/22451

SALTASH Cornwall 403 H 32 – pop. 12 772 – ☎ 0752.

18, 18 St Mellion ✆ 0579 (St Mellion) 50101.

London 246 – Exeter 38 – Plymouth 5 – Truro 49.

Granada Lodge without rest., Callington Rd, Carkeel, PL12 6LF, NW : 1 1/2 m. by A 388 on A 38 at Saltash Service Area ✆ 848408 – TV & P. VISA.
31 rm 27.50/29.50 **st.**

SALTBURN-BY-THE-SEA Cleveland 402 R 20 – pop. 6 066 – ✉ ☎ 0287 Guisborough.

18 Saltburn, Hob Hill ✆ 22812.

4 Station Buildings, Station Sq. ✆ 22422.

London 256 – Middlesbrough 13 – Scarborough 40.

Rushpool Hall, Saltburn Lane, TS12 1HD, S : 1 3/4 m. by A 174 ✆ 624111, Fax 624111, park – TV ☎ P – 100. VISA
M 8.50/15.00 **st.** and a la carte 3.95 – 6.00 – **16 rm** 70.00/95.00 **st.**

SALTHORP Wilts. – see Swindon.

SAMLESBURY Lancs. 402 M 22 – see Preston.

SAMPFORD PEVERELL SERVICE AREA Devon 403 J 31 – ✉ ☎ 0884 Tiverton.

London 184 – Barnstaple 34 – Exeter 20 – Taunton 19.

Travelodge without rest., EX16 7HD, M 5 junction 27 ✆ 821087, Reservations (Toll free) 0800 850950 – TV & P. VISA.
40 rm 24..0/29.50 **t.**

SANCLER = St. Clears.

SANDBACH Cheshire 402 403 404 M 24 – pop. 13 753 – ECD : Tuesday – ☎ 0270.

18 Malkins Bank Municipal, Betchton Rd ✆ 765931 – 9 Middlewich Rd ✆ 762117.

M 6 Service Area (Northbound) ✆ 760460/761879.

London 177 – Liverpool 44 – Manchester 28 – Stoke-on-Trent 16.

Chimney House (Lansbury), Congleton Rd, CW11 OST, E : 1 1/2 m. on A 534 ✆ 764141, Telex 367323, Fax 768916, – TV ☎ P – 70. VISA
M 8.95/14.00 **t.** and a la carte – **50 rm** 74.00/87.00 **t.** – SB (weekends only) 62.00/ 76.00 **st.**

SANDIACRE Derbs. 402 403 404 Q 25 – see Nottingham (Notts.).

SANDOWN I.O.W. 403 404 Q 32 – see Wight (Isle of).

SANDPLACE Cornwall – see Looe.

SANDRINGHAM Norfolk 402 404 V 25 – pop. 431 – ✉ King's Lynn – ☎ 0485 Dersingham.

London 111 – King's Lynn 8 – Norwich 50.

Park House, Sandringham Estate, PE35 6EH, ✆ 543000, Restricted to physically disabled, and their carers « Former Royal residence », heated, , park – rest TV ☎ & P. VISA.
M (buffet lunch)/dinner 11.00 **s.** 3.10 – **16 rm** 47.00/76.00 **st.**

N'oubliez pas qu'il existe des limitations de vitesse au Royaume-Uni en dehors de celles mentionnées sur les panneaux.

– 60 mph (= 96 km/h) sur route.

– 70 mph (= 112 km/h) sur route à chaussées séparées et autoroute.

SANDWICH Kent 404 Y 30 – pop. 4 184 – ECD : Wednesday – ☎ 030 46 (4 fig.) or 0304 (6 fig.).

See : Site★.

⛳, ⛳ Prince's, Sandwich Bay ☎ 611118 – ⛳ Royal St George's ☎ 617308.

ℹ St. Peter's Church, Market St. ☎ 613565 (summer only).

◆London 72 – Canterbury 13 – ◆Dover 12 – Maidstone 41 – Margate 9.

- **Bell,** The Quay, CT13 9EF, ☎ 613388, Fax 615308 – rm TV ☎ P – 50. AE VISA
  M 5.50/13.00 **st.** and a la carte 3.85 – **29 rm** 50.00/95.00 **st.** – SB 77.00/110.00 **st.**

FORD New St. ☎ 612308

SANDY Beds. 404 T 27 – pop. 7 496 – ECD : Thursday – ☎ 0767.

◆London 49 – Bedford 8 – ◆Cambridge 24 – Peterborough 35.

- Sandy Motel without rest., Girtford Bridge, London Rd, SG19 1DH, W : ¾ m. by B 1042 at junction of A 1 and A 603 ☎ 292220, Fax 80452 – TV P.
  58 rm.

at Tempsford N : 3¾ m. by B 1042 on A 1 – ✉ ☎ 0767 Sandy :

- **Anchor** (B.C.B.), Great North Rd, SG19 2AS, on A 1 ☎ 40233, park – TV ☎ P. AE VISA.
  M (carving rest.) 8.00/15.00 **st.** – **10 rm** 38.00/56.00 **st.**

SANDYPARK Devon 403 I 31 – see Chagford.

SARISBURY Hants. 403 404 Q 31 – pop. 5 682 – ✉ Southampton – ☎ 0489 Locks Heath.

◆London 90 – ◆Portsmouth 16 – ◆Southampton 6.

- **Dormy House,** 21 Barnes Lane, Sarisbury Green, SO3 6DA, S : 1 m. ☎ 572626 – TV P
  M (by arrangement) 7.60 **st.** – **10 rm** 17.25/40.25 **st.**

SARN PARK SERVICE AREA Mid Glam. 403 J 29 – ✉ ☎ 0656 Bridgend.

◆London 174 – ◆Cardiff 17 – ◆Swansea 20.

- **Travelodge** without rest, CF32 9RW, ☎ 655332, Fax 645004, Reservations (Toll free) 0800 850950 – TV P. AE VISA.
  40 rm 24.00/29.50 **t.**

SAUNDERSFOOT Dyfed 403 F 28 – pop. 2 196 – ECD : Wednesday – ☎ 0834.

ℹ The Harbour ☎ 811411 (summer only).

◆London 245 – Carmarthen 25 – Fishguard 34 – Tenby 3.

- **St. Brides,** St. Brides Hill, SA69 9NH, ☎ 812304, Telex 48350, Fax 813303, ≤, heated – rm rest TV ☎ P – 80. AE VISA
  M 12.50/17.50 **st.** and a la carte 4.80 – **43 rm** 54.00/85.00 **st.**, **2 suites** 115.00 **st.** – SB (weekends only) 65.00/95.00 **st.**
- **Glen Beach**, Swallow Tree Woods, SA69 9DE, S : ½ m. by B 4316 ☎ 813430, ≤, – TV ☎ P. AE VISA
  M (bar lunch)/dinner 10.00 **st.** and a la carte – **13 rm** 30.00/49.00 **st.** – SB (weekends only) (except July and August) 45.00/70.00 **st.**
- **Malin House,** St. Brides Hill, SA69 9NP, ☎ 812344, – TV P. VISA.
  closed December and January – **M** (bar lunch)/dinner 8.00 **st.** 1.80 – **18 rm** 20.00/40.00 **st.** – SB (October-April) (weekends only) 52.50 **st.**

SAUNDERTON Bucks. 404 R 28 – ✉ Aylesbury – ☎ 084 44 Princes Risborough.

◆London 42 – Aylesbury 9 – ◆Oxford 20.

- **Rose and Crown,** Wycombe Rd, HP17 9NP, on A 4010 ☎ 5299 – TV ☎ P. AE VISA.
  closed 25 to 30 December – **M** *(closed Saturday lunch and Sunday dinner)* a la carte 14.65/23.70 **t.** – **17 rm** 43.45/82.50 **st.** – SB (weekends only) 75.50 **st.**

SAUNTON Devon 403 H 30 – ✉ Braunton – ☎ 0271 Croyde.

◆London 230 – Barnstaple 8 – Exeter 48.

- **Saunton Sands,** EX33 1LQ, ☎ 890212, Fax 890145, ≤ Saunton Sands, squash – TV ☎ P – 120. AE VISA.
  M 11.50/15.50 **t.** and a la carte – **90 rm** 60.00/180.00 **t.** – SB (except summer and Bank Holidays) 70.00/135.00 **st.**
- **Preston House,** EX33 1LG, ☎ 890472, Fax 890555, ≤ Saunton Sands, – TV ☎ P VISA.
  M (bar lunch)/dinner 20.50 **t.** and a la carte 3.50 – **14 rm** 27.50/80.00 **t.**

MICHELIN
NORTH AMERICA
NORTH ATLANTIC OCEAN
EUROPE
AFRICA
SOUTH AMERICA
CIRCLES·THE
WORLD

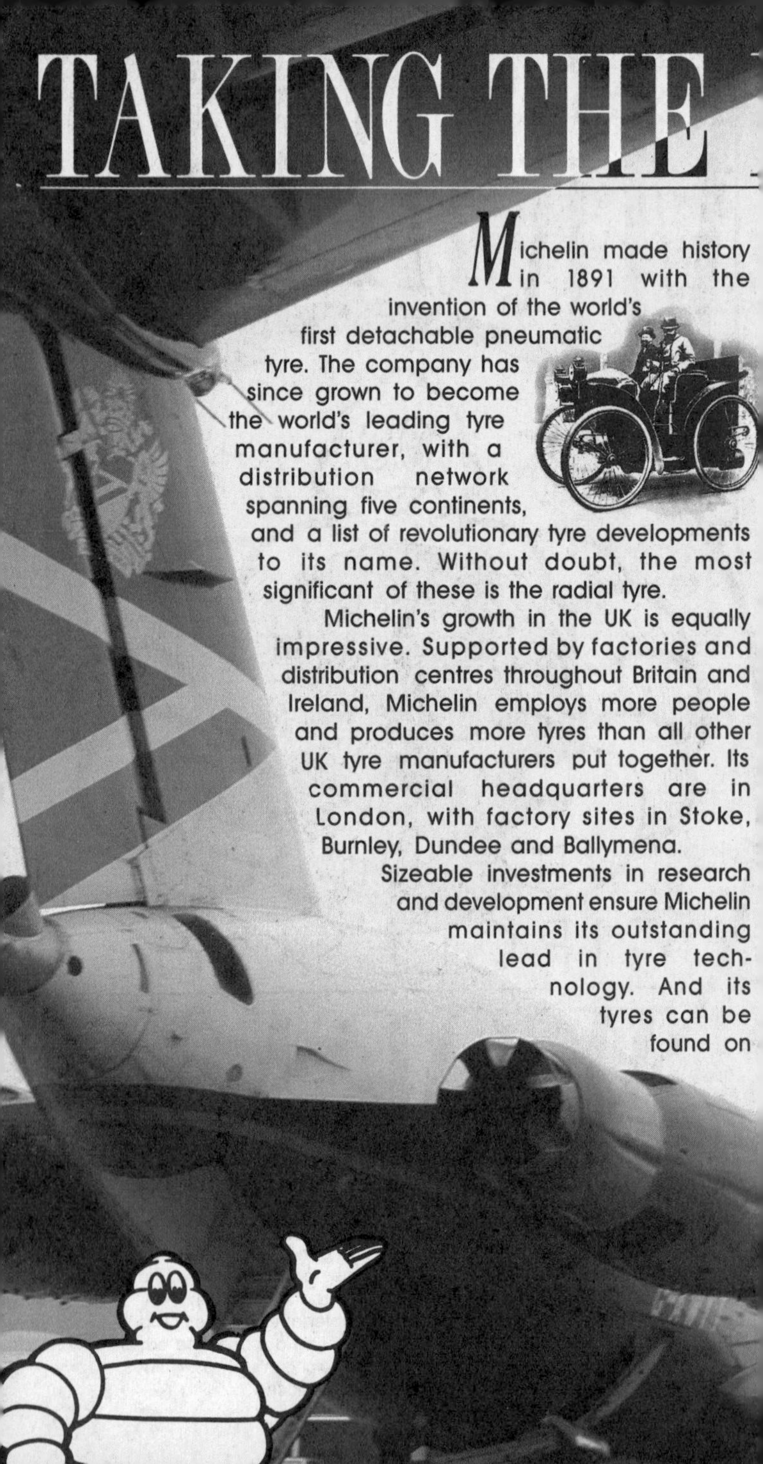

TAKING THE

Michelin made history in 1891 with the invention of the world's first detachable pneumatic tyre. The company has since grown to become the world's leading tyre manufacturer, with a distribution network spanning five continents, and a list of revolutionary tyre developments to its name. Without doubt, the most significant of these is the radial tyre.

Michelin's growth in the UK is equally impressive. Supported by factories and distribution centres throughout Britain and Ireland, Michelin employs more people and produces more tyres than all other UK tyre manufacturers put together. Its commercial headquarters are in London, with factory sites in Stoke, Burnley, Dundee and Ballymena.

Sizeable investments in research and development ensure Michelin maintains its outstanding lead in tyre technology. And its tyres can be found on

EAD

almost every type of wheeled vehicle. Michelin's tallest earthmover tyre measures over 11 feet high and weighs in at more than three tons when fully inflated. Its lightest cycle tyre tips the scales at a mere seven ounces.

GUIDED BY THE BOOK

In response to the growing needs of motorists, Michelin began publishing travel guides at the turn of the century. Using the soon-to-be-famous Michelin system of symbols, the first Red Guide was published in 1900. It bristled with facts, figures and useful commentary. Today, Michelin produces over 200 separate motoring publications spanning Europe, Africa, Mexico, Canada and parts of the U.S.A.

Aided and abetted by the famous Michelin Man, the company's tyres, maps and guides have gained a worldwide reputation. Conceived by the founders of the company, the two Michelin brothers after spotting a pile of tyres, the Michelin Man has become an immensely versatile and instantly recognisable company trademark.

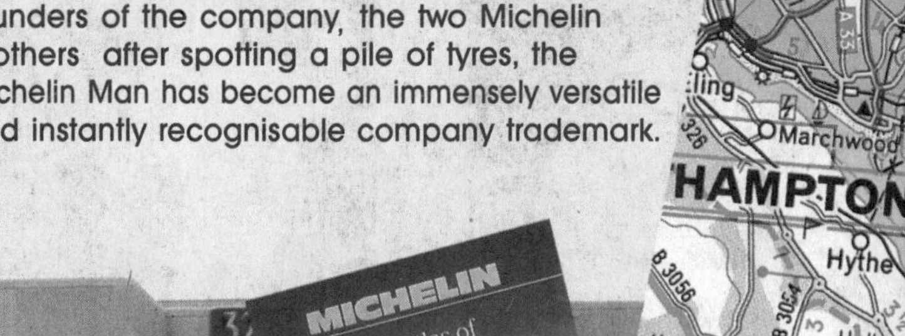

INTO THE N

In common with Michelin's product range, the Michelin Man is designed to last. His staying-power mirrors Michelin's own enduring success well into the last decade of this century. Unique among company symbols, Bibendum first took shape in 1898. He has since taken on an incredible number of guises — everything from a gallant knight armoured for the road, to a nimble-footed mountain climber. Although Bibendum's public image may change with the times, there is no mistaking the Michelin Man. His message remains reassuringly constant.

Bibendum comes to life in an 1898 poster created by the French artist O'Galop.

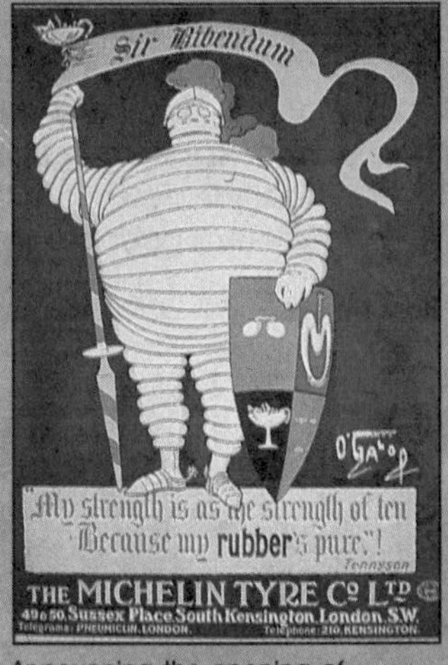

Announcing the opening of Michelin's first London office in 1905.

NETIES

Bibendum brings motorists the best tyres that technology can offer. And his genial face reflects the company's desire to respond to the needs of its customers across all five continents.

A sure-footed Michelin Man confidently takes to the mountains in 1985.

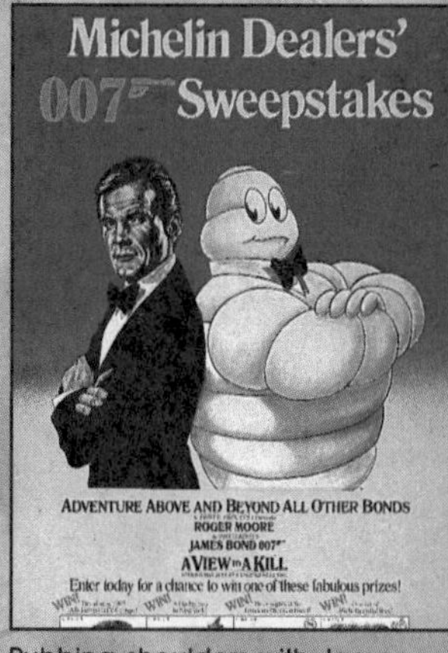

Rubbing shoulders with James Bond in the film "A View to a Kill."

1988 sees Mister Bibendum driving a fast ball for Michelin.

The 1990s Michelin Man is one of the world's most recognizable symbols.

MILES - MO

"Safe to drive and economical to run." These features alone once sold a family car. Times have changed. Today's car is more of a performance machine. With this increased performance comes the need for more grip, improved handling, and greater comfort, durability and reliability.

Michelin's new *MXT* radial is designed to satisfy these demands.

MXT

The Tyre for the Nineties

...ORE-GRIP

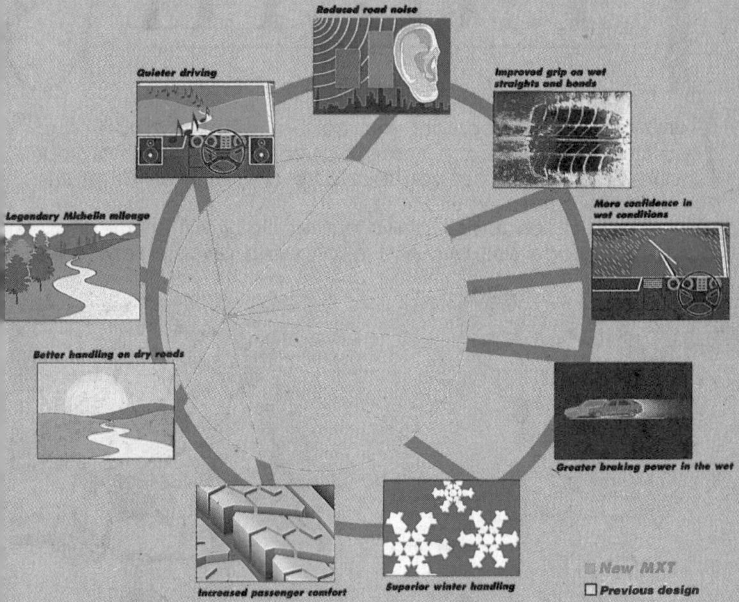

Reduced road noise

Quieter driving

Improved grip on wet straights and bends

More confidence in wet conditions

Legendary Michelin mileage

Better handling on dry roads

Greater braking power in the wet

Increased passenger comfort

Superior winter handling

New MXT

Previous design

Take a look at the *MXT*'s performance features. Compared to Europe's most advanced tyre to date — the Michelin MXL — the *MXT* achieves increased grip in all weather conditions, a quieter ride, and significantly greater braking efficiency in the wet. All this without sacrificing mileage. You get miles more grip. Plus, a quality tyre

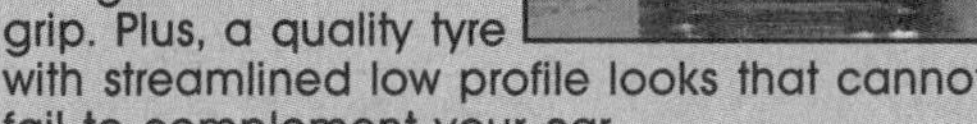

with streamlined low profile looks that cannot fail to complement your car.

For more information about the new *MXT*, ask your local tyre dealer. Or contact our London office:

Michelin Tyre PLC, Marketing Department,
Davy House, Lyon Road, Harrow, Middx., HA1 2DQ
Telephone: 081-861 2121

TYRE TIPS

Tyres are the only contact your car has with the road — four patches of tread, each hardly bigger than the palm of your hand. So it is vital that you take care of your tyres. In return, they will take care of you.
A few simple procedures, carried out regularly, will ensure that your tyres perform well and give a long and reliable service life.

BMW
Ford
Check your car tyre pressures at least once a fortnight, and only when the tyres are cold.
Fit only the tyre size and type recommended by the vehicle manufacturer.
If you are carrying a heavy load, or towing, adjust your tyre pressures according to the vehicle manufacturer's recommendations.
Always ensure your tyres conform to the legal requirements.
Don't forget to check the inflation pressure of your car's spare tyre.
If you spot an irregularity in the tyre, have it checked by your tyre dealer immediately.

MAKE SURE IT'S A MICHELIN

SAWBRIDGEWORTH Herts. 404 U 28 – pop. 8 475 – ECD : Thursday and Saturday – 0279 Bishop's Stortford.

London 26 – ◆Cambridge 32 – Chelmsford 17.

- **The Manor of Groves**, High Wych, CM21 0LA, SW : 1 ½ m. by A 1184 600777, Telex 81492, Fax 600374, heated, park, – – 65. – **M** *(closed Saturday lunch and Sunday dinner)* 16.50 **t.** (lunch) and a la carte 22.45/28.00 **t.** – **32 rm** 65.00/135.00 **st.**

SAWLEY Lancs. 402 M 22 – pop. 179 – 076 586.

London 242 – ◆Blackpool 39 – ◆Leeds 44 – ◆Liverpool 54.

- **Spread Eagle,** BB7 4NH, 0200 (Clitheroe) 41202 – . **M** 12.00/20.00 **st.** and a la carte – **10 rm** 38.00/78.00 **st.** – SB (weekends only) 89.00 **st.**

SAWTRY Cambs. 402 403 T 26 – 0487.

London 71 – ◆Cambridge 25 – Northampton 38 – Peterborough 11.

- Redwings Lodge without rest., PE17 5XT, S : 2 ¾ m. on A1 (Southbound Carriageway) 832778, Fax 496197 – – **39 rm.**

SCALBY North Yorks. 402 S 21 – see Scarborough.

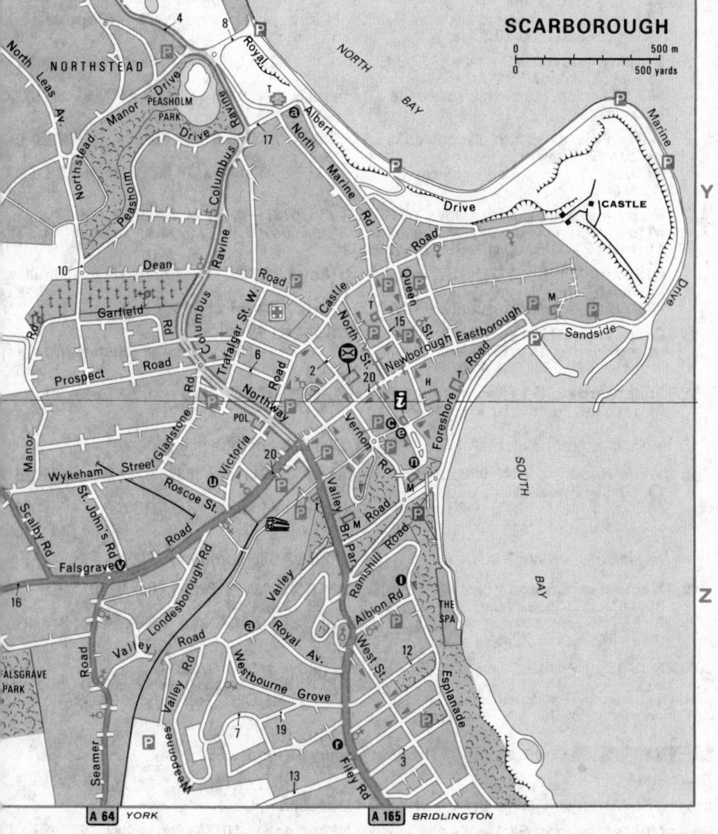

berdeen Walk	Y 2	Avenue Victoria	Z 3	Prince of Wales Terrace	Z 12
astborough	Y	Burniston Road	Y 4	Queen Margaret's Road	Z 13
alsgrave Road	Z	Cambridge Street	Y 6	St. Thomas Street	Y 15
ewborough	Y	Oriel Crescent	Z 7	Stepney Road	Z 16
ictoria Road	YZ	Peasholm Gap	Y 8	Victoria Park	Y 17
Vestborough	Z 20	Peasholm Manor Road	Y 10	Westbourne Road	Z 19

SCARBOROUGH North Yorks. 402 S 21 – pop. 36 665 – ECD : Monday and Wednesday – ☎ 0723.

See : Castle 12C (≤★) *AC* Y.

North Cliff, North Cliff Av. ☎ 360786, NW : 2 m. by A 165 Y – South Cliff, Deepdale Av., off Filey Rd ☎ 360522, S : 1 m. Z – Ganton, Statron Rd ☎ 0944 (Ganton) 70329, SW : 1m. Z.

St. Nicholas Cliff ☎ 373333.

♦London 253 – ♦Kingston-upon-Hull 47 – ♦Leeds 67 – ♦Middlesbrough 52.

Plan on preceding page

Holbeck Hall (Best Western) ⅀, Sea cliff Rd, YO11 2XX, ☎ 374374, Fax 351114, ≤, – TV ☎ P. AE VISA. by A 165 Z
M 9.50/16.95 **st.** and a la carte 5.95 – **29 rm** 47.00/104.00 **st.**, **1 suite** 175.00/250.00 **st** – SB (weekends only) 107.50/117.50 **st.**

Crown (T.H.F.), 7-11 Esplanade, YO11 2AG, ☎ 373491, Telex 52277, Fax 362271, ≤ – rm TV ☎ – 200 Z
81 rm, **1 suite.**

St. Nicholas, St. Nicholas Cliff, YO11 2EU, ☎ 364101, Telex 52351, Fax 500538, ≤, – TV ☎ – 400 Z
139 rm, **5 suites.**

Palm Court, St. Nicholas Cliff, YO11 2ES, ☎ 368161, Fax 371547, – TV ☎ – 100. AE VISA. Z
M (bar lunch Monday to Saturday)/dinner 14.00 **t.** and a la carte 3.75 – **50 rm** 34.00/110.00 **t.** – SB 69.00/79.00 **st.**

Bradley Court (Best Western), 7-9 Filey Rd, YO11 2SE, ☎ 360476, Fax 376661 – TV ☎ P – 40. Z
M 8.95 **t.** (dinner) and lunch a la carte approx. 12.50 **t.** – **38 rm** 27.50/55.00 **t.** – SB 67.00/87.00 **st.**

Clifton (Best Western), Queen's Par., YO12 7HX, ☎ 375691, Fax 364203, ≤ – TV P – 200. AE VISA. Y
M 10.00/15.00 **t.** 4.50 – **65 rm** 28.50/73.00 **t.**, **5 suites** 78.00/83.00 **t.** – SB 66.00/72.00 **st.**

Pickwicks Inn, Huntriss Row, YO11 2ED, ☎ 375787 – TV ☎. AE VISA.
M *(closed Sunday dinner)* (bar lunch Monday to Friday) 6.95/10.50 **st.** and a la carte 3.35 – **11 rm** 24.00/60.00 **st.** – SB 62.00/69.00 **st.** Z

Old Mill, Mill St., YO11 1SZ, via Victoria Rd ☎ 372735, « Restored 18C windmill » – rest TV P Z
closed 20 December-14 January – **M** 7.00 **t.** 3.00 – **14 rm** 18.50/37.00.

Grapevine, 23 Valley Rd, YO11 2LY, ☎ 377088 – AE VISA Z
closed Sunday, 26 to 27 December and 1 to 3 January – **M** (lunch by arrangement)/dinner a la carte 12.40/19.20 **t.** 4.25.

Jade Garden, 121 Falsgrave Rd, YO12 5EA, ☎ 369099, Chinese rest. AE VISA
M a la carte approx. 10.50 **t.** Z

at Scalby NW : 3 m. by A 171 – Z – ✉ ☎ 0723 Scarborough :

Wrea Head ⅀, YO13 0PB, by Barmoor Lane ☎ 378211, Fax 353732, ≤, park – TV ☎ P. AE VISA.
M 10.50/21.50 **t.** 5.95 – **20 rm** 40.00/110.00 **t.**, **1 suite** 120.00/160.00 **t.** – SB 90.00/130.00 **st.**

at Hackness NW : 7 m. by A 171 – Z – ✉ ☎ 0723 Scarborough :

Hackness Grange (Best Western) ⅀, YO13 0JW, ☎ 82345, Fax 82391, ≤, « 18C house », park, – TV ☎ P. AE VISA.
M 7.50/16.75 **t.** and a la carte 5.25 – **26 rm** 51.00/102.00 **t.** – SB (except Bank Holidays) 102.00/116.00 **st.**

CITROEN, DATSUN, PEUGEOT-TALBOT Northway ☎ 363533
DAIHATSU Pickering Rd, West Ayton ☎ 862880
FIAT Manor Rd ☎ 364111
FORD Vine St. ☎ 375581
RENAULT Columbus Ravine ☎ 360791
VAUXHALL-OPEL Seamer Rd ☎ 360335

SCILLY (Isles of) Cornwall 403 ㉚ **The West Country G.** – pop. 2 653.

See : Site★.

Envir. : St. Martin's : Viewpoint★★ – St. Agnes : Horsepoint★.

Helicopter service from St. Mary's and Tresco to Penzance : ☎ 0736 (Penzance) 63871.

St. Mary's Airport : ☎ 0720 (Scillonia) 22677, E : 1 ½ m. from Hugh.

from Hugh Town, St. Mary's to Penzance (Isles of Scilly Steamship Co.) summer only (2 h 30 mn).

Porthcressa Bank, St. Mary's ☎ 0720 (Scillonia) 22536.

Bryher – pop. 66 – ✉ ☎ 0720 Scillonia.

See : Village on Watch Hill (≤★) – Hell Bay★.

Hell Bay 🐦, TR23 0PR, ☎ 22947, Fax 23004, 🌳 – ⇆ rest TV. 🏧 VISA. 🐕
April-September – **M** (bar lunch)/dinner 16.00 **t.** 🍷 4.00 – **10 rm** ☐ -/88.00 **t.**, **4 suites** 110.00 **t.**

Bank Cottage 🐦, TR23 0PR, ☎ 22612, ≤, 🌳 – 🐕
April-October – **M** 8.50 – **5 rm** ☐ (dinner included) 25.00/55.00 **st.**

St. Martin's – ☎ 0720 Scillonia

St. Martin's 🐦, TR25 0QW, ☎ 22092, Fax 22298, ≤ Tean sound and islands, « Idyllic island setting », 🏊, 🌳 – TV ☎. 🏧 AE ⓓ VISA
M 14.00/28.00 **st.** and a la carte 🍷 4.00 – **22 rm** ☐ 120.00/180.00 **st.**, **2 suites** 113.00/195.00 **st.**

St. Mary's – pop. 2 106 – ECD : Wednesday – ✉ St. Mary's – ☎ 0720 Scillonia.

See : Garrison Walk★ (≤★★) – Peninnis Head★.

⛳9 ☎ 22692, N : 1½ m. from Hughtown.

🅘 Porthcressa Bank ☎ 22536.

Tregarthen's (Best Western), Hugh Town, TR21 0PP, ☎ 22540, ≤ – TV ☎
33 rm.

Star Castle 🐦, TR21 0JA, ☎ 22317, « Elizabethan fortress », 🏊, 🌳, 🎾 – TV ☎
Mid March-mid October – **M** (bar lunch)/dinner 15.00 **t.** – **24 rm** ☐ (dinner included) 47.00/60.00 **t.**

Atlantic, Hugh St., Hugh Town, TR21 0PL, ☎ 22417, Fax 23009, ≤ St. Mary's Harbour – ⇆ rest TV ☎. 🏧 VISA
Mid March-mid October – **M** (dinner only) 17.00 **t.** 🍷 4.00 – **23 rm** ☐ (dinner included) 47.00/110.00 **t.**

Carnwethers 🐦, Pelistry Bay, TR21 0NX, ☎ 22415, ≘s, 🏊 heated, 🌳 – ⇆ rest TV. 🐕
End March-early October – **M** 11.00 **st.** 🍷 2.90 – **9 rm** ☐ 24.00/56.00 **st.**

Tremellyn, Church Rd, Hugh Town, TR21 0NA, ☎ 22656, 🌳 – TV Ⓟ. 🐕
April-October – **M** (by arrangement) 10.50 **st.** 🍷 4.00 – **8 rm** ☐ (dinner included) 27.85/66.55 **st.**

Tresco – pop. 285 – ✉ New Grimsby – ☎ 0720 Scillonia.

See : Site★ – Abbey Gardens★ *AC* – Lighthouse Way (≤★★).

Island 🐦, Old Grimsby, TR24 0PU, ☎ 22883, Fax 23008, ≤ St. Martin's and islands, « Sub-tropical gardens », 🏊 heated, park – TV ☎. 🏧 VISA. 🐕
February-October – **M** (dinner only and Sunday lunch)/dinner 27.00 **st.** 🍷 5.00 – **28 rm** ☐ (dinner included) 66.00/212.00 **st.**, **1 suite** (dinner included) 168.00/226.00 **st.**

New Inn, TR24 0QQ, ☎ 22844, ≤, 🏊 heated, 🌳 – ☎. 🐕
M (bar lunch)/dinner 16.50 **t.** 🍷 3.60 – **12 rm** ☐ (dinner included) 45.00/99.00 **t.**

SCOLE Norfolk 404 X 26 – see Diss.

SCOTCH CORNER North Yorks. 402 P 20 – ✉ ☎ 0748 Richmond.

🅘 Rank Motorway Service Area, A 1, ☎ 377677 (summer only).

♦London 235 – ♦Carlisle 70 – ♦Middlesbrough 25 – Newcastle 43.

Scotch Corner, DL10 6NR, ☎ 850900, Telex 587447, Fax 5417 – 🛗 TV ☎ Ⓟ – 🏛 400
86 rm, **4 suites.**

Rank Motor Lodge without rest., Middleton Tyas Lane, D10 6PQ, ☎ 377177 – TV ♿ Ⓟ. 🏧 AE ⓓ VISA
50 rm 27.50/34.50 **st.**

Travelodge without rest., Skeeby, DL10 5EQ, S : 1 m. on A 1 (Northbound carriageway) ☎ 3768, Reservations (Toll free) 0800 850950 – TV ♿ Ⓟ. 🏧 AE VISA. 🐕
40 rm 24.00/29.50 **t.**

SCUNTHORPE Humberside 402 S 23 – pop. 79 043 – ECD : Wednesday – ☎ 0724.

Envir. : Normanby Hall★ (Regency) : Wildlife park★ *AC*, N : 4 m. – Barton-upon-Humber (St. Mary's Church★ 12C, Old St. Peter's Church★ 10C-11C) NE : 13½ m.

⛳18 Normanby Park ☎ 720226, N : 5 m. – ⛳18 Ashby Decoy, Burringham Rd ☎ 842913, SW : 2 m. – ⛳18 Holme Lane, Bottesford ☎ 849185, SE : 4 m. – ⛳9 Kingsway ☎ 840945.

✈ Humberside Airport : ☎ 0652 (Barnetby) 688456, E : 15 m. by A 18.

🅘 Scunthorpe Library, Carlton St. ☎ 860161.

♦London 167 – ♦Leeds 54 – Lincoln 30 – ♦Sheffield 45.

Royal (T.H.F.), Doncaster Rd, DN15 7DE, ℘ 282233, Telex 527479, Fax 281826 – rm TV ☎ P. AE VISA
M *(closed Saturday lunch)* 9.50/13.95 **t.** and a la carte 4.35 – **33 rm** 55.00/60.00 **t.** – SB (weekends only) 62.00 **st.**

Wortley House, Rowland Rd, DN16 1SU, ℘ 842223, Telex 527837, Fax 280646 – TV ☎ P – 250. AE VISA
M 20.00 **st.** and a la carte 4.75 – **38 rm** 58.00/68.00 **st.** – SB (weekends only) 68.00/88.00 **st.**

BMW Old Crosby ℘ 281300
FIAT Normanby Rd ℘ 861191
FORD Station Rd ℘ 840655
HYUNDAI Doncaster Rd ℘ 860212
ROVER Normanby Rd ℘ 856551
VAUXHALL-OPEL Moorwell Rd Industrial Estate ℘ 843284
VAUXHALL Winterton Rd ℘ 861862
VW-AUDI Brigg Rd ℘ 842011

ATS Grange Lane North ℘ 868191
ATS Burringham Rd ℘ 860435

SEACROFT West Yorks. 402 ⑩ – see Leeds.

SEAFORD East Sussex 404 U 31 – pop. 16 367 – ECD : Wednesday – 0323.

East Blatchington ℘ 892597 – Southdown Rd ℘ 890139.

Station Approach ℘ 897426.

London 65 – Brighton 14 – Folkestone 64.

XX **Quincy's,** 42 High St., BN25 1PL, ℘ 895490 – VISA
closed Sunday and Monday – **M** (dinner only) 19.95 **t.** 2.85.

*To visit a town or region : use the **Michelin Green Guides**.*

SEAHOUSES Northumb. 401 402 P 17 – pop. 1 709 (inc. North Sunderland) – ECD : Wednesday – 0665.

Envir. : Farne Islands★ (by boat from harbour).

Beadnell Rd ℘ 720794.

Car Park, Seafield Rd ℘ 720884 (summer only).

London 328 – Edinburgh 80 – Newcastle-upon-Tyne 46.

Beach House, 12a St. Aidans, Seafront, NE68 7SR, ℘ 720337, ←, – rest TV ☎ P. VISA
April-3 November – **M** (bar lunch residents only)/dinner 14.75 **t.** 3.75 – **14 rm** 32.50/61.00 **t.** – SB (October-24 May) 70.00/74.00 **st.**

St. Aidans, Seafront, ℘ 720355, ← – TV P. VISA.
Mid February-mid November – **M** (bar lunch Monday to Saturday)/dinner 15.50 **st.** 4.25 – **10 rm** 25.00/50.00 **st.** – SB (except April-August) 60.00/65.00 **st.**

Olde Ship, 9 Main St., NE68 7RD, ℘ 720200 – TV ☎ P. VISA.
Mid February-November – **M** (bar lunch)/dinner 11.50 **t.** 3.50 – **10 rm** 25.50/55.00 **t.** – SB 66.00/70.00 **st.**

SEALE Surrey 404 R 30 – see Farnham.

SEATOLLER Cumbria – see Keswick.

SEATON BURN Tyne and Wear 402 P 18 – see Newcastle-upon-Tyne.

SEATON CAREW Cleveland 402 Q 20 – see Hartlepool.

SEAVIEW I.O.W. 403 404 Q 31 – see Wight (Isle of).

SEAVINGTON ST. MARY Somerset 403 L 31 – pop. 321 – ✉ Ilminster – 0460 South Petherton.

London 142 – Taunton 14 – Yeovil 11.

Pheasant, Water St., TA19 0QH, ℘ 40502, Fax 42388, – TV ☎ P. AE VISA.
closed 26 December-10 January – **M** *(closed Sunday dinner)* 12.50/20.00 **t.** and a la carte 4.75 – **8 rm** 50.00/70.00 **t.** – SB 94.60 **st.**

SEDGEMOOR SERVICE AREA Somerset – 0934 Weston-Super-Mare

Travelodge without rest., M 5 (Northbound carriageway) between junctions 21 and 22, BS24 0JL, ℘ 750831, Fax 750450, Reservations (Toll free) 0800 850950 – TV P. AE VISA.
40 rm 24.00/29.50 **t.**

SEDLESCOMBE East Sussex 404 V 31 – pop. 1 315 – ✉ Battle – 0424.

London 56 – Hastings 7 – Lewes 26 – Maidstone 27.

Brickwall, The Green, TN33 0QA, ℘ 870253, Fax 870785, heated, – TV ☎ P. AE VISA
M 10.00/15.00 **t.** 3.60 – **24 rm** 43.00/60.00 **t.** – SB 70.00 **st.**

at Cripp's Corner N : 2¼ m. by A 229 on B 2089 – ✉ Robertsbridge – ☎ 058 083 Staplecross :

XX **Olivers,** TN32 5RY, ☎ 870387, – P. VISA
closed Monday, Tuesday and first 3 weeks January – **M** 18.50 **t.** 4.00.

SELBY North Yorks. 402 Q 22 – ☎ 0757.
ee : Selby Abbey Church★★.
Mill Lane, Brayton ☎ 075 782 (Brayton) 622.
Park St. ☎ 703263.
London 202 – ◆Kingston-upon-Hull 36 – ◆Leeds 23 – York 14.

Londesborough Arms (B.C.B.), Market Pl., YO8 0NS, ☎ 707355 – TV ☎ P. AE VISA.
M 8.00/15.00 **st.** – **27 rm** 40.00/54.00 **st.**

ATS Unit 1, Canal rd, Bawtry rd ☎ 703245/702147

SELLING Kent 404 W 30 – pop. 674 – ✉ ☎ 022 785 Faversham.
London 56 – Canterbury 10 – ◆Dover 28 – Maidstone 25.

Parkfield House without rest., Hogben's Hill, ME13 9QX, ☎ 0227 (Canterbury) 752898, – P.
closed 24 to 26 December – **4 rm** 15.00/30.00 **s.**

SEMINGTON Wilts. 403 404 N 29 – ☎ 0380 Devizes.

XX **Highfield House,** BA14 6JN, on A 350 ☎ 870554 – P
M a la carte 14.70/18.90 **t.** 5.00.

SETTLE North Yorks. 402 N 21 – pop. 3 153 – ECD : Wednesday – ☎ 072 92.
Giggleswick ☎ 3912, N : 1 m. on A 65.
Town Hall, Cheapside ☎ 5192.
London 238 – Bradford 34 – Kendal 30 – ◆Leeds 41.

Royal Oak, Market Pl., BD24 9ED, ☎ 2561 – TV ☎ P.
closed Christmas Night – **M** (bar lunch Monday to Saturday)/dinner a la carte 10.95/15.25 **st.** 4.00 – 6.25 – **6 rm** 28.25/47.50 **st.**

OVER Station Rd ☎ 2323

SEVENOAKS Kent 404 U 30 – pop. 24 493 – ECD : Wednesday – ☎ 0732.
ee : Knole★★ (15C-17C) *AC*.
nvir. : Lullingstone (Roman Villa : mosaic panels★) *AC*, N : 6 m.
Woodlands ☎ 095 92 (Shoreham) 3805 – 18 Darenth Valley, Station Rd ☎ 095 92 (Shoreham) 922 – 18 Knole Park, Sea Hollow Rd ☎ 452709 – 9 Wrotham Heath, Seven Mile Lane ☎ 884800.
Buckhurst Lane ☎ 450305.
London 26 – Guildford 40 – Maidstone 17.

XX **Royal Oak** with rm, Upper High St., TN14 5PG, ☎ 451109, Fax 740187 – rest TV ☎ P. AE VISA
M 15.00/18.50 **st.** and a la carte 4.25 – **21 rm** 65.00/80.00 **t.** – SB (weekends only) 85.00 **st.**

at Ivy Hatch E : 4¾ m. by A 25 and A 227 on Coach Rd – ✉ ☎ 0732 Sevenoaks :

X **Le Chantecler** (at The Plough), TN15 0NL, ☎ 810268, – P. VISA
closed Sunday dinner and Monday – **M** 15.00/27.00 **t.** and a la carte.

ITROEN Tonbridge Rd ☎ 453328
AT, MITSUBISHI London Rd ☎ 462800
ENAULT 71 St. Johns Hill ☎ 455174
SAAB Borough Green ☎ 883044
VAUXHALL-OPEL 128 Seal Rd ☎ 451337

SHAFTESBURY Dorset 403 404 N 30 **The West Country G.** – pop. 4 831 – ECD : Wednesday nd Saturday – ☎ 0747.
ee : ≤★ – Gold Hill★ – Local History Museum★*AC*.
nvir. : Wardour Castle★*AC*, NE : 5 m.
8 Bell St. ☎ 53514 (summer only).
London 115 – Bournemouth 31 – ◆Bristol 47 – Dorchester 29 – Salisbury 20.

Grosvenor (T.H.F.), The Commons, SP7 8JA, ☎ 52282, Fax 54755 – TV – 120. AE VISA
M 16.00 **st.** (dinner) 4.95 – **47 rm** 40.00/45.00 **st.** – SB (weekends only) 72.00/79.00 **st.**

Royal Chase (Best Western), Royal Chase Roundabout, SP7 8DB, junction of A 30 and A 350 ☎ 53355, Telex 418414, Fax 51969, , , – TV ☎ P – 50. AE VISA
M a la carte 10.50/19.00 **t.** 4.70 – **34 rm** 59.00/99.00 **t.** – SB (except Christmas and New Year) 88.00 **st.**

at Ludwell (Wilts.) E : 3 m. on A 30 – ✉ ☎ 0747 Shaftesbury (Dorset) :

Grove House, SP7 9ND, on A 30 ℰ 828365, ⩽, – rest TV P. VISA
closed December and January – **M** (bar lunch)/dinner 15.00 **st.** 4.00 – **11 rm** 24.5
55.00 **st.** – SB 69.00/80.00 **st.**

SHALDON Devon 403 J 32 – see Teignmouth.

SHANKLIN I.O.W. 403 404 Q 32 – see Wight (Isle of).

SHAW Wilts. 403 404 N 29 – see Melksham.

SHEDFIELD Hants. 403 404 Q 31 – pop. 3 291 – ✉ Southampton – ☎ 0329 Wickham.
◆London 75 – ◆Portsmouth 13 – ◆Southampton 10.

Meon Valley Golf & Country Club (Best Western), Sandy Lane, SO3 2HQ, off A 33
ℰ 833455, Telex 86272, Fax 833411, ⩽, , , , 18, , park, , squash – rm TV
P – 200 – **84 rm.**

SHEEPWASH Devon 403 H 31 – see Hatherleigh.

SHEERNESS Kent 404 W 29 – pop. 11 087 – ECD : Wednesday – ☎ 0795.
See : ⩽★ from the pier.
Envir. : Minster (abbey : brasses★, effigied tombs★) SE : 2½ m.
Shipping connections with the Continent : to the Netherlands (Vlissingen) (Olau).
Bridge Rd Car Park ℰ 665324.
◆London 52 – Canterbury 24 – Maidstone 20.

Hotels and Restaurants see : Sittingbourne SW : 9 m., ***Maidstone*** SW : 20 m.

FORD High St. ℰ 580058
ROVER New Rd ℰ 664329
SKODA Granville Pl., Granville Rd ℰ 662730

SHEFFIELD South Yorks. 402 403 404 P 23 – pop. 470 685 – ECD : Thursday – ☎ 0742.
See : Cutler's Hall★ CZ A.
18 Tinsley Park ℰ 560237, E : by A 57 BZ – 18 Beauchief, Abbey Lane ℰ 367274, SW : by B 606
AZ – 18 Birley Wood, Birley Lane ℰ 390099, SE : 4½ m. by A 616 BZ – 18 Concorde Park
Shiregreen Lane ℰ 570274, N : 3½ m. by A 6135 BY – 18 Hillsborough, Worrall Rd ℰ 343608 A
– 18 Abbeydale, Twentywell Lane, Dore ℰ 360763.
Town Hall Extension, Union St. ℰ 734671/2.
◆London 174 – ◆Leeds 36 – ◆Liverpool 80 – ◆Manchester 41 – ◆Nottingham 44.

Plans on following pages

Hallam Tower Post House (T.H.F.), Manchester Rd (A 57), S10 5DX, ℰ 670067, Tele
547293, Fax 682620, ⩽, , – rm TV P – 300. AE VISA AZ
M 11.50/15.00 **st.** and a la carte 4.35 – 7.50 – **135 rm** 75.00/85.00 **st.**, **2 suites** 110.00
135.00 **st.** – SB (weekends only) 152.00/175.00 **st.**

St. George (Swallow), Kenwood Rd, S7 1NQ, ℰ 583811, Telex 547030, Fax 500138,
, , , park – TV P – 200. AE VISA AZ
M 11.00/14.00 **st.** and a la carte – **141 rm** 72.00/110.00 **st.**, **1 suite** 95.00/115.00 **st.**
SB (weekends only) 90.00 **st.**

Beauchief (Lansbury), 161 Abbeydale Rd South, S7 2QW, SW : 3½ m. ℰ 620500, Tele
54164, Fax 350197, , – rm TV P – 100. AE VISA.
M 11.00/20.00 **t.** and a la carte 4.50 – **41 rm** 76.00/88.00 **t.** – SB (weekend
only) 76.00/84.00 **st.** on A 625 AZ

Grosvenor House (T.H.F.), Charter Sq., S1 3EH, ℰ 720041, Telex 54312, Fax 757199 –
rm TV P – 400. AE VISA CZ
M 19.95 **st.** and a la carte – 7.60 – **102 rm** 80.00/90.00 **st.**, **1 suite** 160.00/250.00 **st.**
SB (weekends only) 84.00/96.00 **st.**

Charnwood, 10 Sharrow Lane, S11 8AA, ℰ 589411, Fax 555107 – TV P – 80.
AE VISA. CZ
M 10.25/14.95 **t.** and a la carte 6.45 – **21 rm** 86.00/140.00 **t.**

Granada, 340 Prince of Wales Rd, S2 1FF, ℰ 530935, Fax 642731 – TV P. AE
VISA. BZ
M (grill rest.) a la carte approx. 12.00 **t.** – **61 rm** 35.00/39.00 **t.**

Millingtons without rest., 70 Broomgrove Rd, S10 2NA, ℰ 669549 – TV P.
6 rm 21.00/40.00 **t.** AZ

Westbourne House without rest., 25 Westbourne Rd, S10 2QQ, ℰ 660109, – TV P
9 rm. AZ

Zing Vaa, 55 The Moor, S1 4PF, ℰ 722432, Chinese rest. – . AE VISA CZ
M a la carte approx. 14.10 **t.** 3.10.

Nirmal's, 189-193 Glossop Rd, S10 2GW, ℰ 724054, North Indian rest. – AE VISA
closed Sunday lunch and 25-26 December – **M** 25.50 **t.** and a la carte 4.00. CZ

SHEFFIELD
BUILT UP AREA

Street	Grid	No.
arrow Road	BY	4
awtry Road	BY	5
adfield Road	AY	7
Brocco Bank	AZ	8
Broughton Lane	BY	10
Burngreave Road	AY	12
Handsworth Road	BZ	24
Hollinsend Road	BZ	28
Holywell Road	BY	29
Main Road	BZ	32
Meadow Hall Road	BY	33
Middlewood Road	AY	34
Newhall Road	BY	36
Rustlings Road	AZ	39
Westbourne Road	AZ	47
Western Bank	AZ	48
Whitham Road	AZ	49
Woodbourn Road	BYZ	50
Woodhouse Road	BZ	51

Ne confondez pas :

Confort des hôtels : 🏨🏨🏨 ... 🏨, ⌂, ⌂

Confort des restaurants : XXXXX X

Qualité de la table : ✿✿✿, ✿✿, ✿, M

SHEFFIELD

CENTRE

Angel Street .... DY 3
Commercial Street .... DZ 16
Fargate .... CZ
High Street .... DZ
Leopold Street .... CZ 31

West Street .... CZ

Blonk Street .... DY 6
Castle Gate .... DY 13
Charter Row .... CZ 14
Church Street .... CZ 15
Cumberland Street .... CZ 17
Fitzwilliam Gate .... CZ 19
Flat Street .... DZ 20
Furnival Gate .... CZ 21

Furnival Street .... CZ 2
Haymarket .... DY 2
Moorfields .... CY 3
Pinstone Street .... CZ 3
Queen Street .... CY 3
St. Mary's Gate .... CZ 4
Shalesmoor .... CY 4
Snig Hill .... DY 4
Waingate .... DY 4
West Bar Green .... CY 4

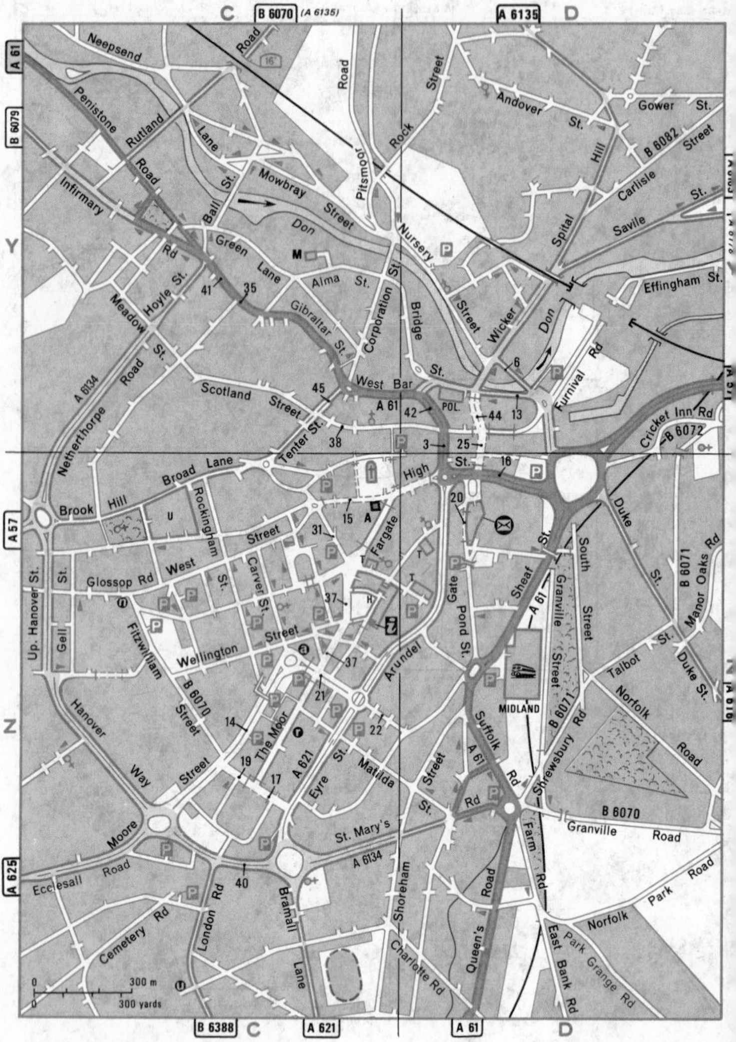

No confondete :

Confort degli alberghi : 🏨 ... 🏠, ⚐, ⌂
Confort dei ristoranti : XXXXX X
Qualità della tavola : ✿✿✿, ✿✿, ✿, M

at Chapeltown N : 6 m. on A 6135 – AY – ✉ ☎ 0742 Sheffield :

Staindrop Lodge, Lane End, S30 4UH, NW : ½ m. on High Green rd ✆ 846727, Fax 846783 – TV ☎ P – 80. AE VISA. *closed 25 and 26 December* – **M** *(closed Saturday lunch, Sunday dinner and Bank Holidays)* 8.50/25.00 **t.** and a la carte 4.75 – **13 rm** 60.00/75.00 **t.** – SB (weekends only) 80.00/83.00 **st.**

XX **Greenhead House,** 84 Buncross Rd, S30 4SF, ✆ 469004 – P. AE VISA *closed Sunday, Monday, first 2 weeks May, 2 weeks August-September and 24 to 30 December* – **M** (booking essential) (dinner only) 27.00 **st.** 5.00.

at Ridgeway (Derbs.) SE : 6¾ m. by A 616 off B 6054 – BZ – ✉ ☎ 0742 Sheffield :

XXX **Old Vicarage,** Ridgeway Moor, S12 3XW, on Marsh Lane rd ✆ 475814, Fax 477079, « Attractively furnished », – P. AE VISA *closed Sunday, Monday, last week August, 26 December-4 January and Bank Holidays* – **M** (lunch by arrangement)/dinner 21.50/30.00 7.00.

at Meadow Head S : 5¼ m. on A 61 – ✉ – ☎ 0708 Sheffield :

Sheffield Moat House (Q.M.H.), Chesterfield Rd South, S8 8BW, ✆ 375376, Telex 547890, Fax 378140, – rm rest TV ☎ P – 500. AE VISA **M** *(closed Saturday lunch)* 10.50/12.50 **st.** and a la carte 3.80 – 7.95 – **89 rm** 69.50/82.00 **st.**, **5 suites** 115.00/155.00 **st.** – SB (weekends only) 72.00/76.00 **st.**

MICHELIN Distribution Centre, 12 Tinsley Park Close, S9 5DE, ✆ 433264, Fax 439279 BY

AUDI 1 Eccleshall Rd, South ✆ 670670
BMW Broad Lane ✆ 755077
CITROEN, FIAT Suffolk Rd ✆ 721378
FORD 53-67 London Rd ✆ 751515
FORD Eccleshall Rd ✆ 686986
HONDA 918 Chesterfield Rd ✆ 748029
HYUNDAI, RENAULT 252 Crookes ✆ 669202
JAGUAR-DAIMLER 200 Sharrow Vale ✆ 684741
LADA 178-184 London Rd ✆ 557394
MAZDA 872 Chesterfield Rd ✆ 748643
MERCEDES-BENZ 300 Cemetery Rd ✆ 663468
MERCEDES-BENZ Hanover Way ✆ 753391
MITSUBISHI Scotland St. ✆ 760567/ 731836
NISSAN 1-7 Meersbrook Rd ✆ 57315
NISSAN 9-15 Manton St., Sheffield ✆ 0742 738947
PEUGEOT-TALBOT Fitzwilliam St. ✆ 756324
PEUGEOT-TALBOT Langsett Rd ✆ 342368
RENAULT Abbeydale Rd Sth. ✆ 369041
ROVER Penistone Rd ✆ 348801
ROVER Tenter St. ✆ 761141
ROVER 286 Sandygate Rd ✆ 302021
ROVER Broadfield Rd ✆ 588121
SAAB 115 Eccleshall Rd South ✆ 369946
SEAT Shalesmoor ✆ 750000
SKODA 39-45 Infirmary Rd ✆ 701971
SKODA 21 Mansfield Rd ✆ 396001
TOYOTA Ellin St. ✆ 768717
VAUXHALL Saville St. ✆ 766600
VAUXHALL Eccleshall Rd ✆ 685922
VOLVO Eccleshall Rd ✆ 753151

ATS 87-91 Clifton St., Attercliffe ✆ 449750/ 449759
ATS Herries Rd ✆ 343986/7

SHELDWICH Kent 404 W 30 – see Faversham.

SHENINGTON Oxon – see Banbury.

SHEPPERTON Surrey 404 S 29 – pop. 9 643 – ☎ 0932 Walton-on-Thames.
London 25.

Plan : see Greater London (South-West)

Shepperton Moat House (Q.M.H.), Felix Lane, TW17 8NP, E : 1¼ m. on B 375 ✆ 241404, Telex 928170, Fax 245231, – TV ☎ P – 300. AE VISA. *closed 26 to 31 December* – **M** *(closed Saturday lunch)* 13.75 **st.** and a la carte 4.50 – **156 rm** 68.50/110.00 **st.** – SB (weekends only) 74.00 **st.** AY a

SHEPTON MALLET Somerset 403 404 M 30 **The West Country G.** – pop. 6 197 – ECD : Wednesday – ☎ 0749.

See : Site★ – SS. Peter and Paul's Church★.

Envir. : Oakhill Manor★*AC*, N : 4 m. off A 37 – Evercreech Church Tower★, SE : 4 m. – Downside Abbey★*AC*, N : 5 m. by A 37 on A 367 – Nunney★, W : 9 m. on A 361.

18 Mendip, Gurney Slade ✆ 840570.

2 Petticoat Lane ✆ 5258 (summer only).

London 127 – Bristol 20 – Southampton 63 – Taunton 31.

XX **Bowlish House** with rm, Wells Rd, BA4 5JD, W : ½ m. on A 371 ✆ 342022, – TV P. VISA *closed 24 to 27 December* – **M** (booking essential) (lunch by arrangement)/dinner 21.00 **st.** 3.50 – 3.50 – **4 rm** 42.00/45.00 **st.**

X **Blostin's,** 29 Waterloo Rd, BA4 5HH, ✆ 343648 – VISA *closed Sunday, Monday, 2 weeks January, 1 weeks June and 1 week November* – **M** (lunch by arrangement)/dinner 13.95 **t.** and a la carte 16.40/20.95 **st.** 4.95.

at Doulting E : 1½ m. on A 361 – ✉ Shepton Mallet – ☎ 074 988 Cranmore :

XX **Brottens Lodge** with rm, BA4 4RB, S : 1 m. ✆ 352, Fax 601, ≤, – TV ☎. VISA. *closed first 2 weeks January* – **M** *(closed Saturday lunch and Sunday)* 18.00/21.00 **st.** 3.50 – 4.50 – **3 rm** 48.00/75.00 **st.**

at Croscombe W : 2 ¼ m. on A 371 – ✉ Wells – ☎ 0749 Shepton Mallet :

The Bull Terrier, Wells, BA5 3QJ, ☎ 343658 – TV. VISA.
M *(closed Sunday dinner and Monday November-March)* a la carte 6.75/14.25 **t.** 4.10
3 rm 18.00/42.00 **t.**

HONDA Townsend Rd ☎ 4422 VW-AUDI Station Rd ☎ 4091

SHERBORNE Dorset 403 404 M 31 **The West Country G.** – pop. 7 405 – ECD : Wednesday – ☎ 0935.

See : Site★ – Abbey★★ – Sherborne Castle★*AC*.

Envir. : Sandford Orcas Manor House★*AC*, N : 4 m. by B 3148 – Purse Caundle Manor★*AC* NE : 5 m. by A 30.

18 Clatcombe ☎ 812475, N : 1 m.

Hound St. ☎ 815341 (summer only).

◆London 128 – Bournemouth 39 – Dorchester 19 – Salisbury 36 – Taunton 31.

Eastbury, Long St., DT9 3BY, ☎ 813131, Telex 46644, Fax 817296, – TV ☎ P – 60 VISA.
M 10.50/19.50 **t.** and a la carte – **15 rm** 62.50/80.00 **t.** – SB (October-April (except Christmas and New Year) 98.00/118.00 **st.**

Half Moon, Half Moon St., DT9 3LN, ☎ 812017 – rm TV ☎ P
15 rm.

Pheasants, 24 Greenhill, DT9 4EW, ☎ 815252 – P. VISA
closed Sunday dinner, Monday and 2 weeks January – **M** 10.50 **t.** (lunch) and a la carte 15.20/18.50 **t.** 3.60.

at Oborne NE : 2 m. by A 30 – ✉ ☎ 0935 Sherborne :

Grange with rm, DT9 4LA, ☎ 813463, ←, – TV ☎ P. VISA.
closed Sunday dinner, 1 to 7 January and 11 August-1 September – **M** (dinner only and Sunday lunch)/dinner 12.00/18.00 **t.** and a la carte 4.60 – **7 rm** 45.00/65.00 **t.**

ALFA-ROMEO, LANCIA Long St. ☎ 3262 ROVER Digby Rd ☎ 2436
MERCEDES-BENZ Yeovil Rd ☎ 3350

SHERBOURNE Warw. – see Warwick.

SHERE Surrey 404 S 30 – see Guildford.

SHERIFF HUTTON North Yorks. 402 Q 21 – pop. 884 – ✉ York – ☎ 034 77.

◆London 313 – York 10.

Rangers House , The Park, YO6 1RH, S : 1 ¼ m. by Strensall rd ☎ 397, – P.
M 18.00 3.00 – **6 rm** 28.50/57.00 – SB (October-March except Easter, Christmas and New Year) 72.00/76.00 **st.**

SHERINGHAM Norfolk 404 X 25 – pop. 6 861 – ECD : Wednesday – ☎ 0263 Cromer.

Envir. : Cromer : SS. Peter and Paul's Church (tower ←★).

18 Sheringham ☎ 822038.

Station Approach ☎ 824329 (summer only).

◆London 128 – Cromer 4 – ◆Norwich 27.

Beacon, 1 Nelson Rd, NR26 8BT, ☎ 822019, – rest P. VISA.
June-September – **6 rm** (dinner included) 24.00/52.00.

SHIFNAL Shropshire 402 403 404 M 25 – pop. 6 094 – ECD : Thursday – ✉ ☎ 0952 Telford.

See : St. Andrew's Church★ 12C-16C.

Envir. : Weston Park★ 17C (paintings★★) *AC*, NE : 5 m.

18 Decker Hill ☎ 460467.

◆London 150 – ◆Birmingham 28 – Shrewsbury 16.

Park House, Park St., TF11 9BA, ☎ 460128, Fax 461658, , , – TV ☎ P – 180
52 rm, 2 suites.

Idsall (at Park House H.), Park St., TF11 9BA, ☎ 460128, Fax 461658, – P.

FORD Park St. ☎ 460631 ROVER Chepside ☎ 460412

SHINFIELD Berks. 404 R 29 – see Reading.

SHIPDHAM Norfolk 404 W 26 – pop. 1 974 – ✉ Thetford – ☎ 0362 Dereham.

◆London 102 – East Dereham 5 – ◆Norwich 21 – Watton 6.

Shipdham Place with rm, Church Close, IP25 7LX, on A 1075 ☎ 820303, – rest ☎ P. VISA
M (booking essential) 10.95/22.50 **t.** 2.80 – **8 rm** 33.00/85.00 **t.** – SB 47.00/114.00 **st.**

SHIPHAM Somerset 403 L 30 – ✉ Winscombe – ☎ 0934 Weston-Super-Mare

Daneswood House, Cuck Hill, BS25 1RD, ☎ 843145, Fax 843824, ≤, 🌳 – 📺 ☎ **P**. AE VISA. ✗
closed 24 to 31 December – **M** *(closed Sunday dinner to non-residents)* 19.95/49.50 **t.** 3.50 – **9 rm** 45.00/75.00 **st.**, **3 suites** 89.50 **st.**

SHIPLEY West Yorks. 402 O 22 – pop. 28 815 – ECD : Wednesday – ☎ 0274 Bradford.
Northcliffe, High Bank Lane ☎ 584085, SW : 1¼ m. by A 650 – 18 Beckfoot Lane, Cottingley, ingley ☎ 563212.
London 216 – Bradford 4 – ◆Leeds 12.

Aagrah, 27 Westgate, BD18 3QX, ☎ 594660, Indian rest. – AE VISA
closed Christmas Day – **M** (booking essential) (dinner only and Sunday lunch)/dinner a la carte 5.45/12.10 **t.** 2.85.

SHIPSTON-ON-STOUR Warw. 403 404 P 27 – pop. 3 072 – ☎ 0608.
London 85 – ◆Birmingham 34 – ◆Oxford 29.

Old Mill with rm, 8 Mill St., CV36 4AW, on B 4035 ☎ 61880, 🌳 – 📺 **P**. AE VISA
M *(closed Sunday dinner and Bank Holidays)* a la carte 16.00/23.15 **t.** 3.25 – **5 rm** 35.00/50.00 **t.** – SB 65.00/85.00 **st.**

at ***Lower Brailes*** E : 4½ m. on B 4035 – ✉ Banbury (Oxon.) – ☎ 060 885 Brailes :

Feldon House with rm, OX15 5HW, ☎ 580, « 19C country house of 17C origins », 🌳 – 📺 ☎ **P**. VISA. ✗
M *(closed Sunday dinner)* 16.75/21.50 **st.** 3.75 – **4 rm** 30.00/55.00 **st.**

at ***Darlingscott*** NW : 2¼ m. by B 4035 on Ilmington rd – ✉ Shipston-on-Stour – ☎ 060 882 Ilmington :

Longdon Manor , CV36 4PW, W : 1 m. ☎ 235, ≤, « Elizabethan manor, country house atmosphere », 🌳 – **P**. ✗
March-November – **M** (by arrangement) 15.00 **s.** – **3 rm** 30.00/50.00 **s.**

ORD Church St. ☎ 61425 SUBARU, ISUZU Tredington ☎ 61544

Per visitare una città o una regione : utilizzate le ***guide verdi Michelin.***

SHIPTON GORGE Dorset – see Bridport.

SHIPTON-UNDER-WYCHWOOD Oxon. 403 404 P 28 – pop. 2 558 – ECD : Wednesday – ☎ 0993.
◆London 81 – ◆Birmingham 50 – Gloucester 37 – ◆Oxford 25.

Shaven Crown, OX7 6BA, ☎ 830330, « 14C hospice » – 📺 **P**. VISA. ✗
M (bar lunch Monday to Saturday)/dinner 21.50 **t.** 4.00 – **9 rm** 30.00/67.00 **t.** – SB (except Bank Holidays) 79.00/85.00 **st.**

Lamb Inn with rm, High St., OX7 6DQ, ☎ 830465 – rest 📺 **P**. AE VISA. ✗
M *(closed Sunday dinner and Monday)* 11.50/18.50 **t.** and a la carte 3.75 – **5 rm** 38.00/58.00 **t.** – SB (weekdays only) 80.00 **st.**

SHIRLEY West Midlands 403 404 O 26 – see Solihull.

SHORNE Kent 404 V 29 – pop. 2 565 – ✉ Gravesend – ☎ 047 482.
◆London 27 – Gravesend 4 – Maidstone 12 – Rochester 4.

Inn on the Lake, DA12 3HB, on A 2 ☎ 3333, Telex 966356, Fax 3175, ≤, , 🌳, park – 📺 ☎ **P** – 150. AE VISA. ✗
M 11.50 **t.** (lunch) and a la carte 14.50/23.75 **t.** 5.00 – **78 rm** 65.00/90.00 **t.**

SHRAWLEY Heref. and Worc. – ✉ ☎ 0905 Worcester.
◆London 152 – ◆Birmingham 45 – Leominster 3.

Lenchford, WR6 6TB, SE : ½ m. on B 4196 ☎ 620229, Fax 621125, ≤, « Riverside setting », heated, 🌳 – 📺 ☎ **P**. AE VISA. ✗
closed 26 to 30 December – **M** *(closed Sunday dinner)* (buffet lunch Monday to Saturday)/dinner 17.00 **st.** and a la carte 3.95 – **16 rm** 42.50/60.00 **st.**

SHREWSBURY Shropshire 402 403 L 25 – pop. 57 731 – ECD : Thursday – ☎ 0743.
See : Abbey Church★ (11C-14C) **D** – St. Mary's Church★ (Jesse Tree window★) **A** – Grope Lane★ (15C).
Envir. : Wroxeter★ (Roman city and baths) *AC*, SE : 6 m. by A 5 on B 4380 – Condover Hall★ (15C) *AC*, S : 5 m. by A 49 – Much Wenlock Priory★, SE : 12 m. by A 49 AZ and A 458.
18 Condover ☎ 722976 – 9 Meole Brace ☎ 64050, S by A 49.
The Square ☎ 50761/50762.
◆London 164 – ◆Birmingham 48 – ◆Cardiff 10 – Chester 43 – Derby 67 – Gloucester 93 – ◆Manchester 68 – ◆Stoke-on-Trent 39 – ◆Swansea 124.

Rowton Castle, SY5 9EP, W : 7 ½ m. on A 458 ℘ 884044, Fax 884949, park – TV ☎ P – 150. AE VISA
M 13.50 **st.** (lunch)and a la carte 13.00/16.25 **st.** 3.88 – **18 rm** 60.00/150.00 **st.** SB 95.00 **st.**

Lion (T.H.F.), Wyle Cop, SY1 1UY, ℘ 53107, Fax 52744 – rm TV ☎ P – 80. AE VISA
M 8.10/18.00 **st.** and a la carte 4.70 – 7.50 – **59 rm** 59.50/115.00 **st.** – SB 80.00 102.00 **st.**

Prince Rupert (Q.M.H.), Butcher Row, SY1 1UQ, ℘ 236000, Telex 35100, Fax 57306 – rest TV ☎ P – 70. AE VISA
M 10.75/16.50 **t.** and a la carte 4.00 – **62 rm** 58.00/72.00 **t.**, **3 suites** 72.00/82.00 **t.** SB (weekends only) 84.00/92.00 **st.**

Radbrook Hall (B.C.B.), Radbrook Rd, SY3 9BQ, SW : 1 ½ m. on A 488 ℘ 236676 Fax 59194, squash – TV ☎ P – 130. AE VISA.
M 8.00/15.00 **st.** – **28 rm** 48.00/62.00 **st.**

Fieldside without rest., 38 London Rd, SY2 6NX, E : 1¼ m. via Abbey Foregate on A 511 ℘ 53143, – TV P. AE VISA.
9 rm 18.00/40.00 **st.**

Cromwells, 11 Dogpole, SY1 1EN, ℘ 61440 – TV
6 rm.

Sandford House without rest., St. Julians Friars, SY1 1XL, ℘ 3829, – TV
9 rm 19.00/37.50 **st.**

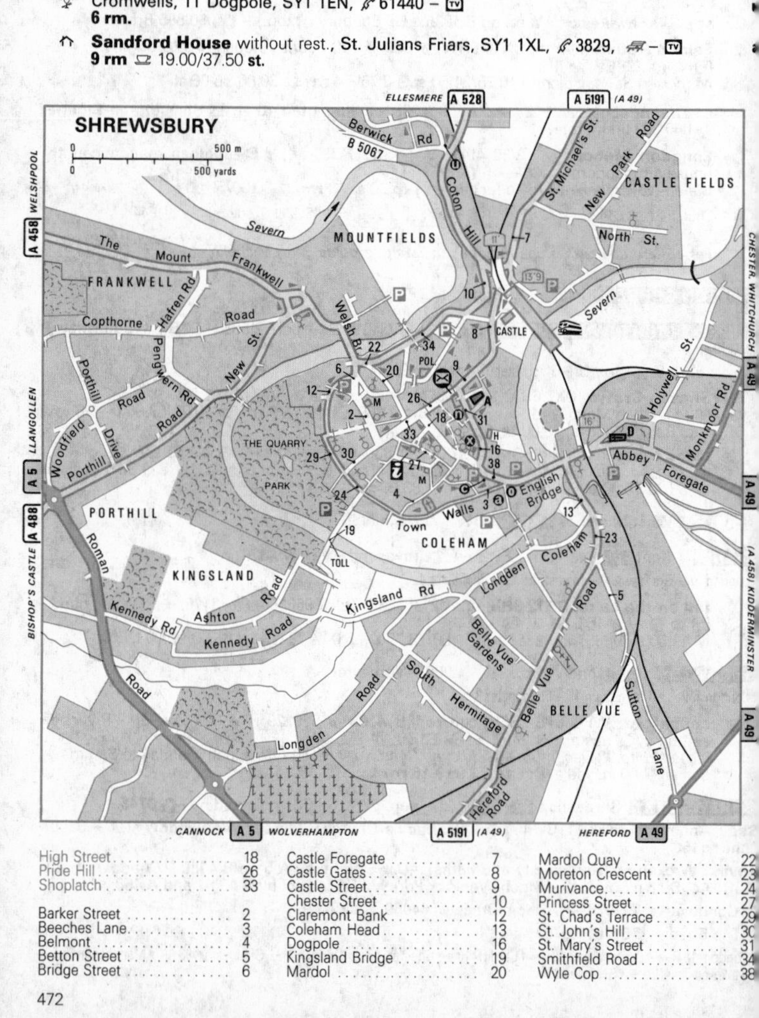

High Street	18
Pride Hill	26
Shoplatch	33
Barker Street	2
Beeches Lane	3
Belmont	4
Betton Street	5
Bridge Street	6
Castle Foregate	7
Castle Gates	8
Castle Street	9
Chester Street	10
Claremont Bank	12
Coleham Head	13
Dogpole	16
Kingsland Bridge	19
Mardol	20
Mardol Quay	22
Moreton Crescent	23
Murivance	24
Princess Street	27
St. Chad's Terrace	29
St. John's Hill	30
St. Mary's Street	31
Smithfield Road	34
Wyle Cop	38

Sydney House, Coton Cres., off Coton Hill, SY1 2LJ, 54681 – TV ☎ P. VISA. x
closed 24 to 31 December – **M** (by arrangement) 9.00 **st.** 3.10 – **7 rm** 24.50/48.00 **st.**

Cornerhouse, 59a Wyle Cop. (1st floor), SY1 1XB, 231991 – AE VISA o
closed Bank Holidays – **M** 13.95 **t.** and a la carte 3.50.

at Albrighton N : 3 m. on A 528 – ✉ Shrewsbury – 0939 Bomere Heath :

Albrighton Hall, Ellesmere Rd, SY4 3AG, 291000, Telex 35726, Fax 291123, , park, squash – TV ☎ P – 200. AE VISA
M 9.50/11.75 **t.** (lunch) and a la carte 12.65/27.25 **t.** – **33 rm** 52.00/120.00 **st.** – SB (weekends only) 93.00/100.00 **st.**

at Dorrington S : 7 m. on A 49 – ✉ Shrewsbury – 074 373 Dorrington :

Country Friends with rm, SY5 7JD, 707, – P. AE VISA
closed 2 weeks July-August, 1 week October and Christmas – **M** *(closed Sunday and Monday)* 16.00 **t.** and a la carte 4.80 – **3 rm** 32.00/42.00 **t.**

at Hanwood SW : 4 m. on A 488 – ✉ 0743 Shrewsbury :

White House, SY5 8LP, 860414, – P.
M (by arrangement) 13.00 **st.** 5.00 – **6 rm** 19.70/50.40 **st.**

TROEN 159 Abbey Foregate 231234
TROEN, DAIHATSU, SAAB Featherbed Lane 241445
ORD Coton Hill 3631
ADA Featherbed Lane 60303
EUGEOT-TALBOT Featherbed Lane 235611
OVER Harlescott 236050
SAAB Westbury Garage 241445
VAUXHALL-OPEL Greyfriars 231321
VOLVO Featherbed Lane 231251
VW-AUDI Featherbed Lane, Harlescott 52471

ATS Lancaster Rd, Harlescott 3954/232231

HURDINGTON Glos. 403 404 N 28 – see Cheltenham.

IBSON Leics. – see Nuneaton (Warw.).

IDFORD Devon 403 K 31 – see Sidmouth.

IDMOUTH Devon 403 K 31 **The West Country G.** – pop. 10 808 – ECD : Thursday – 0395.
nvir. : Seaton, headlands (<★★), E : 9 m. – Branscombe★, E : 9 m. – Colyton★, E : 10 m – icton Gardens★ S : S½m.
Cotmaton Rd 513023.
The Esplanade 516441 (summer only).
London 170 – Exeter 14 – Taunton 27 – Weymouth 45.

Victoria, The Esplanade, Peak Hill, EX10 8RY, 512651, Fax 579154, <, heated, – TV ☎ P. AE VISA.
M 10.00/18.50 **t.** and a la carte – **58 rm** 68.00/110.00 **t.**, **3 suites** 160.00/180.00 **t.** – SB (except summer, Easter, Whitsun and Christmas) 77.00/120.00 **st.**

Riviera, The Esplanade, EX10 8AY, 515201, Fax 577775, < – rest TV ☎ . AE VISA
M 10.50/17.50 **t.** and a la carte 3.75 – **34 rm** 50.00/114.00 **t.** – SB (November-April) (weekends only) 82.00/97.00 **st.**

Belmont, The Esplanade, EX10 8RX, 512555, Fax 579154, <, – TV ☎ P. AE VISA.
M 9.75/15.00 **t.** and a la carte 8.00 – **54 rm** 60.00/132.00 **t.**

Salcombe Hill House, Beatlands Rd, EX10 8JQ, 514697, heated, , – rest TV ☎ P. VISA.
March-October – **M** 8.00/12.00 **t.** and a la carte 4.50 – **32 rm** 32.00/90.00 **t.** – SB (March-May) 62.00/77.00 **st.**

Littlecourt, Seafield Rd, EX10 8HF, 515279, heated, – rest TV P
21 rm.

Abbeydale, Manor Rd, EX10 8RP, 512060, – rest TV ☎ P.
March-October and Christmas – **M** (bar lunch)/dinner 13.00 **t.** 3.00 – **18 rm** (dinner included) 46.00/92.00 **t.**

Mount Pleasant, Salcombe Rd, EX10 8JA, 514694, – TV P.
March-October – **M** (bar lunch)/dinner 11.95 **st.** 3.75 – **16 rm** 24.00/56.00 **st.**

Hunters Moon, Sid Rd, EX10 9AA, 513380, – TV ☎ P
18 rm.

Torbay, Station Rd, EX10 8NW, 513456 – TV ☎. VISA
M 5.00/9.00 **t.** and a la carte 3.50 – **30 rm** 25.00/60.00 **t.** – SB (November-April except Christmas) 36.00/49.30 **st.**

Woodlands, Station Rd, Cotmaton Cross, EX10 8HG, 513120, – P. VISA
M 3.95/8.50 **t.** 3.20 – **29 rm** 23.00/57.20 **t.** – SB (October-May) 40.60/47.20 **st.**

Salcombe Cottage, Hillside Rd, EX10 8JF, ✆ 516829, « 18C thatched cottage », ⅏ rm Ⓟ
M 6.50 **st.** – **4 rm** ⊐ 19.00/34.00 **st.** – SB (October-April) 40.00/42.00 **st.**

Barrington Villa, Salcombe Rd, EX10 8PU, ✆ 514252, – Ⓟ
closed mid October-mid December – **M** (by arrangement) 5.50 **st.** – **9 rm** ⊐ 25.20/53.25

at Sidford N : 2 m. – ✉ 039 55 Sidmouth :

Applegarth, Church St., EX10 9QP, E : on A 3052 ✆ 513174, « Garden » – rest TV
VISA.
M *(closed Sunday dinner and Monday)* (bar lunch Monady to Saturday)/dinner 9.50 **st.** ar a la carte 3.75 – **8 rm** ⊐ 22.50/45.00 **st.** – SB 51.00/53.00 **st.**

FIAT Crossways, Sidford ✆ 513595
ATS Vicarage Rd ✆ 512433

SILCHESTER Hants. 403 404 Q 29 – pop. 1 072 – ✉ Reading (Berks.) – 0734.

◆London 62 – Basingstoke 8 – Reading 14 – Winchester 26.

Romans (Best Western) ⑤, Little London Rd, RG7 2PN, ✆ 700421, Fax 700691, hea ed, , – TV ☎ Ⓟ – 60. AE VISA
closed Christmas-New Year – **M** *(closed Sunday dinner)* 17.00/25.00 **st.** 4.90 – **24 r** ⊐ 62.00/82.00 **st.** – SB (weekends only) 80.00/100.00 **st.**

SILLOTH Cumbria 402 J 19 – 069 73.

Skinburness, Skinburness, CA5 4QT, NE : 2 m. by B 5302 ✆ 32332, Fax 32549, , – TV ☎ Ⓟ – 65. AE VISA
M (bar lunch Monday to Saturday)/dinner 14.95 **t** – **25 rm** ⊐ 40.00/86.00 **t.** – SB 98.0 118.00 **st.**

SIMONSBATH Somerset 403 I 30 The West Country G. – ✉ Minehead – 064 383 Exford.

◆London 200 – Exeter 40 – Minehead 19 – Taunton 38.

Simonsbath House, TA24 7SH, ✆ 259, ≤, « 17C country house », – rest TV
Ⓟ. AE VISA.
closed December and January – **M** (bar lunch)/dinner 17.50 **st.** 3.95 – **7 rm** ⊐ 45.0 92.00 **t.** – SB 122.00 **st.**

SINDLESHAM Berks. – see Reading.

SISSINGHURST Kent 404 V 30 – see Cranbrook.

SITTINGBOURNE Kent 404 W 29 – pop. 35 893 – ECD : Wednesday – 0795.

Wormdale, Newington ✆ 842261.

◆London 44 – Canterbury 16 – Maidstone 13.

Coniston, 70 London Rd, ME10 1NT, ✆ 472131, Fax 428056 – TV ☎ ♿ Ⓟ – 120.
VISA
M 13.50 **t.** and a la carte 3.80 – **57 rm** ⊐ 47.00/74.00 **t.**

FORD Canterbury Rd ✆ 70711
MAZDA High Newington ✆ 842307
RENAULT Chalkwell Rd ✆ 76361
ROVER Salcombe Rd ✆ 512522
TALBOT Teynham ✆ 521286
VAUXHALL-OPEL London Rd, Bapchild ✆ 76222
ATS Crown Quay Lane ✆ 472384/472912

SIX MILE BOTTOM Cambs. – see Newmarket (Suffolk).

SKEGNESS Lincs. 402 404 V 24 – pop. 12 645 – ECD : Thursday – 0754.

North Shore ✆ 3298 – Seacroft ✆ 3020.

Embassy Centre, Grand Parade ✆ 4821 (summer only).

◆London 145 – Lincoln 41.

County, North Par., PE25 2UB, ✆ 2461, ≤ – TV ☎ Ⓟ –
44 rm.

FIAT Beresford Av. ✆ 67131
FORD Wainfleet Rd ✆ 66019
ROVER Roman Bank ✆ 3671
YUGO Clifton Grove ✆ 3589
ATS 66 Alexandra Rd ✆ 67272

SKELTON North Yorks. 402 Q 22 – see York.

SKELWITH BRIDGE Cumbria 402 K 20 – see Ambleside.

SKIPTON North Yorks. 402 N 22 – pop. 13 009 – ECD : Tuesday – 0756.

See : Castle★ (14C) *AC*.

Envir. : Bolton Priory★ E : 6 m.

off NW Bypass ✆ 3922 N : 1 m. on A 65.

8 Victoria Sq. ✆ 792809.

◆London 217 – Kendal 45 – ◆Leeds 26 – Preston 36 – York 43.

Randell's, BD23 2TA, S : 1¼ m. ✆ 700100, Fax 700107, squash – 400.
M 9.95/14.95 **st.** – **61 rm** 62.00/145.00 **st.**

Unicorn, Devonshire Pl., Keighley Rd, BD23 2LP, ✆ 794146 –
M *(closed Sunday)* (buffet lunch)/dinner 12.00 **st.** 3.00 – **10 rm** 36.00/46.00 **st.** – SB 80.00/90.00 **st.**

Travelodge without rest., A 65/A 59 roundabout, Gargrave Rd, BD23 1UD, W : 1¾ m. via Water St., ✆ 798091, Reservations (Toll free) 0800 850950 –
32 rm 24.00/29.50 **t.**

Oats with rm, Chapel Hill, BD23 1NL, ✆ 798118, Fax 792369 –
M *(closed lunch Monday and Saturday and Sunday dinner)* a la carte 19.50/22.00 **t.** – **4 rm** 46.00/56.00 **t.**

ATS Carleton Rd Garage, Carleton Rd ✆ 795741/2

LAIDBURN Lancs. 402 M 22 – pop. 332 – ✉ Clitheroe – 020 06.

London 249 – Burnley 21 – Lancaster 19 – ♦Leeds 48 – Preston 27.

Parrock Head, BB7 3AH, NW : 1 m. ✆ 614, ≤ Bowland Fells, – rest
M (bar lunch)/dinner a la carte 11.50/16.00 **t.** 4.00 – **9 rm** 35.00/57.50 **t.**

Hark to Bounty, BB7 3EP, ✆ 246 –
8 rm.

SLEAFORD Lincs. 402 404 S 25 – pop. 8 247 – ECD : Thursday – 0529.

See : St. Denis' Church★ 12C-15C.

South Rauceby ✆ 052 98 (South Rauceby) 273, W : 1 m. on A 153.

London 119 – ♦Leicester 45 – Lincoln 17 – ♦Nottingham 39.

Lincolnshire Oak, East Rd, NG34 7EQ, NE: 3 m. on A 153 ✆ 413807, Fax 413710, – rest – 140.
M (bar lunch)/dinner 16.00 **st.** – **14 rm** 42.00/60.00 **st.**

Tally Ho Inn, Aswarby, NG34 8SA, S : 4½ m. on A 15 ✆ 052 95 (Culverthorpe) 205, ≤, –
M 10.00 **t.** and a la carte 2.95 – **6 rm** 26.00/38.00 **t.**

FIAT Grantham Rd ✆ 052 98 (Sth. Rauceby) 674
FORD London Rd ✆ 302921
RENAULT 50 Westgate ✆ 305305
ROVER Lincoln Rd ✆ 303034
SKODA Holdingham ✆ 302545
ATS 40 Albion Terr. off Boston Rd ✆ 302908

SLEIGHTS North Yorks. 402 S 20 – see Whitley.

SLOUGH Berks. 404 S 29 – pop. 106 341 – ECD : Wednesday – 0753.

Envir. : Eton (college★★) S : 2 m.

London 29 – ♦Oxford 39 – Reading 19.

Holiday Inn, Ditton Rd, Langley, SL3 8PT, SE : 2½ m. on A 4 ✆ 44244, Telex 848646, Fax 40272, – rm – 300.
M (carving lunch Sunday to Friday) 17.50/19.00 **t.** and a la carte 7.95 – 9.50 – **298 rm** 99.00/123.00 **t.**, **4 suites** 275.00/375.00 **t.** – SB (weekends only) 91.50 **st.**

BMW Petersfield Av. ✆ 821821
FORD Petersfield Av. ✆ 33321
SAAB Beaconsfield Rd ✆ 028 14 (Farnham Common) 5111
VOLVO Petersfield Av. ✆ 23031
VW-AUDI 57 Farnham Rd ✆ 33917
ATS 1a Furnival Av. ✆ 24214/38555/37798

SNEATON North Yorks. 402 S 20 – see Whitby.

SNOWDON (YR WYDDFA) Gwynedd 402 403 H 24.

See : Ascent and ✻★★★ (1 h 15 mn from Llanberis (Pass★★) by Snowdon Mountain Railway AC).

***Hotels and restaurant see : Beddgelert** S : 4 m., **Caernarfon** NW : 9 m.*

SOAR MILL COVE Devon – see Salcombe.

SOHAM Cambs. 404 V 26 – 0353.

Soham By-Pass Motel,, NE : ½ m. on A 142 ✆ 721468 – rm
M (restricted grill menu) – **12 rm.**

SOLIHULL West Midlands 403 404 O 26 – pop. 93 940 – ECD : Wednesday – 021 Birmingham.

Copt Heath, 1220 Warwick Rd ✆ 772650.

Central Library, Homer Rd ✆ 704 6130.

London 109 – ♦Birmingham 7 – ♦Coventry 13 – Warwick 13.

St. John's Swallow, 651 Warwick Rd, B91 1AT, ☎ 711 3000, Telex 33935 Fax 705 6629, – 750.
M *(closed lunch Saturday and Bank Holidays)* 12.50/17.50 **st.** and a la carte 5.00 – **202 r** 72.00/92.00 **st.**, **4 suites** – SB (weekends only) 85.00/95.00 **st.**

George, The Square, B91 3RF, ☎ 711 2121, Telex 334134, Fax 711 3374 – rm – 250.
M 15.00/20.00 **st.** and a la carte 4.55 – 7.00 – **74 rm** 68.00/192.00 **st.** – SB (weekends only) 65.00/72.00 **st.**

Liaison, 761 Old Lode Lane, B92 8JE, N : 2¾ m. by B 425 (Lode Lane) ☎ 743 3993 –
closed Saturday lunch, Monday, 4 to 20 August and 1 to 14 January – **M** 16.50/30.00 **t.** and a la carte 8.25.

at Shirley W : 2½ m. by B 4025 – ✉ Solihull – ☎ 021 Birmingham :

Regency, Stratford Rd, B90 4EB, SE : 2 m. on A 34 ☎ 745 6119, Telex 33440 Fax 733 3801, – rest – 150.
M *(closed Saturday lunch)* 12.00/25.00 **st.** and a la carte – **110 rm** 77.00/89.50 **st.**, **2 suites** 110.00 **st.** – SB (weekends only) 80.00 **st.**

Saracen's Head, Stratford Rd, B90 3AG, ☎ 733 3888, Fax 733 2762 – – 10
M 4.95/5.50 **st.** and a la carte 3.95 – **34 rm** 50.00/64.00 **st.**

Chez Julien, 1036 Stratford RD, Monkspath, B90 4EE, SE : 2½ m. on A 34 ☎ 744 723 Fax 745 4775, French rest. –
closed Saturday lunch, Sunday and Bank Holidays – **M** 7.50 **t.** (lunch) and a la carte 17.10/23.80 **t.** 4.10.

BMW 824 Stratford Rd ☎ 733 3444
DAIMLER-JAGUAR 301 Warwick Rd ☎ 706 2801
FIAT 361-369 Stratford Rd ☎ 056 44 (Tanworth) 2218
FORD 361-369 Stratford Rd ☎ 733 3333
MAZDA 270 Stratford Rd, Shirley ☎ 744 1033
NISSAN Stratford Rd, Shirley ☎ 745 5811
PEUGEOT-TALBOT 386 Warwick Rd ☎ 704 1427
ROVER, ROLLS-ROYCE Stratford Rd, Shirley ☎ 745 5855
SUBARU, ISUZU, SEAT Station Lane ☎ 056 43 (Lapworth) 2933

SOMERTON Somerset 403 L 30 – pop. 4 339 – ECD : Wednesday – ☎ 0458.

See : Site★ – Market place★ (17C Arcaded Cross★) – St Michael's (13C Octagonal South Tower)★.

♦London 138 – ♦Bristol 32 – Taunton 17.

Lynch Country House, 4 Behind Berry, TA11 7PD, ☎ 72316, Fax 74370, ≤, « Attractively converted Regency house », park – rest
M (dinner only) 18.50 **t.** 3.50 – **6 rm** 30.00/95.00 **t.**

SONNING-ON-THAMES Berks. 404 R 29 – pop. 1 469 – ECD : Wednesday – ☎ 0734 Reading.

Sonning-on-Thames ☎ 693332.

♦London 48 – Reading 4.

Great House at Sonning, Thames St., RG4 0UT, ☎ 692277, Telex 849031, Fax 44129 – – 40.
M 15.50/25.90 **st.** and a la carte – **33 rm** 69.00/99.00 **st.**, **3 suites** 140.00 **st.** – SB (weekends only) 110.00 **st.**

French Horn with rm, Thames St., RG4 0TN, ☎ 692204, Fax 442210, ≤ River Thames and gardens –
closed 29 March, 25-26 December and 1 January – **M** 26.50 **st.** (lunch) and a la carte 25.40/30.60 **st.** 5.00 – **10 rm** 75.00/85.00 **st.**, **4 suites** 95.00/120.00 **st.**

SOUTHAM Glos. 403 404 N 28 – see Cheltenham.

SOUTHAMPTON Hants. 403 404 P 31 – pop. 211 321 – ECD : Monday and Wednesday ☎ 0703.

See : Docks★ AY – Tudor House Museum★ (16C) *AC* AZ **M1** – God's House Tower★ 12 (Museum of Archaelogia) AZ **M2** – Bargate★ AZ **B.**

Envir. : Netley (abbey★ ruins 13C) *AC*, SE : 3 m. BZ **A.**

18, 9 West Side Basset Av. ☎ 768407 AY – 18 Fleming Park ☎ 0703 (Eastleigh) 612797, N : 6 m by A 33 AY.

Southampton Airport : ☎ 629600 N : 4 m. BY.

to America (New York) (Cunard) – to the Isle of Wight : East and West Cowes (Red Funnel Services) frequent services daily.

to the Isle of Wight : West Cowes (Red Funnel Services : hydrofoil) frequent services daily (20 mn).

Above Bar Precinct ☎ 221106.

♦London 87 – ♦Bristol 79 – ♦Plymouth 161.

Plans on following pages

Hilton National, Bracken Pl., Chilworth, SO2 3UB, ☎ 702700, Telex 47594, Fax 767233, – rm rest – 200 AY e
132 rm, 2 suites.

Polygon (T.H.F.), Cumberland Pl., SO9 4GD, ☎ 330055, Telex 47175, Fax 332435 – rm – 500. VISA AZ n
M *(closed Saturday lunch)* 10.95/19.75 **st.** and a la carte 4.95 – 7.60 – **117 rm** 75.00/90.00 **st.**, **2 suites** 120.00 **st.** – SB (weekends only) 74.00/80.00 **st.**

Dolphin (T.H.F.), 35 High St., SO9 2DS, ☎ 339955, Telex 477735, Fax 333650 – rm – 90 AZ i
72 rm.

Post House (T.H.F.), Herbert Walker Av., SO1 0HJ, ☎ 330777, Telex 477368, Fax 332510, heated, – rm – 180. VISA AZ o
M *(closed Saturday lunch)* 9.95/13.95 **st.** and a la carte 3.75 – 7.50 – **130 rm** 69.00/89.00 **st.**, **2 suites** 110.00 **st.** – SB (weekends only) 76.00/96.00 **st.**

Southampton Park, 12-13 Cumberland Pl., SO9 4NY, ☎ 223467, Telex 47439, Fax 332538, – rm rest – 200. VISA AZ u
M a la carte approx. 14.45 **st.** – **71 rm** 67.00/85.00 **st.** – SB (weekends only) 70.00/80.00 **st.**

Southampton Moat House (Q.M.H.), 119 Highfield Lane, Portswood, SO9 1YQ, ☎ 559555, Telex 47186, Fax 583910 – – 180. VISA BY e
M *(closed lunch Saturday and Sunday)* 13.50 **st.** and a la carte 5.15 – **66 rm** 60.00/85.00 **st.** – SB (weekends only) 74.80 **st.**

Novotel, 1 West Quay Rd, SO1 0RA, ☎ 330550, Fax 22158, – rm rest – 500 AZ x
121 rm.

Wessex, 66-68 Northlands Rd, SO1 2LH, ☎ 631744, Fax 639243, – . VISA AY r
closed 25 and 26 December – **M** (bar lunch)/dinner 10.00 **s.** and a la carte 3.50 – **34 rm** 38.00/49.50 **st.**

Rosida Garden, 25-27 Hill Lane, S01 5AB, ☎ 228501, Fax 635501, heated, – . VISA AZ r
closed 23 December-2 January – **M** (bar lunch)/dinner a la carte 9.00/12.00 **t.** 3.00 – **28 rm** 45.00/66.00 **t.** – SB (weekends only) (except September) 68.00/85.00 **st.**

Star, 26 High St., SO9 4ZA, ☎ 339939, Fax 335291 – rm – 70. VISA AZ z
closed 26 December-2 January – **M** *(closed Sunday dinner)* a la carte 9.95/11.95 **st.** 3.25 – **45 rm** 30.00/70.00 **st.** – SB (November-August) (weekends only) 66.00/76.00 **st.**

Northlands, Northlands Rd, SO9 3ZW, ☎ 333871, Fax 230360 – . VISA
M *(closed Saturday and Sunday)* (dinner only) 9.70 **st.** 3.20 – **19 rm** 30.00/54.00 **st.** AY a

Hunters Lodge, 25 Landguard Rd, SO1 5DL, ☎ 227919, Fax 230913 – . VISA AZ v
M (by arrangement) 9.00 **st.** 2.50 – **18 rm** 23.00/51.20 **st.**

Earley House, 46 Peartree Av., Bitterne, SO2 7JP, ☎ 448117 – rm . AE.
M 8.50 **t.** – **10 rm** 19.00/45.00 **t.** BY v

Kuti's, 70 London Rd, S01 2AJ, ☎ 221585, Indian rest. AZ a

La Brasserie, 33-34 Oxford St., SO1 1DS, ☎ 635043 – VISA AZ c
closed Saturday lunch, Sunday and Bank Holidays – **M** 8.75/11.75 **t.** and a la carte 3.50.

Brown's Brasserie, Frobisher House, Nelson Gate, Commercial Rd, SO1 0GX, ☎ 332615. AZ s

Kohinoor, 2 The Broadway, Portswood, SO2 1WE, ☎ 582770, Indian rest. – VISA
M 15.00 **t.** (dinner) and a la carte. BY c

Golden Palace, 1st Floor, 17 Above Bar St., SO1 0DX, ☎ 226636, Chinese rest. – VISA AZ e
M 3.30/11.90 **t.** and a la carte 11.50/15.70 **t.** 3.00.

MICHELIN Distribution Centre, Test Lane, SO1 9JX, ☎ 872344, Fax 663617 AY

CITROEN Rochester St. ☎ 331144
FORD 362-364 Shirley Rd ☎ 701700
FORD Palmerston Rd ☎ 228331
PEUGEOT-TALBOT 21-35 St. Denys Rd ☎ 585822
RENAULT Westquay Rd ☎ 639844
RANGE-ROVER The Avenue ☎ 228811
ROVER The Causeway ☎ 865021
ROVER High St., West End ☎ 473773
ROVER, DAIMLER-JAGUAR, LAND-ROVER, VAUXHALL-OPEL Portsmouth Rd, Sholing ☎ 449232
VAUXHALL The Avenue ☎ 226492
VOLVO Millbrook Roundabout ☎ 705600

ATS West Quay Rd ☎ 333231
ATS 88-94 Portswood Rd ☎ 582727

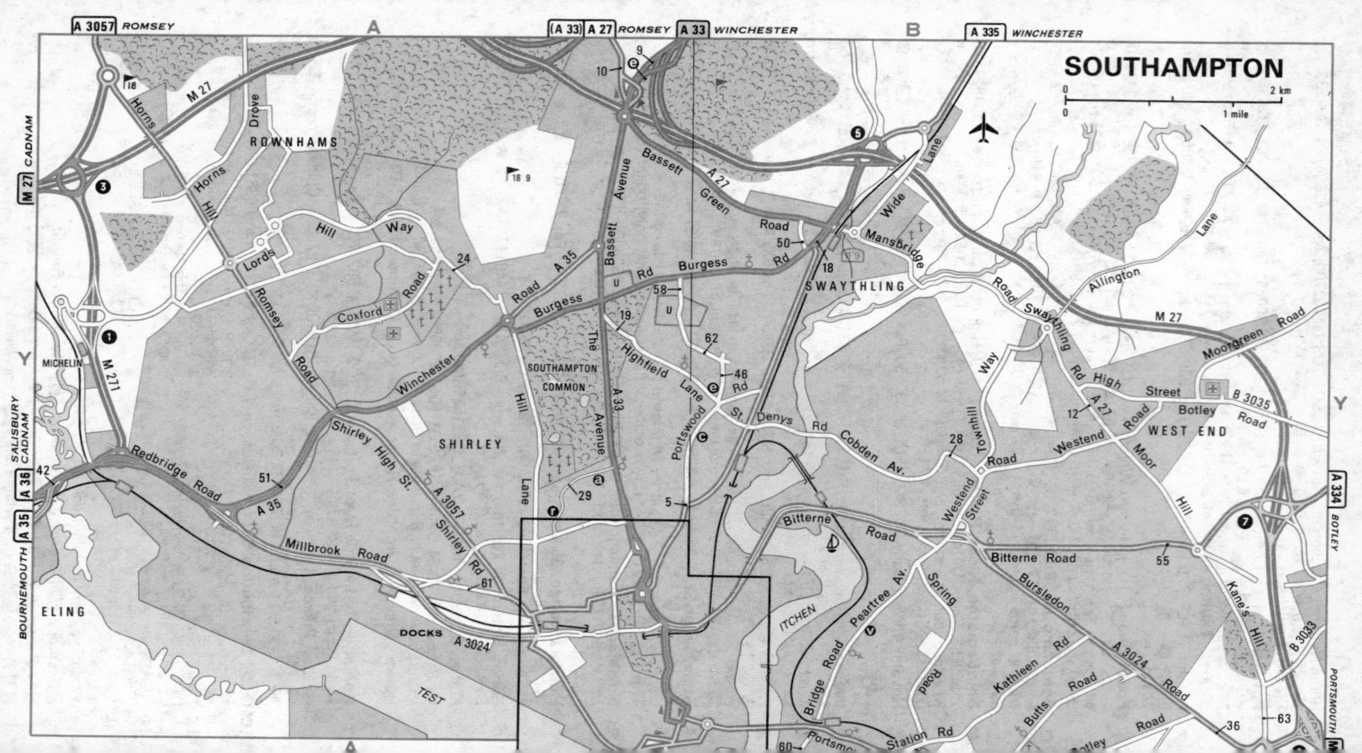
SOUTHAMPTON
0 1 mile
0 2 km
A 3057 ROMSEY
(A 33) A 27 ROMSEY
A 33 WINCHESTER
A 335 WINCHESTER
M 27 CADNAM
A 36 SALISBURY CADNAM
A 35 BOURNEMOUTH
A 334 BOTLEY
PORTSMOUTH
ROWNHAMS
SWAYTHLING
WEST END
SHIRLEY
SOUTHAMPTON COMMON
ELING
DOCKS
ITCHEN
TEST
MICHELIN
M 27
M 271
A 27
A 33
A 35
A 3024
A 3057
B 3035
B 3033
Horns Hill
Drove
Lords Hill Way
Romsey Road
Coxford Road
Winchester Road
Bassett Avenue
Bassett Green Road
Burgess Rd
The Avenue
Hill Lane
Highfield Lane
Portswood
St. Denys Rd
Cobden Av.
Wide Lane
Mansbridge
Swaythling Road
Allington Lane
Moorgreen Road
High Street
Botley Road
Townhill Way
Westend Road
Moor Hill
Westend Street
Bitterne Road
Bursledon Road
Kane's Hill
Spring Road
Peartree Av.
Bridge Road
Kathleen Rd
Butts Road
Station Rd
Shirley High St.
Shirley Rd
Redbridge Road
Millbrook Road

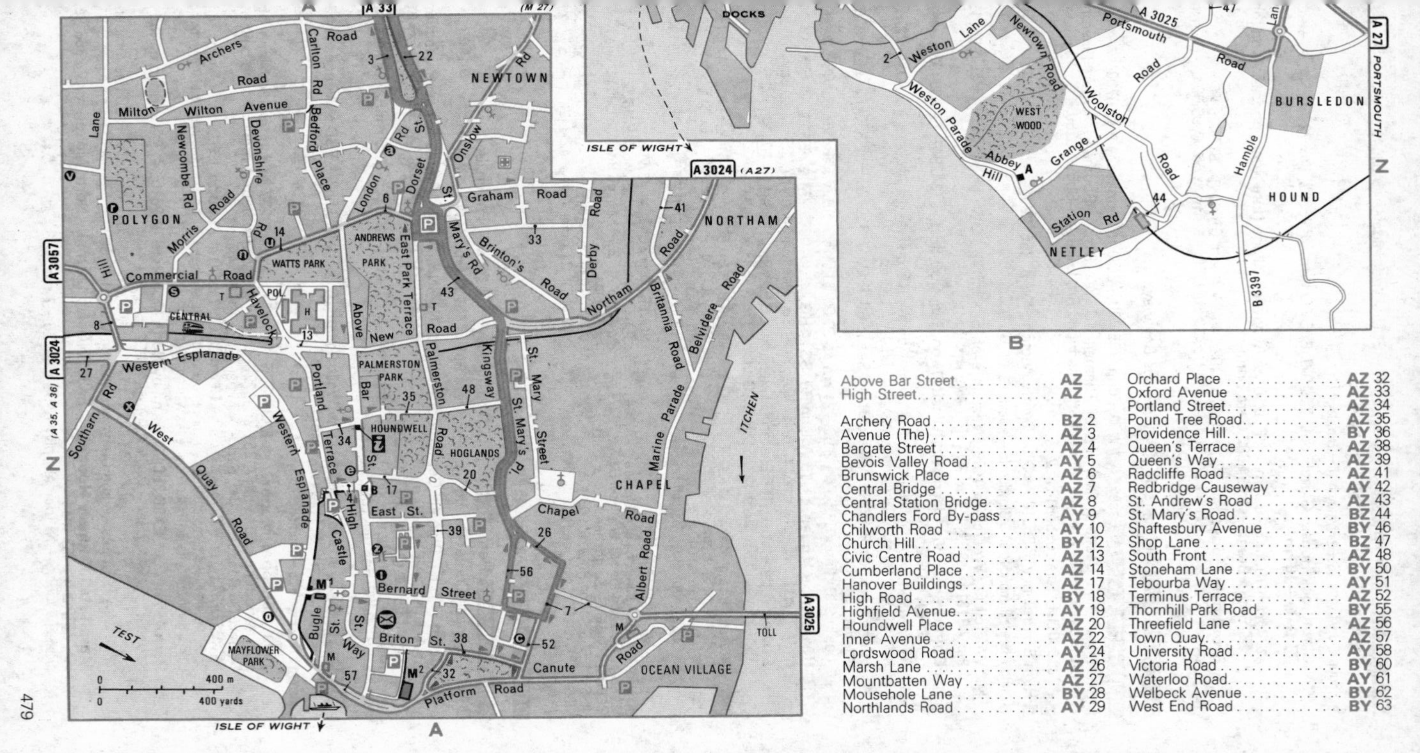

Street	Grid	No.
Above Bar Street	AZ	
High Street	AZ	
Archery Road	BZ	2
Avenue (The)	AZ	3
Bargate Street	AZ	4
Bevois Valley Road	AY	5
Brunswick Place	AZ	6
Central Bridge	AZ	7
Central Station Bridge	AZ	8
Chandlers Ford By-pass	AY	9
Chilworth Road	AY	10
Church Hill	BY	12
Civic Centre Road	AZ	13
Cumberland Place	AZ	14
Hanover Buildings	AZ	17
High Road	BY	18
Highfield Avenue	AY	19
Houndwell Place	AZ	20
Inner Avenue	AZ	22
Lordswood Road	AY	24
Marsh Lane	AZ	26
Mountbatten Way	AZ	27
Mousehole Lane	BY	28
Northlands Road	AY	29
Orchard Place	AZ	32
Oxford Avenue	AZ	33
Portland Street	AZ	34
Pound Tree Road	AZ	35
Providence Hill	BY	36
Queen's Terrace	AZ	38
Queen's Way	AZ	39
Radcliffe Road	AZ	41
Redbridge Causeway	AY	42
St. Andrew's Road	AZ	43
St. Mary's Road	BZ	44
Shaftesbury Avenue	BY	46
Shop Lane	BZ	47
South Front	AZ	48
Stoneham Lane	BY	50
Tebourba Way	AY	51
Terminus Terrace	AZ	52
Thornhill Park Road	BY	55
Threefield Lane	AZ	56
Town Quay	AZ	57
University Road	AY	58
Victoria Road	BY	60
Waterloo Road	AY	61
Welbeck Avenue	BY	62
West End Road	BY	63

SOUTH BRENT Devon 403 I 32 – pop. 2 147 – ECD : Wednesday – ☎ 0364.
Wrangaton ☎ 73229 SW : 2¼ m. by A 38.
♦London 228 – Exeter 28 – ♦Plymouth 16 – Torquay 17.

Glazebrook House, Glazebrook, TQ10 9JE, SW : 1 m. ☎ 73322, Fax 72350, – rm – 10 rm.

at North Huish S : 3¼ m. by B 3210 via Avonwick village (turn right opposite Avon Inn) – ✉ South Brent – ☎ 054 882 Gara Bridge :

Brookdale House, TQ10 9NR, ☎ 402, – rest. VISA.
closed 2 to 24 January – **M** (dinner only) 25.00 **t.** 5.50 – **8 rm** 65.00/95.00 **t.** – SB (November-Easter) 110.00/130.00 **st.**

SOUTH DALTON Humberside 402 S 22 – see Beverley.

SOUTHEND-ON-SEA Essex 404 W 29 – pop. 155 720 – ECD : Wednesday – ☎ 0702.
Envir. : Hadleigh Castle (ruins) ≤★ of Thames *AC*, W : 3 m. – Southend Airport (Historic Aircraft museum) N : 2 m. Belfairs Park, Eastwood Rd, Leigh-on-Sea ☎ 526911.
☎ 340201, Telex 995081 N : 2 m.
High St. Precinct ☎ 355120 – Civic Centre, Victoria Av. ☎ 355122.
♦London 39 – ♦Cambridge 69 – Croydon 46 – ♦Dover 85.

Westcliffe, Westcliffe Par., Westcliffe-on-Sea, SS0 7QW, ☎ 345247, Telex 995013 Fax 431814, ≤ – – 150 – **49 rm.**

Balmoral, 34-36 Valkyrie Rd, Westcliff-on-Sea, SS0 8BU, ☎ 342947, Fax 337828, VISA.
M *(closed Sunday dinner)* (bar lunch)/dinner 8.50 **st.** and a la carte 2.80 – **22 rm** 35.00/48.00 **st.** – SB (weekends only) 55.40/73.00 **st.**

West Park, 11 Park Rd, Westcliff-on-Sea, SS0 7PQ, ☎ 330729, Fax 338162 – VISA.
(bar lunch)/dinner 11.00 **t.** 3.50 – **21 rm** 31.00/51.00 **t.** – SB (weekends only) 50.00 **st.**

Ilfracombe House, 11-13 Wilson Rd, SS1 1HG, ☎ 351000 – AE VISA.
M 9.75 **st.** 2.75 – **13 rm** 28.75/49.45 **st.** – SB (weekends only) 77.00/93.10 **st.**

Strand without rest., 165 Eastern Esplanade, SS1 2YB, ☎ 586611 –
April-November – **8 rm** 15.00/35.00 **s.**

BMW Arterial Rd, Leigh on Sea ☎ 420111
CITROEN 124 High St. Hadleigh ☎ 557372
FIAT 22 Belle Vue Pl. ☎ 610482
FIAT 666-686 London Rd, Westcliff on Sea ☎ 470000
FORD Ness Rd ☎ 296109
HONDA 918 London Rd, Leigh on Sea ☎ 711040
MAZDA 1355 London Rd, Leigh on Sea ☎ 72277
MERCEDES-BENZ Southchurch Rd ☎ 618101
NISSAN 555 Sutton Rd ☎ 619011
NISSAN 1763-1771 London Rd, Leigh on Sea ☎ 75512
PEUGEOT-TALBOT 139-155 West Rd ☎ 347861
RENAULT, ALFA ROMEO, DAIHATSU 536 London Rd, Westcliff-on-Sea ☎ 339602
ROLLS-ROYCE, BENTLEY Station Rd, Thorpe Bay ☎ 582233
ROVER Priory Cres. ☎ 467766
TOYOTA 57 West Rd ☎ 346288/346296
VAUXHALL 33-41 Milton Rd, Westcliff on Sea ☎ 343344
VOLVO 939-953 London Rd, Leigh on Sea ☎ 7233
VW-AUDI 2 Comet Way ☎ 421142

SOUTH LOPHAM Norfolk 404 X 26 – see Diss.

SOUTH MIMMS Herts. 404 T 28 – ECD : Thursday – ✉ ☎ 0707 Potters Bar.
M 25 Bignalls Corner Service Area, Potters Bar ☎ 43233. ♦London 21 – Luton 17.

Crest (T.H.F.), Bignalls Corner, Potters Bar, EN6 3NH, South Mimms Services, junction of A 1 (M), A 6, M 25 on B 197 ☎ 43311, Telex 299162, Fax 46728, – rm rest – 200. AE VISA
M *(closed Saturday lunch)* 12.50/17.00 **st.** and a la carte – 8.45 – **115 rm** 82.00/94.00 **st.** – SB (weekends only) 180.00 **st.**

SOUTH MOLTON Devon 403 I 30 **The West Country G.** – pop. 3 552 – ECD : Wednesday – ☎ 076 95. 1 East St. ☎ 4122 (summer only).
♦London 210 – Exeter 35 – Taunton 39.

❀ **Whitechapel Manor**, EX36 3EG, NE : 4 m. by B 3227 and unmarked lane off roundabout junction with A 361 ☎ 3377, Fax 3797, ≤, « Elizabethan manor house built by Robert De Bassett », park – rest VISA.
M 25.00/37.50 **st.** 6.00 – 7.50 – **10 rm** 58.00/145.00 **st.**, **1 suite** 165.00 **st.**
Spec. Millefeuille of home smoked salmon with a soured cream chive sauce, Confit of quail in goose fat with broad beans, garlic and tarragon, Hot chocolate tart with orange coulis.

Park House, EX36 3ED, N : ½ m. by North Molton rd ☎ 2610, ≤, « Victorian country house », park – rest AE VISA.
closed 10 to 31 January – **M** 17.00 **t.** 4.00 – **7 rm** 36.00/60.00 **t.** – SB (November-March) (except Easter, and Christmas and New Year) 79.00 **st.**

Marsh Hall Country House, EX36 3HQ, N : 1¼ m. by North Molton rd ☎ 2666, ≤ – VISA
closed January – **M** (dinner only) 15.95 **t.** 4.25 – **7 rm** 30.00/60.00 **t.**

at East Buckland NW : 6 ¼ m. by B 3226 – ✉ Barnstaple – ☎ 059 86 Filleigh :

XX **Lower Pitt** with rm, EX32 0TD, ✆ 243, – rest Ⓟ. VISA.
closed 25 December and 1 January – **M** *(closed Sunday and Monday)* (booking essential) (dinner only) a la carte 13.50/17.50 **st.** 3.60 – **3 rm** 30.00/50.00 **st.** – SB (weekdays only) 75.00 **st.**

SOUTH NORMANTON Derbs. 402 403 404 Q 24 – pop. 11 607 (inc. Pinxton) – ECD : Wednesday – ☎ 0773 Ripley.

♦London 130 – Derby 17 – ♦Nottingham 15 – ♦Sheffield 31.

Swallow, Carter Lane East, DE55 2EH, on A 38 ✆ 812000, Telex 377264, Fax 580032, , , – rm rest Ⓟ – 200. AE VISA
M 10.50/15.95 **st.** and a la carte 4.50 – **161 rm** 72.00/110.00 **st.** – SB (weekends only and August) 90.00 **st.**

SOUTH PETHERTON Somerset 403 L 31 – pop. 2 235 – ☎ 0460.

♦London 138 – ♦Bristol 41 – Exeter 41 – Taunton 19 – Yeovil 7.5.

XX **Le Tire Bouchon,** 8 Palmer St., TA13 5DB, ✆ 40272, French rest., – Ⓟ. VISA
closed Sunday dinner and Monday to non-residents and January – **M** (dinner only and Sunday lunch)/dinner 19.50 **st.** 3.75.

SOUTHPORT Merseyside 402 K 23 – pop. 88 596 – ECD : Tuesday – ☎ 0704.

Envir. : Rufford Old Hall★ 15C (the Great Hall★★) *AC*, E : 9 m.

18 Park Rd ✆ 35286 – 18 Hesketh, Cockle Dick's Lane ✆ 30226 – 18 Moss Lane ✆ 24294 – 18 Hillside, Hastings Rd ✆ 69902 – 18 Alt, Park Rd ✆ 30435 – 18 Royal Birkdale, Waterloo Rd ✆ 69903.

112 Lord St. ✆ 33133/500175.

♦London 221 – ♦Liverpool 20 – ♦Manchester 38 – Preston 19.

Prince of Wales (T.H.F), Lord St., PR8 1JS, ✆ 536688, Telex 67415, Fax 543488, – Ⓟ – 400. AE VISA
M (carving lunch)/dinner 10.50 **st.** and a la carte 3.95 – 7.60 – **98 rm** 70.00/85.00 **st.**, **6 suites** 110.00 **st.** – SB (weekends only) 80.00/110.00 **st.**

Scarisbrick, 239 Lord St., PR8 1NZ, ✆ 543000, Fax 533335 – Ⓟ – 120. AE VISA
M 7.30/13.50 **st.** and a la carte – **58 rm** 58.00/70.00 **st.** – SB (weekends only) 50.00/85.00 **st.**

New Bold, Lord St., PR9 0BE, ✆ 532578, Fax 532528 – Ⓟ. AE VISA.
M a la carte 13.35/21.40 **t.** 2.95 – 3.25 – **21 rm** 45.00/50.00 **t.**

Shelbourne, 1 Lord St. West, PR8 2BH, ✆ 541252, – rm Ⓟ. AE VISA.
M 8.50/10.50 **st.** and a la carte 3.20 – **19 rm** 29.00/46.00 **st.** – SB 40.00/60.00 **st.**

Stutelea, Alexandra Rd, PR9 0NB, ✆ 544220, Fax 500232, , , , – Ⓟ. AE VISA.
M (bar lunch)/dinner 12.00 **st.** and a la carte – **12 rm** 35.00/264.00 **st.** – SB (except Bank Holidays) 60.00/69.00 **st.**

Crimond, 28 Knowsley Rd, PR9 0HN, ✆ 536456, Fax 548643, , – rest Ⓟ. AE VISA
M 13.50 **t.** 3.00 – **14 rm** 38.00/60.00 **st.** – SB (weekends only) (except Bank Holidays) 60.00 **st.**

Club House, 15 Leicester St., PR9 0ER, ✆ 533745 – Ⓟ. AE VISA
M (by arrangement) 9.50 **st.** 3.00 – **13 rm** 25.00/40.00 **st.** – SB 60.00/65.00 **st.**

Ambassador, 13 Bath St., PR9 0DP, ✆ 543998 – rest Ⓟ. VISA
closed 28 December-3 January – **M** 8.00 **st.** 3.75 – **8 rm** 26.00/45.00 **st.**

XX Squires, 78-80 King St., PR8 1LG, ✆ 30046 –.

ALFA-ROMEO, LOTUS, SAAB 609 Liverpool Rd ✆ 74114
CITROEN Liverpool Rd ✆ 74127
COLT Aughton Rd ✆ 67904
FIAT 89-91 Bath St. North ✆ 35535
FORD Virginia St. ✆ 31550
LADA Liverpool Rd ✆ 77161
MERCEDES 205 Liverpool Rd ✆ 68515
MITSUBISHI Aughton Rd ✆ 38220
SKODA Portland St. ✆ 34916
TOYOTA Tulketh St. ✆ 30909
VOLVO 51 Weld Rd ✆ 66613
VW-AUDI Zetland St. ✆ 31091

ATS 69 Shakespeare St. ✆ 34434

SOUTHSEA Hants. 403 404 Q 31 – see Portsmouth and Southsea.

SOUTH SHIELDS Tyne and Wear 401 402 P 19 – pop. 86 488 – ECD : Wednesday – ☎ 091 Tyneside.

18 Cleadon Hill ✆ 456 0475, SE : 3 m. – 18 Whitburn, Lizard Lane ✆ 529 2144 SE : 2½ m.

South Foreshore ✆ 455 7411 (summer only) – The Museum and Art Gallery, Ocean Rd ✆ 454 6612.

♦London 284 – ♦Newcastle-upon-Tyne 9.5 – Sunderland 6.

Sea, Sea Rd, NE33 2LD, ✆ 427 0999, Telex 53533, Fax 454 0500 – TV ☎ P. AE VISA
M 8.00 **t.** (lunch) and a la carte 10.65/15.65 **st.** 2.90 – **30 rm** 49.80/60.80 **st.**

ARG Burrow Street ✆ 427 1313
FORD ✆ 455 2227
NISSAN ✆ 455 2101
ATS Western Approach ✆ 454 1060/4247

SOUTHWAITE SERVICE AREA Cumbria 401 402 L 19 – ✉ Carlisle – ☎ 069 74.

♦London 300 – ♦Carlisle 14 – Lancaster 58 – Workington 48.

Granada Lodge without rest., CA4 0NT, on M6 (Southbound carriageway) ✆ 73131 Fax 73669 – rm TV P. AE VISA.
39 rm 27.50/29.50 **t.**

SOUTH WALSHAM Norfolk 404 Y 26 – pop. 543 – ✉ Norwich – ☎ 060 549.

♦London 120 – Great Yarmouth 11 – ♦Norwich 9.

South Walsham Hall H. and Country Club, South Walsham Rd, NR13 6DQ ✆ 378, Fax 519, ←, heated, park, squash – TV ☎ P. AE VISA.
closed 1 to 16 January – **M** 18.00 **t.** and a la carte 4.00 – **17 rm** 40.00/90.00 **st.** – SB (April-October) (weekends only) 95.00/220.00 **st.**

SOUTHWELL Notts. 402 404 R 24 – pop. 6 283 – ECD : Thursday – ☎ 0636.

See : Minster★★ 12C-13C (Chapter house : foliage carving★★ 13C).

♦London 135 – Lincoln 24 – ♦Nottingham 14 – ♦Sheffield 34.

Saracen's Head (T.H.F.), Market Pl., NG25 0HE, ✆ 812701, Telex 377201, Fax 815408 – rm TV ☎ P – 100. AE VISA
M *(closed Saturday lunch)* 16.00 **st.** and a la carte 4.35 – 7.00 – **27 rm** 60.00/120.00 **st** – SB (weekends only) 74.00/84.00 **st.**

Old Forge without rest., 2 Burgage Lane, NG25 0ER, ✆ 812809 – TV P. VISA
5 rm 28.00/45.00 **st.**

FORD Westgate ✆ 813741

"Short Breaks"

Many hotels now offer a special rate for a stay of 2 nights which includes dinner, bed and breakfast.

SOUTHWOLD Suffolk 404 Z 27 – pop. 3 756 – ECD : Wednesday – ☎ 0502.

The Common ✆ 723234, W : ½ m. on A 1095.

Waveney Local Office, Town Hall ✆ 722366 (summer only).

♦London 108 – Great Yarmouth 24 – ♦Ipswich 35 – ♦Norwich 34.

Swan, Market Pl., IP18 6EG, ✆ 722186, Fax 724800, – rest TV ☎ P – 40. AE VISA.
M 20.00/24.00 **t.** – **43 rm** 40.00/96.00 **t.**, **2 suites** 110.00/125.00 **t.** – SB (October-mid March) (weekdays only) (except Christmas, New Year and Bank Holidays) 84.00/116.00 **st.**

Crown, 90 High St., IP18 6DP, ✆ 722275, Telex 97223, Fax 724805 – TV ☎ P. AE VISA
closed first week January – **M** 13.50/16.50 **t.** – 2.50 – **12 rm** 29.00/46.00 **t.**

SOUTH WOODHAM FERRERS Essex 404 V 29 – pop. 6 975 – ✉ ☎ 0245 Chelmsford.

♦London 36 – Chelmsford 12 – Colchester 34 – Southend-on-Sea 13.

Oakland, 2-6 Reeves Way, by Merchant St., CM3 5XE, ✆ 322811, Fax 329201 – TV ☎. AE VISA.
M *(closed Sunday dinner)* 6.00/10.00 **t.** and a la carte 3.75 – **41 rm** 36.00/50.00 **t.**

SOWERBY North Yorks. – see Thirsk.

SPARK BRIDGE Cumbria – see Ulverston.

SPEEN Berks. – see Newbury.

SPELDHURST Kent 404 U 30 – see Royal Tunbridge Wells.

SPRATTON Northants. 404 R 27 – see Northampton.

SPREYTON Devon 403 I 31 – pop. 289 – ✉ Crediton – ☎ 0363 Bow.

♦London 224 – Exeter 23 – ♦Plymouth 42.

Downhayes, EX17 5AR, N : 1½ m. on Bow Rd ✆ 82378, ←, « Converted 16C longhouse », park – rm P.
closed 20 to 28 December – **M** 12.50 – **3 rm** 26.25/45.00.

STADDLEBRIDGE North Yorks. – see Northallerton.

STAFFORD Staffs. 402 403 404 N 25 – pop. 60 915 – ECD : Wednesday – ☎ 0785.

See : High House★ (16C) – St. Mary's Church (Norman font★) Blithfield Hall★ (Elizabethan) *AC*, W : 8 m.

18 Ingestre Park ℰ 0889 (Weston) 270061, E : 6 m. – 9 Newport Rd ℰ 223821.

Ancient High House, Greengate St. ℰ 40204.

♦London 142 – ♦Birmingham 26 – Derby 32 – Shrewsbury 31 – ♦Stoke-on-Trent 17.

- **Tillington Hall** (De Vere), Eccleshall Rd, ST16 1JJ, NW : 1 ½ m. on A 5013 ℰ 53531, Telex 36566, Fax 59223, – TV ☎ P – 70. AE VISA
  M *(closed Saturday lunch)* 9.00/10.50 **t.** and a la carte 4.00 – **90 rm** 78.00/90.00 **t.** – SB (weekends only) (except July and August) 78.00/85.00 **st.**
- **Swan** (B.C.B.), 46 Greengate St., ST16 2JA, ℰ 58142, Fax 223372 – TV ☎ P. AE VISA.
  M (grill rest.) 8.00/15.00 **st.** – **32 rm** 43.00/61.00 **st.**
- **Garth,** Moss Pit, ST17 9JR, S : 2 m. on A 449 ℰ 56124, Telex 36479, Fax 55152, – rm TV ☎ P – 45. AE VISA
  M (bar lunch Saturday) 8.00/12.45 **st.** and a la carte – **60 rm** 49.50/65.00 **t.** – SB (weekends only) 72.00/92.00 **st.**
- Vine, Salter St., ST16 2JU, ℰ 44112, Fax 46612 – TV ☎ P. AE VISA
  M *(closed Sunday dinner)* – **27 rm** 39.50/55.00 **t.** – SB (weekends only) 50.00 **st.**

BMW Lichfield Rd ℰ 46999
CITROEN Astonfields Rd ℰ 223336
DATSUN Lichfield Rd ℰ 59313
FIAT Milford ℰ 661226
FORD Stone Rd ℰ 51331
HONDA Lichfield Rd ℰ 47221
LADA Sandon Rd ℰ 45171
MAZDA Derby St. ℰ 55486
PEUGEOT-TALBOT Newport Rd ℰ 45518/54495
RENAULT Wolverhampton Rd ℰ 52118
ROVER Lichfield Rd ℰ 51366
SAAB Yarlet Bank ℰ 088 97 (Sandon) 248
VAUXHALL-OPEL Walton ℰ 661293

ATS Kenworthy Rd, Astonfields Ind Est. ℰ 223832/58118

STAINES Middlesex 404 S 29 – pop. 51 949 – ECD : Thursday – ☎ 0784.

♦London 26 – Reading 25.

- **Thames Lodge** (T.H.F.), Thames St., TW18 4SF, ℰ 464433, Group Telex 8812552, Fax 454858, – rm rest TV ☎ P – 55. AE VISA
  M *(closed Saturday lunch)* 9.50/15.00 **st.** and a la carte 4.35 – 7.60 – **44 rm** 80.00/95.00 **st.** – SB (weekends only) 84.00/94.00 **st.**

STAMFORD Lincs. 402 404 S 26 – pop. 16 127 – ECD : Thursday – ☎ 0780.

See : Site★★ – St.Martin's Church★ – Lord Burghley's Hospital★ – Browne's Hospital★.

Envir. : Burghley House★★ (16C) (paintings : Heaven Room★★★)*AC*.

18 Burghley Park, St. Martins ℰ 53789 – 18 Luffenham Heath, Ketton ℰ 720205, W : 5 m.

Museum, Broad St. ℰ 55611.

♦London 92 – ♦Leicester 31 – Lincoln 50 – ♦Nottingham 45.

- **The George of Stamford,** 71 St. Martin's, PE9 2LB, ℰ 55171, Telex 32578, Fax 57070, « 17C coaching inn with walled monastic garden » – TV ☎ P – 50. AE VISA
  M a la carte 19.80/27.20 **st.** 5.85 – **46 rm** 69.50/140.00 **st.**, **1 suite** 110.00/130.00 **st.**
- **Lady Anne's,** 37-38 High St., St. Martin's Without, PE9 2LJ, ℰ 53175, – TV ☎ P – 100. AE VISA.
  M 9.50/13.50 **t.** 3.75 – **28 rm** 44.00/75.00 **t.** – SB (weekends only) (October-April) 75.00 **st.**
- **Garden House,** 42 High St., St. Martin's, PE9 2LP, ℰ 63359, Telex 329230, Fax 63339, – TV ☎ P. AE VISA
  M *(closed Sunday dinner)* a la carte 14.60/22.00 **st.** 3.50 – **20 rm** 55.00/125.00 **st.** – SB (weekends only and August) 80.00 **st.**
- **Ram Jam Inn,** Great North Rd, Stretton ✉ Oakham (Leics.), LE15 7QX, NW : 8 m. by B 1081 on A 1 ℰ 410776, Group Telex 342888, – TV ☎ P – 50. AE VISA
  closed Christmas Day – **M** a la carte 8.55/14.50 **t.** 4.00 – 4.00 – **7 rm** 35.00/45.00 **t.**
- Welland House without rest., 19 Broad St., PE9 1PG, ℰ 57028, « 18C town house with antiques », –
  5 rm.
- **Candlesticks** with rm, 1 Church Lane, PE9 2JU, ℰ 64033 – TV P. VISA.
  M *(closed Tuesday lunch and Monday)* 10.00 and a la carte – **4 rm** 30.00/40.00 **t.**

at Collyweston (Northants.) SW : 3 ¾ m. on A 43 – ✉ Stamford – ☎ 078 083 Duddington :

- **Cavalier,** Main St., PE9 3PQ, ℰ 288 – TV P. VISA
  closed 25 December – **M** 8.25 **t.** (lunch) and a la carte 8.60/17.15 **t.** – **4 rm** 28.00/42.00 **st.**

at Empingham W : 5 ¾ m. on A 606 – ✉ Oakham – ☎ 078 086 Empingham :

- **White Horse,** 2 Main St., LE15 8PR, ℰ 221, Fax 521 – TV ☎ P – 60. AE VISA
  M *(closed Sunday dinner)* 8.50/10.60 **st.** and a la carte 3.00 – **12 rm** 21.50/55.00 **st.**

at Normanton Park W : 6½ m. by A 606 on Edith Weston Rd – ✉ Oakham – ☎ 0780 Stamford :

Normanton Park 🐌, South Shore, LE15 8RP, ℘ 720315, Fax 721086, ≤, 🐟, 🌳 – TV ☎ ♿ P. AE VISA. ✈
M *(closed Sunday dinner to non-residents)* 12.75/18.50 **st.** and a la carte 🍷 4.00 – **16 rm** ☕ 43.00/68.00 **st.** – SB 78.00/88.00 **st.**

at Greetham NW : 9½ m. by B 1081 and A 1 on B 668 – ✉ ☎ 0572 Oakham :

Greetham House, Church Lane, LE15 7NJ, ℘ 813078, 🏊, 🌳, 🎾 – 🚭 rm TV P
M 15.00 – **3 rm** ☕ 25.00/40.00 **st.**

FORD Wharf Rd ℘ 55151
PEUGEOT-TALBOT Scotgate ℘ 64741
RENAULT Water St. ℘ 63532
ROVER St. Paul's St. ℘ 52741
TOYOTA Collyweston ℘ 078 083 (Duddington) 271
VAUXHALL West St. ℘ 62571

STANDISH Greater Manchester 402 404 M 23 – pop. 11 504 – ECD : Wednesday – ✉ Wigan – ☎ 0257.

♦London 210 – ♦Liverpool 22 – ♦Manchester 21 – Preston 15.

Kilhey Court (Best Western), Chorley Rd, Worthington, WN1 2XN, E : 1¾ m. by B 5239 on A 5106 ℘ 423083, Telex 67460, Fax 422401, 🏊, 🌳 – TV ☎ P – 🎤 200. AE VISA
M 10.00/17.50 **st.** and a la carte 🍷 4.50 – **54 rm** ☕ 50.00/103.00 **st.** – SB (weekends only) 70.00/90.00 **st.**

The Beeches with rm, School Lane, WN6 0TD, on B 5239 ℘ 426432, Fax 427503 – TV ☎ P. AE VISA. ✈
M *(closed Saturday lunch and Sunday dinner)* 11.20 **st.** and a la carte 🍷 6.60 – ☕ 3.25 – **11 rm** 32.00/46.00 **st.** – SB (weekends only) 30.80/48.00 **st.**

ATS 23 Market St. ℘ 423146/423732

"Short Breaks"

Many hotels now offer a special rate for a stay of 2 nights which includes dinner, bed and breakfast.

STANDLAKE Oxon. 403 404 P 28 – ✉ Witney – ☎ 0865.

♦London 69 – ♦Oxford 12 – Swindon 22.

Old Rectory 🐌 without rest., Church End, OX8 7SG, ℘ 300559, « Part 13C rectory, riverside gardens », 🐟 – TV P. ✈
closed December and January – **3 rm** ☕ 48.00/66.50 **st.**

STANNERSBURN Northumb. – ✉ Hexham – ☎ 0434 Hexham.

♦London 363 – ♦Carlisle 56 – ♦Newcastle-upon-Tyne 46.

Pheasant Inn 🐌, Falstone, NE48 1DD, ℘ 240382 – 🚭 P. ✈
closed 25 December – **M** (bar lunch Monday to Saturday)/dinner 14.00 **st.** and a la carte 🍷 3.75 – **11 rm** ☕ 18.00/42.00 **t.** – SB (October-March) 48.00 **st.**

STANSTEAD ABBOTS Herts. 404 U 28 – pop. 1 906 – ✉ Ware – ☎ 027 979 Roydon.

♦London 22 – ♦Cambridge 37 – Luton 32 – ♦Ipswich 66.

Briggens (Q.M.H.), Stanstead Rd, SG12 8LD, E : 2 m. by A 414 ℘ 2416, Telex 817906, Fax 3685, ≤, « Arboretum », 🏊 heated, ⛳9, 🌳, park, 🎾 – 🛗 TV ☎ P – 🎤 100. AE VISA. ✈
M 18.50/21.50 **t.** and a la carte – ☕ 8.00 – **53 rm** 77.50/110.00 **t.**, **1 suite** 137.50 **t.**

STANSTED AIRPORT Essex 404 U 28 – ✉ Stansted Mountfitchet – ☎ 0279.

Harlequin Round Coppice Rd, CM24 8SE, ℘ 680800, Fax 680890, 🏋, 🏊, 🏊 – 🛗 ▤ TV ☎ ♿ P – 🎤 250. AE VISA. ✈ **M** a la carte 10.40/19.85 **st.** 🍷 4.75 – ☕ 3.75 – **249 rm** 64.45/76.45 **st.**

STANTON HARCOURT Oxon 403 404 P 28 – pop. 774 – ✉ ☎ 0865 Oxford.

♦London 71 – Gloucester 45 – ♦Oxford 13 – Swindon 27.

Harcourt Arms, OX8 1RJ, ℘ 881931 – P. AE VISA
M a la carte 12.45/16.70 **t.** 🍷 3.50.

STANTON ST. QUINTIN Wilts. – see Marlmesbury.

STARBOTTON North Yorks. – see Kettlewell.

STAVERTON Devon 403 I 32 – ✉ Totnes – ☎ 080 426.

Sea Trout Inn, TQ9 6PA, ℘ 274, 🐟 TV ☎ P. AE VISA **M** *(closed Sunday dinner)* (bar lunch Monday to Saturday)/dinner 13.50 **st.** and a la carte 🍷 3.75 – **10 rm** ☕ 37.50/48.00 **st.**

STAVERTON Glos. – see Cheltenham.

STEEPLE ASTON Oxon. 403 404 Q 28 – pop. 1 619 – ECD : Saturday – ☎ 0869.

London 69 – ◆Coventry 38 – ◆Oxford 10.

X **Red Lion,** South St., OX5 3RY, ℘ 40225 – P. VISA
closed Sunday, Monday and 2 weeks September-October – **M** (booking essential) (bar lunch)/dinner 16.50/30.00 **t.** 3.45.

STEVENAGE Herts. 404 T 28 – pop. 74 757 – ECD : Monday and Wednesday – ☎ 0438.

Envir. : Knebworth House (furniture★) S : 3 m.

Aston Lane ℘ 043 888 (Shephall) 424 – 18 Knebworth, Deards End Lane ℘ 812752, S : 1 m.

Central Library, Southgate ℘ 369441.

London 36 – Bedford 25 – ◆Cambridge 27.

Hertfordpark (Q.M.H.), Danestrete, SG1 1EJ, ℘ 350661, Telex 825697, Fax 741880 – rm P – 180. AE VISA
M *(closed lunch Saturday and Sunday)* **t.** and a la carte – **100 rm** 68.00/80.00 **t.** – SB (weekends only) 72.50 **st.**

Novotel, Knebworth Park, SG1 2AX, SW : 1½ m. by A 602 at junction with A 1 (M) ℘ 742299, Telex 826132, Fax 723872, heated – rest P – 130. AE VISA
M 9.50/13.50 **t.** and a la carte 4.50 – 7.00 – **100 rm** 65.00/72.00 **st.**

Stevenage Moat House (Q.M.H.), High St., Old Town, SG1 3AZ, ℘ 359111, Fax 742169, – rm P – 200. AE VISA
M *(closed Saturday lunch)* 11.95 **st.** and a la carte 4.50 – **63 rm** 57.75/70.00 **st.** – SB (weekends only) 67.00/95.00 **st.**

Archways, 15 Hitchin Rd, Old Town, SG1 3BJ, ℘ 316640, Fax 742662, – P. AE VISA
M *(closed Sunday)* 18.00 **st.** and a la carte 3.50 – **37 rm** 37.00/52.00 **st.**

at Broadwater S : 1¾ m. by A 602 on B 197 – ✉ ☎ 0438 Stevenage :

Roebuck Post House (T.H.F.), Old London Rd, SG2 8DS, ℘ 365444, Telex 825505, Fax 741308, – rm P – 50. AE VISA
M *(closed Saturday lunch)* 9.95/12.95 **st.** and a la carte – 7.50 – **54 rm** 65.00/85.00 **st.**

AUDI-VW Lyton Way ℘ 746400
FIAT London Rd ℘ 811011
NISSAN Broadwater Cres. ℘ 315555
PEUGEOT Pound Av. ℘ 356266
ROVER High St. Codicote ℘ 820288
VAUXHALL-OPEL 124-6 High St. ℘ 351113

ATS 4-8 Norton Rd ℘ 313262

STEYNING West Sussex 404 T 31 – pop. 8 318 (inc. Upper Beeding) – ECD : Thursday – ☎ 0903.

See : St. Andrew's Church (the nave★ 12C).

◆London 52 – ◆Brighton 12 – Worthing 10.

Springswells without rest., 9 High St., BN4 3GG, ℘ 812446, , heated, – P. AE VISA.
10 rm 30.00/78.00 **st.**

STILTON Cambs. 404 T 26 – ✉ Peterborough – ☎ 0733.

Bell Inn, Great North Rd, PE7 3RA, ℘ 241066, Fax 245173, « Part 16C Inn », – rm P – 110. AE VISA.
closed Christmas Day – **M** 8.00/12.50 **st.** and a la carte 4.50 – **19 rm** 55.00/90.00 **st.** – SB (weekends only) 80.00/100.00 **st.**

STOBOROUGH Dorset – see Wareham.

STOCKBRIDGE Hants. 403 404 P 30 – pop. 524 – ECD : Wednesday – ☎ 0264 Andover.

◆London 75 – Salisbury 14 – Winchester 9.

Old Three Cups, High St., SO20 6HB, ℘ 810527, « 15C inn », – P. VISA.
closed 25 December-January – **M** *(closed Monday and Sunday dinner)* 6.75/7.50 **t.** and a la carte 3.00 – **8 rm** 22.00/42.00 **st.**

Carbery, Salisbury Hill, SO20 6EZ, on A 30 ℘ 810771, heated, – P.
closed 2 weeks at Christmas – **M** (dinner only) 8.65 **st.** – **11 rm** 17.25/40.25 **st.**

Besonders angenehme Hotels oder Restaurants sind im Führer rot gekennzeichnet.

Sie können uns helfen, wenn Sie uns die Häuser angeben, in denen Sie sich besonders wohl gefühlt haben.

Jährlich erscheint eine komplett überarbeitete Ausgabe aller Roten Michelin-Führer.

... XXXXX ... X

STOCKPORT Greater Manchester 402 403 404 N 23 – pop. 135 489 – ECD : Thursday – ☎ 061 Manchester.

Envir. : Lyme Park★ (16C-18C) *AC*, SE : 4½ m.

18 Marple, Hawk Green ℘ 427 2311 – 18 Heaton Moor ℘ 432 2134 – 18 Bramall Park, 20 Manor Rd ℘ 485 3119 – 18 Davenport, Middlewood Rd, Poynton ℘ 0625 (Poynton) 877321, S : 5 m. – 18 Mellor Townscliffe, Tarben ℘ 427 2208, SE : 7 m. – 18 Hazel Grove, Club House ℘ 483 3217.

9 Princes St. ℘ 474 3320/1.

♦London 201 – ♦Liverpool 42 – ♦Manchester 6 – ♦Sheffield 37 – ♦Stoke-on-Trent 34.

Alma Lodge, 149 Buxton Rd, SK2 6EL, on A 6 ℘ 483 4431, Telex 665026, Fax 483 1983 – rm TV ☎ P – 200. AE VISA
M (bar lunch Saturday) 11.50 **st.** and a la carte 4.55 – 7.00 – **58 rm** 29.50/95.00 **st.** – SB (weekends only) 57.00/65.00 **st.**

Rudyard, 271 Wellington Rd North, Heaton Chapel, SK4 5BP, ℘ 432 2753, Fax 431 0266 – TV ☎ P – 90. AE VISA
M 7.65 **t.** 3.00 – **21 rm** 58.50/68.50 **t.** – SB (weekends only) 57.00/65.00 **st.**

ALFA-ROMEO, JAGUAR, LANCIA, LOTUS 5 Marshland St., Hazel Grove ℘ 456 0800
COLT School Lane, Heaton Chapel ℘ 432 4790
FIAT Heaton Lane ℘ 480 6661
FORD Oak St., Hazel Grove ℘ 483 9431
FORD Adswood Rd ℘ 480 0211
MAZDA Wellington Rd North ℘ 442 6466
PEUGEOT-TALBOT 110 Buxton Rd ℘ 480 0831
RANGE-ROVER, DAIMLER, JAGUAR Town Hall Sq. ℘ 480 7966
RENAULT 91 Heaton Moor Rd ℘ 432 9416
ROVER 35 Buxton Rd ℘ 480 4244
ROVER Wellington Rd North ℘ 443 2000
SAAB 31-33 Buxton Rd ℘ 483 6271
VAUXHALL-OPEL Wellington Rd South ℘ 480 6146
VAUXHALL-OPEL 398 Wellington Rd North ℘ 432 3232
VOLVO Wellington Rd South ℘ 429 7099

ATS Hollingworth Rd, Bredbury ℘ 430 5221

STOCKTON-ON-TEES Cleveland 402 P 20 – pop. 86 699 – ECD : Thursday – ☎ 0642.

18 Eaglescliffe, Yarm Rd ℘ 780098.

Tees-side Airport : ℘ 0325 (Darlington) 332811, SW : 6 m.

Theatre Yard, off High St. ℘ 615080.

♦London 251 – ♦Leeds 61 – ♦Middlesbrough 4.

Swallow, 10 John Walker Sq., TS18 1AQ, ℘ 679721, Telex 587895, Fax 601714, – rm TV ☎ P – 300. AE VISA
M 11.55/20.10 **t.** and a la carte 5.50 – **122 rm** 70.00/95.00 **t.** – SB (except Christmas and New Year) (weekends only) 85.00/95.00 **st.**

at Eaglescliffe S : 3½ m. on A 135 – ✉ ☎ 0642 Stockton-on-Tees :

Parkmore (Best Western), 636 Yarm Rd, TS16 0DH, ℘ 786815, Telex 58298, Fax 790485, – rm TV ☎ P – 100. AE VISA
M 10.50/15.45 **t.** and a la carte 3.75 – **54 rm** 46.00/72.00 **t.**, **1 suite** 65.00/80.00 **t.** – SB (weekends only) 80.00/86.00 **st.**

ARG Portrack Lane ℘ 677777
BMW 45 Norton Rd ℘ 675361
FIAT Commercial St. ℘ 675177
MAZDA 87-91 Oxbridge Lane ℘ 671134
NISSAN Middleway Mandale Industrial Estate ℘ 672617
RENAULT 110 Yarm Rd ℘ 601393
SAAB, SUBARU Chapel St. ℘ 679781
VAUXHALL-OPEL Boathouse Lane ℘ 607804
VOLVO Prince Regent St. ℘ 673251

ATS 18 Brunswick St. ℘ 657733
ATS 112 Norton Rd ℘ 604477

STOKE BRUERNE Northants. 404 R 27 – ✉ Towcester – ☎ 0604 Roade.

♦London 69 – ♦Coventry 33 – Northampton 9 – ♦Oxford 33.

Bruerne's Lock, 5 Canalside, NN12 7SB, ℘ 863654, « Picturesque setting beside the Grand Union Canal » – VISA
closed Sunday dinner, Monday, last 2 weeks February and New Year – **M** 11.50 **t.** (lunch) and a la carte 17.20/23.20 **t.** 4.85.

STOKE BY NAYLAND Suffolk 404 W 28 – pop. 727 – ✉ ☎ 0206 Colchester (Essex).

♦London 60 – Colchester 8 – Ipswich 15.

Angel Inn, Polstead St., CO6 4SA, ℘ 263245, « Part timbered 17C inn » – TV ☎ P. AE VISA.
M a la carte 8.65/22.25 **t.** 3.25 – **6 rm** 35.00/45.00 **st.**

STOKE D'ABERNON Surrey 404 ㊷ – see Cobham.

STOKE FLEMING Devon 403 J 33 – see Dartmouth.

STOKE GABRIEL Devon 403 J 32 – see Totnes.

STOKE MANDEVILLE Bucks. 404 R 28 – see Aylesbury.

STOKE-ON-TRENT Staffs. 402 403 404 N 24 – pop. 272 446 – ECD : Thursday – ☎ 0782.

See : City Museum and Art Gallery★ Y – Gladstone Pottery Museum★ *AC* V – National Garden Festival site U.

Envir. : Little Moreton Hall★★ (16C) *AC*, NW : 8 m. on A 34 U – Wedgwood Visitor's Centre★ S : 1/2 m. by A 519 V.

18 Trentham Park ☎ 642245 V – 18 14 Barlaston Old Rd ☎ 642347 V – 18 Greenway Hall, Stockton Brook ☎ 503158, N : 5 m. U – 18 Alsager, Audley Rd ☎ 0270 (Alsager) 875700, NW : 7 m. U.

1 Glebe St. ☎ 411222 – City Museum and Art Gallery, Bethesda St. ☎ 202173.

◆London 162 – ◆Birmingham 46 – ◆Leicester 59 – ◆Liverpool 58 – ◆Manchester 41 – ◆Sheffield 53.

STOKE-ON-TRENT NEWCASTLE-UNDER-LYME

BUILT UP AREA

Street	Square	No.
Alexandra Road	U	3
Bedford Road	U	4
Brownhills Road	U	12
Church Lane	U	19
Cobridge Road	U	21
Davenport Street	U	23
Elder Road	U	24
Etruria Vale Road	U	27
Grove Road	V	30
Hanley Road	U	31
Heron Street	V	34
High Street	U	35
Higherland	V	37
Manor Street	V	44
Mayne Street	V	45
Moorland Road	U	48
Park Hall Road	V	54
Porthill Road	U	59
Snow Hill	U	63
Stoke Road	U	68
Strand (The)	V	69
Victoria Park Road	U	75
Watlands View	U	76
Williamson Street	U	77

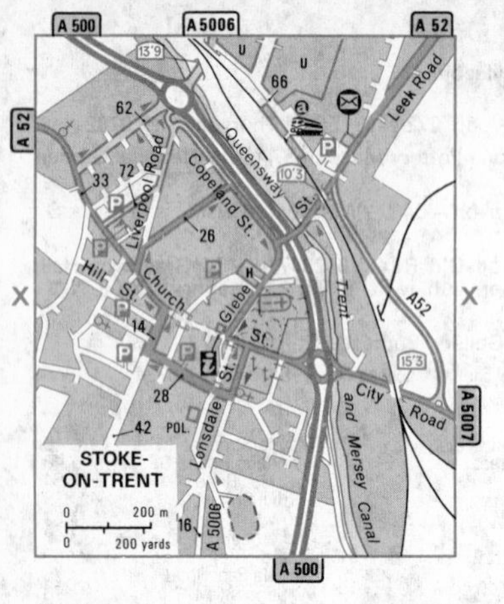

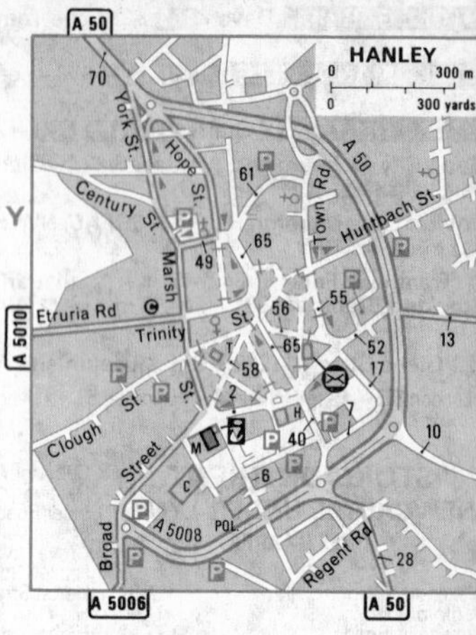

Church Street X	Bucknall New Road . . . . Y 13	New Hall Street . . . . . Y 49
Old Hall Street . . . . . Y 52	Campbell Place . . . . . X 14	Parliament Row . . . . . Y 55
Stafford Street . . . . . Y 65	Campbell Road . . . . . X 16	Percy Street . . . . . Y 56
	Charles Street . . . . . Y 17	Piccadilly . . . . . Y 58
Albion Street . . . . . Y 2	Elenora Street . . . . . X 26	Quadrant Road . . . . . Y 61
Bethesda Street . . . . . Y 6	Fleming Road . . . . . X 28	Shelton Old Road . . . . . X 62
Birch Terrace . . . . . Y 7	Hartshill Road . . . . . X 33	Station Road . . . . . X 66
Botteslow Street . . . . . Y 10	Lichfield Street . . . . . Y 40	Vale Place . . . . . Y 70
	London Road . . . . . X 42	Vale Street . . . . . X 72

🏨 North Stafford, Station Rd, ST4 2AE, ✆ 744477, Telex 36287, Fax 744580 – |♦| ⇆ rm TV ☎ Ⓟ – 🏛 400 X a
67 rm, **2 suites.**

⌂ **White House,** 94 Stone Rd, Trent Vale, ST4 6SP, S : 2¼ m. on A 34 ✆ 642460 – TV ☎ Ⓟ. VISA. ✂ V e
closed 23 December-1 January – **M** (by arrangement) 8.75 **st.** 2.75 – **10 rm** ☕ 21.00/45.00 **st.**

at Hanley N : 2 m. by A 5006 – ✉ ⊙ 0782 Stoke-on-Trent :

🏨 Stakis Grand, 66 Trinity St., ST1 5NB, ✆ 202361, Telex 367264, Fax 286464, ≘s, 🏊 – |♦| TV ☎ ♿ Ⓟ – 🏛 300. AE ⓓ VISA Y c
☕ 7.50 – **128 rm** 70.00/115.00 **t.** – SB 72.00/126.00 **st.**

at Basford NW : 1 ¾ m. by A 500 off A 53 – ✉ ⊙ 0782 Stoke-on-Trent :

🏨 **Haydon House,** Haydon St., ST4 6JD, ✆ 711311, Telex 36600, Fax 717470 – TV ☎ Ⓟ – 🏛 30. AE ⓓ VISA U a
M 16.50 **st.** and a la carte 4.50 – ☕ 6.00 – **19 rm** 58.00/98.00 **st.**, **8 suites** 98.00/110.00 **st.** – SB (weekends only) 90.00/130.00 **st.**

MICHELIN Distribution Centre, Unit No. 2, Jamage Road Industrial Estate, Talke Pits, ST7 1QF, ✆ 771211, Fax 775782 by A 34 U

BMW Pool Dam, Newcastle ✆ 711000
CITROEN Uttoxeter Rd ✆ 599235
DAIHATSU Ashbank ✆ 2426
FIAT Lightwood Rd, Longton ✆ 319212
FORD Clough St. ✆ 202591
FORD King St. ✆ 599333
HONDA Sneyd St., Cobridge ✆ 261593
LADA 292 Waterloo Rd, Cobridge ✆ 202265
MERCEDES-BENZ Clough St. ✆ 202112
NISSAN Victoria Rd, Fenton ✆ 416666
PEUGEOT-TALBOT Leek Rd ✆ 214371
RENAULT Blue Gates, Biddulph ✆ 514444
ROVER Leek Rd, Endon ✆ 503160
ROVER Station Rd, Barlaston ✆ 2014
ROVER Broad St. ✆ 219500
ROVER King St., Longton ✆ 599456
ROVER Brook Lane, Newcastle ✆ 618461
SAAB, TOYOTA, VW Leek Rd, Hanley ✆ 274504
SKODA Leek Rd ✆ 261784
SUBARU, HYUNDAI High St., Tunstall ✆ 838997
VAUXHALL-OPEL Victoria Rd, Hanley ✆ 202200
VAUXHALL-OPEL Bullocks House Rd ✆ 513772
VAUXHALL-OPEL Lightwood Rd ✆ 599199
VOLVO Duke St. ✆ 599799

ATS 25 Smithpool Rd, Fenton ✆ 47081
ATS Lower St., Newcastle-under-Lyme ✆ 622431
ATS 87/89 Waterloo Rd, Burslem ✆ 838493/836591

STOKE PRIOR Heref. and Worc. – see Leominster.

Europe

If the name of the hotel
is not in bold type,
on arrival ask the hotelier his prices.

STONE Glos. 403 404 M 29 – pop. 667 (inc. Ham) – ✉ Berkeley – ☎ 0454 Falfield.
◆London 130 – ◆Bristol 17 – Gloucester 18.

Elms at Stone, GL13 9JX, on A 38 ✆ 260279 – TV ☎ P. VISA
M *(closed Sunday dinner)* 12.95 **t.** (dinner) and lunch a la carte approx. 7.85 **t.** 3.95 – **8 rm** 35.00/45.00 **t.** – SB 62.50 **st.**

BMW, VAUXHALL Manor Close ✆ 710566 FORD Meadowfield Garage ✆ 710386

STONE Heref. and Worc. 403 404 N 26 – see Kidderminster.

STONE Staffs. 402 403 404 N 25 – pop. 12 119 – ECD : Wednesday – ☎ 0785.
18 Barlaston, Meaford Rd ✆ 078 139 (Barlaston) 2795 – 9 Filleybrooks ✆ 813103.
◆London 150 – ◆Birmingham 36 – ◆Stoke-on-Trent 9.

Stone House (Lansbury), ST15 0BQ, S : 1 ¼ m. by A 520 on A 34 ✆ 815531, Telex 367404, Fax 817464, rm TV ☎ P – 200. AE VISA.
M 8.95/14.00 **t.** and a la carte – **48 rm** 74.00/87.00 **t.**, **2 suites** – SB (weekends only) 64.00/76.00 **st.**

Crown, 38 High St., ST15 8AS, ✆ 813535 – TV ☎ P – 150.

FORD Darlaston Rd ✆ 813332

STON EASTON Somerset – see Farrington Gurney.

STONE-IN-OXNEY Kent – see Rye (East Sussex).

STONOR Oxon. 404 R 29 – see Henley-on-Thames.

For maximum information from town plans : consult the conventional signs key.

STONY STRATFORD Bucks. 404 R 27 – ✉ ☎ 0908 Milton Keynes.
◆London 62 – Bedford 27 – ◆Coventry 34 – Northampton 18 – ◆Oxford 31.

Stratfords, 7 St. Paul's Court, 118 High St., MK11 1AJ, ✆ 566577, « Converted Victorian church » – P. AE VISA
closed Saturday lunch and Sunday – **M** 12.50/19.00 **t.**

Peking, 117 High St., MK11 1AT, Chinese (Peking, Szechuan) rest. – .

Bekash Tandoori, 50 High St., MK11 1AQ, ✆ 562249, Indian rest. –.

at Cosgrove (Northants.) N : 2 ½ m. by A 508 – ✉ ☎ 0908 Milton Keynes (Bucks.) :

Old Bakery, Main St., MK19 7JL, ✆ 564940 – TV ☎ P. AE VISA.
M (by arrangement) 8.50 **st.** 4.75 – **8 rm** 28.00/40.00 **st.**

STORRINGTON West Sussex 404 S 31 – pop. 6 915 – ECD : Wednesday – ☎ 090 66 (4 fig.) or 0903 (6 fig.).
Envir. : Parham House★ (Elizabethan) *AC*, W : 1 ½ m.
◆London 54 – ◆Brighton 20 – ◆Portsmouth 36.

Little Thakeham, Merrywood Lane, Thakeham, RH20 3HE, N : 1 ¾ m. by B 2139 ✆ 744416, Fax 745022, ≤ gardens and South downs, « Lutyens house with gardens in the style of Gertrude Jekyll », heated, – TV ☎ P. AE VISA.
closed Christmas-New Year – **M** *(closed* (booking essential) 18.50/32.50 **st.** 4.00 – **7 rm** 90.00/150.00, **2 suites** 210.00.

Abingworth Hall, Thakeham Rd, RH20 3EF, N : 1¾ m. on B 2139 ✆ 0798 (West Chiltington) 813 636, Telex 877835, Fax 813914, heated, – TV ☎ P – 50. AE VISA
M 16.00/28.00 **t.** and a la carte 4.00 – **21 rm** 65.00/150.00 **t.** – SB 130.00/190.00 **st.**

Manley's, Manleys Hill, RH20 4BT, ✆ 742331 – P. AE VISA
closed Sunday dinner and Monday – **M** 17.60/24.00 **t.** (lunch) and a la carte 26.90/29.60 **t.**

STOURBRIDGE West Midlands 403 404 N26 – pop. 55136 – ECD : Thursday – ☎ 0384.
18 Hagley Country Club ✆ 0562 (Hagley) 883701 AU – 18 Worcester Lane, Pedmore ✆ 393062 AU – 18, 18 Highgate Common, Enville ✆ 872551.
◆London 147 – ◆Birmingham 14 – Wolverhampton 10 – Worcester 21.

Plan : see Birmingham p. 2

Talbot, High St., DY8 1DW, ✆ 394350, Group Telex 335464, Fax 371318 – TV ☎ P – 120. AE VISA see plan of Birmingham p.2 AU **a**
M 6.75/12.00 **t.** and a la carte 4.95 – **25 rm** 50.50/156.00 **t.** – SB (weekends only) 118.00/142.00 **st.**

Limes, 260 Hagley Rd, Pedmore, DY9 0RW, SE : 1 ½ m. on A 491 ✆ 0562 (Hagley) 882689, – ☎ P. VISA AU **z**
M (by arrangement) 6.50 **st.** – **11 rm** 24.50/34.50 **st.**

Bon Appetit, 38 Market St., DY8 1AG, ✆ 375372 – P. AE VISA
closed Saturday lunch, Sunday dinner, Monday and 1 to 14 January – **M** 12.50 **t.** (lunch) and a la carte 18.20/21.75 **t.**

at Hagley S : 2 ½ m. by A 491 AU – ✉ Stourbridge – ☎ 0562 Hagley :

Badger Sett Travel Inn, Birmingham Rd, DY9 9JS, NE : 1 ½ m. on A 456 (Eastbound) ℘ 883120, Fax 884416 – ⇔ rm TV ♿ Ⓟ. AE VISA. ✻
M (Beefeater grill) a la carte approx. 12.25 **st.** – ☐ 4.50 – **42 rm** -/27.50 **st.**

at Kinver (Staffs.) W : 5 m. by A 458 – AU – ✉ Stourbridge (West Midlands) – ☎ 0384 Kinver :

XX **Berkley's (Piano Room),** High St., DY7 6HG, ℘ 873679 – Ⓟ. AE VISA
closed Sunday, first 2 weeks February and 26 to 30 December – **M** (dinner only) a la carte 16.20/18.35 **t.** 3.00.

FORD Hagley Rd ℘ 392131
FORD, VOLVO ℘ 442222
NISSAN High St ℘ 393231
RENAULT Norton Rd ℘ 396655
ROVER Hagley Rd ℘ 393022
VAUXHALL-OPEL The Hayes, Lye ℘ 424665
VAUXHALL-OPEL Bridgnorth Rd ℘ 394757
VW-AUDI Birmingham St. ℘ 392626

STOURPORT-ON-SEVERN Heref. and Worc. 403 404 N 26 – pop. 17 880 – ECD : Wednesday – ☎ 029 93 (4 and 5 fig.) or 0299 (6 fig.).

♦London 137 – ♦Birmingham 21 – Worcester 12.

Stourport Moat House (Q.M.H.), 35 Hartlebury Rd, DY13 9LT, E : 1 ¼ m. on B 4193 ℘ 827733, Telex 333676, Fax 378520, park, squash – ⇔ rm TV ☎ Ⓟ – 400. AE VISA
M *(closed Saturday lunch)* 10.50/12.50 **st.** and a la carte 3.95 – **65 rm** ☐ 60.00/80.00 **st.**, **3 suites** 85.00/100.00 **st.** – SB (weekends only) 90.00/225.00 **st.**

Swan, 56 High St., DY13 8BX, ℘ 71661, Fax 827650 – TV ☎ Ⓟ – 50. AE VISA
M 15.00 **t.** – **32 rm** ☐ 42.50/56.00 **t.** – SB (weekends only) 41.00/60.00 **st.**

Oakleigh, 17 York St., DY13 9EE, ℘ 77568, – TV Ⓟ
10 rm.

X **Severn Tandoori,** 11 Bridge St., DY13 8UX, ℘ 3090, Indian rest. – AE VISA
closed Christmas Day – **M** a la carte 10.75/13.85 **t.** 3.15.

STOWMARKET Suffolk 404 W 27 – ☎ 0449.

18 Lower Rd, Onehouse ℘ 044 93 (Rattlesden) 392.

♦London 81 – ♦Cambridge 42 – ♦Ipswich 12 – ♦Norwich 38.

Travelodge without rest., A 45 Westbound, IP14 3PY, NW : 2 m. by A 1038 on A 45 ℘ 615347, Reservations (Toll free) 0800 850950 – TV ♿ Ⓟ. AE VISA
40 rm 24.00/29.50 **st.**

MITSUBISHI, YUGO Dunley ℘ 3357

STOW-ON-THE-WOLD Glos. 403 404 O 28 – pop. 1 596 – ECD : Wednesday – ✉ Cheltenham – ☎ 0451 Cotswold.

Talbot Court ℘ 31082/31971.

♦London 86 – ♦Birmingham 44 – Gloucester 27 – ♦Oxford 30.

Wyck Hill House , GL54 1HY, S : 2¼ m. by A 429 on A 424 ℘ 31936, Fax 32243, ≤, « Victorian country house », park – TV ☎ Ⓟ. AE VISA
M 15.00/36.00 **t.** and a la carte **t.** 5.50 – **30 rm** ☐ 65.00/130.00 **t.**, **1 suite** 130.00/165.00 **t.** – SB (weekends only) 135.00/160.00 **st.**

Grapevine (Best Western), Sheep St., GL54 1AU, ℘ 30344, Fax 32278, « 120 year old grapevine in restaurant » – ⇔ rest TV ☎ Ⓟ. AE VISA. ✻
closed 24 December-17 January and Bank Holidays – **M** (bar lunch)/dinner 23.80 **t.** 6.50 – **17 rm** ☐ 66.00/106.00 **t.** – SB 77.00/153.00 **st.**

Unicorn Crest (T.H.F.), Sheep St., GL54 1HQ, ℘ 30257, Telex 437186, Fax 31090 – ⇔ rm TV ☎ Ⓟ. AE VISA
M (bar lunch Monday to Saturday)/dinner 14.30 **st.** and a la carte – ☐ 7.95 – **20 rm** 60.00/84.00 **t.**

Fosse Manor, Fosse Way, GL54 1JX, S : 1 ¼ m. on A 429 ℘ 30354, Fax 32486, – ⇔ rest TV ☎ Ⓟ – 40. AE VISA
closed 23 December-6 January – **M** 12.95/14.95 **t.** and a la carte 4.20 – **20 rm** ☐ 38.00/80.00 **t.** – SB (except March and September) 77.00/99.00 **st.**

Stow Lodge, The Square, GL54 1AB, ℘ 30485, – ⇔ TV Ⓟ. AE. ✻
closed 20 December-31 January – **M** (bar lunch)/dinner 13.00 **t.** and a la carte 5.00 – **22 rm** ☐ 36.00/70.00 **t.** – SB (November-Easter) 63.00/74.00 **st.**

Cross Keys Cottage without rest., Park St., GL54 1AQ, ℘ 31128, – TV. ✻
closed Christmas-New Year – **3 rm** ☐ -/40.00 **s.**

Limes without rest., Evesham Rd, GL54 1EJ, ℘ 30034, – TV Ⓟ
closed 21 December-2 January – **5 rm** ☐ 17.00/33.00 **s.**

XX **Epicurean,** 1 Park St., GL54 1AQ, ℘ 31613. AE VISA
closed Sunday dinner, Monday and 2 weeks January – **M** 16.50/26.00 **st.** and a la carte 7.50.

at Upper Oddington E : 2 ¼ m. by A 436 – ✉ Moreton-in-Marsh – ☎ 0451 Cotswold :

Horse and Groom Inn, GL56 OXH, ☎ 30584 – TV P. VISA.
closed 25-26 December and 1 January – **M** (bar lunch)/dinner a la carte 7.95/14.10 **t.** 2.80 – **7 rm** 26.50/48.00 **t.** – SB (winters only) 58.00/64.00 **st.**

at Bledington SE : 4 m. by A 436 on B 4450 – ✉ – ☎ 060 871 Kingham (Oxon.) :

Kings Head, OX7 6HD, ☎ 365 – rm TV ☎ P.
M *(closed Sunday dinner)* (bar lunch)/dinner 15.50 **t.** and a la carte 3.00 – **6 rm** 26.00/49.00 **st.**

at Lower Swell W : 1 ¼ m. on B 4068 – ✉ Stow-on-the-Wold – ☎ 0451 Cotswold :

Old Farmhouse, GL54 1LF, ☎ 30232, – rest TV P. VISA
M (dinner only and Sunday lunch)/dinner 12.50 **st.** and a la carte 3.75 – **13 rm** 41.25/61.50 **st.**

AUDI-VW Oddington, Moreton-in-Marsh ☎ 30422

STRATFIELD TURGIS Hants. – pop. 88 – ✉ ☎ 0256 Basingstoke.

London 46 – Basingstoke 8 – Reading 11.

Wellington Arms, RG27 0AS, on A 33 ☎ 882214, Fax 882934, – rm TV ☎ P – 60. AE VISA
M 9.00/23.00 **st.** and a la carte 7.25 – **15 rm** 75.00/100.00 **st.** – SB (weekends only) 87.50 **st.**

In alta stagione, *e soprattutto nelle stazioni turistiche, è prudente prenotare con un certo anticipo. Avvertite immediatamente l'albergatore se non potete più occupare la camera prenotata. Se scrivete ad un albergo all'estero, allegate alla vostra lettera un tagliando-risposta internazionale (disponibile presso gli uffici postali).*

STRATFORD-UPON-AVON Warw. 403 404 P 27 – pop. 20941 – ECD : Thursday – ☎ 0789.

See : Site★ – Shakespeare's birthplace★ (16C)*AC*, AB – Hall's Croft★ (16C)*AC*, A **B**.

Envir. : Charlecote Park (castle 16C : interior★) *AC*, NE : 5 m. by B 4086 B – Wilmcote (Mary Arden's House★★) (16C) *AC*, NW : 5 m. by A 34 A.

18 Tiddington Rd ☎ 414546, E : by B 4086 B.
18 Warwick Rd ☎ 295252 by A 439 B.

Judith Shakespeare's House, 1 High St. ☎ 293127.

London 96 – Birmingham 23 – Coventry 18 – Oxford 40.

STRATFORD-UPON-AVON

Bridge Street	B 8
Henley Street	A 29
High Street	A 31
Sheep Street	AB 35
Wood Street	A 47
Banbury Road	B 2
Benson Road	B 3
Bridge Foot	B 6
Chapel Lane	A 13
Chapel Street	A 14
Church Street	A 16
Clopton Bridge	B 18
College Lane	A 19
Ely Street	A 22
Evesham Place	A 24
Great William Street	A 25
Greenhill Street	A 27
Guild Street	A 28
Scholars Lane	A 33
Tiddington Road	B 38
Trinity Street	A 40
Warwick Road	B 42
Waterside	B 43
Windsor Street	A 45

Town plans : *the names of main shopping streets are indicated in red at the beginning of the list of streets.*

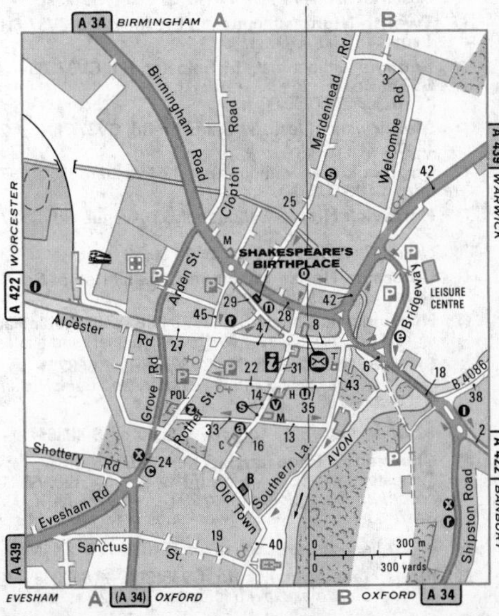

Welcombe, Warwick Rd, CV37 0NR, NE : 1 ½ m. on A 439 ℰ 295252, Telex 31347 Fax 414666, ≤, « 19C mansion in park », – 60. on A 46 B
closed 28 December-3 January – **M** 18.50/27.00 **t.** and a la carte 6.50 – **70 rm** 85.00 135.00 **t.**, **5 suites** 150.00/375.00 **t.** – SB (weekends only) 150.00/160.00 **st.**

Ettington Park, Alderminster, CV37 8BS, SE : 6 ¼ m. on A 34 ℰ 740740, Tele: 311825, Fax 87472, ≤, « Victorian Gothic mansion », park, – rm – 50. on A 34 B
M 15.00/27.50 **st.** and a la carte 10.00 – **43 rm** 95.00/125.00 **st.**, **5 suites** 165.00 185.00 **st.**

Moat House International (Q.M.H.), Bridgefoot, CV37 6YR, ℰ 414411, Telex 311127 Fax 298589, – rm – 350. B
M 13.95 **t.** and a la carte 5.00 – **245 rm** 82.50/110.00 **t.**, **2 suites** 140.00/165.00 **t.** – SB (weekends only) 91.00/115.00 **st.**

Shakespeare (T.H.F.), Chapel St., CV37 6ER, ℰ 294771, Telex 311181, Fax 415411, « 16C timbered inn » – rm – 100. A
M 12.00/17.00 **st.** and a la carte 5.00 – 8.00 – **69 rm** 75.00/105.00 **st.**, **1 suite** 160.00 **st.** – SB (weekends only) (except Easter, Christmas and New Year) 126.00 **st.**

Alveston Manor (T.H.F.), Clopton Bridge, CV37 7HP, ℰ 204581, Telex 31324 Fax 414095, – rm – 150. B
M 25.00 **st.** and a la carte – 7.60 – **103 rm** 77.00/97.00 **st.**, **5 suites** 150.00 **st.** – SB 94.00/124.00 **st.**

Dukes, Payton St., CV37 6UA, ℰ 269300, Fax 414700, – . A
closed Christmas and New Year – **M** *(closed Sunday)* a la carte 13.00/19.25 **t.** 3.75 – **22 rm** 42.50/95.00 **t.** – SB (weekends only) (except Bank Holidays) 85.00/95.00 **st.**

White Swan (T.H.F.), Rother St., CV37 6NH, ℰ 297022, Fax 68773 – rm – 35. A
M 13.00/15.00 **st.** and a la carte 3.75 – 7.00 – **42 rm** 65.00/90.00 **st.** – SB 94.00 **st.**

Falcon (Q.M.H.), Chapel St., CV37 6HA, ℰ 205777, Telex 312522, Fax 414260 – rm – 200. A
M 15.00/16.00 **st.** and a la carte 4.25 – **73 rm** 60.00/99.00 **st.** – SB 84.00/92.00 **st.**

Windmill Park (Best Western), Warwick Rd, CV37 0PY, NE : 3 m. on A 439 ℰ 731173 Fax 731131, park, – rest – 350.
M 9.50/12.75 **st.** and a la carte 4.00 – **100 rm** 65.00/80.00 **st.**

Stratford House, 18 Sheep St., CV37 6EF, ℰ 68288, Fax 295580 – . AB
closed 25 to 28 December – **M** *(closed Sunday and Monday)* 11.50/29.35 **t.** and a la carte – **10 rm** 60.00/90.00 **t.** – SB (weekdays only in Summer) 80.00/100.00 **st.**

Moonraker House without rest., 40 Alcester Rd, CV37 9DB, ℰ 67115, Fax 295504 – . A
closed Christmas Day – **24 rm** 30.00/50.00 **st.**

Twelfth Night without rest., Evesham Pl., CV37 6HT, ℰ 414595 – . A
7 rm 19.00/46.00 **st.**

Sequoia without rest., 51 Shipston Rd, CV37 7LN, ℰ 68852, Fax 414559, – . B
21 rm 27.50/59.00 **st.**

Melita without rest., 37 Shipston Rd, CV37 7LN, ℰ 292432, – . B
12 rm 27.00/52.00 **t.**

Virginia Lodge without rest., 12 Evesham Pl., CV37 6HT, ℰ 292157 – A
6 rm 13.00/36.00 **s.**

Hardwick House without rest., 1 Avenue Rd, CV37 6UY, ℰ 204307 – . B
closed Christmas – **14 rm** 18.00/50.00 **st.**

Caterham House without rest., 58-59 Rother St., CV37 6LT, ℰ 67309 – A
13 rm 27.00/45.00 **st.**

Hussains, 6a Chapel St., CV37 6EP, ℰ 67506, Indian rest. – . A
closed Christmas Day – **M** 15.00 **t.** (dinner) and a la carte 8.60/13.30 **t.** 4.95.

Sir Toby's, 8 Church St., CV37 6HB, ℰ 68822 – . A
closed Sunday, last 3 weeks February and Bank Holidays – **M** (dinner only) a la carte 12.75/18.50 **st.** 3.85.

at Charlecote E : 4 ¾ m. by B 4086 on B 4088 – B – 0789 Stratford upon Avon :

Charlecote Pheasant (Q.M.H.), CV35 9EW, ℰ 470333, Telex 31688, Fax 470222, heated, – rm – 120.
accommodation closed 24 to 29 December – **M** 10.00/12.25 **t.** and a la carte 3.75 – **60 rm** 65.00/115.00 **st.** – SB (weekends only) 83.00/118.00 **st.**

at Wellesbourne E : 5¾ m. on B 4086 – B – Warwick – 0789 Stratford upon Avon :

Kings Head, Warwick Rd, CV35 9LX, ℰ 840206 – .
(closed Christmas Day) a la carte 5.25/8.25 **st.** – **9 rm** 34.00/48.00 **st.**

at Long Marston SW : 7 m. by A 34 – B – off B 4632 – ✉ ☎ 0789 Stratford-upon-Avon :

Kings Lodge ⛺, CV37 8RL, ☎ 720705, « Country house atmosphere », 🌳 – 🅟
closed December and January – **M** (by arrangement) 8.50 **st.** 🌡 2.75 – **3 rm** ☕ 16.50/44.00 **st.**

at Billesley W : 4½ m. by A 422 – A – ✉ Alcester – ☎ 0789 Stratford-upon-Avon :

Billesley Manor (Q.M.H.) ⛺, B49 6NF, ☎ 400888, Telex 312599, Fax 764145, ≤, « Part Elizabethan manor, topiary garden », 🏊, 🏊, 🌳, park, 🎾 – 📺 ☎ 🅟 – 🏛 90. 🏧 AE ⓓ VISA. 🚫
M 17.00/23.00 **t.** and a la carte 🌡 5.40 – **39 rm** ☕ 95.00/155.00 **t.**, **2 suites** 170.00/190.00 **t.** – SB 144.00 **st.**

at Wilmcote NW : 3½ m. by A 3400– A – ✉ ☎ 0789 Stratford-upon-Avon :

Swan House, The Green, CV37 9XJ, ☎ 67030, Fax 204875, 🌳 – 📺 🅟. 🏧 AE VISA. 🚫
accommodation closed 24 to 28 December – **M** (bar lunch)/dinner a la carte 10.75/15.85 **st.** – **12 rm** ☕ 35.00/55.00 **st.** – SB 62.00/72.00 **st.**

Pear Tree Cottage ⛺ without rest., Church Rd, CV37 9UX, ☎ 205889, 🌳 – 📺 🅟
7 rm ☕ 23.00/36.00 **st.**

UDI-VW Western Rd ☎ 294477
ITROEN 23 Weston Rd ☎ 293577
IAT Western Rd ☎ 67159
ORD Arden St. ☎ 67446
IISSAN Avenue Farm Industrial Estate ☎ 69894
EUGEOT-TALBOT Alderminster ☎ 078 987 (Alerminster) 331/419
RENAULT Western Rd ☎ 69237
SAAB Birmingham Rd ☎ 205990

ATS Western Rd ☎ 205591

STRATTON Glos. 403 404 O 28 – see Cirencester.

STREATLEY Berks. 403 404 Q 29 – pop. 1 055 – ✉ ☎ 0491 Goring.
18 Goring Streatley, Rectory Rd ☎ 872688.
London 56 – Oxford 16 – Reading 11.

Swan Diplomat, High St., RG8 9HR, ☎ 873737, Telex 848259, Fax 872554, « ≤ Thames-side setting », 🏊, 🌳 – 📺 ☎ ♿ 🅟 – 🏛 120. 🏧 AE ⓓ VISA
closed 2 to 6 January – **M** *(closed Saturday lunch)* 19.50/22.50 **t.** and a la carte – **45 rm** ☕ 81.00/134.00 **t.**, **1 suite** 170.00/200.00 **t.** – SB (weekends only) 115.00/145.00 **st.**

STREET Somerset 403 L 30 **The West Country G.** – pop. 9 454 – ECD : Wednesday – ☎ 0458.
See : The Shoe Museum★ *AC*.
Envir. : at Somerton★, Market Place★, St. Michaels Church★, S : 6 m. – at High Ham (St. Andrews Church★), SW : 8 m.
London 138 – Bristol 28 – Taunton 20.

Bear, 53 High St., BA16 0EF, ☎ 42021 – 📺 ☎ 🅟 – 🏛 50. 🏧 AE VISA
M (bar lunch Monday to Saturday)/dinner 15.00 **t.** and a la carte 🌡 6.00 – **15 rm** ☕ 50.00/120.00 **t.** – SB (weekends only) 70.00/80.00 **st.**

FIAT 84 West End ☎ 42996
FORD 189 High St. ☎ 47147
ROVER Creeches Lane, Walton ☎ 42735
VAUXHALL-OPEL 12 Main St., Walton ☎ 42275

STRETTON Cheshire 402 403 404 M 23 – see Warrington.

STRETTON Staffs. 402 403 404 P 25 – see Burton-upon-Trent.

STRETTON UNDER FOSSE Warw. 403 404 Q 26 – see Rugby.

STROUD Glos. 403 404 N 28 – pop. 37 791 – ECD : Thursday – ☎ 045 36.
Envir. : Severn Wildfowl Trust★ *AC*, W : 11 m – Painswick★ NE : 3 m.
18, 18 Minchinhampton ☎ 045 383 (Nailsworth) 2642 (Old Course) 3866 (New Course) E : 3 m.
Subscription Rooms ☎ 765768.
London 113 – Bristol 30 – Gloucester 9.

Stonehouse Court, Bristol Rd , Stonehouse, GL10 3RA, W : 3 ¼ m. on A 419 ☎ 045 382 (Stonehouse) 5155, Fax 4611, 🌳 – 📺 ☎ 🅟 – 🏛 150. 🏧 VISA. 🚫
M 10.50/19.50 **t.** and a la carte – **35 rm** ☕ 67.50/80.00 **t.**, **1 suite** – SB (October-April except Christmas-New Year) 98.00/193.00 **st.**

Imperial (B.C.B.), Station Rd, GL5 3AP, ☎ 764077 – 📺 ☎ 🅟. 🏧 AE ⓓ VISA. 🚫
M (grill rest.) 8.00/15.00 **st.** – **25 rm** ☕ 42.00/58.00.

London, 30-31 London Rd, GL5 2AJ, ☎ 759992 – 📺 ☎ 🅟. 🏧 AE ⓓ VISA. 🚫
M 9.85/11.95 **st.** and a la carte 🌡 3.75 – **11 rm** ☕ 25.00/60.00 **st.** – SB (weekends only) (except Bank Holidays) 52.00/68.00 **st.**

Old Vicarage, 167 Slad Rd., GL5 1RD, ☎ 752315, 🌳 – 🚭 rm 📺 🅟. 🚫
closed January – **M** (by arrangement) 10.00 **st.** 🌡 2.20 – **3 rm** ☕ 23.50/29.50 **st.** – SB 42.00/64.00.

XX ⚘ **Oakes** (Oakes), 169 Slad Rd, GL5 1RG, ☎ 759950 – Ⓟ. VISA
closed Sunday dinner, Monday, 2 weeks August and 30 December-29 January – **M** 15.5
34.00 **t.** 5.00.
Spec. Homemade venison sausage with red cabbage, bacon and juniper sauce, Fillet of red mullet with onion, toma and thyme, vermouth cream sauce, Fresh pineapple with praline ice cream, caramel sauce.

at Brimscombe SE : 2 ¼ m. on A 419 – ✉ Stroud – ☎ 0453 Brimscombe :

Burleigh Court ⚘, Burleigh Hill, GL5 2PF, S : ½ m. by Burleigh rd via the Roundabou ☎ 883804, Fax 886870, ≤, heated, – rest TV ☎ Ⓟ. AE VISA.
closed 24 December to 7 January – **M** *(closed Sunday dinner)* 12.00/25.00 **t.** and a la car 3.90 – **17 rm** 54.00/90.00 **st.** – SB 95.00/105.00 **st.**

at Rodborough S : ¾ m. by A 46 – ✉ Stroud – ☎ 0453 Amberley :

Bear of Rodborough (T.H.F.), Rodborough Common, GL5 5DE, SE : 1 ½ m. on Minchi hampton rd ☎ 878522, Telex 437130, Fax 872523, – rm TV ☎ Ⓟ – 60. AE VISA
M 8.50/14.00 **t.** and a la carte 4.35 – 7.00 – **47 rm** 65.00/100.00 **st.** – SB 84.00/94.00 s

at Leonard Stanley W : 4 m. by A 419 – ✉ ☎ 0453 Stroud:

Grey Cottage without rest., GL10 3LU, ☎ 822515, (booking essential), – rm Ⓟ.
closed Christmas – **3 rm** 22.00/48.00 **s.**

ALFA-ROMEO Lansdown Rd ☎ 764845
CITROEN London Rd, Bowbridge ☎ 762861
FIAT Stratford Rd ☎ 764007
FORD London Rd ☎ 751341
MAZDA, HYUNDAI Westward Rd, Ebley ☎ 762000
PEUGEOT-TALBOT Stonehouse ☎ 045 382 (Stonehouse) 2139
ROVER Chestnut Lane ☎ 763671
VAUXHALL-OPEL, BEDFORD Westward Rd ☎ 765522

ATS Dudbridge Rd ☎ 758156

STUCKTON Hants. – see Fordingbridge.

STUDLAND Dorset 403 404 O 32 **The West Country G.** – pop. 559 – ECD : Thursday – ✉ Swanage – ☎ 092 944.
London 130 – Bournemouth 22 – Dorchester 26.

Knoll House, BH19 3AH, ☎ 251, Fax 423, heated, park, – ☎ Ⓟ
April-October – **M** 12.00/14.00 **st.** 3.50 – **78 rm** 50.00/125.00 **st.**

STUDLEY Warw. 403 404 O 27 – ✉ Redditch – ☎ 052 785.

XX **Pepper's,** 45 High St., B80 7HN, ☎ 3183, Indian rest. – AE VISA
closed 25 and 26 December – **M** (dinner only) 15.00 **t.** and a la carte.

STURMINSTER NEWTON Dorset 403 404 N 31 – pop. 1 781 – ☎ 0258.
London 123 – Bournemouth 30 – Bristol 49 – Salisbury 28 – Taunton 41.

XXX **Plumber Manor** ⚘ with rm, DT10 2AF, SW : 1 ¾ m. by A 357 on Hazelbury Bryan r ☎ 72507, Fax 73370, ≤, « 18C manor house », park, – TV ☎ Ⓟ. AE VISA.
closed February – **M** (dinner only) 18.00/25.00 **st.** 4.00 – **16 rm** 50.00/100.00 **st.**

MAZDA Station Rd ☎ 72155

STURTON-BY-STOW Lincs. 402 404 S 24 – pop. 1 040 – ✉ Lincoln – ☎ 0427 Gainsborough
London 149 – Kingston-upon-Hull 45 – Lincoln 9 – Sheffield 46.

Village Farm, High St., LN1 2AE, ☎ 788309, – rm Ⓟ.
April-October – **M** (by arrangement) 9.00 **st.** – **3 rm** 14.00/32.00 **st.** – SB 42.00/46.00 **st.**

FSO, DAIHATSU Tillbridge Lane ☎ 788360

SUDBURY Derbs. 402 403 404 O 25 – pop. 839 – ✉ Derby – ☎ 028 372 Marchington.
See : Sudbury Hall★★ (17C) *AC.*
London 138 – Birmingham 33 – Derby 13 – Stoke-on-Trent 23.

Hotel and restaurant see : Tutbury SE : 6 m., ***Uttoxeter*** W : 4 ½ m.

SUDBURY Suffolk 404 W 27 – pop. 17 723 – ECD : Wednesday – ☎ 0787.
Newton Green ☎ 77501. Public Library, Market Hill ☎ 72092.
London 59 – Cambridge 37 – Colchester 15 – Ipswich 21.

Hill Lodge, Newton Rd, CO10 6RG, ☎ 77568 – rest TV Ⓟ – 70. – **16 rm.**

XX **The Friars,** 17 Friars St., CO10 6AA, ☎ 72940 – AE VISA
closed Sunday except 10 March and Easter – **M** 10.50/13.55 **st.** and a la carte 4.00.

X **Mabey's Brasserie,** 47 Gainsborough St., CO10 7SS, ☎ 74298 – VISA
closed Sunday, Monday, 2 weeks February and 2 weeks August – **M** a la carte 12.15/17.95 **t.** 3.95.

FORD Northern Rd ☎ 73436
VAUXHALL-OPEL Cornard Rd ☎ 72301

ATS Edgeworthy Rd ☎ 74227

SUNDERLAND

Street	Map	No.
Fawcett Street	B	
High Street West	B	15
Holmeside	B	
John Street	B	16
Three Bridges	B	

Street	Map	No.
Albion Place	B	2
Barnes Park Road	A	3
Bedford Street	B	4
Borough Road	B	5
Bridge Street	B	6
Charlton Road	A	8
Chester Road	B	10
Crowtree Road	B	11
Derwent Street	B	12
Harbour View	A	14
Kayll Road	A	17
Livingstone Road	B	18
New Durham Road	B	19
Northern Way	A	20
Ormonde Street	A	21
Pallion Road	A	22
Park Lane	B	23
Queens Road	A	24
Roker Terrace	A	25
St. Luke's Terrace	A	26
St. Mary's Way	B	27
Shields Road	A	29
Southwick Road	B	30
Station Road	A	32
Trimdon Street	A	35
Vine Place	B	36
Wessington Way	A	38

Plans de villes :
Le nom des principales voies commerçantes est inscrit en rouge au début des légendes-rues.

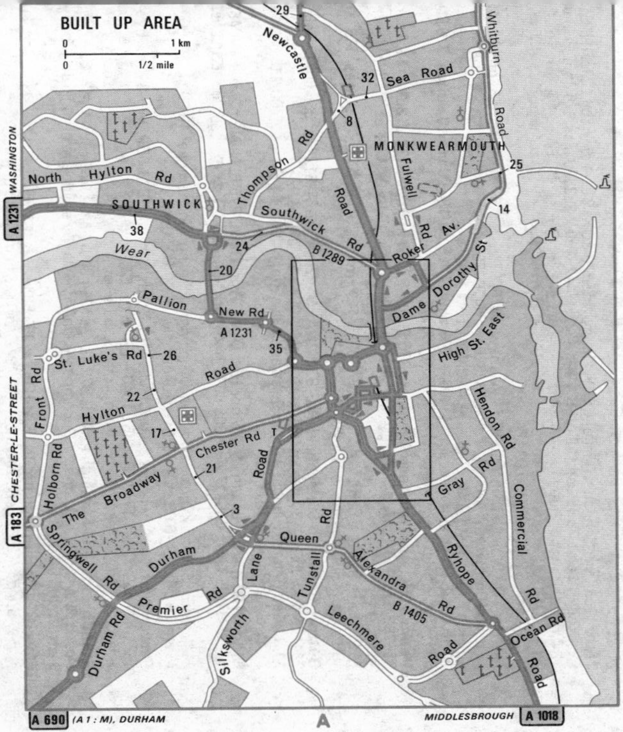

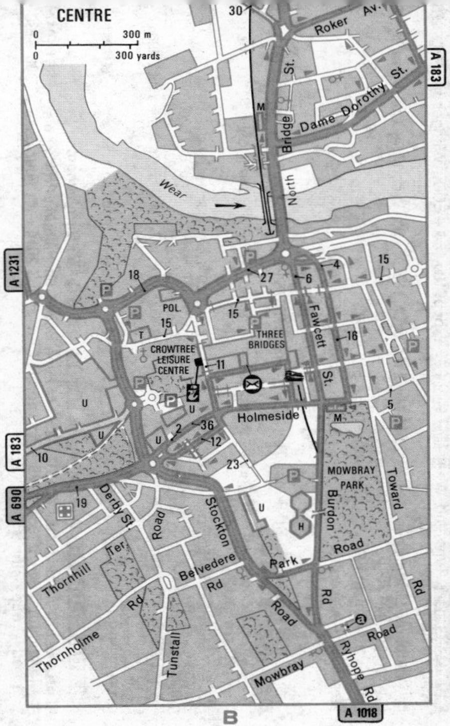

BUILT UP AREA

CENTRE

SUNDERLAND Tyne and Wear 401 402 P 19 – pop. 195 064 – ECD : Wednesday – ☎ 078 (5 and 6 fig.) or 091 (7 fig.).

Whitburn, Lizard Lane ☎ 529 2144 N : 2 m. by A 183 A – Wearside, Coxgreen ☎ 09 (Coxgreen) 534 2518.

Crowtree Leisure Centre, Crowtree Rd ☎ 565 0960.

London 272 – Leeds 92 – Middlesbrough 29 – Newcastle-upon-Tyne 12.

Plan on preceding page

Gelt House, 23 St. Bedes Terr., SR2 8HS, ☎ 567 2990, Fax 510 0724 – rest ☎ AE VISA.
closed Christmas-New Year – **M** *(closed Friday to Sunday)* (dinner only) 8.00 **t.** 2.90 B
22 rm 34.00/40.00 **t.**

AUDI-VW, MERCEDES Newcastle Rd ☎ 548 0235
BMW Ryhope Rd ☎ 523 7373
DAIHATSU, CITROEN Villiers St. ☎ 567 3954
FIAT Villiers St. ☎ 510 0550
FORD Trimdon St. ☎ 514 0311
HONDA Harbour View Garage ☎ 567 7538
MITSUBISHI Nth. Bridge St. ☎ 565 9252
PEUGEOT Newcastle Rd ☎ 548 8811
RENAULT Riverside Rd ☎ 549 5260
ROVER Warwick ☎ 521 0838
VAUXHALL 122-129 High St. West ☎ 567 4805
VOLVO Newcastle Rd ☎ 549 1277

ATS Monkwearmouth Bridge ☎ 565 7694

SUTTON COLDFIELD West Midlands 403 404 O 26 – ☎ 021 Birmingham.

Brooks Rd, Wylde Green ☎ 351 0029 – Pype Hayes, Eachelhurst Rd Walmley ☎ 351 1014 Monmouth Drive ☎ 354 3379 – Thornhill Rd ☎ 353 2014 – Four oaks ☎ 308 6130 Streetly, Little Aston ☎ 353 2066.

London 124 – Birmingham 8 – Coventry 29 – Nottingham 47 – Stoke-on-Trent 40.

Plan: see Birmingham pp. 2 and 3

New Hall (Mt. Charlotte Thistle), Walmley Rd, B76 8QX, SE : 1 ½ m. by Coleshill St Coleshill Rd and Reddicap Hill on B 4148 ☎ 378 2442, Telex 333580, Fax 378 4637, « Par 13C moated manor house », park – rm ☎ – 40. AE VISA.
M 13.00/20.00 **st.** and a la carte – 8.00 – **57 rm** 79.00/160.00 **st.**, **5 suites** 130.00 250.00 **st.** – SB 124.00/130.00 **st.** DT

Belfry (De Vere), Lichfield Rd, Wishaw, B76 9PR, E : 6 ½ by A 453 on A 44 ☎ 0675 (Curdworth) 470301, Telex 338848, Fax 470178, park, squash – rest ☎ – 400. AE VISA. by A 38 DT
M 18.00/35.00 **st.** and a la carte 7.00 – **209 rm** 105.00/135.00 **st.**, **10 suites** 210.00 350.00 **st.** – SB (weekends only) 140.00/220.00 **st.**

Penns Hall, Penns Lane, Walmley, B76 8LH, SE : 2¾ m. by A 5127 ☎ 351 3111, Telex 335789, Fax 313 1297, squash – rm ☎ – 400. AE VISA DT
M 20.00 **st.** and a la carte 4.25 – 7.00 – **109 rm** 90.00/115.00 **st.**, **5 suites** 135.00 165.00 **st.** – SB (weekends only) 82.00/90.00 **st.**

Sutton Court, 60-66 Lichfield Rd, B74 2NA, N : ½ m. on A 5127 ☎ 355 6071, Telex 334175, Fax 355 0083 – rm ☎ – 120. AE VISA. DT
M *(closed Saturday lunch)* 9.95/18.95 **st.** and a la carte 4.00 – **64 rm** 75.00/110.00 **st.** – SB (weekends only) 73.00 **st.**

Moor Hall (Best Western), Moor Hall Drive, Four Oaks, B75 6LN, NE : 2 m. by A 453 ☎ 308 3751, Telex 335127, Fax 308 8974, park – rm ☎ – 250. AE VISA DT
M *(closed Saturday lunch and Sunday dinner)* (carving lunch)/dinner 18.00 **st.** 7.00 – **75 rm** 75.00/140.00 **st.** – SB (weekends only) 76.00/80.00 **st.**

Parson and Clerk without rest., Chester Rd North, Streetly, B73 6SP, W : 3½ m. by A 453 on A 452 ☎ 353 1747, Fax 352 1340 – ☎. AE VISA CT
closed 25 and 26 December – **30 rm** 42.50/53.50 **st.**

Standbridge, 138 Birmingham Rd, B72 1LY, ☎ 354 3007, – rest.
closed 28 May-10 June and 24 December-4 January – **M** (by arrangement) 6.35 **st.** 2.40 – **9 rm** 19.75/39.50 **st.** DT

Flewitt's, 65 Birmingham Rd, B72 1QF, ☎ 355 5836 – . VISA DT
closed Sunday dinner and Monday – **M** 18.00/20.00 **t.** and a la carte 4.25.

SUTTON IN THE ELMS Leics. – see Earl Shilton.

SUTTON SCOTNEY Hants. 403 404 P 30 – ✉ ☎ 0962 Winchester.

London 66 – Reading 32 – Salisbury 21 – Southampton 19.

Travelodge without rest., Sutton Scotney Service Area, SO21 3JY, on A 34 ☎ 760779 (Southside) ☎ 761016 (Northside), Reservations (Toll free) 0800 850950 – . AE VISA.
71 rm 24.00/29.50 **t.**

If you find you cannot take up a hotel booking you have made, please let the hotel know immediately.

WAFFHAM Norfolk 404 W 26 – pop. 4 742 – ECD : Thursday – ☏ 0760.

nvir. : Oxburgh Hall (15C) : Gate house★ *AC*, SW : 7½ m.

Cley Rd ☏ 721611.

ondon 97 – ◆Cambridge 46 – King's Lynn 16 – ◆Norwich 27.

- George, Station St., PE37 7LJ, ☏ 721238 – TV ☎ P – 180
  28 rm.

ATS Unit 2a, Tower Meadow (off Station St.) ☏ 22543

WALCLIFFE Oxon. – see Banbury.

WANAGE Dorset 403 404 O 32 **The West Country G.** – pop. 8 411 – ECD : Thursday – ☏ 0929.

ee : Site★ – Durlston Country Park (≤★★) – The Great Globe★.

nvir. : St. Aldhelm's Head★★ (≤★★★), SW : 4 m. by B 3069 – Corfe Castle★★ (≤★★)*AC*, NW : m. – Old Harry Rocks★★ (Studland Village - St. Nicholas Church★) N : 4½ m. – Studland each (≤★), N : 5 m.

Isle of Purbeck ☏ 092 944 (Purbeck) 361, NW: on B 3351.

White House, Shore Rd ☏ 422885/424932.

London 130 – Bournemouth 22 – Dorchester 26 – ◆Southampton 52.

- **The Pines**, Burlington Rd, BH19 1LT, ☏ 425211, Fax 422075, ≤, – TV ☎ P. VISA – **M** 8.50/21.50 **t.** 3.50 – **45 rm** 35.00/82.00 **t.**
- **Havenhurst,** 3 Cranborne Rd, BH19 1EA, ☏ 424224 – P.
  M 15.00 **st.** – **17 rm** 23.50/47.00 **st.** – SB (October-March) (except Christmas) 48.00/60.00 **st.**
- **Eversden,** 5 Victoria Rd, BH19 1LY, ☏ 423276 – P.
  March-November – **M** 10.00 **t.** 2.00 – **12 rm** 17.00/39.99 **t.** – SB (except June-August) 40.00/46.00 **st.**
- Crowthorne, 24 Cluny Cres., BH19 2BT, ☏ 422108 – rest. – **10 rm.**

WANSEA **(ABERTAWE)** West Glam. 403 I 29 – pop. 172 433 – ECD : Thursday – ☏ 0792.

ee : Maritime Quarter★ B – Maritime and Industrial Museum★ B **M.**

nvir. : Cefn Bryn (✱★★★ from the reservoir) W : 12 m. by A 4118 A – Gower Peninsula★ Rhossili★★★) : West from Swansea by A 4067 A.

xc. : Rhosili (site and ≤★★★) W : 18 m. by A 4118 A.

Morriston ☏ 71079, N : 4 m. by A 48 A – Clyne, Owls Lodge Lane ☏ 401989, SW : off 4067 A – Pontardawe, Cefn Llan ☏ 863118, N : 5 m. A – Langland Bay ☏ 366023, W : 6 m. – Fairwood Park, Upper Killay ☏ 203648 A – Inco, Clydach ☏ 844216 A.

Singleton St. ☏ 468321 – Ty Croeso, Gloucester Pl. ☏ 465204 Oystermouth Sq., The Mumbles 361302 (summer only).

London 191 – ◆Birmingham 136 – ◆Bristol 82 – ◆Cardiff 40 – ◆Liverpool 187 – ◆Stoke-on-Trent 175.

Plan on next page

- **Holiday Inn,** Maritime Quarter, SA1 3SS, ☏ 642020, Telex 48395, Fax 650345, ≤, – rm TV ☎ P – 150. AE VISA. B e
  M 12.75/15.50 **st.** and a la carte 7.95 – 9.25 – **117 rm** 80.00/94.00 **st.** – SB (weekends only) 101.50/120.00 **st.**
- **Forte** (T.H.F.), 39 The Kingsway, SA1 5LS, ☏ 651074, Telex 48309, Fax 456044, – rm TV ☎ P – 250. AE VISA B a
  closed January-April – **M** 12.50/17.50 **st.** and a la carte 5.50 – 9.50 – **98 rm** 85.00/105.00, **1 suite** 125.00 **st.** – SB (weekends only) 96.00 **st.**
- **Fforest** (Lansbury), Pontardulais Rd, Fforestfach, SA5 4BA, NW : 3½ m. on A 483 ☏ 588711, Telex 48105, Fax 586219, – rm TV ☎ P – 200. AE VISA
  M 8.95/14.00 **t.** and a la carte – **34 rm** 68.00/82.00 **t.** – SB (weekends only) 56.00/66.00 **st.**
- **Windsor Lodge,** 15 Mount Pleasant, SA1 6EG, ☏ 642158, Fax 648996, « Contemporary decor », – TV ☎ P. AE VISA B r
  closed Christmas Day – **M** *(closed Sunday)* (booking essential)(lunch by arrangement)/dinner 14.00 **st.** 4.00 – **19 rm** 28.75/51.75 **st.**
- **Beaumont,** 72-73 Walter Rd, SA1 4QA, ☏ 643956, Fax 643044 – TV ☎ P. AE VISA. A n
  closed Christmas – **M** *(bar lunch)/dinner a la carte* 15.40/21.40 **t.** 4.25 – **17 rm** 45.00/80.00 **t.**
- **Tredilion House,** 26 Uplands Cres., Uplands, SA2 0PB, ☏ 470766 – TV ☎ P. VISA. A a
  M (by arrangement) 10.00 **st.** 3.50 – **6 rm** 31.00/48.00 **st.**
- **Alexander** without rest., 3 Sketty Rd, Uplands, SA2 0EU, ☏ 470045 – rest TV ☎. AE VISA. A c
  closed 24 December-2 January – **7 rm** 31.00/45.00 **st.**

SWANSEA

College Street . . . . B 13
Kingsway (The) . . . . B
Oasis Park
Shopping Centre . . . . . B
Oxford Street. . . . . B
Princess Way. . . . . B
Quadrant Centre . . . . B
St. David's Square . . . . . B

Alexandra Road. . . . . B 2
Belle Vue Way . . . . B 4
Carmarthen Road . . . . . . B 7
Christina Street . . . . B 9
Clarence Terrace. . . . . . . B 10
Clase Road . . . . A 12
De La Beche Street . . . . B 14
Dillwyn Street . . . . B 15
East Bank Way . . . . B 16
Fabian Way . . . . B 17
Grove Place . . . . B 18
Martin Street . . . . A 19
Nelson Street . . . . B 20
New Cut Bridge . . . . B 21
Pen-y-Graig Road . . . . . . A 22
Plasmarl By-Pass. . . . . . . A 23
Ravenhill Road . . . . A 24
Station Road . . . . A 25
St. Helen's Road. . . . . . . A 27
St. Mary's Square. . . . . . . B 28
Tawe Bridge . . . . B 29
Terrace Road. . . . . A 30
Union Street . . . . B 32
Uplands Crescent . . . . . . A 34
Walter Road . . . . A 36
Wellington Street . . . . . . B 37
West Way . . . . B 38
William Street . . . . B 39
Woodfield Street. . . . . A 40

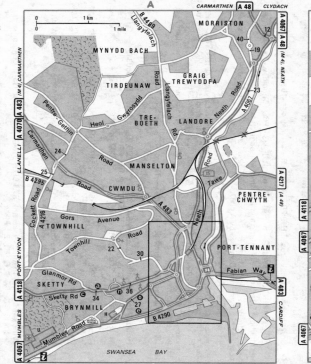

Zum besseren Verständnis der Stadpläne lesen Sie bitte die Zeichenerklärung in der Einleitung

X **Annie's,** 56 St. Helen's Rd, SA1 4BE, ☎ 655603 – VISA A o
closed Monday except summer and Sunday – **M** (booking essential) (dinner only) 12.80 **st.** and a la carte 4.30.

X **Jasmine,** 326 Oystermouth Rd, SA1 3UL, ☎ 652912, Chinese rest. – AE VISA
M 9.00/12.50 **t.** A e

at Swansea Enterprise Park NE : 4 m. by A 4067 off A 48 – ✉ ☎ 0792 Swansea :

Hilton National, Phoenix Way, Llansamlet, SA7 9EG, ☎ 310330, Telex 48589, Fax 797535, – rm rest – 140. AE VISA
M *(closed lunch Saturday and Bank Holidays)* (carving rest.) 9.50/15.00 **st.** and a la carte 4.50 – 8.50 – **112 rm** 76.00/106.00 **st.**, **2 suites** 120.00 **st.** – SB (weekends only) 57.80/98.00 **st.**

at Llanrhidian W : 10 ½ m. by A 4118 A and B 4271 on B 4295 – ✉ Reynoldston – ☎ 0792 Gower :

Fairyhill, SA3 1BS, W : 2 ½ m. by B 4295 (Llangennith rd) ☎ 390139, « Country house atmosphere », park – VISA
closed 25-26 December – **M** (dinner only and Sunday lunch) a la carte 18.70/23.15 **t.** – **11 rm** 65.00/85.00 **t.**

AIMLER-JAGUAR Swansea Enterprise Park 791562
ONDA Valley Way ☎ 771960
EUGEOT-TALBOT Neath Rd ☎ 310200
ENAULT Swansea Ind. Est. ☎ 701801
OVER 511 Carmarthen Rd ☎ 561166
VAUXHALL Neath Rd, Morriston ☎ 310111
VW-AUDI, NSU Gorseinon Rd ☎ 0792 (Gorseinon) 894951

ATS Neath Rd, Hafod ☎ 456379

SWINDON Wilts. 403 404 O 29 **The West Country G.** – pop. 127 348 – ECD : Wednesday – 0793.

ee : Great Western Railway Museum★ *AC* – Railway Village Museum★ *AC*.

, Broome Manor, Pipers Way ☎ 532403, 2 m. from centre – 18 Brunhill Park, Shrivenham 782946, E : 4 m.

32 The Arcade, Brunel Centre ☎ 530328.

London 83 – Bournemouth 69 – ◆Bristol 40 – ◆Coventry 66 – ◆Oxford 29 – Reading 40 – ◆Southampton 65.

Holiday Inn, Pipers Way, SN3 1SH, SE : 1½ m. by Marlborough Road off B 4006 ☎ 512121, Telex 445789, Fax 513114, , squash – rm – 280. AE VISA
M *(closed Saturday lunch)* (carving lunch) 15.50 **st.** and dinner a la carte 16.50/20.55 **st.** 7.25 – 8.95 – **158 rm** 84.00/170.00 **st.** – SB (weekends only) 107.00/157.00 **st.**

Post House (T.H.F.), Marlborough Rd, SN3 6AQ, SE : 2¾ m. on A 4259 ☎ 524601, Telex 444464, Fax 512887, – rm – 80. AE VISA
M 14.00/17.50 **st.** and a la carte 4.35 – 7.50 – **104 rm** 69.00/79.00 **st.** – SB (weekends only) 76.00/92.00 **st.**

Crest (T.H.F.), Oxford Rd, Stratton St. Margaret, SN3 4TL, NE : 3 m. by B 4312 on A 420 ☎ 831333, Telex 444456, Fax 831401 – rm – 80. AE VISA
M *(closed Saturday lunch)* (carving lunch) 13.50/16.25 **st.** and a la carte 4.50 – 7.95 – **93 rm** 77.00/90.00 **st.**, **1 suite** 108.00/115.00 **st.** – SB (weekends only) 76.00/92.00 **st.**

Poplars, Ermin Way, Lower Wanborough, SN4 0AA, E : 4 m. by A 4312 on Wanborough rd ☎ 790774, Fax 790878 – – 30. AE VISA.
M 12.50 **t.** (lunch) and a la carte – 6.50 – **14 rm** 58.00/70.00 **st.**

at Blunsdon N : 4½ m. on A 419 – ✉ ☎ 0793 Swindon :

Blunsdon House (Best Western), The Ridge, SN2 4AD, ☎ 721701, Telex 444491, Fax 721056, park, squash – – 300. AE VISA.
M 12.00/16.00 **t.** and a la carte 5.50 – **88 rm** 82.50/170.00 **t.** – SB (weekends only) 108.00/133.00 **st.**

at Chiseldon S : 6¼ m. by A 4312, A 4259 and A 345 on B 4005 – ✉ ☎ 0793 Swindon :

Chiseldon House, New Rd, SN4 0NE, ☎ 741010, Fax 741059, heated, – VISA.
M 22.50 **st.** (lunch) and a la carte – **21 rm** 60.00/125.00 **st.** – SB 120.00/140.00 **st.**

at Salthrop SW : 5 m. by A 3102 off B 4005 – ✉ ☎ 0793 Swindon :

Salthrop House, SN4 9QP, ←, , park – VISA.
closed Sunday – 18.50/25.00 **st.** and a la carte 5.50 – **8 rm** 85.00/105.00 **st.**

BMW High St. at Wroughton ☎ 812387
CITROEN Kennedy Drive, Eldean ☎ 642717
FORD 30 Marlborough Rd ☎ 20002
PORSCHE Great Western Way ☎ 615000
RENAULT Elgin Drive ☎ 693841
ROVER, DAIMLER-JAGUAR Dorkan Way ☎ 612091
VAUXHALL 13-21 The Street, Moredon ☎ 23457
VAUXHALL Drove Rd ☎ 20971
VW-AUDI, NSU Eldene Drive ☎ 31333

ATS Cheney Manor Ind Est. ☎ 521171
ATS 86 Beatrice St. ☎ 435867

SYMONDS YAT Heref. and Worc. 403 404 M 28 – ✉ Ross-on-Wye – ☎ 0600.
See : Symond's Yat Rock ≤★★.
◆London 126 – Gloucester 23 – Hereford 17 – Newport 31.

Woodlea ⛰, Symonds Yat (West), HR9 6BL, ☎ 890206, ≋, 🌳 – Ⓟ. VISA
closed 1 December-21 February – **M** 10.50 **st.** – **9 rm** ☕ 19.75/45.50 **st.** – SB (weekday only, weekends March and November) (except Easter and Bank Holidays) 52.00/57.50 **st.**

TADCASTER North Yorks. 402 Q 22 – pop. 5 877 – ECD : Wednesday – ☎ 0937.
◆London 176 – Harrogate 16 – ◆Kingston-upon-Hull 47 – ◆Leeds 16 – York 10.

Shann House without rest., 47 Kirkgate, LS24 9AQ, ☎ 833931 – TV Ⓟ. VISA
8 rm ☕ 18.50/28.00 **st.**

ATS Station Rd Ind. Est. ☎ 832626/833969

TALGARTH Powys 403 K 28 – ☎ 0874.
◆London 182 – Brecon 10 – Hereford 29 – ◆Swansea 53.

Olde Masons Arms, LD3 0BB, ☎ 711688, 🌳 – TV Ⓟ – **7 rm.**

TALLAND BAY Cornwall 403 G 32 – see Looe.

TAL-Y-BONT Gwynedd 402 403 I 24 – see Conwy.

TALYBONT-ON-USK Powys. 403 K 28 – ☎ 087 487.
◆London 183 – Abergavenny 14 – Brecon 6 – Newport 39.

Aberclydach House ⛰, Aber Village, LD3 7YS, SW : 1 m. ☎ 361, 🌳 – ⅍ TV ☎ Ⓟ –
11 rm.

TAL-Y-LLYN Gwynedd 402 403 I 25 – pop. 623 (inc. Corris) – ✉ Tywyn – ☎ 065 477 Abergynolwyn. ◆London 224 – Dolgellau 9 – Shrewsbury 60.

Tynycornel, LL36 9AJ, on B 4405 ☎ 282, ≤ lake and mountains, ≋, ≋ heated, 🎣, 🌳
TV ☎ Ⓟ. AE ⓓ VISA
M 12.50/20.00 **t.** and a la carte 🍷 4.35 – **15 rm** ☕ (dinner only) 47.00/94.00 **t.**

Minffordd, LL36 9AJ, NE : 2 ¾ m. by B 4405 on A 487 ☎ 065 473 (Corris) 665, ≤
« Converted 18C farmhouse and inn », 🌳 – ⅍ rest ☎ Ⓟ. ⓓ VISA. ⅍
closed January and February – **M** *(closed Sunday dinner)* (dinner only) 14.75 **st.** 🍷 3.50
6 rm ☕ (dinner included) 56.00/92.00 **st.**

TAMWORTH Staffs. 402 403 404 O 26 – pop. 63 260 – ECD : Wednesday – ☎ 0827.
⛳18 Eagle Drive ☎ 53850, E : 2½m.
ℹ Marmion House, Lichfield St. ☎ 311222.
◆London 128 – ◆Birmingham 12 – ◆Coventry 29 – ◆Leicester 31 – ◆Stoke-on-Trent 37.

Castle, Ladybank, B79 7NB, ☎ 57181, Fax 54303 – TV ☎ – 🏛 140. AE ⓓ VISA
M (dinner only and Sunday lunch)/dinner 16.35 **st.** and a la carte – **34 rm** ☕ 35.00/95.00 **st.** – SB (weekends only) 73.00 **st.**

FORD Gungate ☎ 68411
VW-AUDI Coleshill Rd ☎ 288282
ATS Walting St., Tame Valley Ind. Est. ☎ 281983

TAMWORTH SERVICE AREA Staffs. – ✉ ☎ 0827 Tamworth

Granada Lodge without rest., Green Lane, BT7 6PS, A 5 / M 42 junction 10 ☎ 260120
Fax 260145 – ⅍ TV ♿ Ⓟ. AE ⓓ VISA. ⅍
63 rm 29.00/32.00 **t.**

TATTENHALL Cheshire 402 403 404 L 24 – pop. 1 778 – ☎ 0829.
◆London 200 – ◆Birmingham 71 – Chester 10 – ◆Manchester 38 – ◆Stoke-on-Trent 30.

Pheasant Inn, Higher Burwardsley, CH3 9PF, SE : 1 m. ☎ 70434, Fax 71097, ≤ – TV ☎
Ⓟ. AE ⓓ VISA. ⅍
M (bar lunch)/dinner a la carte 11.50/14.50 **t.** 🍷 2.50 – **6 rm** ☕ 35.00/45.00 **t.** – SB (weekends only) 50.00 **st.**

TAUNTON Somerset 403 K 30 **The West Country G.** – pop. 47 793 – ECD : Thursday – ☎ 0823.
See : Site★ – St. Mary Magdalene's Church★ – Museum★ *AC* – St. James Church★ – Hammet St.★ – The Crescent★ – Bath Alley★.
Envir. : Muchelney★★ (Parish Church★★), E : 14 ½ m. – Wellington Monument (≤★★), W 10 m. – Trull : Church★, S : 2 m. – Bishops Lydeard★ (Church★), NW : 5 m. – Combe Florey★ NW : 7 m. – Wellington Church★, W : 8 m. – Gaulden Manor★*AC*, NW : 9 m. – Midelney Manor★*AC*, E : 12 m.
⛳18 Teignmouth ☎ 73614, N : 2 m. – ⛳18 Corfe, Taunton and Pickeridge ☎ 082 342 (Corfe) 240, S 5 m.
ℹ Public Library, Corporation St. ☎ 274785.
◆London 168 – Bournemouth 69 – ◆Bristol 50 – Exeter 37 – ◆Plymouth 78 – ◆Southampton 93 – Weymouth 50.

Castle, Castle Green, TA1 1NF, ✆ 272671, Telex 46488, Fax 336066, « Part 12C castle with Norman garden » – |‡| TV ☎ ⇔ P – ⛝ 60. AE ① VISA
M 13.90/32.50 **t.** and a la carte 37.40/47.30 **t.** 3.70 – 6.50 – **35** 77.00/198.00 **t.** – SB 145.00/235.00 **st.**

Crest (T.H.F.), Deane Gate Av., TA1 2UA, E : 2½ m. by A 358 at junction with M 5 ✆ 332222, Telex 46703, Fax 332266, – |‡| ✗ rm ▤ rest TV ☎ ♿ P – ⛝ 200. AE ① VISA
M *(closed lunch Saturday and Bank Holidays)* 14.95 **st.** and a la carte – 7.95 – **101 rm** 68.00/80.00 **t.** – SB (weekends only) 78.00 **st.**

County (T.H.F.), East St., TA1 3LT, ✆ 337651, Telex 46484, Fax 334517 – |‡| ✗ rm TV ☎ P – ⛝ 400. AE ① VISA
M 9.95/12.95 **st.** and a la carte 3.95 – 7.00 – **66 rm** 69.00/100.00 **st.** – SB (weekends only) 74.00/94.00 **st.**

Corner House, Park St., TA1 4DQ, ✆ 284683, Telex 46288, Fax 332276 – TV ☎ P. AE VISA. ✗
M 12.00/20.00 **t.** and la carte 4.00 – **32 rm** 40.00/70.00 **t.**

Travel Inn, 81 Bridgwater Rd, TA1 2DU, ✆ 321112, Fax 322054 – ✗ rm TV ♿ P. AE ① VISA. ✗
M (Beefeater grill) a la carte approx. 12.25 **t.** – 4.50 – **40 rm** -/27.50 **t.**

at Hatch Beauchamp SE : 6 m. by A 358 – ✉ Taunton – ☎ 0823 Hatch Beauchamp :

XXX **Farthings** with rm, TA3 6SG, ✆ 480664, « Georgian country house », – TV ☎ P. VISA. ✗
closed 2 weeks January – **M** (lunch residents only)/dinner 20.75 **st.** 4.30 – **6 rm** 65.00/115.00 **st.** – SB 104.00/117.00 **st.**

at Bishop's Hull W : 1¾ m. by A 38 – ✉ ☎ 0823 Taunton :

Meryan House without rest., Bishop's Hull Rd, TA1 5EG, ✆ 337445, – ✗ TV ☎ ♿ P. VISA
12 rm 32.00/50.00 **st.**

AUDI-VW Silver St. ✆ 88371
FIAT Priory Av. ✆ 87611
FORD 151-6 East Reach ✆ 85481
LADA, YUGO 16 Kingston Rd ✆ 88288
RENAULT 138 Bridgwater Rd, Bathpool ✆ 412559
ROVER, DAIMLER-JAGUAR South St. ✆ 88991
SAAB 60 East Reach ✆ 288351
ATS 138 Bridgwater Rd, Bathpool ✆ 412826

TAUNTON DEANE SERVICE AREA Somerset – ✉ ☎ 0823 Taunton

Road Chef Lodge without rest., TA1 4BA, ✆ 332228, Fax 338131 – ✗ TV ☎ ♿ P. AE ① VISA. ✗
39 rm 29.00/35.00 **t.**

TAVISTOCK Devon 403 H 32 **The West Country G.** – pop. 8 508 – ECD : Wednesday – ☎ 0822.

Envir. : Dartmoor National Park★★ – Lydford★★, Lydford Gorge★★ *AC*, N : 9 m. – Morwellham★*AC*, W : 4 m. – at Launceston★, Castle★ *AC* (<★), St. Mary Magdalene Church★ South Gate★ *AC*, NW : 14 m.

18 Down Rd ✆ 612049, SW : 1 m.

Town Hall Buildings, Bedford Sq. ✆ 612938 (summer only).

◆London 239 – Exeter 38 – ◆Plymouth 15.

Bedford (T.H.F.), 1 Plymouth Rd, PL19 8BB, ✆ 613221, Fax 618034 – ✗ rm TV ☎ P – ⛝ 35. AE ① VISA
M 4.95/13.95 **st.** and a la carte 4.35 – 7.00 – **30 rm** 60.00/75.00 **st.** – SB 86.00/93.00 **st.**

X **Neils,** 27 King St., PL19 0DT, ✆ 615550 – VISA
closed Monday – **M** (lunch by arrangement)/dinner 18.50 **t.** 6.00.

at Gulworthy W : 3 m. on A 390 – ✉ ☎ 0822 Tavistock :

XX Horn of Plenty with rm, PL19 8JD, ✆ 832528, < Tamar Valley and Bodmin Moor, – TV ☎ ♿ P
6 rm.

ROVER Plymouth Rd ✆ 612301
ATS 2 Parkwood Rd ✆ 612545

TAYNTON Oxon. – see Burford.

TEESSIDE AIRPORT Durham 402 P 20 – see Darlington.

TEFFONT Wilts. – see Salisbury.

TEIGNMOUTH Devon 403 J 32 **The West Country G.** – pop. 11 995 – ECD : Thursday – ☎ 0626.

18 Exeter Rd ✆ 4194.

ℹ The Den, Sea Front ✆ 779769.

♦London 216 – Exeter 16 – Torquay 8.

- **London,** Bank St., TQ14 8AW, ✆ 776336, Fax 778457, ≘s, ⛆ – |♣| TV ☎ – 🔬 200. AE ⓞ VISA
  M 8.00/14.50 **st.** and a la carte ⅱ 3.60 – **30 rm** ☐ 24.00/80.00 **st.** – SB 48.00/70.00 **st.**
- Cliffden, Dawlish Rd, TQ14 8TE, ✆ 770052, Fax 770973, ≤, 🌳, park – ⇆ rm TV ☎ ♿ Ⓟ
  21 rm.
- **Thomas Luny House,** Teign St., TQ14 8EG, ✆ 772976, « Georgian house built by Thomas Luny », 🌳 – ⇆ rest TV ☎ Ⓟ. ✻
  closed mid December-mid January – **M** (dinner only)(communal dining)(residents only) 13.50 **t.** ⅱ 4.50 – **4 rm** ☐ 27.50/55.00 **t.**
- **Belvedere,** 19 Barnpark Rd, TQ14 8PJ, ✆ 774561 – TV Ⓟ. VISA. ✻
  M 8.00 **st.** ⅱ 3.00 – **13 rm** ☐ 18.50/37.00 **st.**

at Shaldon S : 1 m. on A 379 – ✉ Teignmouth – ☎ 0626 Shaldon :

- **Ness House,** Marine Par., TQ14 0HP, ✆ 873480, Fax 873486, ≤, 🌳 – TV ☎ Ⓟ. AE VISA. ✻
  M 8.50 **st.** (lunch) and a la carte ⅱ 4.00 – **12 rm** ☐ 24.50/72.00 **st.**
- **Glenside,** Ringmore Rd, TQ14 0EP, W : ½ m. on B 3195 ✆ 872448, 🌳 – TV Ⓟ
  closed November – **M** 10.00 **t.** ⅱ 4.50 – **10 rm** ☐ 21.60/59.20 **t.** – SB (October-April except December) 53.90/57.00 **st.**

NISSAN 106 Bitton Park Rd ✆ 772501

TELFORD Shropshire 402 403 404 M 25 – pop. 76 330 – ☎ 0952.

Envir. : Ironbridge Gorge Museum★ (Iron Bridge★★) *AC*, S : 5 m. – Buildwas Abbey★ (ruins 12C) S : 7 m.

18 Great Hay, Sutton Hill ✆ 585642 – 18 Wellington ✆ 244032.

ℹ Shopping Centre ✆ 291370/291723.

♦London 152 – ♦Birmingham 33 – Shrewsbury 12 – ♦Stoke-on-Trent 29.

- **Telford Moat House** (Q.M.H.), Forgegate, Telford Centre, TF3 4NA, ✆ 291291, Telex 35588, Fax 292012, ₺, ≘s, ⛆ – |♣| ⇆ rm ▤ rest TV ☎ ♿ Ⓟ – 🔬 220. AE ⓞ VISA
  closed 24 December-1 January – **M** *(closed Saturday lunch)* 14.50 **t.** and a la carte ⅱ 3.80 – **144 rm** ☐ 66.00/103.00 **st.**, **4 suites** 95.00/121.00 **t.** – SB (weekends only) 75.00/82.00 **st.**
- Holiday Inn, St. Quentin Gate, TF3 4EH, SE : ½ m. ✆ 292500, Telex 359126, Fax 291949, ₺, ≘s, ⛆ – |♣| ⇆ rm ▤ rest TV ☎ ♿ Ⓟ – 🔬 200
  100 rm.
- **Telford H. Golf & Country Club** (Q.M.H.), Great Hay, Sutton Hill, TF7 4DT, S : 4½ m. by A 442 ✆ 585642, Telex 35481, Fax 586602, ≤, ≘s, ⛆, 18, squash – ▤ rest TV ☎ Ⓟ – 🔬 250. AE ⓞ VISA
  M *(closed Saturday lunch)* 7.25/12.00 **st.** and a la carte – **58 rm** ☐ 72.00/80.00 **st.**, **1 suite** 107.50/118.50 **st.** – SB (weekends only) 90.00 **st.**
- **Whitehouse,** Wellington Rd, Muxton, nr. Donnington, TF2 8NG, N : 4½ m. by A 518 ✆ 604276, 🌳 – TV ☎ Ⓟ. AE VISA
  M *(closed Saturday lunch)* 9.00 **t.** (lunch) and a la carte 14.55/20.50 **t.** ⅱ 4.95 – **29 rm** ☐ 47.00/60.00 **t.** – SB (weekends only) 60.00/70.00 **st.**
- Charlton Arms (De Vere), Church St., Wellington, TF1 1DG, ✆ 251351, Fax 222077 – TV ☎ Ⓟ – 🔬 200
  26 rm.
- **Travelodge** without rest., Shawbirch Crossroads, Shawbirch, TF1 3QA, NW : 5¼ m. by M54 and A 518, on A 5223 ✆ 251244, Reservations (Toll Free) 0800 850950 – TV ♿ Ⓟ. AE VISA. ✻
  40 rm 24.00/29.50 **t.**

at Norton S : 7 m. on A 442 – ✉ Shifnal – ☎ 095 271 Norton :

- **Hundred House,** Bridgnorth Rd, TF11 9EE, ✆ 353, Fax 355, « Tastefully decorated inn, antiques », 🌳 – TV ☎ Ⓟ. AE VISA. ✻
  M 13.50/16.50 ⅱ 4.50 – **9 rm** ☐ 59.00/75.00 **t.** – SB (except Christmas) 85.00/95.00 **st.**

FIAT Trench Rd ✆ 605301
PEUGEOT-TALBOT Holyhead Rd ✆ 617272
ROVER, VANDEN-PLAS Market St., Wellington ✆ 290971
TOYOTA Ironbridge Rd ✆ 882100
VAUXHALL-OPEL Holyhead Rd ✆ 618081

ATS Queen St., Madeley ✆ 582820
ATS New St., Oakengates ✆ 613810/612198

TEMPLE SOWERBY Cumbria 401 402 M 20 – pop. 341 – ECD : Thursday – ✉ Penrith – ☎ 076 83 Kirkby Thore.
◆London 297 – ◆Carlisle 31 – Kendal 38.

Temple Sowerby House, CA10 1RZ, ☎ 61578, – rest. VISA
M 20.00 **t.** 3.50 – **12 rm** 41.50/56.00 **t.** – SB (except Bank Holidays) 82.00 **st.**

TEMPSFORD Beds. 404 T 27 – see Sandy.

TENBY (DINBYCH-Y-PYSGOD) Dyfed 403 F 28 – pop. 5 226 – ECD : Wednesday – ☎ 0834.
See : Site★ – Harbour and Sea front★★.
Envir. : Caldey Island★ (boat from Tenby harbour Monday to Friday).
18 The Burrows ☎ 2787. The Craft ☎ 2402 (summer only).
◆London 247 – Carmarthen 27 – Fishguard 36.

Imperial, The Paragon, SA70 7HR, ☎ 3737, Fax 4342, ≤ sea and bay – – 40. VISA.
M (bar lunch)/dinner 12.50 **t.** 3.75 – **45 rm** 36.00/105.00 **t.** – SB 62.00/90.00 **st.**

Fourcroft, Croft Terr., SA70 8AP, ☎ 2886, Fax 2888, ≤, heated, – rest. VISA
April-October – **M** (bar lunch)/dinner 15.00 **st.** 4.00 – **38 rm** 35.00/72.00 **t.** – SB 80.00/90.00 **st.**

Buckingham, Esplanade, SA70 6DU, ☎ 2622, ≤ – . VISA
April-October – **M** 9.50 **st.** 2.75 – **8 rm** 15.00/40.00 **st.** – SB 50.00/55.00 **st.**

at Penally (Penalun) SW : 2 m. by A 4139 – ✉ ☎ 0834 Tenby :

Penally Abbey, SA70 7PY, ☎ 3033, ≤, rm. VISA.
M (bar lunch)/dinner 19.00 4.40 – **11 rm** 38.00/68.00 **st.** – SB 56.00/68.00 **st.**

ROVER Townwall Arcade ☎ 2189

TENTERDEN Kent 404 W 30 – pop. 5 698 – ECD : Wednesday – ☎ 058 06.
9 Woodchurch Rd ☎ 3987.
Town Hall, High St. ☎ 3572 (summer only).
◆ London 57 – Folkestone 26 – Hastings 21 – Maidstone 19.

Little Silver Country, Ashford Rd, St. Michaels, TN30 6SP, N : 1 m. on A 28 ☎ 023 3850 (High Halden) 321, – rest. VISA.
M (booking essential) (lunch by arrangement)/dinner 17.00 **st.** and a la carte 4.00 – **10 rm** 48.00/90.00 **st.**

White Lion, High St., TN30 6BD, ☎ 5077, Fax 4157 – – 35. VISA
M 10.50/13.50 **t.** and a la carte 4.65 – **15 rm** 50.00/70.00 **t.** – SB (weekends only) 64.00 **st.**

Collina House, 5 East Hill, TN30 6RL, ☎ 4852, – . VISA
M 20.00 **st.** 4.50 – **11 rm** 23.00/40.00 **st.**

West Cross House, 2 West Cross, TN30 6JL, ☎ 2224, –
March-October – **M** 8.00 **st.** 2.75 – **7 rm** 14.00/30.00 **st.**

at High Halden NE : 3½ m. on A 28 – ✉ Tenterden – ☎ 0233 High Halden :

Durrants with rm, Hookstead House, TN26 3NE, ☎ 850670, – . VISA.
M *(closed Sunday dinner and Monday)* (dinner only and Sunday lunch)/dinner 15.95 **st.** 3.50 – **4 rm** 30.00/50.00 **st.** – SB 60.00/70.00 **st.**

ROVER High St. ☎ 4444

TETBURY Glos. 403 404 N 29 – pop. 4 467 – ECD : Thursday – ☎ 0666.
Envir. : Westonbirt Arboretum★ *AC*, SW : 3½ m.
9 Westonbirt 066 688 (Westonbirt) 242, S : 3 m.
The Old Court House, 63 Long St. ☎ 53552 (summer only).
◆London 113 – ◆Bristol 27 – Gloucester 19 – Swindon 24.

The Close, 8 Long St., GL8 8AQ, ☎ 502272, Fax 504401, « 16C town house with walled garden », – rest – 25. VISA.
M 15.25/27.50 **t.** 5.25 – 7.50 – **15 rm** 75.00/155.00 **t.** – SB (except Christmas) 150.00/190.00 **st.**

Snooty Fox, Market Pl., GL8 8DD, ☎ 502436, Group Telex 437334, Fax 503479 – . VISA.
M 14.00/18.00 **t.** and a la carte 4.85 – **12 rm** 66.00/110.00 **t.** – SB 98.00/120.00 **st.**

Harry's, 7 New Church St., GL8 8DS, ☎ 503306.

at Westonbirt SW : 2½ m. on A 433 – ✉ Tetbury – ☎ 066 688 Westonbirt :

Hare and Hounds (Best Western), GL8 8QL, ☎ 233, Fax 241, , park, , squash – – 40 – **29 rm.**

at Calcot W : 3 ½ m. on A 4135 – ✉ Tetbury – ☎ 066 689 Leighterton :

🏨 ❁ **Calcot Manor** 🐌, GL8 8YJ, ☎ 890391, Fax 890394, « Converted Cotswolds farm buildings », 🏊 heated, 🌳 – 🚭 rest 📺 ☎ 🅿. AE ⓓ VISA. ✂
closed 2 to 10 January – **M** *(closed Sunday dinner to non-residents)* 25.00/35.00 **t.** 🍷 4.25 – **16 rm** ☕ 80.00/130.00 **t.** – SB (April-October) 135.00/170.00 **st.**
Spec. Fillet of red mullet poached in a mushroom and tomato vinaigarette, Slices of duck breast and crispy leg with sherry vinegar sauce, Calcot's Speciality Apple Dessert.

VW-AUDI London Rd ☎ 502473/503129

TEWKESBURY Glos. 403 404 N 28 – pop. 9 454 – ECD : Thursday – ☎ 0684.

See : Site★ – Abbey Chruch★★ (12C-14C).

Envir. : St. Mary's Church★, Deerhurst S : 6 m.

⛳18 Lincoln, Green Lane ☎ 295405.

ℹ Tewkesbury Museum, 64 Barton St. ☎ 295027.

♦London 108 – ♦Birmingham 39 – Gloucester 11.

🏨 **Tewkesbury Park H. Golf & Country Club** 🐌, Lincoln Green Lane, GL20 7DN, S : 1 ¼ m. by A 38 ☎ 295405, Telex 43563, Fax 292386, ≤, 🏋, 🧖, 🏊, ⛳18, park, 🎾, squash – 📺 ☎ 🅿 – 🏛 150. AE ⓓ VISA. ✂
M *(closed Saturday lunch)* 25.00/40.00 **st.** and a la carte 🍷 4.50 – **78 rm** ☕ 90.00/115.00 **st.**

🏨 **Royal Hop Pole** (T.H.F.), Church St., GL20 5RT, ☎ 293236, Telex 437176, Fax 296680, 🌳 – 🚭 rm 📺 ☎ 🅿. AE ⓓ VISA
M 9.95/14.95 **st.** and a la carte – ☕ 7.95 – **29 rm** 66.00/96.50 **st.** – SB (weekends only) 80.00/100.00 **st.**

🏨 **Bell** (Best Western), 52 Church St., GL20 5SA, ☎ 293293, Fax 295938 – 📺 ☎ 🅿 – 🏛 30. AE ⓓ VISA
M (bar lunch)/dinner 16.95 **st.** 🍷 4.95 – **24 rm** ☕ 58.00/72.00 **st.**, **1 suite** – SB (weekends only) (except Christmas and New Year) 80.00/90.00 **st.**

🏠 **Tudor House,** 51 High St., GL20 5BH, ☎ 297755, Fax 290306, « Part Tudor town house », 🧖 – 📺 ☎ 🅿. AE ⓓ VISA
M *(closed Sunday dinner)* (bar lunch)/dinner 11.95 **t.** and a la carte 🍷 3.50 – **16 rm** ☕ 35.00/80.00 **t.** – SB (weekends only) 64.00 **st.**

🏠 **Jessop House,** 65 Church St., GL20 5RZ, ☎ 292017 – 📺 ☎ 🅿. VISA. ✂
closed Christmas – **M** *(closed Sunday)* (dinner only) a la carte 10.15/18.15 **st.** 🍷 2.95 – **6 rm** ☕ 46.00/57.00 **st.** – SB 70.00 **st.**

at Puckrup N : 2 ½ m. on A 38 – ✉ ☎ 0684 Tewkesbury :

🏨 **Tewkesbury Hall** 🐌, GL20 6EL, ☎ 296200, Fax 850788, ≤, 🌳, park – 🚭 rest 📺 ☎ 🅿 – 🏛 150. AE ⓓ VISA
closed 28 to 30 December – **M** 22.50/30.00 **st.** and a la carte 🍷 3.95 – **16 rm** ☕ 80.00/130.00 **st.** – SB (weekends only) 49.50/64.00 **st.**

at Corse Lawn SW : 6 m. by A 38 and A 438 on B 4211 – ✉ Gloucester – ☎ 045 278 Tirley :

🏨 **Corse Lawn House** 🐌, GL19 4LZ, ☎ 479, Telex 437348, Fax 840, « Queen Anne house », 🏊 heated, 🌳, 🎾 – 📺 ☎ 🅿. AE ⓓ VISA
M (see **Corse Lawn House** below) – **17 rm** ☕ 60.00/85.00 **st.**, **2 suites** 105.00 **st.**

XXX **Corse Lawn House** (at Corse Lawn House H.), GL19 4LZ, ☎ 479, Telex 437348, Fax 840 🌳 – 🅿. AE ⓓ VISA
M 17.50/22.50 **st.** and a la carte 🍷 3.75.

FORD Ashchurch Rd ☎ 292398
NISSAN Bredon ☎ 72333
PEUGEOT-TALBOT Bredon Rd ☎ 297575/293122
ROVER Gloucester Rd ☎ 293122
ⓐ ATS Oldbury Rd ☎ 292461

THAME Oxon. 404 R 28 – pop. 8 300 – ECD : Wednesday – ☎ 084 421.

See : St. Mary's Church★ (13C).

Envir. : Rycote Chapel★ (15C) *AC*, W : 3 ½ m.

ℹ Town Hall, High St. ☎ 2834.

♦London 48 – Aylesbury 9 – ♦Oxford 13.

🏨 **Spread Eagle,** 16 Cornmarket, OX9 2BW, ☎ 3661, Fax 261380 – 📺 ☎ 🅿 – 🏛 200. AE ⓓ VISA. ✂
closed 28 to 30 December – **M** (bar lunch Saturday and Bank Holidays) 15.80/16.80 **st.** and a la carte 🍷 3.75 – ☕ 6.95 – **22 rm** 61.55/95.95 **st.** – SB 93.50/99.50 **st.**

🏠 **Essex House,** Chinnor Rd., OX9 3LS, ☎ 7567, Fax 6420 – 🚭 📺 ☎ 🅿. VISA. ✂
M *(closed Sunday)* (dinner only) 11.95 **st.** 🍷 3.00 – **16 rm** ☕ 30.00/55.00 **st.**

X **Thatchers,** 29-30 Lower High St., OX9 2AA, ☎ 2146, Fax 7413 – 🅿. VISA
closed Saturday lunch and Sunday – **M** 17.50 **t.** and a la carte 🍷 3.75.

at Towersey E : 2 m. by A 4129 – ✉ ☎ 084 421 Thame :

Upper Green Farm without rest., Manor Rd, OX9 3QR, ☎ 2496, « Part 15C, part 16C thatched farmhouse », – TV P.
9 rm 15.00/48.00 **st.**

at Kingsey (Bucks.) E : 2½ m. on A 4129 – ✉ Aylesbury – ☎ 0844 Haddenham :

Foxhill Farm without rest., on A 4129, HP17 8LZ, ☎ 291650, heated, – TV P. – *closed December and January* – **3 rm** 18.00/34.00 **st.**

'AUXHALL 50 Park St. ☎ 5566

THATCHAM Berks. 403 404 Q 29 – ✉ ☎ 0635 Newbury.

London 69 – ◆Bristol 68 – ◆Oxford 30 – Reading 15 – ◆Southampton 40.

Regency Park, Bowling Green Rd., RG13 3RP, NW : 1 ¾ m. by A 4 via Northfield Rd ☎ 71555, Telex 847844, Fax 71571 – rest TV ☎ P – 60. AE VISA
M 13.50/18.95 **st.** and a la carte 5.00 – 7.25 – **49 rm** 75.00/100.00 **st., 1 suite** 185.00 **st.** – SB (weekends only) (except Christmas) 99.00/110.00 **st.**

THAXTED Essex 404 V 28 – pop. 2 177 – ☎ 0371.

London 44 – ◆Cambridge 24 – Colchester 31 – Chelmsford 20.

Four Seasons, Walden Rd, CM6 2RE, NW : ½ m. on B 184 ☎ 830129 – TV ☎ P. AE VISA.
M *(closed Sunday dinner)* 15.50/25.00 **t.** and a la carte 5.50 – **9 rm** 55.00/70.00 **t.** – SB (weekends only) (except Christmas) 98.00 **st.**

at Broxted SW : 3¾ m. by B 1051 – ✉ Great Dunmow – ☎ 0279 Bishop's Stortford :

Whitehall, Church End, CM6 2BZ, on B 1051 ☎ 850603, Fax 850385, ←, « Part 12C and 15C manor house with walled garden », heated, – TV ☎ P. AE VISA. *closed 26 to 30 December* – **M** (dinner only and Sunday lunch)/dinner 29.00 **t.** 5.00 – **16 rm** 70.00/140.00 **t.** – SB (winter only) 142.50 **st.**

THETFORD Norfolk 404 W 26 – pop. 19 591 – ECD : Wednesday – ☎ 0842.

Brandon Rd ☎ 752258. White Hart St. ☎ 752599.

London 83 – ◆Cambridge 32 – ◆Ipswich 33 – King's Lynn 30 – ◆Norwich 29.

Bell (T.H.F.), King St., IP24 2AZ, ☎ 754455, Fax 755552 – rm TV ☎ P – 70. AE VISA
M 10.50/17.85 **st.** and a la carte 3.75 – 7.50 – **47 rm** 66.00/110.00 **st.** – SB 94.00/104.00 **st.**

The Historical Thomas Paine (Best Western), 33 White Hart St., IP24 1AA, ☎ 755631, Fax 766505 – TV ☎ P. AE VISA.
M *(closed lunch Monday and Saturday)* 10.00/14.00 **st.** and a la carte 4.85 – **14 rm** 42.00/58.00 **st.**

Anchor (B.C.B.), Bridge St., IP24 3AE, ☎ 763925 – TV ☎ P – .
M (carving rest.) – **17 rm.**

Wilderness without rest., Earl St., IP24 2AF, ☎ 764646, – TV P.
4 rm 16.00/26.00 **s.**

OVER Guildhall St. ☎ 754427 — ATS Canterbury Way ☎ 755529/755520

THIRSK North Yorks. 402 P 21 – pop. 7 174 – ECD : Wednesday – ☎ 0845.

See : St. Mary's Church★ (Gothic). **Envir.** : Sutton Bank (←★★) E : 6 m. on A 170.

Thornton-Le-Street ☎ 22170.

14 Kirkgate ☎ 22755 (summer only).

London 227 – ◆Leeds 37 – ◆Middlesbrough 24 – York 24.

St. James House without rest., 36 The Green, YO7 1AQ, ☎ 524120, – TV.
April-October – **4 rm** 24.00/36.00.

Brook House without rest., Ingramgate, YO7 1DD, ☎ 522240, – TV P.
closed 2 weeks Christmas – **3 rm** 25.00/30.00 **st.**

at Sowerby S : ½ m. – ✉ ☎ 0845 Thirsk :

Sheppard's with rm, Front St., YO7 1JF, ☎ 523655, Fax 524720 – TV ☎ P. VISA.
closed first week January – **M** a la carte 15.45/21.20 **t.** 4.35 – **12 rm** 45.00/55.00 **st.**

ITROEN Ingramgate ☎ 522243 — ATS Long St. ☎ 22982/22923
EUGEOT Station Rd ☎ 522370

THORNABY-ON-TEES Cleveland 402 Q 20 – pop. 26 319 – ✉ ☎ 0642 Middlesbrough.

London 250 – ◆Leeds 62 – ◆Middlesbrough 3 – York 49.

Post House (T.H.F.), Low Lane, Stainton Village, TS17 9EW, SE : 3½ m. by A 1045 on B 1380 ☎ 591213, Telex 58426, Fax 594989, – rm TV ☎ P – 120. AE VISA
M 6.50/13.95 **st.** 4.50 – 7.50 – **135 rm** 65.00/75.00 **st.** – SB (weekends only) 77.00 **st.**

AUXHALL Acklam Rd ☎ 593333

THORNBURY Avon 403 404 M 29 **The West Country G.** – pop. 11 948 – ECD : Thursday
✉ Bristol – ☎ 0454.

♦London 128 – ♦Bristol 12 – Gloucester 23 – Swindon 43.

Thornbury Castle ⛰, Castle St., BS12 1HH, ✆ 418511, Telex 449986, Fax 41618
« 16C castle, gardens », park – ⇔ rest TV ☎ P. AE VISA. ✻
closed 2 to 12 January – **M** 17.50/29.00 **t.** 3.80 – ☐ 5.00 – **17 rm** 80.00/190.00 **t.**, **1 suit**
190.00 **t.** – SB (November-mid March) 147.00/191.00 **st.**

THORNHILL South Glam. 403 K 29 – see Cardiff.

THORNTHWAITE Cumbria 402 K 20 – see Keswick.

THORNTON CLEVELEYS Lancs. 402 L 22 – ☎ 0253 Blackpool.

♦London 244 – ♦Blackpool 6 – Lancaster 20 – ♦Manchester 44.

Victorian House, Trunnah Rd, FY5 4HF, ✆ 860619, Fax 860350, – TV ☎ P. VISA
closed 2 weeks March – **M** *(closed Monday lunch and Sunday)* 17.50 **st.** (dinner) and a
carte – **3 rm** ☐ 37.50/65.00 **st.**

THORPE Derbs. 402 403 404 O 24 – pop. 227 – ✉ Ashbourne – ☎ 033 529 Thorpe Cloud.

Envir. : N : Dovedale (valley)★★ – Ashbourne (St. Oswald's Church★ 13C) SE : 3 m.

9 at Ashbourne ✆ 0335 (Ashbourne) 42078, SE : 5 m.

♦London 151 – Derby 16 – ♦Sheffield 33 – ♦Stoke-on-Trent 26.

Peveril of the Peak (T.H.F.) ⛰, DE6 2AW, ✆ 333, Fax 507, ←, , ✂ – ⇔ rm TV ☎
– 60. AE VISA
M *(closed Saturday lunch)* 15.35/21.75 **st.** and a la carte 3.95 – ☐ 7.50 – **47 rm** 64.0
95.00 **st.**

THORPE MARKET Norfolk 404 X 25 – pop. 221 – ✉ North Walsham – ☎ 026 379 South
repps. ♦London 130 – ♦Norwich 21.

Green Farm, North Walsham Rd., NR11 8TH, ✆ 833602 – TV ☎ P. VISA
closed 25 to 27 December – **M** (lunch by arrangement) 12.50/15.00 **t.** and a la carte 3.95
5 rm ☐ 50.00/90.00 **t.** – SB 90.00/110.00 **st.**

Elderton Lodge ⛰, Cromer Rd, NR11 8TZ, S : 1 m. on A 149 ✆ 833547, – TV P.
AE VISA – *closed 24 to 26 December* – **M** 11.50 **t.** and a la carte 3.50 – **7 rm** ☐ 25.0
44.00 **t.** – SB 69.00/77.00 **st.**

THORPE ST. ANDREW Norfolk 404 Y 26 – see Norwich.

THORVERTON Devon 403 J 31 – ✉ ☎ 0392 Exeter

Berribridge ⛰, SW : ½ m., EX5 5JR, ✆ 860259, – TV P – **5 rm.**

THREE COCKS (ABERLLYNFI) Powys 403 K 27 – ✉ Brecon – ☎ 049 74 Glasbury.

♦London 184 – Brecon 11 – Hereford 25 – ♦Swansea 55.

Three Cocks with rm, LD3 0SL, on A 438 ✆ 215, – P. VISA. ✻
closed January and December – **M** *(closed Sunday lunch and Tuesday mid September-mi
July)* 20.00 **st.** and a la carte – **7 rm** ☐ 36.00/50.00 **st.** – SB (except Bank Holidays) 76.0
180.00 **st.**

THRESHFIELD North Yorks. 402 N 21 – see Grassington.

THRUSSINGTON Leics. 402 403 404 Q 25 – see Leicester.

THURLESTONE Devon 403 I 33 – see Kingsbridge.

TICKTON Humberside – see Beverley.

TILBURY Essex 404 V 29 – pop. 11 430 – ☎ 037 52.

to Gravesend (Sealink) frequent services daily (5 mn).

♦London 24 – Southend-on-Sea 20.

Hotels and restaurants see : London W : 24 m.

TINTAGEL Cornwall 403 F 32 **The West Country G.** – pop. 1 566 – ECD : Wednesday excep
summer – ☎ 0840 Camelford.

See : Arthur's Castle : site★★★ *AC* – Tintagel Church★ – Old Post Office★ *AC.*

Envir. : Delabole Quarry★ *AC*, SE : 4 m. by B 3263 – Camelford★, SE : 6 m. by B 3263 an
B 3266.

♦London 264 – Exeter 63 – ♦Plymouth 49 – Truro 41.

Bossiney House, Bossiney, PL34 0AX, NE : ½ m. on B 3263 ✆ 770240, , , – P
AE VISA
March-October – **M** (bar lunch)/dinner 12.50 **st.** 3.75 – **18 rm** ☐ 31.00/50.00 **st.**

Old Millfloor ♨, Trebarwith, PL34 0HA, S : 1 ¾ m. by B 3263 ✆ 770234, « Former flour mill », ⛱, park – 📺 🅟. 🚫
Easter-October – **M** (by arrangement) 11.00 and a la carte – **3 rm** ☕ 14.50/29.00.

Old Borough House, Bossiney Rd, PL34 0AY, NE : ½ m. on B 3263 ✆ 770475 – ⛔ rest 🅟. 🚫
M (by arrangement) 8.50 **st.** – **5 rm** ☕ 23.00/36.00 **st.** – SB 38.00/51.00 **st.**

INTERN (TYNDYRN) Gwent 403 404 L 28 – pop. 816 – ECD : Wednesday – ✉ Chepstow – 0291. **See** : Abbey★★ (ruins) *AC.*

Abbey Entrance, Tintern Abbey ✆ 689431 (summer only).

London 137 – ◆Bristol 23 – Gloucester 40 – Newport 22.

Beaufort, NP6 6SF, on A 466 ✆ 689777, Fax 689727, ⛱ – 📺 ☎ 🅟 – 🎤 60. AE VISA
M (bar lunch Monday to Saturday)/dinner 16.95/27.95 **st.** 🍷 4.55 – **24 rm** ☕ 60.00/ 100.00 **st.** – SB 71.00/92.00 **st.**

Royal George, NP6 6SF, on A 466 ✆ 689205, Fax 689448, ⛱ – 📺 ☎ 🅟. AE VISA
M (bar lunch)/dinner 13.50 **t.** and a la carte – **17 rm** ☕ 42.35/58.85 **t.** – SB 65.00/71.50 **st.**

Parva Farmhouse, NP6 6SQ, on A 466 ✆ 689411 – 📺 ☎ 🅟
M 17.00 **st.** 🍷 4.00 – **9 rm** ☕ 28.00/54.00 **st.** – SB 56.00/70.00 **st.**

IVERTON Devon 403 J 31 **The West Country G.** – pop. 14 745 – ECD : Thursday – ☎ 0884.

ee : Museum★ *AC.*

nvir. : at Bickleigh★★, Mill Craft Centre and farms★★ *AC,* Castle★ *AC,* S : 4½ m. – Knightayes Court★ *AC,* N : 2 m. on A 396 – Coldharbour Mill, Uffculme★ *AC,* E : 11 m. by A 373.

Pheonix Lane ✆ 255827 – Junction 27 (M 5) ✆ 821242.

London 190 – Exeter 14 – Taunton 23.

Tiverton, Blundells Rd, EX16 4DB, E : ½ m. on B 3391 ✆ 256120, Fax 258101 – 📺 ☎ ♿ 🅟 – 🎤 250. AE VISA
M 7.50/15.50 **st.** 🍷 3.95 – **75 rm** ☕ 38.00/70.00 **st.** – SB 64.00/74.00 **st.**

at Oakfordbridge NW : 9 m. on A 396 – ✉ Tiverton – ☎ 039 85 Oakford :

Bark House, EX16 9HZ, ✆ 236, ⛱ – 📺 ☎ 🅟. AE VISA
closed January and February – **M** (dinner only)(residents only) 15.00 **st.** 🍷 4.00 – ☕ 6.00 – **6 rm** 18.00/52.00 **st.**

at Bolham N : 1¼ m. on A 396 – ✉ ☎ 0884 Tiverton :

Hartnoll Country House, EX16 7RA, ✆ 252777, Fax 252777, ⛱ – 📺 ☎ 🅟 – **16 rm.**

TROEN 31 Leat St. ✆ 252170

ATS Newport St. ✆ 252062/252950

ODDINGTON SERVICE AREA Beds. 404 S 28 – pop. 4218 – ✉ Luton – ☎ 052 55.

Granada Lodge without rest., Southbound Carriageway, LU5 6HR, ✆ 5150, Fax 5602 – ⛔ 📺 ♿ 🅟. AE VISA. 🚫
43 rm 29.00/32.00 **t.**

ODWICK South Yorks. – pop. 1 661 – ✉ Sheffield – ☎ 0909 Worksop.

London 161 – ◆Nottingham 35 – ◆Sheffield 10.

Red Lion (Lansbury), Worksop Rd, S31 0DJ, on A 57 ✆ 771654, Telex 54120, Fax 773704 – ⛔ rm 📺 ☎ ♿ 🅟 – 🎤 70. AE VISA. 🚫
M *(closed Saturday lunch)* 10.00/15.00 **t.** and a la carte 🍷 4.50 – **29 rm** ☕ 70.00/82.00 **t.** – SB (weekends only) 70.00/77.00 **st.**

ONBRIDGE Kent 404 U 30 – pop. 34 407 – ECD : Wednesday – ☎ 0732.

ee : Tonbridge School★ (1553).

nvir. : Ightham Mote★ (Manor House 14C-15C) *AC,* site★ N : 7 m.

Poult Wood, Higham Lane ✆ 364039, N : 2 m. by A 227.

Tonbridge Castle, Castle St. ✆ 770929.

London 33 – ◆Brighton 37 – Hastings 31 – Maidstone 14.

Rose and Crown (T.H.F.), 125 High St., TN9 1DD, ✆ 357966, Fax 357194, ⛱ – ⛔ rm 📺 ☎ 🅟 – 🎤 80. AE VISA
M 10.50/12.95 **st.** and a la carte 🍷 4.35 – ☕ 7.00 – **50 rm** 60.00/80.00 **st.** – SB (weekends only) 74.00 **st.**

The Office, 163 High St., TN9 1BX, ✆ 353660 – AE VISA
M *(closed Sunday and Bank Holidays)* a la carte 9.70/11.50 **t.**

RD Avebury Av. ✆ 356301
NAULT Sovereign Way ✆ 350288
UXHALL Waterloo Rd ✆ 354035
LVO Hildenborough ✆ 832424

VW-AUDI, NSU, MERCEDES-BENZ Vale Rd ✆ 355822

ATS 61-63 Pembury Rd ✆ 353800/352231

ORCROSS Devon 403 J 33 – see Kingsbridge.

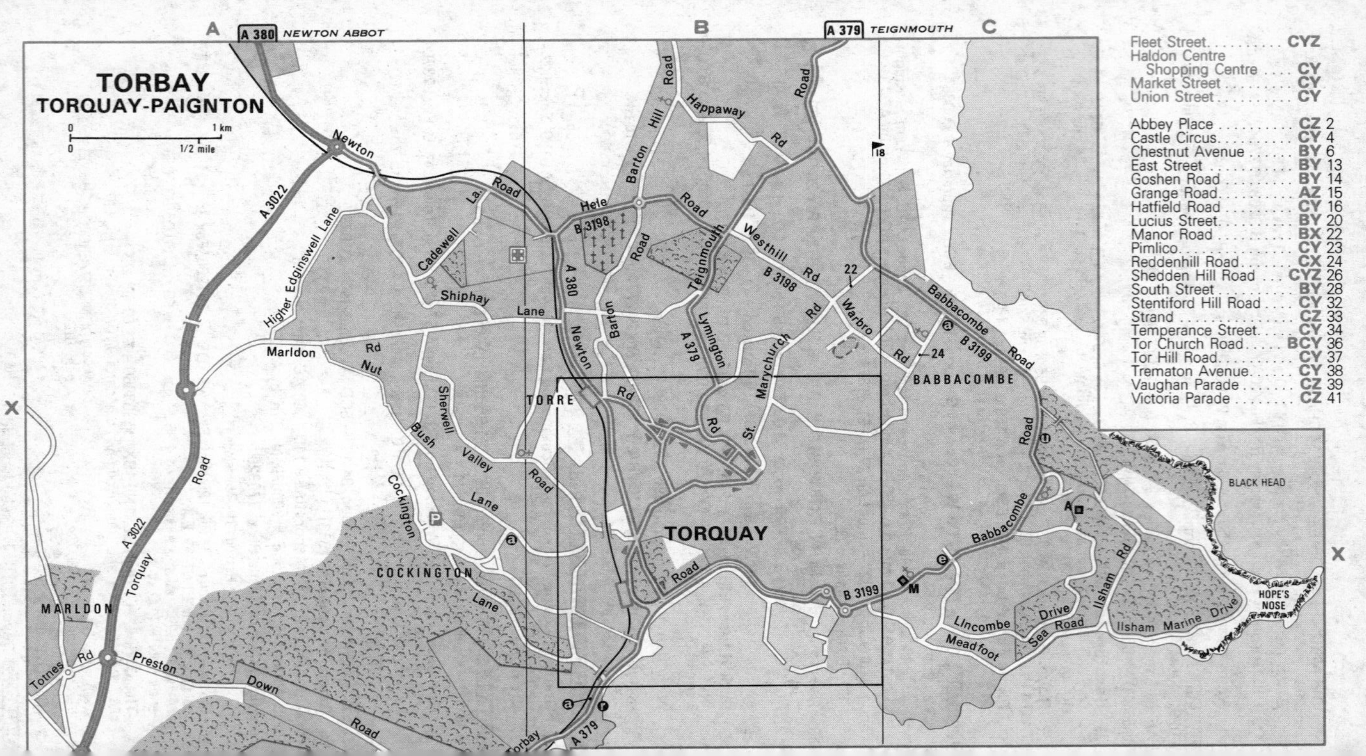

Fleet Street .... CYZ
Haldon Centre
Shopping Centre .... CY
Market Street .... CY
Union Street .... CY

Abbey Place .... CZ 2
Castle Circus.......... CY 4
Chestnut Avenue ..... BY 6
East Street .... BY 13
Goshen Road .... BY 14
Grange Road........... AZ 15
Hatfield Road .... CY 16
Lucius Street........... BY 20
Manor Road .... BX 22
Pimlico............. CY 23
Reddenhill Road........ CX 24
Shedden Hill Road ... CYZ 26
South Street .... BY 28
Stentiford Hill Road .... CY 32
Strand .... CZ 33
Temperance Street..... CY 34
Tor Church Road..... BCY 36
Tor Hill Road........... CY 37
Trematon Avenue...... CY 38
Vaughan Parade .... CZ 39
Victoria Parade .... CZ 41

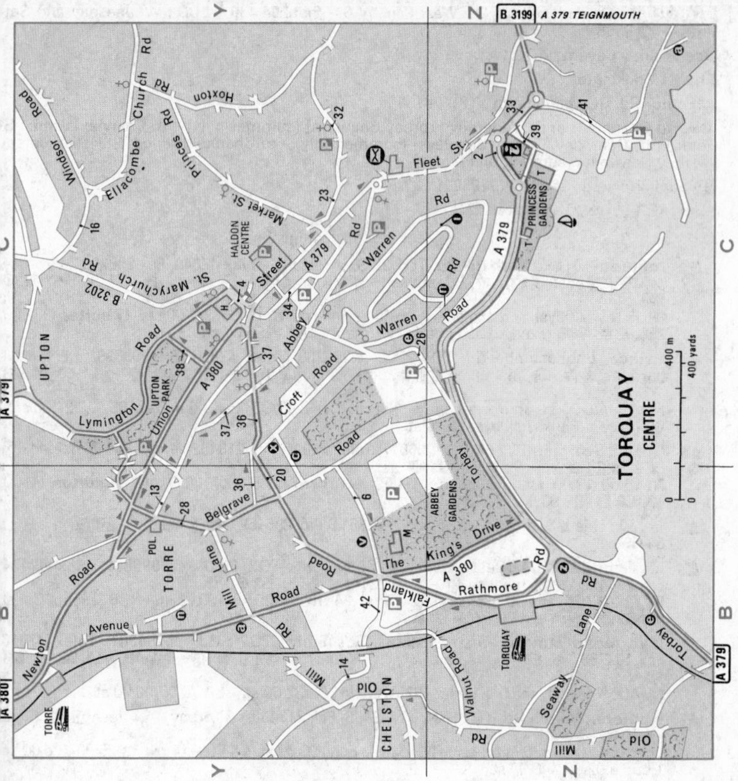

TORQUAY
CENTRE
0 400 m
0 400 yards
B 3199 A 379 TEIGNMOUTH
A 380
A 379
UPTON
Lymington Road
UPTON PARK
Union
St. Marychurch Rd
B 3202
Ellacombe Church Rd
Windsor Road
Princes Rd
Hoxton Rd
Market St.
HALDON CENTRE
Street
Fleet St.
Abbey Rd
Warren Rd
Croft Road
Belgrave Road
TORRE
POL.
Mill Lane
Newton Road
Avenue
Rathmore Rd
Falkland Rd
The King's Drive
ABBEY GARDENS
Torbay Road
Old Mill Rd
CHELSTON
Walnut Road
Seaway Lane
Old Mill Rd
Torbay Rd
TORQUAY
TORRE
PRINCESS GARDENS
See PAIGNTON
Road
Torquay Road
Southfield Avenue
Marldon Rd
King's Ash Road
A 3022
Colley End Road
Totnes Road
ZOO
Penwill Way
Dartmouth Road
A 379
Goodrington Rd
Brixham Road
Long Road
A 3022 BRIXHAM DARTMOUTH
A 385 PLYMOUTH

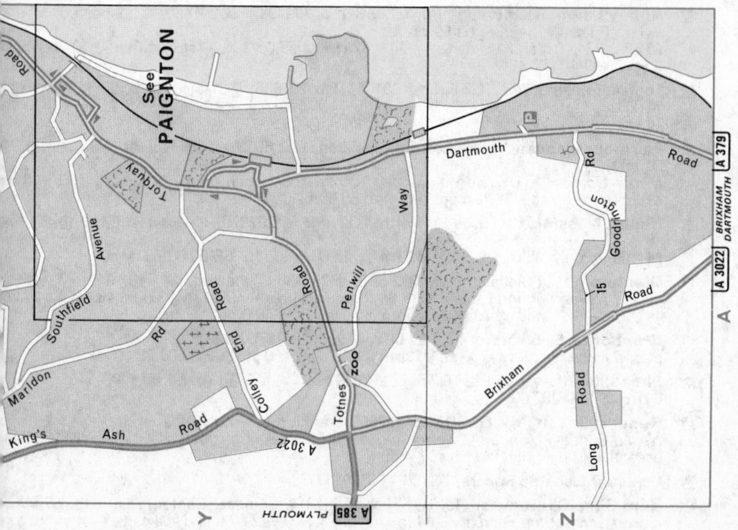

TORQUAY Devon 403 J 32 **The West Country G.** – pop. 54 430 – ECD : Wednesday and Saturday – ☎ 0803.

See : Kent's Cavern★ *AC* CX **A.**

Envir. : Cockington★, W : 1 m. AX.

Petitor Rd, St. Marychurch ☎ 314591 B.

to Channel Islands: Alderney (Torbay Seaways) (summer only) – to Channel Islands: St Peter Port, Guernsey (Torbay Seaways) (summer only) – to Channel Islands: St Helier, Jersey (Torbay Seaways) (summer only).

Vaughan Parade ☎ 297428/296901.

◆London 223 – Exeter 23 – ◆Plymouth 32.

Plans preceding pages

Imperial (T.H.F.), Park Hill Rd, TQ1 2DG, ☎ 294301, Telex 42849, Fax 298293, ≤ Torbay, heated, , squash – rm rest – 350. VISA CZ
M 15.00/27.00 **st.** and a la carte 5.00 – **146 rm** 84.00/172.00 **st.**, **17 suites** 232.00/256.00 **st.** – SB (except Easter and Christmas) 172.00/196.00 **st.**

Palace, Babbacombe Rd, TQ1 3TG, ☎ 200200, Telex 42606, Fax 299899, « Extensive gardens », heated, park, squash – . VISA CX
M 8.50/16.00 **st.** and a la carte – **135 rm** 48.00/90.00 **st.**, **6 suites** 85.00/121.00 **st.** – SB (except Bank Holidays) 98.00 **st.**

Grand, Seafront, TQ2 6NT, ☎ 296677, Telex 42891, Fax 213462, ≤, heated, – – 350. VISA BZ
M 15.00/19.00 **t.** and a la carte 4.50 – **101 rm** 50.00/120.00 **st.**, **11 suites** 60.00/160.00 **t.** – SB 90.00/120.00 **st.**

Corbyn Head, Seafront, TQ2 6RH, ☎ 213611, Fax 296152, ≤, heated – BX
54 rm.

Livermead Cliff (Best Western), Sea Front, TQ2 6RQ, ☎ 299666, Telex 42424, Fax 294496, ≤, heated, – – 70. VISA. BX
M 7.50/13.75 **st.** and a la carte 4.00 – **64 rm** 29.50/100.00 **st.** – SB (except Christmas and New Year) 70.00/94.00 **st.**

Livermead House (Best Western), Sea Front, TQ2 6QJ, ☎ 294361, Telex 42918, Fax 200758, ≤, heated, squash – – 180. VISA BZ
M 7.00/14.00 **st.** and a la carte – **62 rm** 41.00/82.00 **st.** – SB 70.00/90.00 **st.**

Homers, Warren Rd, TQ2 5TN, ☎ 213456, Fax 213458, ≤ Torbay – rest . VISA CZ
closed 4 January-6 February – **M** (dinner only) 25.00 **st.** 4.50 – **14 rm** 25.00/126.00 **st.** **1 suite** 92.00/140.00 **st.**

Roseland, Warren Rd, TQ2 5TT, ☎ 213829, Fax 291266, ≤ Torbay – CY
35 rm.

Abbey Lawn, Scarborough Rd, TQ2 5UQ, ☎ 299199, Fax 291460, ≤, heated, – rm – 50. VISA CY
M 15.00/24.00 **t.** and a la carte 4.20 – **62 rm** 55.00/130.00 **st.**, **1 suite** 95.00/260.00 **st.** – SB 78.00/101.00 **st.**

Toorak, Chestnut Av., TQ2 5JS, ☎ 291444, Fax 291666, heated, – 200 BY
70 rm.

Fairmount House , Herbert Rd, Chelston, TQ2 6RW, ☎ 605446, – rest . VISA AX
March-October – **M** *(closed Sunday dinner)* (bar lunch)/dinner 9.50 **st.** 3.50 – **8 rm** 24.00/48.00 **st.** – SB (except summer) 56.50/62.00 **st.**

Mount Nessing, St. Lukes Rd North, TQ2 5PD, ☎ 292970, ≤ – rest . VISA CZ
M (dinner only) 15.00 **t.** 5.50 – **12 rm** 16.00/41.00 **t.** – SB 50.00/59.00 **st.**

Glenorleigh, 26 Cleveland Rd, TQ2 5BE, ☎ 292135, heated, – . BY
closed November and December – **M** (bar lunch)/dinner 9.00 **st.** 3.50 – **16 rm** 17.00/44.00 **st.** – SB (January-May) (except Bank Holidays) 40.00/52.00 **st.**

Cranborne, 58 Belgrave Rd, TQ2 5HY, ☎ 298046 – . VISA. BY
closed December – **M** 6.00 **st.** – **13 rm** 15.00/36.00 **st.** – SB 32.00/38.00 **st.**

Elmsdale, 70 Avenue Rd, TQ2 5LF, ☎ 295929 – rest . VISA. BY
8 rm 12.00/32.00.

XX **Remy's,** 3 Croft Rd, TQ2 5UN, ☎ 292359, French rest. – VISA CY
closed Sunday, Monday, 2 weeks August and 2 weeks Christmas-New Year – **M** (booking essential) (dinner only) 17.85 **st.** 4.50.

XX Capers, 7 Lisburne Square, TQ1 2PT, ☎ 291177.

XX **Yum Sing,** Old Torwood Rd, TQ1 1PN, ☎ 293314, Chinese (Canton) rest. – . VISA CX
closed Sunday and February – **M** (dinner only) 14.00/22.00 **t.** and a la carte.

at Maidencombe N : 3 ½ m. by A 379 – BX – ✉ ☎ 0803 Torquay :

Orestone Manor House ⛰, Rockhouse Lane, TQ1 4SX, ☎ 328098, Fax 328336, ≤, heated, – TV ☎ P. AE VISA
M (bar lunch)/dinner 17.50 **st.** and a la carte 3.50 – **20 rm** 52.00/104.00 **st.** – SB (October-March) 77.00/94.00 **st.**

at Babbacombe NE : 1 ½ m. – ✉ ☎ 0803 Torquay :

XX **Table,** 135 Babbacombe Rd, TQ1 3SR, ☎ 324292 CX **a**
closed Monday, 1 to 20 February and 1 to 12 September – **M** (booking essential) (dinner only) 23.00/26.00 **t.** 5.00.

AUDI-VW Torwood St. ☎ 298635
FORD Lawes Bridge, Newton Rd ☎ 62021
PEUGEOT-TALBOT 141 Newton Rd ☎ 63626
ROLLS-ROYCE, BENTLEY, FERRARI, VOLVO Lisburne Sq. ☎ 294321
ROVER, MASERATI Lawes Bridge ☎ 612781
ATS 20 Tor Church Rd ☎ 293985
ATS 100 Teignmouth Rd ☎ 329495

TOTLAND BAY I.O.W. 403 404 P 31 – see Wight (Isle of).

TOTNES Devon 403 I 32 **The West Country G.** – pop. 6 133 – ECD : Thursday – ☎ 0803.
See : Site★ – St. Mary's Church★ – Butterwalk★ – Castle (≤★★★) *AC*.
The Plains ☎ 863168 (summer only).
London 224 – Exeter 24 – Plymouth 23 – Torquay 9.

Old Forge at Totnes without rest., Seymour Pl., TQ9 5AY, ☎ 862174, « 14C working forge », – TV P. VISA.
8 rm 30.00/60.00 **st.**

XX **Elbow Room,** 6 North St., TQ9 5NZ, ☎ 863480 – AE VISA
closed Saturday lunch, Sunday and Monday – **M** 8.95 **t.** (lunch) and a la carte 11.40/16.00 **t.** 3.25.

at Stoke Gabriel SE : 4 m. by A 385 – ✉ Totnes – ☎ 080 428 Stoke Gabriel :

Gabriel Court ⛰, TQ9 6SF, ☎ 206, heated, – TV ☎ P. AE VISA
closed February – **M** (dinner only and Sunday lunch)/dinner 25.00 **st.** 3.95 – **20 rm** 40.00/70.00 **st.**

At Tuckenhay S : 4 ¼ m. by A 381 – ✉ Totnes – ☎ 080 423 Harbertonford

X **Poppy's** (at the Maltsters Arms) with rm, Bow Creek, TQ9 7EQ, ☎ 350, Fax 651, ≤, « Riverside setting » – P. AE VISA.
M (Restricted lunch) 18.00/30.00 **st.** and a la carte – **3 rm** (dinner included) 65.00/115.00 **st.**

at Dartington NW : 2 m. on A 385 – ✉ ☎ 0803 Totnes :

Cott Inn, TQ9 6HE, ☎ 863777, Fax 866629, « 14C thatched inn » – TV P. AE VISA.
M (buffet lunch)/dinner 17.50 **t.** and a la carte 2.50 – **6 rm** 45.00/65.00 **t.** – SB (October-March) 75.00/80.00 **st.**

FORD The Stables, Babbage Rd ☎ 862196
VAUXHALL The Plains ☎ 862247
ATS Babbage Rd ☎ 862086

TOTON Notts. 402 403 404 Q 25 – see Nottingham.

TOTTENHILL Norfolk – see King's Lynn.

TOWCESTER Northants. 403 404 R 27 – pop. 5 010 – ☎ 0327.
Woodlands Vale, Farthingstone ☎ 032 736 (Farthingstone) 291, W : 6 m. M 1 junction 16.
London 70 – Birmingham 50 – Northampton 9 – Oxford 36.

Travelodge without rest., A 43, East Towcester by-pass, NN12 0DD, SW : ½ m. by Brackley rd on A 43 ☎ 359105, Reservations (Toll free) 0800 850950 – TV ♿ P. AE VISA.
33 rm 24.00/29.50 **t.**

XX **Vine House** with rm, 100 High St., Paulerspury, NN12 7NA, SE : 3¼ m. by A 5 ☎ 032 733 (Paulerspury) 267, – TV ☎ P. VISA
closed 2 weeks late March, Christmas and New Year – **M** *(closed Saturday lunch, Sunday dinner and Monday)* 32.00 **t.** and a la carte 24.40/30.75 **t.** 3.75 – **6 rm** 53.00/65.00 **t.**

ROVER Quinbury End ☎ 860208

Gli alberghi o ristoranti ameni sono indicati nella guida con un simbolo rosso.

Contribuite a mantenere la guida aggiornata segnalandoci gli alberghi ed i ristoranti dove avete soggiornato piacevolmente.

... XXXXX ... X

TOWERSEY Oxon. 404 R 28 – see Thame.

TRALLWNG = Welshpool.

TRECASTLE Powys 403 J 28 – ☎ 087 482 Sennybridge.
◆London 183 – Brecon 12.

- **Castle,** LD3 8UH, ☎ 354 – TV Ⓟ. VISA
  M (bar lunch)/dinner a la carte 10.65/13.40 **st.** – **8 rm** 33.00/48.00 **st.** – SB 54.00/59.00 **st.**

TREFALDWYN = Montgomery.

TREFDRAETH = Newport (Dyfed).

TREFFYNNON = Holywell.

TREFRIW Gwynedd 402 403 I 24 – see Llanrwst.

TREFYCLAWDD = Knighton.

TREFYNWY = Monmouth.

TREGONY Cornwall 403 F 33 – pop. 670 – ✉ Truro – ☎ 087 253.
◆London 291 – Newquay 18 – Plymouth 53 – Truro 10.

- **Tregony House,** 15 Fore St., TR2 5RN, ☎ 671, – rest Ⓟ.
  March-October – **6 rm** (dinner included) 27.50/60.50.

TREGREHAN Cornwall 403 F 32 – see St. Austell.

TRELLECK **(TRYLEG)** Gwent 403 L 28 – see Monmouth.

TRERICE Cornwall 403 E 32 – see Newquay.

TRESAITH Dyfed – see Aberporth.

TRESCO Cornwall 403 ㉚ – see Scilly (Isles of).

TREYARNON BAY Cornwall 403 E 32 – see Padstow.

TRING Herts. 404 S 28 – pop. 10 610 – ECD : Wednesday – ☎ 044 282 (4 fig.) or 0442 (6 fig.).
See : Church of St. Peter and St. Paul (interior : stone corbels★).
◆London 38 – Aylesbury 7 – Luton 14.

- **Rose and Crown** (Lansbury), High St., HP23 5AH, ☎ 4071, Telex 826538, Fax 890735 – rm TV ☎ Ⓟ – 80. AE VISA.
  M 10.00/17.00 **t.** and a la carte 4.50 – **27 rm** 76.00/88.00 **t.** – SB (weekend only) 80.00/88.00 **st.**
- **Travel Inn,** Tring Hill, HP23 4LD, W : 1 ½ m. on A 41 ☎ 4819, Fax 890787 – rm TV Ⓟ. AE VISA.
  M (Beefeater grill) a la carte approx. 12.25 **t.** – 4.50 – **30 rm** -/27.50 **t.**

HONDA 110 Western Rd ☎ 4144 SAAB London Rd ☎ 890911

TROTTON West Sussex – see Midhurst.

TROUTBECK Cumbria 402 L 20 – see Windermere.

TROWBRIDGE Wilts. 403 404 N 30 **The West Country G.** – pop. 27 299 – ECD : Wednesday – ☎ 022 14 (4 and 5 fig.) or 0225 (6 fig.).
Envir. : Norton St. Philip (The George Inn★★), W : 6 m. – Bratton Castle ※★★, SE : 7 ½ m. by B 3098 – Steeple Ashton★, The Green★, E : 7 m. – Edington (St. Mary, St. Catherine and All Saints Church★), SE : 8 m. – Farleigh Hungerford Castle★ *AC*, (St. Leonards Chapel★), W : 4 m.
ℹ St Stephens Pl. ☎ 777054.
◆London 115 – ◆Bristol 27 – ◆Southampton 55 – Swindon 32.

- **Old Manor** , Trowle, BA14 9BL, NW : 1 m. on A 363 ☎ 777393, Fax 765443, – TV ☎ Ⓟ. AE VISA.
  closed 1 week Christmas – **M** (lunch by arrangement)/dinner a la carte 10.35/18.15 **st.** 2.65 – **14 rm** 38.00/55.00 **st.** – SB 70.00/75.00 **st.**
- **Hilbury Court,** Hilperton Rd, BA14 7JW, E : ¼ m. on A 361 ☎ 752949, – rest TV ☎ Ⓟ. VISA.
  closed 24 December-1 January – **M** *(closed Friday to Sunday and Bank Holidays)* (bar lunch)/dinner 12.00 **st.** 3.20 – **13 rm** 32.00/52.00 **st.**

ITROEN Bradford Rd ℘ 753297
ORD Bradley Rd ℘ 752525
OVER Duke St. ℘ 777222
VAUXHALL-OPEL Town Bridge ℘ 66192

ATS Canal Rd, Ladydown Trading Est. ℘ 753469

TRURO Cornwall 403 E 33 **The West Country G.** – pop. 17 852 – ECD : Thursday – 0872.

ee : Cornwall County Museum★ *AC*.

nvir. : Trewithen★★★, NE : 7½ m. by A 390 – Trelissick garden★★, (≤★★) *AC*, S : 8 m. by A 39 nd B 3289 – at Probus★ Church Tower★ County Demonstration Garden★, NE : 8 m. – Feock Church★), S : 8½ m.

Treliske ℘ 72640, W : 2 m. on A 390.

Municipal Building, Boscawen St. ℘ 74555.

London 295 – Exeter 87 – Penzance 26 – ♦Plymouth 52.

Alverton Manor, Tregolls Rd (A 39), TR1 1XQ, ℘ 76633, Fax 222989, « Mid 19C manor house, former bishops residence and convent », – – 200. AE VISA.
M 11.95 **t.** and a la carte 4.75 – 4.80 – **20 rm** 67.00/190.00 **t.**, **5 suites** 125.00 **t.** – SB (weekends only) 299.00 **st.**

Laniley House without rest., Newquay Rd, nr. Trispen, TR4 9AU, NE : 3½ m. by A 39 and A 3076 on Frogmore rd ℘ 75201, – .
3 rm 22.00/34.00.

Blue Haze without rest., The Parade, Malpas Rd, TR1 1QE, ℘ 223553, – rm .
3 rm 15.00/30.00 **st.**

Conifers without rest., 36 Tregoles Rd, TR1 1LA, ℘ 79925 – .
4 rm 16.00/32.00.

Bay Tree without rest., 28 Ferris Town, TR1 3JM, ℘ 40274 – .
4 rm 16.00/32.00 **s.**

at Blackwater W : 7 m. by A 390 – ✉ Truro – 0872 Truro :

Long's, TR4 8HH, ℘ 561111 – . AE VISA
closed Sunday dinner, Monday, Tuesday and 3 weeks January-February – **M** (dinner only and Sunday lunch)/dinner a la carte 19.75/24.00 **t.**

Pennypots, TR4 8EY, SW : ¾ m. ℘ 820347 – . AE VISA
closed Sunday dinner mid September-mid June, Monday and 2 weeks winter – **M** (dinner only) a la carte 15.75/23.00 **t.**

ORD Lemon Quay ℘ 73933
IERCEDES-BENZ Moresk ℘ 73949
EUGEOT-TALBOT Point Mills, Bissoe ℘ 863073
OVER Lemon Quay ℘ 74321
AUXHALL Fairmantle St. ℘ 76231
VW-AUDI Three Mile Stone ℘ 79301

ATS Tabernacle St. ℘ 74083
ATS Newham Rd ℘ 40353

TRYLEG = Trelleck.

TUCKENHAY Devon – see Totnes.

TUDWEILIOG Gwynedd 402 403 G 25 – pop. 882 – ✉ Pwllheli – 075 887.

London 267 – Caernarfon 25.

Dive Inn, LL53 8PB, W : 2 m. by B 4417 ℘ 246, Seafood – . VISA
closed Monday to Thursday November-March – **M** (booking essential) (bar lunch)/dinner a la carte 11.75/18.25 **t.** 4.00.

TUNBRIDGE WELLS Kent 404 U 30 – see Royal Tunbridge Wells.

TURNERS HILL West Sussex 404 T 30 – 0342 Copthorne.

London 33 – ♦Brighton 24 – Crawley 7.

Alexander House , RH10 4QD, E : 1 m. on B 2110 ℘ 714914, Telex 95611, Fax 717328, ≤, « Tastefully decorated country house », , park, – . AE VISA.
M 35.00 **t.** and a la carte 18.15/31.25 **t.** 6.50 – **7 rm** 90.00/175.00 **t.**, **5 suites** 125.00/250.00 **t.** – SB (November-March) (except Bank Holidays) 182.50/197.50 **st.**

TUTBURY Staffs. 402 403 404 O 25 – pop. 5 099 (inc. Hatton) – ECD : Wednesday – ✉ 0283 Burton-upon-Trent.

London 132 – ♦Birmingham 33 – Derby 11 – ♦Stoke-on-Trent 27.

Ye Olde Dog and Partridge, High St., DE13 9LS, ℘ 813030, Fax 813178, « Part 15C timbered inn », – . AE VISA.
closed 25 and 26 December – **M** (carving lunch)/dinner a la carte 13.35/19.70 **t.** 3.95 – **17 rm** 50.00/72.00 **st.**

TUXFORD Notts. 402 404 R 24 – pop. 2 547 – ECD : Wednesday – ✉ Newark – ☎ 0777.
♦London 141 – ♦Leeds 53 – Lincoln 18 – ♦Nottingham 26 – ♦Sheffield 29.

- **Newcastle Arms,** Market Pl., NG22 0LA, ☎ 870208 – TV ☎ P – 🏔 90. AE VISA
M 15.95 **t.** and a la carte – ☕ 2.50 – **11 rm** 42.00/52.00 **t.**

TWEMLOW GREEN Cheshire 402 403 404 N 24 – see Holmes Chapel.

TWO BRIDGES Devon 403 I 32 **The West Country G.** – ✉ Yelverton – ☎ 0822 Tavistock.
♦London 226 – Exeter 25 – ♦Plymouth 17.

- **Cherrybrook** , PL20 6SP, NE : 1 m. on B 3212 ☎ 88260, ←, – rest P
closed Christmas-New Year – **M** 10.35 **t.** 4.00 – **7 rm** ☕ 20.70/45.00 **st.**

TYDDEWI = St. David's.

TYNDYRN = Tintern.

TYNEMOUTH Tyne and Wear 401 402 P 18 – pop. 17 877 – ECD : Wednesday – ☎ 0632 Nor Shields (6 fig.) or 091 Tyneside (7 fig.).
See : Priory and castle : ruins★ (11C) *AC*.
Spital Dene ☎ 257 4578.
♦London 290 – ♦Newcastle-upon-Tyne 8 – Sunderland 7.

- **Park,** Grand Par., NE30 4JQ, ☎ 257 1406, Fax 257 1716, – rm TV ☎ P – 🏔 40 AE VISA.
closed 2 to 4 January – **M** *(closed lunch Bank Holidays)* 10.50/14.50 **st.** and a la carte 3.9 – **49 rm** ☕ 55.50/68.50 **st.**

VAUXHALL Tynemouth Rd ☎ 257 0346

TYWYN Gwynedd 403 H 26 – ☎ 0654.
High St. ☎ 710070.
♦London 234 – Dolgellau 19 – Shrewsbury 72.

- Riverslea, Aberdovey Rd, LL36 9HS, S : 1 ½ m. on A 493 ☎ 711615, ←, – P.
4 rm.

UCKFIELD East Sussex 404 U 31 – pop. 10 938 – ECD : Wednesday – ☎ 0825.
Envir. : Sheffield Park Gardens★ *AC*, W : 6 m.
Piltdown ☎ 082 572 (Maresfield) 2033, NW : 3 m. by A 272 – , East Sussex Nationa Little Horsted ☎ 75577.
♦London 45 – ♦Brighton 17 – Eastbourne 20 – Maidstone 34.

- **Horsted Place** , Little Horsted, TN22 5TS, S : 2 ½ m. by B 2102 and A 22 on A 2 ☎ 75581, Telex 95548, Fax 75459, ←, « Victorian Gothic country house and gardens , , park, – TV ☎ P – 🏔 25. AE VISA.
closed 1 to 7 January – **M** *(closed Saturday lunch)* 19.00/28.00 **t.** 6.00 – **3 rm** ☕ 125.00 **14 suites** 165.00/310.00 **t.**
- **Hooke Hall,** High St., TN22 1EN, ☎ 761578, Telex 95228, Fax 768025, « Queen Anr town house », – TV ☎ P. VISA.
closed 24 December-1 January – **M** *(closed Sunday to Thursday to non-residents)* (lunc by arrangement)/dinner 20.00 **t.** 4.25 – ☕ 5.75 – **5 rm** 40.00/95.00 **st.**
- **Thai Fantasy,** Ringles Cross, TN22 1HB, N : 1 m. ☎ 763827, Thai rest., – P. VISA
closed Sunday – **M** 8.00/20.00 **t.** and a la carte 5.50.

ROVER 84-86 High St. ☎ 4255

ULLINGSWICK Heref. and Worc. – pop. 261 – ✉ ☎ 0432 Hereford.
♦London 134 – Hereford 12 – Shrewsbury 52 – Worcester 19.

- **Steppes Country House** , HR1 3JG, ☎ 820424, « Converted farmhouse of 14 origins », – rest TV ☎ P
closed 2 weeks January and 2 weeks December – **M** (bar lunch)/dinner 17.50 **st.** 3.45 **5 rm** ☕ 30.00/55.00 **st.** – SB 64.00/86.00 **st.**

ULLSWATER Cumbria 402 L 20 – ✉ Penrith – ☎ 076 84 Pooley Bridge.

See : Lake★ – Lowther Wildlife Park★ *AC*.

ℹ Main Car Park, Glenridding ☎ 085 32 (Glenridding) 414 – at Pooley Bridge, The Square ☎ 530 summer only).

London 296 – Carlisle 25 – Kendal 31 – Penrith 6.

at Howtown SW : 4 m. of Pooley Bridge – ✉ Penrith – ☎ 076 84 Pooley Bridge :

Howtown ⑤, CA10 2ND, ☎ 86514, ≤, ⛱ – P. ✻
last week March-October – **M** (buffet lunch Monday to Saturday)/dinner 10.00 **t.** 3.00 – **14 rm** ☕ 22.00/54.00 **t.**

at Pooley Bridge on B 5320 – ✉ Penrith – ☎ 076 84 Pooley Bridge :

Sharrow Bay Country House ⑤, CA10 2LZ, S : 2 m. on Howtown rd ☎ 86301, Fax 86349, ≤ Ullswater and fells, « Lakeside setting, gardens, tasteful decor » – TV ☎ P. ✻
March-November – **M** *(closed Monday lunch)* (booking essential) 26.00/37.50 **st.** 5.00 – **22 rm** ☕ (dinner included) 80.00/250.00 **st.**, **6 suites** 220.00/250.00 **st.**

at Watermillock on A 592 – ✉ Penrith – ☎ 076 84 Pooley Bridge :

Leeming House (T.H.F.) ⑤, CA11 0JJ, on A 592 ☎ 86622, Telex 64111, Fax 86443, ≤, ⛱, park – ⇔ TV ☎ ♿ P. AE ⓓ VISA
M 29.50 **st.** (dinner) and a la carte 10.90/19.45 **st.** 4.70 – ☕ 8.25 – **40 rm** 70.00/125.00 **st.** – SB 116.00/180.00 **st.**

Rampsbeck ⑤, CA11 0LP, ☎ 86442, ≤, ⛱, park – TV ☎ P. VISA
closed 6 January-23 February – **M** 15.95/25.00 **t.** 4.00 – **19 rm** ☕ 32.00/80.00 **t.** – SB (November-August) 90.00/115.00 **st.**

Old Church ⑤, CA11 0JN, ☎ 86204, Fax 86368, ≤ Ullswater and fells, « Lakeside setting », ⛵, ⛱ – ⇔ rest ☎ P. VISA. ✻
March-November – **M** (dinner) 25.00 **st.** 5.00 – **10 rm** ☕ (dinner included) 68.00/88.00 **st.**

ULVERSTON Cumbria 402 K 21 – pop. 11 976 – ECD : Wednesday – ☎ 0229.

Envir. : Furness Abbey★ (ruins 13C-15C) *AC*, SW : 6½ m.

⛳ Bardsea Park ☎ 52824, SW : 1½ m. on A 5087 – ⛳ Barrow, Rakesmoor, Hawcoat ☎ 0229 Barrow-in-Furness) 25444, SW : 7 m.

ℹ Coronation Hall, County Sq. ☎ 57120.

London 278 – Kendal 25 – Lancaster 36.

Bay Horse Inn, Canal Foot (on the Coast), LA12 9EL, E : 2¼ m. by A 5087, Morecombe Rd and beyond Industrial area ☎ 53972, ≤ – ⇔ P. VISA
closed Monday lunch, Sunday and January-February – **M** (booking essential) 11.50 **t.** (lunch) and a la carte 16.00/20.70 **t.** 4.50.

at Lowick Green N : 5 m. by A 590 on A 5092 – ✉ Ulverston – ☎ 022 986 Greenodd :

Farmers Arms, LA12 8DT, ☎ 861376 – TV ☎ P. AE VISA
closed 26 December and 1 January – **M** 18.50/25.00 **t.** 5.00 – **11 rm** ☕ 28.00/55.00 **t.** – SB (weekends only) (except Bank Holidays) 70.00/92.00 **st.**

at Spark Bridge N : 5½ m. by A 590 off A 5092 – ✉ Ulverston – ☎ 022 985 Lowick Bridge :

Bridgefield House ⑤, LA12 8DA, NW : 1 m. on Nibthwaite Rd ☎ 239, Fax 379, ⛱ – ⇔ rest ☎ P. VISA
M (dinner only) (booking essential) 20.00 **t.** – **5 rm** ☕ 33.00/66.00 **t.**

ATS The Gill ☎ 53442

UMBERLEIGH Devon 403 I 31 – ☎ 0769 High Bickington.

London 215 – Exeter 33 – Plymouth 59 – Taunton 47.

Rising Sun, EX37 9DU, ☎ 60447, ⛵ – TV ☎ P
6 rm.

UNDERBARROW Cumbria 402 L 21 – see Kendal.

UPLYME Devon 403 L 31 – see Lyme Regis.

UPPER ODDINGTON Glos. – see Stow-on-the-Wold.

UPPER SLAUGHTER Glos. 403 404 O 28 – see Bourton-on-the-Water.

UPPINGHAM Leics. 404 R 26 – pop. 2 761 – ECD : Thursday – ☎ 0572.

Envir. : Kirkby Hall★ (ruins 16C), SE : 8 m.

♦London 101 – ♦Leicester 19 – Northampton 28 – ♦Nottingham 35.

- **Garden,** 16 High St. West, LE15 9QD, ℘ 822352, Fax 821156, – rest. VISA.
  M *(closed Sunday)* (bar lunch)/dinner 11.75 **st.** 3.50 – **12 rm** 37.00/48.00 **st.**
- **Rutland House** without rest., 61 High St., East, LE15 9PY, ℘ 822497, –
  5 rm 25.00/35.00 **t.**
- **Lake Isle** with rm, 16 High St. East, LE15 9PZ, ℘ 822951, Fax 822951 – . VISA
  M *(closed Monday lunch, Sunday dinner to non-residents and Bank Holidays)* 10.75 21.00 **t.** 4.85 – **10 rm** 36.00/70.00 **st.** – SB 90.00/100.00 **st.**

at Morcott Service Area E : 4 ¼ m. by A 6003 on A 47 – ✉ Morcott – ☎ 057 287 Uppingham :

- **Travelodge** without rest., Glaston Rd, LE15 8SA, ℘ 719, Reservations (Toll free) 0800 850950 – . VISA.
  40 rm 24.00/29.50 **t.**

at Lyddington SE : 2 m. by A 6003 – ✉ ☎ 0572 Uppingham :

- **Marquess of Exeter** (Best Western), 52 Main St., LE15 9LT, ℘ 822477, Fax 821343 – . VISA.
  M *(closed Saturday lunch and Sunday dinner)* 11.95 **t.** and a la carte 4.50 – **17 rm** 55.00/80.00 **t.** – SB (weekends only) 80.00 **st.**

UPTON ST. LEONARDS Glos. – see Gloucester.

UPTON SNODSBURY Heref. and Worc. 403 404 N 27 – see Worcester.

UPTON UPON SEVERN Heref. and Worc. 403 404 N 27 – pop. 1 537 – ECD : Thursday – ☎ 068 46.

The Pepperpot, Church St. ℘ 4200 (summer only).

♦London 116 – Hereford 25 – Stratford-upon-Avon 29 – Worcester 11.

- **White Lion,** High St., WR8 0HJ, ℘ 2551 – . VISA
  closed 25 and 26 December – **M** 13.50 **t.** and a la carte 5.75 – **10 rm** 46.00/64.00 **t.** – SB 75.00 **st.**
- Star, High St., WR8 0HQ, ℘ 2300, Fax 2929 –
  16 rm.
- **Pool House,** Hanley Rd, WR8 0PA, NW : ½ m. on B 4211 ℘ 2151, ←, – rm VISA.
  closed Christmas – **M** 9.00 **s.** – **9 rm** 19.00/52.00 **st.** – SB (April-mid May) 48.00 78.00 **st.**

USK (BRYNBUGA) Gwent 403 L 28 – pop. 1 783 – ECD : Wednesday – ☎ 029 13.

See : Valley★.

18 at Pontypool ℘ 049 55 (Pontypool) 763655, W : 7 m.

♦London 144 – ♦Bristol 30 – Gloucester 39 – Newport 10.

- **Glen-yr-Afon House,** Pontypool Rd, NP5 1SY, ℘ 2302, – rest VISA
  M *(closed Sunday dinner)* 7.50/20.00 **st.** and a la carte 3.60 – **16 rm** 28.00/45.00 **s.** – SB (except summer) (weekends only) 62.50/67.50 **st.**

at Llangybi S : 2 ½ m. on Llangybi rd – ✉ Usk – ☎ 063 349 Tredunnock :

- **Cwrt Bleddyn,** NP5 1PG, S : 1 m. ℘ 521, Fax 220, , squash – – 200. VISA.
  M 18.95 **t.** and a la carte 3.95 – **36 rm** 62.00/125.00 **t.** – SB (weekdays only) (except Bank Holidays) 100.00/150.00 **st.**

UTTOXETER Staffs. 402 403 404 O 25 – pop. 10 008 – ECD : Thursday – ☎ 088 93 (4 and fig.) or 0889 (6 fig.).

Envir. : Alton Towers (gardens★★) *AC*, NW : 7 ½ m.

18 Wood Lane ℘ 564884.

♦London 145 – ♦Birmingham 33 – Derby 19 – Stafford 13 – ♦Stoke-on-Trent 16.

- White Hart, Carter St., ST14 8EU, ℘ 562437 –
  26 rm.
- **Travelodge** without rest., Ashbourne Rd, ST14 5AA, junction A 50 and B 5030 ℘ 562043 Reservations (Toll free) 0800 850950 – . VISA.
  32 rm 24.00/29.50 **t.**

FIAT Smithfield Rd ℘ 563838
FORD, ISUZU, VAUXHALL Derby Rd ℘ 562301
ATS Smithfield Rd ℘ 563848/565201

VELINDRE (FELINDRE FARCHOG) Dyfed 403 F 27 – see Newport (Dyfed).

VENN OTTERY Devon 403 K 31 – ✉ ☎ 0404 Ottery St. Mary.
London 209 – Exeter 11 – Sidmouth 5.

- **Venn Ottery Barton** ⑤, EX11 1RZ, ℘ 812733, ⛱ – Ⓟ. VISA
M 11.50 **t.** – **16 rm** 26.00/46.00 **t.**

VENTNOR I.O.W. 403 404 Q 32 – see Wight (Isle of).

VERYAN Cornwall 403 F 33 The West Country G. – pop. 880 – ✉ ☎ 0872 Truro.
See : Site★.
London 291 – St. Austell 13 – Truro 13.

- **Nare** ⑤, Carne Beach, TR2 5PF, SW : 1 ¼ m. ℘ 501279, Fax 501856, ≤ Carne Bay, ⛳, heated, ⛱, – TV ☎ Ⓟ. VISA
M (bar lunch Monday to Saturday)/dinner 18.00 **t.** and a la carte – **39 rm** 57.00/136.00 **t.**

at Ruan High Lanes W : 1 ¼ m. on A 3078 – ✉ ☎ 0872 Truro :

- **Hundred House,** TR2 5JR, ℘ 501336, ⛱ – TV Ⓟ. VISA
March-October – **M** (dinner only) 16.00 **st.** 4.50 – **10 rm** 30.00/60.00 **t.**

VOWCHURCH Heref. and Worc. 403 L 27 – pop. 160 – ✉ Hereford – ☎ 0981 Peterchurch.
London 144 – Brecon 27 – Hereford 11.

- **Croft,** HR2 0QE, E : ½ m. on B 4348 ℘ 550226, ≤, ⛱ – TV Ⓟ. VISA.
M (by arrangement) 11.50 **st.** – **7 rm** 20.00/51.00 **st.** – SB (October-March) 59.00/70.00 **st.**

WADDESDON Bucks. 404 R 28 – pop. 1 644 – ECD : Thursday – ☎ 029 665.
See : Waddesdon Manor (Rothschild Collection★★★) *AC.*
London 52 – Aylesbury 6 – Birmingham 66 – Oxford 25.

Hotels see : Aylesbury E : 5 m.

WADESMILL Herts. – see Ware.

WADHURST East Sussex 404 U 30 – pop. 3 643 – ECD : Wednesday – ☎ 089 288.
Dale Hill, Ticehurst ℘ 0580 (Ticehurst) 200112.
London 44 – Hastings 21 – Maidstone 24 – Royal Tunbridge Wells 6.

- **Spindlewood** ⑤, Wallcrouch, TN5 7JG, SE : 2 ¼ m. on B 2099 ℘ 0580 (Ticehurst) 200430, Fax 201132, ≤, ⛱ – TV ☎ Ⓟ. AE VISA.
closed 4 days at Christmas – **M** *(closed Bank Holiday lunch)* 15.00/22.00 **t.** 3.25 – **9 rm** 48.00/80.00 **t.** – SB (October-late May) 87.00/90.00 **st.**
- **Newbarn** ⑤ without rest., Wards Lane, TN5 6HP, E : 3 m. by B 2099 ℘ 2042, ≤ Bewl Water and countryside, ⛱ – Ⓟ.
4 rm 18.00/44.00 **st.**
- **Kirkstone** without rest., Mayfield Lane, TN5 6HX, ℘ 3204, ⛱ – Ⓟ
3 rm 15.00/30.00 **st.**

FIAT Beech Hill ℘ 2126
FORD Cousley Wood ℘ 2375
VAUXHALL Sparrows Green ℘ 3157
VOLVO High St. ℘ 2128

WAKEFIELD West Yorks. 402 P 22 – pop. 74 764 – ECD : Wednesday – ☎ 0924.
Envir. : Pontefract (castle★ : ruins 12C-13C) *AC*, E : 9 m – Nostell Priory★ E : 4 ½ m.
City of Wakefield, Lupset Park, Horbury Rd ℘ 374316, SW : 1 ¼ m. on A 642 – Woodthorpe ℘ 255104, S : 3 m. – Painthorpe House, Painthorpe Lane ℘ 255083, near junction 39 on M 1 – Normanton Snydale Rd ℘ 892943.
Town Hall, Wood St. ℘ 295000/1 (evenings and weekends).
London 188 – Leeds 9 – Manchester 38 – Sheffield 23.

- **Cedar Court,** Denby Dale Rd., Calder Grove, WF4 3QZ, SW : 3 m. on A 636 ℘ 276310, Telex 557647, Fax 280221 – rm TV ☎ Ⓟ – 500. AE VISA
M 8.95/13.50 **t.** and a la carte 3.45 – **146 rm** 87.00/105.00 **t.**, **5 suites** 145.00 **t.** – SB (weekends only) 96.00 **st.**
- **Post House** (T.H.F.), Queen's Drive, Ossett, WF5 9BE, W : 2 ½ m. on A 638 ℘ 276388, Telex 55407, Fax 280277 – rm rest TV ☎ Ⓟ – 150. AE VISA
M *(closed Saturday lunch)* 10.95/13.95 **st.** and a la carte 4.35 – 7.50 – **99 rm** 70.00/90.00 **st.** – SB (weekends only) 76.00/86.00 **st.**
- **Swallow,** Queen St., WF1 1JU, ℘ 372111, Telex 557464, Fax 383648 – rm TV ☎ Ⓟ – 150. AE VISA
M 9.00/13.25 **st.** and a la carte 4.00 – **63 rm** 65.00/80.00 **st.** – SB (weekends only) 75.00 **st.**

BMW Ings Rd ℘ 363796
CITROEN Stanley Rd ℘ 291300
FORD Barnsley Rd ℘ 290290
HONDA Westgate ℘ 666261
LANCIA 509 Leeds Rd ℘ 0532 (Leeds) 822254
PEUGEOT-TALBOT Barnsley Rd ℘ 255904
ROVER Ings Rd ℘ 370100
VAUXHALL Doncaster Rd ℘ 676771

ATS Bethel Pl., Thornes Lane ℘ 371638

WALBERTON West Sussex – see Arundel.

WALKINGTON Humberside 402 S 22 – see Beverley.

WALLASEY Merseyside 402 403 K 23 – pop. 62 465 – ☎ 051 Liverpool.
Bayswater Rd ℘ 639 3630 – Warren,Grove Rd ℘ 639 8223.
to Liverpool (Merseyside Transport) frequent services daily (7-8 mn).
♦London 226 – Birkenhead 3.5 – ♦Liverpool 4.

WALLINGFORD Oxon. 403 404 Q 29 – pop. 9 041 – ECD : Wednesday – ☎ 0491.
9 St. Martin's St. ℘ 35351.
♦London 54 – ♦Oxford 12 – Reading 16.

George (Mt. Charlotte Thistle), 84 High St., OX10 0BS, ℘ 36665, Telex 847468, Fax 2535 – rm TV ☎ P – 100. AE VISA
M 14.50/17.50 **t.** and a la carte 4.25 – 8.00 – **39 rm** 65.00/80.00 **t.**

XXX **Regatta** with rm, 103 High St., OX10 0BL, ℘ 26126, Fax 26337, <, « Thames-side setting » – TV ☎ P. AE VISA.
M *(closed Sunday dinner and Monday)* 12.50/17.50 **t.** and a la carte 6.00 – **3 rm** 60.00/120.00 **st.**

at North Stoke S : 2¾ m. by A 4130 and A 4074 on B 4009 – ✉ ☎ 0491 Wallingford :

Springs , Wallingford Rd, OX10 6BE, ℘ 36687, Telex 849794, Fax 36877, <, heated, , park, – TV ☎ P – 50. AE VISA.
M 17.00/27.00 **t.** and a la carte 5.00 – **35 rm** 65.00/154.00 **st.**, **3 suites** 170.00-200.00 **st.** – SB (weekends only) 130.00/155.00 **st.**

FORD 43 High St. ℘ 38424
PEUGEOT-TALBOT Wood St. ℘ 36017
ROVER 8-10 Watlington Rd, Benson, Nr Wallingford ℘ 38308

En saison, *surtout dans les stations fréquentées, il est prudent de retenir à l'avance.*
Cependant, si vous ne pouvez pas occuper la chambre que vous avez retenue, prévenez immédiatement l'hôtelier.
Si vous écrivez à un hôtel à l'étranger, joignez à votre lettre un coupon-réponse international (disponible dans les bureaux de poste).

WALLSEND Tyne and Wear 401 402 P 18 – see Newcastle-upon-Tyne.

WALSALL West Midlands 403 404 O 26 – pop. 177 923 – ECD : Thursday – ☎ 0922.
Calderfields, Aldridge Rd ℘ 32243, N : 1 m. CT – Broadway ℘ 22710, S : 1 m.
♦London 126 – ♦Birmingham 9 – ♦Coventry 29 – Shrewsbury 36.

Plan of enlarged area : see Birmingham pp. 2 and 3

Crest (T.H.F.), Birmingham Rd, WS5 3AB, SE : 1½ m. on A 34 ℘ 33555, Telex 335479 Fax 612034 – rm rest TV ☎ P – 50. AE VISA CT e
M 12.50/16.50 **st.** and a la carte 4.50 – 7.95 – **101 rm** 71.00/100.00 **st.** – SB (weekends only) 72.00/90.00 **st.**

Friendly Lodge, 20 Wolverhampton Rd, West Bentley, WS2 0BS, W : 2½ m. on A 454 ℘ 724444, Telex 334854, Fax 723148, , , – rm TV ☎ P – 180. AE VISA. BT a
M (carving rest.) 9.65/16.00 **st.** and a la carte 4.00 – 5.00 – **120 rm** 52.00/73.00 **st.** – SB (weekends only) 70.00/75.00 **st.**

at Walsall Wood NE : 3½ m. on A 461 – CT – ✉ Walsall – ☎ 0543 Brownhills :

Barons Court (Best Western), Walsall Rd, WS9 9AH, ℘ 452020, Telex 333061, Fax 361276, , – TV ☎ P – 110. AE VISA
M *(closed Sunday dinner and Bank Holidays)* a la carte 15.00/25.00 **St.** 3.95 – **100 rm** 54.00/95.00 **st.** – SB 80.00/110.00 **st.**

FORD Wolverhampton St. ℘ 721212
FORD Wolverhampton Rd ℘ 402000
LADA, PROTON 152 Green Lane ℘ 645347
PEUGEOT-TALBOT Paddock Lane, off Charlotte St. ℘ 721188
RENAULT Day St. ℘ 720202
TOYOTA Lichfield Rd, Willenhall ℘ 0922 (Bloxwich) 493000
VAUXHALL-OPEL Broadway ℘ 720500

ATS Leamore Trading Est., Fryers Rd, Bloxwich ℘ 478631

WALSGRAVE ON SOWE West Midlands – see Coventry.

WALTHAM ABBEY Essex 404 U 28 – pop. 16 498 – ☎ 0992 Lea Valley.
Royal Epping Forest, Chingford ℘ 081 (London) 529 6407.
♦London 15 – ♦Cambridge 44 – ♦Ipswich 66 – Luton 30 – Southend-on-Sea 35.

Swallow, Old Shire Lane, EN9 3LX, SE : 1½ m. on A 121 ℘ 717170, Telex 916596, Fax 711841, , , – rm rest TV ☎ P – 200. AE VISA
M 18.00/20.50 **st.** and a la carte 5.25 – **163 rm** 55.00/130.00 **st.** – SB (weekends only) 98.00/105.00 **st.**

WALTON-ON-THAMES Surrey 404 S 29 – ECD : Wednesday – ✉ ☎ 0932.
Town Hall, New Zealand Av. ✆ 228844.
London 23 – ♦Brighton 54 – ♦Portsmouth 61 – ♦Southampton 65.

Plan : see Greater London (South-West)

Ashley Park, Ashley Park Rd, KT12 1JP, ✆ 220196, Fax 248721 – TV ☎ P – 60
28 rm.

XX **La Malmaison,** 17 Queens Rd, Hersham, KT12 5ND, ✆ 227412, French rest. – VISA
closed Saturday lunch and Sunday – **M** 14.50 **t.** (lunch) and a la carte 17.80/27.10 **t.** 4.20.

WALTON ON THE HILL Surrey – ✉ ☎ 0737 Tadworth.
London 19 – ♦Brighton 38.

XX Ebenezer Cottage, 36 Walton St., KT20 7RT, ✆ 813166, « 17C cottage » – .

WANSFORD Cambs. 404 S 26 – see Peterborough.

WANTAGE Oxon. 403 404 P 29 – pop. 9 708 – ECD : Thursday – ☎ 023 57.
Envir. : White Horse ←★.
London 75 – ♦Bristol 58 – ♦Oxford 15 – Reading 25.

Hotels and restaurants see : Swindon NW : 15 m.

ROVER Wallingford St. ✆ 3355
VW-AUDI Grove Rd ✆ 65511
ATS 76 Grove St. ✆ 66466/7

WARE Herts. 404 T 28 – pop. 15 344 – ECD : Thursday – ☎ 0920.
Chadwell Springs, Hertford Rd ✆ 463647.
London 24 – ♦Cambridge 30 – Luton 22.

Hanbury Manor, Thundridge, SG12 0SD, N : 1 ¾ m. by A 1170 on A 10 ✆ 487722, Telex 817515, Fax 487692, ←, « Jacobean style mansion in extensive grounds, walled garden », squash – rm rest TV ☎ P – 120. AE VISA.
M (booking essential) 21.50/38.00 **st.** and a la carte 6.00 – **90 rm** 135.00/195.00 **st.**, **5 suites** 225.00/325.00 **st.**

Ware Moat House (Q.M.H.), Baldock St., SG12 9DR, N : ½ m. on A 1170 ✆ 465011, Telex 817417, Fax 468016 – rm rest TV ☎ P – 120. AE VISA
closed 26 to 31 December – **M** *(closed Saturday lunch)* 12.50/14.50 **t.** and a la carte 4.85 – **50 rm** 70.00/85.00 **t.**

at Wadesmill N : 2 ¼ m. by A 1170 on A 10 – ✉ ☎ 0920 Ware :

Feathers Inn (B.C.B.), SG1 2ON, ✆ 462606 – TV ☎ P – 50. AE VISA.
M 15.00 **st.** – **22 rm** 44.50/59.50 **st.**

at Cold Christmas NE : 3 ¼ m. by A 1170 off A 10 – ✉ ☎ 0920 Ware :

XX **Fabdens Park** with rm, SG12 0UE, ✆ 463484, ←, « Attractively furnished part 15C house », park – TV ☎ P
closed February, 29 March and September – **M** *(closed Sunday and Monday)* (booking essential) (dinner only) 27.50 **t.** – **2 rm** 75.00/85.00 **st.**, **1 suite** 85.00 **st.**

WAREHAM Dorset 403 404 N 31 The West Country G. – pop. 2 771 – ECD : Wednesday – ☎ 0929.
See : Site★ – St. Martin's Church★★.
Envir. : Blue Pool★*AC*, S : 3 m. on A 351 – Smedmore★*AC*, S : 7 m. by A 351 – Bovington : Tank Museum★*AC*, W : 7 m. on A 352 – Lulworth Cove★, SW : 11 m. by A 352.
Lakey Hill, Hyde ✆ 471776 – 18 Sandford Rd ✆ 554147, NE : 1 m. on A 35.
Town Hall, East St. ✆ 552740.
London 123 – Bournemouth 13 – Weymouth 19.

Priory, Church Green, BH20 4ND, ✆ 551666, Telex 41143, Fax 554519, ←, « Tastefully renovated part 16C priory, riverside gardens », – TV ☎ P. AE VISA.
M 14.00/25.00 **t.** and a la carte 3.75 – **17 rm** 65.00/135.00 **t.**, **2 suites** 160.00 **t.** – SB (October-April) (except Bank Holidays) 132.00/200.50 **st.**

Kemps Country House, East Stoke, BH20 6AL, W : 2 ¾ m. on A 352 ✆ 0929 (Bindon Abbey) 462563, Fax 405287, – rest TV ☎ P. AE VISA.
M 7.50/14.95 **t.** and a la carte 3.25 – **15 rm** 54.00/79.00 **t.** – SB 75.00/125.00 **st.**

at Stoborough S : ½ m. on A 351 – ✉ ☎ 0929 Wareham :

Springfield Country, Grange Rd, BH20 5AL, ✆ 552177, Fax 551862, heated, – TV ☎ P – 25. AE VISA
M (bar lunch)/dinner 13.50 **t.** and a la carte 4.50 – **32 rm** 60.00/89.00 **t.** – SB 101.00/118.00 **st.**

Europe

Wenn der Name eines Hotels dünn gedruckt ist,
hat uns der Hotelier Preise
und Öffnungszeiten nicht angegeben.

WARMINSTER Wilts. 403 404 N 30 **The West Country G.** – pop. 14 826 – ECD : Wednesday – ☎ 0985.

Envir. : Longleat House★★★ *AC* SW : 6 m. – Bratton Castle (≤★★), NE : 6 m – Westbury H (White Horse★, ≤★), N : 6 m.

18 West Wiltshire, Elm Hill ☎ 212702.

Central Car Park, Three Horseshoes Mall ☎ 218548.

◆London 111 – ◆Bristol 29 – Exeter 74 – ◆Southampton 47.

Bishopstrow House ⑤, Boreham Rd, BA12 9HH, SE : 1 ½ m. on B 3414 ☎ 21231. Telex 444829, Fax 216769, ≤, « Tastefully furnished country house », ≘s, ⛱ heated, ⛱, ⛱, park, ✗ – TV ☎ P – 🏛 35. AE VISA
M 14.00/29.50 **t.** 9.50 – ☕ 6.50 – **29 rm** 80.00/110.00 **t.**, **3 suites** 260.00/272.00 **t.** SB (winter only) 162.00/304.00 **st.**

Granada Lodge without rest., BA12 8PF, NW : 1 m. by B 3414 on A 36 ☎ 21953 Fax 214380 – ⇔ TV ♿ P. AE VISA. ✗
32 rm 27.50/29.50 **st.**

Old Bell, 42 Market Pl., BA12 9AN, ☎ 216611, Fax 217111 – TV ☎ P. AE VISA
M a la carte 8.50/16.45 **t.** 3.00 – **24 rm** ☕ 36.00/54.00 **t.**

AUDI-VW 36 Victoria Rd ☎ 212893
FORD Boreham Rd ☎ 214777
MERCEDES-BENZ Corsley Heath ☎ 037 388 (Chapmanslade) 383
ROVER George St. ☎ 212808
VOLVO Fairfield Rd ☎ 213525

WARREN ROW Berks. – see Knowl Hill.

Die Stadtpläne sind eingenordet (Norden = oben).

WARREN STREET Kent – ✉ ☎ 0622 Maidstone.

◆London 51 – Folkestone 28 – Maidstone 12.

Harrow Inn, ME17 2ED, ☎ 858727, ⛱ – ☎ P. VISA. ✗
M 13.00 **st.** and a la carte 6.75 – **7 rm** ☕ 35.00/58.00 **st.** – SB (weekends only) 90.00 **st.**

WARRINGTON Cheshire 402 403 404 M 23 – pop. 81 366 – ECD : Thursday – ☎ 0925.

See : St. Elphin's Church (chancel★ 14C).

18 Hill Warren ☎ 61620, S : 3 m. – 18 Walton Hall, Warrington Rd ☎ 66775, S : 2 m. – 18 Kelvi Close, Birchwood ☎ 818819.

Rylands St. ☎ 36501/444400 ext. 2112.

◆London 195 – Chester 20 – ◆Liverpool 18 – ◆Manchester 21 – Preston 28.

Garden Court Holiday Inn, Woolston Grange Av., Woolston, WA1 4PX, E : 3¼ m. by A 57 at junction with M 6 ☎ 838779, Fax 838859 – |‡| ▤ rest TV ☎ ♿ P. AE VISA
M (dinner only) 15.00 **st.** and a la carte – ☕ 5.50 – **100 rm** 35.00/52.00 **st.**

Fir Grove, Knutsford Old Rd, WA4 2LD, SE : 2 m. by A 50 ☎ 67471, Telex 628117 Fax 601092 – TV ☎ P – 🏛 150. AE VISA. ✗
closed 25 December – **M** *(closed Saturday lunch and Bank Holidays)* 10.75 **st.** and a la cart 3.60 – **40 rm** ☕ 49.00/70.00 **st.**

at Stretton S : 3½ m. by A 49 on B 5356 – ✉ ☎ 0925 Warrington :

Old Vicarage, Stretton Rd, WA4 4NS, ☎ 73706, ⛱ – |‡| TV ☎ P. AE VISA
M 9.25/14.50 **t.** and a la carte 4.50 – **25 rm** ☕ 60.00/85.00 **t.** – SB (weekends only) (except Christmas) 70.00 **st.**

BMW Farrell St. ☎ 35987
FORD Winwick Rd ☎ 51111
HYUNDAI 194-196 Knutsford Rd ☎ 68444
ROVER Winwick St. ☎ 50011
ATS Grange Av., Latchford ☎ 32613

WARWICK Warw. 403 404 P 27 – pop. 21 701 – ECD : Thursday – ☎ 0926.

See : Castle★★ (14C) *AC* Y – St. Mary's Church★ (12C-18C) Y **A** – Lord Leycester's Hospital★ Y **B.**

9 The Racecourse ☎ 494316 Y.

The Court House, Jury St. ☎ 492212.

◆London 96 – ◆Birmingham 20 – ◆Coventry 11 – ◆Oxford 43.

Plan opposite

Park Cottage without rest., 113 West St., CV34 6AH, ☎ 410319, Fax 410319 – TV ☎ P ✗ Y e
closed Christmas-New Year – **4 rm** ☕ 36.00/50.00 **st.**

Pageant Lodge without rest., 2 Castle Lane, CV34 4BU, ☎ 491244 – TV. ✗ Y u
4 rm ☕ 20.00/40.00 **st.**

✗✗ **Randolph's,** 19-21 Coten End, CV34 4NT, ☎ 491292 – VISA Y i
closed Sunday and 24 to 31 December – **M** (dinner only) (booking essential) 30.00 **t** and a la carte **t.** 4.50.

WARWICK
ROYAL LEAMINGTON SPA

es plans de villes
ont disposés le Nord en haut.

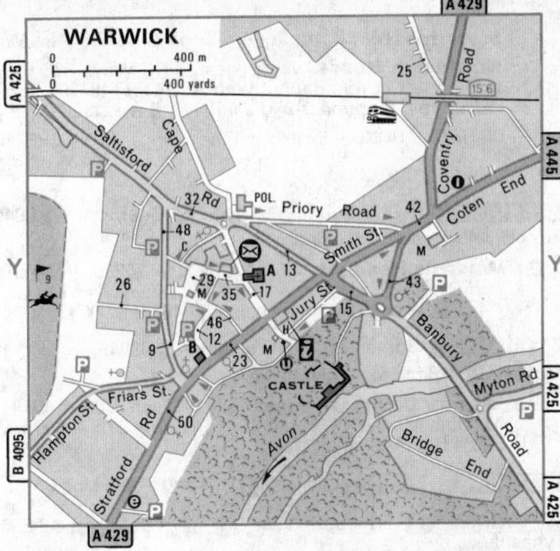

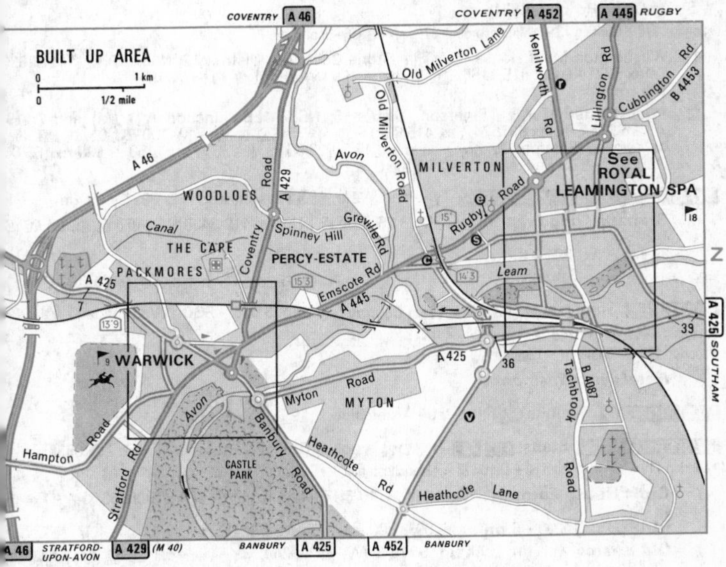

at Barford S : 4 ½ m. on A 429 – Z – ✉ 0926 Warwick :

Glebe, Church St., CV35 8BS, on B 4462 ✆ 624218, Fax 624625, – rest [TV] [P] – 120. AE VISA
M 18.50 **t.** (dinner) and a la carte 7.50 – **36 rm** 79.50/110.00 **t.**

at Longbridge SW : 2 m. on A 429 – Z – ✉ 0926 Warwick :

Hilton National, Stratford Rd, CV34 6RE, junction of A 429, A 46 and A 41 ✆ 499555, Telex 312468, Fax 410020, – rm [TV] [P] – 200. AE VISA.
M *(closed Saturday lunch)* 12.95/15.95 **st.** and a la carte 4.50 – 8.95 – **180 rm** 75.00/105.00 **st.** – SB (weekends only) 90.00 **st.**

at Sherbourne SW : 2 ¾ m. by A 429 – Z – ✉ 0926 Warwick :

Old Rectory without rest., Vicarage Lane, CV35 8AB, at junction with A 46 ✆ 624562, – [TV] [P]
closed 23 to 29 December – **14 rm** 27.00/42.00 **st.**

at Hatton NW : 3 ½m. by A 425–on A 4177 Z – ✉ Warwick – ☎ 0926 Haseley Knob

Northleigh House without rest., Five Ways Rd, CV35 7HZ, NW : 2 ½ m. by A 417 turning left at roundabout with A 4141 ☎ 484203, – TV P *closed mid December-mid January* – **6 rm** 26.00/45.00 **st.**

BMW, DIAHATSU, HONDA Heathcote Lane ☎ 452288
FIAT Wharf St. ☎ 496231
PORSCHE Birmingham Rd ☎ 491731
VOLVO Nelson Lane ☎ 400642

WASDALE HEAD Cumbria 402 K 20 – ✉ Gosforth – ☎ 09406 Wasdale.
◆London 324 – Kendal 72 – Workington 30.

Wasdale Head Inn, CA20 1EX, ☎ 26229, ≤ Wasdale Head – ☎ P. VISA
mid March-mid November and 29 December-mid January – **M** (bar lunch)/dinner 14.50 4.50 – **10 rm** (dinner included) 45.50/87.00 **t.**

WASHFORD Somerset – ✉ Watchet – ☎ 0984.
◆London 178 – ◆Bristol 55 – Tauton 16.

Langtry Country House, TA23 0NT, on A 39 ☎ 40484, – TV P. VISA.
M (dinner only) 11.50 **t.** and a la carte 2.95 – **6 rm** 36.00/48.00 **t.**, **1 suite** 48.00 **t.** SB 64.00/68.00 **st.**

WASHINGBOROUGH Lincs. 402 404 S 24 – see Lincoln.

WASHINGTON Tyne and Wear 401 402 P 19 – pop. 48 856 – ECD : Wednesday – ✉ ☎ 09 Tyneside.
Stone Cellar Rd ☎ 417 8346.
◆London 278 – Durham 13 – ◆Middlesbrough 32 – ◆Newcastle-upon-Tyne 7.

Washington Moat House (Q.M.H.), Stone Cellar Rd, District 12, NE37 1PH, ☎ 417 262 Telex 537143, Fax 415 1166, , , squash – rm TV ☎ P – 180
106 rm.

Post House (T.H.F.), Emerson, District 5, NE37 1LB, junction A 1 (M) and A 19 ☎ 416 2264, Telex 537574, Fax 415 3371 – rm TV ☎ P – 100. AE VISA
M *(closed Saturday lunch)* a la carte 13.30/23.65 **st.** 4.35 – 7.50 – **138 rm** 65.00 75.00 **st.** – SB (weekends only) 76.00 **st.**

WASHINGTON SERVICE AREA Tyne and Wear – ✉ Washington – ☎ 091 Tyneside

Granada Lodge without rest., DH3 2SJ, on A 1 (M) ☎ 410 3436 – TV P. AE VISA.
35 rm 27.50/29.50 **t.**

ARG Village Lane ☎ 415 0066
FORD Parsons Rd ☎ 4167700

WATCHET Somerset 403 J 30 **The West Country G.** – pop. 3 055 – ECD : Wednesday – ☎ 0984
Envir. : Cleeve Abbey★★ *AC*, SW : 2 m.
◆London 180 – ◆Bristol 57 – Taunton 18.

Hotel see : Washford

WATERHEAD Cumbria 402 L 20 – see Ambleside.

WATERHOUSES Staffs. 402 403 404 O 24 – pop. 1 018 – ✉ Stoke-on-Trent – ☎ 0538.
◆London 115 – ◆Birmingham 63 – Derby 23 – ◆Manchester 39 – ◆Stoke-on-Trent 17.

Croft House Farm, Waterfall, ST10 3HZ, N : 1 m. by A 523 ☎ 308553, – T P.
M 18.00 **st.** 3.00 – **6 rm** 17.00/31.00 **st.** – SB 46.00/50.00 **st.**

XX **Old Beams** with rm, Leek Rd, ST10 3HW, ☎ 308254, – rest TV ☎ P. AE VISA.
closed 2 weeks January – **M** *(closed Sunday dinner and Monday)* (booking essential) 12.75/26.50 **t.** 6.00 – **6 rm** 50.00/85.00 **t.** – SB (winter only) 100.00/140.00 **st.**

WATERINGBURY Kent 404 V 30 – see Maidstone.

WATERMILLOCK Cumbria 402 L 20 – see Ullswater.

WATERROW Somerset – see Wiveliscombe.

VATFORD Herts. 404 S 29 – pop. 109 503 – ECD : Wednesday – ☎ 0923.

ondon 21 – Aylesbury 23.

Plan : see Greater London (North-West)

Hilton National, Elton Way, WD2 8HA, Watford By-Pass, E : 3½ m. on A 41 at junction A 4008 ☎ 35881, Telex 923422, Fax 220836, – TV ☎ P – 450. AE VISA
M *(closed Saturday lunch)* 15.75 **t.** and a la carte 4.50 – 8.50 – **195 rm** 80.00/110.00 **t.**, **1 suite** 150.00 **t.** BT **e**

Dean Park (Q.M.H.), 30-40 St. Albans Rd, WD1 1RN, ☎ 229212, Telex 8813610, Fax 54638 – rm TV ☎ – 250. AE VISA. AT **c**
M *(closed Saturday lunch)* 12.00/14.00 **st.** and a la carte – **88 rm** 73.00/83.00 **st.**, **2 suites** 95.00 **st.** – SB 80.00 **st.**

UDI-VW 68 Chalk Hill ☎ 55055
ORD 201 High St. ☎ 37211
ONDA High Rd at Bushey Heath ☎ 081 (London) 50 3311
EUGEOT-TALBOT Aldenham ☎ 852177
VAUXHALL 73-75 High Rd ☎ 081 (London) 950 6146
VAUXHALL 329 St. Albans Rd ☎ 31716
ATS Lyon Way, Hatfield Rd, St. Albans ☎ 52314/5

VATH-IN-NIDDERDALE North Yorks. – see Pateley Bridge.

VDIG (GOODWICK) Dyfed – see Fishguard.

WEEDON BEC Northants. 403 404 Q 27 – pop. 2 361 – ECD : Wednesday – ✉ Northampton – ☎ 0327 Daventry.

London 74 – ♦Coventry 18 – Northampton 8 – ♦Oxford 41.

Heyford Manor (Lansbury), High St., Flore, NN7 4LP, E : 1½ m. on A 45 ☎ 349022, Telex 312437, Fax 349017, – rm TV ☎ P – 60
56 rm.

Heart of England (B.C.B.), Daventry Rd, NN7 4QD, ☎ 40335, – TV ☎ P
12 rm.

WELLAND Heref. and Worc. 403 404 N 27 – see Great Malvern.

WELLESBOURNE Warw. 403 404 P 27 – see Stratford-Upon-Avon.

WELLINGBOROUGH Northants. 404 R 27 – pop. 38 598 – ECD : Thursday – ☎ 0933.

Harrowden Hall, Great Harrowden ☎ 677 234 – Rushden, Kimbolton Rd, Chelveston ☎ 312581.

Library, Pebble Lane ☎ 228101.

London 73 – ♦Cambridge 43 – ♦Leicester 34 – Northampton 10.

Hind (Q.M.H.), Sheep St., NN8 1BY, ☎ 222827, Fax 441921 – rest TV ☎ P – 80. AE VISA
closed Christmas and New Year – **M** 20.00 **st.** and a la carte 3.95 – **34 rm** 58.00/76.00 **st.** – SB (weekends only) 70.00/76.00 **st.**

Columbia, 19 Northampton Rd, NN8 3HG, ☎ 229333, Fax 440418 – TV ☎ P. AE VISA.
closed Christmas – **M** 6.95/11.50 **st.** and a la carte 3.20 – **29 rm** 43.00/54.00 **st.** – SB (weekends only) 54.00 **st.**

at Hinwick (Beds.) SE : 6½ m. by A 509 via Wollaston – ✉ – ☎ 0933 Wellingborough (Northants.) :

XX **Flemish House,** NN9 7JE, ☎ 50012, Fax 316811 – P. AE VISA
closed Sunday dinner and Bank Holiday Mondays – **M** 10.00/33.00 **t.** and a la carte.

OVER Finedon Rd ☎ 76651
SKODA Talbot Rd ☎ 223924

WELLINGTON HEATH Heref. and Worc. 403 404 M 27 – see Ledbury.

WELLS Somerset 403 404 M 30 **The West Country G.** – pop. 9 252 – ECD : Wednesday – ☎ 0749.

See : Site★★ – Cathedral★★★ – Vicar's Close★ – Bishop's Palace★*AC* (<★★ of east end of cathedral).

Envir. : Wookey Hole★★*AC* (Caves★, Papermill★, Fairground collection★), NW : 2 m.

East Horrington Rd ☎ 72868.

Town Hall, Market Pl. ☎ 72552.

♦London 132 – ♦Bristol 20 – ♦Southampton 68 – Taunton 28.

Swan (Best Western), 11 Sadler St., BA5 2RX, ☎ 78877, Telex 449658, Fax 77647 – TV ☎ P – 60. AE VISA
M 10.50/14.50 **t.** and a la carte 4.50 – **32 rm** 55.00/82.50 **t.** – SB 95.00/105.00 **st.**

Star, 14 High St., BA5 2SQ, ☎ 73055, Fax 72654 – TV. AE VISA
M 6.25/13.50 **st.** and a la carte 4.50 – 5.25 – **12 rm** 39.00/45.00 **st.** – SB 64.00 **st.**

at Worth W : 2 ¾ m. by A 371 on B 3139 – ☎ 0749 Wells :

Worth House, BA5 1LW, ☎ 72041, – P. VISA.
M (bar lunch)/dinner 12.00/16.00 **st.** – **7 rm** 20.00/40.00 **st.** – SB 50.00 **st.**

CITROEN Long St., Croscombe ☎ 26601
ROVER, LAND-ROVER Glastonbury Rd ☎ 72626
VAUXHALL-OPEL Westfield Rd ☎ 74437

WELLS-NEXT-THE-SEA Norfolk 404 W 25 – ☎ 0328 Fakenham.

Staithe St. ☎ 710885.

◆London 117 – King's Lynn 31 – ◆Norwich 36.

Moorings, 6 Freeman St., NR23 1BA, ☎ 710949
closed Thursday lunch, Tuesday and Wednesday – **M** (booking essential) 15.00/20.00 **t.**

FORD Polka Rd ☎ 710213

WELSH HOOK Dyfed – see Fishguard.

WELSHPOOL **(TRALLWNG)** Powys 402 403 K 26 – pop. 4 869 – ECD : Thursday – ☎ 0938.

Envir. : Powis Castle★★ S : 1 m.

Y Golfa Hill ☎ 3377.

Vicarage Garden Car Park ☎ 552043.

◆London 182 – ◆Birmingham 64 – Chester 45 – Shrewsbury 19.

Royal Oak, The Cross, SY21 7DG, ☎ 552217 – TV ☎ P. AE VISA.
M 9.00/12.00 **t.** and a la carte 3.50 – **25 rm** 32.50/57.50 **t.** – SB (weekends only) 60.0
64.00 **st.**

Tynllwyn Farm, SY21 9BW, N : 1 ½ m. on A 490 ☎ 553175, ≤, « Working farm »
TV P.
M 6.50 **s.** – **6 rm** 14.00/24.00 **s.** – SB (October-March) 36.00 **st.**

FORD Salop Rd ☎ 552391
VAUXHALL-OPEL Newtown Rd ☎ 554444

WELWYN Herts. 404 T 28 – pop. 9 961 (inc. Codicote) – ECD : Wednesday – ☎ 0438.

◆London 30 – Bedford 31 – ◆Cambridge 32.

Heath Lodge, Danesbury Park Rd, AL6 9SN, NE : 2 m. by B 197, Canonsfield Rd an
Potters Heath Rd ☎ 840000, Telex 827618, Fax 8500, , park – rm rest TV ☎ P
50. AE VISA
M a la carte 18.65/31.65 **st.** – **8.95** – **25 rm** 72.00 **st.**, **22 suites** 150.00 **st.**

COLT 54 Great North Rd ☎ 5911
FORD By Pass Rd ☎ 6123

WELWYN GARDEN CITY Herts. 404 T 28 – pop. 40 665 – ECD : Wednesday – ☎ 0707 We
wyn Garden.

Panshanger ☎ 339507 – Mannicotts, High Oaks Rd ☎ 322722.

The Campus West ☎ 332880.

◆London 28 – Bedford 34 – ◆Cambridge 34.

Crest (T.H.F.), Homestead Lane, AL7 4LX, SW : 1 ¼ m. by B 195 and Heronswood Rd o
Cole Green Lane ☎ 324336, Telex 261523, Fax 326447, – rm TV ☎ P – 8
AE VISA
M 12.50/23.50 **st.** and a la carte – 7.95 – **58 rm** 74.00/87.00 **st.** – SB (weekend
only) 94.00 **st.**

LADA Great North Rd ☎ 070 72 (Hatfield) 64567
ATS 17 Tewin rd. ☎ 371619

WENTBRIDGE West Yorks. 402 404 Q 23 – ✉ ☎ 0977 Pontefract.

◆London 183 – ◆Leeds 19 – ◆Nottingham 55 – ◆Sheffield 28.

Wentbridge House, Great North Rd, WF8 3JJ, ☎ 620444, Fax 620148, – TV ☎ P
120. AE VISA.
closed Christmas Night – **M** 17.80 **t.** (lunch) and a la carte 22.75/31.45 **t.** 5.75 – **12 rm**
60.00/100.00 **st.**

WEOBLEY Heref. and Worc. 403 L 27 – pop. 1 080 – ECD : Wednesday – ✉ Hereford
☎ 0544.

◆London 145 – Brecon 30 – Hereford 12 – Leominster 9.

Red Lion, Broad St., HR4 8SE, ☎ 318220, – TV ☎ P
7 rm.

WEST BAGBOROUGH Somerset 403 K 30 – ✉ Taunton – ☎ 0823.

◆London 176 – ◆Bristol 49 – Minehead 19 – Tauton 8.

Higher House, TA4 3EF, ☎ 432996, ≤, heated, – TV ☎ P. VISA
M (communal dining) (dinner only) 15.00 **st.** 4.50 – **6 rm** 27.00/55.00 **st.** – SB 60.00
85.00 **st.**

WEST BAY Dorset 403 L 31 – see Bridport.

WEST BEXINGTON Dorset – ✉ Dorchester – ☎ 0308 Burton Bradstock.

London 150 – Bournemouth 43 – Bridport 6 – Weymouth 13.

Manor, Beach Rd, DT2 9DF, ℘ 897616, ≤, 🐾 – TV ☎ P. AE VISA.
M 13.50/17.45 **t.** 2.95 – **13 rm** 35.95/59.90 **t.** – SB 82.50/89.50 **st.**

WEST BRIDGFORD Notts. 403 404 Q 25 – see Nottingham.

WEST BROMWICH West Midlands 403 404 O 26 – see Birmingham.

WESTBROOK Wilts. – see Melksham.

WEST CHILTINGTON West Sussex 404 S 31 – pop. 2 044 – ECD : Wednesday and Thursday – ✉ Pulborough – ☎ 0798.

Broadford Bridge Rd ℘ 3574.

London 50 – Brighton 22 – Worthing 12.

Roundabout (Best Western), Monkmead Lane, RH20 2PF, S : 1 ¼ m. ℘ 813838, Fax 812962, – TV ☎ P – 45. AE VISA
M 11.00/18.35 **st.** and a la carte 4.95 – **20 rm** 60.00/96.75 **st.** – SB 89.00/96.00 **st.**

WEST COKER Somerset 403 404 M 31 – see Yeovil.

WESTERHAM Kent 404 U 30 – pop. 3 392 – ECD : Wednesday – ☎ 0959.

Envir. : Chartwell★ (Sir Winston Churchill's country home, Museum) *AC*, S : 2 m.

London 24 – Brighton 45 – Maidstone 22.

Kings Arms, Market Sq., TN16 1AN, ℘ 62990 – TV ☎ P
17 rm.

XXX **Cope's Oyster House,** Quebec Sq., Brasted Rd, TN16 1TE, on A 25 ℘ 62139, Fax 62877, – P. AE VISA
closed Saturday lunch and Sunday dinner – **M** 26.00 **t.** and a la carte 21.00/44.00 **t.**

VW-AUDI London Rd ℘ 64333

WEST HADDON Northants. 403 404 Q 26 – see Rugby.

WEST HUNTSPILL Somerset 403 L 30 – see Bridgwater.

WESTLETON Suffolk 404 Y 27 – pop. 493 – ECD : Wednesday – ✉ Saxmundham – ☎ 072 873.

London 72 – Cambridge 72 – Ipswich 28 – Norwich 31.

Crown, IP17 3AD, ℘ 273, – rest TV ☎ P.
19 rm.

WEST LULWORTH Dorset 403 404 N 32 – pop. 910 – ECD : Wednesday – ✉ Wareham – ☎ 092 941.

See : Lulworth Cove★.

London 129 – Bournemouth 21 – Dorchester 17 – Weymouth 19.

Cromwell House, Main Rd, BH20 5RJ, ℘ 253, Fax 566, ≤, – TV ☎ P
14 rm.

Gatton House, Main Rd, BH20 5RU, ℘ 252, – rest TV P. VISA
closed 2 to 14 January – **M** 15.00 **st.** 3.50 – **8 rm** 25.00/50.00 **st.** – SB (October-March) 65.00/80.00 **st.**

WEST MALVERN Heref. and Worc. 403 404 M 27 – see Great Malvern.

WEST MERSEA Essex 404 W 28 – pop. 5 245 – ✉ Colchester – ☎ 0206.

London 58 – Chelmsford 27 – Colchester 9.5.

XX **Le Champenois, Blackwater H.** with rm, 20-22 Church Rd, CO5 8QH, ℘ 383338 – TV P. AE VISA.
closed 8 January-4 February – **M** *(closed Tuesday lunch and Sunday dinner)* 13.50 **t.** (lunch) and a la carte 13.70/23.60 **t.** 4.20 – **7 rm** 28.00/65.00 **t.** – SB (except Sunday, Christmas and Bank Holidays) 70.00/85.00 **st.**

WESTON Devon 403 K 31 – see Honiton.

WESTONBIRT Glos. 403 404 N 29 – see Tetbury.

WESTON FAVELL Northants. 404 R 27 – see Northampton.

WESTON-ON-THE-GREEN Oxon. 403 404 Q 28 – pop. 479 – ✉ ☎ 0869 Bletchington.
◆London 65 – ◆Birmingham 61 – Northampton 33 – ◆Oxford 8.

Weston Manor (Best Western), on A 43, OX6 8QL, ☎ 50621, Telex 83409, Fax 50901, heated, park, squash – TV ☎ P – 30. AE VISA.
M 17.00/21.00 **t.** and a la carte 5.65 – **36 rm** 75.00/110.00 **t.**, **1 suite** 80.00/120.00 **t.** SB 100.00/110.00 **st.**

WESTON-SUPER-MARE Avon 403 K 29 **The West Country G.** – pop. 60 821 – ECD : Thursday – ☎ 0934.

See : Sea front ≤★★.

18 Worlebury, Monks Hill ☎ 623214, 2 m. from station BY – 18 Uphill Rd ☎ 621360 AZ.

Beach Lawns ☎ 626838.

◆London 147 – ◆Bristol 24 – Taunton 32.

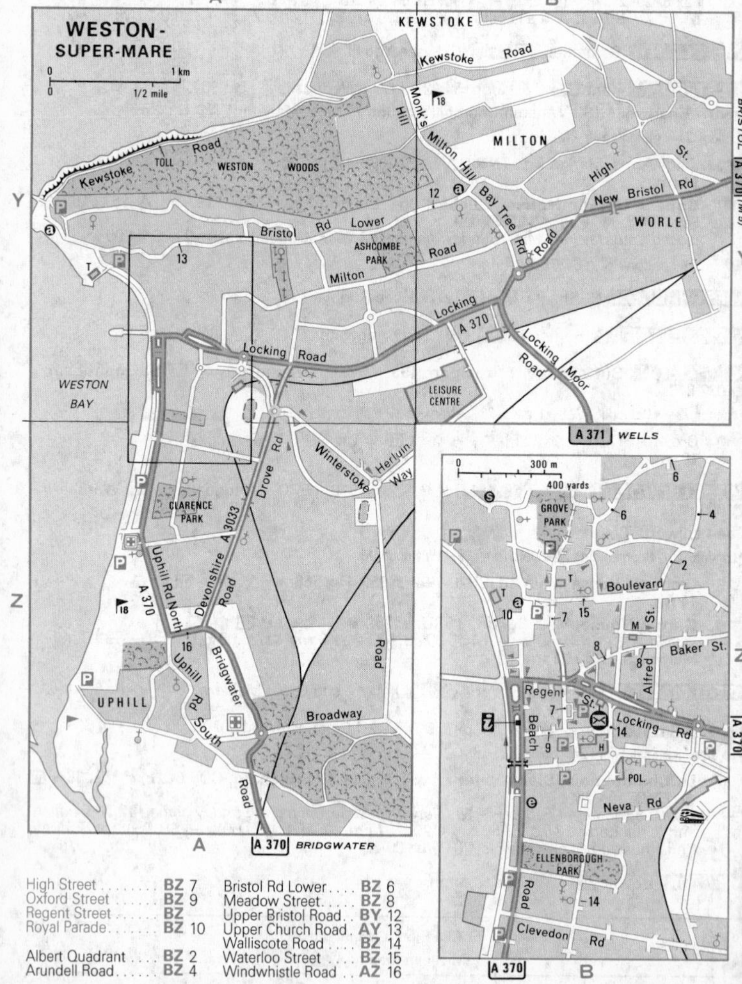

High Street	BZ 7	Bristol Rd Lower	BZ 6
Oxford Street	BZ 9	Meadow Street	BZ 8
Regent Street	BZ	Upper Bristol Road	BY 12
Royal Parade	BZ 10	Upper Church Road	AY 13
		Walliscote Road	BZ 14
Albert Quadrant	BZ 2	Waterloo Street	BZ 15
Arundell Road	BZ 4	Windwhistle Road	AZ 16

Grand Atlantic (T.H.F.), Beach Rd, BS23 1BA, ℘ 626543, Fax 415048, ≤, heated, – rm – 200. AE VISA BZ **e**
M 9.50/12.95 **st.** and a la carte 4.05 – 7.50 – **76 rm** 59.00/109.00 **st.** – SB 80.00/108.00 **st.**

Royal Pier (Best Western), 55-57 Birnbeck Rd, BS23 2EJ, ℘ 626644, Fax 624169, ≤ Weston Bay and Bristol Channel – – 65. AE VISA. AY **a**
M 11.80/14.00 **t.** and a la carte 4.00 – **38 rm** 46.50/66.00 **t.**, **2 suites** 77.00 **t.** – SB 72.50/83.50 **st.**

Berni Royal (B.C.B.), South Par., BS23 1JN, ℘ 623601, – – 40. AE VISA. BZ **a**
M 15.00 **st.** – **36 rm** 48.50/70.00 **st.**

Queenswood, 17 Victoria Park, BS23 2HZ, ℘ 416141, Fax 621759, ≤ – . AE VISA BZ **s**
closed Christmas and New Year – **M** (bar lunch)/dinner 11.50 **st.** 3.00 – **18 rm** 29.50/59.00 **st.**

Duets, 103 Upper Bristol Rd, BS22 8ND, ℘ 413428 – VISA BY **a**
closed Sunday dinner, Monday and 2 weeks January – **M** (lunch by arrangement)/dinner 12.95 **t.** and a la carte 16.65/18.65 **st.** 4.50.

ALFA-ROMEO Hewish ℘ 832078
AUDI-VW Winterstoke Rd ℘ 632541
CITROEN Baker St. ℘ 623995
FORD Winterstoke Rd ℘ 628291
HONDA Bridgwater Rd ℘ 0934 (Bleadon) 812244
NISSAN Herwin Way ℘ 416454
PEUGEOT-TALBOT Broadway ℘ 0934 (Bleadon) 812479
RENAULT Locking Rd ℘ 414007
ROVER Alfred St. ℘ 621451
VAUXHALL-OPEL Winterstoke Rd ℘ 419526
VOLVO 106-110 Milton Rd ℘ 626428

WESTON-UNDER-PENYARD Heref. and Worc. 403 404 M 28 – see Ross-On-Wye.

WEST PENNARD Somerset 403 M 30 – see Glastonbury.

WEST RUNTON Norfolk 404 X 25 – ECD : Wednesday – ✉ Cromer – 026 375.

Links Country Park Hotel ℘ 691.

♦London 135 – King's Lynn 42 – ♦Norwich 24.

Links Country Park, Sandy Lane, NR27 9QH, ℘ 691, Fax 8264, , , 9, , – – 50. VISA
M (bar lunch Monday to Saturday)/dinner 17.20 **st.** and a la carte 3.75 – **31 rm** (dinner included) 67.00/150.00 **st.** – SB 96.00/115.00 **st.**

Mirabelle, 7 Station Rd, NR27 9QD, ℘ 396 – . AE VISA
closed Sunday dinner November-May, Monday and first 2 weeks November – **M** 14.50/20.00 **t.** and a la carte 3.75.

WEST SCRAFTON North Yorks. – see Middleham.

WEST STOUR Dorset – pop. 144 – ✉ Gillingham – 074 785 East Stour.

♦London 119 – Bournemouth 35 – Salisbury 28 – Yeovil 15.

Ship Inn, SP8 5RP, on A 30 ℘ 640, – – **6 rm.**

WEST WITTON North Yorks. 402 O 21 – pop. 338 – ✉ Leyburn – 0969 Wensleydale.

♦London 241 – Kendal 39 – ♦Leeds 60 – York 53.

Wensleydale Heifer, Main St., DL8 4LS, ℘ 22322, Fax 24183, – . AE VISA
M (bar lunch Monday to Saturday)/dinner 17.50 **st.** 3.95 – **19 rm** 45.00/70.00 **st.**

WETHERAL Cumbria 401 402 L 19 – see Carlisle.

WETHERBY West Yorks. 402 P 22 – pop. 9 467 – ECD : Wednesday – 0937.

18 Linton Lane ℘ 63375.

Council Offices, 24 Westgate ℘ 62706.

♦London 208 – Harrogate 8 – ♦Leeds 13 – York 14.

Wood Hall , Trip Lane, Linton, LS22 4JA, SW : 3 m. by A 661 and Winton Rd ℘ 67271, Fax 64353, ≤, « Part Jacobean and Georgian country house in park », , – . AE VISA
M *(closed Saturday lunch)* 16.95/29.50 **t.** and a la carte 8.00 – **20 rm** 85.00/105.00 **t.**, **2 suites** 145.00/225.00 **t.** – SB (weekends only) 150.00/170.00 **st.**

Penguin, Leeds Rd, LS22 5HE, junction A 58 and A 1 ℘ 63881, Telex 556428, Fax 580062 – rm – 160. AE VISA
M (carving lunch)/dinner a la carte 13.00/17.50 **st.** 3.50 – 7.00 – **72 rm** 63.00/75.00 **st.** – SB (weekends only) 75.00/90.00 **st.**

Linton Spring , Sicklinghall Rd, LS22 4AF, W : 1 ¾ m. by A 661 ℘ 65353, Fax 67579, , park – – **8 rm**, **1 suite.**

ROVER North St. ℘ 62623

WETHERSFIELD Essex 404 V 28 – ✉ ☎ 0371 Great Dunmow

XX **Dicken's,** The Green, CM7 4BS, ☎ 850723 – Ⓟ. VISA
closed Sunday dinner, Monday, February and Bank Holidays – **M** a la carte 19.60/23.75 ₰ 5.00.

WEYBOURNE Norfolk 404 X 25 – pop. 553 – ✉ Holt – ☎ 026 370.

♦London 128 – Cromer 7.5 – ♦Norwich 26.

Maltings, The Street, NR25 6SY, on A 149 ☎ 731, – TV ☎ Ⓟ
21 rm.

WEYBRIDGE Surrey 404 S 29 – pop. 50 031 (inc. Walton-on-Thames) – ECD : Wednesday – ☎ 0932.

18, 9 St George's Hill ☎ 842406 – 18 New Zealand, Woodham Lane ☎ 093 23 (Woodham) 45049.

♦London 23.

Plan : see Greater London (South-West)

Ship Thistle (Mt. Charlotte Thistle), Monument Green, High St., KT13 8BQ, ☎ 84836, Telex 894271, Fax 857153 – TV ☎ Ⓟ – 110. AE VISA by A 3050 AY
M 10.00/14.00 **st.** and a la carte – 7.75 – **39 rm** 79.00/100.00 **st.** – SB 88.00 **st.**

XXX **Casa Romana,** 2 Temple Hall, Monument Hill, KT13 8RH, ☎ 843470, Italian rest. – Ⓟ. AE VISA by A 3050 AY
closed Saturday lunch and 25-26 December – **M** 14.95/16.50 **t.** and a la carte ₰ 4.00.

XX Colony, 3 Balfour Rd, KT13 8HE, ☎ 842766, Chinese (Peking) rest. by A 317 AZ

X Gaylord, 73 Queens Rd, KT13 9UQ, E : ¾ m. on A 317 ☎ 842895, Indian rest. by A 317 AZ

FORD Brooklands Rd ☎ 093 23 (Byfleet) 52941
MERCEDES Spinney Hill, Addlestone ☎ 093 287 (Ottershaw) 3726
ROVER 30 Queens Rd ☎ 842233
TOYOTA 51-59 Baker St. ☎ 848247
VAUXHALL-OPEL New Haw Rd ☎ 853101
VOLVO 168 Oatlands Drive ☎ 854422

Le piante topografiche sono orientate col Nord in alto.

WEYMOUTH Dorset 403 404 M 32 **The West Country G.** – pop. 38 384 – ECD : Wednesday – ☎ 0305.

See : Boat Trip★ (Weymouth Bay and Portland Harbour).

Envir. : Chesil Beach★★ (from Portland★ (S : 1½ m.) to Abbotsbury) – at Abbotsbury★★, NW : 9 m. by B 3157 Swannery Gardens★*AC*, Sub Tropical Gardens★*AC*, St. Catherines Chapel★*AC*.

18 Weymouth, off Manor roundabout ☎ 784994.

Shipping connections with the Continent : to France (Cherbourg) (Sealink) (summer only) (Weymouth Maritime Services) (restricted service in winter) – to Channel Islands : Jersey (St. Helier, via Guernsey and Alderney) (Weymouth Maritime Services).

to Channel Islands : Guernsey (St. Peter Port) and Jersey (St. Helier) (Condor : hydrofoil) (summer only).

Pavilion Theatre Complex, The Esplanade ☎ 772444 (summer only) – The Esplanade ☎ 785747.

♦London 142 – Bournemouth 35 – ♦Bristol 68 – Exeter 59 – Swindon 94.

Streamside, 29 Preston Rd, Overcombe, DT3 6PX, NE : 2 m. on A 353 ☎ 833121, – TV ☎ Ⓟ. AE VISA
M 9.95 **t.** (dinner) and a la carte 10.15/21.20 **t.** – **15 rm** 42.00/64.00 **t.** – SB (October-April) 60.00/80.00 **st.**

Glenburn, 42 Preston Rd, Overcombe, DT3 6PZ, NE : 2 m. on A 353 ☎ 832353 – TV Ⓟ. VISA.
M 10.00 **t.** and a la carte ₰ 3.75 – **13 rm** 27.00/52.00 **t.** – SB (October-March) 65.00/72.00 **st.**

Rex, 29 The Esplanade, DT4 8DN, ☎ 760400 – TV ☎. AE VISA
M (dinner only) 6.50 **t.** and a la carte ₰ 3.00 – **31 rm** 33.00/66.00 **t.** – SB 56.00/64.00 **st.**

Sou'West Lodge without rest., Rodwell Rd, DT4 8QT, ☎ 783749 – TV Ⓟ
closed 2 weeks Christmas – **9 rm** 15.50/38.00 **st.**

FIAT 172 Dorchester Rd ☎ 786311
FORD 48-62 Dorchester Rd ☎ 782222

WHALLEY Lancs. 402 M 22 – pop. 4 745 – ✉ Blackburn – ☎ 025 482.

9 Long Leese Barn, Clerkhill ☎ 2236.

♦London 233 – ♦Blackpool 32 – Burnley 12 – ♦Manchester 28 – Preston 15.

Mytton Fold Farm, Whalley Rd., Langho, BB6 8AB, SW : 1 ¾ m. ☎ 0254 (Blackburn) 240662, Fax 248119, – TV ☎ Ⓟ. VISA.
M 7.50 **t.** (lunch) and a la carte 9.90/19.70 **t.** ₰ 3.75 – **27 rm** 46.00/60.00 **t.** – SB (weekends only) (except Christmas and New Year) 67.50 **st.**

XX **Northcote Manor** with rm, Northcote Rd, Langho, BB6 8BE, SW : 2 m. on A 59 ☎ 0254 (Blackburn) 240555, Fax 246568, – TV ☎ Ⓟ. AE VISA.
M 14.00 **t.** (lunch) and a la carte 19.05/30.10 **t.** – **6 rm** 60.00/70.00 **t.**

WHAPLODE Lincs. 402 404 T 25 – pop. 1 885 – ✉ Spalding – ☎ 0406 Holbeach.
♦London 106 – Lincoln 45 – ♦Leicester 61 – ♦Norwich 60.

Guy Wells without rest., Eastgate, PE12 6TZ, E : ½ m. by A 151 ☎ 22239, « Queen Anne house », – P.
closed last 2 weeks December and first week January – **3 rm** 20.00/30.00 **st.**

WHARRAM-LE-STREET North Yorks. – see Malton.

WHEATLEY Oxon. 403 404 Q 28 – see Oxford.

WHEDDON CROSS Somerset 403 J 30 – ✉ Minehead – ☎ 0643 Timberscombe.
See : Vantage Point★.
♦London 191 – Exeter 36 – Taunton 29.

Higherley House, TA24 7EB, W : ½ m. on B 3224 ☎ 841582, ←, – P. VISA
M 12.00 **st.** 1.75 – **5 rm** 16.75/53.00 **st.** – SB (winter only) 48.00/58.00 **st.**

WHETSTONE Leics. – see Leicester.

WHIMPLE Devon 403 J 31 – see Exeter.

WHITBY North Yorks. 402 S 20 – pop. 12 982 – ECD : Wednesday – ☎ 0947.
See : Abbey ruins★ (13C) *AC*, Old St. Mary's Church★ (12C), East Terrace ←★.
18 Low Straggleton ☎ 602768.
New Quay Rd ☎ 602674.
♦London 257 – ♦Middlesbrough 31 – Scarborough 21 – York 45.

Larpool Hall Country House, Larpool Lane, YO22 4ND, ☎ 602737, ←, – rest TV ☎ P. VISA.
M 9.50/25.00 **t.** and a la carte 3.95 – **12 rm** 28.50/60.00 **t.** – SB (except Bank Holidays) 70.00/90.00 **st.**

at Sneaton S : 3 m. by A 171 on B 1416 – ✉ ☎ 0947 Whitby :

Sneaton Hall, YO22 5HP, ☎ 605929, – TV P. VISA
M (bar lunch)/dinner 13.00 **t.** 3.00 – **8 rm** 29.00/45.00 **t.** – SB 60.00/65.00 **st.**

at Sleights SW : 4 m. by A 171 on A 169 – ✉ Bruggswath – ☎ 0947 Whitby :

Willow Dale without rest., 17 Carr Hill Lane, Briggswath, YO21 1RS, N : ½ m. by A 169 ☎ 810525, – TV P
3 rm.

at Dunsley W : 3¼ m. by A 171 – ✉ ☎ 0947 Whitby :

Dunsley Hall, YO21 3TL, ☎ 83437, ←, , , , – TV P. VISA
M *(closed Sunday)* (dinner only) 15.00 **t.** 3.45 – **7 rm** 50.00/64.00 **t.** – SB (October-June) (except Sunday and Bank Holidays) 70.00/75.00 **st.**

FORD Silver St. ☎ 602237
NISSAN Castle Park ☎ 602841
RENAULT 18 Silver St. ☎ 602093
ROVER 6 Upgang Lane ☎ 603321
ROVER ☎ 0287 (Castleton) 660203
VAUXHALL Argyle Rd ☎ 602898/602238

WHITCHURCH Bucks. 404 R 28 – ✉ ☎ 0296 Aylesbury.
♦London 50 – Luton 27 – ♦Oxford 32.

XX **Priory** with rm, 70-72 High St., HP22 4JS, ☎ 641239, « Tudor house », – TV ☎ P. AE VISA
M *(closed Sunday)* 21.00/35.00 **t.** 4.75 – **11 rm** 57.00/103.50 **t.**

WHITCHURCH Shropshire 402 403 404 L 25 – pop. 7 246 – ECD : Wednesday – ☎ 0948.
18 Hill Valley, Terrick Rd ☎ 3584, N : 1 m.
Civic Centre, High St. ☎ 4577.
♦London 171 – ♦Birmingham 54 – Chester 22 – ♦Manchester 43 – Shrewsbury 20.

Redbrook Hunting Lodge, Wrexham Rd, SY13 3ET, W : 2 ½ m. on A 525 ☎ 094 873 (Redbrook Maelor) 204, Fax 533, – TV ☎ P. AE VISA.
M 9.25 **t.** and a la carte 3.00 – **12 rm** 40.00/55.00 **t.**

FORD Brownlow St. ☎ 2826
RENAULT Wrexham Rd ☎ 2257
ROVER Newport Rd ☎ 3333
ATS The Wharf, Mill St. ☎ 2491/2701

WHITEBROOK Gwent – see Monmouth.

WHITFIELD Kent 404 X 30 – see Dover.

Great Britain and Ireland are covered entirely at a scale of 16 miles to 1 inch by our map « Main roads » 986.

WHITLAND **(HENDY-GWYN)** Dyfed 403 G 28 – pop. 1 342 – ECD : Wednesday – ☎ 0994.
◆London 235 – Carmarthen 15 – Haverfordwest 17.

⌂ **Cilpost Farm** ⛰, SA34 0RP, N : 1 ¼ m. by North Rd ☎ 240280, ≤, « Working dair farm », ☰, ⌂, ⚘ – Ⓟ. ✗
April-September – **7 rm** ☐ 15.00/20.00.

BMW Green Bower ☎ 0437 (Haverfordwest) 86251 — ATS Emporium Garage, Market St. ☎ 240587

WHITSTABLE Kent 404 X 29 – pop. 26 227 – ECD : Wednesday – ☎ 0227.
Envir. : Herne Bay : Reculver (church twin towers★ *AC*), E : 8 ½ m.
⛳18 Chestfield Rd ☎ 022 779 (Chestfield) 4411, SE : 2 m. by A 299 – ⛳9 Collingwood Rd ☎ 272020
ℹ Horsebridge ☎ 275482.
◆London 59 – ◆Dover 22 – Maidstone 28 – Margate 19.

✗ **Shapla,** 36 Harbour St., CT5 1AJ, ☎ 262454, Indian rest – AE ⓓ VISA
M a la carte approx. 7.10 **t.** 3.10.

FORD Tankerton Rd ☎ 770880 — RENAULT Tower Par. ☎ 261477

WHITTLE-LE-WOODS Lancs. 402 M 23 – see Chorley.

WHITWELL-ON-THE-HILL North Yorks. 402 R 21 – pop. 131 – ✉ York – ☎ 065 381.
◆London 223 – Malton 5 – York 12.

🏨 **Whitwell Hall Country House** ⛰, YO6 7JJ, ☎ 551, Fax 554, ≤, ⌂, ⚘, park, ✗ – ⇆ rest TV ☎ Ⓟ – 🏛 40. AE VISA. ✗
M 11.00/21.50 **st.** 4.00 – **23 rm** ☐ 54.00/105.00 **st.** – SB (November-April) 90.00 **st.**

WICKHAM Hants. 403 404 Q 31 – pop. 3 485 – ECD : Wednesday – ☎ 0329.
◆London 74 – ◆Portsmouth 12 – ◆Southampton 11 – Winchester 16.

🏨 Old House, The Square, PO17 5JG, ☎ 833049, Fax 833672, « Queen Anne house », ⚘ – TV ☎ Ⓟ. AE ⓓ VISA. ✗
closed 2 weeks Easter, 2 weeks July-August and 2 weeks at Christmas – **M** *(closed lunch Monday and Saturday and Sunday)* – **12 rm** ☐ 70.00/90.00 **st.**

WIDEGATES Cornwall 403 G 32 – see Looe.

WIDNES Cheshire 402 403 404 L 23 – pop. 55 973 – ☎ 051 Liverpool.
⛳18 Highfield Rd ☎ 424 2440 – ⛳18 Dundalk Rd ☎ 424 0989.
ℹ Municipal Building Kingsway ☎ 424 2061.
◆London 205 – ◆Liverpool 19 – ◆Manchester 27 – ◆Stoke-on-Trent 42.

🏨 **Hillcrest,** Cronton Lane, Cronton, WA8 9AR, N : 2 m. by A 568 on A 5080 ☎ 424 1616, Telex 627098, Fax 495 1348 – TV ☎ Ⓟ. AE ⓓ VISA
M *(closed Saturday lunch)* 10.50 **st.** and a la carte 3.90 – **57 rm** ☐ 45.00/52.50 **st.** – SB (June-September) (weekends only) 70.00/90.00 **st.**

CITROEN Ditton Rd ☎ 4244516
PEUGEOT-TALBOT Hole Rd ☎ 4242207
VAUXHALL 200 Peelhouse Lane ☎ 4231661
YUGO Halebank Rd ☎ 4862840
ATS Hale Rd, Halebank ☎ 424 3011/2945

WIGHT (Isle of) 403 404 PQ 31 32 – pop. 118 594.
⛴ from East to West Cowes to Southampton (Red Funnel Services) frequent services daily – from Yarmouth to Lymington (Sealink) frequent services daily (30 mn) – from Fishbourne to Portsmouth (Sealink) frequent services daily (35 mn).
⛴ from West Cowes to Southampton (Red Funnel services : hydrofoil) frequent services daily (20 mn) – from Ryde to Southsea (Hovertravel to Southsea Clarence Pier) summer frequent services daily – from Ryde to Portsmouth (Sealink to Portsmouth Harbour) frequent services daily (15 mn).

PEUGEOT-TALBOT Church Rd ☎ 872121

Chale – pop. 561 – ECD : Thursday – ✉ Ventnor – ☎ 0983 Isle of Wight.
Newport 9.

🏨 **Clarendon,** Newport Rd, PO38 2HA, ☎ 730431, ≤, ⚘ – TV Ⓟ.
M 10.00/12.00 **st.** and a la carte 3.00 – **13 rm** ☐ 21.00/45.00 **t.** – SB (October-May) 60.00/64.00 **st.**

Cowes – pop. 16 371 – ECD : Wednesday – ✉ ☎ 0983 Isle of Wight.

Envir. : Osborne House★ (19C) *AC*, E : 1 m.

Osborne, East Cowes ☎ 295421, E : by A 3021 – Crossfield Av. ☎ 292303.

4 Marina Walk ☎ 291914 (summer only).

Newport 4.

Fountain (Lansbury), High St., PO31 7AW, ☎ 292397, Telex 86481 – TV ☎. AE VISA.
M 8.75 **t.** (lunch) and a la carte 9.90/17.75 **t.** – **20 rm** 48.00/60.00 **t.** – SB (weekends only) 60.00 **st.**

Freshwater Bay – pop. 5 073 – ECD : Thursday – ✉ ☎ 0983 Isle of Wight.

Afton Down ☎ 752955.

Newport 13.

Blenheim House, Gate Lane, PO40 9QD, ☎ 752858, heated – rest TV P.
June-October – **M** (by arrangement) 7.00 – **8 rm** 17.50/35.00.

Newport – pop. 19 758 – ECD : Thursday – ✉ ☎ 0983 Isle of Wight.

Envir. : Shorwell (St. Peter's Church★ 15C) SW : 5 m. – Carisbrooke Castle★★ (12C-16C) (keep ≤★) *AC*, SW : 1½ m.

St. George's Down, Shide ☎ 525076, SE : 1 m.

Town Lane Car Park ☎ 525450 (summer only).

AUDI-VW, MERCEDES-BENZ Medina Av. ☎ 523232
SUBARU Blackwater ☎ 523684
ATS 44-50 South St. ☎ 522881

Niton – ✉ Isle of Wight – ☎ 0983 Niton.

Pine Ridge, The Undercliff, PO38 2LY, ☎ 730802, – TV ☎ P. VISA
M 19.00 **t.** 3.10 – **8 rm** 23.00/62.00 **t.** – SB (October-27 May) 110.00 **st.**

ROVER Elmfield ☎ 62717

Sandown – ✉ ☎ 0983 Isle of Wight.

Fairway Lake ☎ 403217.

Grange, Alverstone, PO36 0EZ, NW : 2 m. ☎ 403729, – rest P
March-October – **M** 11.50 **st.** – **6 rm** 16.50/36.00 **st.**

Seaview – ✉ ☎ 0983 Isle of Wight

Seaview, High St., PO34 5EX, ☎ 612711, Fax 613729 – TV ☎ P. AE VISA
M *(closed Sunday dinner except Bank Holidays)* 15.00 **t.** and a la carte 3.30 – **16 rm** 44.00/80.00 **t.**

Shanklin – pop. 8 109 – ECD : Wednesday – ✉ ☎ 0983 Isle of Wight.

See : Old Village (thatched cottages)★ – The Chine★ *AC*.

Envir. : Brading★ (Roman Villa : mosaics★ *AC*) N : 3 ½ m. – Brading : St. Mary's Church★.

67 High St. ☎ 862942.

Newport 9.

Cliff Tops (Best Western), 1-5 Park Rd, PO37 6BB, ☎ 863262, Fax 867139, ≤, , , , – TV ☎ P – 220. AE VISA
M (bar lunch Monday to Saturday)/dinner 15.95 **st.** and a la carte 3.55 – **88 rm** 64.00/102.00 **st.** – SB 99.00 **st.**

Bourne Hall Country, Luccombe Rd, PO37 6RR, ☎ 862820, , heated, , , – TV ☎ P. AE VISA.
closed January and February – **M** *(closed Saturday lunch)* (bar lunch Monday to Friday)/dinner 14.50 **t.** and a la carte 8.00 – **28 rm** 40.00/70.00 **t.** – SB (October-May) 61.50 **st.**

Queensmead, 12 Queens Rd, PO37 6AN, ☎ 862342, heated, – rest TV P. VISA
March-November and Christmas – **M** (bar lunch)/dinner 8.00 **s.** and a la carte 3.50 – **31 rm** 31.00/62.00 **st.** – SB (except summer and Bank Holidays) 50.00/62.00 **st.**

Carlton, (entrance on Park Rd) Eastcliff Promenade, PO37 6AY, ☎ 862517, ≤, – TV P. VISA
M (residents only) – **13 rm** (dinner included) 27.00/54.00 **t.**

Apse Manor Country House, Apse Manor Rd, PO37 7PN, W : 1½ m. by A 3020 ☎ 866651, – rest TV ☎ P
M (dinner only) 10.00 **t.** – **7 rm** 30.00/46.00 **st.** – SB (November-March) 50.00/60.00 **st.**

Luccombe Chine Country, Luccombe Chine, PO37 6RH, S : 2¼ m. by A 3055 ℘ 862037, ≤, – TV P. VISA.
closed December and January – **M** 11.50 **t.** 5.00 – **8 rm** (dinner included) 49.00/68.00 **t.** – SB (April-October) 55.00 **st.**

Delphi Cliff, 7 St. Boniface Cliff Rd, PO37 6ET, ℘ 862179, ≤, – rest P.
March-October – **M** 5.00 **st.** – **11 rm** 12.50/33.00 **st.**

Totland Bay – pop. 2 316 – ECD : Wednesday – ✉ 0983 Isle of Wight.

Envir. : Alum Bay (coloured sands★) and the Needles★, SW : 1 m.

Newport 13.

Country Garden, Church Hill, PO39 0ET, on B 3322 ℘ 754521, Telex 94017218, ≤, – TV P. AE VISA
restricted service November and January – **M** 17.85/15.70 **t.** and a la carte 3.95 – **18 rm** 32.00/75.00 **t.**, **1 suite** 68.00/85.00 **t.** – SB 63.00/85.00 **st.**

Sentry Mead, Madeira Rd, PO39 0BJ, ℘ 753212, – rest TV P. AE
M (bar lunch)/dinner 8.50 **t.** 2.00 – **14 rm** 26.00/52.00 **t.**

Nodes, Alum Bay Old Rd, PO39 0HZ, SW : 1 ½ m. by B 3322 ℘ 752859, – TV P
M 8.50 **st.** 3.00 – **11 rm** 17.00/43.00 **st.** – SB (October-April) 40.00/45.00 **st.**

Westgrange Country, Alum Bay Old Rd, PO39 0HZ, SW : 1½ m. by B 3322 ℘ 752227, – P. VISA.
March-October **M** 9.50 **st.** 4.25 – **13 rm** 27.00/72.50 **st.**

Littledene Lodge without rest., Granville Rd, PO39 0AX, ℘ 752411 – P
March-October – **6 rm** 17.00/32.00 **t.**

Ventnor – pop. 7 956 – ECD : Wednesday – ✉ 0983 Isle of Wight.

Envir. : St. Catherine's Point (≤★ from the car park), W : 5 m.

Steephill, Down Rd ℘ 853326.

34 High St. ℘ 853625 (summer only).

Newport 10.

Madeira Hall, Trinity Rd, PO38 1NS, ℘ 852624, Fax 854906, heated, – rest TV P. VISA.
closed January and February – **M** 12.95 **t.** 2.85 – **8 rm** 30.00/90.00 **t.**

at Bonchurch – ✉ 0983 Isle of Wight :

Winterbourne, via Bonchurch Shute, PO38 1RQ, ℘ 852535, Fax 853056, ≤ gardens and sea, « Country house and gardens », heated – TV P. AE VISA
Mid March-mid November – **M** (bar lunch)/dinner 14.00 **t.** – **19 rm** 44.00/106.00 **t.**

Highfield, 87 Leeson Rd, Upper Bonchurch, PO38 1PU, on A 3055 ℘ 852800, ≤, – rest TV P. VISA
March-November – **M** 6.50/14.00 **t.** 3.50 – **12 rm** 29.00/46.00 **t.** – SB (except summer) 57.90 **st.**

Lake, Shore Rd, PO38 1RF, ℘ 852613, – P
March-October – **M** (dinner only) 8.00 **t.** 3.25 – **21 rm** 24.00/34.00 **t.**

Horseshoe Bay, Shore Rd, PO38 1RN, ℘ 852487, ≤ – rest TV P.
April-December – **M** 7.50 4.00 – **6 rm** (dinner included) 19.00/24.00 **s.** – SB (except summer) 106.00/120.00 **st.**

at St. Lawrence – ✉ 0983 Ventnor :

Lawyers Rest, Undercliff Drive, PO38 1XF, ℘ 852610, ≤, – rest P. AE VISA.
March-October and weekends in winter – **M** *(closed Monday to non-residents)* 13.50 **t.** (dinner) and a la carte 5.00 – **8 rm** (dinner included) 39.10/78.20 **t.**

FORD Victoria St. ℘ 852650 ROVER Mill Rd ℘ 760436

WILLENHALL West Midlands 403 404 N 26 – see Coventry.

WILLERBY Humberside 402 S 22 – see Kingston-upon-Hull.

WILLERSEY Heref. and Worc. 403 404 O 27 – see Broadway.

WILLERSEY HILL Glos. 403 404 O 27 – see Broadway (Heref. and Worc.).

WILLITON Somerset 403 K 30 **The West Country G.** – pop. 2 410 – ECD : Saturday – ✉ Taunton – 0984.

♦London 177 – Minehead 8 – Taunton 16.

White House, 11 Long St., TA4 4QW, ℘ 32306 – rest TV P
Mid May-October – **M** (dinner only) 26.00 **t.** 6.50 – **12 rm** 45.00/75.00 **t.** – SB (Mid May-October) 104.00/115.00 **st.**

Fairfield House, 51 Long St., TA4 4QY, ℘ 32636 – P. VISA.
March-October – **M** (dinner only) 11.00 **st.** and a la carte 4.25 – **5 rm** 23.00/40.00 **st.**

⌂ **Curdon Mill** ⛰, Lower Vellow, TA4 4LS, SE : 2½ m. by A 358 on Stogumber rd ✆ 56522, ≤, « Converted water mill on working farm », heated, ⛰, ⛰, park – ⛰ TV P. ⛰
M *(closed Monday and Tuesday)* 20.00 **t.** and a la carte 3.50 – **6 rm** 25.00/60.00 **t.**

EUGEOT-TALBOT High St. ✆ 32761 ROVER West Quantoxhead ✆ 32437

WILMCOTE Warw. 403 404 O 27 – see Stratford-upon-Avon.

WILMINGTON East Sussex 404 U 31 – see Eastbourne.

WILMINGTON Devon 403 K 31 – see Honiton.

WILMSLOW Cheshire 402 403 404 N 24 – pop. 28 827 – ECD : Wednesday – ✆ 0625.

Great Warford, Mobberley ✆ 056 587 (Mobberley) 2579.

London 189 – ♦Liverpool 38 – ♦Manchester 12 – ♦Stoke-on-Trent 27.

Stanneylands ⛰, Stanneylands Rd, SK9 4EY, N : 1 m. by A 34 ✆ 525225, Telex 8950511, Fax 537282, « Gardens » – rest TV ☎ ♿ P – 🏛 90. AE VISA. ⛰
M *(closed Sunday dinner)* 10.50/22.50 **t.** and a la carte 3.60 – 8.50 – **33 rm** 78.00/85.00 **t.** – SB (weekends only) 95.00/140.00 **st.**

Wilmslow Moat House (Q.M.H.), Oversley Ford, Altrincham Rd, SK9 4LR, NW : 2 ¾ m. on A 538 ✆ 529201, Telex 666401, Fax 531876, ⛰, ⛰, squash – TV ☎ P – 🏛 300. AE VISA
M 9.85/18.15 **t.** and a la carte – 6.50 – **125 rm** 70.00/80.00 **st.**

at Handforth N : 3 m. on A 34 – ✉ ✆ 0625 Wilmslow :

Belfry, Stanley Rd, SK9 3LD, ✆ 061 (Manchester) 437 0511, Telex 666358, Fax 499 0597, ⛰ – TV ☎ ♿ P – 🏛 100. AE VISA. ⛰
closed 25-26 December and 1 January – **M** 11.00/21.50 **t.** and a la carte 4.80 – 8.00 – **78 rm** 73.50/84.50 **t.**, **3 suites** 84.50/94.00 **t.**

BMW Manchester Rd ✆ 529955
PORSCHE Green Lane ✆ 526392
RENAULT Knutsford Rd ✆ 523669
TOYOTA Station Rd, Styal ✆ 524145
VAUXHALL-OPEL Water Lane ✆ 527311

Die Preise — Einzelheiten über die in diesem Führer angegebenen Preise finden Sie in der Einleitung.

WIMBORNE MINSTER Dorset 403 404 O 31 **The West Country G.** – pop. 14 193 – ECD : Wednesday – ✆ 0202 Wimborne.

See : Site★.

Envir. : Bere Regis Church★ (Roof★★) W : 11 m.

18 Broadstone, Wentworth Drive ✆ 693363 – 9 Ashley Wood ✆ 0258 (Blandford) 452253, NW : 8 m.

29 High St. ✆ 886116/841025 (summer only).

♦London 112 – Bournemouth 10 – Dorchester 23 – Salisbury 27 – ♦Southampton 30.

Beechleas, 17 Poole Rd, BH21 1QA, ✆ 841684, ⛰ – ⛰ rm TV ☎ P. VISA. ⛰
closed Christmas-January – **M** (dinner only) 15.00 **t.** 4.85 – 7.00 – **7 rm** 59.50/69.50 **t.**

Stour Lodge, 21 Julians Rd, BH21 1EF, on A 31 (Dorchester rd) ✆ 888003, ⛰ – TV P
closed 20 December-5 January – **M** (by arrangement) 15.00 **st.** 2.00 – **3 rm** 25.00/45.00 **st.**

at Horton N : 6 m. by B 3078 – ✉ Wimborne Minster – ✆ 0258 Witchampton :

Northill House ⛰, BH21 7HL, NW : ½ m. ✆ 840407, ⛰ – ⛰ rest TV ☎ P. VISA. ⛰
closed 20 December-15 February – **M** (bar lunch)/dinner 11.00 **st.** 3.00 – **9 rm** 28.00/52.00 **st.**

Horton Inn, Cranborne Rd, BH21 5AD, NW : 1 m. ✆ 840252 – TV P. VISA
M (bar meals Sunday dinner and Monday) a la carte 16.15/19.95 **t.** 4.95 – **5 rm** 40.00/50.00 **t.**

at Broadstone S : 3¼ m. by A 349 on B 3074 – ✉ Poole – ✆ 0202 Broadstone :

Fairlight ⛰, 1 Golf Links Rd, BH18 8BE, ✆ 694316, ⛰ – ⛰ rest TV P. VISA
M 15.50 **t.** 4.10 – **10 rm** 26.00/46.00 **t.** – SB (winter only) 88.00 **st.**

FORD 1 Brook Rd ✆ 886211
FORD Poole Rd ✆ 886211
VAUXHALL-OPEL Walford Bridge ✆ 842414

WINCHESTER Hants. 403 404 P 30 – pop. 34 127 – ECD : Thursday – ✆ 0962.

See : Site★★ – Cathedral★★★ (11C-13C) B – St. Cross Hospital★★ (12C-15C) A – Winchester College★ (14C) B **B** – Castle (Great Hall★) B – Pilgrim's Hall★ (14C) B **E.**

Envir. : Marwell Zoological Park★★ *AC*, SE : 5 m. on A 333 A.

18 Hockley, Turjford ✆ 713678 B – 18 Royal Winchester ✆ 52462 A.

The Guildhall, The Broadway ✆ 840500/87871.

♦London 72 – ♦Bristol 76 – ♦Oxford 52 – ♦Southampton 12.

WINCHESTER

High Street . . . . B

Alresford Road . . . . A 2
Andover Road . . . . B 3
Bereweeke Road . . . . A 5
Bridge Street . . . . B 6
Broadway (The) . . . . B 8
Chilbolton Avenue . . . . A 9
City Road . . . . B 10
Clifton Terrace . . . . B 12
East Hill . . . . B 15
Eastgate Street . . . . B 16
Easton Lane . . . . A 18
Friarsgate . . . . B 19
Garnier Road . . . . A 20
Kingsgate Road . . . . A 22
Magdalen Hill . . . . B 23
Middle Brook Street . . . . B 24
Morestead Road . . . . A 25
Park Road . . . . A
Quarry Road . . . . A
St. George's Street . . . . B
St. Paul's Hill . . . . B
St. Peter's Street . . . . B
Southgate Street . . . . B
Stoney Lane . . . . A
Stockbridge Road . . . . B
Sussex Street . . . . B
Union Street . . . . B
Upper High Street . . . . B

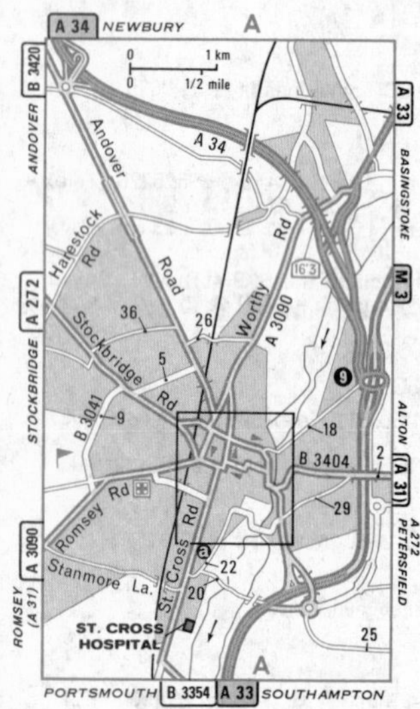

Lainston House 🐎, Sparsholt, SO21 2LT, NW : 3½ m. by A 272 ☎ 63588, Telex 477375, Fax 72672, ≤, « 17C manor house », park, – TV ☎ P – 60. AE VISA
M 18.50/34.50 **t.** and a la carte 5.00 – 9.00 – **29 rm** 95.00/150.00 **t.**, **3 suites** 230.00 **t.** – SB (weekends only) 180.00 **st.** by A 272 A

Wessex (T.H.F.), Paternoster Row, SO23 9LQ, ☎ 61611, Telex 47419, Fax 841503, ≤ – rm TV ☎ P – 80. AE VISA B
M 14.00/19.00 **st.** and a la carte – 8.20 – **93 rm** 86.00/108.00 **st.**, **1 suite** 125.00 **st.** – SB (weekends only) 102.00/120.00 **st.**

Royal (Best Western), St. Peter St., SO23 8BS, ☎ 840840, Telex 477071, Fax 841582, – TV ☎ P – 80 B
59 rm.

Winchester Moat House (Q.M.H.), Worthy Lane, SO23 7AB, ☎ 868102, Fax 840862, – rm rest TV ☎ P – 140. AE VISA B
M *(closed Saturday lunch)* 13.50/16.50 **st.** and a la carte 4.00 – 6.50 – **72 rm** 70.00/85.00 – SB (weekends only) 79.00/85.00 **st.**

The Wykeham Arms, 75 Kingsgate St., SO23 9PE, ☎ 53834, – rest TV ☎ P
M *(closed Monday dinner and Sunday)* (in bar) 11.50/14.50 **st.** and a la carte 3.15 – **7 rm** 55.00/65.00 **st.** B

Florum House, 47 St. Cross Rd, SO23 9PS, ☎ 840427, – TV P. VISA A
M (by arrangement) (communal dining) 9.25 **st.** 3.50 – **6 rm** 36.00/48.00 **st.** – SB (winter only) 60.00/72.00 **st.**

Brann's, 9 Great Minster St., The Square, SO23 9HA, ☎ 64004 – AE VISA B
closed Sunday dinner and Bank Holidays – **M** 27.50 **t.** and a la carte 3.60.

ASTON-MARTIN Hursley ☎ 75218
FORD Hyde St ☎ 64161
PEUGEOT-TALBOT, CITROEN 2-4 St. Cross Rd ☎ 843636
ROVER Easton Lane, The By-pass ☎ 842842
VAUXHALL Stockbridge Rd ☎ 63344
VOLVO Kingsworthy ☎ 881414
VW-AUDI St. Cross Rd ☎ 66331

ATS 61 Bar End Rd ☎ 65021

Europe

Se il nome di un albergo è stampato in carattere magro, chiedete arrivando le condizioni che vi saranno praticate.

WINDERMERE Cumbria 402 L 20 – pop. 6 835 – ECD : Thursday – ☎ 096 62.

ee : Lake★★.

nvir. : Kirkstone Pass (on Windermere ≤★), N : 7 m. by A 592 Y.

Cleabarrow ℘ 3123 by A 5074 Z on B 5284.

Victoria St. ℘ 6499.

at Bowness : The Glebe ℘ 2895 (summer only).

London 274 – ◆Blackpool 55 – ◆Carlisle 46 – Kendal 10.

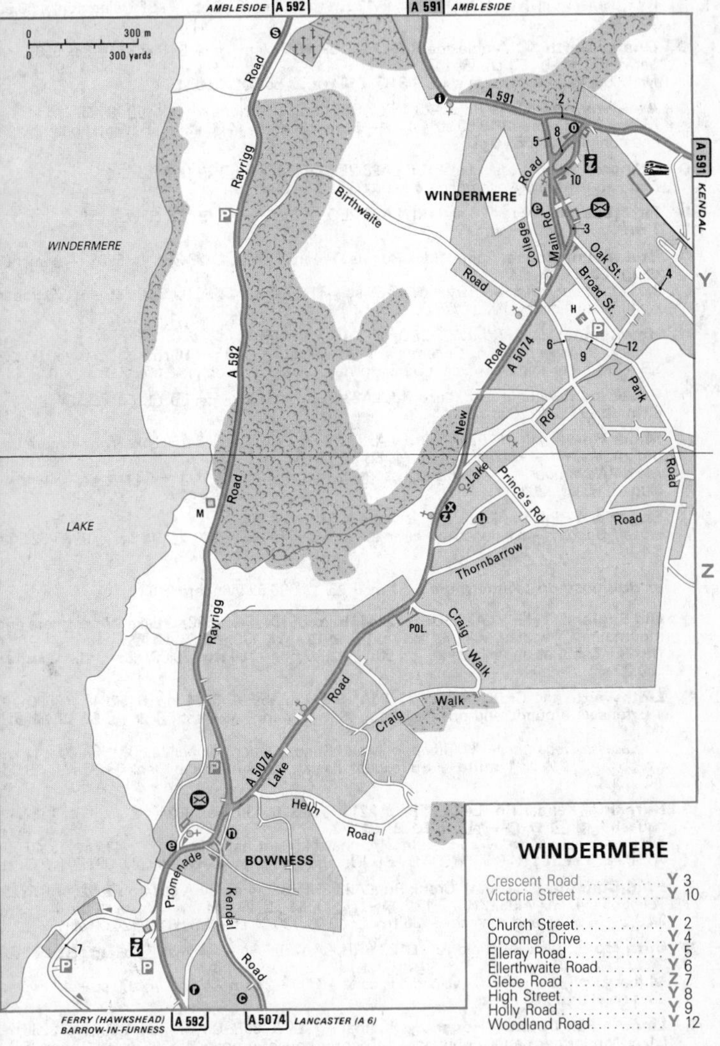

If you find you cannot take up a hotel booking you have made, please let the hotel know immediately.

Prévenez immédiatement l'hôtelier si vous ne pouvez pas occuper la chambre que vous avez retenue.

Merewood Country House ⅋, Ecclerigg, LA23 1LH, NW : 2 ½ m. on A 591 Y ✆ 648 Fax 2128, ⛬, park – ⊭ rest TV ☎ P – 🎤 25. ⬚ AE ⦿ VISA. ⚔
M (bar lunch Monday to Saturday)/dinner 19.95 **st.** 🍷 4.50 – **16 rm** ☕ 65.00/160.00 **st.**

Holbeck Ghyll ⅋, Holbeck Lane, LA23 1LU, NW : 3 ¼ m. by A 591 ✆ 05394 (Ambleside) 32375, <, ⛬ – ⊭ rest TV ☎ P. ⬚ VISA by A 591 Y
closed January – **M** (dinner only and Sunday lunch)/dinner 20.00 **t.** 🍷 3.75 – **14 rm** ☕ (dinner included) 60.00/120.00 **t.** – SB (November-May) 80.00/100.00 **st.** by A 591 Y

Cedar Manor, Ambleside Rd, LA23 1AX, ✆ 3192, ⛬ – ⊭ rest TV ☎ P. ⬚ VISA
M (dinner only) 17.00 **t.** 🍷 4.00 – **12 rm** ☕ 38.00/64.00 **t.** – SB (winter only) 60.00/68.00 **st.** Y

Quarry Garth ⅋, Ambleside Rd, LA23 1LF, NW : 2 m. on A 591 ✆ 3761, Fax 6584, ⛬, park – TV ☎ P. ⬚ AE ⦿ VISA by A 591 Y
M 12.50/18.00 **t.** and a la carte 🍷 3.95 – **10 rm** ☕ 55.00/110.00 **t.**

Archway, 13 College Rd, LA23 1BY, ✆ 5613, « Victoriana » – ⊭ TV ☎. AE. ⚔
M (by arrangement) 13.50 **st.** 🍷 4.20 – **5 rm** ☕ 19.00/44.00 **st.** – SB (winter only) (weekends only) 58.00/65.00 **st.** Y

Glencree without rest., Lake Rd, LA23 2EQ, ✆ 5822 – TV P. ⬚ VISA. ⚔ Z
Mid February-mid November – **5 rm** ☕ 35.00/54.00 **st.**

Fir Trees without rest., Lake Rd, LA23 2EQ, ✆ 2272 – TV P. ⬚ AE VISA. ⚔ Z
7 rm ☕ 33.00/43.00 **st.**

Braemount House, Sunny Bank Rd (via Queens Drive), LA23 2EN, ✆ 5967 – ⊭ rest TV ☎ P. ⬚ AE ⦿ VISA Z
closed January and February – **M** 13.50 **st.** 🍷 4.50 – **4 rm** ☕ 35.00/52.00 **st.** – SB (October-April) (Bank holidays) 62.00/75.00 **st.**

Hawksmoor, Lake Rd, LA23 2EQ, ✆ 2110, ⛬ – TV P. ⚔ Z
closed 4 November-26 December – **M** 9.50 **st.** 🍷 2.60 – **10 rm** ☕ 25.00/50.00 **t.** SB (November-mid May except Bank Holidays) (weekdays only) 49.00/62.00 **st.**

Rosemount without rest., Lake Rd, LA23 2EQ, ✆ 3739 – ⊭ TV P. ⬚ VISA. ⚔
8 rm ☕ 22.00/40.00 **st.** Z

Miller Howe with rm, Rayrigg Rd, LA23 1EY, ✆ 2536, Fax 5664, < Lake Windermere and mountains, ⛬ – ⊭ rest ▤ rest P. ⬚ AE ⦿ VISA Y
March-November – **M** (booking essential) (dinner only) 30.00 **t.** – **13 rm** ☕ (dinner included) 85.00/120.00 **t.**

Roger's, 4 High St., LA23 1AF, ✆ 4954 – ⬚ AE ⦿ VISA Y
closed Sunday – **M** (lunch by arrangement)/dinner 9.95 **t.** and a la carte 16.75/22.30 **t.** 🍷 4.10.

at Bowness-on-Windermere S : 1 m. – ✉ ⚙ 096 62 Windermere :

Old England (T.H.F.), LA23 3DF, ✆ 2444, Telex 65194, Fax 3432, < Lake Windermere and mountains, ⛱ heated, ⛬ – ⇅ ⊭ rm TV ☎ P – 🎤 170. ⬚ AE ⦿ VISA Z
M 7.95/23.50 **st.** and a la carte 🍷 4.50 – ☕ 7.50 – **80 rm** 70.00/125.00 **st.**, **2 suites** 150.00 **st.**

Linthwaite ⅋, Crook Rd, LA23 3JA, S : ¾ m. by A 5074 on B 5284 ✆ 3688, < « Extensive grounds and private lake », ⛵, ⛬, park – ⊭ rest TV ☎ P. ⬚ AE ⦿ VISA ⚔
Mid March-December – **M** (dinner only and Sunday lunch)/dinner 16.50 **st.** 🍷 4.00 – **12 rm** ☕ 65.00/98.00 **st.**, **1 suite** – SB (except Easter, Christmas and Bank Holidays) 98.00/118.00 **st.** by A 5074 Z

Burnside, Kendal Rd, LA23 3EP, ✆ 2211, Telex 65430, Fax 3824, <, 🏋, ≘s, ⛱, ⛬, squash – ⇅ TV ☎ P – 🎤 80. ⬚ AE ⦿ VISA Z
M (bar lunch Monday to Saturday)/dinner 14.50 **st.** and a la carte – **41 rm** ☕ 40.00/76.00 **st.**, **3 suites** 84.00/104.00 **st.** – SB (October-March) (weekends only) 82.00/108.00 **st.**

Wild Boar (Best Western), Crook Rd, LA23 3NF, SE : 4 m. by A 5074 on B 5284 ✆ 5225, Telex 65464, Fax 2498, ⛬ – TV ☎ P – 🎤 40. ⬚ AE ⦿ VISA by A 5074 Z
M 9.20/18.50 **st.** and a la carte – **36 rm** ☕ 40.00/130.00 **st.** – SB 88.00/124.00 **st.**

Burn How, Back Belsfield Rd, LA23 3HH, ✆ 6226, ⛬ – ⊭ rest TV ☎ P. ⬚ AE VISA. ⚔
M (bar lunch)/dinner 20.00 **st.** and a la carte 🍷 4.00 – **26 rm** ☕ 43.00/66.00 **st.** – SB (weekdays only) 65.00/85.00 **st.** Z

Lindeth Fell Country House ⅋, Kendal Rd, LA23 3JP, S : 1 m. on A 5074 ✆ 3286, < Lake Windermere and mountains, « Country house atmosphere », ⛵, ⛬, park, ⚔ – ⊭ rest TV ☎ P. ⬚ VISA. ⚔ by A 5074 Z
Mid March-October – **M** (bar lunch)/dinner 17.00 **st.** 🍷 3.25 – **14 rm** ☕ 44.00/99.00 **st.**

Bordriggs Country House ⅋, Longtail Hill, LA23 3LD, S : 1 m. by A 592 ✆ 3567, Fax 6949, ⛱ heated, ⛬ – ⊭ TV ☎ P. ⚔ by A 592 Z
Mid February-mid November – **M** (dinner only) 12.50 **t.** 🍷 4.00 – **11 rm** ☕ 30.00/120.00 **st.** – SB (February-April) 70.00 **st.**

White Foss without rest., Longtail Hill, LA23 3JD, S : ¾ m. by A 592 ✆ 6593, – Ⓟ. by A 592 Y
3 rm -/40.00 **st.**

Brooklands, Ferry View, LA23 3JB, S : ¾ m. on A 5074 ✆ 2344 – rm Ⓟ
M 12.00 **st.** 2.90 – **6 rm** 17.00/34.00 **st.** – SB (November-March) (weekends only) (except Christmas and New Year) 50.00/54.00 **st.** on A 5074 Z

Gilpin Lodge with rm, Crook Rd, LA23 3NE, SE : 2 ½ m. by A 5074 on B 5284 ✆ 88818, Fax 88058, ←, – rest TV ☎ Ⓟ. AE VISA. by A 5074 Z
M (dinner only) 21.00 **t.** 4.75 – **6 rm** 60.00/110.00 **t.** – SB (November-April) (except Easter, Christmas and New Year) 70.00/120.00 **st.**

Porthole Eating House, 3 Ash St., LA23 3EB, ✆ 2793 – AE VISA Z **n**
closed Tuesday and mid December-mid February – **M** (dinner only) a la carte 15.25/20.00 **t.** 4.00.

at Troutbeck N : 4 m. by A 592 – Y – ✉ Windermere – ☎ 053 94 Ambleside :

Mortal Man, LA23 1PL, ✆ 33193, ← Garburn Hill and Troutbeck Valley, – TV Ⓟ
12 rm.

HONDA Kendal Rd ✆ 2000
PEUGEOT-TALBOT Main Rd ✆ 2441
ROVER Rayrigg ✆ 2451

WINDSOR Berks. 404 S 29 – pop. 30 832 (inc. Eton) – ECD : Wednesday – ☎ 0753.
See : Site★★★ (Town Centre★) – Castle★★★ (St. George's Chapel★★★, State Appartments★★★) Z – Windsor Park★.
Envir. : Eton (College★) N : 1 m. Z – Runnymede (signing of the Magna Carta, 1215, museum) AC, SE : 4 m. by A 308 Y.
Central Station, Thames St. ✆ 852010.
♦London 28 – Reading 19 – ♦Southampton 59.

Plan on next page

Oakley Court (Q.M.H.), Windsor Rd, Water Oakley, SL4 5UR, W : 3 m. on A 308 ✆ 0628 (Maidenhead) 74141, Telex 849958, Fax 37011, ←, « Part Gothic mansion on banks of River Thames », , park – TV ☎ Ⓟ – 100 by A 308 Y
91 rm, 1 suite.

Castle (T.H.F.), High St., SL4 1LJ, ✆ 851011, Telex 849220, Fax 830244 – TV ☎ Ⓟ – 400. AE VISA Z **c**
M 16.00/18.00 **st.** and a la carte 5.00 – 7.60 – **102 rm** 80.00/120.00 **st.**, **1 suite** 135.00/170.00 **st.** – SB (weekends only) 114.00/134.00 **st.**

Sir Christopher Wren's House, Thames St., SL4 1PX, ✆ 861354, Telex 847938, Fax 860172, ←, – TV ☎ Ⓟ – 50. AE VISA Z **v**
M *(closed Saturday lunch)* 15.50 **st.** (lunch) and a la carte 20.45/23.00 **st.** – **38 rm** 79.00/114.00 **st.**, **1 suite** 160.00 **st.** – SB (weekends only) 110.00 **st.**

Aurora Garden, 14 Bolton Av., SL4 3JF, ✆ 868686, Fax 831394, – TV ☎ Ⓟ – 40. AE VISA Z **a**
M 12.50/25.00 **st.** 4.50 – **14 rm** 63.50/75.00 **st.** – SB (weekends only) 78.00/88.00 **st.**

Ye Harte and Garter (B.C.B.), 21 High St., SL4 1LR, ✆ 863426, Fax 830527 – rest TV – 100. VISA. Z **e**
M 15.00 **st.** – **50 rm** 52.00/85.00 **st.**

Royal Adelaide, Kings Rd, SL4 2AG, ✆ 863916, Fax 830682 – TV ☎ Ⓟ – 50. Z **n**
41 rm.

Fairlight Lodge, 41 Frances Rd, SL4 3AQ, ✆ 861207 – rest TV Ⓟ. AE VISA. Z **z**
M approx. 9.40 **t.** 3.00 – **10 rm** 34.00/51.00 **t.**

Trinity without rest., 18 Trinity Pl., SL4 3AT, ✆ 864186 – TV. VISA Z **i**
9 rm 18.00/42.00 **st.**

VAUXHALL-OPEL 72-74 Arthur Rd ✆ 860131

WINDSOR

High Street	Z	13
King Edward Court Centre	Z	
Peascod Street	Z	
St. Leonard's Road	Z	
Thames Street	Z	24
Bexley Street	Z	2
Bolton Road	Y	3
Castle Hill	Z	4
Claremont Road	Z	6
Clarence Crescent	Z	7
Clewer Crescent Road	Z	8
Goswell Road	Z	9
Grove Road	Z	10
High Street (DATCHET)	Y	12
Horton Road	Y	14
Keats Lane	Z	16
Peascod Street	Z	17
Ragstone Road	Y	18
River Street	Z	19
Stovell Road	Z	20
Thames Avenue	Z	22
Trinity Place	Z	25
Windsor Bridge	Z	26
Windsor Road	Y	28

North is at the top on all town plans.

M 4 READING
A 355 SLOUGH WEST
A 332 SLOUGH
UPTON
Upton Court Road
UPTON PARK
MYRKE
M 4
A 332
ETON WICK
Y
B 3026
Wick Road
ETON
Slough Rd
Pococks Lane
Datchet Rd
Slough By-Pass
Slough Rd
Eton Rd
Southlea Rd
London Rd
B 376
DATCHET
WINDSOR
A 308 MAIDENHEAD
B 3024
THE HOME PARK
Hatch Lane
B 3173
B 3022
St. Leonard's Road
SPITAL
King's Road
Albert Road
Southlea Road
B 3021
Thames
0 2 km
0 1 mile
A 332 ASCOT
A 308 STAINES

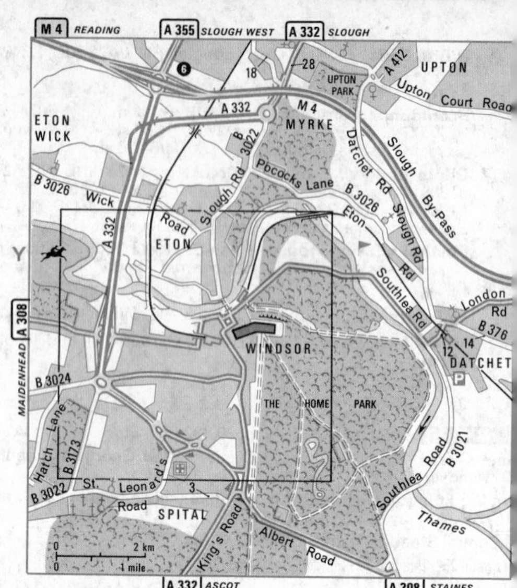

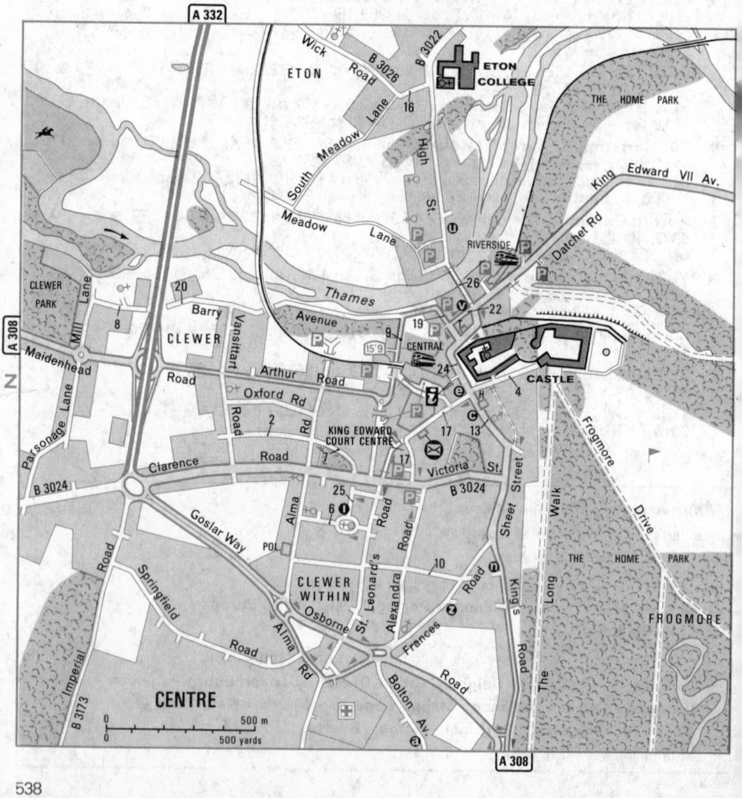

A 332
ETON
Wick Road
B 3026
B 3022
ETON COLLEGE
THE HOME PARK
South Meadow Lane
High St.
Meadow Lane
King Edward VII Av.
Datchet Rd
RIVERSIDE
Thames
CLEWER PARK
Mill Lane
Barry Avenue
CLEWER
Vansittart Road
CENTRAL
CASTLE
A 308
Z
Maidenhead Road
Arthur Road
Oxford Rd
KING EDWARD COURT CENTRE
Parsonage Lane
Clarence Road
Victoria St.
Frogmore Drive
B 3024
Goslar Way
Alma Road
Sheet Street
The Long Walk
POL
THE HOME PARK
CLEWER WITHIN
St. Leonard's Road
Alexandra Road
King's Road
FROGMORE
Springfield Road
Osborne Road
Frances Road
Imperial Road
Alma Rd
Bolton Av.
B 3173
CENTRE
0 500 m
0 500 yards
A 308

WINGHAM Kent 404 X 30 – pop. 1 429 – ☎ 0227 Canterbury.
♦London 66 – Canterbury 7 – ♦Dover 19 – Margate 14.

X **Four Seasons,** 109 High St., CT3 1BU, ☎ 720286, – AE VISA
closed Saturday lunch, Sunday dinner, Tuesday and first week January – **M** 9.95 **t.** and a la carte 3.00.

WINSFORD Somerset 403 J 30 **The West Country G.** – pop. 340 – ECD : Thursday – ✉ Minehead – ☎ 064 385.
See : Site★.
♦London 194 – Exeter 31 – Minehead 10 – Taunton 32.

Royal Oak Inn, TA24 7JE, ☎ 455, Fax 388, « Attractive 12C thatched inn » – TV ☎ P. AE VISA
closed 2 days at Christmas – **M** (bar lunch Monday to Saturday)/dinner 22.50 **st.** – **14 rm** 60.00/80.00 **st.** – SB (weekdays only) 104.50 **st.**

WINSLEY Wilts. 403 404 N 29 – see Bath (Avon).

WINTERBOURNE Avon 403 404 M 29 – see Bristol.

WINTERINGHAM Humberside 402 S 22 – pop. 932 – ✉ ☎ 0724 Scunthorpe.
♦London 176 – ♦Kingston-upon-Hull 16 – ♦Sheffield 67.

XXX **Winteringham Fields** with rm, DN15 9PF, ☎ 733096, « Part 16C manor house », – rm TV ☎ P. VISA.
closed first 2 weeks March, first week August and Christmas – **M** *(closed lunch Monday, Saturday and Sunday)* 15.00/33.00 **st.** and a la carte 4.00 – 4.50 – **6 rm** 55.00/85.00 **st.**

WISBECH Cambs. 402 404 U 25 – pop. 22 932 – ECD : Wednesday – ☎ 0945.
Envir. : March (St. Wendreda's Church 15C : the Angel roof★) SW : 10 m. – Long Sutton(St. Mary's Church★ : Gothic) NW : 10 m.
District Library, Ely Pl. ☎ 583263.
♦London 106 – ♦Cambridge 47 – ♦Leicester 62 – ♦Norwich 57.

White Lion, 5 South Brink, PE13 1JD, ☎ 584813 – TV ☎ P. AE VISA
M 9.00/11.50 **t.** and a la carte 4.50 – **18 rm** 35.00/59.95 **t.** – SB (weekends only) 68.00 **st.**

FORD Elm Rd ☎ 582681
ROVER 46 Norwich Rd ☎ 584342
VAUXHALL-OPEL Elm High Rd ☎ 582471
ATS North End ☎ 583214

WITCOMBE Glos. – see Gloucester.

WITHAM Essex 404 V 28 – pop. 21 875 – ECD : Wednesday – ☎ 0376.
♦London 42 – ♦Cambridge 46 – Chelmsford 9 – Colchester 13.

White Hart (B.C.B.), 39 Newland St., CM8 2AF, ☎ 512245 – TV ☎ P – 50. AE VISA.
M 15.00 **st.** – **18 rm** 41.50/53.50.

XX **Lian,** High House, Newland St., CM8 2AF, ☎ 510684, Chinese rest. AE VISA
M 20.00 **t.** and a la carte 5.90.

at Rivenhall End NE : 1 ½ m. by B 1389 on A 12 (Southbound Carriageway) – ✉ ☎ 0376 Witham :

Rivenhall Resort, CM8 3BH, ☎ 516969, Fax 513674, squash – rm TV ☎ P – 50. AE VISA
M 11.50/12.95 **st.** and a la carte – 6.50 – **48 rm** 45.00/55.00 **t.** – SB (weekends only) 64.00/91.00 **st.**

FORD Colchester Rd ☎ 513496
NISSAN London Rd ☎ 515575
ROVER Newland St. ☎ 513272
ATS Moss Rd Ind Est. East, Unit 15 ☎ 518360/515671

WITHERSLACK Cumbria 402 L 21 – see Grange-over-Sands.

WITHINGTON Glos. 403 404 O 28 – pop. 500 – ☎ 024 289.
♦London 91 – Gloucester 15 – ♦Oxford 35 – Swindon 24.

Halewell , GL54 4BN, ☎ 238, ←, « Part 15C monastery, country house atmosphere », heated, , , park – rest TV P. VISA
M (booking essential) (communal dining) (dinner only, residents only) 15.00 **st.** – **6 rm** 47.00/72.00 **st.**

WITHYPOOL Somerset 403 J 30 The West Country G. – pop. 231 – ECD : Thursday – ✉ ☎ 064 383 Exford.

◆London 204 – Exeter 34 – Taunton 36.

Royal Oak Inn, TA24 7QP, ☎ 506, Fax 659, – TV ☎ P. AE VISA
closed 25 and 26 December – **M** (bar lunch Monday to Saturday)/dinner 19.00 and a la carte 3.20 – **8 rm** ☐ 27.00/60.00 **t.**

WITNEY Oxon 403 404 P 28 – ☎ 0993.

◆London 69 – Gloucester 39 – ◆Oxford 19.

Witney Lodge, Ducklington Lane, OX8 7TJ, S : 1½ m. on A 415 ☎ 779777, Telex 8345 Fax 703467 – TV ☎ ♿ P – 🔺 120. AE VISA
M 10.50/12.00 **st.** and a la carte 4.35 – ☐ 4.25 – **74 rm** 65.00/78.00 **st.** – SB (weekends only) 88.00/90.00 **st.**

WIVELISCOMBE Somerset 403 K 30 The West Country G. – pop. 1 457 – ECD : Thursday ☎ 0984.

◆London 185 – Barnstaple 38 – Exeter 37 – Taunton 14.

Langley House , Langley Marsh, TA4 2UF, NW : ½ m. ☎ 23318, Fax 24573, « Country house atmosphere », – rest TV ☎ P. AE VISA
M (booking essential) (lunch by arrangement)/dinner 21.70/26.50 **st.** 4.00 – **8 rm** ☐ 57.50/105.00 **st.** – SB (except Bank Holidays) 126.40/148.00 **st.**

Jews Farm House , Huish Champflower, TA4 2HL, ☎ 24218, ≤, « 13C farmhouse », park – P.
April-October – **M** (by arrangement) 15.00 **s.** – **3 rm** ☐ 30.00/60.00 **s.**

Deepleigh , Langley Marsh, TA4 2UU, NW : 1 m. Whitefield rd ☎ 23379, « Converted part 16C farmhouse », – TV P.
M 12.50 **st.** 3.65 – **5 rm** ☐ 30.00/48.00 **st.** – SB 58.00/66.00 **st.**

at Waterrow SW : 2½ m. by B 3227 – ✉ ☎ 0984 Wiveliscombe :

Hurstone , TA4 2AT, E : ½ m. ☎ 23441, ≤ Tone Valley, « Converted farmhouse », park – TV ☎ P. AE VISA
M *(closed lunch Monday and Tuesday)* 12.50/18.50 4.00 – **5 rm** ☐ -/74.00 **st.** – SB (weekends only) 87.50/95.00 **st.**

Michelin n'accroche pas de panonceau aux hôtels et restaurants qu'il signale.

WOBURN Beds. 404 S 28 – pop. 824 – ECD : Wednesday – ✉ Milton Keynes – ☎ 0525.

See : Woburn Abbey★★ (18C) *AC*, Wild Animal Kingdom★★ *AC*.

Heritage Centre, 12 Bedford St. (summer only).

◆London 49 – Bedford 13 – Luton 13 – Northampton 24.

Bedford Arms (Mt. Charlotte Thistle), 1 George St., MK17 9PX, ☎ 290441, Telex 825205 Fax 290432 – rm TV ☎ P – 🔺 60. AE VISA
M 14.75/17.50 **st.** and a la carte 4.25 – ☐ 7.50 – **54 rm** 68.00/92.00 **st.**, **1 suite** 110.00 118.00 **st.** – SB (except Easter and Christmas) 95.00/120.00 **st.**

XXX Paris House, Woburn Park, MK17 9QP, SE : 2¼ m. on A 4012 ☎ 290692, « Reconstructed timbered house in Park », – P.

WOKING Surrey 404 S 30 – pop. 92 667 – ECD : Monday – ☎ 048 62.

18, 18 Hoebridge Golf Centre, Old Woking Rd ☎ 0483 (Woking) 722611, SE : 1 m – 18 Woking Pond Rd, Hook Heath ☎ 760053 – 18 West Hill, Brookwood ☎ 048 67 (Brookwood) 4365 – 18 Worplesdon, Heath House Rd ☎ 048 67(Brookwood) 89876 – 9 Windlemere, Windlesham Rd, West End ☎ 0276 (Lightwater) 858727.

◆London 31 – Guildford 7 – Reading 24.

X **Chez Comus,** 5 High St., Knaphill, GU21 2PG, W : 3¼ m. by High St. and Victoria way off A 324 ☎ 0483 (Brookwood) 797800 – VISA
M 11.95 **t.** (lunch) and a la carte 17.40/21.45 **t.** 2.85.

WOKINGHAM Berks. 404 R 29 – pop. 30 773 – ECD : Wednesday – ☎ 0734.

18 Easthampstead Park ☎ 0344 (Bracknell) 424066 – 9 Sandford Lane, Hurst ☎ 345143.

◆London 43 – Reading 7 – ◆Southampton 52.

St. Annes Manor (Stakis), London Rd, RG11 1ST, E : 1½ m. on A 329 ☎ 772550, Telex 847342, Fax 772526, park – rm rest TV ☎ ♿ P – 🔺 300. AE VISA
M 13.00/19.00 **t.** and a la carte – ☐ 7.50 – **126 rm** 89.00/118.00 **t.**, **4 suites** 150.00 **t.** – SB 92.00/144.00 **st.**

Edward Court, Wellington Rd, RG11 2AN, ☎ 775886, Fax 772018 – TV ☎ ♿ P – 🔺 35 AE VISA.
closed 24 December-2 January – **M** *(closed Sunday dinner and Bank Holiday Mondays)* 16.00/18.50 **st.** – **25 rm** ☐ 58.00/82.00 **st.**

FORD 245 Finchampstead Rd ☎ 794776

WOLF'S CASTLE **(CAS-BLAIDD)** Dyfed 403 F 28 – ✉ Haverfordwest – ☎ 043 787 Treffgarne.
London 258 – Fishguard 7 – Haverfordwest 8.

XX **Wolfscastle Country** with rm, SA62 5LZ, on A 40 ☎ 225, Fax 383, squash – TV ☎ P. AE VISA
M (lunch by arrangement) a la carte 12.40/19.25 **t.** 3.25 – **15 rm** 30.00/50.00 **t.** – SB (October-June) (weekends only) 53.00/65.00 **st.**

WOLVERHAMPTON West Midlands 402 403 404 N 26 – pop. 263 501 – ECD : Thursday – ☎ 0902.
See : St. Peter's Church★ (15C) B A.
Oxley Park, Bushbury ☎ 20506, N : 1 ½ m. A – Pattingham ☎ 700342 – Penn Common ☎ 341142, SW : by A 449 A – Danescourt Rd, Tettenhall ☎ 751065.
18 Queen's Sq. ☎ 312051.
London 132 – ◆Birmingham 15 – ◆Liverpool 89 – Shrewsbury 30.

Plan of Enlarged Area : see Birmingham pp. 2 and 3

WOLVERHAMPTON

Darlington Street B
Mander Centre B
Victoria Street B 24
Wulfrun Centre B

Alfred Squire Road A 2
Birmingham New Road A 3
Bridgnorth Road A 6
Cleveland Street B 7
Garrick Street B 8
Lichfield Road A 10
Lichfield Street B 12

Market Street B 14
Princess Street B 15
Queen Square B 17
Railway Drive B 20
Salop Street B 22
Thompson Avenue A 23
Wolverhampton Road A 26

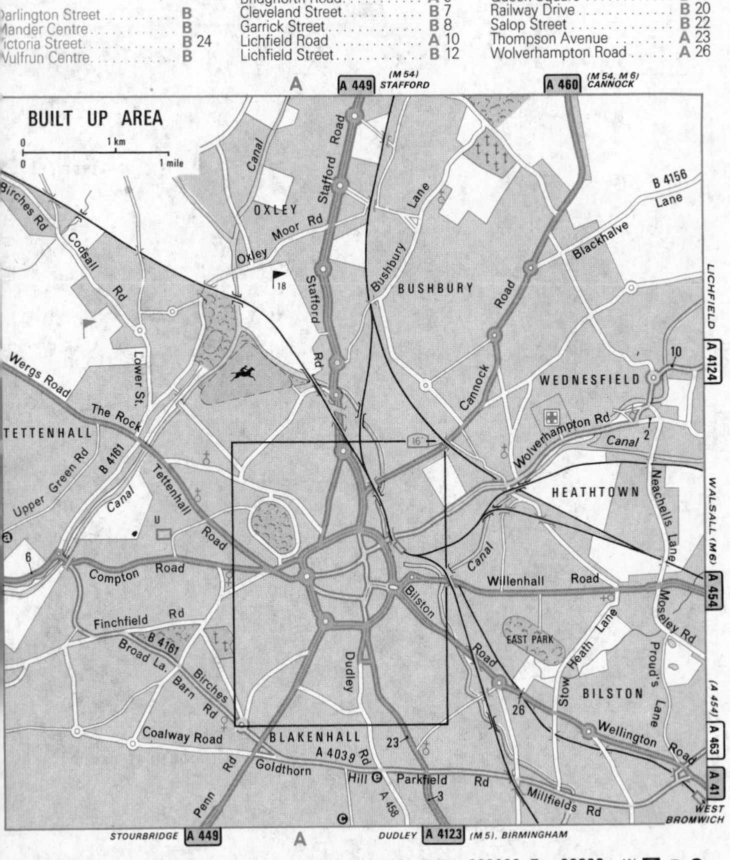

Victoria Park, Lichfield St., WV1 4DB, ☎ 29922, Telex 338083, Fax 29923 – TV ☎ P – 220. AE VISA.
M 8.50/12.95 **t.** and a la carte 3.75 – 7.50 – **117 rm** 70.00/80.00 **t.**, **1 suite** 110.00 **t.**

Goldthorn, 126 Penn Rd, WV3 0ER, ☎ 29216, Telex 339516, Fax 710419 – TV ☎ P – 50. AE VISA
closed 24 to 27 December – **M** *(closed Saturday lunch)* 9.95/10.95 **st.** and a la carte 3.75 – 6.50 – **93 rm** 52.50/75.00 **st.** – SB (weekends only) 77.00/102.00 **st.** B i

Mount, Mount Rd, Tettenhall Wood, WV6 8HL, W : 2 ½ m. by A 454 ✆ 75205 Fax 745263, – rm – 160.
M *(closed Saturday lunch)* 14.00 **st.** and a la carte 4.45 – 7.00 – **48 rm** 66.00/76.50 **st.** – **1 suite** 86.00/96.00 **st.** – SB (weekends only) 66.00/73.00 **st.** A

Park Hall, Park Drive, off Ednam Rd, Goldthorn Park, WV4 5AJ, S : 2 m. by A 44 ✆ 331121, Telex 333546, Fax 344760, – rm – 400.
M *(closed Saturday lunch)* 10.00/15.00 **st.** and a la carte 4.50 – 7.00 – **56 rm** 53.00/76.50 **st.**, **1 suite** 86.00 **st.** – SB 63.00 **st.** A

Dudleys, Dudley Rd, WV4 6BD, ✆ 333001, Fax 343424 –
10 rm. A

Ely House, 53 Teltenhall Rd, WV3 9NB, ✆ 311311, Fax 21098 – – 30
19 rm. B

at Pattingham (Shropshire) W : 6 ¼ m. by A 454 – A – 0902 Pattingham :

Patshull Park (Best Western), Patshull Park, WV6 7HR, W : 1 ¾ m. by Patshull R ✆ 700100, Telex 334849, Fax 700874, park – – 100
48 rm.

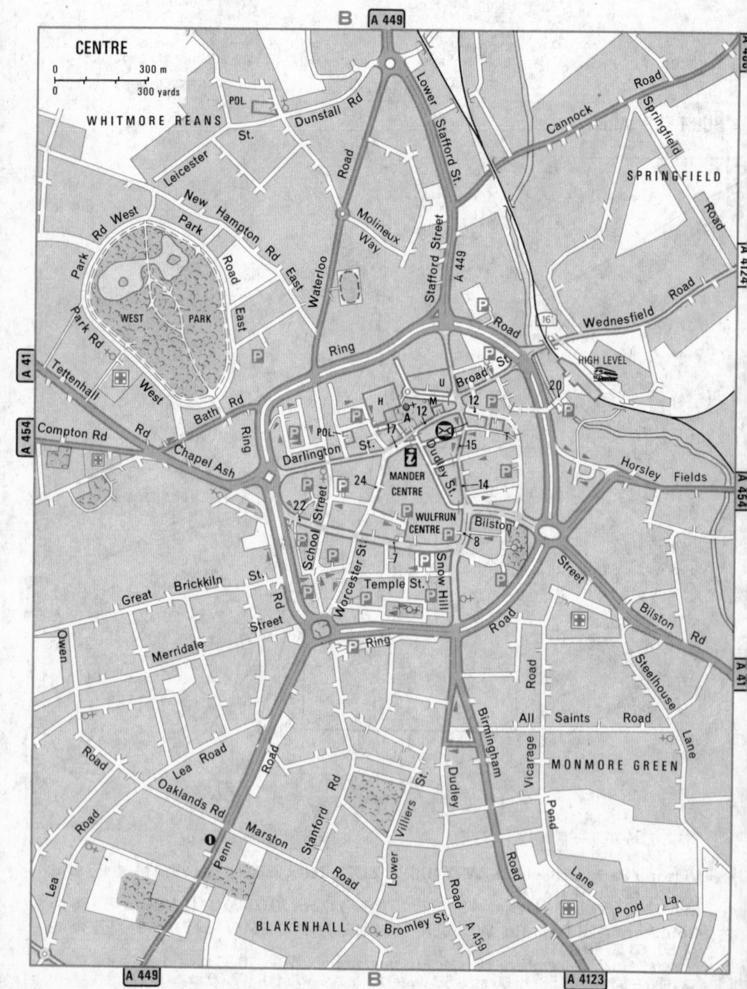

LFA-ROMEO, CITROEN Merridale Lane ✆ 23295
MW, VW-AUDI Rabey St. ✆ 54602/54952
ORD Bilston Rd ✆ 51515/53030
IERCEDES-BENZ Penn Rd ✆ 27897
EUGEOT-TALBOT Oxford St., Bilston ✆ 353000
ENAULT Bilston Rd ✆ 53111
OVER Chapel Ash ✆ 311611/714607
OVER Wolverhampton Rd, Wednesfield
✆ 731372
SKODA, ROVER Vulcan Rd, Bilston ✆ 402222
VAUXHALL-OPEL Dudley Rd ✆ 58000
VAUXHALL-OPEL 67-71 Bilston Rd ✆ 352352/607559
VOLVO Parkfield Rd ✆ 333211

ATS 35-39 Wednesfield Rd ✆ 55055
ATS 2 Willenhall rd ✆ 871417

WOOBURN COMMON Bucks. – see Beaconsfield.

WOODBRIDGE Suffolk 404 X 27 – pop. 9 697 – ECD : Wednesday – 039 43 (4 fig.) or 0394 5 fig.).

, Bromeswell Heath ✆ 2038 – 18 Waldringfield Heath, Newbourne Rd ✆ 0473 (Waldringfield) 36768 – 9 Grove Farm, Cretingham ✆ 072 882 (Cretingham) 275.

London 81 – Great Yarmouth 45 – ◆Ipswich 8 – ◆Norwich 47.

Seckford Hall, IP13 6NU, SW : 1¼ m. by A 12 ✆ 385678, Telex 987446, Fax 380610, « Part Tudor country house », park – 100. AE VISA
closed Christmas Day – **M** 10.50 **st.** (lunch) and a la carte 13.85/18.50 **st.** 3.50 – **27 rm** 64.00/80.00 **st.**, **7 suites** 90.00/120.00 **st.** – SB 105.00/140.00 **st.**

Crown (T.H.F.), Thoroughfare, IP12 1AD, ✆ 4242, Fax 7192 – rm. AE VISA
M (bar lunch Monday to Saturday)/dinner 12.95 **st.** and a la carte – **20 rm** 60.00/80.00 **st.** – SB (weekends only) 84.00/94.00 **st.**

ORD 60 Ipswich Rd ✆ 3333
ORD Bawdsey ✆ 411368
ROVER Melton Rd ✆ (039 43) 3456

WOODHALL SPA Lincs. 402 404 T 24 – pop. 2 526 – ECD : Wednesday – 0526.

Envir. : Tattershall Castle★ (15C Keep) *AC*, SE : 3½ m.

18 The Broadway ✆ 52511.

◆London 138 – Lincoln 18.

Golf, The Broadway, LN10 6SG, ✆ 53535, Fax 53096, – rm – 100. AE VISA
M (bar lunch Monday to Saturday)/dinner 14.50 **st.** and a la carte 4.50 – **50 rm** 70.00/90.00 **st.** – SB 70.00/95.00 **st.**

Dower House, Manor Estate, via Spa Rd, LN10 6PY, ✆ 52588, « Country house atmosphere », – . AE VISA
M (bar lunch)/dinner 12.50 **st.** and a la carte 3.05 – **7 rm** 35.00/48.00 **st.**

Oglee, 16 Stanhope Av., LN10 6SP, ✆ 53512, – . VISA
M (by arrangement) 8.00 3.00 – **5 rm** 17.00/36.00 **s.**

Duns, The Broadway, LN10 6SQ, ✆ 52969 –
M (by arrangement) 7.00 **st.** – **6 rm** 15.00/40.00 **st.**

WOODSTOCK Oxon. 403 404 P 28 – pop. 3 057 – ECD : Wednesday – 0993.

See : Blenheim Palace★★★ (18C) (park and gardens★★★) *AC*.

Envir. : Rousham (Manor House gardens : statues★) NE : 5 m. – Ditchley Park★ (Renaissance) *AC*, NW : 6 m.

Hensington Rd ✆ 811038 (summer only).

◆London 65 – Gloucester 47 – ◆Oxford 8.

Bear (T.H.F.), Park St., OX7 1SZ, ✆ 811511, Telex 837921, Fax 813380, « Part 16C inn » – 30. AE VISA
M 17.95/38.00 **st.** and a la carte 5.80 – 8.75 – **41 rm** 80.00/110.00 **st.**, **4 suites** 150.00/180.00 **st.** – SB 124.00/154.00 **st.**

Feathers, Market St., OX7 1SX, ✆ 812291, Fax 813158, « Tastefully furnished » – rest. AE VISA
M 19.50/26.50 and a la carte 18.00 – **14 rm** 75.00/145.00 **t.** – SB (November-March) 145.00 **st.**

ROVER 2 Oxford St. ✆ 811286

WOODY BAY Devon 403 I 30 – see Lynton.

Pleasant hotels and restaurants are shown in the Guide by a red sign.

Please send us the names of any where you have enjoyed your stay.

Your Michelin Guide will be even better.

…

XXXXX … X

WOOLACOMBE Devon 403 H 30 **The West Country G.** – pop. 1 171 – ECD : Wednesday – 0271.

Envir. : Mortehoe★★ – Morte Point (vantage point★) – Mortehoe Church★.

Hall 70, Beach Rd 870553 (summer only).

◆London 237 – Barnstaple 15 – Exeter 55.

- **Little Beach,** The Esplanade, EX34 7DJ, 870398, ←, – TV ☎ P. VISA
  February-October – **M** (residents only) (bar lunch)/dinner 10.50 3.00 – **10 rm** 25.00/60.00 **st.** – SB (February-24 May) 55.00/60.00 **st.**
- Waters Fall, Beach Rd, EX34 7AD, 870365, ←, – rest P
  17 rm.

at Mortehoe N : ½ m. – ✉ 0271 Woolacombe :

- **Watersmeet,** The Esplanade, EX34 7EB, 870333, Fax 870890, ← Morte Bay, heated, – rest TV ☎ P. AE VISA.
  Mid February-November and Christmas – **M** (dinner only) 19.50 **st.** 4.25 – **26 rm** 60.00/130.00 **st.**
- **Sunnycliffe,** Chapel Hill, EX34 7EB, 870597, ← – rest TV P.
  closed December and January – **M** (dinner only) 12.00 **st.** – **8 rm** 23.00/40.00 **st.** – SB 57.00/70.00 **st.**

WOOLER Northumb. 401 402 N 17 – pop. 1 925 – ECD : Thursday – 0668.

Envir. : Chillingham Wild Cattle★ in Chillingham Park E : 6 m.

9 Doddington 81956, NE : 2 m.

Bus Station Car Park, High St. 81602 (summer only).

◆London 332 – ◆Edinburgh 62 – ◆Newcastle-upon-Tyne 46.

- Ryecroft, 28 Ryecroft Way, NE71 6AB, 81459 – ☎ P
  9 rm.

FORD, SUZUKI Haughead 81316

"Short Breaks"

Many hotels now offer a special rate for a stay of 2 nights which includes dinner, bed and breakfast.

WOOLHOPE Heref. and Worc. 403 404 M 27 – ✉ Hereford – 043 277 Fownhope.

◆London 127 – Gloucester 25 – Hereford 8 – Worcester 25.

- Butchers Arms, HR1 4RF, E : ½ m. on Putley rd 281, ←, – TV P.
  3 rm.

WOOLLEY EDGE SERVICE AREA West Yorks. – ✉ 0924 Wakefield

- **Granada Lodge** without rest., WF4 4LQ, M 1 between junctions 38 and 39 830371, Fax 830609 – rm TV P. AE VISA.
  31 rm 27.50/29.50 **st.**

WORCESTER Heref. and Worc. 403 404 N 27 – pop. 75 466 – ECD : Thursday – 0905.

See : Cathedral★★ (13C-15C) (crypt★★ 11C) – The Commandery★ (15C) *AC* B.

Envir. : Great Witley : Witley Court (ruins) and the Parish Church of St. Michael and All Saints (Baroque interior★★) NW : 12 m. by A 443.

18 Boughton Park 422555, W : 1m. – 9 The Fairway, Tolladine Rd 21074.

Guildhall, High St. 726311.

◆London 124 – ◆Birmingham 26 – ◆Bristol 61 – ◆Cardiff 74.

Plan opposite

- Fownes, City Walls Rd, WR1 2AP, 613151, Telex 335021, Fax 23742, « Converted glove factory », – TV ☎ P – 125 **a**
  58 rm, 3 suites.
- Star, Foregate St., 24308, Telex 33075, Fax 23440 – TV ☎ P – 100 **u**
  46 rm.
- **Giffard** (T.H.F.), High St., WR1 2QR, 726262, Telex 338869, Fax 723458 – rm TV ☎ P – 120. AE VISA **r**
  M *(closed Saturday lunch)* 8.50/11.50 **st.** and a la carte 4.35 – **101 rm** 60.00/80.00 **st.**, **2 suites** 75.00/95.00 **st.** – SB (weekends only) 84.00/96.00 **st.**
- **Ye Olde Talbot** (Lansbury), Friar St., WR1 2NA, 23573, Telex 333315, Fax 612760 – rm TV ☎ P. AE VISA **e**
  M 8.95/14.00 **t.** and a la carte – **29 rm** 63.00/76.00 **t.** – SB (weekends only) 64.00/76.00 **st.**
- **Brown's,** 24 Quay St., WR1 2JN, 26263, « Attractively converted riverside corn mill » – AE VISA **c**
  closed Saturday lunch, Sunday dinner, 24 to 31 December and Bank Holiday Mondays – **M** 18.00/26.00 **t.** 3.00.

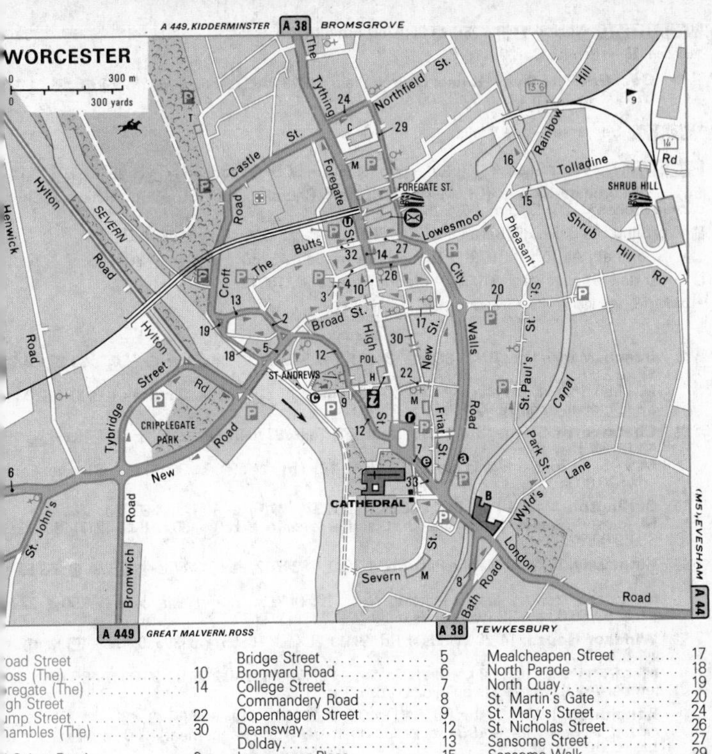

oad Street
oss (The) 10
regate (The) 14
gh Street
ump Street 22
hambles (The) 30

l Saints Road 2
ngel Place 3
ngel Street 4

Bridge Street 5
Bromyard Road 6
College Street 7
Commandery Road 8
Copenhagen Street 9
Deansway 12
Dolday 13
Lowesmoor Place 15
Lowesmoor Terrace 16

Mealcheapen Street 17
North Parade 18
North Quay 19
St. Martin's Gate 20
St. Mary's Street 24
St. Nicholas Street 26
Sansome Street 27
Sansome Walk 29
Shaw Street 32
Sidbury 33

at Upton Snodsbury E : 6 m. by A 44 on A 422 – ✉ Worcester – ☎ 090 560 Upton Snodsbury :

Upton House, WR7 4NR, on B 4082 (beside church) ☎ 226, « Tastefully furnished », – ⇝ rm TV **P**.
M (by arrangement) 18.50 **st.** – **3 rm** 40.00/60.00 **st.**

at Leigh W : 5 m. by A 4103 – ✉ Worcester – ☎ 0886 Leigh Sinton :

Leigh Court, WR6 5LB, ☎ 32275, park – **P**
28 March-6 October – **M** (by arrangement) 11.00 **st.** – **3 rm** 18.00/33.00 **st.**

ICHELIN Distribution Centre, Blackpole Trading Estate, WR3 8TJ, ☎ **55626, Fax 754188** by 38

AIMLER, JAGUAR Castle St. ☎ 726116
AT Malvern Rd, Powick ☎ 830361
ORD Bath Rd ☎ 763123
ONDA Pershore Rd, Stoulton ☎ 840661
ADA Droitwich Rd ☎ 58538
IAZDA Kempsey ☎ 821132
ERCEDES-BENZ Farrier St. ☎ 613711
ISSAN Bransford Rd ☎ 428101
EUGEOT-TALBOT Bath Rd ☎ 820777
ENAULT St. Martins Gate ☎ 21215
ENAULT The Butts ☎ 24252

ROVER Castle St. ☎ 723100
SAAB Kempsey ☎ 821132
SKODA Bromsgrove St. ☎ 23532
SUBARU, ISUZU Pierpoint St. ☎ 25786
VAUXHALL-OPEL Hallow ☎ 640228
VAUXHALL-OPEL Brook St. ☎ 726222
VOLVO Bromyard Rd ☎ 748282
VW-AUDI Hallow Rd ☎ 640228

ATS Little London, Barbourne ☎ 24009/28543

ORFIELD Shropshire – see Bridgnorth.

ORSLEY Greater Manchester 402 403 404 MN 23 – see Manchester.

Si vous cherchez un hôtel tranquille,
consultez d'abord les cartes de l'introduction
ou repérez dans le texte les établissements indiqués avec le signe ou .

WORSTEAD Norfolk 404 Y 25 – ☎ 069 260 Smallburgh.
♦London 128 – ♦Norwich 19.

- **Geoffrey The Dyer House,** Church Plain, NR28 9AL, ☎ 562 – rm TV P.
M 7.00 **s.** – **4 rm** 16.00/32.00 **s.**

WORTH Somerset – see Wells.

WORTHING West Sussex 404 S 31 – pop. 90 687 – ECD : Wednesday – ☎ 0903.
Envir. : Shoreham-by-Sea (St. Mary of Haura's Church★ 12C-13C – St. Nichola's Chur carved arches★ 12C) E : 5 m. by A 259 BY.
18 Worthing Hill Barn, Hill Barn Lane ☎ 37301 BY – 18, 18 Links Rd ☎ 60801 AY.
Shoreham Airport : ☎ 079 17 (Shoreham-by-Sea) 452304, E : 4 m. by A 27 BY.
Town Hall, Chapel Rd ☎ 210022 – Marine Parade ☎ 210022.
♦London 59 – ♦Brighton 11 – ♦Southampton 50.

Plan opposite

- **Beach,** Marine Par., BN11 3QJ, ☎ 34001, Fax 34567, ← – TV ☎ P – . AE VISA AZ
M 11.50/16.00 **t.** and a la carte 4.00 – **84 rm** 45.50/77.50 **t.**, **3 suites** 106.00/112.00 **t** SB (October-April) 75.00/100.00 **st.**
- **Chatsworth,** Steyne, BN11 3DU, ☎ 36103, Telex 877046, Fax 823726 – TV ☎ – 15 AE VISA. BZ
M 9.85/13.75 **t.** and a la carte 3.75 – **105 rm** 52.00/130.00 **t.** – SB (weekend only) 70.00 **st.**
- **Burlington,** Marine Par., BN11 3QL, ☎ 211222 – TV ☎ – . AE VISA.
M *(closed Sunday dinner)* 13.00 **st.** and a la carte 3.50 – **30 rm** 42.00/80.00 **st.** SB 69.00/72.00 **st.** AZ
- **Kingsway,** 117-119 Marine Par., BN11 3QQ, ☎ 37542, Fax 204173 – TV ☎ P. AE VISA AZ
M *(closed Monday lunch)* (carving rest.) 10.50/13.50 **t.** and a la carte 4.50 – **22 r** 42.50/66.00 **t.** – SB (weekends only) 70.00/109.00 **st.**
- **Windsor House,** 14-20 Windsor Rd, BN11 2LX, ☎ 39655, Fax 39655, – TV ☎ P. VISA. BY
M (carving rest.) 10.50/11.50 and a la carte 3.50 – **33 rm** 23.50/90.00 **t.** – SB (Mid Se tember-April) (weekends only) 52.00/62.00 **st.**
- **Bonchurch,** 1 Winchester Rd, BN11 4DJ, ☎ 202492 – rest TV P. AZ
closed 1 week May and 3 weeks October – **M** (by arrangement) 8.00 **st.** 2.00 – **7 r** 13.00/32.00 **st.**
- **Beacons,** 18 Shelley Rd, BN11 1TV, ☎ 30948 – TV P. VISA BZ
M 7.95 **st.** – **5 rm** 18.50/37.00 **st.**
- **South Dene,** 41 Warwick Gdns, BN11 1PF, ☎ 32909 – TV. BZ
closed 23 December-3 January – **M** (by arrangement) – **6 rm** 14.00/32.00.
- XX **Trenchers,** 118-120 Portland Rd, BN11 1QA, ☎ 820287 – AE VISA BZ
closed Saturday lunch, Sunday and Monday – **M** 19.50/24.00 **t.** and a la carte 28.20/38.50
- XX **Paragon,** 9-10 Brunswick Rd, BN11 3NG, ☎ 33367 – AE VISA AZ
closed Sunday, Christmas and New Year – **M** 18.50 **st.** and a la carte 13.95/22.70 **st.** 3.75
- X **Grapes,** 3 Bath Pl., BN11 3BA, ☎ 32424, Bistro – AE VISA BZ
closed lunch Saturday and Bank Holidays and Sunday – **M** 12.50 **t.** (dinner) and a carte 11.00/15.50 **t.** 3.50.

at Findon N : 4 m. by A 24 – AY – ✉ Worthing – ☎ 0903 Findon :

- **Findon Manor** , High St., BN14 0TA, ☎ 872733, « Part 16C stone and flint house » – TV ☎ P. AE VISA
closed 25 December-1 January – **M** *(closed lunch Monday and Saturday and Sunday dinner)* 10.50 **t.** (lunch) and a la carte 10.85/18.90 **t.** – **10 rm** 55.00/100.00 **t.**

at Angmering W : 6¼ m. by A 259 – AY – ✉ ☎ 0903 Worthing :

- XX Belties, High St., BN16 4AE, ☎ 787080.

at East Preston W : 6½ m. by A 259 – AY – off B 2225 – ✉ Littlehampton – ☎ 0903 Rustington :

- XX **Old Forge,** The Street, BN16 1JJ, ☎ 782040, « 17C cottage » – P. AE VISA
closed Sunday dinner and Monday – **M** 10.00 **st.** (lunch) and a la carte 12.70/28.50 **st** 3.80.

ALFA-ROMEO Lancing ☎ 766981
FIAT 123 Upper Brighton Rd ☎ 36065
NISSAN Broadwater Rd ☎ 206091
RENAULT Portland Rd ☎ 200820/823442
ROVER Broadwater Rd ☎ 31111
SAAB, PEUGEOT-TALBOT St. Lawrence Av. ☎ 207703

SKODA Tarring ☎ 34363
TALBOT Broadwater Rd ☎ 262338
VAUXHALL-OPEL Goring Rd ☎ 42389
VOLVO 187 Findon Rd ☎ 090 671 (Findon) 3022

ATS 34 Thorn Rd ☎ 37640/820971

WORTHING

Street	Grid	No.
apel Road	BZ	
ildbourne Centre	BZ	
ontague Street	BZ	
ontague Place Shopping Centre	BZ	
uth Street (WORTHING)	BZ	
oadwater Road	BZ	3
oadwater Street West	BY	5
oadway (The)	BZ	6
ougham Road	BY	7
unswick Road	AZ	8
Church Road	AY	12
Cowper Road	AZ	13
Crockhurst Hill	AY	14
Durrington Hill	AY	15
Eriswell Road	ABZ	16
Goring Street	AY	17
Goring Way	AY	18
Grafton Road	BZ	20
High Street	BZ	21
Liverpool Road	BZ	22
Mulberry Lane	AY	24
Portland Road	BZ	25
Rectory Road	AY	26
Reigate Road	AY	27
Sompting Avenue	BY	28
Sompting Road	BY	29
South Street (WEST TARRING)	AY, AZ	30
Southfarm Road	ABZ	31
Steyne (The)	BZ	32
Steyne Garden	BZ	33
Stoke Abbot Road	BZ	34
Tennyson Road	AZ	36
Thorn Road	AZ	37
Union Place	BZ	38
Warwick Road	BZ	40
Warwick Street	BZ	41
West Street	BZ	42
Western Place	BZ	44
Wykeham Road	AZ	45

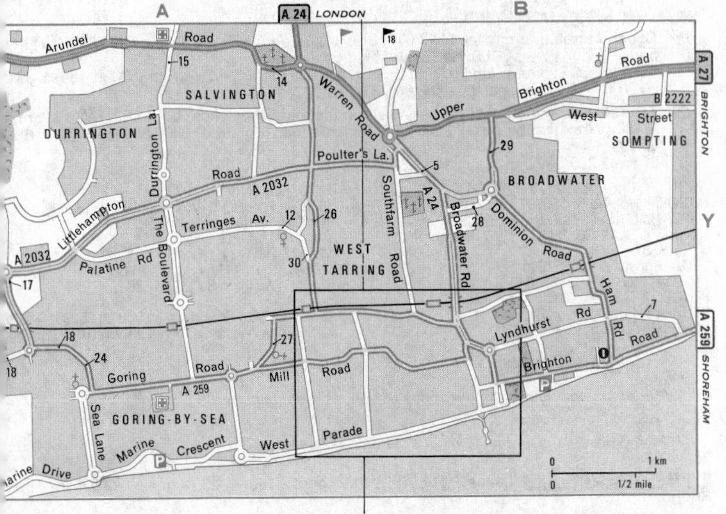

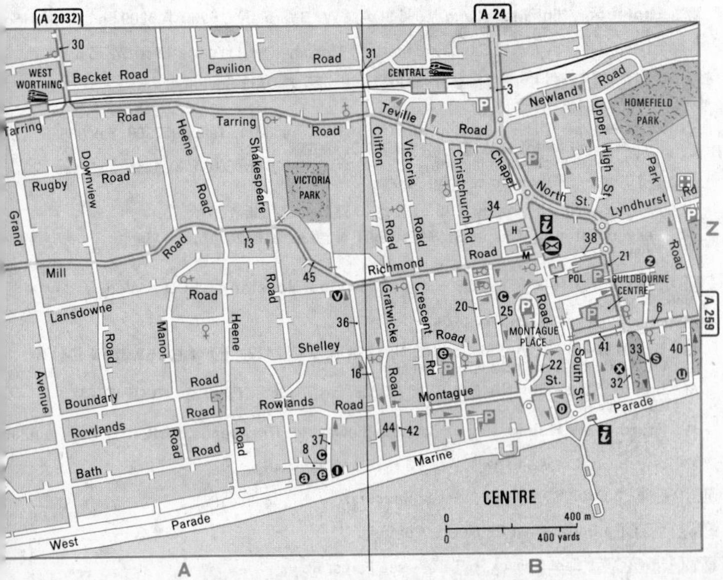

(A 2032)
A 24
WEST WORTHING
Becket Road
Pavilion Road
CENTRAL
Tarring Road
Teville Road
Newland Road
HOMEFIELD PARK
Upper High St.
Park Road
Rugby Road
Downview
Heene Road
Shakespeare
VICTORIA PARK
Clifton Road
Victoria Road
Christchurch Rd
Chapel Road
North St.
Lyndhurst Rd
Grand Avenue
Mill Road
Richmond Road
Lansdowne Road
Manor Road
Shelley
Gratwicke Road
Crescent Road
MONTAGUE PLACE
GUILDBOURNE CENTRE
South St.
Boundary Road
Rowlands Road
Montague St.
Parade
Bath Road
Marine Parade
West Parade
Z
A 259
CENTRE
0 400 m
0 400 yards
A
B

WRAFTON Devon 403 H 30 – see Braunton.

WRAY Lancs. 402 M 21 – ✉ Lancaster – ☎ 052 42 Lancaster.
◆London 258 – ◆Blackpool 44 – Kendal 24 – Lancaster 10.

- Lane Head, Millhouses, LA2 8NF, E : 1 ¼ m. ℘ 21148 – TV P
4 rm.

WREXHAM **(WRECSAM)** Clwyd 402 403 L 24 – pop. 39 929 – ECD : Wednesday – ☎ 0978.
See : St. Giles' Church★.
Envir. : Erddig House★ (17C-18C) *AC*, SW : 2 m.
Holt Rd ℘ 261033, NE : 1 ¾ m.
Memorial Hall, Town Centre ℘ 357845 (summer only).
◆London 192 – Chester 12 – Shrewsbury 28.

- **Cross Lanes,** Marchwiel, LL13 0TF, SE : 3 ½ m. on A 525 ℘ 780555, Fax 780568, park – TV ☎ P – 100. AE VISA
M *(closed Saturday lunch)* 9.95/13.95 **t.** and a la carte 4.25 – 4.00 – **18 rm** 35.00/70.00 **t.** – SB (weekends only) 65.00/78.00 **st.**
- **Travelodge** without rest., Croes-Foel roundabout, Rhostyllen, LL14 4EJ, SW : 3 ½ m. on A 483 (Wrexham by-pass) ℘ 365705, Reservations (Toll free) 0800 850950 – TV P. AE VISA.
31 rm 24.00/29.50 **t.**

AUDI-VW Rhosrobin ℘ 291177
CITROEN Holt Rd ℘ 356707
FORD Holt Rd ℘ 290690
HYUNDAI, SUBARU, ISUZU New Broughton ℘ 757838
LADA Rhostyllen ℘ 357996
MAZDA Market Pl. ℘ 351648
PEUGEOT-TALBOT Castle St. ℘ 270271
RENAULT Regent St. ℘ 356822
ROVER Wrexham Rd ℘ 842369
SEAT Llay New Rd ℘ 720074
SKODA, HYUNDAI Wrexham Rd ℘ 263438
TOYOTA Wrexham Rd ℘ 840578
VAUXHALL-OPEL Mold Rd ℘ 290077
VOLVO Hill St. ℘ 262685
VW-AUDI Llay New Rd ℘ 291177
YUGO Wrexham Rd ℘ 350328

ATS Dolydd Rd, Croesnewydd ℘ 352301/35292
ATS Eagles Meadow, Clwyd ℘ 366510

"Short Breaks" (SB)

De nombreux hôtels proposent des conditions avantageuses
pour un séjour de deux nuits
comprenant la chambre, le dîner et le petit déjeuner.

WRIGHTINGTON BAR Lancs. 402 404 L 23 – pop. 3 160 – ✉ Wigan – ☎ 025 75 Apple Bridge.
◆London 210 – ◆Liverpool 24 – ◆Manchester 30 – Preston 15.

- XXX **Highmoor,** High Moor Lane, WN6 9QA, SW : 3 ½ m. by B 5250, A 5209 and Robin Hood Lane ℘ 2364 – P. AE VISA
closed Saturday lunch, Sunday dinner and Monday – **M** a la carte 17.50/24.75 **t.** 4.80.

WROTHAM HEATH Kent 404 U 30 – pop. 1 669 – ✉ ☎ 0732 Sevenoaks.
◆London 35 – Maidstone 10.

- **Post House** (T.H.F.), London Rd, TN15 7RS, ℘ 883311, Telex 957309, Fax 885850, – rm TV ☎ P – 60. AE VISA
M 13.25/16.95 **st.** and a la carte 4.50 – 8.50 – **116 rm** 80.00/90.00 **st.**, **2 suites** 120.00/140.00 **st.** – SB (weekends only) 94.00 **st.**

at Ryarsh NE : 3 ½ m. by A 20 – ✉ ☎ 0732 West Malling :

- Heavers Farm, Chapel St., ME19 5JU, N : ½ m. ℘ 842074, – P
3 rm.

WROXHAM Norfolk 404 Y 25 – pop. 2 954 (inc. Hoveton) – ECD : Wednesday – ✉ ☎ 0603 Norwich.
◆London 118 – Great Yarmouth 21 – ◆Norwich 7.

- **Kings Head** (B.C.B.), Station Rd, NR12 8UR, ℘ 782429 – TV ☎ P. AE VISA.
M 15.00 **st.** – **6 rm** 36.50/48.50 **st.**
- Broads, Station Rd, NR12 8UR, ℘ 782869, Fax 784066 – TV ☎ P. AE VISA
26 rm 30.00/52.00 **t.**
- **Staitheway House** without rest., Staitheway Rd, The Avenue, NR12 8TH, SW : ½ m. by A 1151 ℘ 783347, – P.
closed Christmas and New Year – **3 rm** 18.20/34.40 **s.**

WROXTON Oxon. 403 404 P 27 – see Banbury.

WYBOSTON Beds. – see St. Neots (Cambs.).

WYCH CROSS East Sussex 404 U 30 – see Forest Row.

WYE Kent 404 W 30 – pop. 1 396 – ECD : Wednesday – ✉ Ashford – ☎ 0233.
London 61 – Folkestone 21 – Maidstone 24 – Margate 28.

Woodmans Arms Auberge, Hassell Street, TN25 5JE, E : 4 m. by Hastingleigh rd off Waltham rd ☎ 023 375 (Elmsted) 250, – ⊁ TV P.
closed 1 to 14 April and 2 to 29 September – **M** (booking essential) (dinner only, residents only) 17.25 **st.** 4.50 – **3 rm** 63.25/80.50 **st.**

ROVER Bridge St. ☎ 812331

WYMONDHAM Norfolk 404 X 26 – pop. 9 088 – ECD : Wednesday – ☎ 0953.
London 110 – Cambridge 53 – Norwich 9.

Sinclair, 28 Market St., NR18 0BB, ☎ 606721, Fax 601361 – TV ☎ P. AE VISA.
M 12.50/15.00 **t.** and a la carte 3.85 – **20 rm** 39.00/49.00 **t.** – SB 60.00/70.00 **st.**

Jennings, 16 Damgate St., NR18 0BQ, ☎ 603533. AE VISA
closed Sunday, Monday, 1 week spring, 1 week summer and Bank Holidays – **M** (booking essential) (lunch by arrangement)/dinner 22.50 **t.** 3.50.

WYNDS POINT Heref. and Worc. 403 404 M 27 – see Great Malvern.

WYRE PIDDLE Heref. and Worc. – see Pershore.

YARM Cleveland 402 P 20 – pop. 6 360 – ☎ 0642 Middlesbrough.
London 242 – Middlesbrough 8.

Crathorne Hall, Crathorne, TS15 0AR, S : 3½ m. by A 67 ☎ 700398, Telex 587426, Fax 700814, « Converted Edwardian mansion », , park – TV ☎ P – 150. AE VISA.
M 16.00/18.00 **st.** and a la carte – **38 rm** 80.00/110.00 **st.**, **1 suite** 120.00 **st.** – SB (weekends only and August) 100.00 **st.**

YATELEY Surrey 404 R 29 – pop. 14 121 – ECD : Wednesday – ✉ Camberley – ☎ 0252.
London 37 – Reading 12 – Southampton 58.

Casa Dei Cesari, Handford Lane, Cricket Hill, GU17 7BA, ☎ 873275, – TV ☎ P. AE VISA.
closed Christmas – **M** (Italian rest.) a la carte 17.75/23.00 **t.** 4.00 – **36 rm** 50.00/120.00 **st.**

YATTENDON Berks. 403 404 Q 29 – pop. 568 – ECD : Saturday – ✉ Newbury – ☎ 0635 Hermitage.
London 62 – Newbury 8 – Reading 12.

Royal Oak with rm, The Square, RG16 0UF, ☎ 201325, Fax 201926, – TV ☎ P. AE VISA.
closed Christmas Day – **M** *(closed Sunday dinner)* (booking essential) a la carte approx. 25.30 **t.** – **5 rm** 60.00/80.00 **t.** – SB (weekends only) (except Christmas and New Year) 100.00 **st.**

YELVERTON Devon 403 H 32 – ☎ 0822.
Golf Links Rd ☎ 853618.
London 234 – Exeter 33 – Plymouth 9.

Moorland Links, PL20 6DA, S : 2 m. on A 386 ☎ 852245, Telex 45616, Fax 855004, ≤, , – ⊁ rm TV ☎ P – 170. AE VISA
closed 26 December-3 January – **M** *(closed Saturday lunch)* a la carte 12.50/22.45 **t.** – **29 rm** 57.50/84.70 **t.**, **1 suite** 95.00/100.00 **t.** – SB (weekends only) 95.00 **st.**

Overcombe, Horrabridge, PL20 7RN, N : 1¼ m. on A 386 ☎ 853501, ≤, – ⊁ rest TV P. VISA
M 10.50 **st.** 2.80 – **11 rm** 18.00/41.00 **st.** – SB (October-May) 53.00/63.00 **st.**

Harrabeer Country House, Harrowbeer Lane, PL20 6EA, ☎ 853302, , – ⊁ rest TV ☎ P. AE VISA.
M 12.00 **st.** 3.50 – **7 rm** 21.00/47.00 **st.** – SB (weekdays only) (except Bank Holidays) 85.00/87.00 **st.**

YEOVIL Somerset 403 404 M 31 **The West Country G.** – pop. 36 114 – ECD : Monday and Thursday – ☎ 0935.
See : St. John the Baptist Church★.
Envir. : Montacute House★★*AC*, W : 4 m. on A 3088 – Fleet Air Arm Museum★★*AC*, NW : 8 m. by A 37 – Long Sutton★ (Church★★), NW : 10 m. – Huish Episcopi : Church Tower★★, NW : 13 m. – Martock : All Saints Church★★, W : 7 m. – Cadbury Castle (≤★★), NE : 11 m. by A 359 – Ham Hill (≤★★), W : 4 m. – Tintinhull House★*AC*, NW : 5 m.
Sherborne Rd ☎ 75949.
Petters House, Petters Way ☎ 71279.
London 136 – Exeter 48 – Southampton 72 – Taunton 26.

Yeovil Court, West Coker Rd., BA20 2NE, SW : 2 m. on A 30 ✆ 093 586 (West Coker) 3746, Fax 3990, – 📺 ☎ 🅿 – 50. AE VISA
M *(closed Saturday lunch)* 9.50/19.00 **t.** and a la carte 12.95/21.75 **st.** 4.95 – **18 rm** 44.00/59.00 **st.**, **1 suite** 75.00/85.00 **st.** – SB (weekends only) 55.00/75.00 **st.**

Manor Crest (T.H.F.), Hendford Rd, BA20 1TG, ✆ 23116, Telex 46580, Fax 706607, – rm rest 📺 ☎ 🅿 – 60. AE VISA
M *(closed Saturday lunch)* 9.50/16.00 **st.** and a la carte – 7.95 – **41 rm** 64.00/76.00 **st.** – SB 76.00/84.00 **st.**

Travelodge without rest., Podimore, BA22 8JG, N : 9 ½ m. by A 37 on A 303 ✆ 840074 Reservations (Toll free) 0800 850950 – 📺 & 🅿. AE VISA.
31 rm 24.00/29.50 **t.**

at Barwick S : 2 m. by A 30 off A 37 – ✉ ☎ 0935 Yeovil :

XX **Little Barwick House** with rm, BA22 9TD, ✆ 23902, ←, – rest rest 📺 ☎ 🅿. AE VISA
closed Christmas-New Year – **M** *(closed Sunday to non-residents)* (booking essential) (dinner only) 18.90/20.90 **t.** 4.20 – **6 rm** 47.00/70.00 **st.** – SB (October-March) 80.00 **st.**

at West Coker SW : 3 ½ m. on A 30 – ✉ ☎ 0935 Yeovil :

Four Acres, High St., BA22 9AJ, ✆ 2555, Telex 46666, Fax 3929, – 📺 ☎ 🅿. AE VISA
M 16.00 **st.** and a la carte 3.25 – **25 rm** 45.00/62.00 **st.** – SB (weekends only) 69.50/74.00 **st.**

at East Chinnock SW : 5 m. on A 30 – ✉ Yeovil – ☎ 093 586 West Coker :

Barrows Country House, Weston St., BA22 9EJ, ✆ 2390, – 🅿.
closed 24 December-2 January – **M** 6.00 **s.** 2.00 – 3.00 – **6 rm** 13.00/30.00 **s.**

at Montacute W : 5 ½ m. on A 3088 – ✉ Yeovil – ☎ 0935 Martock :

Kings Arms, Bishopston, TA15 6UU, ✆ 822513, – rest 📺 ☎ 🅿. AE VISA
M (buffet lunch)/dinner a la carte 12.95/15.20 **t.** 3.50 – **11 rm** 42.00/72.00 **t.** – SB 55.00/89.00 **st.**

XX **Milk House** with rm, The Borough, TA15 6XB, ✆ 823823, – . VISA.
M *(closed Sunday, Monday and Tuesday)* (dinner only) 14.00/20.00 **st.** 3.20 – **2 rm** 40.00/58.00 **st.**

FORD West Henford ✆ 27421
NISSAN Marston Magna ✆ 850386
ROVER, DAIMLER, JAGUAR Market St. ✆ 75242
SAAB 12 Oxford Rd ✆ 26701
VAUXHALL-OPEL Addlewell Lane ✆ 74842
VOLVO Reckleford ✆ 72381

ATS Penmill Trading Est., Lyde Rd ✆ 75580 71780

Y-FENNI = Abergavenny.

YORK North Yorks. 402 Q 22 – pop. 123 126 – ECD : Monday and Wednesday – ☎ 0904.

See : Site★★★ – Minster★★★ (13C-15C) (Stained Glass★★★ Chapter House★★★, ✻★★ from tower, *AC*, 275 steps) CDY – National Railway Museum★★★ CY – City Walls★★ (14C) CDYZ – Castle Museum★*AC* DZ **M2** – Jorvik Viking Centre★ DY **M1** – Fairfax House★ DY **A** – The Shambles★ DY.

18 Lords Moor Lane, Strensall ✆ 491840, NE : 6 m. by Huntington Rd BY – 9 Heworth, Muncaster Gate ✆ 424618 B – 18 Pike Hills, Tadcaster Rd, Copmanthorpe ✆ 706566, W : 3 m AZ – 18 Fulford, Heslington Lane ✆ 413579, S : 2 m. Z.

De Grey Rooms, Exhibition Sq. ✆ 621756 – York Railway Station, Outer Concourse ✆ 643700

♦London 203 – ♦Kingston-upon-Hull 38 – ♦Leeds 26 – ♦Middlesbrough 51 – ♦Nottingham 88 – ♦Sheffield 62.

Plan opposite

Middlethorpe Hall, Bishopthorpe Rd, YO2 1QP, S : 1 m. ✆ 641241, Telex 57802 Fax 620176, ←, « William and Mary house, gardens », park – 📺 ☎ 🅿 – 30. AE VISA. by A 19 BZ
M 16.90/28.50 **st.** and a la carte 23.55/36.90 **st.** 8.90 – **Grill** *(April-September)* (dinner only) 31.50 **st.** 8.90 – 9.50 – **26 rm** 85.00/125.00 **st.**, **5 suites** 170.00/195.00 **st.** – SB (November-April) (except Bank Holidays) 156.00/222.00 **st.**

Holiday Inn York Cliffords Tower, 1 Tower St., YO1 1SB, ✆ 648111, Telex 57566 Fax 610317 – rm rest 📺 ☎ & 🅿 – 150. AE VISA DY
M *(closed Saturday lunch)* 9.95/14.50 **st.** and a la carte 7.75 – 7.95 – **126 rm** 86.00/100.00 **t.**, **2 suites** 115.00 **t.** – SB (weekends only) 108.00/116.00 **st.**

Viking (Q.M.H.), North St., YO1 1JF, ✆ 659822, Telex 57937, Fax 641793, ←, – rest 📺 ☎ 🅿 – 250. AE VISA. CY
M 8.75/30.00 **st.** and a la carte 4.50 – **187 rm** 70.00/90.00 **st.**, **1 suite** 160.00/220.00 **st.** – SB (weekends only) 96.00/104.00 **st.**

YORK

Street	Grid	No.
Blake Street	CY	5
Coney Street	CY	13
Davygate	CY	16
Lendal	CY	32
Parliament Street	DY	42
Shambles (The)	DY	54
Stonegate	CY	58
Bishopgate Street	CZ	3
Bishophill Senior	CZ	4
Campleshon Road	AZ	7

Street	Grid	No.
Church Street	DY	8
Clifford Street	DY	10
Colliergate	DY	12
Cromwell Road	CZ	15
Deangate	DY	18
Duncombe Place	CY	20
Fawcett Street	DZ	21
Fetter Lane	CY	22
Goodramgate	DY	25
High Ousegate	DY	26
High Petergate	CY	28
Knavesmire Road	AZ	29
Leeman Road	AY, CY	30
Lord Mayor's Walk	DX	33

Street	Grid	No.
Low Petergate	DY	35
Melrosegate	BY	36
Museum Street	CY	39
Pavement	DY	43
Peasholme Green	DY	45
Penley's Grove Street	DX	46
Queen Street	CZ	49
St. Helen's Road	AZ	50
St. Leonard's Place	CY	52
St. Maurice's Road	DXY	53
Station Road	CY	55
Stonebow (The)	DY	56
Tower Street	DZ	59
University Road	BZ	60

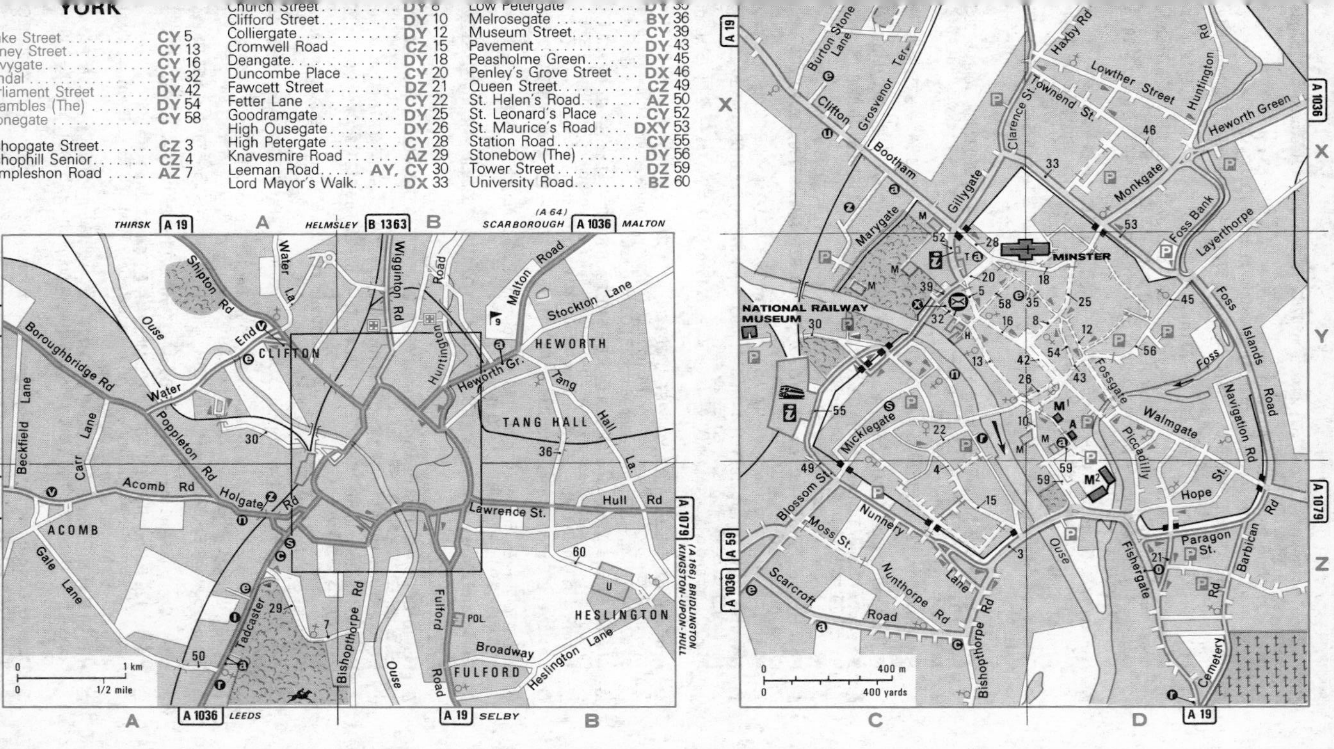

Judges' Lodging, 9 Lendal, YO1 2AQ, ✆ 638733, Telex 57200, « Restored 18C judges lodgings » – TV ☎ P. AE VISA CY
M (bar lunch)/dinner 12.50 **t.** and a la carte 4.50 – 5.50 – **13 rm** 50.00/110.00 **t.** – SB (November-March except Christmas, New Year and Easter) 100.00/120.00 **st.**

The Grange, Clifton, YO3 6AA, ✆ 644744, Telex 57210, Fax 612453, « Regency town house » – TV ☎ & P – 40. AE VISA. CX
M 13.50/19.50 **st.** and a la carte 3.75 – **29 rm** 80.00/120.00 **st.** – SB 125.00/185.00 **st.**

Mount Royale, The Mount, YO2 2DA, ✆ 628856, Telex 57414, Fax 611171, « Tasteful decor and furnishings », heated, – TV ☎ P. AE VISA. AZ
closed 23 to 31 December – **M** *(closed lunch Saturday and Sunday)* 14.95/30.00 **t.** – **20 rm** 75.00/95.00 **t.**, **1 suite** 95.00 **t.**

Hudsons, 60 Bootham, YO3 7BZ, ✆ 621267 – TV ☎ P. AE VISA. CX
closed Sunday lunch – **M** (bar lunch)/dinner 20.00 **t.** and a la carte 4.50 – **28 rm** 45.00/72.00 **st.** – SB 78.00/88.00 **st.**

Dean Court (Best Western), Duncombe Pl., YO1 2EF, ✆ 625082, Telex 57584, Fax 620305 – TV ☎ CY
41 rm.

York Pavilion, 45 Main St., Fulford, YO1 4PJ, S : 1 m. on A 19 ✆ 622099, Telex 57305, Fax 626939, – TV ☎ P. AE VISA. on A19 B
M 18.95 **t.** and a la carte 4.75 – **21 rm** 63.00/83.00 **t.**

Ambassador, 123-125 The Mount, YO2 2DA, ✆ 641316, Fax 640259, – TV ☎ P. VISA AZ
M (bar lunch)/dinner 18.50 **t.** and a la carte – **19 rm** 54.00/90.00 **t.** – SB 88.00/110.00 **st.**

Swallow Chase, Tascaster Rd, YO2 2QQ, ✆ 701000, Telex 57582, Fax 702308, , – rm TV ☎ & P – 100. AE VISA AZ
M 25.00 **st.** and a la carte 4.75 – **112 rm** 83.00/140.00 **st.** – SB 95.00/110.00 **st.**

Post House (T.H.F.), Tadcaster Rd, YO2 2QF, ✆ 707921, Telex 57798, Fax 702804, – rm TV ☎ P – 100. AE VISA AZ
M 11.10/14.10 **st.** and a la carte – 7.50 – **147 rm** 65.00/85.00 **st.** – SB 80.00/100.00 **st.**

Novotel York, Fishergate, YO1 4AD, ✆ 611660, Telex 57556, Fax 610925, heated – rest TV ☎ & P – 300. AE VISA DZ
M 20.00 **st.** and a la carte 4.50 – 6.50 – **124 rm** 58.00/72.00 **st.** – SB (weekends only) 90.00/100.00 **st.**

Arndale, 290 Tadcaster Rd, YO2 2ET, ✆ 702424, – rest TV P. AZ
closed Christmas and New Year – **M** *(closed Thursday)* (dinner only) 11.95 **st.** – **9 rm** 40.00/56.00 **st.** – SB (November-March) 51.00/69.00 **st.**

Clifton Bridge, Water End, YO3 6LL, ✆ 610510, Fax 640208 – TV ☎ P. AE VISA
closed 25 December-1 January – **M** (bar lunch)/dinner a la carte 6.30/11.15 **st.** 3.55 – **14 rm** 35.00/58.00 **st.** – SB (November-March) 62.00/78.00 **st.** AY

Cottage, 3 Clifton Green, YO3 6LH, ✆ 643711, Fax 611230 – TV ☎ P. AE VISA AY
closed Christmas and New Year – **M** (dinner only) 9.50 **t.** and a la carte 4.50 – **19 rm** 30.00/60.00 **t.** – SB 68.00/78.00 **st.**

Grasmead House without rest., 1 Scarcroft Hill, YO2 1DF, ✆ 629996 – rm TV. VISA CZ
6 rm -/48.00 **st.**

Heworth Court, 76-78 Heworth Green, YO3 7TQ, ✆ 425156, Telex 57571, Fax 415290 – TV ☎ P. AE VISA. BY
M 8.50/13.50 **t.** and a la carte 4.40 – **26 rm** 36.00/62.00 **t.** – SB 68.00/75.00 **st.**

Kilima, 129 Holgate Rd, YO2 4DE, ✆ 658844, Telex 57928, Fax 612083, – rest TV ☎ & P. AE VISA AZ
M 16.75 **t.** (dinner) and a la carte 4.35 – **15 rm** 41.00/62.00 **t.** – SB (except Easter, Christmas and New Year) 76.00/94.00 **st.**

Town House, 98-104 Holgate Rd, YO2 4BB, ✆ 636171, Fax 623044 – TV ☎ P. VISA AZ
closed 22 December-2 January – **M** (bar lunch)/dinner 12.50 **t.** and a la carte 3.60 – **23 rm** 20.00/56.00 **t.** – SB (November-March) 60.00 **st.**

Field House, 2 St. Georges Pl., YO2 2DR, ✆ 639572, – rest TV ☎ P. AE VISA AZ
closed Christmas – **M** (dinner only) 10.50 **st.** – **17 rm** 23.00/60.00 **st.** – SB 60.00/80.00 **st.**

Priory, 126 Fulford Rd, YO1 4BE, ✆ 625280, – TV P. AE VISA. DZ
closed Christmas – **M** (dinner only) a la carte 8.55/13.75 **st.** 3.75 – **19 rm** 22.00/45.00 **st.** – SB (winter only) 65.00/70.00 **st.**

Hill, 60 York Rd, Acomb, YO2 5LW, ✆ 790777, – rest TV ☎ P. AE VISA.
closed mid December-mid January – **M** (bar lunch)/dinner 15.00 **st.** 5.40 – **10 rm** 39.50/70.00 **st.** AZ

Curzon Lodge and Stable Cottages without rest., 23 Tadcaster Rd, YO2 2QG ✆ 703157 – TV P. AZ
closed Christmas and New Year – **10 rm** 34.00/52.00 **st.**

⌂ **Hobbits** without rest., 9 St. Peter's Grove, Clifton, YO3 6AQ, ℘ 624538 – ⇔ rm TV P. VISA CX **e**
closed 24 to 26 December – **5 rm** ⊒ 20.00/45.00 **st.**

⌂ **Crook Lodge,** 26 St. Mary's, Bootham, YO3 7DD, ℘ 655614 – TV P. VISA.
M 9.00 **st.** 3.00 – **7 rm** ⊒ 21.50/40.00 **st.** – SB (November-March) 45.00/49.00 **st.** CX **z**

XX **Melton's,** 7 Scarcroft Rd, YO2 1ND, ℘ 634341 – VISA.
closed Sunday, Monday, 29 March, 25 August-2 September and 22 December – **M** a la carte 15.50/20.40 **st.** 4.00. CZ **c**

XX **Restaurant Français** with rm, 103 The Mount, YO2 2AX, ℘ 647339 – TV ☎. VISA. CZ **e**
closed Sunday – **M** (dinner only) 23.00 **t.** and a la carte 3.45 – **6 rm** ⊒ 37.50/75.00 **st.**

X **19 Grape Lane,** 19 Grape Lane, YO1 2HU, ℘ 636366, English rest. – VISA CY **e**
closed Sunday, Monday, last 2 weeks January and last 2 weeks September – **M** 16.50 **t.** (dinner) and a la carte 17.25/25.50 **t.**

X **McCoy's,** 17 Skeldergate, YO1 1DH, ℘ 612191. AE VISA CY **r**
closed 25 December and 1 January – **M** a la carte 12.90/20.20 **t.**

X **Tony's,** 39 Tanner Row, YO1 1JP, ℘ 659622, Greek rest. – AE VISA CY **s**
closed Sunday and Monday – **M** (dinner only) 10.50 **t.** and a la carte 8.70/11.80 **t.**

at Kexby E : 6 ¾ m. on A 1079 B – ✉ York – ☎ 075 95 Wilberfoss :

Kexby Bridge, Hull Rd, YO4 5LD, ℘ 8223, Fax 8822, – ⇔ rm TV ☎ P – 100. VISA.
M 10.95/22.00 **st.** and a la carte 3.50 – **32 rm** ⊒ 50.00/75.00 **st.** – SB 70.00 **st.**

at Bilbrough SW : 5 ½ m. by A 1036 – AZ – off A 64 – ✉ York – ☎ 0937 Tadcaster :

Bilbrough Manor , YO2 3PH, ℘ 834002, Fax 834724, ←, « Tastefully decorated Victorian manor », , park – TV ☎ P. AE VISA.
closed 25 to 29 December – **M** 17.50/29.50 **t.** 8.50 – **12 rm** ⊒ 75.00/135.00 **t.** – SB (October-March) 103.00/147.00 **st.**

at Skelton NW : 3 m. on A 19 – AY – ✉ ☎ 0904 York :

Fairfield Manor, Shipton Rd, YO3 6XW, ℘ 625621, Fax 612725, – TV ☎ P
M 10.50/15.00 **t.** and a la carte 4.75 – **22 rm** ⊒ 49.00/77.00 **t.** – SB (except Bank Holidays) 70.00/77.00 **st.**

LFA-ROMEO Leeman Rd ℘ 622772
OLT Fulford ℘ 633139
IAT Piccadilly ℘ 634321
ORD Piccadilly ℘ 625371
ORD, VAUXHALL-OPEL 117 Long St. ℘ 0347 (Easingwold) 21694
AGUAR, DAIMLER Layerthorpe ℘ 658252
ADA Leeman Rd ℘ 659241
MAZDA 17 Layerthorpe ℘ 658809
PEUGEOT-TALBOT The Stonebow ℘ 655118
TOYOTA 172 Fulford Rd ℘ 652947
VAUXHALL-OPEL Malton Rd ℘ 426688
VOLVO 88-96 Walmgate ℘ 653798

ATS 2 James St. ℘ 412372/410375
ATS 36 Holgate Rd ℘ 654411

YOXFORD Suffolk 404 Y 27 – pop. 690 – ✉ Saxmundham – ☎ 072 877.
London 95 – Ipswich 25 – Norwich 55.

Satis House, Brook St., IP17 3EX, ℘ 418, , – ⇔ rest TV ☎ P. AE VISA.
M *(closed Sunday and Monday to non-residents)* 16.75 **t.** and a la carte 3.95 – **7 rm** ⊒ 39.50/59.00 **st.** – SB (except Bank Holidays) 71.50/84.00 **st.**

YR ORSEDD = Rossett.

YR WYDDFA = Snowdon.

YR WYDDGRUG = Mold.

Scotland

Place with at least :

one hotel or restaurant .... ● Tongue
one pleasant hotel .... 🏨, ⌂, ✗ with rm
one quiet, secluded hotel ....
one restaurant with ..... ✿, ✿✿, ✿✿✿, M
See this town for establishments
located in its vicinity .... ABERDEEN

La località possiede come minimo :

una risorsa alberghiera .... ● Tongu
un albergo ameno .... 🏨, ⌂, ✗ with rr
un albergo molto tranquillo, isolato .....
un'ottima tavola con .... ✿, ✿✿, ✿✿✿,
La località raggruppa nel suo testo
le risorse dei dintorni .... ABERDEE

Localité offrant au moins :

une ressource hôtelière .... ● Tongue
un hôtel agréable .... 🏨, ⌂, ✗ with rm
un hôtel très tranquille, isolé ....
une bonne table à ...... ✿, ✿✿, ✿✿✿, M
Localité groupant dans le texte
les ressources de ses environs .. ABERDEEN

Ort mit mindestens :

einem Hotel oder Restaurant ...... ● Tongu
einem angenehmen Hotel .. 🏨, ⌂, ✗ with rr
einem sehr ruhigen und abgelegenen Hotel
einem Restaurant mit .... ✿, ✿✿, ✿✿✿,
Ort mit Angaben über Hotels und Restaurant
in seiner Umgebung .... ABERDEE

SHETLAND ISLANDS
ISLE OF UNST
Hillswick
Brae
MAINLAND
Walls
Whiteness
Lerwick
ISLE OF WESTRAY
MAINLAND
Dounby
Loch Harray
Stromness
Kirkwall
ORKNEY ISLANDS
St. Margaret's Hope
Thurso
Tongue
Forsinard
Wick
Altnaharra
A 9
Rogart
Lairg
Brora
Golspie
ONAR BRIDGE
Ardgay
Dornoch
Tain
Cromarty
Strathpeffer
Muir of Ord
Beauly
INVERNESS
Nairn
Forres
A 96
Elgin
Buckie
Cullen
Banff
Fordyce
St. Combs
A 952
A 98
Rothes
Marnoch
Peterhead
Craigellachie
Aberlour
Advie
Farr
A 9
Drumnadrochit
Lewiston
Grantown-on-Spey
Insch
Oldmeldrum
Pitcaple
Ellon
Newburgh
Dulnain Bridge
oyers
Invermoriston
Boat of Garten
Kildrummy
Inverurie
Whitebridge
Aviemore
Fort Augustus
Kincraig
ABERDEEN
Newtonmore
Kingussie
Laggan
Ballater
Aboyne
Banchory
A 92
Braemar
Netherley

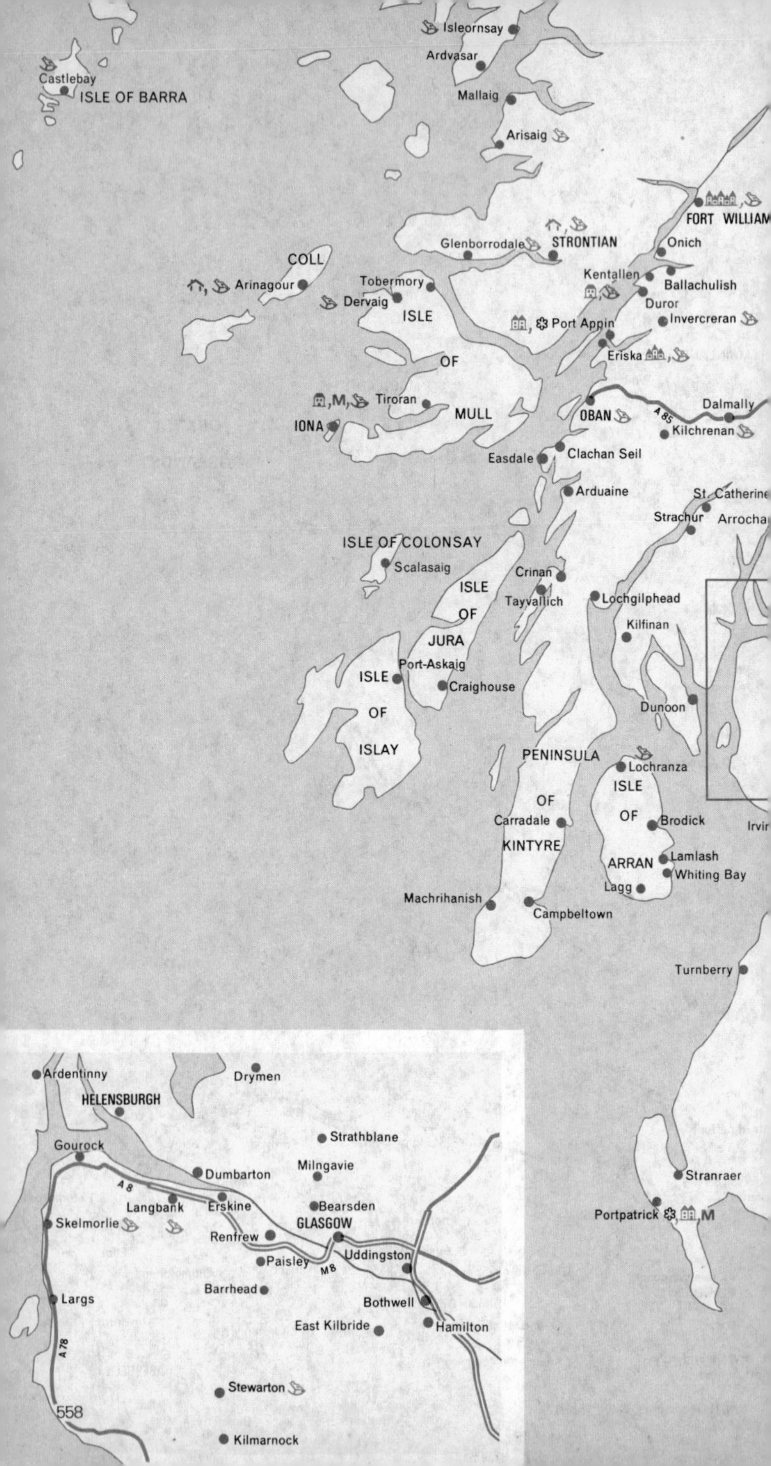

Isleornsay
Ardvasar
Castlebay
ISLE OF BARRA
Mallaig
Arisaig
FORT WILLIAM
Glenborrodale
STRONTIAN
Onich
COLL
Arinagour
Tobermory
Dervaig
Kentallen
Ballachulish
Duror
ISLE
OF
MULL
Port Appin
Invercreran
Eriska
Tiroran
IONA
OBAN
A 85
Dalmally
Kilchrenan
Easdale
Clachan Seil
Arduaine
St. Catherine
Strachur
Arrocha
ISLE OF COLONSAY
Scalasaig
Crinan
Tayvallich
Lochgilphead
ISLE
OF
JURA
Kilfinan
Port-Askaig
Craighouse
ISLE
OF
ISLAY
Dunoon
PENINSULA
OF
KINTYRE
Carradale
Lochranza
ISLE
OF
ARRAN
Brodick
Irvir
Lamlash
Whiting Bay
Lagg
Machrihanish
Campbeltown
Turnberry
Ardentinny
Drymen
HELENSBURGH
Strathblane
Gourock
Milngavie
Dumbarton
A 8
Langbank
Erskine
Bearsden
Skelmorlie
GLASGOW
Renfrew
Uddingston
Paisley
M8
Barrhead
Largs
Bothwell
East Kilbride
Hamilton
A 78
Stewarton
Kilmarnock
Stranraer
Portpatrick
M

Invermoriston
Whitebridge
Fort Augustus
Aviemore
Kincraig
Kildrummy
ABERDEEN
Newtonmore
Kingussie
Laggan
Ballater
Aboyne
Banchory
Netherley
Braemar
Stonehaven
A 92
A 9
Blair Atholl
Edzell
Kirkmichael
PITLOCHRY
Montrose
Forfar
Aberfeldy
Blairgowrie
Kenmore
Meigle
A 92
Arbroath
Dunkeld
Auchterhouse
Kinclaven
KILLIN
A 85
DUNDEE
Crianlarich
St. Fillans
CRIEFF
PERTH
Wormit
Glencarse
Balquhidder
Lochearnhead
STRATHYRE
A 9
Cupar
St. Andrews
Auchterarder
Ladybank
Peat Inn
Brig o'Turk
Callander
Crail
KINROSS
A 84
Dunblane
Markinch
Anstruther
Port of Menteith
Doune
M 90
Bridge of Allan
GLENROTHES
LEVEN
Aberfoyle
STIRLING
KIRKCALDY
DUNFERMLINE
Burntisland
Airth
North Berwick
Aberdour
Denny
GULLANE
Aberlady
Dunbar
FALKIRK
South-Queensferry
East Linton
A 80
A 90
Linlithgow
Musselburgh
Haddington
Uphall
Edinburgh
Gifford
Livingston
M 8
A 68
Dolphinton
Lanark
Lauder
Greenlaw
Peebles
Walkerburn
Quothquan
Galashiels
KELSO
MELROSE
Troon
Prestwick
Tweedsmuir
Selkirk
Ayr
A 74
HAWICK
Roberton
Moffat
Beattock
Eskdalemuir
Thornhill
Dalry
Lockerbie
New Galloway
Dumfries
Canonbie
Newton Stewart
Gretna
Castle Douglas
Dalbeattie
Gatehouse of Fleet
Colvend
Sandyhills
Creetown
Wigtown
Kirkcudbright
Rockcliffe
Auchencairn
Whithorn (Isle of)

ABERDEEN Aberdeen. (Grampian) **401** N 12 **Scotland G** – pop. 186 757 – ECD : Wednesda and Saturday – ☎ 0224.

See : Site★★ – Old Aberdeen★★ X – St. Machar's Cathedral★★ (West front★★★, heraldi ceiling★★★) X **A** – Mercat Cross★★ Y **B** – Art Gallery★★ Y **M** – King's College Chapel★ (Crow spire★★★, medieval fittings★★★) X **D** – Brig o'Balgownie★ by Don Street X – Maritime Mu seum★ Z **M1** – Provost Skene's House★ (Painted ceiling★★) Y **E** – Marischal College★ Y **U**.

Envir. : Deeside★★ and Lin O'Dee★ Tour of 64 m., W : by A 93 X – Grampian Castle country★ (Craigievar★★★) W : 27 m. by A 944 X and B 9119 – Crathes Castle★★, SW : 14 m. by A 93 X Kildrummy★, NW : 36 m. by A 944 X – Castle Fraser★ (exterior★★) W : 16 m. by A 944 X Pitmedden Gardens★★, N : 16 m. by A 92 X and B 999 – Haddo House★, NW : 26 m. by A 92 X and B 9005.

18 Bon Accord, 19 Golf Rd ☎ 633464 X – 18 St. Fittick's Rd, Balnagask ☎ 876407 X – 18 Westhi Westhill Heights Skene ☎ 740159 by A 944 X – 18, 18, 9 Hazelhead ☎ 321830, W : 3 m. b A 944 X – 18 King's Links, Golf Rd ☎ 632269 Y – 18, 18 Royal Aberdeen, Balgownie, Bridge c Don ☎ 702571, 2 m. by A 92 X – 18, 9 Murcar, Bridge of Don ☎ 704345, NE : 5 m. X.

✈ Aberdeen Airport ☎ 722331, NW : 7 m. by A 96 X – **Terminal** : Bus Station, Guild S (adjacent to Railway Station).

☎ 0345 090700.

by P & O Ferries : (Orkney & Shetland Services) : to Shetland Islands : Lerwick 1 weekl – to Stromness, Orkney Island 1 weekly.

ℹ St. Nicholas House, Broad St. ☎ 632727.
Railway Station, Guild St. (summer only).

◆Edinburgh 130 – ◆Dundee 67.

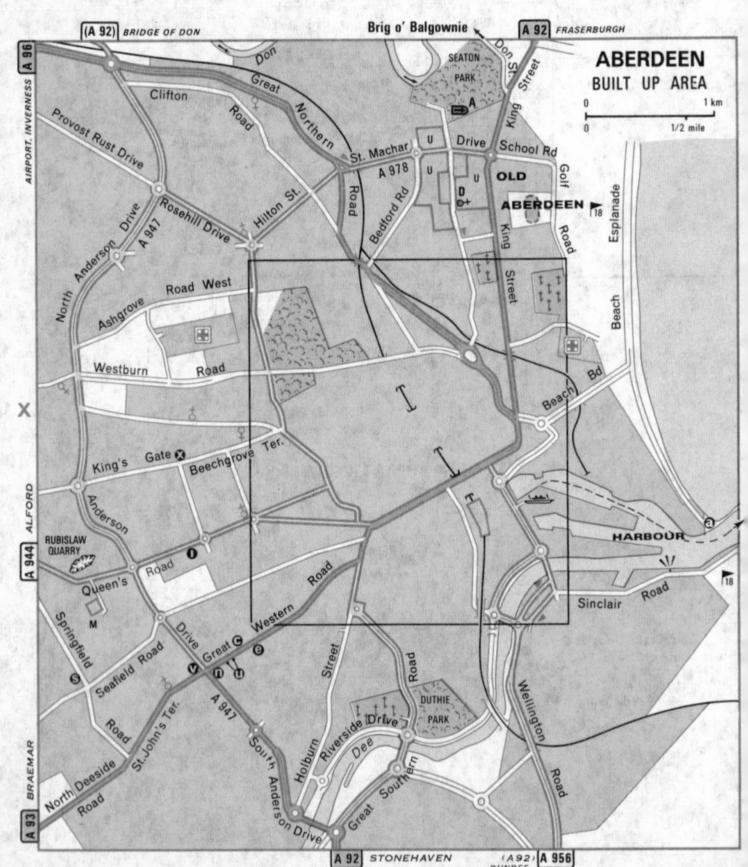

Caledonian Thistle (Mt. Charlotte Thistle), 10-14 Union Terr., AB9 1HE, ℘ 640233, Telex 73758, Fax 641627, – rm – 45. AE VISA Z i
M 9.00/18.00 **t.** and a la carte – 7.75 – **77 rm** 70.00/105.00 **st.**, **3 suites.**

Stakis Tree Tops, 161 Springfield Rd, AB9 2QH, ℘ 313377, Telex 73794, Fax 312028, – rm – 600. AE VISA X s
M 9.50/15.00 **t.** and a la carte – 7.50 – **112 rm** 79.00/103.00 **t.**, **2 suites** 103.00 **t.** – SB 80.00/138.00 **st.**

Ardoe House, South Deeside Rd, Blairs, AB1 5YP, SW : 5 m. on B 9077 – X – ℘ 867355, Fax 861283, park – 120
17 rm, **2 suites.**

Amatola, 448 Great Western Rd, AB1 6NP, ℘ 318724, Telex 739743, Fax 312716 – rm – 400. AE VISA X v
M *(closed Saturday lunch)* 8.95/10.95 **st.** and a la carte 4.45 – 7.00 – **54 rm** 60.00/70.00 **st.** – SB (weekends only) 59.00/75.00 **st.**

P.T.O. →

ABERDEEN

eorge Street . . . . **Y**
t. Nicolas Street . . . . **Y** 30
hopping Centre . . . . **Y**
nion Street . . . . **Z**

road Street . . . . **Y** 6
astle Street . . . . **Y** 7
ollege Street . . . . **Z** 9
raigie Loanings . . . . **Y** 12

East North Street . . . . **Y** 16
Great Southern Road . . . . . **Z** 18
Guild Street . . . . **Z** 19
Justice Street . . . . **Y** 21
Loch Street . . . . **Y** 22
Millburn Street . . . . **Z** 23
Regent Quay . . . . **Z** 24
Rosemount Terrace . . . . . . **Y** 25
Rosemount Viaduct . . . . . . **Y** 26
St. Andrew Street . . . . **Y** 28
St. Swithin Street . . . . **Z** 31
School Hill . . . . **YZ** 32

South Esplanade West . . . . **Z** 33
South Mount Street . . . . . . **Y** 34
Springbank Terrace . . . . . . **Z** 35
Spring Garden . . . . **Y** 36
Trinity Quay . . . . **Z** 37
Union Terrace . . . . **Z** 39
Upperkirkgate . . . . **Y** 40
Victoria Street . . . . **Z** 42
Waverley Place . . . . **Z** 43
Wellington Place . . . . **Z** 45
Wellington Road . . . . **Z** 47
Woolmanhill . . . . **Y** 48

New Marcliffe, 51-53 Queen's Rd, AB9 2PE, ☎ 321371, Telex 73225, Fax 311162 – TV ☎ P – 400. AE VISA. X
M *(closed Sunday)* 15.50/17.50 **st.** (dinner) and a la carte 4.00 – **27 rm** 65.00/95.00 st – SB (weekends only) 68.00/74.00 **st.**

Atholl, 54 King's Gate, AB9 2YN, ☎ 323505, Fax 321555 – TV ☎ P – 50 X
35 rm.

Malacca, 349 Great Western Rd, AB1 6NW, ☎ 588901, Fax 571621 – TV ☎ P X
18 rm.

Cedars without rest., 339 Great Western Rd, AB1 6NW, ☎ 583225, Fax 583225 – TV P AE – **13 rm** 25.00/38.00 **st.** X

Corner House, 385 Great Western Rd, AB1 6NY, ☎ 313063 – rest TV ☎ P X
20 rm.

Fourways, 435 Great Western Rd, AB1 6NJ, ☎ 310218 – TV P.
M 8.00 **t.** – **7 rm** 18.00/30.00 **t.** X

Bracklinn without rest., 348 Great Western Rd, AB1 6LX, ☎ 317060 – TV X
6 rm 16.00/30.00 **st.**

Aberdeen Rendez-vous, 218-222 George St., AB1 1BS, ☎ 633610, Chinese (Peking) rest. – ▤. AE VISA Y
M a la carte approx. 12.00 **st.** 3.80.

Atlantis, 16-17 Bon Accord Cres., AB1 2DR, ☎ 591403, Seafood – AE VISA Z
closed Saturday lunch, Sunday, 25 December and 1 January – **M** a la carte 18.50/24.00 st

Nargile, 77-79 Skene St., AB1 1QD, ☎ 636093, Turkish rest. Y

Silver Darling, Pocra Quay, North Pier Rd, AB2 1DQ, ☎ 576229, French Seafood rest. – AE VISA X
closed lunch Saturday, Sunday and Bank Holidays and 23 December-7 January
M (booking essential) 14.75 **t.** (lunch) and a la carte approx. 25.65 **t.** 4.50.

at Altens S : 3 m. on A 956 – X – ✉ 0224 Aberdeen :

Skean Dhu Altens (Mt. Charlotte Thistle), Souterhead Rd, AB1 4LF, ☎ 877000, Telex 739631, Fax 896964, heated – rest ▤ rest TV ☎ P – 350. AE VISA
M 13.00/16.00 **t.** and a la carte 3.75 – 6.95 – **221 rm** 70.00/83.00 **t.**, **1 suite** 150.00/160.00 **t.**

at Cults SW : 4 m. on A 93 – X – ✉ 0224 Aberdeen :

Faradays, 2 Kirk Brae, AB1 9SQ, ☎ 869666 – P. VISA
closed Sunday May-September, Monday and 1 to 14 January – **M** a la carte 11.10/14.40 t 4.80.

at Maryculter SW : 8 m. on B 9077 – X – ✉ 0224 Aberdeen :

Maryculter House , South Deeside Rd, AB1 0BB, ☎ 732124, Fax 733510, « Part 13th house on River Dee », – TV ☎ P – 55. AE VISA.
M *(closed Sunday)* (dinner only) 25.00 **t.** 5.00 – **10 rm** 65.00/100.00 **t.** – SB (weekends only) 70.00/80.00 **st.**

at Westhill W : 6½ m. by A 944 – X – ✉ 0224 Aberdeen :

Westhill, Kinmundy Drive, AB3 6TT, ☎ 740388, Telex 739925, Fax 744354, – TV ☎ P – 250. AE VISA
M 12.00/30.00 **s.** and a la carte 3.75 – **52 rm** 42.50/55.00 **st.**

at Bucksburn NW : 4 m. by A 96 – X – on A 947 – ✉ 0224 Aberdeen :

Bucksburn Moat House (Q.M.H.), Oldmeldrum Rd, AB2 9LN, ☎ 713911, Telex 73108 Fax 714020, – rm TV ☎ P – 180. AE VISA
closed 25 and 26 December – **M** *(closed saturday lunch)* 14.50/19.00 **st.** and a la carte – 7.25 – **97 rm** 70.00/78.00 **s.**, **1 suite** 100.00/133.00 **s.** – SB (weekends only) 96.00/200.90 **st.**

at Dyce NW : 5½ m. by A 96 – X – on A 947 – ✉ 0224 Aberdeen :

Holiday Inn, Riverview Drive, Farburn, AB2 0AZ, ☎ 770011, Telex 739651, Fax 722347, – rm ▤ TV ☎ P – 380. AE VISA
M 13.50/16.00 **st.** and a la carte – 8.95 – **153 rm** 92.00/106.00 **st.**, **1 suite** 165.00/185.00 **st.**

at Aberdeen Airport NW : 6 m. by A 96 – X – ✉ 0224 Aberdeen :

Aberdeen Airport Skean Dhu (Mt. Charlotte Thistle), Argyll Rd, AB2 0DU, ☎ 725252 Telex 739239, Fax 72301, heated – rm TV ☎ P – 600. AE VISA
M 9.00/14.50 **st.** and a la carte 4.75 – 6.95 – **148 rm** 65.00/150.00 **st.**

MICHELIN Distribution Centre, Wellington Rd, AB9 2JZ, ☎ 875075, Fax 878474 by A 956 X

BMW Grey St. ☎ 313355
FIAT 870 Gt Northern Rd ☎ 695573
FORD Menzies Rd ☎ 248800
FORD Lang Stracht ☎ 697772
FORD Gt. Western Rd ☎ 594277
MERCEDES-BENZ 366 King St. ☎ 634211
NISSAN North Andason Drive ☎ 681111
PEUGEOT Broadford Rd, Bridge of Don ☎ 826300
RENAULT 78 Powis Terr. ☎ 481313
ROVER Lang Stracht ☎ 685511
ROVER 19 Justice Mill Lane ☎ 596151
VAUXHALL-OPEL 16 Dee St. ☎ 589216

ATS Beach Boulevard ☎ 592727
ATS 214 Hardgate ☎ 589461

ABERDOUR Fife. (Fife) 401 K 15 **Scotland G** – pop. 1 460 – ECD : Wednesday – ☎ 0383.

See : Site★ – Castle★.

Dodhead, Burntisland ☎ 0592 (Burntisland) 873247, E : 5 m. on A 92 – Seaside Pl. ☎ 860688.

Edinburgh 17 – Dunfermline 7.

Woodside, 80 High St., KY3 0SW, ☎ 860328, Fax 860920, – TV ☎ P
20 rm, 1 suite.

ABERFELDY Perth. (Tayside) 401 I 14 **Scotland G** – pop. 1 477 – ECD : Wednesday – ☎ 0887.

See : Site★.

Envir. : St. Mary's Church (Painted ceiling★) NE : 2 m. by A 827 – Loch Tay★★, SW : 6 m. by A 827.

Taybridge Rd ☎ 20535.

8 Dunkeld St. ☎ 20276 (summer only).

Edinburgh 76 – ◆Glasgow 73 – ◆Oban 77 – Perth 32.

Atkins at Farleyer House, PH15 2JE, W : 2 m. on B 846 ☎ 20332, Fax 29430, ≤ Tay Valley, park – rest TV ☎ P. AE VISA.
M *(closed Monday lunch)* 20.00/30.00 **t.** 8.50 – **11 rm** 50.00/200.00 **t.**

SUBARU, FORD Dunkeld St. ☎ 20254

ABERFOYLE Stirling (Central) 401 G 15 – pop. 546 – ECD : Wednesday – ✉ Stirling – ☎ 087 72.

Braeval ☎ 493.

Main St. ☎ 352 (summer only).

Edinburgh 56 – ◆Glasgow 27.

✿ **Braeval Old Mill,** (Nairn), FK8 3UY, E : 1 m. by A 821 on A 81 (Callander Rd) ☎ 711 – P. AE VISA
closed Monday, 2 weeks February, 1 week June, 2 weeks November, 25-26 December and 1-2 January – **M** (booking essential) (dinner only and Sunday lunch)/dinner a la carte 19.40/26.40 **t.**
Spec. Soufflé of smoked salmon and dill, Pigeon breasts with green lentils and a blackcurrant sauce, White chocolate ice cream with a dark chocolate sauce.

ABERLADY E. Lothian. (Lothian) 401 L 15 – pop. 884 – ECD : Wednesday – ☎ 087 57.

Kilspindie, ☎ 358.

Edinburgh 16 – Haddington 5 – North Berwick 7.5.

Green Craig Country House, SW : ¾ m. on A 198, EH32 0PY, ☎ 301, Fax 440, ≤, – TV ☎ P. AE VISA.
closed 25 December and January – **M** (bar lunch)/dinner 21.00 **t.** anda la carte 3.50 – 6.50 – **5 rm** 50.00/60.00 **t.**, **1 suite** 85.00/105.00 **t.**

Kilspindie House, Main St., EH32 0RE, ☎ 682 – TV ☎ P. VISA
M (bar lunch)/dinner 11.00 **t.** and a la carte 3.85 – **26 rm** 33.00/56.00 **t.** – SB (October-April) 60.00/70.00 **st.**

ABERLOUR Banff. (Grampian) 401 K 11 – pop. 879 – ECD : Wednesday – ☎ 034 05.

Envir. : Dufftown (Glenfiddich Distillery★) SE : 4 m. by A 941 – Huntly Castle (Heraldic carvings★★★) E : 1 ½ m. by A 941 and A 920.

Edinburgh 189 – ◆Aberdeen 59 – ◆Inverness 54.

Hotels see : Rothes N : 4 m.

LAND-ROVER, RANGE-ROVER 15-19 High St. ☎ 505

ABOYNE Aberdeen. (Grampian) 401 L 12 – pop. 1 477 – ECD : Thursday – ☎ 0339 (4 fig.) or 033 98 (5 fig.).

Envir. : Craigievar Castle★★★ (17C) *AC*, NE : 12 m.

Formaston Park ☎ 86328, E : end of Village – Tarland ☎ 033 981 (Tarland) 413, NW : 5 m.

Ballater Rd Car Park ☎ 86060 (summer only).

Edinburgh 131 – ◆Aberdeen 30 – ◆Dundee 68.

Birse Lodge, Charlestown Rd, AB3 5EL, ☎ 86253, – ☎ P. AE VISA
M (bar lunch)/dinner 16.00 **t.** 3.75 – **15 rm** 35.00/70.00 **t.** – SB (winter only and July) 70.00 **st.**

Hazlehurst Lodge, Ballater Rd, AB3 5HY, ☎ 86921, – rm P. VISA
closed January – **M** 21.50 **t.** 5.00 – **3 rm** 24.50/38.00 **t.**

ROVER Main Rd ☎ 86440

Your recommendation is self-evident if you always walk into a hotel Guide in hand.

ACHILTIBUIE Ross and Cromarty. (Highland) 401 D 9 – ☎ 085 482.
◆Edinburgh 243 – ◆Inverness 84 – Ullapool 25.

Summer Isles ⛰, IV26 2YG, ☎ 282, « ≤ Picturesque setting overlooking Summer Isles », – rest Ⓟ
Easter-mid October – **M** (booking essential) (dinner only) 27.50 **st.** – **11 rm** 40.00/90.00 **st.**

ADVIE Moray. (Highland) 401 J 11 – ✉ Grantown-on-Spey – ☎ 080 75.
◆Edinburgh 153 – ◆Inverness 46.

Tulchan Lodge ⛰, PH26 3PW, on B 9102 ☎ 200, Telex 75405, Fax 234, ≤ Spey Valley, « Victorian sporting lodge », park, – ☎ Ⓟ.
February-September – **M** (booking essential for non-residents) (communal dining) 20.00/32.00 **t.** – **11 rm** 124.00/220.00 **t.**

AIRTH Stirling. (Central) 401 I 15 – pop. 972 – ✉ Falkirk – ☎ 0324.
◆Edinburgh 30 – Dunfermline 14 – Falkirk 7 – Stirling 8.

Airth Castle ⛰, FK2 8JF, ☎ 83411, Telex 777975, Fax 83419, ≤, « Castle and stables in extensive grounds », park – TV ☎ & Ⓟ – 400. AE VISA.
M 12.00/19.50 **st.** and a la carte 5.00 – **47 rm** 70.00/90.00 **st.** – SB (weekends only) 79.50 **st.**

ALTENS Aberdeen. (Grampian) – see Aberdeen.

ALTNAHARRA Sutherland. (Highland) 401 G 9 – ✉ Lairg – ☎ 054 981.
◆Edinburgh 239 – ◆Inverness 83 – Thurso 61.

Altnaharra ⛰, IV27 4UE, ☎ 222, ≤, – rest Ⓟ. VISA
March-October – **M** (bar lunch)/dinner 13.50 **t.** 4.50 – **20 rm** 36.50/73.00 **t.** – SB (except June-August) 80.00 **st.**

ANSTRUTHER Fife. (Fife) 401 L 15 – pop. 2 865 – ECD : Wednesday – ☎ 0333.
See : Scottish Fisheries Museum★★ – Crail, NE : 5 m. (Site★★) – Old Town★★ – Upper Crail★.
Envir. : The East Neuk★★ (coastline from Crail to St. Monance by A 917) – Kellie Castle★, NW : 7 m. by A 959.
9 Marsfield ☎ 310956.
Scottish Fisheries Museum ☎ 310628.
◆Edinburgh 46 – ◆Dundee 23 – Dunfermline 34.

Craw's Nest, Bankwell Rd, KY10 3DS, ☎ 310691, Telex 727049, Fax 312216, – TV ☎ Ⓟ – 180. AE VISA.
M 9.00/15.50 **t.** and a la carte – **50 rm** 32.00/73.00 **st.** – SB (except July-August) 75.00/85.00 **st.**

Cellar, 24 East Green, KY10 3AA, ☎ 310378, Seafood – . AE VISA
closed lunch Monday to Thursday, Sunday and 1 week Christmas-New Year – **M** 25.00 **t.** (dinner) and lunch a la carte 10.50/15.75 **t.**

ARBROATH Angus. (Tayside) 401 M 14 **Scotland G** – pop. 23 934 – ECD : Wednesday – ☎ 0241.
See : Site★ – Abbey★ *AC.*
Envir. : St. Vigeans Museum★ by A 92.
18 Elliot ☎ 72272, S : 1 m.
Market Pl., ☎ 72690 and 76680.
◆Edinburgh 72 – ◆Aberdeen 51 – ◆Dundee 16.

Letham Grange ⛰, Colliston, DD11 4RL, NW : 4 ¾ m. by A 933 ☎ 024 189 (Gowanbank) 373, Fax 414, ≤, 18, park – TV ☎ Ⓟ – 30. AE VISA.
M 10.50/17.00 **t.** – **19 rm** 57.00/90.00 **t.**, **1 suite** 135.00 **t.** – SB 90.00/128.00 **st.**

FORD Millgate ☎ 73051 ROVER Montrose Rd ☎ 72919

ARDENTINNY Argyll. (Strathclyde) 401 F 15 – ECD : Wednesday – ✉ Dunoon – ☎ 036 981.
◆Edinburgh 107 – Dunoon 13 – ◆Glasgow 64 – ◆Oban 71.

Ardentinny ⛰, PA23 8TR, ☎ 209, ≤ Loch Long, – rest TV Ⓟ. AE VISA
Mid March-October – **M** 18.00 **t.** (dinner) and a la carte 10.35/16.00 **t.** 3.95 – **11 rm** 27.00/70.00 **st.** – SB (March, April and October) 59.00 **st.**

N'oubliez pas qu'il existe des limitations de vitesse au Royaume-Uni en dehors de celles mentionnées sur les panneaux.

– 60 mph (= 96 km/h) sur route.
– 70 mph (= 112 km/h) sur route à chaussées séparées et autoroute.

RDEONAIG Perth. (Central) 401 H 14 – see Killin.

RDGAY Sutherland 401 G10.
Edinburgh 205 – ◆Inverness 49 – Wick 77

Ardgay House, IV24 3DH, ✆ 345, – P
closed January – **M** 12.00 **st.** 4.00 – **6 rm** 14.00/38.00 **st.**

RDROSSAN Ayr. (Strathclyde) 401 402 F 17 – pop. 11 386 – ECD : Wednesday – 0294.
by Caledonian MacBrayne : to the Isle of Arran : Brodick, summer : 3-5 daily, winter : weekly (55 mn).
Ferry Terminal Building, Ardrossan Harbour ✆ 601063 (summer only).
Edinburgh 75 – ◆Ayr 18 – ◆Glasgow 32.

Hotels see : Kilmarnock SE : 11 ½ m., ***Largs*** N : 11 ½ m.

RDUAINE Argyll. (Strathclyde) 401 D 15 – ECD : Wednesday – ✉ Oban – 085 22 Kilmelford.
Edinburgh 142 – ◆Oban 20.

Loch Melfort, PA34 4XG, ✆ 233, Fax 214, ← Sound of Jura, , park – P. VISA
closed 2 January-10 March – **M** (bar lunch)/dinner 25.00 **t.** 6.00 – **23 rm** 50.00/60.00 **t.**

RDVASAR Inverness. (Highland) 401 C 12 – see Skye (Isle of).

RINAGOUR Argyll. (Strathclyde) 401 A 14 – see Coll (Isle of).

RISAIG Inverness. (Highland) 401 C 13 – ECD : Thursday – 068 75.
ee : Site★ – ←★ of Sound of Arisaig.
nvir. : Silver Sands of Morar★, N : 6 m. by A 830.
Edinburgh 172 – ◆Inverness 102 – ◆Oban 88.

Arisaig House, Beasdale, PH39 4NR, SE : 3 ¼ m. on A 830 ✆ 622, Telex 777279, Fax 626, ←, , park – rest P. VISA.
9 March-mid November – **M** (booking essential) (restricted lunch)/dinner 33.00 **t.** 8.50 – 4.00 – **15 rm** 44.00/176.00 **t.**

Arisaig, PH39 4NH, ✆ 210, ← – rest P. VISA
M (bar lunch)/dinner 21.00 **t.** and a la carte 4.20 – **15 rm** 30.00/80.00 **t.**

Old Library Lodge with rm, High St., PH39 4NH, ✆ 651, ← Loch nan Ceall and Inner Hebridean Isles – P. VISA.
Easter-October – **M** (restricted lunch)/dinner 17.50 **t.** and a la carte approx. 15.60 **t.** 3.75 – **7 rm** 20.00/56.00 **t.**

RMADALE Inverness. (Highland) 401 C 12 – Shipping Services : see Skye (Isle of).

RRAN (Isle of) Bute. (Strathclyde) 401 402 DE 16 17 **Scotland G** – pop. 4 726.
ee : Site★★ – Brodick Castle★★.
by Caledonian MacBrayne : from Brodick to Ardrossan summer : 3-5 daily, winter : weekly (55 mn) – from Lochranza to Claonaig (Kintyre Peninsula)(summer only) : 7 daily 30 mn).

Brodick – pop. 884 – ECD : Wednesday – ✉ 0770 Brodick.
18 Brodick ✆ 2349, ½ m. from Pier – 9 Machrie Bay ✆ 267.
The Pier ✆ 2140.

Auchrannie Country House, KA27 8BZ, ✆ 2234, Fax 2812, – P. VISA.
M *(closed lunch November-March)* 9.75/20.00 **t.** and a la carte 3.00 – **12 rm** 50.00/95.00 **t.**

Lagg – ✉ Kilmory – 077 087 Sliddery

Lagg, KA27 8PQ, ✆ 255, – P
M 12.50/17.00 **t.** 3.40 – **15 rm** 30.00/70.00 **t.**

Lamlash – pop. 908 – ECD : Wednesday except summer – ✉ Brodick – 077 06 Lamlash.
18 ✆ 296.

Glenisle, Shore Rd, KA27 8LS, ✆ 258, ←, – P. VISA
M (bar lunch)/dinner 12.00 **t.** 3.65 – **13 rm** 26.00/52.00 **t.**

Lochranza – ✉ 077 083 Lochranza.
9 ✆ 273.

Butt Lodge, KA27 8JF, SE : ½ m. by Brodick Rd ✆ 240, ←, – P. VISA.
April-October – **M** 11.50 **st.** – **5 rm** -/52.00 **st.**

Whiting Bay – ECD : Wednesday except summer – ✉ Brodick – ☎ 077 07 Whitir Bay.

⛳18 ✆ 487.

⌂ **Royal,** Shore Rd, KA27 8PZ, ✆ 286, ≤, 🌳 – ☎ Ⓟ
closed November-February – **M** 8.00 **st.** – **5 rm** ☕ 21.00/56.00 **st.**

⌂ **View Bank** 🐎, Golf Course Rd, KA27 8QT, ✆ 326, ≤, 🌳 – Ⓟ
closed Christmas and New Year – **M** 6.50 **st.** – **7 rm** ☕ (dinner included) 17.50/35.00 **s.**

ARROCHAR Dunbarton (Strathclyde) 401 F 15 – ☎ 030 12.
◆Edinburgh 83 – ◆Glasgow 35 – ◆Oban 57.

⌂ **Mansfield,** G83 7AG, ✆ 282, Fax 692, ≤, 🌳 – ⊁ 📺 Ⓟ. ✻
M (by arrangement) 8.00 **st.** – **5 rm** ☕ 20.00/28.00 **st.**

AUCHENCAIRN Kirkcudbright. (Dumfries and Galloway) 401 402 I 19 – ✉ Castle Douglas ☎ 055 664.
◆Edinburgh 98 – ◆Dumfries 21 – Stranraer 62.

⌂ **Bluehill Farm** 🐎 without rest., DG7 1QW, W : 1 m. by A 711 ✆ 228, ≤, 🌳, park ⊁ rm Ⓟ. ✻
June-September – **3 rm** ☕ 15.00/34.00.

AUCHTERARDER Perth. (Tayside) 401 I 15 – pop. 2 838 – ECD : Wednesday – ☎ 0764.
⛳18 Orchil Rd ✆ 62804, SW : 1 ½ m. – ⛳18, ⛳18, ⛳18, ⛳18 Gleneagles ✆ 076 46 (Gleneagles) 3543.
🅘 90 High St. ✆ 63450.
◆Edinburgh 55 – ◆Glasgow 45 – Perth 14.

🏨 **Gleneagles,** PH3 1NF, SW : 1 ½ m. by A 9 ✆ 62231, Telex 76105, Fax 62134, ≤, « Championship golf courses and extensive leisure facilities », 🏊, ⛳18, 🎣, 🌳, park, 🎾, squash 🛗 ⊁ rm ▤ rest 📺 ☎ ♿ Ⓟ – 🎤 300. 🅂 AE ⓓ VISA
M 21.50/34.00 **t.** and a la carte – ☕ 12.00 – **221 rm** 110.00/225.00 **t.**, **20 suites** 280.0 610.00 **t.**

🏨 **Auchterarder House** 🐎, PH3 1DZ, N : 1 ½ m. on B 8062 ✆ 63646, Fax 62939, « Scottish Jacobean house », 🌳, park – ⊁ rest 📺 ☎ Ⓟ. 🅂 AE ⓓ VISA
M (booking essential) 30.00/50.00 **t.** 🍷 5.50 – **11 rm** ☕ 60.00/160.00 **t.**, **2 suites** 200.00 **t.**

🏨 **Cairn Lodge** 🐎, Orchill Rd, PH3 1LX, ✆ 62634, 🌳 – 📺 ☎ Ⓟ. 🅂 AE VISA. ✻
closed 2 weeks January-February – **M** 11.50 **t.** (lunch) and a la carte 22.50/32.00 **t.** – **5 rr** ☕ 50.00/85.00 **t.**

🏨 **Collearn House,** PH3 1DF, ✆ 63553, Fax 63059, 🌳 – 📺 ☎ Ⓟ. 🅂 AE ⓓ VISA. ✻
M 18.00/24.00 **t.** and a la carte 🍷 3.75 – **8 rm** ☕ 45.00/70.00 **t.** – SB 85.00/125.00 **st.**

AUCHTERHOUSE Angus. (Tayside) 401 K 14 – ✉ Dundee – ☎ 082 626.
◆Edinburgh 69 – ◆Dundee 7 – Perth 24.

XXX **Old Mansion House** 🐎 with rm, DD3 0QN, ✆ 366, Fax 400, ≤, « 15-17C countr house », 🏊 heated, 🌳, park, 🎾, squash – 📺 ☎ Ⓟ. 🅂 AE ⓓ VISA
closed 30 December-7 January – **M** 14.95 **st.** (lunch) and a la carte 20.00/25.00 **st.** 🍷 3.75 **6 rm** ☕ 65.00/90.00 **t.**

AULTBEA Ross and Cromarty. (Highland) 401 D 10 – ECD : Wednesday – ☎ 044 582.
◆Edinburgh 234 – ◆Inverness 79 – Kyle of Lochalsh 80.

🏨 **Aultbea,** IV22 2HX, ✆ 201, Fax 214, ≤ – 📺 ☎ Ⓟ. 🅂 VISA
M (bar lunch)/dinner 15.00/30.00 **t.** and a la carte 🍷 3.25 – **8 rm** ☕ 30.00/60.00 **t.** – S (November-March) 60.00 **st.**

AVIEMORE Inverness. (Highland) 401 I 12 **Scotland G** – pop. 1 510 – ECD : Wednesday Winter sports – ☎ 0479.
See : Site★.
Envir. : ✲★★★ from Cairn Gorm (alt. 4 084 ft.) SE : 8 ½ m. by B 970 (chair lift *AC*) – Highlan Wildlife Park★, S : by A 9.
🅘 Grampian Rd ✆ 810363.
◆Edinburgh 129 – ◆Inverness 29 – Perth 85.

🏨 **Stakis Four Seasons,** Aviemore Centre, PH22 1PF, ✆ 810681, Telex 75213, Fax 810862 ≤ Cairngorms, 🏋, ≘s, 🏊 – 🛗 ⊁ rm 📺 ☎ Ⓟ – 🎤 100. 🅂 AE ⓓ VISA
M (dancing Saturday) 7.00/15.00 and a la carte – ☕ 7.50 – **86 rm** 56.00/104.00 **t.**, **2 suite** – SB 68.00/102.00 **st.**

🏨 **Corrour House** 🐎, Inverdruie, PH22 1QH, SE : 1 m. on B 970 ✆ 810220, 🌳 – ⊁ res 📺 ☎ Ⓟ. 🅂 VISA
closed 1 November-27 December – **M** (dinner only) 13.00/15.00 **st.** 🍷 3.00 – **8 rm** ☕ 24.00 48.00 **st.** – SB 60.00/72.00 **st.**

FORD 62 Grampian Rd ✆ 810232

YR Ayr. (Strathclyde) 401 402 G 17 **Scotland G** – pop. 48 493 – ECD : Wednesday – ☎ 0292.
nvir. : Alloway★ (Burns' Cottage and Museum★) S : 3 m. by B 7024 BZ – Culzean Castle★
Setting★★★, Oval staircase★★) SW : 14 m. by A 719 BZ.
Belleisle ℘ 41258 BZ – 18 Dalmilling, Westwood Av., Whitletts ℘ 63893 BZ.
39 Sandgate ℘ 284196.
Edinburgh 81 – ◆Glasgow 35.

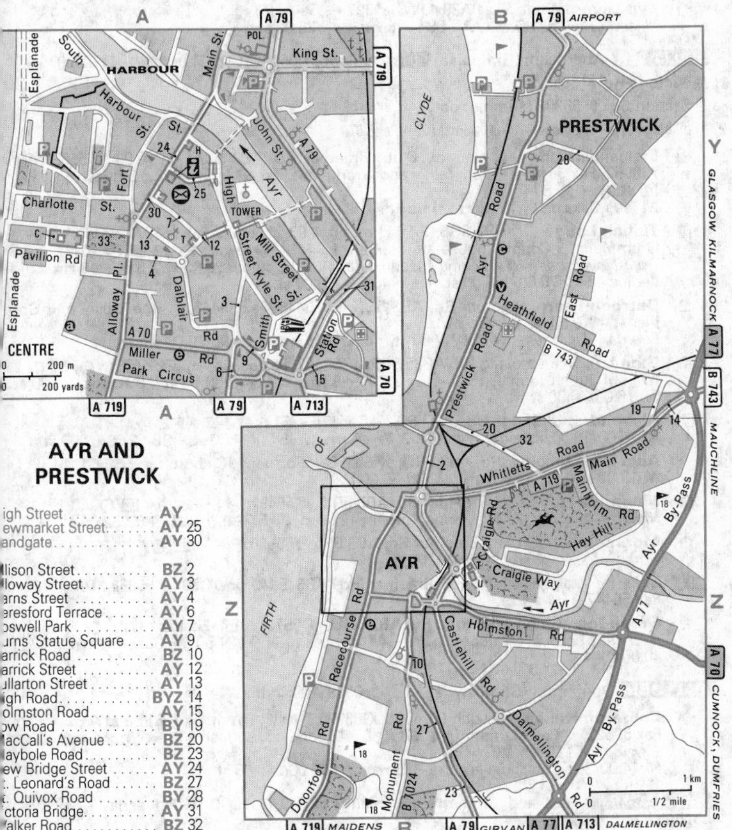

AYR AND PRESTWICK

igh Street	AY
ewmarket Street	AY 25
andgate	AY 30
llison Street	BZ 2
lloway Street	AY 3
arns Street	AY 4
eresford Terrace	AY 6
oswell Park	AY 7
urns' Statue Square	AY 9
arrick Road	BZ 10
arrick Street	AY 12
ullarton Street	AY 13
igh Road	BYZ 14
olmston Road	AY 15
ow Road	BY 19
acCall's Avenue	BZ 20
aybole Road	BZ 23
ew Bridge Street	AY 24
t. Leonard's Road	BZ 27
t. Quivox Road	BY 28
ictoria Bridge	AY 31
alker Road	BZ 32
ellington Square	AY 33

Fairfield House, 12 Fairfield Rd, KA7 2AR, ℘ 267461, Telex 778833, Fax 261456, ⛝, ⛝, ⛝ – ⛝ TV ☎ P. ⛝ AE ⓓ VISA. ⛝ — AY **a**
M 14.50/40.00 **st.** and a la carte 🍷 7.75 – **39 rm** ☕ 75.00/200.00 **st.**

Kylestrome, 11 Miller rd, KA7 2AX, ℘ 262474 – TV ☎ P – ⛝ 40. ⛝ AE ⓓ VISA — AY **e**
M 7.95/12.00 **t.** and a la carte 🍷 4.50 – **13 rm** ☕ 45.00/70.00 **t.** – SB 130.00/150.00 **st.**

Pickwick, 19 Racecourse Rd, KA7 2TD, ℘ 260111, Fax 285348 – TV ☎ P. ⛝ AE ⓓ VISA. ⛝ — BZ **e**
M 7.95/14.50 **t.** and a la carte 🍷 4.50 – **15 rm** ☕ 40.00/80.00 **t.** – SB 85.00/95.00 **st.**

at Alloway S : 3 m. on A 719 – BZ – ✉ ☎ 0292 Ayr :

Balgarth, 8 Dunure Rd, Doonfoot, KA7 4HR, on A 719 ℘ 42441, ⛝ – TV ☎ P
15 rm.

LFA-ROMEO, FIAT Galloway Av. ℘ 260416
AIMLER, JAGUAR, LAND-ROVER, RANGE-ROVER
3 Holmston Rd ℘ 266944
UZUKI Cambuslea Rd ℘ 266146
IERCEDES-BENZ Heathfield Industrial Estate
℘ 282727
TOYOTA 65 Peebles St. ℘ 267606
VAUXHALL 196 Prestwick Rd ℘ 261631
VOLVO Burn's Statue Sq. ℘ 282711
VW-AUDI 24 Dalblair Rd ℘ 269522

BALLACHULISH Argyll. (Highland) 401 E 13 – ECD : Wednesday – 085 52.

Envir. : Glen Coe★★, E : 6 m. by A 82.

296 (summer only).

Edinburgh 117 – Inverness 80 – Kyle of Lochalsh 90 – Oban 38.

Ballachulish, PA39 4JY, W : 2¼ m. by A 82 on A 828 606, Fax 629, ←, – rest
. VISA
M (bar lunch)/dinner 17.00 **st.** and a la carte 4.00 – **30 rm** 39.50/98.00 **st.** – SB 65.00

Lyn Leven, White St., PA39 4JW, 392, ←, –
closed Christmas Day – **M** 7.50 **t.** – **8 rm** –/36.00 **st.**

BALLATER Aberdeen. (Grampian) 401 K 12 – pop. 1 051 – ECD : Thursday – 033 97.

Victoria Rd 55567.

Station Sq. 55306 (summer only).

Edinburgh 111 – Aberdeen 41 – Inverness 70 – Perth 67.

Craigendarroch H. & Country Club, Braemar Rd, AB3 5XA, on A 93 55858, Tel
739952, Fax 55447, ← Dee Valley and Grampians, , , , , , squash – r
 – 80
M (see **Oaks** below) – **49 rm**, **1 suite.**

Tullich Lodge , AB3 5SB, E : 1½ m. on A 93 55406, Fax 55397, ← Dee Valley ar
Grampians, « Country house atmosphere », – rest . VISA
April-November – **M** (booking essential) (bar lunch)/dinner 20.00 **st.** 3.50 – **10 rm** (di
ner included) 70.00/158.00 **st.** – SB 148.00/158.00 **st.**

Darroch Learg, Braemar Rd, AB3 5UX, 55443, Fax 55443, ← Dee Valley and Gran
pians, – . VISA
February-October – **M** 7.50/17.50 **st.** 4.00 – **23 rm** 24.00/70.00 **st.**

Glen Lui, 14 Invercauld Rd, AB35 5RP, 55402, Fax 55545, ←, – . VIS
M (bar lunch)/dinner 15.00 **st.** 3.00 – **8 rm** 25.00/50.00 **st.**, **2 suites** 70.00 **st.**
SB 75.00/85.00 **st.**

Alexandra, 12 Bridge Sq., AB3 5QJ, 55376 – . VISA
M 10.00/18.00 **st.** and a la carte 3.40 – **6 rm** 15.00/44.00 **st.** – SB 52.00/62.00 **st.**

Auld Kirk, Braemar Rd, AB3 5RQ, 55762, « Former 19C church » – . VISA
M 13.00 **st.** 3.50 – **6 rm** 22.00/38.00 **t.**

Moorside House, 26 Braemar Rd, AB3 5RL, 55492, – rest . VISA.
March-November – **M** (by arrangement) 12.00 **st.** 5.50 – **9 rm** 21.00/32.00 **st.**

Morvada without rest., Braemar Rd, AB3 5RL, 55501, –
April-October – **7 rm** 20.00/32.00.

XXX Oaks (at Craigendarroch H.), Braemar Rd, AB3 5XA, on A 93 55858, Telex 73995
Fax 55447 – .

X **Green Inn** with rm, 9 Victoria Rd, AB3 5QQ, 55701 – . VISA
restricted service October-March – **M** a la carte 11.00/21.50 **t.** 3.25 – **3 rm** 25.0
40.00 **t.**

BALLOCH Dunbarton (Strathclyde) – 0389 Alexandria

Cameron House , Loch Lomond, G83 8QZ, NW : 1½ m. by A 811 and A 82 5556
Fax 59522, ← Loch Lomond, , , , , park, , squash – rm rest
– 300. VISA.
M 14.00/30.00 **st.** and a la carte – **63 rm** 100.00/240.00 **st.**

BALMACARA Ross and Cromarty. (Highland) 401 D 12 – ECD : Wednesday – Kyle
Lochalsh – 059 986.

Edinburgh 197 – Kyle of Lochalsh 4.5.

Balmacara, IV40 8DH, 283, ← coast and mountains – . VISA
M 8.00/14.00 **st.** 3.00 – **29 rm** 27.00/47.00 **st.**

BALQUHIDDER Perth. (Central) 401 G 14 – see Strathyre.

BANAVIE Inverness. (Highland) 401 E 13 – see Fort William.

ANCHORY Kincardine. (Grampian) 401 M 12 – pop. 4 683 – ECD : Thursday – ☎ 033 02.

nvir. : Crathes Castle★★, E : 2 m. by A 93 – Craigievar Castle★★★, N : 17 m. by A 980 – Castle aser★ (exterior★★), N : 14 m. by A 980 and B 977.

Kinneskie ☎ 2365 – Torphins ☎ 033 982 (Torphins) 493, NW : 6 m.

Dee St. Car Park ☎ 2000 (summer only).

Edinburgh 118 – Aberdeen 17 – Dundee 55 – Inverness 94.

Invery House, Bridge of Feugh, AB3 3NJ, S : 1 ½ m. on B 974 ☎ 4782, Telex 73737, Fax 4712, ≤, « Georgian mansion, gardens », park – rest TV ☎ P – 30. AE VISA.
closed 4 to 26 January – **M** 19.50/31.50 **st.** 5.00 – **13 rm** 95.00/165.00 **st.**, **1 suite** 165.00/225.00 **st.** – SB (October-March) 150.00/190.00 **st.**

Raemoir House, AB3 4ED, N : 2 ½ m. on A 980 ☎ 4884, Fax 2171, ≤, « 18C mansion with 16C Ha-House », park, – TV ☎ P – 50. AE VISA
M (bar lunch Monday to Saturday)/dinner 19.50 **t.** and a la carte 3.85 – **21 rm** 55.00/90.00 **t.**, **4 suites** 110.00/120.00 **t.** – SB (except Christmas and New Year) 95.00/104.50 **st.**

Banchory Lodge, Dee St., AB3 3HS, ☎ 2625, ≤, « Part 18C house on River Dee », – TV ☎ P. AE VISA
closed 18 December-29 January – **M** 12.50/25.00 **st.** 4.25 – **23 rm** 55.00/110.00.

Tor-na-Coille, Inchmarlo Rd, AB31 4AB, ☎ 2242, Fax 4012, – TV ☎ P – 50. AE VISA
M (bar lunch Monday to Saturday)/dinner 15.50 **t.** and a la carte 3.70 – **24 rm** 39.50/82.50 – SB (weekends only) 87.00 **st.**

ENAULT North Deeside Rd ☎ 2847

BANFF Banff. (Grampian) 401 M 10 **Scotland G** – pop. 3 843 – ECD : Wednesday – ☎ 026 12.

ee : Site★ – Duff House★ – Mercat Cross★.

Duff House Royal, The Barnyards ☎ 2062, S : ½ m.

Collie Lodge ☎ 2419.

Edinburgh 177 – Aberdeen 47 – Fraserburgh 26 – Inverness 74.

Banff Springs, Golden Knowes Rd, AB4 2JE, W : ¾ m. on A 98 ☎ 2881, ≤ – TV ☎ P – 200
28 rm, **2 suites.**

Eden House, AB4 3NT, S : 5 m. by A 98 and A 947 on Scatlertie Dunlugas rd ☎ 282, ≤, « Part 18C former shooting lodge overlooking River Deveron Valley », park, – P.
closed Christmas and New Year – **M** 17.50 **st.** – **9 rm** 27.50/55.00 **st.**

ORD Bridge Rd ☎ 2673 ATS Carmelite St. ☎ 2234

BARRA (Isle of) Inverness. (Outer Hebrides) (Western Isles) 401 X 12 13 – pop. 1 232.

at North Bay ☎ 041 889 1311.

by Caledonian MacBrayne : from Castlebay to Oban : – to Lochboisdale (South Uist).

Castlebay – ✉ ☎ 087 14 Castlebay.

☎ 336 (summer only).

Isle of Barra, Tangusdale Beach, PA80 5XY, NW : 2 m. on A 888 ☎ 383, Fax 385, ≤ sea and mountains – P. VISA
April-September – **M** (bar lunch)/dinner 14.90 **st.** 3.80 – **30 rm** 35.00/60.00 **st.** – SB (weekdays only) 79.00 **st.**

BARRHEAD Renfrew. (Strathclyde) 401 402 G 16 – pop. 18 419 – ECD : Tuesday – ✉ 041 Glasgow.

Edinburgh 56 – Ayr 32 – Glasgow 10.

Dalmeny Park, Lochlibo Rd, G78 1LG, SW : ½ m. on A 736 ☎ 881 9211, « Gardens » – TV ☎ P. AE VISA
M *(closed Saturday lunch)* 7.95/16.50 **t.** and a la carte 3.10 – **20 rm** 27.00/77.00 **t.**

ATS Glasgow Rd, Crossmill ☎ 881 5651

BEARSDEN Dunbarton. (Strathclyde) 401 G 16 – pop. 27 146 – ECD : Tuesday and Saturday – ✉ ☎ 041 Glasgow.

Windyhill ☎ 942 2349.

Edinburgh 51 – Glasgow 5.

October, 128 Drymen Rd, G61 3RB, ☎ 942 7272 – VISA
closed Sunday dinner, 1 week Easter, first 2 weeks August, 2 January and Bank Holidays – **M** 9.75 **t.** (lunch) and a la carte 18.50/24.90 **t.** 3.95.

La Bavarde, 19 New Kirk Rd, G61 9JS, ☎ 942 2202 – AE VISA
closed Sunday, Monday, last 3 weeks July and 2 weeks Christmas-New Year – **M** 7.60/17.20 **t.** and a la carte 3.50.

ORSCHE, FERRARI Maxwell Av. ☎ 943 1155

BEATTOCK Dumfries. (Dumfries and Galloway) 401 402 J 18 – ✉ Moffat – ☎ 068 33.
◆Edinburgh 60 – ◆Carlisle 41 – ◆Dumfries 20 – ◆Glasgow 59.

Auchen Castle, DG10 9SH, N : 2 m. by A 74 ☎ 407, Fax 667, ≤, park – TV ☎ P 30
25 rm.

BEAULY Inverness. (Highland) 401 G 11 – pop. 1 135 – ECD : Thursday – ☎ 0463.
◆Edinburgh 169 – ◆Inverness 13 – ◆Wick 125.

Priory, The Square, IV4 7BX, ☎ 782309, Fax 782531 – TV ☎. AE VISA
M a la carte 7.50/16.85 **st.** 3.50 – **11 rm** 26.95/49.50 **st.** – SB (weekends only) 60.00 70.00 **st.**

Chrialdon, Station Rd, IV4 7EH, ☎ 782336, – rest TV P
M 10.75 **st.** – **7 rm** 18.00/38.00 **st.**

SUBARU High St. ☎ 782266 FIAT West End ☎ 21721

BELLOCHANTUY Argyll. (Strathclyde) 401 C 17 – see Kintyre (Peninsula).

BENBECULA Inverness. (Western Isles) 401 X 11 – see Uist (Isles of).

BIRSAY Orkney (Orkney Islands) 401 K 6 – see Orkney Islands (Mainland).

BLAIR ATHOLL Perth. (Tayside) 401 I 13 – pop. 516 – ☎ 079 681.
See : Blair Castle★★★.
Envir. : Queens View★★, S : 9 m. by A 9 and B 8019 – Falls of Bruar★ W : 3 m.
9 ☎ 407, S : ½ m.
◆Edinburgh 78 – ◆Inverness 78 – Perth 34.

Atholl Arms, PH18 5SG, ☎ 205 – TV ☎ P
30 rm.

BLAIRGOWRIE Perth. (Tayside) 401 J 14 – pop. 7 028 – ☎ 0250.
18, 18, 9 Rosemount ☎ 2594.
Wellmeadow ☎ 2960.
◆Edinburgh 60 – ◆Dundee 19 – Perth 16.

Kinloch House , PH10 6SG, W : 3 m. on A 923 ☎ 025 084 (Essendy) 237, Fax 333, « Country house atmosphere », , park – rest ☎ P. AE VISA
closed 10 to 30 December – **M** 12.50/19.50 **st.** – **13 rm** 40.50/108.00 **st.**

Altamount House , Coupar Angus Rd, PH10 6JN, on A 923 ☎ 3512, – TV ☎ P VISA.
closed 4 January-12 February – **M** *(closed Sunday dinner)* (bar lunch Monday to Saturday) dinner 15.50 **t.** 3.50 – **7 rm** 30.00/60.00 **t.**

Rosemount Golf, Golf Course Rd, PH10 6LJ, SE : 1 ¾ m. by A 923 ☎ 2604, – TV P. VISA.
M (bar lunch)/dinner 14.50 **st.** and a la carte 3.00 – **12 rm** 30.00/45.00 **st.** – SB (October-April) 57.00/67.00 **st.**

BLAIRLOGIE Stirling. (Central) – see Stirling.

BOAT OF GARTEN Inverness. (Highland) 401 I 12 – ECD : Thursday – ☎ 047 983.
18 ☎ 351.
◆Edinburgh 133 – ◆Inverness 28 – ◆Perth 89.

The Boat (Best Western), PH24 3BH, ☎ 258, Fax 414, – TV ☎ P. AE VISA
M (bar lunch)/dinner 16.50 **st.** and a la carte 5.00 – **32 rm** 42.00/83.00 **st.** – SB 76.00 106.00 **st.**

Heathbank, Spey Avenue, PH24 3BD, ☎ 234, – P.
closed November-28 December – **M** 12.00 **t.** – **8 rm** 16.00/45.00 **t.** – SB 52.00/64.00 st

BONAR BRIDGE Sutherland (Highland) 401 G 10 – ✉ Invershin-by-Lairg – ☎ 054 982 Invershin
◆Edinburgh 206 – ◆Inverness 50 – ◆Wick 76.

Kyle House without rest., Dornock Rd, IV24 3EB, ☎ 360 – P.
April-September – **6 rm** 25.00/28.00.

at Invershin W : 3 m. on A 836 – ☎ 054 982 Invershin

Gneiss House without rest., Batchraggan, IV27 4ET, ☎ 282 – P. AE VISA.
closed last 2 weeks October, Christmas and New Year – **3 rm** 20.00/30.00 **st.**

Michelin puts no plaque or sign
on the hotels and restaurants mentioned in this Guide.

BOTHWELL Lanark. (Strathclyde) 401 402 H 16 Scotland G – ✉ Glasgow – ☎ 0698.
See : Castle★.
Envir. : Blantyre : David Livingstone Centre (Museum★) off A 724.
18 Blantyre Rd ☎ 853177.
Edinburgh 39 – ◆Glasgow 8.5.

Silvertrees, 27-29 Silverwells Cres., G71 8DP, ☎ 852311, Fax 852311 (extn. 200), – TV ☎ P – 120. AE VISA
closed Christmas and New Year – **M** *(closed Sunday dinner)* 9.00/11.50 **t.** and a la carte 5.00 – **24 rm** 52.50/60.00 **t.**, **2 suites** 60.00/65.00 **t.**

BRAE Shetland (Shetland Islands) 401 P 2 – see Shetland Islands (Mainland).

BRAEMAR Aberdeen. (Grampian) 401 J 12 – ECD : Thursday except summer – ☎ 033 97 (5 fig.) or 033 83 (3 fig.).
Envir. : Lin O' Dee★, W : 7 m.
18 Cluniebank Rd ☎ 41618.
Balnellan Rd ☎ 41600 (summer only).
Edinburgh 85 – ◆Aberdeen 58 – ◆Dundee 51 – Perth 51.

Invercauld Arms (Mt. Charlotte Thistle), AB3 5YR, ☎ 41605, Fax 41428 – TV ☎ P – 40. AE VISA
M 14.50/21.00 **st.** 4.20 – **68 rm** 54.50/80.00 **st.** – SB 60.50/90.00 **st.**

Braemar Lodge, Glenshee Rd, AB3 5YQ, ☎ 41627, – rest TV P. VISA
closed April-Spring Bank Holiday, November and December – **M** (dinner only) 19.50 **st.** 3.25 – **7 rm** 24.00/60.00 **st.**

BRESSAY (Isle of) Shetland (Shetland Islands) 401 Q 3 –Shipping services : see Shetland Islands.

BRIDGE OF ALLAN Stirling. (Central) 401 I 15 – pop. 4 551 – ECD : Wednesday – ☎ 0786.
Envir. : Dollar (Castle Campbell★ (site★★★) E : 12 m. by A 91 – Wallace Monument (★★) S : 2 m. by A 9 – Doune★ (Castle★, Motor Museum★) NW : 7 m. by A 9 and B 824.
Sunnylaw ☎ 83232, N : ½ m. by A 9.
Edinburgh 21 – ◆Dundee 54 – ◆Glasgow 33.

Royal, 55 Henderson St., FK9 4HG, ☎ 832284, Fax 834377, – TV ☎ P – 100
32 rm.

BRIG O'TURK Perth. (Central) 401 G 15 – ✉ Callander – ☎ 08776.
Edinburgh 58 – ◆Glasgow 36 – Perth 47.

Dundarroch and the Byre, Trossachs, FK17 8HT, ☎ 200, ≤, – TV P. AE VISA.
closed 20 January-17 February and 2 weeks November – **M** *(closed Tuesday November-March)* 12.35 **t.** and a la carte 2.65 – **3 rm** 30.00/56.00 **t.** – SB (winter only except Easter, Christmas and New Year) 68.00 **st.**

BRODICK Bute. (Strathclyde) 401 402 E 17 – see Arran (Isle of).

BRORA Sutherland. (Highland) 401 I 9 – pop. 1 728 – ECD : Wednesday – ☎ 0408.
18 Golf Rd ☎ 21417.
Edinburgh 234 – ◆Inverness 78 – ◆Wick 49.

Royal Marine, Golf Rd, KW9 6QS, ☎ 21252, – TV ☎ P. AE VISA
M 8.95/16.50 **st.** 3.50 – **11 rm** 50.00/95.00 **st.** – SB 96.00/125.00 **st.**

Tigh Farm, without rest. Golf Rd, KW9 6QS, ☎ 21332, – P
3 rm 18.50/29.00 **s.**

BROUGHTY FERRY Angus. (Tayside) 401 L 14 – see Dundee.

BUCKIE Banff. (Grampian) 401 L 10 – pop. 7 869 – ECD : Wednesday – ✉ Drybridge – ☎ 0542.
18 Buckpool, Barrhill Rd ☎ 32236 – 18 Strathlene ☎ 31798, E : ½ m.
High St. ☎ 34853 (summer only).
Edinburgh 195 – ◆Aberdeen 66 – ◆Inverness 56.

Old Monastery, AB5 2JB, SE : 3½ m. by A 942 ☎ 32660, ≤, « Former chapel overlooking Spey Bay » – P. AE VISA
closed Sunday, Monday, 2 weeks November and 3 weeks January – **M** a la carte 9.75/18.00 **t.** 5.00.

VAUXHALL-OPEL Marine Place ☎ 32327

BUCKSBURN Aberdeen. (Grampian) 401 N 12 – see Aberdeen.

BUNCHREW Inverness. (Highland) – see Inverness.

BUNESSAN Argyll. (Strathclyde) 401 B 15 – see Mull (Isle of).

BURNTISLAND Fife. (Fife) 401 K 15 – pop. 6 025 – 0592.

♦Edinburgh 20 – Dunfermline 10 – Kirkcaldy 6.

Inchview, 69 Kinghorn Rd, KY3 9EB, 872239 – . AE VISA.
M 8.45/13.95 **t.** and a la carte 3.30 – **12 rm** 33.50/47.50 **st.**

BUSBY Lanark. (Strathclyde) 401 402 H 16 – see Glasgow.

BUTE (Isle of) Bute. (Strathclyde) 401 402 E 16 – pop. 7733.

18 Canada Hill, Rothesay 2244.

by Caledonian MacBrayne : from Tothesay to Wemyss Bay : frequent services dail (30 mn) – from Rhubodach to Colintraive : frequent services daily (5 mn).

CAIRNGORM (Mountains) Inverness. (Highland) 401 J 12 **Scotland G.**

See : Mountains★★ (✻★★ from Cairn Gorm) (alt. 4 048 ft.) (chairlift *AC*) Highland wildlif Park★.

Hotels see : Aviemore NW, ***Braemar*** SE.

CAIRNRYAN Wigtown. (Dumfries and Galloway) 401 402 E 19.

by P & O European Ferries : to Larne 4-6 daily (2 h 15 mn).

♦ Edinburgh 126 – ♦ Ayr 45 – Stranraer 6.5.

Hotel see : Stranraer S : 6 ½ m.

CALLANDER Perth. (Central) 401 H 15 **Scotland G** – pop. 2 286 – ECD : Wednesday excep summer – 0877.

See : Site★.

Envir. : The Trossachs★★★: Loch Katrine★★ – Hilltop Viewpoint (✻★★★) W : 10 m. by A 821 Inchmahone Priory (Monument★) S : 6 m. by A 81 and B 8034.

18 Aveland Rd 30090.

Leny Rd 30342 (from March, Ancaster Sq 30342).

♦Edinburgh 52 – ♦Glasgow 43 – ♦Oban 71 – Perth 41.

Roman Camp, Main St., FK17 8BG, 30003, Fax 31533, <, « 17C hunting lodge i extensive gardens », , park – rest . AE VISA
M 15.00/25.00 **t.** 5.00 – **11 rm** 65.00/105.00 **t.**, **3 suites** 115.00/135.00 **t.**

Lubnaig, Leny Feus, FK17 8AS, 30376, – rest
Easter-October – **M** (dinner only) (residents only) 12.00 **t.** – **10 rm** 27.00/49.00 **t.**

Brook Linn, Leny Feus, FK17 8AU, 30103, <, –
Easter-October – **M** 9.00 **t.** 3.90 – **7 rm** 15.00/36.00 **t.**

Highland House, 8 South Church St., FK17 8BN, 30269 – . AE VISA
March-November, Christmas and New Year – **M** 15.00 **st.** 3.00 – **10 rm** 16.00/38.00 s – SB (except summer and Bank Holidays) 52.00/66.00 **st.**

East Mains House without rest., Bridgend, FK17 8AG, 30080, –
5 rm.

CAMPBELTOWN Argyll. (Strathclyde) 401 D 17 – see Kintyre (Peninsula).

CANNA (Isle of) Inverness. (Highland) 401 A 12 – Shipping Services : see Mallaig.

CANONBIE Dumfries. (Dumfries and Galloway) 401 402 L 18 – 038 73 (5 fig.) or 054 1 (3 fig.).

♦Edinburgh 80 – ♦Carlisle 15 – ♦Dumfries 34.

Riverside Inn with rm, DG19 0UX, 71295 – rest . VISA.
closed last 2 weeks February and first 2 weeks November – **M** *(closed Sunday)* (bookin essential) (bar lunch)/dinner 17.50 **t.** – **6 rm** 45.00/70.00 **t.** – SB (November-April) 75.0 85.00 **st.**

CARFRAEMILL Berwick. (Borders) 401 402 L 16 – see Lauder.

CARRADALE Argyll. (Strathclyde) 401 D 17 – see Kintyre (Peninsula).

CASTLEBAY Inverness. (Outer Hebrides) (Western Isles) 401 X 13 – see Barra (Isle of).

Si vous écrivez à un hôtel à l'étranger,
joignez à votre lettre un coupon-réponse international.
(disponible dans les bureaux de poste).

CASTLE DOUGLAS Kirkcudbright. (Dumfries and Galloway) 401 402 I 19 **Scotland G** – pop. 3 546 – ECD : Thursday – ☎ 0556.

Envir. : Threave Garden★★ and Castle★, SW : 3 m. by A 75.

Abercromby Rd ☎ 2801.

Markethill ☎ 2611 (summer only).

♦Edinburgh 98 – ♦Ayr 49 – ♦Dumfries 18 – Stranraer 57.

King's Arms, St. Andrew St., DG7 1EL, ☎ 2626 – TV P
14 rm.

FORD, LADA Oakwell Rd ☎ 2805
ROVER Morris House ☎ 2560
VAUXHALL-OPEL King St. ☎ 2038
ATS Station Yard ☎ 3121/2

CLACHAN SEIL Argyll. (Strathclyde) 401 D 15 – ECD : Wednesday – ✉ Oban – ☎ 085 23 Balvicar.

♦Edinburgh 137 – ♦Oban 14.

Willowburn, Isle of Seil, PA34 4TJ, ☎ 276, ←, – TV P. VISA
April-October – **M** 12.00 **t.** 3.80 – **6 rm** 21.00/50.00 **t.**

Old Clachan Farmhouse, Clachan, PA34 4RH, ☎ 493, ←, « 18C former drovers inn » – P. VISA.
closed 21 December-8 January – **M** 15.00 **st.** – **3 rm** 15.00/40.00 **st.**

CLAONAIG (Cap) Argyll. (Strathclyde) 401 402 D 16 – Shipping Services : see Kintyre (Peninsula).

La guida cambia, cambiate la guida ogni anno.

CLARENCEFIELD Dumfries. (Dumfries and Galloway) – see Dumfries.

CLEISH Fife. (Tayside) 401 J 15 – see Kinross.

COLINTRAIVE Argyll. (Strathclyde) 401 402 E 16 – ☎ 070 084.

by Caledonian MacBrayne : to Rhubodach (Isle of Bute) : frequent services daily (5 mn).

♦Edinburgh 127 – ♦Glasgow 81 – ♦Oban 81.

COLL (Isle of) Argyll. (Strathclyde) 401 A 14 – pop. 153.

by Caledonian MacBrayne : from Arinagour to Oban : 3 weekly – from Arinagour to Tobermory (Isle of Mull) 3 weekly – from Arinagour to Isle of Tiree : 3 weekly.

Arinagour – ✉ ☎ 087 93 Coll

Tigh-Na-Mara without rest., PA78 6SY, ☎ 354, ← Mull and Treshnish Isles, « Idyllic Hebridean setting », – P
closed December-mid January – **8 rm** 14.50/34.00 **t.**

COLONSAY (Isle of) Argyll. (Strathclyde) 401 B 15 – pop. 132 – ☎ 095 12 Colonsay.

☎ 316.

by Caledonian MacBrayne : summer only, from Scalasaig to Oban 3 weekly (2 h 30 mn).

Scalasaig – ECD : Wednesday – ✉ ☎ 095 12 Colonsay

Isle of Colonsay, PA61 7YP, ☎ 316, Fax 353, ←, « 18C inn », – rest P. AE VISA
closed 14 January-28 February and 5 November-27 December – **M** (bar lunch)/dinner 14.25 **st.** 3.75 – **11 rm** 45.00/90.00 **st.** – SB (except summer) 86.00 **st.**

COLVEND Kircudbright. (Dumfries and Galloway) – ✉ Dalbeattie – ☎ 055 663 Rockcliffe.

Sandyhills ☎ 398, E : 1¼ m.

♦Edinburgh 99 – ♦Dumfries 19.

Clonyard House, DG5 4QW, NW : 1 m. on A 710 ☎ 372, – TV ☎ P. VISA
M (bar lunch)/dinner a la carte 7.00/13.10 **t.** 3.20 – **9 rm** 30.00/50.00 **t.** – SB (November-March) 60.00 **st.**

CRAIGELLACHIE Banff. (Grampian) 401 K 11 – ☎ 0340.

♦Edinburgh 190 – ♦Aberdeen 58 – ♦Inverness 53.

Craigellachie, Victoria Street, AB3 9SS, ☎ 881 204, Fax 881 253, – TV ☎ P. AE VISA
M 18.50/40.00 **t.** and a la carte 4.75 – **30 rm** 47.50/99.00 **t.**

CRAIGHOUSE Argyll. (Strathclyde) 401 C 16 – see Jura (Isle of).

CRAIL Fife 401 M 15 – ☎ 0333.

♦Edinburgh 50 – ♦Dundee 23 – Dunfermline 38.

Caiplie, 53 High St., KY10 3RA, ☎ 50564 – **7 rm.**

CREETOWN Wigtownshire. (Dumfries and Galloway) 401 402 G 19 – ☎ 067 182.
◆Edinburgh 118 – ◆Dumfries 38 – ◆Glasgow 100 – Stranraer 37.

- Hills of Burns, Hill St., DG8 7HF, ☎ 487, ←, – TV ☎ P
  M (dinner only) – **5 rm**, **1 suite.**

CRIANLARICH Perth. (Central) 401 G 16 – ☎ 083 83.
◆Edinburgh 82 – ◆Glasgow 52 – Perth 53.

- **Allt-Chaorain House**, FK20 8RU, NW : 1 m. on A 82 ☎ 283, ←, – TV P. VISA
  Mid March-October – **M** 12.00 **t.** – **9 rm** 33.00/78.00 **t.**

CRIEFF Perth. (Tayside) 401 I 14 **Scotland G** – pop. 5 101 – ECD : Wednesday – ☎ 0764.
See : Site★.
Envir. : Drummond Castle★ *AC*, S : 2 m. by A 822 – Tullibardine Chapel★, S : 6 m. by – Upper Strathearn★ (Loch Earn★★) NW : 12 m. by A B5.
18 Perth Rd ☎ 2909 – 9 Peat Rd, Muthill ☎ 3319, S : 3 m. on A 822.
High St. ☎ 2578 (summer only).
◆Edinburgh 60 – ◆Glasgow 50 – ◆Oban 76 – Perth 18.

- **Murraypark,** Connaught Terr., PH7 3DJ, ☎ 3731, Fax 5311, – TV ☎ P. AE VISA
  M 11.50/18.50 **t.** and a la carte 4.00 – **13 rm** 37.75/58.00 **t.**, **1 suite** 65.00 **t.**
- **Gwydyr House,** Comrie Rd, PH7 4BP, on A 85 ☎ 3277, ←, – TV P
  28 March-October – **M** 8.50 **t.** 3.10 – **10 rm** 12.25/29.00 **t.**
- **Leven House,** Comrie Rd, PH7 4BA, on A 85 ☎ 2529, ← – rest P
  M 10.00 **st.** 2.50 – **10 rm** 15.00/40.00 **st.** – SB 44.00/55.00 **st.**

at Sma'Glen NE : 4 m. by A 85 on A 822 – ✉ ☎ 0764 Crieff :

- **Foulford Inn**, PH7 3LN, ☎ 2407, ← – P. VISA
  closed February – **M** 7.00/12.00 **t.** and a la carte 4.00 – **10 rm** 14.00/34.00 **t.** – SB 45.00/55.00 **st.**

VAUXHALL, SUZUKI Comrie Rd ☎ 2125

CRINAN Argyll. (Strathclyde) 401 D 15 – ✉ Lochgilphead – ☎ 054 683.
See : Site★.
Envir. : Kilmory Knap (Macmillan's Cross★) SW : 14 m.
◆Edinburgh 137 – ◆Glasgow 91 – ◆Oban 36.

- **Crinan,** PA31 8SR, ☎ 261, Fax 292, « ← commanding setting, overlooking Loch Crinan and Sound of Jura », – TV ☎ P. VISA.
  closed 1 week Christmas – **M** (buffet lunch)/dinner 25.00 **t.** 5.50 – (see also **Lock 16** below) – **22 rm** 60.00/170.00 **t.** – SB (November-Easter except New Year) 90.00 **st.**
- XX **Lock 16** (at Crinan H.), PA31 8SR, ☎ 261, Seafood, « ← commanding setting, overlooking Loch Crinan and Sound of Jura » – P. VISA
  closed Monday and Christmas – **M** (booking essential) (dinner only) 23.50/35.00 **t.**

CROMARTY Ross and Cromarty. (Highland) 401 H 10 – pop. 685 – ECD : Wednesday – ☎ 038 17.
◆Edinburgh 182 – ◆Inverness 26 – ◆Wick 126.

- **Royal,** Marine Terr., IV11 8YN, ☎ 217, ← – TV P. AE VISA
  M *(closed Sunday dinner)* 8.00/14.00 **st.** 3.00 – **10 rm** 22.00/44.00 **st.**
- XX **Thistles,** 20 Church St., IV11 8XA, ☎ 471 –
  closed Sunday dinner and Monday except Bank Holidays and 25 to 30 December – **M** a la carte 13.00/20.00 **st.** 5.00.

CROSSFORD Fife. (Fife) 401 J 15 – see Dunfermline.

CULLEN Banff. (Grampian) 401 L 10 **Scotland G** – pop. 1 378 – ECD : Wednesday – ☎ 0542.
See : Auld Kirk★ (Sacrament house★, carved panels★).
Envir. : Deskford Church (Sacrament house★) S : 4 m. by B 9018 – Portsoy★, E : 5 ½ m. by A 98.
18 The Links ☎ 40685.
20 Seafield St. ☎ 40757 (summer only).
◆Edinburgh 189 – ◆Aberdeen 59 – Banff 12 – ◆Inverness 61.

- **Bayview,** Seafield St., AB56 2SU, ☎ 41031, ← – TV ☎. VISA.
  closed November – **M** (bar lunch)/dinner 13.50 **st.** 3.50 – **6 rm** 30.00/48.00 **st.**
- Mayfield House, Seafield Place, AB5 2TE, ☎ 40819, – **3 rm.**

CULLODEN Inverness. (Highland) 401 H 11 – see Inverness.

CULNAKNOCK Inverness. (Highland) 401 B 11 – see Skye (Isle of).

CULTS Aberdeen. (Grampian) 401 N 12 – see Aberdeen.

CUPAR Fife. (Fife) 401 K 15 – pop. 6 662 – ECD : Thursday – ☎ 0334.

ℹ Fluthers car park ℘ 55555 (summer only).

◆Edinburgh 45 – ◆Dundee 15 – Perth 23.

✗ **Ostler's Close,** Bonnygate, KY15 4BU, ℘ 55574 – VISA
closed 2 weeks June – **M** *(closed Monday and Sunday)* a la carte 18.40/22.00 **t.** 3.40.

ATS St. Catherine St. ℘ 54003

DALBEATTIE Kirkcudbright. (Dumfries and Galloway) 401 402 I 19 – pop. 3 891 – ☎ 0556.

ℹ Town Hall ℘ 610117.

◆Edinburgh 94 – ◆Ayr 56 – ◆Dumfries 14 – Stranraer 62.

Auchenskeoch Lodge , DG5 4PG, SE : 5 m. on B 793 ℘ 038 778 (Southwick) 277, , , park – & P. VISA
Easter-October – **M** (by arrangement) 11.00 **st.** – **5 rm** 26.00/40.00 **st.** – SB (spring and autumn) 56.00/60.00 **st.**

DALIBURGH Inverness. (Outer Hebrides) (Western Isles) 401 X 12 – see Uist (South) (Isles of).

DALMALLY Argyll. (Strathclyde) 401 F 14 – ✉ ☎ 083 82.

◆Edinburgh 99 – ◆Glasgow 69 – ◆Oban 24 – Perth 70.

Craig Villa, PA33 1AX, on A 85 ℘ 255, ←, – P.
April-October – **M** 11.00 **st.** – **6 rm** 25.00/40.00 **st.**

DALRY (ST. JOHN'S TOWN OF) Kirkcudbright. (Dumfries and Galloway) 401 402 H 18 – ✉ Castle Douglas – ☎ 064 43.

◆Edinburgh 82 – ◆Dumfries 27 – ◆Glasgow 66 – Stranraer 47.

Lochinvar, Main St., DG7 3UP, ℘ 210 – P. AE VISA
M 6.50/14.95 **st.** and a la carte 3.50 – **16 rm** 25.00/60.00 **t.**

DENNY Stirling. (Central) 401 I 15 – pop. 23 172 – ☎ 0324.

◆Edinburgh 34 – ◆Glasgow 25 – Stirling 7.

Topps Farm , Fintry Rd, FK6 5JF, W : 4 m. on B 818 ℘ 822471, ← – & P
M 10.00 **st.** 4.00 – **8 rm** 25.00/34.00 **st.**

DERVAIG Argyll. (Strathclyde) 401 B 14 – see Mull (Isle of).

DIRLETON E. Lothian. (Lothian) 401 402 L 15 – see Gullane.

DOLPHINTON Lanark. (Strathclyde) 401 J 16 – ✉ West Linton – ☎ 0968.

◆Edinburgh 26 – Hawick 43 – ◆Glasgow 41.

Dolphinton House , EH46 7AB, ℘ 82286, – rest ☎ P. AE VISA
M 7.50/24.95 **t.** 4.70 – **12 rm** 50.00/100.00 **t.** – SB 109.95/119.50 **st.**

DORNIE Ross and Cromarty. (Highland) 401 D 12 – ✉ Kyle of Lochalsh – ☎ 059 985.

◆Edinburgh 212 – ◆Inverness 74 – Kyle of Lochalsh 8.

Loch Duich, IV40 8DY, ℘ 213, ← Eilean Donan Castle and hills, – P. VISA.
April-October – **M** (bar lunch)/dinner 15.00 **t.** 5.60 – **18 rm** 22.00/44.00 **t.**

DORNOCH Sutherland. (Highland) 401 H 10 **Scotland G** – pop. 1 006 – ECD : Thursday – ☎ 0862.

18 Royal Dornoch, Golf Rd ℘ 810219.

ℹ The Square, ℘ 810400.

◆Edinburgh 219 – ◆Inverness 63 – ◆Wick 65.

Dornoch Castle, Castle St., IV25 3SD, ℘ 810216, « Former bishop's palace, part 16C », – rest ☎ P. AE VISA
Mid April-end October – **M** 10.50/14.50 **st.** and a la carte 3.40 – **19 rm** 32.00/68.00 **st.** – SB 79.00/95.00 **st.**

PEUGEOT Evelix Service Station (on A 9) ℘ 810255

*Es ist empfehlenswert, **in der Hauptsaison** und vor allem in Urlaubsorten, Hotelzimmer im voraus zu bestellen.*
Benachrichtigen Sie sofort das Hotel, wenn Sie ein bestelltes Zimmer nicht belegen können.
Wenn Sie an ein Hotel im Ausland schreiben, fügen Sie Ihrem Brief einen internationalen Antwortschein bei (im Postamt erhältlich).

DOUNBY Orkney. (Orkney Islands) 401 K 6 – see Orkney Islands (Mainland).

DOUNE Perth. (Central) 401 H 15 **Scotland G** – pop. 1 020 – ECD : Wednesday – 0786.

See : Site★ – Castle★.

Envir. : Doune Motor Museum★, NW : 1 m. by A 84.

♦Edinburgh 45 – ♦Glasgow 35 – Perth 33 – Stirling 8.

Broughton's, Blair Drummond, FK9 4XE, S : 3 m. by A 84 on A 873 ℘ 841897, – . VISA
closed Sunday dinner, Monday, last 2 weeks January, first 2 weeks February and first week September – **M** (booking essential) 10.50/18.00 **t.** and a la carte lunch approx. 7.50 **t.** 3.50.

DRUMNADROCHIT Inverness. (Highland) 401 G 11 – pop. 542 – ✉ Milton – 045 62.

Envir. : Loch Ness★★ – Loch Ness Monster Exhibition★.

♦Edinburgh 172 – ♦Inverness 16 – Kyle of Lochalsh 66.

Polmaily House, IV3 6XT, W : 2 m. on A 831 ℘ 343, « Country house atmosphere », park, – rest . VISA.
April-October – **M** (bar lunch, residents only)/dinner 29.00 **st.** 4.00 – **9 rm** 40.00/90.00 **st.**

DRYMEN Stirling. (Central) 401 G 15 – pop. 771 – ECD : Wednesday – 0360.

Envir. : Loch Lomond★★, W : 3 m.

♦Edinburgh 64 – ♦Glasgow 18 – Stirling 22.

Buchanan Highland, Main St., G63 0BQ, ℘ 60588, Fax 60943, , , , , squash – TV – 130. AE VISA
M 15.00/30.00 **t.** and a la carte 4.25 – **50 rm** 60.00/95.00 **t.** – SB 80.00/110.00 **st.**

DULNAIN BRIDGE Inverness. (Highland) 401 J 12 – ECD : Wednesday – ✉ Grantown-on-Spey (Moray Highland) – 047 985.

♦Edinburgh 140 – ♦Inverness 31 – Perth 96.

Muckrach Lodge, PH26 3LY, W : ½ m. on A 938 ℘ 257, ≤, – TV . AE VISA
M 12.00/23.50 **t.** and lunch a la carte – **10 rm** 33.00/66.00 **t.**

Auchendean Lodge, PH26 3LU, S : 1 m. on A 95 ℘ 347, ≤ Spey Valley and Cairngorms – rest TV
closed early November-mid December – **M** (dinner only) 19.50 **st.** 3.00 – **7 rm** 29.00/55.00 **st.**

DUMBARTON Dunbarton. (Strathclyde) 401 G 16 – pop. 23 204 – 0389.

See : Dumbarton Castel site★.

Envir. : Loch Lomond★★, N : 6 m. by A 82 – Helensburgh (Hill House★) NW 10 m. by A 814.

Milton, by Dumbarton A 82 ℘ 42306.

♦Edinburgh 64 – ♦Glasgow 12 – Greenock 17.

Travelodge without rest., Milton, G82 2TY, E : 3 m. by A 814 on A 82 ℘ 65202 Reservations (Toll free) 0800 850950 – TV . AE VISA.
32 rm 24.00/29.50 **t.**

DUMFRIES Dumfries. (Dumfries and Galloway) 401 402 J 18 **Scotland G** – pop. 31 307 – ECD : Thursday – 0387.

See : Site★ – Midsteeple★ A **A** – Lincluden College (Tomb★) by College Str. A.

Envir. : Sweetheart Abbey★, S : 8¼ m. by A 710 A – Caerlaverock Castle★, SE : 9 m. by B 725 B – Ruthwell Cross★, SE : 16 m. by B 725 B – Glenkiln (Sculptures★) E : 10 m. by A 75 B – Kippford★, SW : 18 m. by A 710 or A 711 A – Drumlanrig Castle★★, NW : 18 m. by A 76 A.

18 Laurieston Av. ℘ 53582 A – 18 Southerness ℘ 88677 A – 18 Dumfries and County, Edinburgh rd ℘ 53585, NE : 1 m. B – 9 Lochmaben ℘ 03887 (Lochmaden) 810552, NE : 1 m. B.

Whitesands ℘ 53862.

♦Edinburgh 80 – ♦Ayr 59 – ♦Carlisle 34 – ♦Glasgow 79 – ♦Manchester 155 – ♦Newcastle-upon-Tyne 91.

Plan opposite

Station, 49 Lovers Walk, DG1 1LT, ℘ 54316, Fax 50388 – TV – 60. AE VISA B e
M (carving lunch)/dinner 17.50 **t.** and a la carte 4.00 – **32 rm** 40.00/95.00 **t.** – SB (weekends only) 75.00/90.00 **st.**

FIAT 78-90 Glasgow St. ℘ 64875
FORD Main Rd ℘ 710491
VOLVO Annan Rd ℘ 61437

ATS Glasgow St. ℘ 63837/8

DUMFRIES

igh Street . . . . A 18
ldermanhill Road . . . . B 2
ank Street . . . . A 3
uccleuch Street . . . . A 4
ardoness Street . . . . B 5
assalands . . . . A 6
astle Street . . . . A 7
astle Douglas Road . . . . . . A 8
atherine Street . . . . B 9
orberry Avenue . . . . A 10
Eastfield Rd . . . . B 12
Friars Vennel . . . . A 13
Galloway Street . . . . A 14
Glebe Street . . . . B 15
Great King Street . . . . A 16
Hermitage Drive . . . . A 17
Laurieknowe . . . . A 20
Loreburn Street . . . . A 21
Nith Street . . . . AB 22
Queen Street . . . . B 23
Queensberry Street . . . . A 24
Rae Street . . . . B 26
St. Mary's Street . . . . B 27
St. Michael Street . . . . B 28
St. Michael's Bridge Road . . . . A 30
Shakespeare Street . . . . B 31
Union Street . . . . A 32
Whitesands . . . . A 34

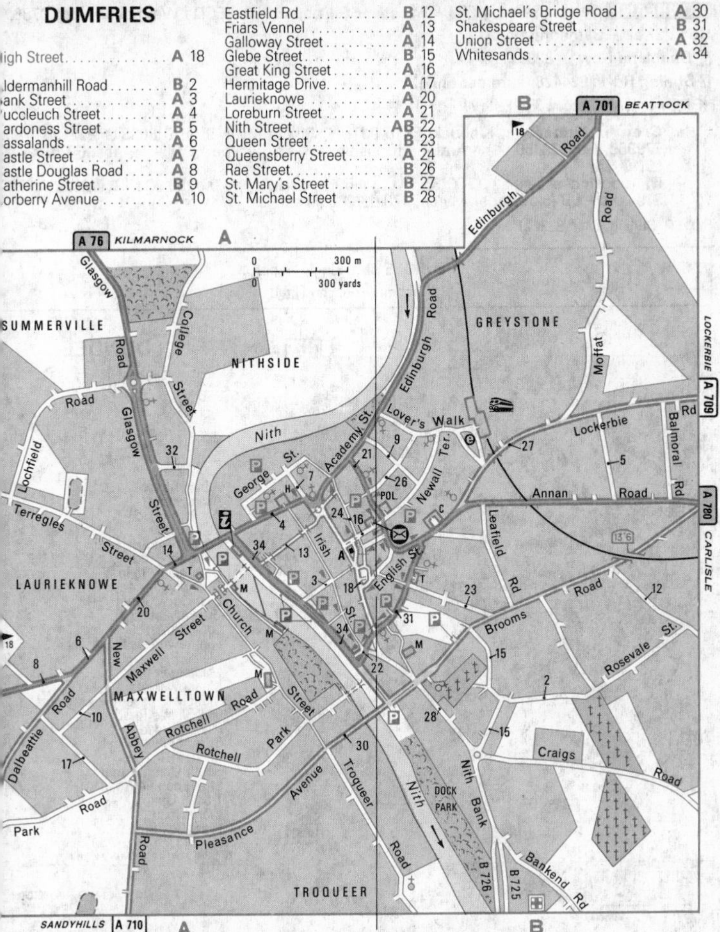

DUNAIN PARK Inverness. (Highland) – see Inverness.

DUNBAR E. Lothian. (Lothian) 401 M 15 **Scotland G** – pop. 5 795 – ECD : Wednesday – ☎ 0368.

See : Tolbooth★ – John Muir's Birthplace★.

Envir. : Museum of Flight★, W : 5 m. by A 1087 and A 1 – Preston Mill★, W : 6 m. by A 1087, A 1 and B 1407 – Tyninghame★, NW : 6 m. by A 1 and A 198 – Tantallon Castle★★, NW : 10 m. by A 1087, A 1 and A 198.

Winterfield, North Rd ℘ 62280 – East Links ℘ 62317, S : ½ m.

Town House, High St. ℘ 63353.

◆Edinburgh 28 – ◆Newcastle-upon-Tyne 90.

Redheuch, Bayswell Park, EH42 1AE, ℘ 62793 – TV ☎. AE VISA
M (lunch by arrangement)/dinner a la carte 9.75/14.20 **t.** 2.75 – **10 rm** 35.00/55.00 **t.** – SB (weekends only) 59.00/65.00 **st.**

Courtyard, Woodbrush Brae, EH42 1HB, ℘ 64169 – TV P. VISA
M *(closed Sunday dinner)* a la carte 11.30/14.60 **t.** 3.25 – **6 rm** 17.50/45.00 **t.**

St Beys, 2 Bayswell Rd, EH42 1AB, ℘ 63571 – TV
6 rm.

Marine, 7 Marine Rd, EH42 1AR, ℘ 63315, ← – rest
M 5.00 **st.** – **9 rm** 12.00/24.00 **st.**

DUNBLANE Perth. (Central) 401 I 15 **Scotland G** – pop. 6 783 – ECD : Wednesday – ☎ 0786.

See : Site★ – Cathedral★★.

Dunblane New ☎ 823711.

Stirling Rd ☎ 824428 (summer only).

◆Edinburgh 42 – ◆Glasgow 33 – Perth 29.

Cromlix House ⛰, Kinbuck, FK15 9JT, N : 3 ¼ m. by A 9 on B 8033 ☎ 822125, Tele 779959, Fax 825450, ≤, « Antique furnishings », 🎣, park, 🎾 – ⚡ rest 📺 ☎ 🅿. AE ⓓ VISA
M (booking essential) 30.00/35.00 **t.** 🍷 4.50 – **6 rm** ☕ 95.00/130.00 **t.**, **8 suites** 165.00 215.00 **t.** – SB (November-March) 170.00/260.00 **st.**

ROVER Stirling Rd ☎ 823271

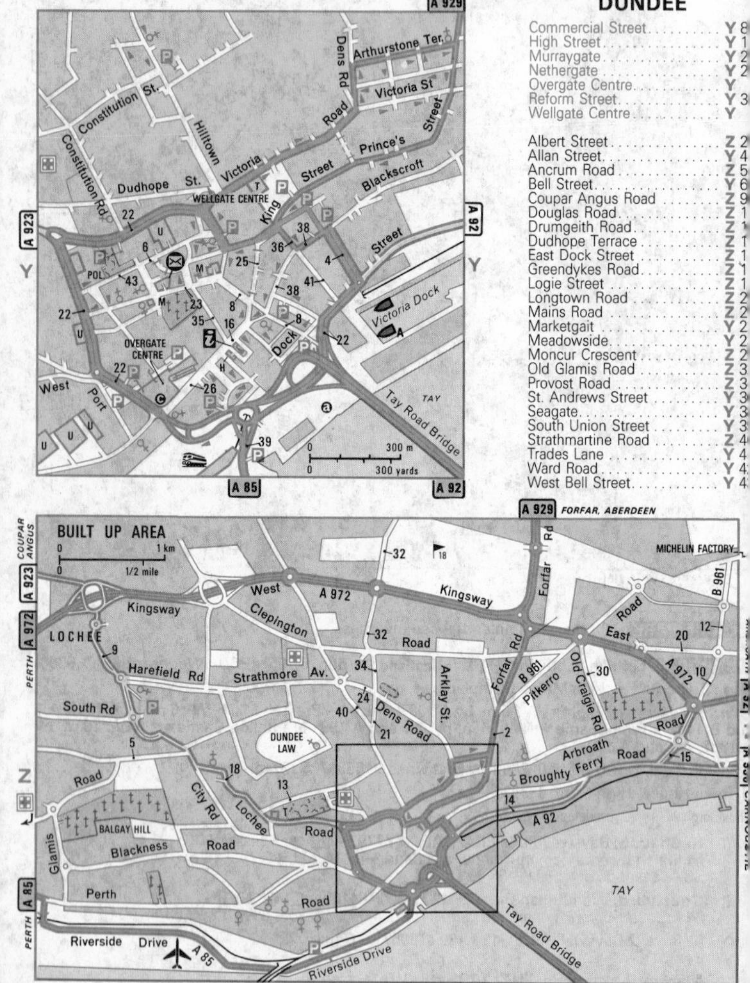

DUNDEE

DUNDEE Angus. (Tayside) 401 L 14 **Scotland G** – pop. 172 294 – ECD : Wednesday – ☎ 0382.

See : The Frigate Unicorn★ Y A – R. RS Discovery★ Y B.

18 Caird Park ☎ 453606 off Kingsway Bypass at Mains Loan Z – 18 Camperdown Park ☎ 623398, NW : 2 m. by A 923 Z – 18 Downfield, Turnberry Av. ☎ 825595 – 18, 18 Monifieth Golf Links, Princes St. ☎ 532767.

Dundee Airport : ☎ 643242, SW : 1 ½ m. Z.

4 City Sq. ☎ 27723.

◆Edinburgh 63 – ◆Aberdeen 67 – ◆Glasgow 83.

Plan opposite

Stakis Earl Grey, Earl Grey Pl., DD1 4DE, ☎ 29271, Telex 76569, Fax 200072, ≤, – rest TV ☎ & P – 200. AE VISA. Y a
M 8.50/14.75 and a la carte – 7.50 – **102 rm** 68.00/102.00 t., **2 suites** 130.00 t. – SB 80.00/144.00 **st.**

Angus Thistle (Mt. Charlotte Thistle), 101 Marketgait, DD1 1QU, ☎ 26874, Telex 76456, Fax 22564 – rm TV ☎ P – 450. AE VISA Y c
M 8.00/13.00 **st.** and a la carte – 7.75 – **53 rm** 60.00/95.00 **st.**, **5 suites** – SB 70.00 **st.**

Swallow, Kingsway West (Dundee Ring Rd), DD2 5JT, W : 4 ¾ m. at junction A 85 and A 972 Z ☎ 641122, Telex 76694, Fax 568340, – rm rest TV ☎ & P. AE VISA
M *(closed Saturday lunch)* 10.25/16.50 **st.** and a la carte 4.50 – **110 rm** 75.00/195.00 **st.** – SB 85.00 **st.**

at Broughty Ferry E : 4 ½ m. by A 930 – Z – (Dundee Rd) – ✉ ☎ 0382 Dundee :

Tayview without rest., 71-73 St. Vincent St., DD5 2EZ, ☎ 79438 – . VISA.
11 rm 35.00/60.00 **t.**

CITROEN Clepington Rd ☎ 28483
FIAT, LADA MacAlpine Rd ☎ 818004
FORD Balfield Rd ☎ 60191
HONDA Queen St., Broughty Ferry ☎ 77257
HYUNDAI 25 Rosebank St. ☎ 25406
MAZDA 72-76 Monyfeith Rd, Broughty Ferry ☎ 77992
RENAULT Riverside Drive ☎ 644401
ROVER 64 Ward Rd ☎ 24013
TOYOTA East Kingsway ☎ 457667
VAUXHALL East Dock St. ☎ 26521
VOLVO Riverside Drive ☎ 643295
ATS 332 Clepington Rd ☎ 88327

DUNDONNELL Ross and Cromarty. (Highland) 401 E 10 – ✉ Garve – ☎ 085 483.

◆Edinburgh 215 – ◆ Inverness 59.

Dundonnell, IV23 2QS, ☎ 204, Fax 366, ≤ Dundonnell Valley – TV ☎ P. VISA
M (bar lunch)/dinner 16.50 **t.** and a la carte 3.75 – **24 rm** 37.00/68.00 **t.** – SB 80.00/100.00 **st.**

DUNFERMLINE Fife. (Fife) 401 J 15 **Scotland G** – pop. 52 105 – ECD : Wednesday – ☎ 0383.

See : Site★ – Abbey★ (Norman nave★★).

Envir. : Culross★★★ (Palace★★ and Study★) E : 7 m. by A 994.

18 Canmore, Venturefair ☎ 724969, N : 1 m. – 18 Pitreavie, Queensferry Rd ☎ 722591 – 18 Pitfirrane, Crossford ☎ 723534.

Glen Bridge Car Park ☎ 720999 (summer only).

◆Edinburgh 16 – ◆Dundee 48 – Motherwell 39.

King Malcolm Thistle (Mt. Charlotte Thistle), Queensferry Rd, KY11 5DS, S : 1 m. on A 823 ☎ 722611, Telex 727721, Fax 730865 – rm rest TV ☎ P – 120. AE VISA
M 16.00 **st.** and a la carte – 7.75 – **48 rm** 49.00/70.00 **st.** – SB 74.00 **st.**

at Crossford SW : 1 ¾ m. on A 994 – ✉ ☎ 0383 Dunfermline :

Keavil House (Best Western) , Main St., KY12 8QW, ☎ 736258, Telex 728227, Fax 621600, – TV ☎ & P – 150. AE VISA
M 14.50/18.50 **st.** 3.75 – **32 rm** 55.00/75.00 **st.** – SB 84.00/95.00 **st.**

FIAT 128-140 Pittencrieff St. ☎ 722565
RENAULT Headwell Av. ☎ 721914
ROVER 18 Halbeath Rd ☎ 731041
VAUXHALL, BEDFORD, OPEL 3 Carnock Rd ☎ 721511
ATS 14 Dickson St., Elgin St. Est. ☎ 722802

DUNKELD Perth. (Tayside) 401 J 14 **Scotland G** – ECD : Thursday – ☎ 035 02.

See : Site★ – Cathedral Street★.

9 Fungarth ☎ 524, N : 1 m. on A 923.

The Cross ☎ 688 (summer only).

◆Edinburgh 58 – ◆Aberdeen 88 – ◆Inverness 98 – Perth 14.

Kinnaird , Dalguise, PH8 0LB, NW : 6 ¾ m. by A 9 on B 898 ☎ 079 682 440 (Ballinluig), Fax 289, ≤ Tay valley and hills, « Sporting estate, antique furnishings », park, – rest TV ☎ P. VISA.
closed February – **M** 20.00/37.50 **st.** 7.50 – **8 rm** 75.00/145.00 **st.**, **1 suite** 185.00 **st.** – SB (October-May) (except Christmas and New Year) 110.00/162.00 **st.**

Stakis Dunkeld House ⑤, PH8 0HX, ☎ 771, Telex 76657, Fax 8924, ←, « Tayside setting », Ⓛ, ⌂s, ☐, ⌂, ⌂, park, ⚘ – |⌂| ⇆ rm ☐ ☎ Ⓟ – ⚑ 70. ☐ AE ⓘ VISA. ⚘
M 15.00/22.50 – ☐ 7.50 – **89 rm** 86.00/99.00 **st.**, **3 suites** 135.50 **t.** – SB 100.00/238.00 **st**

Bheinne Mhor, Perth Rd, Birnam, PH8 0DH, S : ¾ m. by A 923 ☎ 779, ⌂ – ⇆ rest Ⓟ ⚘
closed December and January – **M** 9.00 **st.** – **4 rm** ☐ 14.50/31.00 **st.** – SB (October-Easter 44.50/47.50 **st.**

DUNOON Argyll. (Strathclyde) 401 F 16 – pop. 8 797 – ECD : Wednesday – ☎ 0369.

18 Cowal, Ardenslate Rd ☎ 2216, NE : boundary.

⛴ by Caledonian MacBrayne : from Dunoon Pier to Gourock Railway Pier : frequent services daily (20 mn) – by Western Ferries : from Hunters Quay to McInroy's Point, Gourock frequent services daily (20 mn).

ℹ 7 Alexandra Par. ☎ 3785.

♦Edinburgh 73 – ♦Glasgow 27 – ♦Oban 77.

Enmore, Marine Par., Kirn, PA23 8HH, N : 1 m. on A 815 ☎ 2230, ← Firth of Clyde, ⌂ squash – ⇆ rest ☐ ☎ Ⓟ. ☐ ⓘ VISA
closed 3 weeks Christmas-New Year – **M** 15.00/18.50 **t.** ⌂ 4.25 – **12 rm** ☐ 38.00/106.00 **t.** – SB (November-April) 96.00/126.00 **st.**

RENAULT Shore St., Inverary ☎ 0499 (Inverary) 2150
ROVER, LAND-ROVER, FORD East Bay Promenade ☎ 3094
ⓘ ATS 247 Argyll St. ☎ 2853

Entrez à l'hôtel le Guide à la main, vous montrerez ainsi, qu'il vous conduit là en confiance.

DUNVEGAN Inverness. (Highland) 401 A 11 – see Skye (Isle of).

DUROR Argyll. (Strathclyde) 401 E 14 – ✉ Appin – ☎ 063 174.

♦Edinburgh 125 – Fort William 19 – ♦Oban 31.

Stewart (Best Western) ⑤, Glen Duror, PA38 4BW, ☎ 268, Telex 94014994, Fax 328, ←, ⌂s, ⌂ – ⇆ rest ☐ ☎ Ⓟ. ☐ AE ⓘ VISA
April-December – **M** (bar lunch)/dinner 25.00 **t.** ⌂ 4.50 – **19 rm** ☐ 35.00/70.00 **t.** – SB 100.00 **st.**

DYCE Aberdeen. (Grampian) 401 N 12 – see Aberdeen.

EASDALE Argyll. (Strathclyde) 401 D 15 – ✉ Oban – ☎ 085 23 Balvicar.

♦Edinburgh 140 – ♦Glasgow 120 – ♦Oban 17.

Easdale Inn ⑤, Isle of Seil, PA34 4RF, ☎ 256, ← – ☐ Ⓟ
Easter-October – **M** (bar lunch)/dinner 12.50 **t.** ⌂ 2.50 – **7 rm** ☐ (dinner included) 35.00/80.00 **t.**

EAST KILBRIDE Lanark. (Strathclyde) 401 402 H 16 – pop. 70 454 – ECD : Wednesday – ☎ 035 52.

♦Edinburgh 46 – ♦Ayr 35 – ♦Glasgow 10.

Bruce (Swallow), 35 Cornwall St., G74 1AF, ☎ 29771, Telex 778428, Fax 42216 – |⌂| ⇆ rm ☐ ☎ Ⓟ – ⚑ 200
79 rm.

Stuart, 2 Cornwall Way, G74 1JR, ☎ 21161, Telex 778504, Fax 64410 – |⌂| ☐ ☎ – ⚑ 200. ☐ AE ⓘ VISA
M 10.00/11.50 **t.** and a la carte ⌂ 3.50 – **38 rm** ☐ 43.00/50.00 **t.**, **1 suite** 55.00/65.00 **t.**

Crutherland Country House ⑤, Strathaven Rd, G75 0QZ, SE : 2 m. on A 726 ☎ 37633, Fax 37633, ⌂ – ☐ ☎ Ⓟ. ☐ AE VISA
closed 1 and 2 January – **M** 8.50/16.95 **t.** and a la carte ⌂ 5.80 – **18 rm** ☐ 50.00/95.00 **t.**, **1 suite** 75.00/90.00 **t.** – SB (weekends only) 90.00 **st.**

EAST LINTON E. Lothian. (Lothian) 401 M 16 – pop. 1 190 – ECD : Wednesday – ☎ 0620.

♦Edinburgh 22 – ♦Newcastle-upon-Tyne 96.

Harvesters, Station Rd, EH40 3DP, ☎ 860395, ⌂ – ☐ ☎ Ⓟ. ☐ AE ⓘ VISA
M a la carte 7.90/13.45 **t.** ⌂ 4.45 – **11 rm** ☐ 28.00/62.00 **t.** – SB (weekends only) 74.00/78.00 **st.**

ECKFORD Roxburgh. (Borders) 401 M 17 – see Kelso.

EDAY (Isle of) Orkney. (Orkney Islands) 401 L 6 – Shipping services : see Orkney Islands (Mainland : Kirkwall).

EDDLESTON Peebles. (Borders) 401 402 K 16 – see Peebles.

DINBURGH Midlothian. (Lothian) 401 K 16 **Scotland G** – pop. 408 822 – ☎ 031.

ee : Site★★★ – International Festival★★★ (August) – Castle★★ (Site★★★, ≤★★ ✱★★★, Great all: hammerbeam roof★★, Palace block: Honours of Scotland★★★) DZ – Abbey and Palace of olyroodhouse★★ (Plasterwork ceilings★★★) BV – Royal Mile★★ : Gladstone's Land★ EYZ **A**, St. iles' Cathedral★★ (Crown Spire★★★) EZ – Canongate Tolbooth★ EY **B** Victoria Street★ EZ **84** – oyal Museum of Scotland★★, EZ **M2** – New Town★★ : Charlotte Square★★★ CY **14**, Royal useum of Scotland (Antiquities★★) EY **M3** – The Georgian House★ CY **D** – National Portrait allery★ EY **M3** – Princes Street and Gardens : National Gallery of Scotland★★★ DY **M4** – Scott lonument★ EY **F** Calton Hill EY : ✱★★★ from Nelson Monument – Royal Botanic Gardens★★★ / – Edinburgh Zoo★★ AV – Scottish Agricultural Museum★ by A 90 AV – Craigmillar Castle★ X.

nvir. : Rosslyn Chapel★★, Apprentice Pillar★★★, S : 7 m. by A 701 BX – Hopetoun House★★ / : 10½ m. by A 90 AV – Forth Bridges★★ W : 7½m. by A 90 AV – Dalmeny (site★) W : 7 m. by 90 AV.

; Silverknowes, Parkway, ☎ 336 3843, W : 4 m. AV – 18 Liberton, Gilmerton Rd ☎ 664 8580, E : 3 m. on A 7 BX – 18 Craigmillar Park, Observatory Rd ☎ 667 2837 BX – 18 Carrick Knowe, lendevon Park ☎ 337 1096, W : 5 m. AX – 18 Swanston Rd, Fairmilehead ☎ 445 2239, S : 4 m. y A 702 AX – 18 Lothianburn, Biggar Rd ☎ 445 2206, S : 4½ m. by A 702 BX – 18, 18 Braidhills o 1, Braidhills No 2, Braids United ☎ 447 6666. BX

✈ ☎ 333 1000, Telex 727615, W : 6 m. by A 8 AV – **Terminal** : Waverley Bridge.

☎ 0345 090700.

Waverley Market, Princes St., ☎ 557 1700 – Edinburgh Airport ☎ 333 2167.

Glasgow 46 – ◆Newcastle-upon-Tyne 105.

Plans on following pages

Caledonian (Q.M.H.), Princes St., EH1 2AB, ☎ 225 2433, Telex 72179, Fax 225 6632 – 🛗 ⇸ rm TV ☎ ♿ P – 🎓 400. AE ⓓ VISA. ✗ CY **n**
M (see **Pompadour** below) – ☕ 9.75 – **221 rm** 110.00/175.00 **t.**, **16 suites** 240.00/650.00 **t.** – SB (weekends only) 134.00/172.00 **st.**

Sheraton, 1 Festival Square, EH3 9SR, ☎ 229 9131, Telex 72398, Fax 228 4510, Ⓛ, ≘s, ⛾ – 🛗 ⇸ rm ▤ TV ☎ ♿ P – 🎓 450. AE ⓓ VISA. ✗ CDZ **v**
M 15.75/19.75 **t.** and a la carte 🍷 4.50 – ☕ 10.25 – **247 rm** 100.00/165.00 **t.**, **16 suites** 130.00/485.00 **t.**

George (Inter-Continental), 19-21 George St., EH2 2PB, ☎ 225 1251, Telex 72570, Fax 226 5644 – 🛗 ⇸ rm ▤ rest TV ☎ P – 🎓 180. AE ⓓ VISA DY **z**
M 14.00/25.00 **t.** and a la carte 🍷 7.50 – ☕ 9.50 – **193 rm** 93.50/132.00 **st.**, **2 suites** 225.00/374.00 **st.** – SB (weekends only) 123.50 **st.**

Carlton Highland, 1-29 North Bridge, EH1 1SD, ☎ 556 7277, Telex 727001, Fax 556 2691, Ⓛ, ≘s, ⛾, squash – 🛗 ▤ rest TV ☎ ♿ – 🎓 350 EY **s**
M 13.00/15.00 **t.** and a la carte 🍷 4.25 – **201 rm** ☕ 82.00/116.00 **t.**, **4 suites** 250.00 **t.** – SB (weekends only) (winter only) 80.00/84.00 **st.**

Howard, 32-36 Gt. King St., EH3 6QH, ☎ 557 3500, Fax 557 6515, « Georgian town houses » – 🛗 TV ☎ P – 🎓 35. AE ⓓ VISA. ✗ DY **s**
M No 36 *(closed Saturday lunch)* 14.75/30.00 **t.** and a la carte 🍷 5.00 – **16 rm** ☕ 95.00/250.00 **t.** – SB (except August and Christmas) (weekends only) 85.00/120.00 **st.**

Dalmachoy H. Golf & Country Club 🐎, Kirknewton, EH27 8EB, SW : 7 m. on A 71– AX ☎ 333 1845, Telex 772205, Fax 335 3203, ≤, Ⓛ, ≘s, ⛾, 18, 🎾, park, 🎾, squash – 🛗 ⇸ rm ▤ rest TV ☎ ♿ P – 🎓 260. AE ⓓ VISA. ✗
M 12.50/18.50 **t.** and a la carte 🍷 5.75 – **114 rm** ☕ 93.00/108.00 **t.**, **1 suite** 115.00/150.00 **t.** – SB 110.00/140.00 **st.**

Hilton National, Bells Mills, 69 Belford Rd, EH4 3DG, ☎ 332 2545, Telex 727979, Fax 332 3805 – 🛗 ⇸ rm TV ☎ ♿ P – 🎓 120. AE ⓓ VISA CY **i**
M *(closed Saturday lunch)* a la carte 14.00/26.00 **st.** 🍷 4.50 – ☕ 8.50 – **143 rm** 90.00/120.00 **st.**, **1 suite** 175.00 **st.** – SB (weekends only) 80.00/85.00 **st.**

Scandic Crown, 80 High St., EH1 1TH, ☎ 557 9797, Telex 727298, Fax 557 9789, Ⓛ, ≘s, ⛾ – 🛗 ⇸ rm ▤ rest TV ☎ ♿ P – 🎓 200. AE ⓓ VISA. ✗ EY **z**
M 9.95/12.95 **st.** and a la carte 🍷 4.25 – ☕ 7.50 – **228 rm** 79.00/130.00 **st.**, **10 suites** 205.00/280.00 **st.**

Capital (Q.M.H.), Clermiston Rd, EH12 6UG, ☎ 334 3391, Telex 728284, Fax 334 9712, Ⓛ, ≘s, ⛾ – 🛗 ⇸ rm TV ☎ ♿ P – 🎓 400 – **99 rm.** AV **n**

Roxburghe (Best Western), 38 Charlotte Sq., EH2 4HG, ☎ 225 3921, Telex 727054, Fax 220 2518 – 🛗 TV ☎ ♿ – 🎓 200 – **73 rm**, **2 suites.** DY **o**

Royal Scott (Swallow), 111 Glasgow Rd, EH12 8NF, W : 4½ m. on A 8 ☎ 334 9191, Telex 727197, Fax 316 4507, Ⓛ, ≘s, ⛾ – 🛗 ⇸ rm TV ☎ P – 🎓 250. AE ⓓ VISA
M 15.00/16.00 **st.** and a la carte 🍷 4.50 – **254 rm** ☕ 82.00/110.00 **st.**, **4 suites** 150.00 **st.** – SB (weekends only) 95.00 **st.** by A 8 AV

Royal Terrace, 18 Royal Terrace, EH7 5AQ, ☎ 557 3222, Telex 727182, Fax 557 5334, Ⓛ, ≘s, 🌳 – 🛗 ⇸ rm TV ☎ – 🎓 60 EY **i**
97 rm, **1 suite.**

King James Thistle (Mt. Charlotte Thistle), 107 Leith St., EH1 3SW, ☎ 556 0111, Telex 727200, Fax 557 5333 – 🛗 ⇸ rm TV ☎ P – 🎓 250. AE ⓓ VISA EY **u**
M 9.50/14.50 **st.** and a la carte ☕ 7.75 – **142 rm** 65.00/115.00 **st.**, **5 suites** – SB 105.00 **st.**

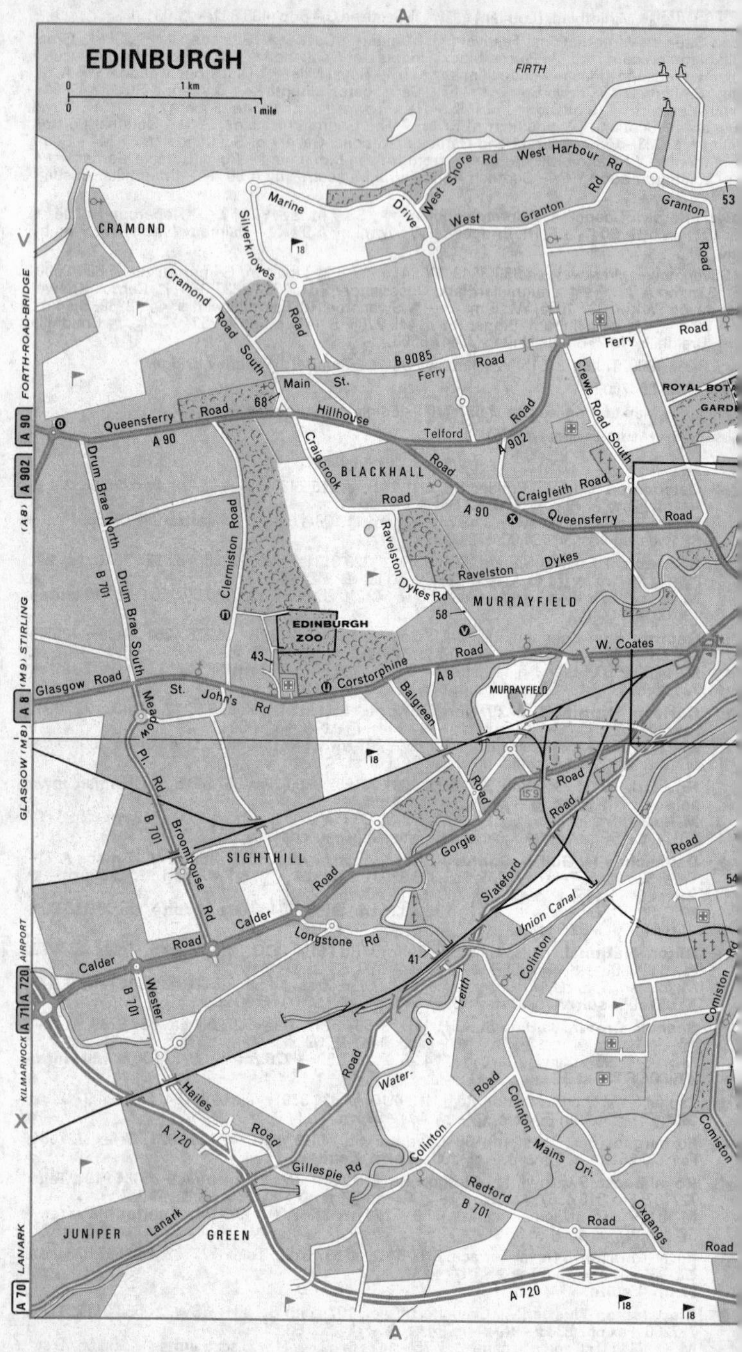
EDINBURGH
0 1 km
0 1 mile
FIRTH
CRAMOND
BLACKHALL
MURRAYFIELD
EDINBURGH ZOO
SIGHTHILL
JUNIPER GREEN
ROYAL BOTA
GARDE
MURRAYFIELD
Queensferry Road
Glasgow Road
St. John's Rd
Corstorphine Road
Calder Road
Gorgie Road
Slateford Road
Union Canal
Water of Leith
Colinton Road
Lanark Road
Gillespie Rd
Redford Road
Oxgangs Road
Comiston Rd
West Granton Road
West Harbour Rd
West Shore Rd
Marine Drive
Silverknowes Road
Cramond Road South
Main St.
Hillhouse Road
Ferry Road
B 9085
Telford Road
Crewe Road South
Craigleith Road
Craigcrook Road
Clermiston Road
Drum Brae North
Drum Brae South
Ravelston Dykes Rd
Ravelston Dykes
Balgreen Road
W. Coates
Meadow Pl. Rd
Broomhouse Rd
Longstone Rd
Wester Hailes Road
Colinton Mains Dri.
A 90
A 902
A 8
A 720
B 701
68
43
58
41
53
54
18
FORTH-ROAD-BRIDGE
A 90
A 902
(A 8)
(M 9) STIRLING
GLASGOW (M 8)
A 8
AIRPORT
KILMARNOCK
A 720
A 71
LANARK
A 70
A
V
X

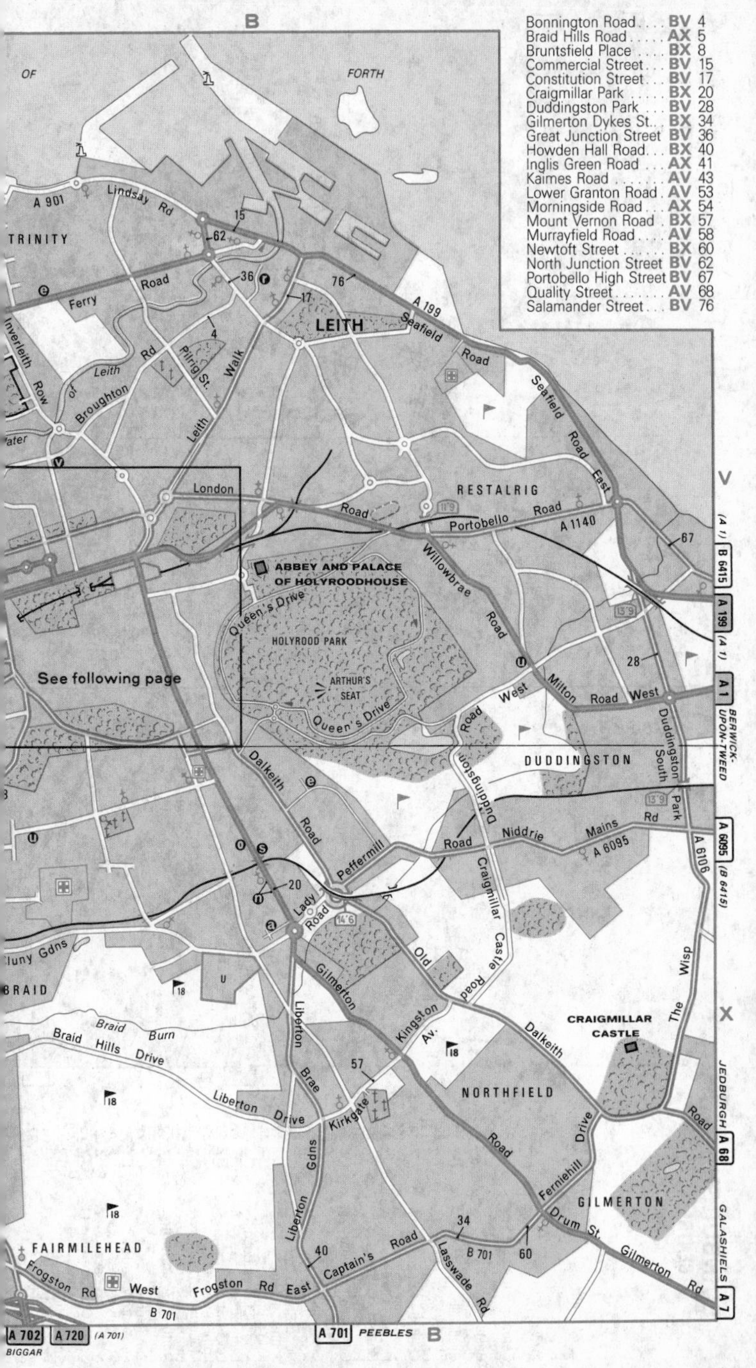
Bonnington Road . . . . BV 4
Braid Hills Road . . . . . AX 5
Bruntsfield Place . . . . . BX 8
Commercial Street . . . BV 15
Constitution Street . . . BV 17
Craigmillar Park . . . . . BX 20
Duddingston Park . . . . BV 28
Gilmerton Dykes St. . . BX 34
Great Junction Street BV 36
Howden Hall Road. . . . BX 40
Inglis Green Road . . . . AX 41
Kaimes Road . . . . AV 43
Lower Granton Road . AV 53
Morningside Road . . . . AX 54
Mount Vernon Road . . BX 57
Murrayfield Road . . . . AV 58
Newtoft Street . . . . . . BX 60
North Junction Street BV 62
Portobello High Street BV 67
Quality Street . . . . AV 68
Salamander Street . . . BV 76
B
OF
FORTH
A 901
Lindsay Rd
TRINITY
Ferry
Road
LEITH
A 199
Seafield
Road
Inverleith
Row
Leith
Broughton
Rd
Pilrig St.
Leith
Walk
Seafield
Road
East
RESTALRIG
London
Road
Portobello
Road
A 1140
V
Willowbrae
Road
ABBEY AND PALACE
OF HOLYROODHOUSE
Queen's Drive
HOLYROOD PARK
ARTHUR'S
SEAT
Queen's Drive
See following page
Milton
Road
West
Road
West
Duddingston
DUDDINGSTON
Duddingston
South
Park
Dalkeith
Road
Peffermill
Road
Niddrie
Mains
Rd
A 6095
Craigmillar
Castle
Road
A 6106
The
Wisp
Lady
Road
Old
Cluny Gdns
BRAID
Gilmerton
Liberton
Brae
Kingston
Av.
X
CRAIGMILLAR
CASTLE
Dalkeith
Road
Braid
Burn
Braid
Hills
Drive
Liberton
Drive
Kirkgate
NORTHFIELD
Road
Ferniehill
Drive
GILMERTON
Liberton
Gdns
FAIRMILEHEAD
Frogston
Rd
West
Frogston
Rd
East
Captain's
Road
B 701
Lasswade
Rd
Drum
St.
Gilmerton
Rd
B 701
(A 1)
B 6415
A 199
(A 1)
A 1
BERWICK-
UPON-TWEED
A 6095
(B 6415)
JEDBURGH
A 68
GALASHIELS
A 7
A 702
A 720
(A 701)
BIGGAR
A 701
PEEBLES
B

EDINBURGH
CENTRE

Castle Street	DY	
Frederick Street	DY	
George Street	DY	
Hanover Street	DY	
High Street	EYZ	37
Lawnmarket	EYZ	46
Princes Street	DY	
St. James Centre	EY	
Waverley Market	EY	

Bernard Terrace	EZ	3
Bread Street	DZ	6
Bristo Place	EZ	7
Candlemaker Row	EZ	9
Castlehill	DZ	10
Chambers Street	EZ	12
Chapel Street	EZ	13
Charlotte Square	CY	14
Deanhaugh Street	CY	23
Douglas Gardens	CY	25
Drummond Street	EZ	27
Forrest Road	EZ	31
Gardner's Crescent	CZ	32
George IV Bridge	EZ	33
Grassmarket	DZ	35
Home Street	DZ	38
Hope Street	CY	39
Johnston Terrace	DZ	42
King's Bridge	DZ	44
King's Stables Road	DZ	45
Leith Street	EY	47
Leven Street	DZ	48
Lothian Street	EZ	51
Mound (The)	DY	55
North Bridge	EY	61
North St. Andrew Street	EY	66
Raeburn Place	CY	69
Randolph Crescent	CY	71
St. Andrew Square	EY	73
St. Mary's Street	EY	75
Shandwick Place	CYZ	77
South Charlotte Street	DY	78
South St. David Street	DEY	79
Spittal Street	DZ	83
Victoria Street	EZ	84
Waterloo Place	EY	87
Waverley Bridge	EY	89

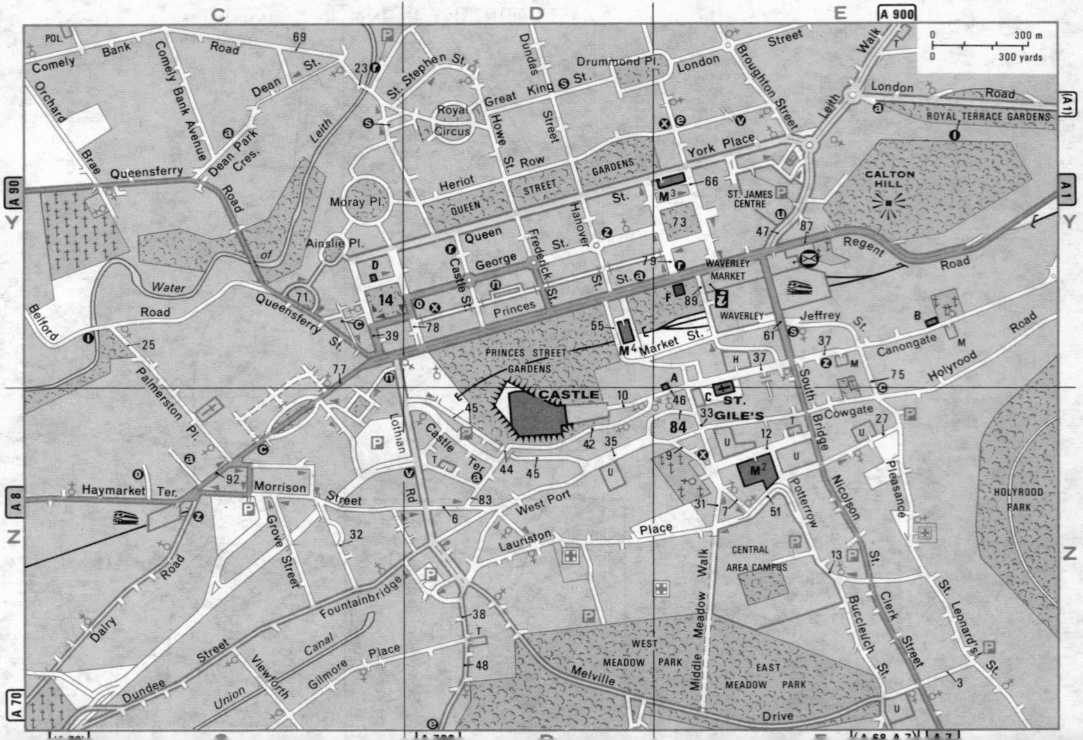

Bruntsfield (Best Western), 69-74 Bruntsfield Pl., EH10 4HH, ☎ 229 1393, Telex 727897, Fax 229 5634 – TV ☎ P – 25. AE VISA DZ **e**
M 8.50/16.50 **st.** and a la carte 3.75 – 5.50 – **52 rm** 65.00/120.00 **st.**

Ellersly House, 4 Ellersly Rd, EH12 6HZ, ☎ 337 6888, Fax 313 2543, – rm TV ☎ P – 45. AE VISA AV **v**
M 8.75/14.25 **st.** and a la carte 4.75 – 7.50 – **54 rm** 75.00/87.00 **st.** – SB 64.00/90.00 **st.**

Holiday Inn, Queens Ferry Rd, EH4 3HL, ☎ 332 2442, Telex 72541, Fax 332 3408, – rm rest TV ☎ P – 200 AV **x**
118 rm, **1 suite.**

Barnton Thistle (Mt. Charlotte Thistle), 562 Queensferry Rd, EH4 6AS, ☎ 339 1144, Telex 727928, Fax 339 5521, – rm TV ☎ P – 100. AE VISA AV **o**
M 9.00 **t.** (lunch) and a la carte 12.00/25.00 **t.** – 7.75 – **47 rm** 65.00/95.00 **st.**, **3 suites** – SB 99.00 **st.**

Stakis Grosvenor, Grosvenor St., EH12 5EF, ☎ 226 6001, Telex 72445, Fax 220 2387 – rm TV ☎ – 160. AE VISA CZ **a**
M (grill rest.) 13.50 and a la carte – 7.25 – **135 rm** 77.00/109.50 **t.**, **1 suite** 135.50 **t.** – SB 82.00/162.00 **st.**

Post House (T.H.F.), Corstorphine Rd, EH12 6UA, ☎ 334 0390, Telex 727103, Fax 334 9237, – rm TV ☎ P – 130. AE VISA AV **u**
M 9.00/15.00 **st.** and a la carte 4.65 – 7.50 – **206 rm** 68.00/80.00 **st.**, **1 suite.**

Mount Royal, 53 Princes St., EH2 2DG, ☎ 225 7161, Telex 727641, Fax 220 4671 – TV ☎ – 50 DY **a**
158 rm, **1 suite.**

Lady Nairne (B.C.B.), 228 Willowbrae Rd, EH8 7NG, ☎ 661 3396, Fax 652 2789 – TV ☎ P – 120. AE VISA. BV **u**
M 8.00/15.00 **st.** – **33 rm** 48.00/64.50 **st.**

Albany, 39-43 Albany St., EH1 3QY, ☎ 556 0397, Telex 727079 – TV ☎. VISA
M *(closed lunch Saturday and Sunday)* a la carte 13.20/21.95 **st.** 6.30 – **20 rm** 60.00/85.00 **st.** – SB (October-April) 130.00 **st.** EY **v**

Old Waverley, 43 Princes St., EH2 2BY, ☎ 556 4648, Telex 727050, Fax 557 6316 – TV ☎. AE VISA EY **r**
M (carving lunch) 6.00/12.00 **t.** and a la carte 3.95 – **66 rm** 60.00/98.00 **t.** – SB (weekends only) 72.00/104.00 **st.**

Christopher North House, 6 Gloucester Pl., EH3 6EF, ☎ 225 2720 – TV. AE VISA. CY **s**
M (bar lunch)/dinner a la carte approx. 15.50 **t.** **11 rm** 36.00/70.00 **st.**

Iona, 17 Strathearn Pl., EH9 2AL, ☎ 447 6264, Fax 452 8574, – TV ☎ P. VISA
M 6.20/15.00 **t.** and a la carte 3.50 – **21 rm** 30.00/52.00 **t.** BX **u**

Dorstan, 7 Priestfield Rd, EH16 5HJ, ☎ 667 6721 – rest TV ☎. VISA.
closed Christmas and New Year – **M** 10.00 **t.** – **12 rm** 17.00/43.00 **t.** BX **e**

Buchan without rest., 3 Coates Gdns, EH12 5LG, ☎ 337 1045 – TV CZ **o**
11 rm 18.00/48.00 **st.**

Greenside without rest., 9 Royal Terr., EH7 5AB, ☎ 557 0022, – EY **a**
closed November and December – **13 rm** 25.30/45.00 **t.**

International without rest., 37 Mayfield Gdns, EH9 2BX, ☎ 667 2511 – TV.
7 rm 18.00/42.00 **st.** BX **s**

Galloway without rest., 22 Dean Park Cres., EH4 1PH, ☎ 332 3672 – TV CY **a**
10 rm 25.00/38.00 **t.**

Ravensdown without rest., 248 Ferry Rd, EH5 3AN, ☎ 552 5438 – TV. BV **e**
7 rm 30.00/32.00 **st.**

Southdown without rest., 20 Craigmillar Park, EH16 5PS, ☎ 667 2410 – TV P.
6 rm 20.00/32.00 **st.** BX **n**

Parklands without rest., 20 Mayfield Gdns, EH9 2BZ, ☎ 667 7184. BX **o**
6 rm 22.00/38.00 **s.**

Glenisla, 12 Lygon Rd, EH16 5QB, ☎ 667 4098 – BX **a**
8 rm.

St. Margarets without rest., 18 Craigmillar Park, EH16 5PS, ☎ 667 2202 – TV P.
April-December – **8 rm** 25.00/34.00 **st.** BX **n**

XXXX **Pompadour** (at Caledonian H.), Princes St., EH1 2AB, ☎ 225 2433 – P. AE VISA
M 15.75/51.00 **st.** and a la carte 6.75. CY **n**

XX **Vintners Room,** The Vaults, 87 Giles St., Leith, EH6 6BZ, ☎ 554 6767 – . AE VISA
closed Sunday and 2 weeks Christmas – **M** 11.00 **t.** (lunch) and a la carte 17.00/22.00 **t.** 4.50. BV **r**

XX **Martins,** 70 Rose St., North Lane, EH2 3DX, ☎ 225 3106 – . AE VISA DY **n**
closed Saturday lunch, Sunday, Monday and 22 December-21 January – **M** (booking essential) 15.00 **t.** (lunch) and a la carte 19.15/25.25 **t.** 5.00.

XX **L'Auberge,** 56 St. Mary's St., EH1 1SX, ☎ 556 5888, French rest. – . AE VISA
closed 25-26 December and 1-2 January – **M** 12.00/33.00 **t.** and a la carte 7.00. EYZ **c**

XX **Raffaelli,** 10-11 Randolph Pl., EH3 7TA, ✆ 225 6060, Fax 225 8830, Italian rest. – VISA CY
closed Saturday lunch, Sunday, 25-26 December and 1-2 January – **M** a la carte 13.1 22.50 **t.** 4.30.

XX **Lancer's Brasserie,** 5 Hamilton Pl., Stockbridge, EH3 5BA, ✆ 332 3444, North Indi rest. – AE VISA CY
M a la carte 8.70/18.10 **t.**

XX **Umberto,** 29-33 Dublin St., EH3 6NL, ✆ 556 2231, Italian rest. – AE VISA
closed Saturday and Sunday lunch and Sunday dinner in winter – **M** 7.95 **t.** (lunch) and a carte 9.90/18.75 **t.** 4.15. EY

XX **Merchants,** 17 Merchant St., (under bridge), EH1 2QD, ✆ 225 4009 – AE VISA
closed Sunday, 25-26 December and 1 January – **M** (booking essential) 15.00/25.00 **t.** and la carte 3.50. EZ

XX **Indian Cavalry Club,** 3 Atholl Pl., EH3 8HP, ✆ 228 3282, Indian rest. – AE
M 5.95/13.95 **t.** and a la carte 4.00. CZ

XX **Debbretts,** 33-36 Castle Terr., EH1 2EL, ✆ 229 1181 – AE VISA DZ
closed Sunday lunch, Sunday dinner except August, 25-26 December and 1-2 January
M 10.50/22.50 **t.** and a la carte 16.40/23.25 **t.** 5.75.

XX **Cosmo,** 58a North Castle St., EH2 3LU, ✆ 226 6743, Italian rest. – VISA DY
closed Saturday lunch, Sunday and Monday – **M** a la carte 13.80/21.00 **t.** 3.90.

XX Premier Mandarin, 8b Abercromby Pl., EH3 6LB, ✆ 556 2321, Chinese rest. EY

X **Le Marche Noir,** 2-4 Eyre Pl., EH3 5EP, ✆ 558 1608 – VISA BV
M *(closed lunch Saturday and Sunday)* 13.00/20.50 **t.** 3.50.

X **Alp-Horn,** 167 Rose St., EH2 4LS, ✆ 225 4787, Swiss rest. – . VISA DY
closed Sunday, 2 weeks January and 2 weeks July – **M** 10.50/19.00 **t.** and a la carte 4.6

X **Verandah,** 17 Dalry Rd, EH11 2BQ, ✆ 337 5828, North Indian rest. – AE
M a la carte 10.75/15.95 **t.** 3.25. CZ

ALFA-ROMEO, DAIHATSU 22 Canning St. ✆ 229 5561
CITROEN 13 Lauriston Gdns ✆ 229 4207
FORD Baileyfield Rd ✆ 669 6261
FORD Fountainbridge ✆ 229 3331
FORD 12 West Mayfield ✆ 667 1900
FORD Craighall Rd ✆ 552 5524
PEUGEOT-TALBOT Lochrin Tollcross ✆ 229 8911
PORSCHE, FERRARI 300 Colinton Rd ✆ 441 6805
RENAULT 553 Gorgie Rd ✆ 444 1673
ROVER, LAND-ROVER, RANGE-ROVER Westfield Av. ✆ 337 3222
ROVER Lanark Rd ✆ 443 2936
ROVER 70 Slateford Rd ✆ 337 1252
VOLVO 38 Seafield Rd East ✆ 669 8301
VOLVO Bankhead ✆ 442 3333
VW-AUDI-NSU 454 Gorgie Rd ✆ 346 1661
VW-AUDI-NSU Marionville Rd ✆ 652 1691

ATS 167 Bonnington Rd, Leith ✆ 554 6617
ATS 6 Gylemuir Rd, Corstorphine ✆ 334 6174/5

EDZELL Angus. (Tayside) 401 M 13 **Scotland G** – pop. 751 – ECD : Thursday – 035 64.
Envir. : Castle★ (The Pleasance★★★) W : 1 ¼ m.
18 at Brechin ✆ 035 62 (Brechin) 2383, S : 5 ½ m.
◆Edinburgh 94 – ◆Aberdeen 36 – ◆Dundee 31.

Glenesk, High St., DD9 7TF, ✆ 319, Fax 7333, , , , – – 100. VISA
M 7.50/10.50 **t.** 3.50 **25 rm** 34.00/60.00 **t.** – SB (October-March and July) 75.00 78.00 **st.**

EGILSAY (Isle of) Orkney. (Orkney Islands) 401 L 6 – Shipping Services : see Orkney Island (Mainland : Kirkwall).

EIGG (Isle of) Inverness. (Highland) 401 B 13 – Shipping Services : see Mallaig.

ELGIN Moray. (Grampian) 401 K 11 **Scotland G** – pop. 18 702 – ECD : Wednesday – 0343.
See : Site★ – Cathedral★ (Chapter House★★).
18 Hardhillock, Birnie Rd ✆ 2338, S : 1 m. – 9 Hopeman ✆ 830578, N : 7 m.
17 High St. ✆ 543388 and 542666.
◆Edinburgh 198 – ◆Aberdeen 68 – Fraserburgh 61 – ◆Inverness 39.

Mansion House, The Haugh, IV30 1AW, via Haugh Rd and Murdocks Wynd ✆ 54881 Fax 547916, , , , – . VISA.
M 10.00/20.00 **t.** and a la carte 3.50 – **18 rm** 49.60/100.00 **t.** – SB (weekends only (except Christmas and New Year) 90.00/100.00 **st.**

Park House, South St., IV30 1JB, ✆ 547695 – . VISA
M 5.20/16.00 **t.** and a la carte 3.50 – **6 rm** 35.00/55.00 **t.** – SB (weekends only 140.00 **st.**

FORD East Rd ✆ 2176
PEUGEOT 27 Greyfriars St. ✆ 7416
ROVER Station Rd ✆ 541133
VAUXHALL-OPEL Edgar Rd ✆ 7688
VW-AUDI Blackfriars Rd ✆ 44977

ATS Moycroft ✆ 546333

ELLON Aberdeen. (Grampian) 401 N 11 – pop. 6 304 – ECD : Wednesday – ☎ 0358.

nvir. : Pitmedden Gardens★★, SW : 5 m. by A 920 – Haddo House★, NW : 8 m. by B 9005 – yvie Castle★ NW : 14 m. by B 9005 and A 947.

McDonald ☎ 20576.

Market St. Car Park ☎ 20730 (summer only).

Edinburgh 147 – ◆Aberdeen 17 – Fraserburgh 27.

Hotels see : **Newburgh** SE : 5½ m.

ORD 99 Station Rd ☎ 20206

ERISKA (Isle of) Argyll. (Strathclyde) 401 D 14 – ✉ Oban – ☎ 063 172 Ledaig

Isle of Eriska ⛰, PA37 1SD, ☎ 371, Telex 777040, Fax 531, ≤ Lismore and mountains, « Country house atmosphere », park, – TV ☎ ♿ P. VISA.
22 March-27 October – **M** 12.00/33.00 **t.** 5.00 – **16 rm** 69.00/270.00 **t.**

ERSKINE Renfrew. (Strathclyde) 401 402 G 16 – ☎ 041 Glasgow.

Edinburgh 55 – ◆Glasgow 9.

Crest (T.H.F.) ⛰, Erskine Bridge, PA8 6AN, on A 726 ☎ 812 0123, Telex 777713, Fax 812 7642, ≤, , , – rm rest TV ☎ P – 600. AE VISA
M *(closed lunch Saturday and Bank Holiday Mondays)* a la carte 12.50/15.50 **st.** 3.95 – 8.45 – **166 rm** 73.00/85.00 **st.**

ESKDALEMUIR Dumfries. (Dumfries and Galloway) 401 402 K 18 – ✉ Langholm – ☎ 054 16.

Edinburgh 71 – ◆Carlisle 33 – ◆Dumfries 28.

Hart Manor ⛰, DG13 0QQ, S : ½ m. on B 709 ☎ 73217, ≤ – P.
M *(closed dinner to non-residents Sunday and Monday)* (bar lunch)/dinner 16.00 **t.** 4.50 – **7 rm** 28.50/50.50 **t.**

FALKIRK Stirling. (Central) 401 I 16 – pop. 36 372 – ECD : Wednesday – ☎ 0324.

Grangemouth ☎ 711500, E : 3 m – 18 Stirling Rd, Camenon ☎ 611061 – 18 86 Bernhead Rd, arbert ☎ 562415, N : 3 m.

The Steeple, High St. ☎ 20244.

Edinburgh 26 – Dunfermline 18 – ◆Glasgow 25 – Motherwell 27 – Perth 43.

Stakis Park, Camelon Rd, Arnothill, FK1 5RY, ☎ 28331, Telex 776502, Fax 611593 – rm TV ☎ P – 200. AE VISA
7.50 – **55 rm** 61.50/85.00 **t.** – SB 70.00/114.00 **st.**

Pierre's, 140 Grahams Rd, FK2 7BQ, ☎ 35843, French rest. – P. AE VISA
closed Saturday lunch, Sunday, Monday and 1 to 5 January – **M** 7.50/11.45 **t.** and a la carte 4.00.

at Polmont SE : 3 m. on A 803 – ✉ ☎ 0324 Polmont :

Inchyra Grange (Best Western), Grange Rd, via Boness Rd – Kirk entry, FK2 0YB, ☎ 711911, Telex 777693, Fax 716134, , , , – TV ☎ P – 220. AE VISA
M *(closed Saturday lunch)* 9.50/14.00 **t.** and a la carte 3.95 – **33 rm** 66.00/100.00 **t.** – SB (except Christmas-New Year) (weekends only) 90.00/102.00 **st.**

ORD Callendar Rd ☎ 21511
HYUNDAI, SAMBURA, ISUZU High Station Rd ☎ 24221
MAZDA Main St. ☎ 22584
TOYOTA Lady's Mill ☎ 35935
TOYOTA Winchester Av., Denny ☎ 824387
VAUXHALL-OPEL 76-80 Grahams Rd ☎ 21234
VOLVO West End ☎ 613333

ATS Burnbank Rd ☎ 22958

FARR Inverness. (Highland) 401 H 11 – ✉ Inverness – ☎ 080 83.

Edinburgh 155 – ◆Inverness 10.

Dunlichity Lodge ⛰, Dunlichity, IV1 2AN, W : 2 m. ☎ 282, ≤, , – P
May-September – **M** 11.50 **st.** 2.95 – **3 rm** 28.00/44.00 **st.**

FEOLIN Argyll. (Strathclyde) 401 B 16 – Shipping Services : see Jura (Isle of).

When travelling for business or pleasure
in England, Wales, Scotland and Ireland :

– use the series of five maps
(nos 401, 402, 403, 404 and 405) at a scale of 1:400 000
– they are the perfect complement to this Guide
as towns underlined in red on the maps will be found in this Guide.

FETLAR (Isle of) Shetland. (Shetland Islands) 401 R 2 – Shipping Services : see Shetlan Islands.

FIONNPHORT Argyll. (Strathclyde) 401 A 15 – Shipping Services : see Mull (Isle of).

FISHNISH Argyll. (Strathclyde) 401 C 14 – Shipping Services : see Mull (Isle of).

FLOTTA (Isle of) Orkney. (Orkney Islands) 401 K 7 – Shipping Services : see Orkney Islands

FORDYCE Banff. (Grampian) 401 L 11 – pop. 145 – 0261 Portsoy.

♦Edinburgh 187 – ♦Aberdeen 57 – ♦Inverness 65.

X **Hawthorne,** Church St., AB4 2SL, 43003 – P. VISA
closed Sunday dinner, Monday, Tuesday in winter and 2 weeks January – **M** a la carte 7.50 17.75 **t.**

FORFAR Angus. (Tayside) 401 L 14 – pop. 12 652 – ECD : Thursday – 0307.

Envir. : Glamis★ (Castle★★, Angus Folk Museum★) SW : 5½ m. by A 94.

18 Cunninghill, Arbroath Rd 62120, E : 1 m. on A 932.

The Library, West High St. 67876 (summer only).

♦Edinburgh 75 – ♦Aberdeen 55 – ♦Dundee 12 – Perth 31.

Royal, Castle St., DD8 3AE, 62691, Fax 62691, – TV P. AE VISA.
M 12.00/15.00 **t.** 3.50 – **19 rm** 39.00/65.00 **t.** – SB (except New Year) (weekends only 65.00/75.00 **st.**

FORD Kirriemuir Rd 62347
PEUGEOT-TALBOT Lochside Rd 62676
ROVER 128 Castle St. 62542
ATS Queenswell Rd 64501/2

FORRES Moray. (Grampian) 401 J 11 **Scotland G.** – pop. 8 346 – ECD : Wednesday – 0309.

See : Sueno's Stone★★.

Envir. : Brodie Castle★ W : 4 m. by A 96.

18 Muiryshade 72949, SE : by B 9010.

Falconer Museum, Talbooth St. 72938 (summer only).

♦Edinburgh 165 – ♦Aberdeen 80 – ♦Inverness 27.

Ramnee, Victoria Rd, IV36 0BN, 72410, – TV P – 100. AE VISA
M 7.50/15.25 **st.** and a la carte 3.30 – **20 rm** 34.50/65.00 **st.** – SB (weekends only 83.00 **st.**

Knockomie, Grantown Rd, IV36 0SG, S : 1½ m. on A 940 73146, Fax 73146, TV P – 50. VISA
M 9.25/12.95 **st.** and a la carte 4.25 – **7 rm** 40.00/70.00 **st.** – SB (October-Apri 80.00 **st.**

Parkmount House, St. Leonards Rd, IV36 0DW, 73312, – rest TV P. VIS
closed Christmas – **M** 15.95 **t.** 3.25 – **6 rm** 29.00/46.00 **t.** – SB (November-March 70.00/80.00 **st.**

FIAT Tytler St. 72122
FORD Market St. 72677
ROVER Greshop Ind Estate 74709

FORSINARD Sutherland. (Highland) – 064 17 Halladale.

♦Edinburgh 271 – Thurso 30 – ♦Wick 51.

Forsinard, KW13 6YT, 221, – rest P. VISA
M 15.00/20.00 **t.** 3.00 – **10 rm** 30.00/60.00 **st.**

FORT AUGUSTUS Inverness. (Highland) 401 F 12 – pop. 573 – 0320.

9 Markethill 6460.

Car Park 6367 (summer only).

♦Edinburgh 166 – Fort William 32 – ♦Inverness 36 – Kyle of Lochalsh 57.

Lovat Arms, PH32 2BE, 6206, – TV P. VISA
M (bar lunch)/dinner 15.50 **st.** 3.85 – **25 rm** 29.00/58.00 **st.**

FORT WILLIAM Inverness. (Highland) 401 E 13 **Scotland G** – pop. 10 805 – ECD : Wednesda except summer – 0397.

See : Site★.

Envir. : Ben Nevis★★, SE : 4 m. – Road to the Isles★★ (Glenfinnan★, Arisaig★ (★★ of Sound o Arisaig), Silver Sands of Morar★, Mallaig★) NW : 46 m. by A 830 – Glen Nevis★, SE.

18 North Rd 4464, N : 3 m. on A 82.

Cameron Sq. 3781.

♦Edinburgh 133 – ♦Glasgow 104 – ♦Inverness 68 – ♦Oban 50.

Inverlochy Castle ⚘, Torlundy, PH33 6SN, NE : 3 m. on A 82 ☏ 702177, Telex 776229, Fax 702953, ≤ garden, loch and mountains, « Victorian castle in extensive grounds », ⚲, ⛱, park, ✂ – TV ☎ P. AE VISA. ✗
Mid March-mid November – **M** (booking essential) 33.00/43.00 **st.** 5.00 – **15 rm** 121.00/165.00 **t.**, **1 suite** 185.00/250.00 **st.**

Mercury (Mt. Charlotte Thistle), Achintore Rd, PH33 6RW, SW : 2 m. on A 82 ☏ 703117, Telex 778454, ≤ – lift TV ☎ P
M (carving rest.) – **86 rm.**

Guisachan, Alma Rd, PH33 6HA, ☏ 703797, ≤, ⛱ – ✗ rm P. ✗
closed 22 December-5 January – **M** 8.00 **t.** – **14 rm** 15.00/26.00 **t.**

Cabana House, Union Rd, PH33 6RB, ☏ 705991. ✗
M 15.00 **st.** – **3 rm** -/35.00 **st.** – SB (winter only) 56.00/60.00 **st.**

Factor's House with rm, Torlundy, PH33 6SN, NE : 3 ½ m. on A 82 ☏ 705767, Telex 776229, Fax 702953, ⛱ – TV ☎ P. AE VISA. ✗
closed mid December-mid January – **M** *(closed lunch and Monday to non-residents)* (bar lunch)/dinner 23.00 **t.** 5.00 – **7 rm** 57.50/86.25 **t.**

at Banavie N : 3 m. by A 82 and A 830 on B 8004 – ✉ Fort William – ☎ 0397 Corpach :

Moorings, PH33 7LY, ☏ 772797, Fax 441, ≤, ⛱ – ✗ rest TV ☎ P. AE VISA. ✗
closed Christmas Day – **M** (bar lunch)/dinner 25.00 **t.** and a la carte 3.00 – **21 rm** 50.00/76.00 **t.** – SB (except Christmas) 90.00/110.00 **st.**

OVER Gordon Sq. ☏ 2345/2346

FOYERS Inverness. (Highland) 401 G 12 – ☎ 045 63 Gorthleck.

See : Loch Ness★★.

Edinburgh 176 – ◆Inverness 18.

Foyers, IV1 2XT, N : ½ m. on B 852 ☏ 216, ≤ Loch Ness and mountains, ⚲, ⛱ – ✗ P. VISA. ✗
M 11.50/16.00 **t.** and a la carte 3.50 – **8 rm** 35.00/70.00 **t.**

"Short Breaks"

Many hotels now offer a special rate for a stay of 2 nights which includes dinner, bed and breakfast.

GAIRLOCH Ross and Cromarty. (Highland) 401 C 10 – ECD : Wednesday except summer – ☎ 0445.

Envir. : Inverewe Gardens★★★, NE : 8 m. by A 832 – Wester Ross★★★ (Gairloch to Ullapool★ via Loch Maree★★★, Inverewe Gardens★★★, Falls of Measach★ and Loch Broom★★) NE : 56 m. by A 832 and A 835 – Wester Ross★★★ (Gairloch to Kyle of Lochalsh via Victoria Falls★ Loch Maree★★★, and Plockton★) S : 102 m. by A 832, A 896 and A 890.

Gairloch ☏ 2407, S : 1 m. on A 832.

Achtercairn ☏ 2130.

Edinburgh 228 – ◆Inverness 72 – Kyle of Lochalsh 68.

Shieldaig Lodge ⚘, IV21 2AW, S : 4½ m. by A 832 on B 8056 ☏ 044 583 (Badachro) 250, ≤ Gair Loch, « Former hunting lodge on lochside », ⚲, ⛱ – ✗ rest P
April-October – **M** (bar lunch)/dinner 15.00 **t.** 4.50 – **13 rm** 38.00/62.00 **t.**

Kerrysdale House without rest., IV21 2AL, S : 3 m. on A 832 ☏ 2292, ⛱ – ✗ rm P. ✗
March-November – **3 rm** 17.00/27.00 **st.**

GALASHIELS Selkirk. (Borders) 401 402 L 17 – pop. 12 206 – ECD : Wednesday – ☎ 0896.

Envir. : Abbotsford★★ SE : 2 m. by A 7 – Melrose Abbey★★ SE : 4 m. by A 7 and A 6091.

Ladhope, ☏ 3724, NE : ¼ m. – 9 Torwoodlee, ☏ 2260, N : 1 m. on A 7.

Bank St. ☏ 55551 (summer only).

Edinburgh 34 – ◆Carlisle 61 – ◆Glasgow 71 – ◆Newcastle-upon-Tyne 74.

Woodlands House, Windyknowe Rd, TD1 1RQ, NW : ¾ m. by A 72 and Hall St. ☏ 4722, ⛱ – TV ☎ P. VISA
M 9.95/19.95 **t.** and a la carte 3.50 – **9 rm** 40.00/60.00 **t.** – SB (weekends only) 84.00 **st.**

Kingsknowes, Selkirk Rd, TD1 3HY, SE : 1 ½ m. on A 7 ☏ 58375, ≤, ⛱, ✂ – TV ☎ P. AE VISA
M 8.50/12.50 **st.** and a la carte 4.50 – **11 rm** 43.00/60.00 **st.** – SB (October-May) (except Bank Holidays) 80.00/90.00 **st.**

ATS Paton St. ☏ 3271/2

GATEHOUSE OF FLEET Kirkcudbright. (Dumfries and Galloway) 401 402 H 19 – pop. 894 – ECD : Thursday – ☎ 055 74.

Gatehouse ☏ 252.

Car Park ☏ 212 (summer only).

Edinburgh 113 – ◆Dumfries 33 – Stranraer 42.

- **Cally Palace**, DG7 2DL, E : ½ m. on B 727 ✆ 341, Fax 522, ←, heated, park – rest ☎ Ⓟ. VISA
  closed January and February – **M** 10.00/18.00 **t.** and a la carte 4.00 – **48 rm** 40.0 80.00 **t.**, **7 suites** 90.00 **t.** – SB (except summer) 80.00/100.00 **st.**
- **Murray Arms** (Best Western), High St., DG7 2HY, ✆ 207, Fax 370, park – Ⓟ. AE VISA
  M (bar lunch)/dinner 15.00 **st.** and a la carte 3.50 – **12 rm** 35.00/70.00 **st.**, **1 sui** 75.00/80.00 **st.** – SB 84.00/95.00 **st.**

GATTONSIDE Roxburgh. (Borders) – see Melrose.

GIFFNOCK Renfrew. (Strathclyde) 401 ④ 402 ⑨ – see Glasgow.

GIFFORD E. Lothian. (Lothian) 401 L 16 – pop. 665 – ECD : Monday and Wednesday
✉ Haddington – 062 081 – Gifford ✆ 267, SW : 1 m.
♦Edinburgh 20 – Hawick 50.

- Tweeddale Arms, High St., EH41 4QU, ✆ 240, Fax 488 – ☎ Ⓟ – **15 rm.**

GLASGOW Lanark. (Strathclyde) 401 402 H 16 **Scotland G** – pop. 754 586 – 041.

See : Site★★★ – Burrell Collection★★★ AX **M1** – Cathedral★★★ DYZ – Tolbooth Steeple★ DZ A Hunterian Art Gallery★★ (Whistler Collection★★★, Mackintosh wing★★★) CY **M2** – Art Galle and Museum Kelvingrove★★ CY – City Chambers★ DZ **C** – Glasgow School of Art★ CY B Museum of Transport★★ (Scottish cars★★★, Clyde Room of Ship Models★★★) AV M3 – Poll House★ (Spanish paintings★★) AX **D.**

Envir. : Trossachs★★★, N : by A 739 AV and A 81 – Loch Lomond★★, NW : by A 82 AV – Cly Estuary★ (Dumbarton Castle Site★, Hill House★, Helensburgh) by A 82, AV – Bothwell Castle and David Livingstone Centre (Museum★) SE : 9 m. by A 724 BX.

18 Linn Park, Simshill Rd ✆ 637 5871, S : 4 m. BX – 18 Lethamhill, Cumbernauld Rd ✆ 770 62 BV – 18, 18 Cawder, Cadder Rd ✆ 772 7101 BV – 18 Deaconsbank ✆ 638 7044 AX – 9 Alexand Park, Alexandra Par. ✆ 556 3211 BV – 9 Knightswood, Lincoln Av. ✆ 959 2131, W : 4 m. AV 9 Kings Park, Croftpark Av., S : 4 m. by B 766 BX.

Access to Oban by helicopter.

✈ Glasgow Airport : ✆ 887 1111, W : 8 m. by M 8 AV – **Terminal** : Coach service from Glasgo Central and Queen Street main line Railway Stations and from Anderston Cross and Buchana Bus Stations.

✈ see also Prestwick.

ℹ 35 St. Vincent Pl. ✆ 204 4400 – Glasgow Airport, Inchinnon Rd ✆ 848 4440.

♦Edinburgh 46 – ♦Manchester 221.

Plans on following pages

- **Holiday Inn**, 500 Argyle St., Anderston, G3 8RR, ✆ 226 5577, Telex 77635 Fax 221 9202, squash – rm ☎ Ⓟ – 700. AE VISA
  M (buffet meals) 17.90 **st.** and a la carte 7.65 – 9.85 – **293 rm** 99.00/140.00 s **5 suites** 200.00/1230.00 **st.** CZ
- **Forte Albany** (T.H.F.), Bothwell St., G2 7EN, ✆ 248 2656, Telex 77440, Fax 221 8986, ← rm ☎ Ⓟ – 1 000. AE VISA CZ
  M 12.50 **st.** and a la carte 3.95 – 8.50 – **251 rm** 95.00/105.00 **st.**, **3 suites** 210.0 250.00 **st.** – SB (weekends only) 104.00/124.00 **st.**
- **One Devonshire Gardens**, 1 Devonshire Gdns, G12 OUX, ✆ 339 2001, Fax 337 166 « Opulent interior design » – ☎. AE VISA. AV
  M *(closed Saturday lunch)* 19.25/39.50 **t.** and a la carte – 6.50 – **16 rm** 105.00/150.00 **2 suites** 175.00 **t.**
- Moat House International (Q.M.H.), Congress Rd, G3 8QT, ✆ 204 0733, Telex 77624 Fax 221 2022, ← – rm ☎ Ⓟ – 800 CZ
  285 rm, **15 suites.**
- **Hospitality Inn** (Mt. Charlotte Thistle), 36 Cambridge St., G2 3HN, ✆ 332 3311, Tele 777334, Fax 332 4050 – ☎ Ⓟ – 1 500. AE VISA DY
  M 13.75/16.50 **st.** and a la carte – 8.50 – **313 rm** 80.00/105.00 **st.**, **3 suites** 180.00 **st.** SB 75.00/85.00 **st.**
- Stakis Grosvenor, Grosvenor Terr., Great Western Rd, G12 0TA, ✆ 339 8811, Tele 776247, Fax 334 0710 – ☎ Ⓟ – 250. AE VISA CY
  7.50 – **93 rm** 84.50/109.50 **t.**, **2 suites** 156.00 **s.** – SB 82.00/136.00 **st.**
- **Copthorne** (Best Western), George Sq., G2 1DS, ✆ 332 6711, Telex 77814 Fax 332 4264 – ☎ – 100. AE VISA. DZ
  M *(closed lunch Saturday, Sunday and Bank Holiday Mondays)* (carving rest.) 14.00/15.00 s and a la carte 4.95 – 7.90 – **135 rm** 84.00/96.00 **st.**, **5 suites** 115.00/140.00 **st.**
- White House without rest., 12 Cleveden Cres., G12 0PA, ✆ 339 9375, Telex 77758 Fax 337 1430 – ☎ – 25 – **20 rm**, **11 suites.** AV

Swallow, 517 Paisley Rd West, G51 1RW, ☎ 427 3146, Telex 778795, Fax 427 4059, – rm rest – 250 AX **a**
119 rm.

Tinto Firs Thistle (Mt. Charlotte Thistle), 470 Kilmarnock Rd, G43 2BB, ☎ 637 2353, Telex 778329, Fax 633 1340 – – 60. AE VISA AX **c**
M 8.00/12.50 **st.** and a la carte – 7.75 – **25 rm** 65.00/85.00 **st.**, **2 suites** – SB 90.00 **st.**

Kelvin Park Lorne (Q.M.H.), 923 Sauchiehall St., G3 7TE, ☎ 334 4891, Telex 778935, Fax 337 1659 – – 175. AE VISA CY **a**
M *(closed Saturday lunch)* 9.95/14.25 **st.** and a la carte 4.95 – 6.50 – **99 rm** 65.00/130.00 **st.**

Crest (T.H.F.), 377 Argyle St., G2 8LL, ☎ 248 2355, Telex 779652, Fax 221 1014 – rm – 80. AE VISA. CZ **x**
M *(closed lunch Saturday, Sunday, Monday and Bank Holidays)* 9.25/15.95 **t.** and a la carte – 7.95 – **121 rm** 60.00/90.00 **st.**

Stakis Ingram, 201 Ingram St., G1 1DQ, ☎ 248 4401, Telex 776470, Fax 226 5149 – rm – 200. AE VISA DZ **c**
M 8.50/12.95 **t.** – 7.25 – **90 rm** 69.00/91.00 **t.** – SB 70.00/114.00 **st.**

Jury's Pond (Stakis), 2-4 Shelley Rd, off Great Western Rd, G12 0XP, ☎ 334 8161, Telex 776573, Fax 334 3846, – rm – 50 AV **i**
137 rm.

Albion without rest., 405-407 North Woodside Rd, G20 6NN, ☎ 339 8620 – . AE VISA. CY **u**
16 rm 35.00/45.00 **st.**

Town House, 4 Hughenden Terr., G12 9XR, ☎ 357 0862 – rest . AV **a**
M 16.00 **st.** 5.00 – **10 rm** 40.00/49.00 **st.**

Dalmeny, 62 St. Andrews Drive, Nithsdale Cross, Pollokshields, G41 5EZ, ☎ 427 1106 – . AE VISA AX **o**
M (by arrangement) – **8 rm** 26.50/50.00 **st.**

Kirklee without rest., 11 Kensington Gate, G12 9LG, ☎ 334 5555 – . AV **c**
10 rm 37.50/49.00 **st.**

XXX **North Rotunda,** 28 Tunnel St. (2nd floor), G3 8HL, ☎ 204 1238, Fax 226 4264, French rest. – . AE VISA CZ **u**
closed Saturday lunch, Sunday, 25-26 December, 1-2 January and Bank Holiday Mondays – **M** 10.75/19.00 **t.** and a la carte 4.95.

XXX Killermont House, 2022 Maryhill Rd, Maryhill Park, G20 0AB, ☎ 946 5412, – by A 81 AV

XXX **Fountain,** 2 Woodside Cres., G3 7UL, ☎ 332 6396 – AE VISA CY **c**
closed Saturday lunch and Sunday – **M** 9.00/13.95 **t.** and a la carte.

XX **Buttery,** 652 Argyle St., G3 8UF, ☎ 221 8188, Fax 204 4639 – . AE VISA
closed Saturday lunch, Sunday and Bank Holidays – **M** 12.50 **st.** (lunch) and a la carte 17.55/26.00 **t.** CZ **e**

XX **Rogano,** 11 Exchange Pl., G1 3AN, ☎ 248 4055, Fax 248 2608, Seafood, « Art deco » – AE VISA DZ **i**
closed Sunday and Bank Holidays – **M** a la carte 22.95/27.95 **t.**

XX Cafe India, 171 North St., G3 7DL, ☎ 248 4074, Indian rest. – CY **e**

XX Ho Wong, 82 York St., G2 3LE, ☎ 221 3550, Chinese (Peking) rest. – rest CZ **v**

XX Amber Royale, 336 Arghle St., G2 8LY, ☎ 221 2550, Chinese rest. – rest CZ **o**

X **Ubiquitous Chip,** 12 Ashton Lane, off Byres Rd, G12 8SJ, ☎ 334 5007 – AE VISA
closed 25 and 31 December-1 January – **M** a la carte 14.70/22.80 **t.** AV **e**

X Shish Mahal, 45 Gibson St., G12 8NW, ☎ 339 8256, Indian and Pakistani rest. – CY **s**

at Giffnock (Renfrew.) (Strathclyde) S : 5¼ m. by A 77 – AX – ✉ 041 Glasgow :

MacDonald Thistle (Mt. Charlotte Thistle), Eastwood Toll, G46 6RA, at intersection of A 77 and A 726 ☎ 638 2225, Telex 779138, Fax 638 6231, – – 100. AE VISA
M 8.00/14.00 **st.** and a la carte – 7.75 – **52 rm** 60.00/90.00 **st.**, **4 suites** – SB 80.00 **st.**

Redhurst (B.C.B.), 77 Eastwoodmains Rd, G46 6QE, ☎ 638 6465 – . AE VISA.
M 15.00 **st.** – **17 rm** 43.50/64.50 **st.**

X Turban Tandoori, 2 Station Rd, G46 6JF, ☎ 638 0069, Indian rest.

at Busby S : 5½ m. by A 727 – AX – on A 726 – ✉ 041 Glasgow :

Busby, 1 Field Rd, Clarkston, G76 8RX, ☎ 644 2661 – – **14 rm.**

at Glasgow Airport (Renfrew.) (Strathclyde) W : 8 m. by M 8 – AV – ✉ 041 Glasgow :

Excelsior (T.H.F.), Abbotsinch, PA3 2TR, ☎ 887 1212, Telex 777733, Fax 887 3738 – rm – 400. AE VISA.
M (carving rest.) 13.50 **st.** and a la carte 7.00 – 9.00 – **283 rm** 80.00/90.00 **st.**, **5 suites** 120.00 **st.** – SB (weekends only) (except Easter, Christmas and New Year) 80.00/100.00 **st.**

GLASGOW
BUILT UP AREA

Street	Grid	No.
...aggs Road	AX	68
...arriet Street	AX	70
...elen Street	AV	72
...olmfauld Road	AV	73
...olmlea Road	BX	74
...ospital Street	BX	75
...mes Street	BX	79
...ng's Drive	BX	83
...ng's Park Road	BX	84
Lamont Road	BV	88
Langside Av.	AX	89
Langside Road	BX	90
Lincoln Avenue	AV	91
Lyoncross Road	AX	97
Meiklerig Crescent	AX	98
Minard Rd	AX	101
Moss Road	AV	103
Nether Auldhouse Road	AX	104
Prospecthill Road	BX	112
Provan Road	BV	114
Red Road	BV	118
Riverford Road	AX	119
Sandwood Road	AV	123
Shields Road	AX	124
Todd Street	BV	131
Westmuir Place	BX	136
Westmuir Street	BX	138

For Street Index see Glasgow p. 6

A 803 KIRKINTILLOCH B

BISHOPBRIGGS

SPRINGBURN PARK

See following pages

ALEXANDRA PARK

GLASGOW GREEN

RICHMOND PARK

TOLLCROSS PARK

RUTHERGLEN

KING'S PARK

CLYDE

MICHELIN

STIRLING A 80

EDINBURGH M 8

A 8 (M 74, M 8)

M 74, CARLISLE A 74

A 724 HAMILTON

EAST-KILBRIDE A 749

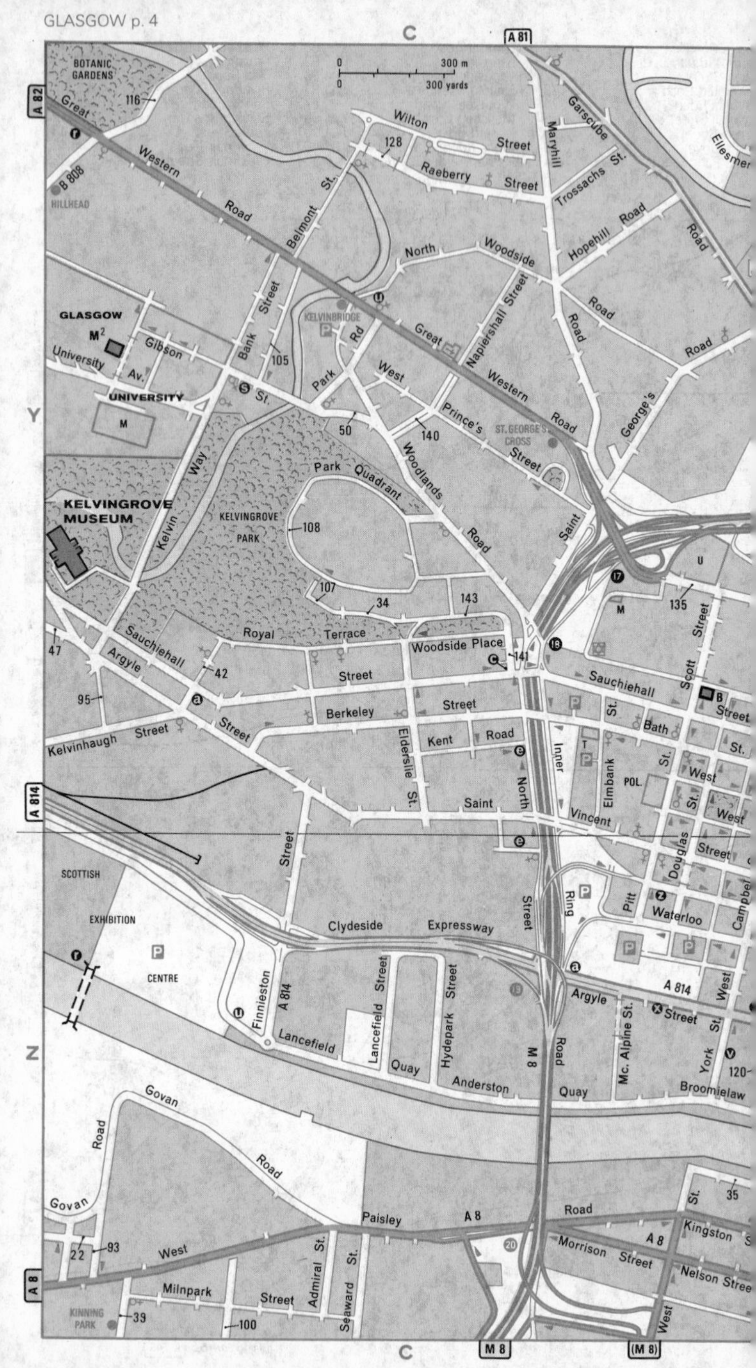
C
A 81
A 82
BOTANIC GARDENS
Great Western Road
B 808
HILLHEAD
Wilton Street
Raeberry Street
Maryhill Road
Garscube Road
Trossachs St.
Hopehill Road
Belmont St.
Bank Street
North Woodside Road
Napiershall Street
KELVINBRIDGE
Park Rd
GLASGOW
University Av.
Gibson St.
UNIVERSITY
West Prince's Street
ST. GEORGE'S CROSS
Saint George's Road
Kelvin Way
KELVINGROVE MUSEUM
KELVINGROVE PARK
Park Quadrant
Woodlands Road
Royal Terrace
Woodside Place
Sauchiehall Street
Argyle Street
Berkeley Street
Kelvinhaugh Street
Kent Road
Elderslie St.
North Street
Saint Vincent Street
Inner Ring Road
Elmbank St.
Scott Street
Bath St.
West Regent St.
West George St.
Douglas St.
Pitt St.
Waterloo Street
Campbell St.
A 814
SCOTTISH EXHIBITION CENTRE
Clydeside Expressway
Finnieston Street
Lancefield Street
Lancefield Quay
Hydepark Street
Anderston Quay
M 8
Mc. Alpine St.
York St.
West St.
Broomielaw
Govan Road
Paisley Road West
A 8
Kingston St.
Morrison Street
Nelson Street
Milnpark Street
Admiral St.
Seaward St.
KINNING PARK
West St.
M 8
(M 8)
Y
Z
300 m
300 yards

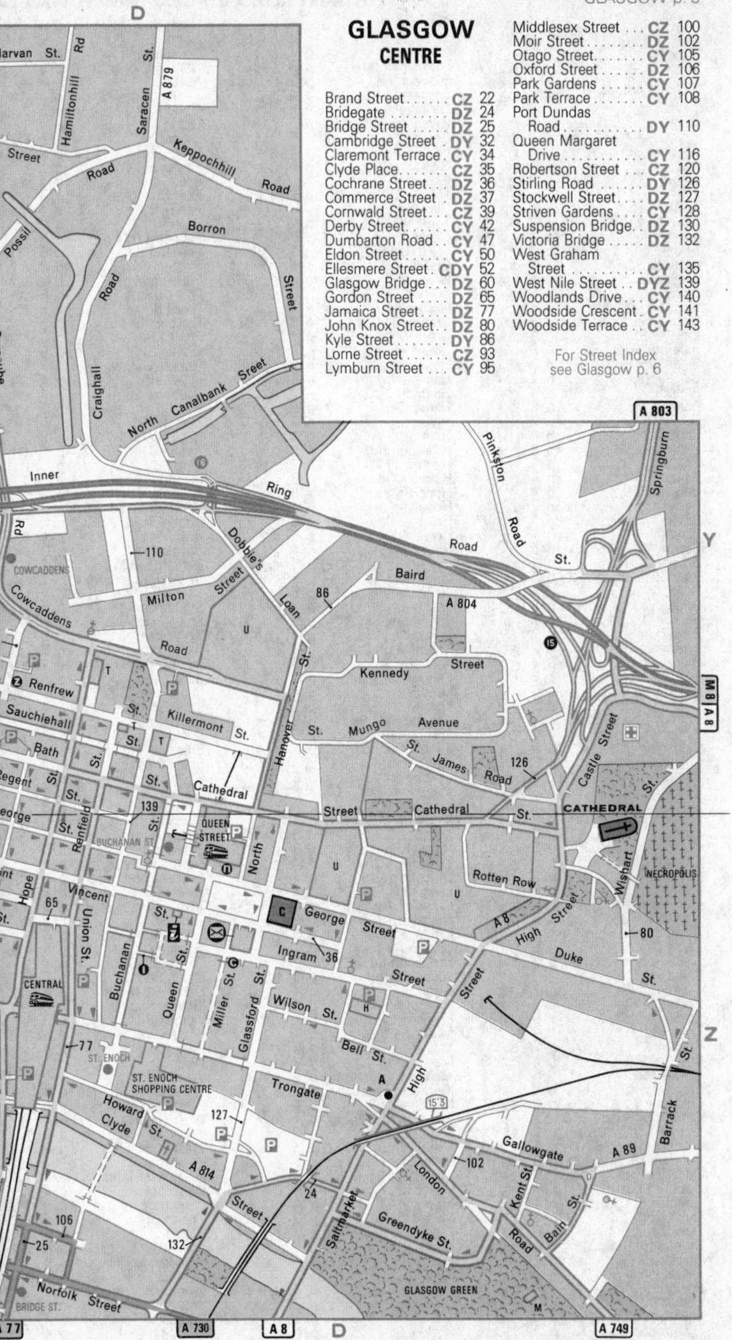

GLASGOW
CENTRE
Brand Street CZ 22
Bridegate DZ 24
Bridge Street DZ 25
Cambridge Street DY 32
Claremont Terrace CY 34
Clyde Place CZ 35
Cochrane Street DZ 36
Commerce Street DZ 37
Cornwald Street CZ 39
Derby Street CY 42
Dumbarton Road CY 47
Eldon Street CY 50
Ellesmere Street CDY 52
Glasgow Bridge DZ 60
Gordon Street DZ 65
Jamaica Street DZ 77
John Knox Street DZ 80
Kyle Street DY 86
Lorne Street CZ 93
Lymburn Street CY 95
Middlesex Street CZ 100
Moir Street DZ 102
Otago Street CY 105
Oxford Street DZ 106
Park Gardens CY 107
Park Terrace CY 108
Port Dundas Road DY 110
Queen Margaret Drive CY 116
Robertson Street CZ 120
Stirling Road DY 126
Stockwell Street DZ 127
Striven Gardens CY 128
Suspension Bridge DZ 130
Victoria Bridge DZ 132
West Graham Street CY 135
West Nile Street DYZ 139
Woodlands Drive CY 140
Woodside Crescent CY 141
Woodside Terrace CY 143
For Street Index see Glasgow p. 6
D
Y
Z
A 803
A 879
A 804
A 8
M 8
A 89
A 814
A 77
A 730
A 749
Saracen St.
Hamiltonhill Rd
Keppochhill Road
Possil Road
Borron Street
Craighall Road
North Canalbank Street
Inner Ring Road
Pinkston Road
Springburn Road
Baird St.
Dobbie's Loan
Milton Street
Cowcaddens Road
COWCADDENS
Kennedy Street
St. Mungo Avenue
St. James Road
Castle Street
Hanover St.
North St.
Renfrew St.
Sauchiehall St.
Killermont St.
Bath St.
Regent St.
Cathedral St.
George St.
Renfield St.
BUCHANAN ST.
QUEEN STREET
CATHEDRAL
NECROPOLIS
Wishart St.
Rotten Row
High Street
Duke St.
Hope St.
Vincent St.
Union St.
Buchanan St.
Queen St.
Miller St.
Glassford St.
Ingram Street
Wilson St.
Bell St.
Trongate
CENTRAL
ST. ENOCH
ST. ENOCH SHOPPING CENTRE
Howard St.
Clyde Street
Gallowgate
Barrack St.
London Road
Kent St.
Bain St.
Saltmarket
Greendyke St.
GLASGOW GREEN
Norfolk Street
BRIDGE ST.

STREET INDEX TO GLASGOW TOWN PLA

Street	Page	Grid	No.
Argyle St.	p. 4	CZ	
Buchanan St.	p. 5	DZ	
Gordon St.	p. 5	DZ	65
Jamaica St.	p. 5	DZ	77
Oswald St.	p. 5	DZ	
Renfield St.	p. 5	DZ	
St. Enoch Shopping Centre		DZ	
St. Vincent St.	p. 5	DZ	
Sauchiehall St.	p. 5	DY	
Trongate	p. 5	DZ	
Union St.	p. 5	DZ	
Admiral St.	p. 4	CZ	
Aikenhead Rd	p. 3	BX	2
Alexandra Par.	p. 3	BV	3
Anderston Quay	p. 4	CZ	
Anniesland Rd	p. 2	AV	
Argyle St.	p. 4	CZ	
Bain St.	p. 5	DZ	
Baird St.	p. 5	DY	
Balgrayhill	p. 3	BV	4
Ballater St.	p. 3	BX	6
Balmore Rd	p. 3	BV	
Balornock Rd	p. 3	BV	8
Balshagray Av.	p. 2	AV	9
Bank St.	p. 4	CY	
Barrack St.	p. 5	DZ	
Barrhead Rd	p. 2	AX	
Bath St.	p. 4	CY	
Battlefield Rd	p. 3	BX	12
Bell St.	p. 5	DZ	
Belmont St.	p. 4	CY	
Berkeley St.	p. 4	CY	
Berryknowes Rd	p. 2	AX	15
Bilsland Drive	p. 3	BV	16
Blairbeth Rd	p. 3	BX	18
Borron St.	p. 5	DY	
Boydstone Rd	p. 2	AX	
Braidcraft Rd.	p. 2	AX	20
Brand St.	p. 4	CZ	22
Bridegate	p. 5	DZ	24
Bridge St.	p. 5	DZ	25
Brockburn Rd	p. 2	AX	
Broomfield Rd	p. 3	BV	
Broomielaw	p. 4	CZ	
Broomloan Rd	p. 2	AV	26
Brownside Rd	p. 3	BX	
Buchanan St.	p. 5	DZ	
Burnhill Chapel St.	p. 3	BX	28
Byres Rd	p. 2	AV	29
Caldarvan St.	p. 5	DY	
Caledonia Rd	p. 3	BX	30
Cambridge St.	p. 5	DY	32
Cambuslang Rd	p. 3	BX	
Cardowan Rd	p. 3	BV	
Carmunnock Rd	p. 3	BX	33
Carntyne Rd	p. 3	BV	
Carntynehall Rd	p. 3	BV	
Castle St.	p. 5	DY	
Cathcart Rd	p. 3	BX	
Cathedral St.	p. 5	DY	
Claremont Ter.	p. 4	CY	34
Clarkston Rd	p. 3	BX	
Clyde Place	p. 4	CZ	35
Clyde St.	p. 5	DZ	
Clyde Tunnel	p. 2	AV	
Clydeside Expressway	p. 2	AV	
Cochrane St.	p. 5	DZ	36
Commerce St.	p. 5	DZ	37
Cook St.	p. 3	BV	38
Corkerhill Rd	p. 2	AX	
Cornwald St.	p. 4	CZ	39
Cowcaddens St.	p. 5	DY	
Craighall Rd	p. 5	DY	
Croftfoot Rd	p. 3	BX	
Crookston Rd	p. 2	AX	
Crow Rd	p. 2	AV	
Cumbernauld Rd	p. 3	BV	40
Dalmarnock Rd.	p. 3	BX	
Derby St.	p. 4	CY	42
Dobbie's Loan	p. 5	DY	
Douglas St.	p. 4	CZ	
Duke's Rd	p. 3	BX	
Duke St.	p. 5	DZ	
Dumbarton Rd	p. 4	CY	47
Dumbreck Rd	p. 2	AX	
East Kilbride Rd	p. 3	BX	
Edinburgh Rd	p. 3	BV	
Edmiston Drive	p. 2	AV	48
Eglinton Rd	p. 3	BX	
Eglinton St.	p. 3	BX	
Elderslie St.	p. 4	CY	
Eldon St.	p. 4	CY	50
Elmbank St.	p. 4	CY	
Farmeloan Rd	p. 3	BX	53
Fenwick Rd.	p. 2	AX	55
Finnieston St.	p. 4	CZ	
Gallowgate	p. 5	DZ	
Garscube Rd.	p. 5	DY	
George St.	p. 5	DZ	
Gibson St.	p. 4	CY	
Glasgow Bridge	p. 5	DZ	60
Glasgow Rd (PAISLEY)	p. 2	AX	62
Glasgow Rd (RENFREW)	p. 2	AV	
Glasgow Rd (RUTHERGLEN)	p. 3	BX	
Glassford St.	p. 5	DZ	
Gorbals St.	p. 3	BX	63
Gordon St.	p. 5	DZ	65
Govan Rd	p. 4	CZ	
Grange Rd	p. 3	BX	67
Great Western Rd	p. 4	CY	
Greendyke St.	p. 5	DZ	
Haggs Rd	p. 2	AX	68
Hamiltonhill Rd.	p. 5	DY	
Hardgate Rd	p. 2	AV	
Harriet St.	p. 2	AX	70
Helen St.	p. 2	AV	72
High St.	p. 5	DZ	
Hillington Rd.	p. 2	AV	
Holmfauld Rd	p. 2	AV	73
Holmlea Rd.	p. 3	BX	74
Hope St.	p. 5	DZ	
Hopehill Rd.	p. 4	CY	
Hospital St.	p. 3	BX	75
Howard St.	p. 5	DZ	
Hydepark St.	p. 4	CZ	
Ingram St.	p. 5	DZ	
Inner Ring Rd	p. 5	DY	
Jamaica St.	p. 5	DZ	77
James St.	p. 3	BX	79
John Knox St.	p. 5	DZ	80
Kelvin Way	p. 4	CY	
Kelvinhaugh St.	p. 4	CY	
Kennedy St.	p. 5	DY	
Kennishead Rd	p. 2	AX	
Kent Rd	p. 4	CY	
Kent St.	p. 5	DZ	
Keppoch Hill Rd	p. 5	DY	
Killermont St.	p. 5	DY	
Kilmarnock Rd	p. 2	AX	
King's Drive	p. 3	BX	83
King's Park Av.	p. 3	BX	
Kings Park Rd.	p. 3	BX	84
Kingston St.	p. 4	CZ	
Kingsway	p. 2	AV	
Kyle St.	p. 5	DY	86
Lamont Rd	p. 3	BV	88
Lancefield Quay	p. 4	CZ	
Lancefield St.	p. 4	CZ	
Langlands Rd	p. 2	AV	
Langside Av.	p. 2	AX	89
Langside Drive	p. 2	AX	
Langside Rd	p. 3	BX	90
Lincoln Av.	p. 2	AV	91
Linthaugh Rd	p. 2	AX	
London Rd	p. 3	BX	
Lorne St.	p. 4	CZ	93
Lymburn St.	p. 4	CY	95
Lyoncross Rd	p. 2	AX	97
McAlpine St.	p. 4	CZ	
Main St.	p. 3	BX	
Maryhill Rd	p. 4	CY	
Meiklerig Crescent	p. 2	AX	98
Merrylee Rd	p. 2	AX	
Middlesex St.	p. 4	CZ	100
Milnpark St.	p. 4	CZ	
Milton St.	p. 5	DY	
Mill St.	p. 3	BX	
Miller St.	p. 5	DZ	
Minard Rd.	p. 2	AX	101
Moir St.	p. 5	DZ	102
Morrison St.	p. 4	CZ	
Moss Rd	p. 2	AV	103
Mosspark Blvd.	p. 2	AX	
Napiershall St.	p. 4	CY	
Nelson St.	p. 4	CZ	
Nether Auldhouse Rd.	p. 2	AX	104
Newlands Rd	p. 2	AX	
Nitshill Rd	p. 2	AX	
Norfolk St.	p. 5	DZ	
North St.	p. 4	CY	
North Canalbank St.	p. 5	DY	
North Hanover St.	p. 5	DY	
North Woodside Rd	p. 4	CY	
Oswald St.	p. 5	DZ	
Otago St.	p. 4	CY	1
Oxford St.	p. 5	DZ	1
Paisley Rd	p. 2	AV	
Paisley Rd West	p. 2	AX	
Park Gdns	p. 4	CY	1
Park Quadrant	p. 4	CY	
Park Ter	p. 4	CY	1
Peat Rd	p. 2	AX	
Petershill Rd	p. 3	BV	
Pinkston Rd	p. 5	DY	
Pitt St.	p. 4	CZ	
Pollokshaws Rd.	p. 2	AX	
Port Dundas Rd	p. 5	DY	1
Possil Rd	p. 5	DY	
Prospecthill Rd	p. 3	BX	1
Provan Rd	p. 3	BV	1
Queen St.	p. 5	DZ	
Queen Margaret Drive	p. 4	CY	1
Raeberry St.	p. 4	CY	
Red Rd.	p. 3	BV	1
Renfield St.	p. 5	DZ	
Renfrew Rd	p. 2	AV	
Renfrew St.	p. 5	DY	
Ring Rd	p. 3	BV	
Riverford Road	p. 2	AX	1
Robertson St.	p. 4	CZ	1
Robroyston Rd	p. 3	BV	
Rotten Row	p. 5	DZ	
Royal Ter.	p. 4	CY	
Royston Rd	p. 3	BV	
Rutherglen Rd	p. 3	BX	
St. Andrew's Drive	p. 2	AX	
St. George's Rd	p. 4	CY	
St. James Rd.	p. 5	DY	
St. Mungo Av.	p. 5	DY	
St. Vincent St	p. 5	DZ	
Saltmarket	p. 5	DZ	
Sandwood Rd	p. 2	AV	1
Saracen St.	p. 5	DY	
Sauchiehall St.	p. 5	DY	
Scott St.	p. 4	CY	
Seaward St.	p. 4	CZ	
Shettleston Rd	p. 3	BX	
Shieldhall Rd	p. 2	AV	
Shields Rd	p. 2	AX	1
Southbrae Drive	p. 2	AV	
Springburn Rd.	p. 3	BV	
Springfield Rd	p. 3	BX	
Stirling Rd	p. 5	DY	1
Stockwell St.	p. 5	DZ	1
Stonelaw Rd	p. 3	BX	
Striven Gdns	p. 4	CY	1
Suspension Bridge	p. 5	DZ	1
Thornliebank Rd	p. 2	AX	
Titwood Rd	p. 2	AX	
Todd St.	p. 3	BV	1
Tollcross Rd.	p. 3	BX	
Trongate	p. 5	DZ	
Trossachs St.	p. 4	CY	
Union St.	p. 5	DZ	
University Av.	p. 4	CY	
Victoria Bridge.	p. 5	DZ	1
Victoria Rd	p. 3	BX	
Wallacewell Rd	p. 3	BV	
Waterloo St.	p. 4	CZ	
West St.	p. 4	CZ	
West Campbell St.	p. 4	CZ	
West George St.	p. 5	DZ	
West Graham St.	p. 4	CY	1
Westmuir Place	p. 3	BX	1
Westmuir St.	p. 3	BX	1
West Nile St.	p. 5	DYZ	1
West Paisley Rd	p. 4	CZ	
West Prince's St.	p. 4	CY	
West Regent St.	p. 5	DY	
Wilson St.	p. 5	DZ	
Wilton St.	p. 4	CY	
Wishart St.	p. 5	DZ	
Woodlands Drive	p. 4	CY	1
Woodlands Rd	p. 4	CY	
Woodside Crescent	p. 4	CY	14
Woodside Place	p. 4	CY	
Woodside Ter	p. 4	CY	14
York St.	p. 4	CZ	

ICHELIN Distribution Centre, 60 Cunningham Rd, Rutherglen, G73 1PP, ☏ **643 2101,** ax 647 5267 p. 3 BX

ORD Hilton Gdns ☏ 954 1500
ORD 34 Fenwick Rd ☏ 637 7161
ORD Pollockshaws Rd ☏ 423 6644
ONDA Maxwell Rd ☏ 429 4298
ISSAN 77-81 Dumbarton Rd ☏ 334 1241
PEL-VAUXHALL 10 Holmbank Av. ☏ 649 9321
ORSCHE Maxwell Av. Bearsden ☏ 943 1155
ENAULT 64 Kirkintilloch Rd ☏ 772 6481
OVER, MAZDA 215 Queensborough Gdns
357 1234
OVER, VAUXHALL Vineycombe St. ☏ 334 4761
SAAB 162 Crow Rd ☏ 334 4661
VAUXHALL-OPEL St. Georges Rd ☏ 332 2626
VOLVO 2413-2493 London Rd ☏ 778 8501
VOLVO Bothwell Rd, Hamilton ☏ 728 4100
VW-AUDI 384-402 Tintallon Rd ☏ 637 2241

ATS 192 Finnieston St. ☏ 248 6761
ATS Rutherglen Ind Est., Glasgow Rd, Rutherglen ☏ 647 9341
ATS 1 Sawmillfield St., off Garscube Rd ☏ 332 1945

If you find you cannot take up a hotel booking you have made, please let the hotel know immediately.

GLENBORRODALE Argyll. (Highland) 401 C 13 – ✉ Acharacle – ☎ 097 24.

Edinburgh 151 – ♦Inverness 108 – ♦Oban 72.

Glenborrodale Castle ⛰, Ardnamurchan, PH36 4JP, ☏ 266, Telex 778815, Fax 224, ≤ Loch Sunart and gardens, « Victorian castle in extensive gardens », ⛫, park, ✗ – TV ☎ P. VISA.
Easter-October – **M** (booking essential) (buffet lunch, residents only)/dinner 27.50/30.00 **t.** 8.50 – **15 rm** ⊐ 100.00/190.00 **t.**

GLENCARSE Perth. (Tayside) 401 K 14 – ECD : Wednesday – ✉ Perth – ☎ 073 886.

Edinburgh 47 – ♦Dundee 16 – Perth 6.5.

Newton House, PH2 7LX, ☏ 250, Fax 717, – TV ☎ P. VISA
M 19.00 **t.** and a la carte 4.95 – **10 rm** ⊐ 44.00/64.00 **t.** – SB 88.00/96.00 **st.**

GLENCRIPESDALE Argyll. (Highland) – see Strontian.

GLENROTHES Fife. (Fife) 401 K 15 – pop. 33 639 – ECD : Tuesday – ☎ 0592.

Envir. : Falkland (Palace of Falkland★ ; village★) N : 5 m. by A 92 and A 912.

Thornton ☏ 771111, S : 3 m. – 18 Golf Course Rd ☏ 758686 – 18 Balbirnie Park ☏ 752006 – Leslie ☏ 741449, W : 3 m. on A 911.

Glenrothes House, North St. ☏ 756684.

Edinburgh 33 – ♦Dundee 25 – Stirling 36.

Albany (B.C.B.), 1 North St., KY7 5NA, ☏ 752292, Fax 756451 – TV ☎ P – 200
M (grill rest.) – **29 rm.**

at Markinch NE : 1 ¾ by A 911 and A 92 on the B 9130 – ✉ ☎ 0592 Glenrothes :

Balbirnie House ⛰, Balbirnie Park, KY7 6NE, ☏ 610066, Fax 610529, « Part 18C mansion », , park – TV ☎ ♿ P – 170. VISA
M 15.00/28.00 **t.** 4.00 – ⊐ 8.50 – **28 rm** 59.00/110.00 **t.**, **3 suites** 140.00 **t.** – SB (weekends only) 122.00/142.00 **st.**

at Leslie W : 3 m. by A 911 – ✉ Leslie – ☎ 0592 Glenrothes :

Rescobie, Valley Drive, KY6 3BQ, ☏ 742143, – TV ☎ P. VISA.
closed Christmas Day – **M** 8.50/13.50 **t.** and a la carte 3.00 – **8 rm** ⊐ 43.00/65.00 **t.**

EUGEOT-TALBOT North St. ☏ 752262

GOLSPIE Sutherland. (Highland) 401 I 10 – pop. 1 385 – ECD : Wednesday – ✉ ☎ 040 83.

Ferry Rd ☏ 3266.

Edinburgh 228 – ♦Inverness 72 – ♦Wick 54.

Golf Links, Church St., KW10 6TT, ☏ 3408, ≤, – TV P. VISA
M 7.00/13.50 **t.** and dinner a la carte 3.00 – **8 rm** ⊐ 25.50/44.00 **t.**

AT Old Bank Rd ☏ 3411
AT West End, Brora ☏ 21721
ROVER Station Rd ☏ 3205

GOUROCK Renfrew. (Strathclyde) 401 F 16 – pop. 11 087 – ECD : Wednesday – ☎ 0475.

by Caledonian MacBrayne : from Railway Pier to Dunoon Pier: frequent services daily (20 mn) – by Western Ferries : from McInroy's Point to Hunters Quay, Dunoon: frequent services daily (20 mn).

by Caledonian MacBrayne and Clyde Marine Motoring Co. Ltd. to Helensburgh via Kilcreggan : 3-7 daily (exept Sunday).

Pierhead ☏ 39467 (summer only).

Edinburgh 71 – ♦Ayr 47 – ♦Glasgow 27.

Stakis Gantock, Cloch Rd, PA15 1AR, SW : 2 m. on A 770 ℘ 34671, Telex 77858 Fax 32490, ≤ Firth of Clyde, ⛹, ♨, 🏊, 🎾 – 🛗 ⇔ rm 📺 ☎ 🅟 – 🔔 200. 🔲 AE ⓪ VISA
M 7.50/15.00 **t.** and a la carte – ☐ 7.50 – **99 rm** 65.50/91.50 **t.**, **2 suites** 135.50 **t.** SB 80.00/148.00 **st.**

FIAT Manor Cres. ℘ 32356

GRAEMSAY (Isle of) Orkney. (Orkney Islands) 401 K 7 – Shipping Services : see Orkne Islands.

GRANTOWN-ON-SPEY Moray. (Highland) 401 J 12 – pop. 1 800 – ECD : Thursday – ⓢ 0479

18 Golf Course Rd ℘ 2079, East town boundary.

ℹ 54 High St. ℘ 2773.

♦Edinburgh 143 – ♦Inverness 34 – Perth 99.

Garth, The Square, PH26 3HN, ℘ 2836, Fax 2116, 🌳 – ⇔ rest 📺 ☎ 🅟. 🔲 VISA. ✗
M (bar lunch)/dinner 21.00 **t.** and a la carte 🍷 3.50 – **17 rm** ☐ 28.00/56.00 **t.** – SB (wint only) 75.00/88.00 **st.**

Dunstaffnage House ⛰, Dunstaffnage Brae, PH26 3JR, via Woodside Av. ℘ 2000, 🌳 – ⇔ 📺 🅟. 🔲 VISA
closed 15 November-20 December and 6 January-15 March – **M** 16.50 **t.** – **6 rm** ☐ 25.0 42.00 **s.**

Culdearn House, Woodlands Terrace, PH26 3JU, ℘ 2106, 🌳 – ⇔ rest 📺 🅟. 🔲 VIS ✗
March-October – **M** 12.50 **t.** – **8 rm** ☐ 19.95/39.90 **t.** – SB 58.95 **st.**

FORD Woodland Service Centre ℘ 2289 ROVER Chapel Rd ℘ 2037

GREAT CUMBRAE ISLAND Bute. (Strathclyde) 401 402 F 16 – pop. 1 611 – ⓢ 047 553 Mil port.

⛴ by Caledonian MacBrayne : from Cumbrae Slip to Largs frequent services daily (10 mn)

GREENLAW Berwick. (Borders) 401 402 M 16 – pop. 608 – ✉ Duns – ⓢ 089 084 Leitholm.

Envir. : Manderston★, NE : 9 m. by B 6355 and A 6105.

♦Edinburgh 39 – ♦Newcastle-upon-Tyne 70.

Purves Hall ⛰, TD10 6UJ, SE : 4 m. by A 697 ℘ 558, 🏊 heated, 🌳, park, 🎾 – 📺 ☎ 🅟 🔲 AE ⓪ VISA
M 8.95/15.95 **t.** and a la carte 🍷 3.00 – **7 rm** ☐ 32.00/60.00 **t.** – SB (except summer) 78.0 83.00 **st.**

GRETNA Dumfries. (Dumfries and Galloway) 401 402 K 19 – pop. 2 737 – ECD : Wednesday ⓢ 046 13 (3 fig.) or 0461 (5 fig.).

ℹ Annan Rd ℘ 37834 (summer only).

♦Edinburgh 91 – ♦Carlisle 10 – ♦Dumfries 24.

Gretna Chase, CA6 5JB, S : ¼ m. on B 721 ✉ Carlisle (Cumbria) ℘ 37517, « Gardens – 📺 🅟. 🔲 AE ⓪ VISA. ✗
closed January – **M** *(closed Sunday to non-residents)* (lunch by arrangement)/dinner a carte 9.90/15.90 **t.** 🍷 2.75 – **9 rm** ☐ 33.00/80.00 **t.**

Travelodge without rest., A 74 Trunk Rd, Gretna Green ✉ Carlisle (Cumbria), CA6 5H NW : 1½ m. by B 721 on A 74 ℘ 37566, Fax 37752, Reservations (Toll free) 0800 850950 📺 ♿ 🅟. 🔲 AE VISA. ✗
41 rm 24.00/29.50 **t.**

GULLANE E. Lothian. (Lothian) 401 L 15 – pop. 2 124 – ECD : Wednesday – ⓢ 0620.

Envir. : Dirleton★ (Castle★) E : 2 m. by A 198.

18, 18, 18 Gullane ℘ 843115 – 18 The Honourable Company of Edinburgh Golfers, Muirfie ℘ 842123.

♦Edinburgh 19 – North Berwick 5.

Greywalls ⛰, Duncur Rd, Muirfield, EH31 2EG, ℘ 842144, Fax 842241, ≤ gardens an golf course, « Lutyens house, gardens by Gertrude Jekyll », 🎾 – 📺 ☎ 🅟. 🔲 AE ⓪ VI
April-November – **M** 14.00/27.00 **t.** 🍷 5.70 – **22 rm** ☐ 77.00/132.00 **t.**

✗ ✿ **La Potinière** (Hilary Brown), Main St., EH31 2AA, ℘ 843214 – 🅟
closed lunch Friday and Saturday, dinner Sunday to Thursday, Wednesday, 1 week Jur and October – **M** 15.50/21.50 **t.** 🍷 3.50.
Spec. Tomato and mint soup, Poached chicken breast with lentils and wild mushrooms, Iced orange soufflé w caramelised oranges.

at Dirleton NE : 2 m. by A 198 – ✉ ⓢ 062 085 Dirleton :

✗✗ **Open Arms** with rm, EH39 5EG, ℘ 241, Fax 570, « Tastefully converted ston cottages », 🌳 – 📺 ☎ 🅟. 🔲 VISA
M (bar lunch Monday to Saturday)/dinner 19.75 **t.** and a la carte 🍷 6.50 – **7 rm** ☐ 70.0 98.00 **t.** – SB (October-May) 99.00/120.00 **st.**

HADDINGTON E. Lothian. (Lothian) 401 L 16 **Scotland G** – pop. 7 988 – ECD : Thursday – ☎ 062 082.

See : Site★ – High Street★.

Envir. : Gifford★, S : 4 m. by B 8369 – Stenton★, E : 7 m. – Lennoxlove★, S : 1 m.

Amisfield Park, ☎ 3627.

Edinburgh 17 – Hawick 53 – ◆Newcastle-upon-Tyne 101.

XX **Brown's** with rm, 1 West Rd, EH41 3RD, ☎ 2254 – TV ☎ P. AE VISA.
M (dinner only and Sunday lunch)(booking essential)/dinner 21.50 **t.** – **5 rm** 49.50/62.50 **t.**

HAMILTON SERVICE AREA Lanark. (strathclyde) 401 402 H 16 – pop. 51 441 – ☎ 0698.

Edinburgh 38 – ◆Glasgow 12.

RoadChef Lodge without rest., GA2 5BA, M 74 between junctions 6 and 5 (Northbound carriageway) ☎ 891904, Fax 891682 – TV ☎ P – 30. AE VISA.
closed 25 December – **36 rm** 34.00/39.00 **st.**

HARRIS (Isle of) Inverness. (Outer Hebrides) (Western Isles) 401 Z 10 – pop. 2 137.

See : St. Clement's Church, Rodel (tomb★).

by Caledonian MacBrayne : from Kyles Scalpay to the Isle of Scalpay : 6-12 daily (10 mn) – from Tarbert to Uig (Isle of Skye) summer only : 2-4 daily (1 h 45 mn) – from Tarbert to Lochmaddy (Isle of Uist) : Monday/Saturday 1-2 weekly.

Scarista – ✉ ☎ 085 985 Scarista

Scarista House, PA85 3HX, from Tarbert, SW : 15 m. on A 859 ☎ 238, ≤ beach and mountains, – rest ☎ P
May-September – **M** *(closed lunch to non-residents)* (booking essential) (bar lunch)/dinner 22.50 **st.** 4.50 – **7 rm** 50.00/80.00 **st.**

Tarbert – pop. 479 – ECD : Thursday – ✉ ☎ 0859 Harris.

☎ 2011 (summer only).

Harris, PA85 3DL, ☎ 2154, Fax 2281, – rest P. VISA
M 7.00/14.50 **t.** 3.10 – **24 rm** 26.00/55.00 **st.** – SB (except June-August) (weekends only) 58.50/66.40 **st.**

Prices — For full details of the prices quoted in the guide, consult the introduction.

HAWICK Roxburgh. (Borders) 401 402 L 17 **Scotland G** – pop. 16 213 – ECD : Tuesday – ☎ 0450.

Envir. : Jedburgh★ (Abbey★★-Mary Queen of Scots House★-Canongate Bridge★) NE : 11 m. by A 698 and B 6358 – Waterloo Monument (※★★) NE : 12 m. by A 698, A 68 and B 6400 – Hermitage Castle★, S : 16 m. by B 6399.

Vertish Hill ☎ 72293, S : 1½ m.

Common Haugh Car Park ☎ 72547 (summer only).

Edinburgh 51 – ◆Ayr 122 – ◆Carlisle 44 – ◆Dumfries 63 – Motherwell 76 – ◆Newcastle-upon-Tyne 62.

Kirklands, West Stewart Pl., TD9 8BH, ☎ 72263, – TV ☎ P. AE VISA
M 11.00/13.50 **st.** and a la carte 3.50 – **13 rm** 35.00/60.00 **t.** – SB (except summer) (weekends only) 52.00/55.00 **st.**

at ***Newmill*** SW : 4 m. on A 7 – ✉ ☎ 0450 Hawick :

X **Old Forge,** TD9 0JU, ☎ 85298 – P. VISA
closed Sunday, Monday, 2 weeks May and 2 weeks November – **M** (dinner only) 13.95 **st.** 4.25.

PEUGEOT-TALBOT 29 Commercial Rd ☎ 72287
VW-AUDI Commercial Rd ☎ 73211
ATS Victoria Rd ☎ 73369

HEITON Roxburgh. (Borders) – see Kelso.

HELENSBURGH Dunbarton. (Strathclyde) 401 F 15 – pop. 16 432 – ECD : Wednesday – ☎ 0436.

See : Hill House★.

Envir. : Loch Lomond★★, NE : 5 m. by B 832.

by Caledonian MacBrayne and Clyde Marine Motoring Co. Ltd. to Gourock via Kilcreggan : 7 daily (except Sunday).

The Clock Tower, ☎ 72642 (summer only).

Edinburgh 68 – ◆Glasgow 22.

Commodore Toby, 112 West Clyde St., G84 8ER, ☎ 76924, Telex 778740, ≤ – TV ☎ P – 180. AE VISA
M 7.95/15.00 **st.** – **45 rm** 51.00/71.00 **st.**, **1 suite.**

at Rhu NW : 2 m. on A 814 – ✉ ☎ 0436 Rhu :

Rosslea Hall (Best Western) ⛰, Ferry Rd, G84 8NF, ✆ 820684, Telex 77869 Fax 820897, ≤, 🌳 – 📺 ☎ ♿ 🅟 – 🏛 100. 💳 AE ⓓ VISA
M 13.00/15.00 **t.** and a la carte 🍷 4.00 – **31 rm** ☕ 59.00/75.00 **t.** – SB 90.00/100.00 **st.**

RENAULT 103 East Clyde St. ✆ 76021 TOYOTA 5-7 John Street ✆ 72779

HILLSWICK Shetland. (Shetland Islands) 401 P 2 – see Shetland Islands (Mainland).

HOY (Isle of) Orkney. (Orkney Islands) 401 K 7 – see Orkney Islands.

INSCH Aberdeen. (Grampian) 401 M 11 – ☎ 0464.

♦Edinburgh 55 – ♦Aberdeen 55.

Leslie Castle ⛰, Leslie, AB5 6NX, SW : 4 ¼ m. by B 992 ✆ 20869, « 17C fortified baronial house » – 📺 ☎ 🅟. 💳 AE VISA. ✱
M (communal dining) (lunch by arrangement)/dinner 22.00 **t.** 🍷 4.00 – **5 rm** ☕ 80.00/110.00 **st.**

INVERCRERAN Argyll. (Strathclyde) 401 E 14 – ✉ ☎ 063 173 Appin.

♦Edinburgh 142 – Fort William 29 – ♦Oban 19.

Invercreran Country House ⛰, Glen Creran, PA38 4BJ, ✆ 414, Fax 532, ≤ Glen Creran and mountains, ≘s, 🌳, park – ⇔ 📺 ☎ 🅟. 💳 VISA. ✱
March-October – **M** 20.00/22.50 **st.** 🍷 5.00 – **7 rm** ☕ 47.50/125.00 **st.**

INVERMORISTON Inverness. (Highland) 401 G 12 – ☎ 0320 Glenmoriston.

See : Loch Ness★★.

♦Edinburgh 168 – ♦Inverness 29 – Kyle of Lochalsh 56.

Glenmoriston Arms, IV3 6YA, ✆ 51206, 🎣 – 📺 ☎ 🅟. 💳 VISA
M (bar lunch)/dinner 15.00 **st.** and a la carte 🍷 3.95 – **8 rm** ☕ 30.00/56.00 **st.** – SB (October-May) 77.00 **st.**

INVERNESS Inverness. (Highland) 401 H 11 **Scotland G** – pop. 38 204 – ECD : Wednesday – ☎ 0463.

See : Site★ – Museum and Art Gallery★ **M.**

Envir. : Loch Ness★★ by A 82 – Loch Ness Monster Exhibition★ – Cawdor Castle★, E : 14 m. by A 82, A 96 and B 9090 – Clava Cairns★, E : 10 m. by B 9006 – Culloden Moor, E : 6 m. by B 9006 – Fortrose (Cathedral Site★) N : 16 m. by B 865, A 9 and A 832.

⛳18 ✆ 239882, S : 1 m. by Culcabock Rd.
⛳18 Torvean, Glenurquhart Rd ✆ 237543, W : 1 m.

✈ Dalcross Airport : ✆ 232471, NE : 8 m. by A 96.

🚗 ✆ 0345 090700.

ℹ 23 Church St. ✆ 234353.

♦Edinburgh 156 – ♦Aberdeen 107 – ♦Dundee 134.

Plan opposite

Kingsmills (Swallow), Culcabock Rd, IV2 3LP, ✆ 237166, Telex 75566, Fax 225208, ≘s, 🏊, 🌳 – ⇔ rm 📺 ☎ 🅟. 💳 AE ⓓ VISA
M 15.00/16.75 **st.** and a la carte 🍷 6.50 – **32 rm** ☕ 64.00/104.00 **st.**, **6 suites** 120.00/195.00 **st.** – SB (weekends only) 95.00/108.00 **st.**

Caledonian, 33 Church St., IV1 1DX, ✆ 235181, Telex 75232, Fax 711206, 🏋, ≘s, 🏊 – 📺 ☎ 🅟 – 🏛 200. 💳 AE ⓓ VISA
M 7.25/26.90 **st.** and a la carte 🍷 4.45 – ☕ 7.00 – **96 rm** 64.00/86.00 **st.**, **4 suites** 86.00/129.00 **st.** – SB 65.00/96.00 **st.**

Craigmonie (Best Western), 9 Annfield Rd, IV2 3HX, ✆ 231649, Telex 9401330 Fax 233720, 🏋, ≘s, 🏊 – 🛗 📺 ☎ 🅟 – 🏛 140. 💳 AE ⓓ VISA
M 9.95/17.00 **t.** and a la carte 🍷 5.00 – **32 rm** ☕ 58.00/98.00 **t.**, **3 suites** 125.00/180.00 **t.** – SB (weekends only) (except Christmas and New Year) 96.00/116.00 **st.**

Glenmoriston, 20 Ness Bank, IV2 4SF, ✆ 223777 – 📺 ☎ 🅟. 💳 AE VISA. ✱
M (lunch by arrangement)/dinner 18.50 **st.** and a la carte 🍷 3.85 – **19 rm** ☕ 42.50/70.00 **st.** – SB (winter only) (weekends only) 80.00/110.00 **st.**

Glendruidh House ⛰, Old Edinburgh Rd, IV1 2AA, SW : 2 m. ✆ 226499, 🌳 – ⇔ 📺 🅟. 💳 AE ⓓ VISA. ✱
M (residents only) 13.00/15.00 **st.** and a la carte 🍷 4.00 – **7 rm** ☕ 45.00/55.00 **st.**

Ballifeary House, 10 Ballifeary Rd, IV3 5PJ, ✆ 235572, 🌳 – ⇔ 📺 🅟. ✱
Mid March-mid October – **M** 10.00 **st.** 🍷 3.50 – **8 rm** ☕ 23.00/46.00 **st.**

Firs without rest., Dores Rd, IV2 4QU, S : 1 ¼ m. on B 862 ✆ 225197, ≤, « Antique furnishings », 🌳 – ⇔ 🅟. ✱
5 rm ☕ 35.00/50.00 **st.**

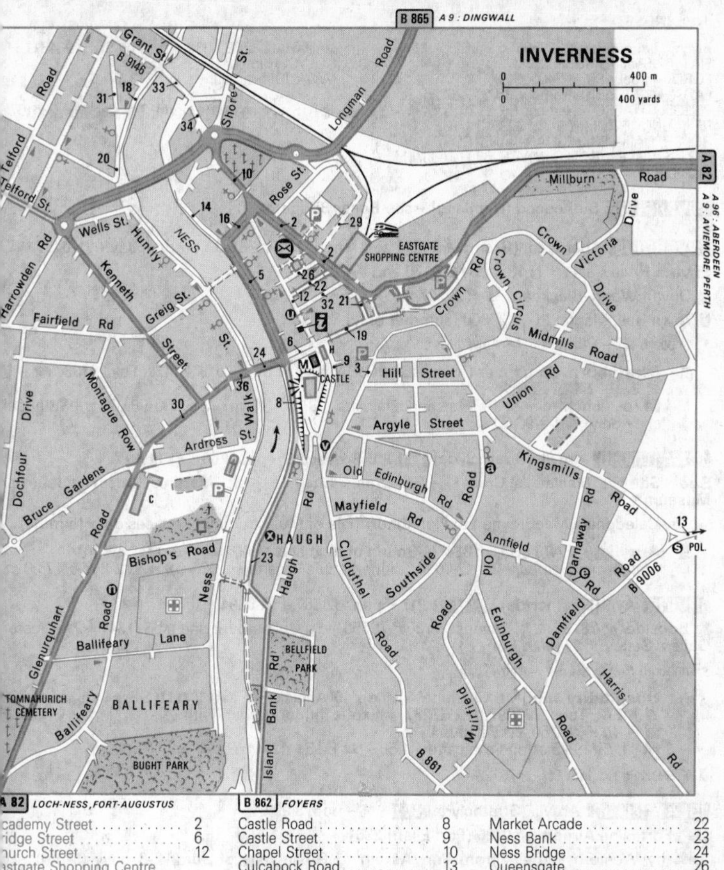

cademy Street	2	Castle Road	8	Market Arcade	22
ridge Street	6	Castle Street	9	Ness Bank	23
hurch Street	12	Chapel Street	10	Ness Bridge	24
astgate Shopping Centre		Culcabock Road	13	Queensgate	26
igh Street	19	Douglas Row	14	Strothers Lane	29
nion Street	32	Friars Lane	16	Tomnahurich Street	30
		Gilbert Street	18	Waterloo Bridge	33
rdconnel Street	3	Huntly Place	20	Waterloo Place	34
ank Street	5	Inglis Street	21	Young Street	36

⌂ **Craigside Lodge,** 4 Gordon Terr., IV2 3HD, ☎ 231576, ≤ – ⇔ TV. ✱ **v**
M (by arrangement) 8.00 **st.** – **6 rm** ☐ 16.00/32.00 **st.**

⌂ **Old Rectory,** 9 Southside Rd, IV2 3BG, ☎ 220969, ✿ – ⇔ **P**. ✱ **a**
closed 20 December-3 January – **M** by arrangement 8.00 – **4 rm** ☐ 24.00/30.00 **s.**

at Culloden E : 3 m. by A 96 – ✉ ☎ 0463 Inverness :

Culloden House ⛰, IV1 2NZ, ☎ 790461, Telex 75402, Fax 792181, ≤, ≋s, ✿, park, ✱ – TV ☎ **P**. AE ① VISA
M 29.50 **t.** (dinner) and a la carte 13.10/26.00 **t.** 🍷 3.50 – **19 rm** ☐ 95.00/155.00 **t.**, **1 suite** 165.00 **t.** – SB (November-April) 150.00 **st.**

at Dunain Park SW : 2 ½ m. on A 82 – ✉ ☎ 0463 Inverness :

Dunain Park ⛰, IV3 6JN, ☎ 230512, Fax 224532, ≤, « Country house and gardens », ≋s, ▢, park – ⇔ rest TV ☎ **P**. AE ① VISA
M (dinner only) 25.00 **t.** 🍷 3.50 – **6 rm** ☐ 80.00/110.00 **t.**, **2 suites** 110.00/130.00 **t.**

at Bunchrew W : 3 m. on A 862 – ✉ ☎ 0463 Inverness :

Bunchrew House ⛰, IV3 6TA, ☎ 234917, ≤ Beauly Firth, « 17C mansion », ⛰, ✿, park – ⇔ rest TV ☎ **P**. AE VISA. ✱
M 9.50/19.50 **t.** 🍷 3.50 – **6 rm** ☐ 55.00/105.00 **t.** – SB 102.00/150.00 **st.**

P.T.O. →

BMW Harbour Rd ℘ 236566
FIAT 62 Seafield Rd ℘ 235777
FORD Harbour Rd ℘ 710000
LADA, MITSUBISHI Harbour Rd ℘ 226226
PEUGEOT-TALBOT Harbour Rd ℘ 231536
RENAULT 16 Telford St. ℘ 222848
ROVER, DAIMLER-JAGUAR, LAND-ROVER, RANGE-ROVER, ROLLS-ROYCE 66 Harbour Rd ℘ 220011
VAUXHALL-OPEL 112 Academy St. ℘ 234311
VOLVO Harbour Rd ℘ 230885
VW-AUDI Harbour Rd ℘ 231313

ATS Carsegate Rd North, The Carse ℘ 236167

INVERSHIN Sutherland (Highland) – see Bonar Bridge.

INVERURIE Aberdeen. (Grampian) 401 M 12 – pop. 7 701 – ECD : Wednesday – 0467.

Envir. : Fyvie Castle★ N 13 m. by B 9170 and A 47.

18 Davah Wood, Blackhall Rd ℘ 20207.

Town Hall, Market Pl. ℘ 20600 (summer only).

♦Edinburgh 147 – ♦Aberdeen 17 – ♦Inverness 90.

Strathburn, Burghmuir Drive, AB5 9GY, NW : 1 ¼ by A 96 ℘ 24422, Fax 25133, – ☎ ♿ P. AE VISA.
M (bar lunch)/dinner 22.75 **st.** and a la carte 3.25 – **15 rm** 33.00/58.00 **st.** – SB (weekends only) 72.00/90.00 **st.**

IONA (Isle of) Argyll. (Strathclyde) 401 A 15 **Scotland G** – pop. 268 – 068 17.

See : Site★ – Maclean's Cross★ – St. Oran's Chapel★ – St. Martin's Cross★ – Infirmary Museum★.

by Caledonian MacBrayne : to Fionnphort (Isle of Mull) frequent services daily (5 mn).

Argyll, PA76 6SJ, ℘ 334, ≤ Sound of Iona and Mull, – rest. VISA
March-mid October – **M** 12.00 **st.** (dinner) and a la carte 3.50 – **19 rm** 34.00/77.00 **st.**

IRVINE Ayr. (Strathclyde) 401 402 F 17 – pop. 32 507 – 0294.

18 Bogside ℘ 78139 – 18 Ravens Park ℘ 79550 – 18 Gailes-by-Irvine ℘ 311347 – 18 Western Gailes, Gailes ℘ 311649.

♦Edinburgh 75 – Ayr 14 – ♦Glasgow 29.

Hospitality Inn (Mt. Charlotte Thistle), 46 Annick Rd, KA11 4LD, SE : 1 m. on B 708 ℘ 74272, Telex 777097, Fax 77287, « Exotic indoor garden with », , 9 – rm ☎ ♿ P – 250. AE VISA
M 11.75/19.25 **st.** and a la carte 4.50 – 6.95 – **127 rm** 65.00/92.00 **st.**

ATS 9 Kyle Rd, Ind. Est. ℘ 78727

ISLAY (Isle of) Argyll. (Strathclyde) 401 B 16 – pop. 3 997.

Port Ellen Airport: ℘ 0496 (Port Ellen) 2361.

by Western Ferries : from Port Askaig to Feolin (Isle of Jura) 2-8 daily (5-mn) – by Caledonian MacBrayne : from Port Ellen to Kennacraig (Kintyre Peninsula) 1-2 daily – from Port Askaig to Kennacraig (Kintyre Peninsula) Monday/Saturday 1-2 daily.

at Bowmore, The Square ℘ 049 681 (Bowmore) 254.

Port Askaig – ECD : Tuesday – ✉ 049 684 Port Askaig.

Port Askaig, PA46 7RD, ℘ 245, Fax 295, ≤ Sound of Islay and Jura, – TV P
M 6.50/12.00 **st.** 3.95 – **9 rm** 25.00/50.00 **st.** – SB 64.00/70.00 **st.**

ISLEORNSAY Inverness. (Highland) 401 C 12 – see Skye (Isle of).

JEDBURGH Roxburgh. (Borders) 401 402 M 17 **Scotland G** – pop. 4 053 – ECD : Thursday – 0835.

See : Site★ – Abbey★★ – Mary Queen of Scots House★ – Canongate Bridge★.

Envir. : Waterloo Monument (※★★) N : 3 m. by A 68 and B 6400.

9 Dunion Rd ℘ 63587, W : 1 m.

Murray's Green ℘ 63435/63688.

♦Edinburgh 48 – ♦Carlisle 54 – ♦Newcastle-upon-Tyne 57.

Glenfriars, The Friars, TD8 6BN, ℘ 62000, – TV P. AE VISA
M (lunch by arrangement)/dinner 14.00 **st.** 3.50 – **6 rm** 30.00/60.00 **st.** – SB (except Christmas and New Year) 75.00/83.00 **st.**

Spinney without rest., Langlee, TD8 6PB, S : 2 m. on A 68 ℘ 63525, – P.
March-October – **3 rm** 31.00 **st.**

JOHN O'GROATS Caithness. (Highland) 401 K 8 – Shipping Services : see Orkney Islands.

JURA (Isle of) Argyll. (Strathclyde) 401 C 15 – pop. 239.

by Western Ferries : from Feolin to Port Askaig (Isle of Islay) 2-8 daily (5-mn).

Craighouse – ECD : Tuesday – ✉ 049 682 Jura.

Jura, PA60 7XU, 243, ≤ Small Isles Bay, – **16 rm, 1 suite.**

KELSO Roxburgh. (Borders) 401 402 M 17 **Scotland G** – pop. 5 547 – ECD : Wednesday – 0573.

See : Site★ – Market Square★★ – ≤★ from Kelso Bridge.

Envir. : Mellerstain★★ (ceilings★★★-Library★★★) NW : 6 m. by A 6089 – Floors Castle★, NW : m. by A 6089 – Smailholm Tower★ (★★) NW : 6 m. by A 6089 and B 6397 – Ladykirk (Kirk o'Steil★) NE : 16 m. by A 698, A 697, A 6112 and B 6437 – Flodden Field, NE : 11 m. by A 698 and A 697.

Racecourse Rd 23009.

Turret House 23464 (summer only).

Edinburgh 44 – Hawick 21 – ◆Newcastle-upon-Tyne 68.

Ednam House, Bridge St., TD5 7HT, 24168, Fax 26319, ≤, – TV ☎ P. VISA
closed 24 December-9 January – **M** (bar lunch Monday to Saturday)/dinner 15.50 **t.** 3.50 – **32 rm** 36.00/73.00 **t.**

at Heiton SW : 3 m. by A 698 – ✉ Kelso – 057 35 Roxburgh :

Sunlaws House, TD5 8JZ, 331, Telex 728147, Fax 611, ≤, « Victorian country house », park, – TV ☎ P. AE VISA.
M 15.50/25.00 **t.** and a la carte 5.50 – **22 rm** 60.00/145.00 **t.** – SB (except September-November, Christmas and New Year) 125.00/140.00 **st.**

at Eckford SW : 4½ m. by A 698 – ✉ Kelso – 057 34 Morebattle :

XX **Marlefield Country House** with rm, TD5 8ED, NE : 2 m. on B 6401 561, Fax 393, ≤, – rest TV ☎ P. VISA.
M (dinner only and Sunday lunch in winter)/dinner 13.50 **t.** and a la carte – **6 rm** 50.00/65.00 **t.**

PEUGEOT-TALBOT Sheddon Par. Rd 24488
RENAULT Golf Course Rd 24720
ROVER, JAGUAR Bridge St. 24345
ATS The Butts 24997/8

KENMORE Perth. (Tayside) 401 I 14 – ECD : Thursday except summer – ✉ Aberfeldy – 088 73.

See : Site★.

Envir. : Loch Tay★★ – Ben Lawers★★, SW : 8 m. by A 827.

Taymouth Castle 228.

Edinburgh 82 – ◆Dundee 60 – ◆Oban 71 – Perth 38.

Kenmore, PH15 2NU, 205, Fax 262, 18, – rest TV ☎ P. AE VISA.
M 12.00/16.95 **t.** 3.95 – **38 rm** 40.00/70.00 **st.** – SB (weekends only) (November-March) 60.00 **st.**

KENNACRAIG Argyll. (Strathclyde) 401 D 16 – Shipping Services : see Kintyre (Peninsula).

KENSALEYRE Inverness. (Highland) 401 B 11 – see Skye (Isle of).

KENTALLEN Argyll. (Highland) 401 E 14 – 063 174 Duror.

Edinburgh 123 – Fort William 17 – ◆Oban 33.

Ardsheal House, PA38 4BX, SW : ¾ m. by A 828 227, Fax 342, ≤, « Country house in lochside setting », park, – rest P. VISA
Easter-October – **M** 15.00/28.00 **t.** – **13 rm** 48.00/92.00 **t.**

XX **Holly Tree** with rm, Kentallen Pier, PA38 4BY, 292, Fax 345, ≤ Loch Linnhe and mountains, – rest TV ☎ P. AE VISA
closed mid January-mid February and mid November-mid December – **M** 12.50/25.00 **t.** and a la carte – **10 rm** 63.00/118.00 **t.** – SB (winter only) 110.00 **st.**

KILCHOAN Argyll. (Highland) 401 B 13 – ✉ Acharacle – 097 23.

by Caledonian MacBrayne : to Tobermory (Isle of Mull) summer only Monday/Saturday 6 daily (35 mn).

Edinburgh 163 – ◆Inverness 120 – ◆Oban 92.

***En saison,** surtout dans les stations fréquentées, il est prudent de retenir à l'avance.*
Cependant, si vous ne pouvez pas occuper la chambre que vous avez retenue, prévenez immédiatement l'hôtelier.
Si vous écrivez à un hôtel à l'étranger, joignez à votre lettre un coupon-réponse international (disponible dans les bureaux de poste).

KILCHRENAN Argyll. (Strathclyde) 401 E 14 – ✉ Taynuilt – ☎ 086 63.
♦Edinburgh 117 – ♦Glasgow 87 – ♦Oban 18.

Ardanaiseig ⛰, PA35 1HE, NE : 4 m. ☎ 333, Fax 222, ≤ gardens and Loch Awe « Country house in extensive informal gardens on Loch Awe », park, – TV ☎ AE VISA
Mid April-late October – **M** 20.00/31.00 **st.** – **14 rm** (dinner included) 88.00/210.00 **t.** SB 136.00/192.00 **st.**

Taychreggan ⛰, Lochaweside, PA35 1HQ, SE : 1 ¼ m. ☎ 211, Fax 244, ≤ Loch Awe « Lochside setting », park – ☎ P
March-October – **M** (bar lunch)/dinner 25.00 **t.** 6.00 – **16 rm** 50.00/69.00 **t.**

KILCREGGAN Dunbarton. (Strathclyde) 401 F 16 – Shipping Services : see Gourock.

KILDRUMMY Aberdeen. (Grampian) 401 L 12 **Scotland G** – ✉ Alford – ☎ 097 55.
See : Castle★.
Envir. : Craigievar Castle★★★, SE : 13 m. by A 944 and A 980 – Huntly Castle (Heraldic carvings★★) N : 15 m. by A 97.
♦Edinburgh 137 – ♦Aberdeen 35.

Kildrummy Castle (Best Western) ⛰, AB3 8RA, S : 1 ¼ m. on A 97 ☎ 71288, Telex 94012529, Fax 71345, ≤ gardens and Kildrummy Castle, « 19C mansion in extensive park », – rest TV ☎ P. AE VISA
M 13.50/20.00 **t.** and a la carte 4.25 – **16 rm** 49.00/90.00 **t.** – SB (except summer) 90.00/130.00 **st.**

KILFINAN Argyll. (Strathclyde) 401 E 16 – ✉ Tighnabruaich – ☎ 070 082.
♦Edinburgh 124 – ♦Glasgow 78 – ♦Oban 78.

Kilfinan ⛰ with rm, Tighnabruaich, PA21 2AP, ☎ 201, Fax 205, – TV ☎ P. AE VISA
M (bar lunch)/dinner 26.00 **t.** and a la carte 4.20 – **11 rm** 35.00/48.00 **t.**

KILLIECRANKIE Perth. (Tayside) 401 I 13 – see Pitlochry.

KILLIN Perth. (Central) 401 H 14 – pop. 545 – ECD : Wednesday – ☎ 056 72.
Envir. : Loch Tay★★, Ben Lawers★★, NE : 8 m. by A 827 – Kenmore★, NE : 17 m. by A 827.
9 ☎ 312.
Main St. ☎ 254 (summer only).
♦Edinburgh 72 – ♦Dundee 65 – Perth 43 – ♦Oban 54.

Morenish Lodge ⛰, FK21 8TX, NE : 2 ½ m. on A 827 ☎ 258, ≤ Loch Tay and hills, – P. VISA.
Easter-October – **M** *(closed lunch to non-residents)* (bar lunch)/dinner 15.00 **t.** 3.20 – **13 rm** 24.00/48.00 **t.**

Fairview House, Main St., FK21 8UT, ☎ 667 – P
M 7.00 – **7 rm** 12.00/28.00 **t.**

at Ardeonaig NE : 7 ¼ m. – ✉ ☎ 056 72 Killin :

Ardeonaig ⛰, South Loch Tayside, FK21 8SU, ☎ 400, park – P. AE VISA
closed November and December – **M** (bar lunch)/dinner 17.50 **t.** 3.25 – **12 rm** 25.00/50.00 **t.** – SB 70.00/80.00 **st.**

KILMARNOCK Ayr. (Strathclyde) 401 402 G 17 **Scotland G** – pop. 51 799 – ECD : Wednesday – ☎ 0563.
See : Dean Castle (Arms and armour collection★ – musical instruments★).
18 Annanhill, Irvine Rd ☎ 21644, W : 1 m. – 18 Caprington, Ayr Rd ☎ 21915.
62 Bank St., ☎ 39090.
♦Edinburgh 62 – ♦Ayr 13 – ♦Dumfries 58 – ♦Glasgow 22.

Howard Park (Swallow), 136 Glasgow Rd, KA3 1UT, N : 2 m. on B 7038 ☎ 31211, Group Telex 53168, Fax 27795 – rm TV ☎ P – 150
46 rm.

ATS Riccarton Rd, Hurlford ☎ 20111

KILNINVER Argyll. (Strathclyde) 401 D 14 – see Oban.

KINCLAVEN Perth. (Tayside) 401 J 14 – ✉ Stanley – ☎ 025 083 Meikleour.
♦Edinburgh 56 – Perth 12.

Ballathie House (Best Western) ⛰, PH1 4QN, ☎ 268, Telex 76216, Fax 396, ≤, « Country house in extensive grounds on banks of River Tay », park, – TV ☎ P. AE VISA.
closed 17 February-1 March – **M** 12.50/22.00 **t.** and a la carte 4.40 – **27 rm** 47.00/125.00 **t.**, **1 suite** 115.00/150.00 **t.**

KINCRAIG Inverness. (Highland) 401 I 12 – ECD : Wednesday – ✉ Kingussie – ☎ 054 04.
Edinburgh 119 – ◆Inverness 37 – Perth 75.

- **Ossian,** PH21 1NA, ☎ 242, ←, ↘, 🌳 – Ⓟ. AE VISA
  closed January and November – **M** (bar lunch)/dinner 15.00 **st.** and a la carte 🌡 3.50 – **9 rm** ▭ 24.00/48.00 **st.**

KINGUSSIE Inverness. (Highland) 401 H 12 – pop. 1 140 – ECD : Wednesday – ☎ 0540.
☎ 661374, N : ½ m. from town shops by A 9.
King St. ☎ (054 02) 297 (summer only).
Edinburgh 117 – ◆Inverness 41 – Perth 73.

- **Osprey,** Ruthven Rd, PH21 1EN, ☎ 661510 – Ⓟ. AE ⓓ VISA
  closed November and December – **M** (dinner only) 20.00 **st.** 🌡 3.75 – **8 rm** ▭ 25.00/70.00 **st.**
- **Homewood Lodge,** Newtonmore Rd, PH21 1HD, ☎ 661507, ←, 🌳 – ⇎ Ⓟ
  closed Christmas – **M** 13.95 **st.** – **4 rm** ▭ 20.95/34.95 **st.**
- XX **The Cross** with rm, 25-27 High St., PH21 1HX, ☎ 661762 – ⇎. ✻
  closed Sunday, Monday, 3 weeks May and 4 weeks November-December – **M** (booking essential) (dinner only) 29.50 **st.** 🌡 2.50 – **3 rm** ▭ (dinner included) 55.00/110.00 **st.**

KINLOCHBERVIE Sutherland. (Highland) 401 E 8 – ECD : Wednesday – ✉ Lairg – ☎ 097 182.
Envir. : Cape Wrath★★★ (✻★★) SE : 28½ m. by B 801 and A 838.
Edinburgh 276 – Thurso 93 – Ullapool 61.

- **Kinlochbervie** ⑤, IV27 4RP, ☎ 275, Fax 438, ← Loch Inchard and sea – ⇎ rest TV ☎ Ⓟ. AE ⓓ VISA
  restricted service January-February – **M** (booking essential) 25.00 **st.** (dinner) and a la carte 🌡 3.40 – **14 rm** ▭ 50.00/70.00 **st.** – SB 110.50/130.00 **st.**
- **Old School** ⑤, Inshegra, IV27 4RH, SE : 1½ m. ☎ 383, ← – TV ☎ Ⓟ. VISA
  M 12.10 **t.** 🌡 2.50 – **6 rm** ▭ 20.00/40.00 **t.**

"Short Breaks"

Many hotels now offer a special rate for a stay of 2 nights which includes dinner, bed and breakfast.

KINROSS Kinross. (Tayside) 401 J 15 – pop. 3 493 – ECD : Thursday – ☎ 0577.
Green Hotel, ☎ 63467 – 18 Beeches Park ☎ 62237 – 9 Milnathort ☎ 64069, N : 2 m.
Kinross Service Area (off junction 6, M 90) ☎ 63680 (summer only).
Edinburgh 28 – Dunfermline 13 – Perth 18 – Stirling 25.

- **Windlestrae,** The Muirs, KY13 7AS, ☎ 63217, Fax 64733, 🌳 – TV ☎ Ⓟ – 🎪 70. AE ⓓ VISA
  M 10.95/18.50 **t.** and a la carte 🌡 5.25 – **18 rm** ▭ 50.00/70.00 **t.** – SB (October-April) 96.00/106.00 **st.**
- **Green** (Best Western), 2 The Muirs, KY13 7AS, ☎ 63467, Telex 76684, Fax 63180, « Gardens », Ⅎ₆, ≘s, ☒, 18, ↘, squash – TV ☎ Ⓟ – 🎪 120. AE ⓓ VISA
  M (bar lunch)/dinner 16.00 **t.** and a la carte 🌡 4.50 – **40 rm** ▭ 53.00/80.00 **t.** – SB (except Christmas and New Year) 90.00/115.00 **st.**
- **Granada Lodge** without rest., Kincardine Rd, KY13 7NQ, W : 1 m. by A 922 on A 977 ☎ 64646, Fax 64108 – ⇎ TV ☎ ♿ Ⓟ. AE ⓓ VISA. ✻
  35 rm 27.50/29.50 **t.**

at Cleish SW : 4½ m. by B 996 off B 9097 – ✉ Kinross – ☎ 057 75 Cleish Hills :

- **Nivingston House** ⑤, KY13 7LS, ☎ 216, Fax 238, ←, 🌳 – TV ☎ Ⓟ. AE VISA
  M 16.00/28.00 **st.** 🌡 5.00 – **17 rm** ▭ 55.00/110.00 **st.**

FORD High St. ☎ 62424

KINTYRE (Peninsula) Argyll. (Strathclyde) 401 D 16 17 **Scotland G.**
See : Carradale★ – Saddell (grave stones★).
✈ at Campbeltown (Machrihanish Airport) : ☎ 0586 (Campbeltown) 53021.
⛴ by Caledonian MacBrayne : from Claonaig to Lochranza (Isle of Arran) summer only 8-10 daily (30 mn) – from Kennacraig to Port Ellen (Isle of Islay) 1-2 daily – from Kennacraig to Port Askaig (Isle of Islay) Monday/Saturday 1-2 daily.

Campbeltown – ECD : Wednesday – ✉ ☎ 0586 Campbeltown.
ℹ ☎ 52056.
◆Edinburgh 176.

- **Seafield,** Kilkerran Rd, PA28 6JL, ☎ 54385, 🌳 – TV ☎ Ⓟ. VISA
  M 17.50 **st.** 🌡 4.00 – **9 rm** ▭ 27.50/44.00 **t.**

ATS Burnside St. ☎ 54404

Carradale – ECD : Wednesday – ✉ ☎ 058 33 Carradale.

9 ℘ 387.

♦Edinburgh 164 – ♦Glasgow 121 – ♦Oban 74.

Carradale, PA28 6RY, ℘ 223, ≤, sauna, garden, squash – TV P. VISA
March-October – **M** 9.00/18.50 **st.** 4.50 – **15 rm** 41.00/62.00 **st.** – SB (except March) 76.00/96.00 **st.**

Machrihanish – pop. 540 – ✉ Campbeltown – ☎ 058 681 Machrihanish.

18, 9 ℘ 213.

Ardell House, PA28 6PT, ℘ 235, ≤, garden – TV P
closed November-February – **M** 15.00 **t.** 6.00 – **10 rm** 24.00/60.00 **t.**

KIRKCALDY Fife. (Fife) 401 K 15 **Scotland G** – pop. 46 356 – ECD : Wednesday – ☎ 0592.

18 Balwearie Rd ℘ 260370 – 18 Dunnikier Park, Dunnikier Way ℘ 261599, North boundary.

Esplanade ℘ 267775 (summer only).

♦Edinburgh 27 – ♦Dundee 32 – ♦Glasgow 54.

at West Wemyss NE : 4½ m. by A 955 – ✉ ☎ 0592 Kirkcaldy :

Belvedere , Coxstool, KY1 4SN, ℘ 54167, ≤ – TV ☎ P. VISA.
closed 25 December-8 January – **M** *(closed Sunday)* 13.50/16.50 **t.** – **20 rm** 39.00/50.00 **t.**, **1 suite** 58.00 **t.**

BMW Bennochy Rd ℘ 262191
CITROEN, VAUXHALL-OPEL 24 Victoria Rd ℘ 264755
FORD Forth Av. ℘ 261199
HYUNDAI, SUZUKI Meldrum Rd ℘ 200354
ROVER, JAGUAR 27 Rosslyn St. ℘ 51997
SAAB 180-186 St. Clair St. ℘ 52291
VOLVO 8 Abbotshall Rd ℘ 262141

KIRKCUDBRIGHT Kirkcudbright. (Dumfries and Galloway) 401 402 H 19 **Scotland G** – pop. 3 352 – ECD : Thursday – ☎ 0557.

See : Site★. **Envir.** : Dundrennan Abbey★, SE : 5 m. by A 711.

18 Stirling Cres. ℘ 30542.

Harbour Sq. ℘ 30494 (summer only).

♦Edinburgh 108 – ♦Dumfries 28 – Stranraer 50.

Selkirk Arms, Old High St., DG6 4JG, ℘ 30402, Fax 31639, garden – TV ☎ P. AE VISA
M 13.75 **st.** (dinner) and a la carte 9.65/22.50 **st.** 2.80 – **15 rm** 36.50/65.00 **st.** – SB (except Christmas and New Year) 84.00/90.00 **st.**

ROVER Mews Lane ℘ 30412

KIRKMICHAEL Perth. (Tayside) 401 J 13 – ✉ Blairgowrie – ☎ 025 081 Strathardle.

♦Edinburgh 74 – Perth 30 – Pitlochry 12.

Log Cabin , Blairgowrie, PH10 7NB, W : 1 m. ℘ 288, ≤, « Scandinavian pine chalet » – P. AE VISA
M (bar lunch Monday to Saturday)/dinner 15.95 **t.** – **12 rm** 32.95/45.90 **t.**

KIRKWALL Orkney. (Orkney Islands) 401 L 7 – see Orkney Islands (Mainland).

KYLEAKIN Inverness. (Highland) 401 C 12 – Shipping Services : see Skye (Isle of).

KYLE OF LOCHALSH Ross and Cromarty. (Highland) 401 C 12 **Scotland G** – pop. 803 – ECD : Thursday – ☎ 0599.

Envir. : Eilean Donan Castle★ (Site★★) E : 8 m. by A 87 – Plockton★, N : 6 m.

by Caledonian MacBrayne : to Kyleakin (Isle of Skye) frequent services daily (5 mn).

by Caledonian MacBrayne : to Mallaig: 3 weekly (summer only) (2 h).

Car Park ℘ 4276 (summer only).

♦Edinburgh 204 – ♦Dundee 182 – ♦Inverness 82 – ♦Oban 125.

Lochalsh, Ferry Rd, IV40 8AF, ℘ 4202, Telex 75318, Fax 4881, ≤ Skye Ferry and hills – TV ☎ P. AE VISA
M 10.00/21.00 **t.** and a la carte 8.50 – **38 rm** 62.00/135.00 **t.** – SB (October-April) (except summer) 79.00 **st.**

FORD Main Rd ℘ 4329

KYLES SCALPAY Inverness. (Western Isles) (Highland) 401 Z 10 – Shipping Services : see Harris (Isle of).

LADYBANK Fife (fife) 401 K 15 – ☎ 0337.

♦Edinburgh 38 – ♦Dundee 20 – ♦Stirling 40.

Redlands Country Lodge , KY7 7SH, E : 1 m. on B 938 ℘ 31091, garden – rest TV P.
closed last week February-first week March – **M** 12.00 **t.** 2.90 – **4 rm** 24.50/40.00 **t.**

AGG Bute. (Strathclyde) – see Arran (Isle of).

AGGAN Inverness. (Highland) 401 H 12 – ✉ Newtonmore – ☎ 052 84.
Edinburgh 110 – ♦Inverness 52 – Perth 66.

Gaskmore House, PH20 1BS, E : ¾ m. on A 86 ☎ 250, Fax 207, ≤ Grampian mountains – ⇔ rest TV ☎ ♿ P. VISA
closed November – **M** 8.50/20.00 **t.** and a la carte 4.40 – **10 rm** 27.50/55.00 **t.**, **1 suite** 65.00 **t.** – SB (October-March) 80.00 **st.**

AIDE Ross and Cromarty. (Highland) 401 D 10 – ✉ Achnasheen – ☎ 044 582 Aultbea.
nvir. : Inverewe Gardens★★★, S : 8 m. by A 832.
Edinburgh 232 – ♦Inverness 76.

Hotel see : Aultbea SW : 1 m.

AIRG Sutherland. (Highland) 401 G9 – pop. 628 – ECD : Wednesday – ☎ 0549.
Edinburgh 218 – ♦Inverness 61 – ♦Wick 72.

Sutherland Arms, IV27 4AT, ☎ 2291, Fax 2261, ≤, – TV ☎ P. AE VISA
May-October – **25 rm** 48.00/78.00 **t.**

AMLASH Bute. (Strathclyde) 401 E 17 – see Arran (Isle of).

ANARK Lanark. (Strathclyde) 401 402 I 16 **Scotland G** – pop. 9 673 – ECD : Thursday – ☎ 0555. **See** : New Lanark★.
Horsemarket, Ladyacre Rd ☎ 61661.
Edinburgh 34 – ♦Carlisle 78 – ♦ Glasgow 28.

Ristorante La Vigna, 40 Wellgate, ML11 9DT, ☎ 4320, Italian rest. – AE VISA
closed Sunday lunch, 6 to 12 January and first 3 weeks September – **M** (booking essential) a la carte 14.70/22.60 **t.** 3.95.

TROEN 30 West Port ☎ 2581

ANGBANK Renfrew. (Strathclyde) 401 G 16 – ECD : Saturday – ☎ 047 554.
Edinburgh 63 – ♦Glasgow 17 – Greenock 7.

Gleddoch House ⛰, PA14 6YE, SE : 1 m. by B 789 ☎ 711, Telex 779801, Fax 201, ≤ Clyde and countryside, 18, , park, squash – TV ☎ P. AE VISA
closed 26 to 27 December and 1 to 3 January – **M** *(closed Saturday lunch)* 16.50/32.50 **t.** and a la carte 5.00 – **32 rm** 85.00/125.00 **t.**, **1 suite** 160.00 **t.** – SB (weekends only) 132.00 **st.**

ARGS Ayr. (Strathclyde) 401 402 F 16 **Scotland G** – pop. 9 619 – ECD : Wednesday – ☎ 0475.
ee : Skelmorlie Aisle★ (Monument★ and ceiling★).
Irvine Rd ☎ 673594, S : 1 m. – 18 Routenburn, ☎ 673230.
by Caledonian MacBrayne : to Cumbrae Slip (Great Cumbrae Island) frequent services aily (10 mn).
Promenade ☎ 673765.
Edinburgh 76 – ♦Ayr 32 – ♦Glasgow 30.

Glen Eldon, 2 Barr Cres., KA30 8PX, ☎ 673381 – ⇔ rest TV ☎ P. VISA.
closed mid January-mid March – **M** (dinner only) 10.00 **t.** – **9 rm** 25.00/50.00 **t.**

AUDER Berwick. (Borders) 401 402 L 16 **Scotland G** – pop. 799 – ECD : Thursday – ☎ 057 82.
ee : Thirlestane Castle (Plasterwork ceilings★★).
☎ 409, W : ½ m.
Edinburgh 27 – Hawick 31 – ♦Newcastle-upon-Tyne 78.

Hotels see : Galashiels S : 9 m.

ERWICK Shetland. (Shetland Islands) 401 Q 3 – see Shetland Islands (Mainland).

ESLIE Fife. (Fife) 401 K 15 – see Glenrothes.

EVEN Fife. (Fife) 401 K 15 – pop. 8 596 – ECD : Thursday – ☎ 0333.
Links Rd ☎ 21390 – 18 Leven Municipal ☎ 207057 – 18 Lundin, Golf Rd, Lundin Links 320202. South St. ☎ 29464.
Edinburgh 36 – ♦Dundee 23 – ♦Glasgow 65.

Old Manor, Leven Rd, Lundin Links, KY8 6AJ, E : 2 m. on A 915 ☎ 320368, Telex 727606, Fax 320911, ≤, – TV ☎ P. AE VISA.
M 9.50/15.95 **st.** and a la carte 3.50 – **19 rm** 55.00/75.00 **st.** – SB (weekends only) 100.00 **st.**

AT Scoonie Rd ☎ 27003 ROVER The Promenade ☎ 23449

LEWIS (Isle of) Ross and Cromarty. (Outer Hebrides) (Western Isles) 401 Z 8 **Scotland G.**

See : Callanish Standing Stones★★ – Carloway Broch★.

by Caledonian MacBrayne : from Stornoway to Ullapool Monday/Saturday 1-4 dai (3 h 30 mn).

Uig – ECD : Wednesday – ✉ Uig – ☎ 085 175 Timsgarry.

Baile-Na-Cille, Timsgarry, PA86 9JD, ☎ 242, ≤ Uig bay and mountains, rest ℗
April-mid October – **M** (lunch by arrangement) 15.00/16.00 **st.** 3.75 – **12 rm** (dinner included) 33.00/90.00 **st.**

FORD Sandwick Rd ☎ 5553
ROVER 11-16 Bayhead St. ☎ 3246
VAUXHALL-OPEL Bayhead St. ☎ 2888

LEWISTON Inverness. (Highland) 401 G 12 – ☎ 045 62 Drumnadrochit.

See : Loch Ness★★.

◆Edinburgh 173 – ◆Inverness 17.

Lewiston Arms, IV3 6UN, ☎ 225, – ℗. VISA
M (bar lunch)/dinner a la carte 5.00/13.00 **t.** 3.50 – **8 rm** 15.00/30.00 **t.**

LINLITHGOW W. Lothian. (Lothian) 401 J 16 – pop. 9 524 – ☎ 0506.

See : Site★★ – Linlithgow Palace★★ (gateway★, fountain★★, Great Hall : Fireplace★★) – Ol Town★ – St. Michaels Church★.

Envir. : Cairnpapple Hill★ S : 2 m.

Braehead ☎ 842585, S : 1 m – Avingath Hill ☎ 826030.

Burgh Halls, The Cross ☎ 844600.

◆Edinburgh 19 – Falkirk 9 – ◆Glasgow 35.

XXX **Champany Inn,** Champany, EH49 7LU, NE : 2 m. on A 803 at junction with A 9 ☎ 050 683 (Philipstoun) 4532, Fax 4302, « Converted horse-mill », – ℗. AE VISA
closed Saturday lunch, Sunday and 24 December-12 January – **M** (grill rest.) 13.75 s (lunch) and a la carte 22.00/32.00 **t.** 3.75.

LISMORE (Isle of) Argyll. (Strathclyde) 401 D 14 – pop. 156.

by Caledonian MacBrayne : from Achnacroish to Oban Monday/Saturday 2-4 dai (50 mn).

Hotels see : Oban.

LIVINGSTON Midlothian. (Lothian) 401 J 16 – pop. 38 594 – ☎ 0506.

◆Edinburgh 16 – Falkirk 23 – ◆Glasgow 32.

Hilton National, Almondview, Almondvale, EH54 6QB, ☎ 31222, Telex 727680, Fax 3466 – rm ℗ – 100
120 rm.

LOCHALINE Argyll. (Highland) 401 C 14.

by Caledonian MacBrayne : to Fishnish (Isle of Mull) Monday/Saturday frequent service daily 9 daily (15 mn).

◆Edinburgh 129 – ◆Inverness 109 – Kyle of Lochalsh 116 – ◆Oban 6.

Hotels see : Mull (Isle of).

LOCHBOISDALE Inverness. (Western Isles) 401 Y 12 – Shipping Services-: see Uist (South (Isles of).

LOCHCARRON Ross and Cromarty. (Highland) 401 D 11 **Scotland G** – ECD : Thursday ☎ 052 02.

Envir. : Plockton★, S : 17 m. by A 896 and A 890.

Main St. ☎ 241 (summer only).

◆Edinburgh 221 – ◆Inverness 65 – Kyle of Lochalsh 23.

Lochcarron, IV54 8YS, ☎ 226, ≤ Loch Carron – ☎ ℗. VISA
M 12.00/18.00 **t.** 3.75 – **11 rm** 26.50/57.00 **t.**

LOCHEARNHEAD Perth. (Central) 401 H 14 – ECD : Wednesday – ☎ 056 73.

◆Edinburgh 65 – ◆Glasgow 56 – ◆Oban 57 – Perth 36.

Mansewood Country House, FK19 8NS, S : ½ m. on A 84 ☎ 213, – rest ℗. VISA.
M 10.00 **st.** 3.80 – **8 rm** 18.00/41.50 **st.**

*When in a hurry use the **Michelin Main Road Maps**:*
970 Europe, 980 Greece, 984 Germany, 985 Scandinavia-Finland,
986 Great Britain and Ireland, 987 Germany-Austria-Benelux, 988 Italy,
989 France, 990 Spain-Portugal and 991 Yugoslavia.

LOCHGILPHEAD Argyll. (Strathclyde) 401 D 15 – pop. 2 391 – ECD : Tuesday – ☎ 0546.
Blarbuie Rd ☎ 2340.
Lochnell St. ☎ 2344 (summer only).
Edinburgh 130 – ◆Glasgow 84 – ◆Oban 38.

Stag, Argyll St., PA31 8NE, ☎ 2496 – TV ☎ P. VISA
M (bar lunch) 16.00 **t.** and a la carte 3.50 – **17 rm** 27.50/49.50 **t.** – SB (except summer) (weekends only) 68.85/76.00 **st.**

LOCH HARRAY Orkney. (Orkney Islands) 401 K 6 – see Orkney Islands (Mainland).

LOCHINVER Sutherland. (Highland) 401 E 9 – ECD : Tuesday – ✉ Lairg – ☎ 057 14.
Main St. ☎ 330 (summer only).
Edinburgh 251 – ◆Inverness 95 – ◆Wick 105.

Inver Lodge, IV27 4LU, ☎ 496, Telex 75206, ≤ Lochinver bay, Suilven and Canisp Mountains, park – TV ☎ P. AE VISA
June-mid November – **M** (Bar lunch Monday to Saturday)/dinner 25.00 **st.** 5.00 – **20 rm** 69.00/103.00 **st.** – SB 112.00/138.00 **st.**

Ardglas without rest., Baddidarroch rd, IV27 4LI, ☎ 257, ≤ Loch Inver – P
March-November – **8 rm** 12.00/24.00.

LOCHRANZA Bute. (Strathclyde) 401 402 E 16 – see Arran (Isle of).

LOCKERBIE Dumfries. (Dumfries and Galloway) 401 402 J 18 – pop. 3 545 – ECD : Tuesday – ☎ 057 62.
Corrie Rd ☎ 3363.
Edinburgh 74 – ◆Carlisle 27 – ◆Dumfries 13 – ◆Glasgow 73.

Dryfesdale, DG11 2SF, NW : 1 m. by A 74 ☎ 2427, Fax 4187, ≤, – TV ☎ P. AE VISA
M 9.00/12.00 **t.** and a la carte 3.50 – **15 rm** 40.00/60.00 **t.** – SB (November-May) (weekends only) 85.00/90.00 **st.**

Lockerbie House, Boreland Rd, DG11 2RG, N : 1 m. on B 723 ☎ 3939, Fax 3046, ≤, park – TV ☎ P – 80. AE VISA
M (bar lunch by arrangement)/dinner 9.00 **st.** and a la carte 3.95 – **27 rm** 38.50/75.00 **st.**

Keine bezahlte Reklame im Michelin-Führer.

MACHRIHANISH Argyll. (Strathclyde) 401 C 17 – see Kintyre (Peninsula).

MAINLAND Orkney. (Orkney Islands) 401 KL 6 – see Orkney Islands.

MAINLAND Shetland. (Shetland Islands) 401 PQ 3 – see Shetland Islands.

MALLAIG Inverness. (Highland) 401 C 12 – pop. 998 – ECD : Wednesday – ☎ 0687.
See : Site★.
Envir. : Silver Sands of Morar★, S : by A 830 – Arisaig, S : 9 m. by A 830.
by Caledonian MacBrayne : to Armadale (Isle of Skye) (except Tuesday, Thursday and Sunday) 1 daily.
by Caledonian MacBrayne : to Isles of Eigg, Muck, Rhum, Canna, return Mallaig Monday/Saturday 3-7 weekly – to Kyle of Lochalsh: 3 weekly (summer only) (2 h).
☎ 2170 (summer only).
Edinburgh 179 – ◆ Inverness 110 – ◆Oban 96.

MARKINCH Fife. (Fife) 401 K 15 – see Glenrothes.

MARNOCH Aberdeen. (Grampian) 401 L 11 – ✉ ☎ 0466 Huntly
Edinburgh 170 – ◆Aberdeen 40 – ◆Inverness 77.

Old Manse of Marnoch, AB5 5RS, on B 9117 ☎ 780873, – P
M (Residents only) (communal dining) 6.50/12.50 **t.** 4.00 – **4 rm** 25.50/44.00 **t.**

MARYCULTER Aberdeen. (Grampian) 401 N 12 – see Aberdeen.

MEIGLE Perth. (Tayside) 401 K 14 – ☎ 082 84.
See : Museum★★ (Early Christian Monuments★★).
Envir. : Glamis Castle★★ NE : 7 m. by A 94.
Edinburgh 62 – ◆Dundee 13 – Perth 18.

Kings of Kinloch, Coupar Angus Rd, PH12 8QX, W : 1 m. on A 94 ☎ 273, ≤, – TV P. VISA
M 8.50/9.50 **st.** and a la carte 3.50 – **6 rm** 40.00/70.00 **st.**

MELROSE Roxburgh. (Borders) 401 402 L 17 **Scotland G** – pop. 2 143 – ECD : Thursday – ☏ 089 682.

See : Site★ – Abbey★★ (Decorative sculpture★★★).

Envir. : Eildon Hill North (✳★★★) – Scott's View★★ – Abbotsford★★, W : 4 m. by A 6091 – Dryburgh Abbey★★★ (setting★★★) SE : 4 m. by A 6091.

⛳9 Dingleton ℘ 2855, South boundary.

ℹ Priorwood Gdns, near Abbey ℘ 2555 (summer only).

◆Edinburgh 38 – Hawick 19 – ◆Newcastle-upon-Tyne 70.

- **Burts,** Market Sq., TD6 9PN, ℘ 2285, Fax 2870, – TV ☎ P. AE VISA
  closed 24 to 27 December and 2-3 January – **M** 15.00/17.00 **t.** and a la carte 3.75 – **21 rm** 38.00/64.00 **t.** – SB 45.00/50.00 **st.**

  at Gattonside NW : 2¼ m. by A 6091 on B 6360 – ✉ ☏ 089 682 Melrose :

- **Hoebridge Inn,** TD6 9LZ, ℘ 3082 – P. VISA
  closed Monday, 2 weeks April, 1 week October, 25 December and 1 January – **M** (dinner only) a la carte 11.00/15.85 **t.** 3.65.

HONDA St. Dunstans ℘ 2048

MILLPORT Bute. (Strathclyde) 401 402 F 16 – Shipping Services : see Great Cumbrae Island.

MILNGAVIE Dunbarton. (Strathclyde) 401 H 16 – pop. 12 030 – ECD : Tuesday and Saturday – ✉ ☏ 041 Glasgow.

⛳18 Dougalston ℘ 956 5750 – ⛳18, ⛳18 Hilton Park ℘ 956 5124.

◆Edinburgh 53 – ◆Glasgow 7.

- **Black Bull Thistle** (Mt.Charlotte Thistle), Main St., G62 6BH, ℘ 956 2291, Telex 778323, Fax 956 1896 – TV ☎ P – 100. AE VISA
  M 7.00/13.00 **t.** and a la carte – 7.75 – **27 rm** 55.00/75.00 **st.** – SB 84.00 **st.**

ROVER Main St. ℘ 956 2255 VAUXHALL-OPEL Glasgow Rd ℘ 956 1126

☛ *Questa Guida non contiene pubblicità a pagamento.*

MOFFAT Dumfries. (Dumfries and Galloway) 401 402 J 17 **Scotland G** – pop. 1 990 – ECD : Wednesday – ☏ 0683.

Envir. : Grey Mare's Tail (waterfall)★★ NE : 9 m. – Tweed Valley★★ N : 6 m.

⛳18 Coasthill ℘ 20020.

ℹ Church Gate ℘ 20620 (summer only).

◆Edinburgh 61 – ◆Dumfries 22 – ◆Carlisle 43 – ◆Glasgow 60.

- **Well View** 🔇, Ballplay Rd, DG10 9JU, E : ¾ m. by Selkirk Rd (A 708) ℘ 20184, ≤, – TV P. VISA
  M 8.00/14.00 **t.** – **7 rm** 21.00/68.00 **t.**
- **Beechwood Country House** 🔇, up Harthope Pl., by Academy Rd, DG10 9RS, ℘ 20210, ≤, – rest TV ☎ P. AE VISA
  closed January – **M** (bar lunch Monday to Saturday)/dinner 16.50 **t.** 3.50 – **7 rm** 43.75/62.30 **t.**
- **Moffat House,** High St., DG10 9HL, ℘ 20039, Fax 21288, – rest TV ☎ P. AE VISA
  M (bar lunch)/dinner a la carte 13.75/16.00 **t.** 4.75 – **20 rm** 35.00/60.00 **t.**

MONTROSE Angus. (Tayside) 401 M 13 **Scotland G** – pop. 12 127 – ECD : Wednesday – ☏ 0674.

Envir. : Brechin (Round Tower★) W : 7 m. by A 935 – Aberlemno Stones★ (summer only) W : 13 m. by A 935 and B 9134 – Glen Esk★ (via Brechin and Edzell) 29 m. by A 935, B 9667, B 966, B 974 and A 937 – Cairn O'Mount Road★ (≤★★) N : 20 m. by A 937 and B 974.

⛳18, ⛳18 Montrose Links Trust, Triall Drive ℘ 72932, E : 1 m. by A 92.

ℹ The Library, High St ℘ 72000 (summer only).

◆Edinburgh 92 – ◆Aberdeen 39 – ◆Dundee 29.

- Park, 61 John St., DD10 8RJ, ℘ 73415, Telex 76367, Fax 77091, – TV ☎ P – 150. **59 rm.**

MUCK (Isle of) Inverness. (Highland) 401 B 13 – Shipping Services : see Mallaig.

MUIR OF ORD Ross and Cromarty. (Highland) 401 G 11 – pop. 1 693 – ☏ 0463 Inverness.

⛳18 Great North Rd ℘ 870825.

◆Edinburgh 173 – ◆Inverness 10 – Wick 121.

- **Dower House** 🔇, Highfield, IV6 7XN, N : 1 m. on A 862 ℘ 870090, « Tasteful decor », – rest TV ☎ P. AE VISA.
  closed Christmas – **M** (lunch by arrangement)/dinner 22.00 **t.** 5.00 – **4 rm** 57.00/96.00 **t.**, **1 suite** 96.00 **t.** – SB (winter only) (except Christmas and New Year) 79.00/92.00 **st.**

MULL (Isle of) Argyll. (Strathclyde) 401 C 14 **Scotland G** – pop. 2 605.

See : Site★ – Calgary Bay★★ – Isle of Iona★ – Torosay Castle (Gardens★ – ≤★).

by Caledonian MacBrayne: from Craignure to Oban: 1-3 daily – from Fishnish to Lochaline Monday/Saturday frequent services daily. 9 daily (15 mn) – from Tobermory to Arinagour (Isle of Coll) 3 weekly – from Tobermory to Isle of Tiree 3 weekly – from Tobermory to Oban 3 weekly.

by Caledonian MacBrayne : from Fionnphort to Isle of Iona frequent services daily in summer, restricted service in winter (5 mn) – from Tobermory to Kilchoan summer only Monday/Saturday 3-6 daily (35 mn).

Main St. at Tobermory ✆ 0688 (Tobermory) 2182.

Dervaig – ✉ Tobermory – ☎ 068 84 Dervaig.

Druimnacroish, PA75 6QW, S : 2 m. by B 8073 and Salen rd ✆ 274, ≤ Bellart Glen, « Converted steading », – rest TV ☎ P. AE VISA
Mid April-mid October – **M** (dinner only) 20.00 **st.** 3.00 – **6 rm** 45.00/90.00 **st.**

Tiroran – ✉ ☎ 068 15 Tiroran.

Tiroran House, PA69 6ES, ✆ 232, ≤ Loch Scridain, « Country house atmosphere », , park – rest P.
June-2 October – **M** (light lunch residents only)/dinner 27.00 **st.** 3.75 – **9 rm** 70.00/140.00 **st.**

Tobermory – pop. 843 – ECD : Wednesday – ✉ ☎ 0688 Tobermory.

Tobermory ✆ 2020.

Main St. ✆ 2182.

Harbour House, 59 Main St., PA75 6NT, ✆ 2209, ≤ – VISA
M (dinner only) 12.50 **t.** 3.00 – **9 rm** 19.00/46.00 **st.**

Tobermory, 53 Main St., PA75 6NT, ✆ 2091, ≤
M (dinner only) 14.00 **t.** 3.50 – **15 rm** 22.00/52.00 **t.**

Ulva House, Strongarbh, PA75 6PR, ✆ 2044, ≤ Tobermory Harbour and Calve Island, – P
April-October – **M** 13.95 **t.** 3.95 – **6 rm** 21.00/53.00 **t.**

MUSSELBURGH E. Lothian. (Lothian) 401 K 16 – ☎ 031.

Monktonhall ✆ 665 2005 – Royal Musselburgh, Prestongrange House ✆ 0875 (Prestonpans) 810276.

Edinburgh 6 – Berwick 54 – Glasgow 53.

Granada Lodge without rest., Old Craighall, EH21 8RE, S : 1 ½ m. by B6415 at junction with A1 ✆ 653 6070, Fax 653 6106 – TV P. AE VISA.
44 rm 27.50/29.50 **t.**

NAIRN Nairn. (Highland) 401 I 11 **Scotland G** – pop. 7 366 – ECD : Wednesday – ☎ 0667.

Envir. : Cawdor Castle★, S : 7 m. by A 9090 – Brodie Castle★, E : 2 m. – Forres (Sueno's Stone★★) E : 11 m. by A 96 and B 9011 – Fort George★ W : 10 m. by A 96 and B 9006.

18, 9 Seabank Rd ✆ 52103 – 18 Nairn Dunbar, Lochloy Rd ✆ 52741.

62 King St. ✆ 52753 (summer only).

Edinburgh 172 – Aberdeen 91 – Inverness 16.

Golf View, Seabank Rd, IV12 4HD, ✆ 52301, Telex 75134, Fax 55267, ≤, heated, , – TV ☎ P – 130. AE VISA
M 19.00 **t.** (dinner) and a la carte – **45 rm** (dinner included) 52.00/126.00 **t.**, **3 suites** 130.00/150.00 **t.** – SB 78.00/98.00 **st.**

Lochloy House, Lochloy Rd, Lochloy, IV12 5WE, NE : 2½ m. ✆ 55355, Fax 54809, ≤, « Country house atmosphere », , , park, – P
M *(closed lunch Saturday and Sunday)* 12.00/25.00 **t.** and a la carte 2.50 – **6 rm** 37.50/75.00 **s.**

Clifton, Viewfield St., IV12 4HW, ✆ 53119, Fax 52836, ≤, « Tasteful decor, antiques », – P. AE VISA
March-October – **M** (booking essential) 15.00/20.00 **t.** and a la carte – **16 rm** 48.00/85.00 **t.**

Links, 1 Seafield St., IV12 4HN, ✆ 53321, – TV P. VISA.
M (Bar lunch)/dinner 12.00 **st.** – **10 rm** 22.00/52.00 **st.** – SB (October-May) 65.00/76.00 **st.**

Carnach House, Delnies, IV12 5NT, W : 2¼ m. on A 96 ✆ 52094, – rest TV ☎ P. AE VISA
M (bar lunch)/dinner 25.00 **t.** (dinner) and a la carte 3.50 – **14 rm** 28.50/57.00 **t.** – SB (November-February) (weekends only) 67.00 **st.**

Sunny Brae, Marine Rd, IV12 4EA, ✆ 52309, ≤, – TV P
March-October – **M** 7.50 **st.** 3.00 – **10 rm** 16.50/35.00 **st.**

SO Inverness Rd ✆ 52335

NETHERLEY Kincardine. (Grampian) 401 N 12 – ✉ ☏ 0569 Stonehaven
◆Edinburgh 117 – ◆Aberdeen 8 – ◆Dundee 54.

XX **Lairhillock,** AB3 2QS, NE : 1 ½ m. by B 979 on Portlethan rd ☏ 30001, Fax 31175 – Ⓟ. AE ⓓ VISA
closed Sunday dinner and Monday – **M** (bar lunch Tuesday to Saturday)/dinner 25.00 ♁ 4.80.

NEWBURGH Aberdeen. (Grampian) 401 N 12 – ☏ 035 86.
◆Edinburgh 144 – ◆Aberdeen 14 – Fraserburgh 33.

Udny Arms, Main St., AB4 0BL, ☏ 89444, Fax 89012, – TV ☎ Ⓟ – 80. VISA
M a la carte 11.15/18.40 **t.** ♁ 5.75 – ☕ 3.75 – **26 rm** 46.00/68.00 **t.** – SB (weekends only) 77.00/120.00 **st.**

NEW GALLOWAY Kirkcudbright. (Dumfries and Galloway) 401 402 H 18 – pop. 290 ☏ 064 42.
9 ☏ 2794, S : on A 762.
◆Edinburgh 88 – ◆Ayr 36 – Dumfries 25.

Leamington, High St., DG7 3RN, ☏ 327 – Ⓟ. VISA.
closed 30 October-2 December – **M** 9.00 **t.** ♁ 3.20 – **10 rm** ☕ 12.50/34.00 **t.**

NEWMILL Roxburgh. (Borders) 401 402 L 17 – see Harwick.

NEW SCONE Perth. (Tayside) 401 J 14 – see Perth.

NEWTONMORE Inverness. (Highland) 401 H 12 – pop. 1 010 – ECD : Wednesday – ☏ 054 03
18 Golf Course Rd ☏ 328.
◆Edinburgh 113 – ◆Inverness 43 – Perth 69.

Ard-na-Coille, Kingussie Rd, PH20 1AY, ☏ 214, Fax 453, ← – rest Ⓟ
closed 1 week April, 1 week September, November and December – **M** (lunch by arrangement)/dinner 22.50 **t.** ♁ 4.50 – **7 rm** ☕ (dinner included) 52.50/119.00 **t.** – SB (except mid May-mid September, December and Bank Holidays) 60.00/75.00 **st.**

Pines ⛰, Station Rd, PH20 1AR, ☏ 271, ←, – Ⓟ.
May-late October – **M** 9.00 **st.** – **6 rm** ☕ (dinner included) 29.00/58.00 **st.**

NEWTON STEWART Wigtown. (Dumfries and Galloway) 401 402 G 19 – pop. 3 212 – ECD Wednesday – ☏ 0671.
Envir. : Galloway Forest Parks★, N : Queen's Way★ (Newton Stewart to New Galloway) 19 m by A 712.
18 Mains off Park, Glenluce ☏ 058 13 (Glenluce) 420 – 9 Kirroughtree Av., Minnigaff ☏ 2172.
Dashwood Sq. ☏ 2431 (summer only).
◆Edinburgh 131 – ◆Dumfries 51 – ◆Glasgow 87 – Stranraer 24.

Kirroughtree ⛰, DG8 6AN, NE : 1 ½ m. on A 712 ☏ 2141, Fax 2425, ← woodland and River Cree, « Country house and gardens », park, – rest TV ☎ Ⓟ. AE ⓓ VISA
closed early January-early February – **M** 25.00 **t.** (dinner) and a la carte ♁ 4.50 – **21 rm** ☕ 52.00/114.00 **t.**, **1 suite** 128.00 **t.** – SB 113.00/144.00 **st.**

Creebridge House ⛰, Minnigaff, DG8 6NP, ☏ 2121, – TV ☎ Ⓟ. VISA
M (bar lunch)/dinner 13.50 **t.** and a la carte ♁ 4.45 – **18 rm** ☕ 35.00/65.00 **t.** – SB 60.00/86.00 **st.**

Bruce, 88 Queen St., DG8 6JL, ☏ 2294 – TV ☎ Ⓟ. AE ⓓ VISA
closed December and January – **M** 11.00/17.00 **st.** ♁ 3.75 – **18 rm** ☕ 35.00/58.00 **st.** SB 70.00 **st.**

Crown, 101 Queen St., DG8 6JW, ☏ 2727 – rest TV Ⓟ. VISA
M (bar lunch)/dinner 11.50 **t.** and a la carte ♁ 3.60 – **10 rm** ☕ 19.00/42.00 **t.** – SB 55.00/64.00 **st.**

Rowallan House ⛰, Corsbie Rd, DG8 6JB, ☏ 2520, – rest TV Ⓟ.
closed November – **M** 15.00 **t.** ♁ 3.50 – **6 rm** ☕ 24.00/48.00 **t.**

RENAULT Duncan Park, Wigtown ☏ 098 84 (Wigtown) 3287
VOLVO, CITROEN Minnigaff Holm Park Ind Est ☏ 3101
VW-AUDI Queen St. ☏ 2112

NORTH BERWICK E. Lothian. (Lothian) 401 L 15 **Scotland G** – pop. 4 861 – ECD : Thursday ☏ 0620.
Envir. : Tantallon Castle★★ (Site★★★) E : 3 m. by A 198 – Tyninghame★, S : 6 m. by A 198 Preston Mill★, S : 8 m. by A 198 and B 1407 – Museum of Flight★, S : 10 m. by A 198 and B 1407.
18 Beach Rd ☏ 2135 – 18 East Links ☏ 2726 – 18 Glen, East Links ☏ 2221.
Quality St. ☏ 2197.
◆Edinburgh 24 – ◆Newcastle-upon-Tyne 102.

Marine (T.H.F.), 18 Cromwell Rd, EH39 4LZ, 2406, Telex 72550, Fax 4480, ≤ golf course and Firth of Forth, heated, squash – rm – 300.
M 9.50/20.00 **st.** 4.00 – 7.50 – **78 rm** 75.00/95.00 **st.**, **5 suites** 130.00/175.00 **st.** – SB 98.00/110.00 **st.**

Point Garry, 20 West Bay Rd, EH39 4AW, 2380, ≤ –
Mid March-October – **M** (bar lunch)/dinner 12.95 **t.** and a la carte 3.90 – **16 rm** 19.80/83.50 **t.**

Blenheim House, 14 Westgate, EH39 4AF, 2385, Fax 4010, ≤, –
closed January and February – **10 rm** 25.00/80.00 **st.**

Nether Abbey, 20 Dirleton Av., EH39 4BQ, 2802, Fax 5298 –
M (bar lunch)/dinner a la carte 11.20/15.45 **t.** 3.25 – **16 rm** 23.00/32.00 **t.** – SB 40.00/60.00 **t.**

Craigview without rest., 5 Beach Rd, EH39 4AB, 2257 –
3 rm 13.50/35.00 **st.**, **1 suite** 45.00 **st.**

Hardings, 2 Station Rd, EH39 4AU, 4737 –
closed Tuesday dinner, Sunday, Monday, 4 weeks January-February and 1 week October – **M** 11.50/18.00 **t.** 4.80.

ORD 52 Dunbar Rd 2232

ORTH RONALDSAY (Isle of) Orkney. (Orkney Islands) 401 M 5 – Shipping Services : see rkney Islands (Mainland : Kirkwall).

OBAN Argyll. (Strathclyde) 401 D 14 **Scotland G** – pop. 7 476 – ECD : Thursday – 0631.

ee : Site★.

nvir. : Loch Awe★★ – Inverary★★ (Castle★★-Interior★★★) – Loch Fyne★★ – Bonawe Furnace★ Cruachan Power Station★ – Auchindrain★ – Crinan★, 83 m. by A 85, A 819, A 83 and A 816 – ea Life Centre★, N : 11 m. by A 828.

Glencruitten Rd 62868.

ccess to Glasgow by helicopter.

by Caledonian MacBrayne : to Craignure (Isle of Mull) 1-3 daily – to Castlebay (Isle of arra) – to Lochboisdale (South Uist) 3-5 weekly – to Arinagour (Isle of Coll) : 3 weekly – to Isle Tiree 3 weekly – to Scalasaig (Isle of Colonsay) summer only: 3 weekly (2 h 30 mn) – to chnacroish (Isle of Lismore) Monday/Saturday 2-4 daily (50 mn) – to Tobermory (Isle of Mull) weekly.

Argyll Sq. 63122.

Edinburgh 123 – ◆Dundee 116 – ◆Glasgow 93 – ◆Inverness 118.

Columba, North Pier, PA34 5QD, 62183, Telex 728256, Fax 64683, ≤ –
M 11.00/25.00 **st.** and a la carte 4.75 – **50 rm** 60.00/80.00 **st.** – SB 65.00/95.00 **st.**

Manor House, Gallanach Rd, PA34 4LS, 62087, ≤ – rest
closed January – **M** 5.00/19.50 **t.** and a la carte 2.50 – **11 rm** (dinner included) 80.00/140.00 **t.**

Dungrianach without rest., Pulpit Hill, PA34 4LX, 62840, ≤ Oban, Sound and Isle of Kerrara, –
April-October – **3 rm** 28.00/30.00 **st.**

Corriemar, Esplanade, PA34 5AQ, 62476, ≤ – rest
April-September – **M** 10.00 **t.** 3.00 – **14 rm** 25.00/50.00 **t.**

at Kilninver SW : 8 m. on A 816 – Oban – 085 26 Kilninver :

Knipoch, PA34 4QT, NE : 1 ½ m. on A 816 251, Fax 249, ≤, « Tastefully furnished », –
Mid February-mid November – **M** (lunch by arrangement)/dinner 33.00 **t.** 4.00 – **17 rm** 53.00/106.00 **t.**

ORD Soroba Rd 63061
OVER, LAND ROVER Airds Pl. 63173
VOLVO Breadalbane Pl. 63066

OLDMELDRUM Aberdeen. (Grampian) 401 N 11 – pop. 1 343 – ECD : Wednesday – 065 12.

Envir. : Pitmedden Gardens★★, E : 5 m. by A 920 – Haddo House★, N : 9 m. by B 9170 and 9005 – Fyvie Castle★, N : 8 m. by A 947.

2212, E : off A 947.

Edinburgh 148 – ◆Aberdeen 18 – Fraserburgh 30 – ◆Inverness 89.

Meldrum House, AB5 0AE, N : 1 ½ m. on A 947 2294, ≤, « Part 13C baronial house, country house atmosphere », park –
closed mid December-mid March – **M** (bar lunch)/dinner 24.00 **st.** – **11 rm** 55.00/100.00 **st.** – SB (weekends only) 100.00 **st.**

ENAULT Station Rd 3928

Use this year's Guide.

ONICH Inverness. (Highland) 401 E 13 – ECD : Saturday except summer – ✉ Fort William
☎ 085 53.

♦Edinburgh 123 – ♦Glasgow 93 – ♦Inverness 79 – ♦Oban 39.

Allt-Nan-Ros, PH33 6RY, on A 82 ☎ 210, Fax 462, ≤ Loch Linnhe and mountains, – rest TV ☎ P. AE VISA
Easter-November – **M** 17.00 **st.** (dinner) lunch a la carte – **21 rm** 43.00/136.00 **st.**

The Lodge on the Loch, Creag Dhu, PH33 6RY, on A 82 ☎ 238, Fax 463, ≤ Loch Linn and mountains, – rest TV ☎ ♿ P. VISA
closed 3 to 31 January and 1 November-20 December – **M** 8.00/18.50 **t.** and a la ca
4.50 – **20 rm** 29.50/95.00 **st.**

Onich, PH33 6RY, on A 82 ☎ 214, Fax 484, ≤ Loch Linnhe and mountains, – TV ☎
AE VISA
closed 1 to 18 January – **M** 9.00/20.00 **t.** and a la carte 3.55 – **26 rm** 32.50/65.00
SB (except summer) 64.00.

Cuilcheanna House , PH33 6SD, ☎ 226, ≤, – rest P
Easter-mid October – **M** 11.00 **t.** 3.00 – **8 rm** 25.00/44.00 **t.**

Utilisez le guide de l'année.

ORKNEY ISLANDS Orkney. (Orkney Islands) 401 KL 6 and 7 **Scotland G** – pop. 19 040.

see Mainland : Kirkwall.

see Mainland : Kirkwall and Stromness.

by Thomas & Bews : from Burwick (South Ronaldsay) to John O'Groats summer on 2-5 daily (45 mn) – by P & O Ferries : from Stromness to Scrabster Monday/Saturday (1 dail (1 h 50 mn) – from Stromness to Limerick via Aberdeen 1 weekly.

HOY

Old Man of Hoy **Scotland G.**

See : Old Man of Hoy★★★ (sandstone stack).

MAINLAND

Birsay **Scotland G** – ✉ ☎ 085 672 Birsay.

See : Brough of Birsay (site★★).

Dounby – ✉ Dounby – ☎ 085 677 Harray.

Smithfield, KW17 2HT, ☎ 215 – P
April-September – **M** (bar lunch)/dinner 25.00 **st.** – **6 rm** 16.00/40.00 **s.**

Kirkwall **Scotland G** – pop. 5 947 – ECD : Wednesday – ✉ ☎ 0856 Kirkwall.

See : Site★★ – St. Magnus Cathedral★★ – Earl's Palace★ – Tankerness House Museum★

Envir. : Italian Chapel★ – Corrigall Farm Museum★.

18 Grainbank ☎ 2457, W : 1 m.

Kirkwall Airport : ☎ 2421, Telex 75473, S : 3½ m.

by Orkney Islands Shipping Co. : to Westray via Eday, Stronsay, Sanday and Pap Westray 3 weekly – to North Ronaldsay 1 weekly – to Shapinsay 2-4 daily (25 mn).

Broad St. ☎ 2856.

Kirkwall, Harbour St., KW15 1LF, ☎ 2232, Fax 2812, ≤ – TV ☎
44 rm.

Foveran , St. Ola, KW15 1SF, SW : 3 m. on A 964 ☎ 2389, ≤, « Overlooking Scap Flow » – P. VISA
March-October – **M** *(closed Sunday)* (dinner only) a la carte 10.60/15.60 **st.** 3.25 – **8 rm** 26.00/42.00 **st.**

West End, Main St., KW15 1BU, ☎ 2368, Fax 6181 – TV ☎ P. VISA
M 5.00/15.00 **st.** 3.50 – **16 rm** 28.00/40.00 **st.**

Lynnfield , Holm Rd, KW15 1RX, S : 1¼ m. on A 961 ☎ 2505, – TV P
9 rm.

Ayre, Ayre Rd, KW15 1QX, ☎ 3001, Fax 3001 – TV ☎ P. VISA
M a la carte 4.05/16.20 **st.** 3.00 – **34 rm** 26.00/58.00 **st.**

St. Ola, Harbour St., KW15 1LE, ☎ 5090 – TV ☎.
closed Christmas – **M** 8.00 **st.** – **6 rm** 20.00/34.00 **st.**

Brekk-Ness , Muddisdale Rd, W : 1 m. by Pickaquay Rd ☎ 4317 – TV P
M (by arrangement) – **11 rm.**

COLT, TALBOT Gt Western Rd ☎ 2805
FIAT Junction Rd ☎ 2158
FORD Castle St. ☎ 3212
RENAULT Gt Western Rd ☎ 2601

VAUXHALL Burnmouth Rd ☎ 2950

ATS Junction Rd ☎ 2361

Loch Harray – ✉ Loch Harray – ☎ 085 677 Harray.

Merkister ⛰, KW17 2LF, off A 986 ☎ 366, ≤, – TV ☎ P. VISA
April-October – **M** (bar lunch)/dinner 20.00 **st.** and a la carte 3.75 – **15 rm** 28.75/49.50 **st.**

St. Margarets Hope – ☎ 0856 Orkney Islands.

X **Creel** with rm, Front St., KW17 2SL, ☎ 83311 – P. VISA.
closed Tuesday, Wednesday and Thursday in winter, Monday and January – **M** (dinner only) a la carte 8.25/14.65 **t.** 3.30 – **2 rm** 20.00/36.00 **t.**

Stromness **Scotland G** – pop. 1 816 – ECD : Thursday – ✉ ☎ 0856 Stromness.

See : Site★ – Pier Arts Centre (Collection of abstract art★).

Envir. : Old Man of Hoy★★★ – Maes Howe★★ E : 4 m. – Skara Brae★★ (Prehistoric Village) N : 7½ m.

Ness ☎ 850772.

by P & O Ferries : Orkney and Shetland Services : to Scrabster Monday/Saturday (1 daily) (1 h 50 mn).

Ferry Terminal Building, Pierhead ☎ 850716.

UT SKERRIES Shetland. (Shetland Islands) 401 R 2 – Shipping Services : see Shetland ands (Mainland : Lerwick).

We suggest:
For a successful tour, that you prepare it in advance.
Michelin maps and guides will give you much useful information on route planning, places of interest, accommodation, prices etc.

AISLEY Renfrew. (Strathclyde) 401 402 G 16 **Scotland G** – pop. 84 330 – ECD : Tuesday – 041 Glasgow.

ee : Museum and Art gallery (Paisley Shawl Section★).

Barshaw Park ☎ 889 2908, E : 1 m. of Paisley Cross off A 737.

Town Hall, Abbey Close, ☎ 889 0711.

Edinburgh 53 – ♦Ayr 35 – ♦Glasgow 7.5 – Greenock 17.

Stakis Watermill, Lonend, PA1 1SR, ☎ 889 3201, Fax 889 5938 – rm TV ☎ P. AE VISA
M 7.95/10.00 **t.** and a la carte – 7.50 – **51 rm** 59.50/81.00 **t.** – SB 70.00/114.00 **st.**

TROEN East Lane ☎ 889 8526
AT 4-8 Lochfield Rd ☎ 884 2281
ORD 37-41 Lonend ☎ 887 0191
PEUGEOT-TALBOT 7 West St. ☎ 889 0011
ROVER 46 New Sneddon St. ☎ 889 7882
VAUXHALL-OPEL 69 Espedair St. ☎ 889 5254

APA WESTRAY (Isle of) Orkney. (Orkney Islands) 401 L 5 – Shipping Services : see Orkney lands (Mainland : Kirkwall).

EAT INN Fife. (Fife) 401 L 15 – ✉ Cupar – ☎ 033 484.

Edinburgh 45 – Dundee 21 – Perth 28.

XXX ✿ **The Peat Inn** (Wilson) ⛰ with rm, KY15 5LH, ☎ 206, Fax 530, – rest TV ☎ ♿ P. AE VISA.
closed 2 weeks January and 2 weeks November – **M** *(closed Sunday and Monday)* (booking essential) 15.50/35.00 **st.** and a la carte 24.50/28.00 **st.** 6.00 –, **8 suites** 80.00/120.00 **st.**
Spec. Breast of pigeon on a pastry case filled with wild mushrooms, Loin of spring lamb in its juices flavoured with rosemary (May-August), A trio of nut desserts.

EEBLES Peebles. (Borders) 401 402 K 17 – pop. 6 404 – ECD : Wednesday – ☎ 0721.

nvir. : Traquair House★★, SE : 7 m.

Kirkland St. ☎ 20197 – West Linton ☎ 0968 (West Linton) 60463.

Chambers Institute, High St. ☎ 20138 (summer only).

Edinburgh 24 – Hawick 31 – ♦Glasgow 53.

Peebles Hydro, Innerleithen Rd, EH45 8LX, ☎ 20602, Telex 72568, Fax 22999, ≤, , park, , squash – TV ☎ P – 400. AE VISA.
M 10.50/16.00 **st.** 4.00 – **132 rm** 50.50/100.50 **st.**, **2 suites** 108.00/128.00 **st.** – SB 79.50/125.00 **st.**

Tweedbridge House, Chambers Terr., EH45 9DZ, ☎ 20590, Fax 22793, ≤, – rest TV ☎ P. AE VISA.
M (bar lunch)/dinner a la carte 10.65/19.70 **st.** 4.00 – **5 rm** 35.00/70.00 **st.** – SB 60.00/85.00 **st.**

Cringletie House ⛰, EH45 8PL, N : 3 m. on A 703 ✆ 072 13 (Eddleston) 233, Fax 2 ≤, « Country house in extensive grounds », park, – rest VISA
closed 2 January-8 March – **M** (restricted lunch Monday to Saturday)/dinner 20.00 **t.** 4 – **13 rm** 39.00/72.00 **t.** – SB (March-May and October-December) (except Christm 94.00/106.00 **st.**

Park, Innerleithen Rd, EH45 8BA, ✆ 20451, Group Telex 72568, Fax 22999, – AE VISA
M (bar lunch)/dinner 19.25 **t.** 4.50 – **25 rm** 41.00/90.00 **t.**

Tontine (T.H.F.), 39 High St., EH45 8AJ, ✆ 20892, Fax 29732 – – 25. VISA
M (bar lunch)/dinner 20.00 **st.** and a la carte 4.35 – **36 rm** 45.00/60.00 **st.**

CITROEN, LANCIA George St. ✆ 20545 — ROVER, LAND-ROVER Innerleithen Rd ✆ 20627

PENNAN Aberdeen. (Grampian) 401 N 10 – pop. 92 – ✉ 034 66 New Aberdour.
◆Edinburgh 181 – ◆Aberdeen 51 – Fraserburgh 12 – ◆Inverness 85.

Pennan Inn, 17-19 Main St., AB4 4JB, ✆ 201 –
closed 25-26 December and 1-2 January – **M** *(closed dinner Sunday and Monday)* (lunch)/dinner 20.00 **st.** and a la carte 3.50 – **6 rm** 30.00/35.00 **st.**

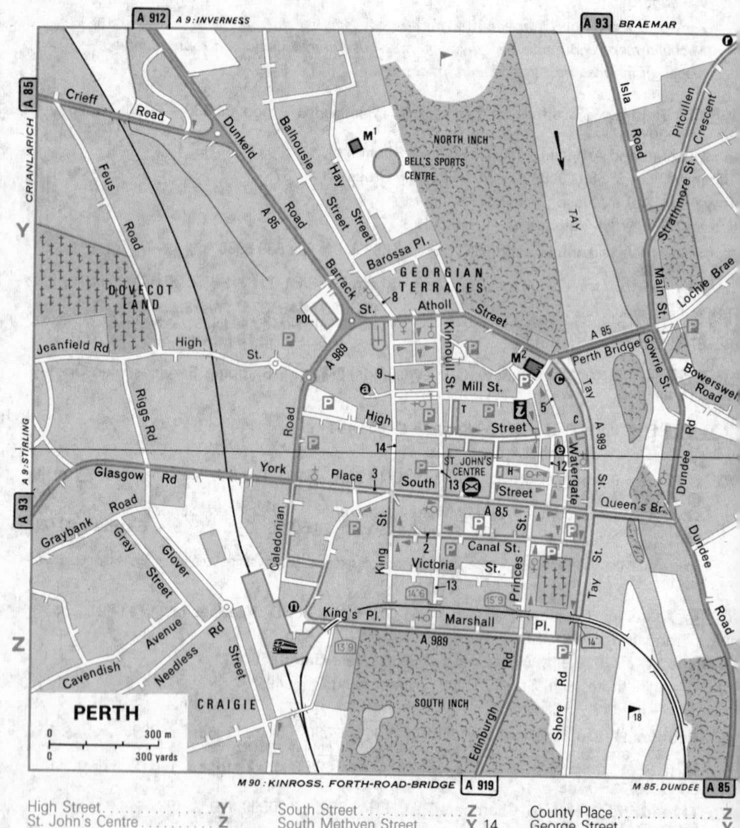

High Street	Y		South Street	Z		County Place	Z
St. John's Centre	Z		South Methven Street	Y	14	George Street	Y
St. John Street	Z	12				Melville Street	Y
Scott Street	Z	13	Charterhouse Lane	Z	2	North Methven Street	Y

PERTH Perth. (Tayside) 401 J 14 **Scotland G** – pop. 41 916 – ECD : Wednesday – ☎ 0738.

See : Black Watch Regimental Museum★ Y **M1** – Georgian terraces★ Y – Museum and Art Gallery★ Y **M2** – Branklyn Garden★ by A 85 Z – Kinnoull Hill (≤★) by Bowerswell Rd Y.

Envir. : Scone Palace★★, N : 2 m. by A 93 Y – Huntingtower Castle★, NW : 3 m. by A 9 Y – Elcho Castle★, SE : by A 912 Z – Abernethy Round Tower★, SE : 8 m. by A 912 Z and A 913 – Cairnwell (✲★★) N : 40 m. by A 93 Y.

18 Craigie Hill, Cherrybank ℘ 24377, West boundary, by A 9 Z – 18 King James VI, Moncrieffe Island ℘ 25170 Y – 18 Murrayshall ℘ 52784 Y – 18 Royal Perth Golfing Society ℘ 22265 Y – 18 North Inch ℘ 39911 Y.

The Round House, Marshall Pl. ℘ 38353.

Edinburgh 44 – ♦Aberdeen 86 – ♦Dundee 22 – Dunfermline 29 – ♦Glasgow 64 – ♦Inverness 112 – ♦Oban 94.

Plan opposite

Hunting Tower ⛰, Crieff Rd, PH1 3JT, W : 3½ m. by A 85 ℘ 83771, Fax 83777, ⌂ – TV ☎ P on A 85 Y
24 rm.

Royal George (T.H.F.), Tay St., PH1 5LD, ℘ 24455, Fax 30345 – ⇋ rm TV ☎ P – 100. Y **c**
AE VISA
M (bar lunch Monday to Saturday)/dinner 12.95 **st.** and a la carte 4.35 – 7.00 – **43 rm** 60.00/85.00 **st.** – SB 80.00/110.00 **st.**

Station, Leonard St., PH2 8HE, ℘ 24141, Telex 76481, Fax 39912, ⌂ – ⇋ rm TV ☎ P – 300. AE VISA. Z **n**
M 16.50 **st.** and a la carte 4.00 – 5.00 – **68 rm** 49.00/66.00 **st.**, **2 suites** – SB (weekends only) 70.00/78.00 **st.**

Stakis City Mills, West Mill St., PH1 5QP, ℘ 28281, Fax 43423 – ⇋ rm TV ☎ P – 200. AE VISA Y **a**
M 8.00/11.00 **t.** and a la carte – 7.50 – **76 rm** 59.50/81.00 **t.**

Pitcullen, 17 Pitcullen Cres., PH2 7HT, NE : ¾ m. on A 94 ℘ 26506 – ⇋ rest TV P. Y **r**
M 9.00 **s.** – **6 rm** 17.00/30.00 **st.**

Timothy's, 24 St. John St., PH1 5SP, ℘ 26641, Smörrebrod – VISA Y **e**
closed Sunday, Monday, 3 weeks July and 2 weeks Christmas-New Year – **M** a la carte 7.15/12.95 **t.** 3.90.

at New Scone NE : 2½ m. on A 94 – Y – ✉ ☎ 0738 Perth :

Murrayshall House ⛰, PH2 7PH, E : 1½ m. by A 94 ℘ 51171, Fax 52595, ≤, 18, ⌂, park, ✂ – TV ☎ P. AE VISA
M 17.50/37.50 **t.** 4.50 – **16 rm** 75.90/125.00 **t.**, **3 suites** 120.00/240.00 **t.** – SB (November to March) 15.00/170.00 **st.**

BMW, ROLLS-ROYCE 50-56 Leonard St. ℘ 30001
CITROEN 60 South St. ℘ 23335
FORD Riggs Rd ℘ 25121/25129
LAND ROVER, RANGE ROVER Glenearn Rd ℘ 20811
ROVER Dunkeld Rd ℘ 39993
VAUXHALL Dunkeld Rd ℘ 26241
VOLVO Arran Rd, North Muirton ℘ 22156
VW-AUDI Dunkeld Rd ℘ 25252

ATS Inveralmond Ind Est., Ruthvenfield Rd ℘ 29481

PETERHEAD Aberdeen. (Grampian) 401 O 11 – pop. 16 804 – ECD : Wednesday – ☎ 0779.

18 Craigewan Links ℘ 72149.

54 Broad St. ℘ 71904 (summer only).

Edinburgh 165 – ♦Aberdeen 35 – Fraserburgh 18.

Waterside Inn, Fraserburgh Rd, AB4 7BN, NW : 2 m. on A 952 ℘ 71121, Telex 739413, Fax 70670, ⌂, ⌂, ⌂ – TV ☎ P – 200. AE VISA
closed 25 and 26 December – **M** 7.50/13.95 **st.** and a la carte 3.75 – **110 rm** 50.00/85.00 **st.** – SB 73.00/87.00 **st.**

VAUXHALL-OPEL West Rd ℘ 72440

PITCAPLE Aberdeen. (Grampian) 401 M 12 – ☎ 046 76.

♦Edinburgh 51 – ♦Aberdeen 21.

Pittodrie House ⛰, AB5 9HS, SW : 1¾ m. by Chapel of Garioch rd ℘ 444, Telex 739935, Fax 648, ≤, « Country house atmosphere », ⌂, park, ✂, squash – TV ☎ P – 60. AE VISA
M 12.50/32.50 **t.** and a la carte – **27 rm** 75.00/90.00 **t.** – SB (November-March) 129.00 **st.**

PITLOCHRY Perth. (Tayside) 401 I 13 **Scotland G** – pop. 2 194 – ECD : Thursday – ☎ 0796.

See : Site★.

18 Golf Course Rd ℘ 2792.

22 Atholl Rd ℘ 2215 and 2751.

♦Edinburgh 71 – ♦Inverness 85 – Perth 27.

Green Park ♨, Clunie Bridge Rd, PH16 5JY, ☎ 3248, ←, 🌳 – ⛔ rest 📺 ☎ 🅟. 🅔 VISA
24 March-26 October – **M** (bar lunch)/dinner 16.50 **st.** 🍷 3.50 – **37 rm** 🛏 29.00/70.00 t
SB (26 March-5 May) 80.00 **st.**

Pine Trees ♨, Strathview Terr., PH16 5QR, ☎ 2121, Fax 2460, ←, 🌳 – 📺 🅟. 🅔 VISA.
M 12.00 **t.** (lunch) and a la carte – **18 rm** 🛏 35.00/70.00 **t.** – SB (mid October-Mar
80.00 **st.**

Port-an-Eilean ♨, Strathtummel, PH16 5RU, NW : 10½ m. by A 924 on B 80
☎ 088 24 (Tummel Bridge) 233, ← Loch Tummel and mountains, « Lochside Victori
sporting lodge », 🐟, 🌳, park – 🅟
May-September – **M** (bar lunch, residents only)/dinner 13.50 **t.** 🍷 3.60 – **8 rm** 🛏 30.(
52.00 **t.**

Queen's View ♨, Strathtummel, PH16 5NR, NW : 6 ½ m. by A 924 on B 8019 ☎ 32
← Loch Tummel and mountains, 🐟, 🌳 – 🅟. 🅔 AE ⓓ VISA.
April-October – **M** 16.10/18.50 **t.** and a la carte 🍷 4.75 – **10 rm** 🛏 25.60/61.20 **t.**

Birchwood, 2 East Moulin Rd, PH16 5DW, ☎ 2477, 🌳 – ⛔ rest 📺 ☎ 🅟. 🅔 VISA
March-November – **M** 9.00/14.00 **st.** and a la carte 🍷 4.00 – **16 rm** 🛏 32.00/65.00 **t.**

Knockendarroch, Higher Oakfield, PH16 5HT, ☎ 3473, ←, 🌳 – ⛔ rest 📺 🅟
12 rm.

Airdaniar, 160 Atholl Rd, PH16 5AR, ☎ 2266, 🌳 – ⛔ rest 📺 ☎ 🅟. 🅔 VISA
closed January – **M** (bar lunch)/dinner 16.00 **st.** 🍷 3.75 – **9 rm** 🛏 -/59.00 **st.** – SB (m
October-Easter) (except Christmas-New Year) 60.00/68.00 **st.**

Acarsaid, 8 Atholl Rd, PH16 5BX, ☎ 2389 – ⛔ rest 📺 ☎ 🅟. 🅔 VISA.
closed 2 January-2 March – **M** 15.00 **t.** (dinner) and lunch a la carte 🍷 3.50 – **18**
🛏 22.50/53.00 **t.**

Claymore, 162 Atholl Rd, PH16 5AR, ☎ 2888, 🌳 – ⛔ rest 📺 ☎ 🅟. 🅔 VISA
closed January and November – **M** (bar lunch)/dinner 14.95 **t.** – **12 rm** 🛏 27.50/55.00 t

Balrobin, Higher Oakfield, PH16 5HT, ☎ 2901, ←, 🌳 – ⛔ rest 📺 🅟
April-October – **M** 9.00 **t.** 🍷 3.00 – **12 rm** 🛏 22.00/48.00 **t.**

Craig Urrard, 10 Atholl Rd, PH16 5BX, ☎ 2346, 🌳 – ⛔ rest 📺 🅟
12 rm.

Dundarave House without rest., Strathview Terr., PH16 5AT, ☎ 3109, 🌳 – 📺 🅟
March-late October – **7 rm** 🛏 22.50/49.00 **s.**

XX **East Haugh House** with rm, East Haugh, PH16 5JS, SE : 2 m. by A 924 ☎ 3121, 🌳 –
🅟. 🅔 VISA.
M (bar lunch Monday to Saturday)/dinner 16.95 **t.** and a la carte 🍷 4.75 – **6 rm** 🛏 30.0
78.00 **t.** – SB 60.00/95.00 **st.**

at Killiecrankie NW : 4 m. by A 924 and B 8019 on B 8079 – ✉ ☎ 0796 Pitlochry :

Killiecrankie ♨, PH16 5LG, ☎ 3220, Fax 2451, ←, 🌳 – ⛔ rest 📺 ☎ 🅟
March- early November – **M** (bar lunch)/dinner 25.00 **t.** 🍷 3.50 – **11 rm** 🛏 31.50/75.50 **t.**

FORD, SUBARU Atholl Rd ☎ 2471

PLOCKTON Ross and Cromarty. (Highland) 401 D 11 – pop. 425 – ☎ 059 984.

♦Edinburgh 210 – ♦Inverness 88.

Haven, Innes St., IV52 8TW, ☎ 223, ←, 🌳 – 📺 ☎ 🅟. 🅔 VISA.
closed 20 December-10 February – **M** (bar lunch)/dinner 17.50 **t.** 🍷 4.00 – **13 rm** 🛏 28.0
56.00 **t.**

POLMONT Stirling. (Central) 401 402 I 16 – see Falkirk.

POOLEWE Ross and Cromarty. (Highland) 401 D 10 – ECD : Thursday – ✉ Achnasheen ☎ 044 586.

See : Inverewe Gardens★★★.

♦Edinburgh 241 – ♦Inverness 85.

Pool House ♨, IV22 2LE, ☎ 272, ← Loch Ewe – ⛔ rest 📺 🅟. 🅔 VISA.
M (bar lunch)/dinner 13.50 **st.** – **13 rm** 🛏 29.00/58.00 **st.**

ORT APPIN Argyll. (Strathclyde) 401 D 14 – ECD : Thursday – ☎ 063 173 Appin.

dinburgh 136 – Ballachulish 20 – ♦Oban 24.

✿ **Airds** (Betty Allen) ⚘, PA38 4DF, ✆ 236, Fax 535, ≤ Loch Linnhe and hills of Kingairloch, « Former ferry inn on lochside », 🚗 – ⇔ rest TV ☎ P. ✈
closed mid January-early March – **M** (restricted lunch)/dinner 32.00 **t.** 5.50 – **13 rm** ⊐ 70.00/125.00 **t.**, **1 suite** 124.00/152.00 **t.** – SB (mid November-mid April, except Easter, Christmas and New Year) 150.00/190.00 **st.**
Spec. Mousseline of scallops with a champagne and chive sauce, Roast rack of lamb with crab apple mint jelly, Walnut fudge tart.

ORT ASKAIG Argyll. (Strathclyde) 401 B 16 – see Islay (Isle of).

ORT OF MENTEITH Perth. 401 H15 – ☎ 087 75.

dinburgh 53 – ♦Glasgow 30 – ♦Stirling 17.

Lake ⚘, FK8 3RA, ✆ 258, Fax 671, ≤ – ⇔ rest TV ☎ P. VISA. ✈
closed January – **M** *(dinner only and Sunday lunch)/dinner* 18.50 **t.** and a la carte 3.20 – **14 rm** ⊐ 50.00/120.00 **t.** – SB 130.00 **st.**

ORTPATRICK Wigtown. (Dumfries and Galloway) 401 402 E 19 – pop. 595 – ECD : Thursday
✉ Stranraer – ☎ 077 681.

, 9 Dunskey ✆ 81273.

Edinburgh 141 – ♦Ayr 60 – ♦Dumfries 80 – Stranraer 9.

✿ **Knockinaam Lodge** ⚘, DG9 9AD, SE : 3¼ m. by A 77 off B 7042 ✆ 471, Fax 435, « Country house in picturesque coastal setting », 🐟, 🚗, park – ⇔ rest TV ☎ P. AE ⓓ VISA
closed 4 January-mid March – **M** (booking essential) 18.00/28.00 **t.** 5.50 – **10 rm** ⊐ (dinner included) 85.00/170.00 **t.** – SB (mid-March-Easter and November-24 December) 126.00/153.00 **st.**
Spec. Assiette de homard Ecossais aux épices, Grenadin de bourgeois grillé sur citronelle et nage de coriandre, Pièce de boeuf poêlée a la moelle et au vin de Bordeaux.

Fernhill, Heugh Rd, DG9 8TD, ✆ 220, Fax 596, ≤, 🚗 – ⇔ rest TV ☎ P. AE ⓓ VISA
closed 25 and 26 December – **M** 14.50 **t.** (dinner) and a la carte 3.50 – **21 rm** ⊐ 35.00/90.00 **t.** – SB 75.00/110.00 **st.**

Broomknowe, School Brae, DG9 8LG, ✆ 365, ≤, 🚗 – ⇔ TV P
closed October-February – **M** (by arrangement) 6.50 **s.** – **3 rm** ⊐ -/26.00 **s.**

Blinkbonnie, School Brae, DG9 8LG, ✆ 282, ≤, 🚗 – P
February-October – **M** (by arrangement) 8.00 **t.** – **6 rm** ⊐ 12.00/28.00 **t.**

Si vous écrivez à un hôtel à l'étranger,
joignez à votre lettre un coupon-réponse international.
(disponible dans les bureaux de poste).

PORTREE Inverness. (Highland) 401 B 11 – see Skye (Isle of).

PRESTWICK Ayr. (Strathclyde) 401 402 G 17 – pop. 13 355 – ECD : Wednesday – ☎ 0292.

8 East Rd ✆ 77101 BY – 18 Links Rd ✆ 77404.

✈ ✆ 79822, Telex 778792 – **Terminal** : Buchanan Bus Station.

✈ see also Glasgow.

Prestwick Airport ✆ 79822 – Boydfield Gdns ✆ 79946.

Edinburgh 78 – ♦Ayr 2 – ♦Glasgow 32.

Plan of Built up Area : see Ayr

Carlton, 187 Ayr Rd, KA9 1TP, ✆ 76811 – ⇔ TV ☎ P. AE ⓓ VISA — BY **v**
M (carving rest.) 7.65 **t.** – **37 rm** ⊐ 45.00/60.00 **t.**

Kincraig without rest., 39 Ayr Rd, KA9 1SY, ✆ 79480 – TV P — BY **c**
6 rm ⊐ 13.00/40.00 **st.**

ROVER 1 Monkton Rd ✆ 77415

QUOTHQUAN Lanark. (Strathclyde) 401 J 27 – ✉ ☎ 0899 Biggar.

Edinburgh 32 – ♦Dumfries 50 – ♦Glasgow 36.

Shieldhill ⚘, ML12 6NA, NE : ¾ m. ✆ 20035, Fax 21092, ≤, « Victorian country house, 12C origins », 🚗 – ⇔ TV ☎ P – 🏛 25. AE ⓓ VISA. ✈
M 19.95/23.95 **t.** and a la carte 4.00 – **11 rm** ⊐ 80.00/137.00 **t.** – SB (except summer) 112.00/157.50 **st.**

RAASAY (Isle of) Inverness. (Highland) 401 B 11 – pop. 182 –see Skye (Isle of).

⛴ by Caledonian MacBrayne : to Sconser (Isle of Skye) Monday/Saturday 3-5 daily (15 mn).

RENFREW Renfrew. (Strathclyde) 401 G 16 – pop. 21 456 – ECD : Wednesday – ☎ 0- Glasgow.

◆Edinburgh 53 – ◆Glasgow 7.

- Stakis Normandy, Inchinnan Rd, PA4 9EJ, ☎ 886 4100, Telex 778897, Fax 885 2366 – rm TV ☎ P – 1000 **142 rm.**
- **Glynhill,** 169 Paisley Rd, PA4 8XB, ☎ 886 5555, Telex 779536, Fax 885 2838, – rm TV ☎ P – 350. AE VISA. **M** 9.50/16.00 **st.** and a la carte 3.75 – **125 rm** 69.00/99.00 **st.**

PEUGEOT-TALBOT 18-20 Fulbar St. ☎ 886 3354 VAUXHALL-OPEL Porterfield Rd ☎ 886 2777

RHU Dunbarton. (Strathclyde) 401 402 F 15 – see Helensburgh.

RHUBODACH Bute. (Strathclyde) 401 402 E 16 – Shipping Services : see Bute (Isle of).

RHUM (Isle of) Inverness. (Highland) 401 B 13 – Shipping Services : see Mallaig.

ROBERTON Roxburgh. (Borders) 401 402 L 17 – ✉ Hawick – ☎ 0750 Ettrick Valley.

◆Edinburgh 56 – ◆Carlisle 46 – Hawick 55.

- **West Buccleuch**, Ettrick Valley, TD9 7NQ, W : 8 m. on B 711 ☎ 62230, ←, P. VISA **M** (bar lunch)/dinner a la carte 10.50/15.00 **st.** 3.50 – **7 rm** 17.00/39.00 **st.** – SB 49.0 55.00 **st.**

ROCKCLIFFE Kirkcudbright. (Dumfries and Galloway) 401 402 I 19 – ✉ Dalbeattie ☎ 055 663.

◆Edinburgh 100 – ◆Dumfries 20 – Stranraer 69.

- **Baron's Craig**, DG5 4QF, ☎ 225, ←, park – TV ☎ P. VISA *Easter-mid October* – **M** 10.00/18.50 **t.** – **25 rm** 38.50/96.00 **t.**

En saison, surtout dans les stations fréquentées, il est prudent de retenir à l'avance. Cependant, si vous ne pouvez pas occuper la chambre que vous avez retenue, prévenez immédiatement l'hôtelier. Si vous écrivez à un hôtel à l'étranger, joignez à votre lettre un coupon-réponse international (disponible dans les bureaux de poste).

ROGART Sutherland. (Highland) 401 H 9 – ☎ 040 84.

◆Edinburgh 229 – ◆Inverness 73 – ◆Wick 63.

- **Rovie Farm**, IV28 3TZ, W : ¾ m. by A 839 ☎ 209, ←, « Working farm », park – *April-October* – **M** 8.50 **st.** – **6 rm** 13.50/27.00 **st.**

ROTHES Moray. (Grampian) 401 K 11 – pop. 1 414 – ECD : Wednesday – ☎ 034 03.

◆Edinburgh 192 – ◆Aberdeen 62 – Fraserburgh 58 – ◆Inverness 49.

- **Rothes Glen**, IV33 7AH, N : 3 m. on A 941 ☎ 254, Fax 566, ←, « Country hous atmosphere », park – TV ☎ P. AE VISA *closed 25 December-1 February* – **M** 12.00/22.50 **st.** 4.50 – **16 rm** 60.00/92.50 **st.** SB (April-October) (weekends only) 105.00 **st.**

ROUSAY (Isle of) Orkney. (Orkney Islands) 401 K 6 – Shipping Services : see Orkney Island (Mainland : Kirkwall).

ST. ANDREWS Fife. (Fife) 401 L 14 **Scotland G** – pop. 10 525 – ECD : Thursday – ☎ 0334.

See : Site★★ – Cathedral★ – West Port★.

Envir. : The East Neuk★★ (coastline from Crail to St. Monance) SE : 16 m. by A 917 – Leuchar Parish Church★, NW : 6 m. by A 91 and A 919 – Ceres★ (Fife Folk Museum) W : 9 m. by B 939 Kellie Castle★, S : 9 m. by B 9131 and B 9171.

18 Old Course, 18 Eden Course, 18 Jubilee Course, 18 New Course, 9 Balgove Cours St. Andrews Links ☎ 74637 – 9 St. Michaels ☎ 033 483 (Leuchars) 365, N : 5 m.

South St. ☎ 72021.

◆Edinburgh 51 – ◆Dundee 14 – Stirling 51.

- **St. Andrews Old Course,** Old Station Rd, KY16 9SP, ☎ 74371, Telex 76280, Fax 77668 ← golf courses and sea, – rest TV ☎ P – 150. AE VISA **M** 22.50 **st.** (dinner) and a la carte 15.00/29.75 **t.** 6.00 – 9.50 – **108 rm** 125.00 200.00 **st.**, **17 suites** 250.00/395.00 **st.** – SB 144.00/225.00 **st.**
- **Rusacks** (T.H.F.), 16 Pilmour Links, KY16 9JQ, ☎ 74321, Fax 77896, ←, – rm TV ☎ P – 50. AE VISA **M** 10.00/29.50 **st.** 4.50 – 9.00 – **48 rm** 80.00/135.00 **st.**, **2 suites** 150.00 **st.** SB 160.00/170.00 **st.**

Rufflets, Strathkinness Low Rd, KY16 9TX, W : 1 ½ m. on B 939 ☎ 72594, Fax 78703, ≤, « Country house, gardens » – TV ☎ P. AE VISA. ✻
closed mid January-mid February – **M** 10.50/21.00 **st.** and a la carte 5.80 – **20 rm** 46.00/120.00 **st.** – SB (November-April) 96.00/104.00 **st.**

St. Andrews Golf, 40 The Scores, KY16 9AS, ☎ 72611, Telex 94013267, Fax 72188, ≤, – TV ☎ – 150. AE VISA
M 10.75/16.75 **t.** and a la carte 4.00 – **23 rm** 57.00/110.00 **t.** – SB (November-March) 78.00 **st.**

The Scores (Best Western), 76 The Scores, KY16 9BB, ☎ 72451, Telex 94012061, Fax 73947, ≤, – TV ☎. AE VISA
closed 24 to 26 December – **M** (bar lunch)/dinner 17.50 **st.** and a la carte 4.00 – **30 rm** 62.00/120.00 **st.**

Russell, 26 The Scores, KY16 9AS, ☎ 73447, ≤ – TV ☎. AE VISA. ✻
closed 1 to 14 January – **M** 15.00 **t.** (dinner) and a la carte 3.50 – **7 rm** 45.00/60.00 **t.** – SB (winter only) 70.00/75.00 **st.**

ST. BOSWELLS Roxburgh. (Borders) 401 402 L 17 – pop. 1 086 – ☎ 0835.
Envir. : Dryburgh Abbey★★ (Setting★★★).
☎ 22359, off A 68 at St. Boswells Green.
Edinburgh 39 – ♦Glasgow 79 – Hawick 17 – ♦Newcastle-upon-Tyne 66.

Hotels see: Melrose NW : 4 ½ m.

ST. CATHERINES Argyll. (Strathclyde) 401 E 15 – ✉ Cairndow – ☎ 0499 Inveraray.
Envir. : Inveraray★★ (Castle★★-interior★★★) NW : 12 m. by A 815 and A 83 – Auchindrain★, NE : 18 m. by A 815 and A 83 SW.
Edinburgh 99 – ♦Glasgow 53 – ♦Oban 53.

Thistle House without rest., PA25 8AZ, on A 815 ☎ 2209, ≤, – rest P
April-October – **5 rm** 14.50/29.00 **st.**

ST. COMBS Aberdeen. (Grampian) 401 O 11 – pop. 817 – ECD : Wednesday – ✉ Fraserburgh – ☎ 034 65 Inverallochy.
♦Edinburgh 173 – ♦Aberdeen 43 – Fraserburgh 6.

Tufted Duck ⑤, AB4 5YS, ☎ 2481, Fax 2475, ≤ – TV ☎ P. AE VISA. ✻
M a la carte 11.70/19.70 3.75 – **15 rm** 28.50/48.00 **st.**

ST. FILLANS Perth. (Tayside) 401 H 14 – ECD : Wednesday – ☎ 076 485.
☎ 312.
♦Edinburgh 67 – ♦Glasgow 57 – ♦Oban 64 – Perth 30.

Four Seasons, PH6 2NF, ☎ 333, ≤ Loch Earn and mountains – rest TV ☎ P. AE VISA
closed January and February – **M** 10.95 14.35/20.20 **t.** (lunch) and a la carte **t.** 3.85 – **12 rm** 35.00/75.00 – SB (winter only) 88.00/96.00 **st.**

Achray House, PH6 2NF, ☎ 231, ≤ Loch Earn and mountains, – P. AE VISA. ✻
March-October – **M** (bar lunch)/dinner 18.00 **st.** and a la carte 3.00 – **5 rm** 26.00/48.00 **st.**

ST. MARGARETS HOPE Orkney. (Orkney Islands) 401 K 6 – see Orkney Islands.

SANDAY (Isle of) Orkney. (Orkney Islands) 401 M 6 – Shipping Services : see Orkney Islands (Mainland : Kirkwall).

SANDYHILLS Kirkcudbright. (Dumfries and Galloway) 401 402 I 19 – ✉ Dalbeattie – ☎ 038 778 Southwick.
♦Edinburgh 99 – ♦Ayr 62 – ♦Dumfries 19 – Stranraer 68.

Cairngill House ⑤, DG5 4NZ, ☎ 681, ≤, , ✻ – TV P
closed December-February – **M** 13.00 **st.** 3.00 – **8 rm** 27.00/48.00 **st.**

SCALASAIG Argyll. (Strathclyde) 401 B 15 – see Colonsay (Isle of).

SCALPAY (Isle of) Inverness. (Highland) 401 A 10 – Shipping Services : see Harris (Isle of).

SCARISTA Inverness. (Outer Hebrides) (Western Isles) – see Harris (Isle of).

SCOURIE Sutherland. (Highland) 401 E 8 – ✉ Lairg – ☎ 0971.
◆Edinburgh 263 – ◆Inverness 107.

- **Eddrachilles** ⛰, Badcall Bay, IV27 4TH, S : 2½ m. on A 894 ✆ 2080, ≤ Badcall Bay an islands, ⛱ – TV ☎ Ⓟ. ✱
March-October – **M** (bar lunch)/dinner 9.25 **t.** and a la carte 🍷 2.60 – **11 rm** ☕ 41.65 63.30 **t.**
- **Scourie** ⛰, IV27 4SX, ✆ 2396, Fax 2423, ≤, 🎣 – ☎ Ⓟ. AE ⓓ VISA
Mid March-late October – **M** (bar lunch)/dinner 12.00 **t.** 🍷 3.50 – **20 rm** ☕ 23.00/80.00 **t.**

SCRABSTER Caithness. (Highland) 401 J 8 – Shipping Services : see Thurso.

SELKIRK Selkirk. (Borders) 401 402 L 17 **Scotland G** – pop. 5 469 – ☎ 0750.
Envir. : Bowhill★★, W : 3 m. by A 708.
⛳9 Selkirk Hills ✆ 20621, S : 1 m.
ℹ Halliwell's House ✆ 20054 (summer only).
◆Edinburgh 40 – ◆Glasgow 73 – Hawick 11 – ◆Newcastle-upon-Tyne 73.

- **Philipburn House** ⛰, TD7 5LS, W : 1 m. at junction A 707 and A 708 ✆ 20747 Fax 21690, 🏊 heated, ⛱ – 🚭 rest TV ☎ Ⓟ. AE ⓓ VISA. ✱
M 11.50/21.50 **t.** and a la carte 🍷 4.95 – **16 rm** ☕ 42.00/60.00 **t.** – SB (closed July, August Easter, Christmas and New Year) (weekends only) 105.00/120.00 **st.**

SHAPINSAY (Isle of) Orkney. (Orkney Islands) 401 L 6 – Shipping Services : see Orkney Islands (Mainland : Kirkwall).

Les prix	Pour toutes précisions sur les prix indiqués dans ce guide, reportez-vous à l'introduction.

SHETLAND ISLANDS Shetland. (Shetland Islands) 401 PQ 3 **Scotland G** – pop. 27 271.
See : Site★ – Up Helly Aa★★ (last Tuesday in January).
✈ see Mainland : Lerwick and Sumburgh.
✈ Unst Airport : at Baltasound ✆ 095 781 (Baltasound) 404/7.
⛴ Shipping connections with the Continent : from Lerwick to Faroe Islands (Thorshavn) (Smyril Line) summer only – to Norway (Bergen) (Smyril Line) summer only – to Iceland (Seydisfjordur via Thorshavn) (Smyril Line) summer only – by P & O Ferries : Orkney and Shetland Services : from Lerwick to Aberdeen 1 weekly – by Shetland Islands Council : from Lerwick (Mainland) to Bressay frequent services daily (5 mn) – from Laxo (Mainland) to Symbister (Isle of Whalsay) frequent services daily (30 mn) – from Toft (Mainland) to Ulsta (Isle of Yell) frequent services daily (20 mn) – from Gutcher (Isle of Yell) to Belmont (Isle of Unst) frequent services daily (restricted on Sunday) (10 mn) – from Gutcher (Isle of Yell) to Oddsta (Isle of Fetlar) 2-3 daily (25 mn).
⛴ by Shetland Islands Council: from Fair Isle to Sumburgh (Gruntness) 1 weekly (2 h 30 mn) – from Lerwick (Mainland) to Skerries 2 weekly (2 h 20 mn).

MAINLAND

Brae – ✉ ☎ 080 622 Brae.

- **Busta House** ⛰, ZE2 9QN, SW : 1½ m. ✆ 506, Telex 9312100218, Fax 588, ≤, « Part 16C and 18C country house », ⛱ – 🚭 rest TV ☎ Ⓟ. AE ⓓ VISA
closed 22 December-3 January – **M** (bar lunch)/dinner 20.25 **t.** – **20 rm** ☕ 50.00/73.00 **t.**

Hillswick – ✉ ☎ 080 623 Hillswick.

- **St. Magnus Bay,** ZE2 9RW, ✆ 372, Fax 373, ≤, 🎣, ⛱ – TV Ⓟ. VISA
M (bar lunch)/dinner 25.00 **st.** and a la carte 🍷 3.75 – **25 rm** ☕ 30.00/54.00 **st.**

Lerwick **Scotland G** – pop. 7 223 – ECD : Wednesday – ✉ ☎ 0595 Lerwick.
See : Clickhimin Broch★ – Shetland Croft House Museum★ – Mousa Broch★★★ (island site) S : 13 m.
⛳18 Dale ✆ 369, NW : 3½ m. on A 970.
✈ Tingwall Airport : ✆ 3535/2024, NW : 6½ m. by A 971.
ℹ The Market Cross ✆ 3434.

- **Shetland,** Holmsgarth Rd, ZE1 0PW, ✆ 5515, Telex 75432, Fax 5828, ≤, 🎣, 🏊 – 🛗 🚭 rm TV ☎ ♿ Ⓟ – 🎤 200. AE ⓓ VISA
M 6.50/14.50 **st.** and a la carte – **63 rm** ☕ 58.00/66.00 **st.**, **1 suite** 90.00 **st.**
- Kveldsro House, Greenfield Pl., ZE1 0AN, ✆ 2195 – TV ☎ Ⓟ. VISA. ✱
closed Christmas-New Year – **M** 9.50/15.00 **t.** 🍷 3.10 – **14 rm.**

ROVER, NISSAN North Rd ✆ 2709
SUZUKI, MAZDA Holms Garth ✆ 2896
ATS 3 Gremista Ind Est. ✆ 3857

Sumburgh – ✉ ☎ 0950 Sumburgh.
See : Jarlshof★★ (prehistoric village).
✈ ✆ 60654, Telex 75451.

Walls – ✉ Walls – ☎ 0595 77 Shetland

✗ **Burrastow House** ⛰ with rm, ZE2 9PB, SW : 2 ½ m. ☎ 307, ≤, « 18C House overlooking Vaila Sound » – Ⓟ
March-September – **M** *(closed Tuesday)* (bar lunch)/dinner 17.50 **st.** – **2 rm** ☐ 51.00/92.00 **st.**

Whiteness – ✉ Whiteness – ☎ 059 584 Gott.

Westings, Wormadale, ZE2 9LJ, SE : 2 m. on A 971 ☎ 242, ≤ The Deeps and Islands – TV Ⓟ
6 rm.

SHIELDAIG Ross and Cromarty. (Highland) 401 D 11 – ✉ Strathcarron – ☎ 052 05.
◆Edinburgh 226 – ◆Inverness 70 – Kyle of Lochalsh 36.

Tigh-An Eilean, IV54 8XN, ☎ 251, ≤ Shieldaig Islands and Loch, « Attractively furnished inn » – Ⓟ. VISA
Easter-October – **M** (dinner only) 13.95 **t.** – **12 rm** ☐ 25.30/54.50 **t.**

SKEABOST Inverness. (Highland) 401 B 11 – see Skye (Isle of).

SKELMORLIE Ayr. (Strathclyde) 401 F 16 – pop. 1 606 – ECD : Wednesday – ☎ 0475 Wemyss Bay.
8 ☎ 520152, E: off A 78.
◆Edinburgh 78 – ◆Ayr 39 – ◆Glasgow 32.

Manor Park ⛰, PA17 5HE, S : 2 ¾ m. on A 78 ☎ 520832, ≤ gardens and Firth of Clyde, « Extensive gardens », park – TV ☎ Ⓟ. AE VISA.
M 15.00/17.50 **t.** and a la carte 5.00 – **23 rm** ☐ 40.00/100.00 **t.** – SB 90.00/115.00 **st.**

Redcliffe, 25 Shore Rd, PA17 5EH, on A 78 ☎ 521036, Fax 521894, ≤, – TV ☎ Ⓟ
9 rm.

SKYE (Isle of) Inverness. (Highland) 401 B 11 and 12 **Scotland G** – pop. 8 139.
See : Site★★ – Cuillin Hills★★★.
by Caledonian MacBrayne : from Kyleakin to Kyle of Lochalsh : frequent services daily (5 mn) – from Armadale to Mallaig Monday/Saturday 3 weekly – from Uig to Tarbert (Isle of Harris) Monday/Saturday: 1-2 daily (1 h 45 mn direct) (4 h 45 mn via Lochmaddy) – from Uig to Lochmaddy (North Uist) Monday/Saturday 1-2 daily (1 h 45 mn direct)(3 h 55 mn via Tarbert) – from Sconser to Isle of Raasay ; Monday/Saturday 3-5 daily (15 mn).

Ardvasar 401 C 12 – ✉ ☎ 047 14 Ardvasar.

Ardvasar, ✉ Sleat, IV45 8RS, ☎ 223, – Ⓟ. VISA
accommodation closed January and February – **M** *(closed 25 December and 1-2 January)* (bar lunch)/dinner a la carte approx. 15.00 **t.** 5.00 – **10 rm** ☐ 25.00/55.00 **t.**

Culnaknock 401 B 11 – ✉ Portree – ☎ 047 062 Staffin.

Glenview Inn, IV51 9JH, ☎ 248, ≤ – TV Ⓟ. VISA
Easter-October – **M** *(closed Sunday dinner)* (bar lunch)/dinner 20.00 **st.** – **5 rm** ☐ 25.00/55.00 **st.**

Dunvegan **Scotland G** – ✉ ☎ 047 022 Dunvegan.
See : Dunvegan Castle★.

Harlosh ⛰, IV55 8ZG, SE : 6 m. by A 863 ☎ 367, ≤ Loch Bracadale and Islands – rest Ⓟ. VISA.
April-October – **M** (dinner only) a la carte 14.20/21.00 **t.** 3.50 – **6 rm** ☐ -/60.00 **t.**

✗ **Three Chimneys,** Colbost, IV55 8ZT, NW : 5 ¾ m. by A 863 on B 884 ☎ 047 081 (Glendale) 258 – rest Ⓟ. VISA
April-October – **M** *(closed Sunday)* (booking essential) (restricted lunch)/dinner a la carte 16.50/34.00 **t.** 4.00.

Isleornsay – ✉ ☎ 047 13 Isleornsay.

Kinloch Lodge ⛰, IV43 8QY, ✉ Sleat, N : 3 ½ m. by A 851 ☎ 333, Fax 277, ≤ Loch Na Dal, « Country house atmosphere », , – rest Ⓟ. VISA
Mid March-November – **M** (dinner only) 30.00 **st.** 3.00 – **10 rm** ☐ 90.00/160.00 **st.**

Kensaleyre – ✉ Portree – ☎ 047 032 Skeabost Bridge.

Kensaleyre House ⛰, IV51 9XE, on A 856 ☎ 210, ≤ Loch Snizort Beag, « Country house atmosphere » – Ⓟ
Easter-October – **M** 10.00 **st.** 2.80 – **5 rm** ☐ 30.00/36.00 **st.**

Portree **Scotland G** – pop. 1 533 – ECD : Wednesday – ✉ ☎ 0478 Portree.

See : Site★★ – Skye Croft Museum★, N : 18 m. by A 850 and A 856 – Trotternish Peninsula★★, N : 40 m. by A 850, A 856 and A 855.

ℹ Meall House ✆ 2137.

Rosedale, Beaumont Cres., IV51 9DB, ✆ 3131, ≤ harbour – TV ☎ P
June-September – **M** (bar lunch, residents only)/dinner 15.00 **t.** – **23 rm** 30.00/64.00 **t.**

Kings Haven without rest., 11 Bosville Terr., IV51 9DJ, ✆ 2290 – TV.
closed December-February – **6 rm** -/50.00 **t.**

ROVER, FORD, RENAULT Dunvegan Rd ✆ 2554

Raasay Isle of – ✉ Kyle of Lochalsh – ☎ 047 862 Raasay.

Isle of Raasay, IV40 8PB, ✆ 222, ≤ Narrows of Raasay and Skye, – rest TV
P – *April-September* – **M** (bar lunch)/dinner 15.00 **t.** – **12 rm** 26.00/52.00 **t.** – SB (May-September) 76.00/80.00 **st.**

Skeabost – ECD : Wednesday – ✉ ☎ 047 032 Skeabost Bridge.

Skeabost House, IV51 9NP, ✆ 202, ≤ Loch Snizort Beag, « Country house atmosphere », 9, , , park – TV ☎ P
April-October – **M** (buffet lunch)/dinner 16.50 **t.** 4.50 – **21 rm** 32.00/80.00 **t.**

SMA'GLEN Perth. (Tayside) 401 I 14 – see Crieff.

SOUTH QUEENSFERRY W. Lothian. (Lothian) 401 J 16 **Scotland G** – pop. 7 485 – ECD : Wednesday – ☎ 031 Edinburgh.

See : Forth Bridges★★.

Envir. : Dalmeny (St. Cuthbert's Church★ – Dalmeny House★) E : 2 m. by B 924 – Hopetoun House★★, W : 2 m. by A 904 – Abercorn Parish Church (Hopetoun Loft★) W : 3 m. by A 904.

♦Edinburgh 9 – Dunfermline 7 – ♦Glasgow 41.

Forth Bridges Moat House (Q.M.H.), EH30 9SF, junction A 90 and Forth Bridge ✆ 331 1199, Telex 727430, Fax 319 1733, ≤ Firth of Forth and Bridges, , , , squash – rest TV ☎ P – 120. AE VISA
M 11.95/13.05 **st.** and a la carte 4.50 – 7.50 – **108 rm** 65.00/82.00 **st.** – SB (weekends only) 79.00 **st.**

STEWARTON Ayr. (Strathclyde) 401 402 G 16 – pop. 6 319 – ECD : Wednesday and Saturday – ☎ 0560.

♦Edinburgh 68 – ♦Ayr 21 – ♦Glasgow 22.

XXX **Chapeltoun House** with rm, KA3 3ED, SW : 2 ½ m. by A 735 off B 769 ✆ 82696, Fax 85100, « Country house in extensive grounds », , , park – TV ☎ P. AE VISA.
closed first 2 weeks January – **M** 16.00/25.50 **t.** – **8 rm** 69.00/125.00 **t.**

STIRLING Stirling. (Central) 401 I 15 **Scotland G** – pop. 36 640 – ECD : Wednesday – ☎ 0786.

See : Site★★ – Castle★★ (Site★★★-external elevations★★★-Stirling Heads★★★) B – Argyll and Sutherland Highlanders Regimental Museum★ B **M** – Argyll's Lodging★ (Renaissance decoration★) B **A** – Church of the Holy Rude★ B **B**.

Envir. : Wallace Monument (✻★★) N : 2 ½ m. by A 9 – A – and B 998 – Dunblane★ (Cathedral★) N : 6 ½ m. by A 9 – A – Doune★ (Castle★-Motor Museum★) NW : 8 m. by A 84 – A – M 9 and B 824 – Bannockburn, S : 2 m. by A 9 – A.

18 Queens Rd ✆ 73801 – B – 9 Alva Rd, Tillicoultry ✆ 0259 (Tillicoultry) 50124, E : 9 m. by A 9 – A.

✆ 73085.

ℹ Dumbarton Rd ✆ 75019 – Broad St. ✆ 79901 (summer only).

♦Edinburgh 37 – Dunfermline 23 – Falkirk 14 – ♦Glasgow 28 – Greenock 52 – Motherwell 30 – ♦Oban 87 – Perth 35.

Plan opposite

Park Lodge, 32 Park Terr., FK8 2JS, ✆ 74862, « Tastefully decorated Georgian house, antiques », – TV ☎ P. VISA
closed Christmas and New Year – **M** 11.50/17.50 **st.** and a la carte 4.50 – **9 rm** 75.00/150.00 **st.** B **a**

Granada Lodge without rest., Pirnhall roundabout, Snabhead, FK7 8EU, S : 3 m. ✆ 813614, Fax 815033 – TV P. AE VISA.
37 rm 27.50/29.50 **t.**

at Blairlogie NE : 4 ½ m. by A 9 on A 91 – A – ✉ Stirling – ☎ 0259 Alva :

Blairlogie House, FK9 5QE, ✆ 61441, , park – TV ☎ P. VISA
closed 2 weeks Christmas-New Year – **M** *(closed Sunday)* a la carte 12.40/18.00 **st.** 3.60 – **7 rm** 36.50/56.50 **st.**

FIAT 42-44 Causeway Head Rd ✆ 62426
VAUXHALL 119-139 Glasgow Rd ✆ 0786 (Bannockburn) 811234

ATS 45 Drip Rd ✆ 50770

STIRLING

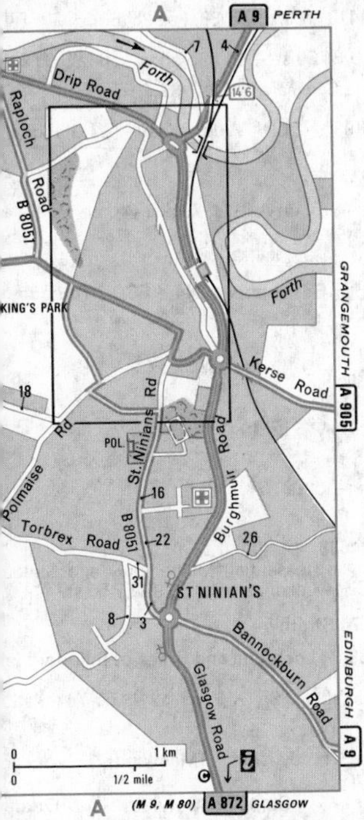

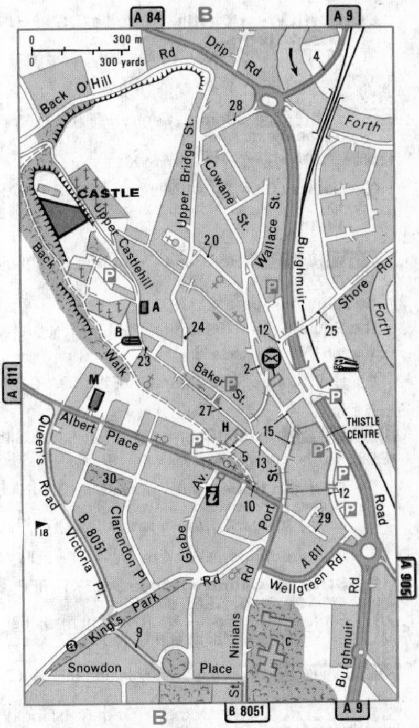

STONEHAVEN Kincardine. (Grampian) 401 N 13 **Scotland G** – pop. 7 834 – ECD : Wednesday – ☎ 0569.

Envir. : Dunnottar Castle★★ (site★★★) S : 2 m. by A 92 – Muchalls Castle (plasterwork ceilings★★) N : 5 m. by A 92.

Cowie ☎ 62124, N : 1 m. on Aberdeen Rd.

The Square ☎ 62806 (summer only).

Edinburgh 114 – ◆Aberdeen 16 – ◆Dundee 51.

Hotel see : **Netherley** N : 6 m.

ATS 64-72 Barclay St. ☎ 62077

STORNOWAY Ross and Cromarty. (Outer Hebrides) (Western Isles) 401 A 9 – see Lewis (Isle of).

STRACHUR Argyll. (Strathclyde) 401 E 15 – ECD : Wednesday – ✉ Cairndow – ☎ 036 986.

Edinburgh 104 – ◆Glasgow 58 – ◆Oban 58.

Creggans Inn, PA27 8BX, on A 815 ☎ 279, Telex 777694, Fax 637, ≤ Loch Fyne, – TV ☎ & P. AE VISA
M (bar lunch Monday to Saturday)/dinner a la carte 14.55/26.20 **t.** 4.65 – **21 rm** 40.00/116.00 **t.** – SB (April-October) 108.00/136.00 **st.**

Europe

Si le nom d'un hôtel figure en petits caractères,
demandez à l'arrivée
les conditions à l'hôtelier.

STRANRAER Wigtown. (Dumfries and Galloway) 401 402 E 19 **Scotland G** – pop. 10 766
ECD : Wednesday – ☎ 0776.

Envir. : Logan Botanic Garden★, S : 13 m. by A 77, A 716 and B 7065.

Creachmore by Stranraer, Leswalt ℘ 87245, NW : 2 m.

by Sealink : to Larne frequent services daily (2 h 20 mn).

Port Rodie Car Park ℘ 2595 (summer only).

◆Edinburgh 132 – ◆Ayr 51 – ◆Dumfries 75.

North West Castle, Portrodie, DG9 8EH, ℘ 4413, Telex 777088, Fax 2646, – 60.
M 19.00/17.50 **st.** and a la carte – **78 rm** 45.00/84.00 **st.** – SB (October-April) 88.00 **st.**

ROVER Leswalt Rd ℘ 3636 — ATS Commerce Rd ℘ 2131

STRATHBLANE Stirling. (Central) 401 H 16 – pop. 1 933 – ECD : Wednesday – ✉ Glasgow
☎ 0360 Blanefield.

◆Edinburgh 52 – ◆Glasgow 11 – Stirling 26.

Country Club, 41 Milngavie Rd, G63 9AH, S : ¾ m. on A 81 ℘ 70491, park –
10 rm.

STRATHPEFFER Ross and Cromarty. (Highland) 401 G 11 – pop. 1 244 – ECD : Thursday
☎ 0997.

Strathpeffer Spa ℘ 21219.

The Square ℘ 21415 (summer only).

◆Edinburgh 174 – ◆Inverness 18.

Holly Lodge, Golf Course Rd, IV14 9AR, ℘ 21254, –
7 rm.

STRATHYRE Perth. (Central) 401 H 15 – ✉ Callander – ☎ 087 74.

◆Edinburgh 62 – ◆Glasgow 53 – Perth 42.

Creagan House with rm, FK18 8ND, on A 84 ℘ 638, ≤ –
closed February and 1 week October – **M** (booking essential) (dinner only and Sunda
lunch) 16.00 **t.** 3.75 – **5 rm** 25.00/43.00 **t.** – SB (weekends only) 50.00/57.50 **st.**

at Balquhidder NW : 4 m. by A 84 – ✉ ☎ 087 74 Strathyre :

Stronvar Country House, FK19 8PB, ℘ 688, ≤ Loch Voil and Braes of Balquhidde
– . AE VISA.
February-October – **M** (bar lunch)/dinner 15.00 **st.** 3.95 – **5 rm** 49.50/75.00 **st.**
SB (February, March and October) 77.00 **st.**

STROMNESS Orkney. (Orkney Islands) 401 K 7 – see Orkney Islands (Mainland).

STRONSAY (Isle of) Orkney. (Orkney Islands) 401 M 6 – Shipping Services : see Orkne
Islands (Mainland : Kirkwall).

STRONTIAN Argyll. (Highland) 401 D 13 – ✉ ☎ 0967.

◆Edinburgh 139 – Fort William 23 – ◆Oban 66.

Kilcamb Lodge, PH36 4HY, ℘ 2257, ≤, , park – rest .
Easter-mid October – **M** (bar lunch)/dinner 20.00 **t.** 5.00 – **9 rm** (dinner includ
ed) 45.50/100.00 **t.**

at Glencripesdale W : 15½ m. by A 884, Laudale rd and Forestry Commission Track
✉ Acharacle – ☎ 096 785 Salen :

Glencripesdale House, Loch Sunart, Acharacle, PH36 4JH, ℘ 263, ≤ Loch Sunar
and Ben Laga, , , park – rest .
March-October and Christmas-New Year (booking advisable) – **4 rm** (dinner included
56.00/112.00 **st.**

SUMBURGH Shetland. (Shetland Islands) 401 Q 4 – see Shetland Islands (Mainland).

TAIN Ross and Cromarty. (Highland) 401 H 10 – pop. 3 428 – ECD : Thursday – ☎ 0862.

℘ 2314.

◆Edinburgh 191 – ◆Inverness 35 – ◆Wick 91.

Royal, High St., IV19 1AB, ℘ 2013, Fax 3450 – . AE VISA
M (bar lunch)/dinner 20.00 **t.** – **25 rm** 27.50/55.00 **t.**

Morangie, Morangie Rd, IV19 1PY, ℘ 2281, Fax 2872 – . AE VISA.
M 5.90/13.50 **t.** and a la carte 3.30 – **11 rm** 30.00/45.00 **t.**

VAUXHALL Knockbreck Rd ℘ 2175

TARBERT Inverness. (Outer Hebrides) (Western Isles) 401 Z 10 – see Harris (Isle of).

TAYINLOAN Argyll. (Strathclyde) 401 D 16 – Shipping Services : see Gigha (Isle of).

TAYVALLICH Argyll. (Strathclyde) 401 D 15 – ✉ Lochgilphead – ☎ 054 67.

Edinburgh 141 – ◆Glasgow 95 – ◆Oban 40.

X **Tayvallich Inn,** by Lochgilphead, PA31 8PR, ℘ 282, ≤ – P. VISA
April-October and Friday and Saturday in winter – **M** a la carte 5.70/14.60 **t.** 3.50.

THORNHILL Dumfries. (Dumfries and Galloway) 401 402 I 18 **Scotland G** – pop. 1 449 – ECD : Thursday – ☎ 0848.

Envir. : Drumlanrig Castle★★, NW : 4 m. by A 76.

18 Blacknest ℘ 30546.

◆Edinburgh 64 – ◆Ayr 44 – ◆Dumfries 15 – ◆Glasgow 63.

Trigony House, Closeburn, DG3 5EZ, S : 1½ m. on A 76 ℘ 31211, , – TV ☎ P. VISA.
M *(bar lunch)/dinner a la carte* 10.50/15.45 **t.** 4.50 – **9 rm** 29.50/54.00 **st.**

THURSO Caithness. (Highland) 401 J 8 **Scotland G** – pop. 8 828 – ECD : Thursday – ☎ 084 786.

Envir. : Coast road to Durness via Strathy Point★ (≤★★★) – Torrisdale Bay★ – Ben Loyal★★ – Coldbackie (≤★★) – Ben Hope★ – Loch Eriboll (≤★★★) W : 74 m. by A 836 and A 838.

18 Newlands of Geise ℘ 63807 – 18 Reay ℘ 084 781 (Reay) 288.

by P & O Ferries : Orkney and Shetland Services : from Scrabster to Stromness (Orkney Islands) 1 daily (1 h 50 mn) Monday/Saturday.

Riverside ℘ 62371 (summer only).

◆Edinburgh 289 – ◆Inverness 133 – ◆Wick 21.

Forss House , Bridge of Forss, KW14 7XY, W : 5½ m. on A 836 ℘ 202, ≤, , , park – TV ☎ P
7 rm.

CITROEN Couper Sq. Riverside ℘ 62777 | FORD Mansons Lane ℘ 63101

TIREE (Isle of) Argyll. (Strathclyde) 401 Z 14 – pop. 780.

℘ 087 92 (Scarinish) 456.

by Caledonian MacBrayne : to Arinagour (Isle of Coll): 3 weekly (– to Oban 3 weekly – to Tobermory (Isle of Mull) 3 weekly.

TIRORAN Argyll. (Strathclyde) 401 B 14 – see Mull (Isle of).

TOBERMORY Argyll. (Strathclyde) 401 B 14 – see Mull (Isle of).

TONGUE Sutherland. (Highland) 401 G 8 – ECD : Saturday – ✉ Lairg – ☎ 084 755.

Envir. : Coast road east via Coldbackie (≤★★) – Ben Loyal★★ – Torrisdale Bay★ – Strathy Point★ (≤★★★) E : 24 m. by A 836 – Coast road west via Ben Hope★ – Loch Eriboll (≤★★★) – Cape Wrath★★★ (≤★★) W : 44 m. by A 838.

◆Edinburgh 257 – ◆Inverness 101 – Thurso 43.

Ben Loyal, Main St., IV27 4XE, ℘ 216, ≤ – P. VISA
M (bar lunch)/dinner 12.50 **t.** 3.30 – **15 rm** 20.00/58.00 **t.** – SB 47.00/75.00 **st.**

Craggan , Talmine, Melness, IV27 47S, ℘ 278, ≤ – P
4 rm.

TROON Ayr. (Strathclyde) 401 402 G 17 – pop. 14 035 – ECD : Wednesday – ☎ 0292.

18, 18, 18 Harling Drive ℘ 312464 – 18, 18, 18 Royal Troon, Craigend Rd ℘ 311555 – 18 Kilmarnock (Barassie), 29 Hillhouse Rd ℘ 311077 – 18, 18, 18 Royal Troon, Craigend Rd ℘ 311555 – 18, 18 Hillhouse Rd, Barassie ℘ 311077.

Municipal Buildings, South Beach ℘ 317696 (summer only).

◆Edinburgh 77 – ◆Ayr 7 – ◆Glasgow 31.

Marine Highland, 8 Crosbie Rd, KA10 6HE, ℘ 314444, Telex 777595, Fax 316922, ≤, , , squash – TV ☎ P – 220. AE VISA
M 9.95/18.50 **t.** and a la carte 5.00 – **66 rm** 80.00/120.00 **t.**, **6 suites** 170.00 **t.** – SB 90.00/130.00 **st.**

Piersland House, 15 Craigend Rd, KA10 6HD, ℘ 314747, Fax 315613, – TV ☎ P. AE VISA
M 10.95/19.50 **t.** and a la carte 4.25 – **15 rm** 48.00/95.00 **t.**, **4 suites** 74.00 **t.** – SB (October-April) (weekends only) 70.00 **st.**

Ardneil, 51 St. Meddans St., KA10 6NU, ☎ 311611 – TV P. VISA
M 13.75/15.75 **t.** and a la carte – **9 rm** 22.50/48.00 **t.**

Campbell's, 3 South Beach, KA10 6EF, ☎ 314421 – VISA
closed Sunday, Monday and first 2 weeks January – **M** 10.95 **t.** (lunch) and a la carte 13.15/22.50 **t.** 3.65.

DAIHATSU St. Meddans St. ☎ 312099 — FORD 72-76 Portland St. ☎ 312312

TURNBERRY Ayr. (Strathclyde) 401 402 F 18 – ECD : Wednesday – ✉ Girvan – ☎ 0655.

18, 18 Turnberry Hotel ☎ 31000.

◆Edinburgh 97 – ◆Ayr 15 – ◆Glasgow 51 – Stranraer 36.

Turnberry, Maidens Rd, KA26 9LT, on A 719 ☎ 31000, Telex 777779, Fax 31706, ≤ golf course and bay, 18, – TV P – 170 VISA
M 16.50/29.50 **t.** and a la carte 7.50 – **115 rm** 145.00/190.00 **t.**, **10 suites** 265.00/400.00 **t.**

TWEEDSMUIR Peebles. (Borders) 401 402 J 17 – ✉ Biggar (Lanark) – ☎ 089 97.

◆Edinburgh 38 – ◆Carlisle 58 – ◆Dumfries 57 – ◆Glasgow 37.

Crook Inn, ML12 6QN, N : 1 m. on A 701 ☎ 272, ≤, – P. VISA
M (Bar lunch Monday to Saturday)/dinner a la carte 9.60/13.15 **st.** 3.75 – **7 rm** 30.00/52.00 **st.** – SB (weekdays only) 60.00/66.00 **st.**

UDDINGSTON Lanark. (Strathclyde) 401 402 H 16 – pop. 10 681 – ECD : Wednesday – ✉ Glasgow – ☎ 0698.

◆Edinburgh 41 – ◆Glasgow 10.

Redstones, 8-10 Glasgow Rd, G71 7AS, ☎ 813774, Fax 815319 – TV P. VISA
closed 1 and 2 January – **M** *(closed Sunday dinner)* 13.95/25.00 **t.** and a la carte 3.80 – **18 rm** 50.50/70.00 **t.** – SB (weekends only) 105.00/130.00 **st.**

Il Buongustaio, 84 Main St., ML6 6LT, ☎ 816000, Italian rest. – VISA
M *(closed Sunday and Tuesday)* 4.95 **t.** (lunch) and a la carte 15.75/37.55 **t.** 4.00.

UIG Ross and Cromarty. (Outer Hebrides) (Western Isles) 401 Y 9 – see Lewis (Isle of).

UIST (Isles of) Inverness. (Western Isles) 401 XY 11 and 12 – pop. 3 677.

✈ see Benbecula.

by Caledonian MacBrayne : from Lochboisdale to Oban 4 weekly – from Lochmaddy to Uig (Isle of Skye) Monday/Saturday 1-2 daily – from Lochmaddy to Tarbert (Isle of Harris) summer only: 1 weekly.

Benbecula – ✉ Liniclate – ☎ 0870 Benbecula.

✈ Benbecula Airport : ☎ 2051.

Dark Island, PA88 5PJ, ☎ 2414 – TV P. VISA.
M 6.50/12.50 **t.** and a la carte 3.50 – **42 rm** 22.00/100.00 **t.**

Daliburgh (South Uist) – ✉ ☎ 087 84 Lochboisdale.

Borrodale, PA81 5SS, ☎ 444, ≤, – TV P. VISA
M 7.50/12.50 **t.** 5.50 – **13 rm** 23.00/45.00 **t.** – SB (inter only) (weekends only) 60.00/68.60 **st.**

ULLAPOOL Ross and Cromarty. (Highland) 401 E 10 **Scotland G** – pop. 1 006 – ECD : Tuesday except summer – ☎ 0854.

See : Site★.

Envir. : Falls of Measach★★ in the Corrieshalloch Gorge★, S : 11 m. by A 835 – Loch Broom★★, Loch Assynt★★ and Lochinver, N : 37 m. by A 835 and A 837.

Exc. : Inverewe Gardens★★★ W : 50 m. by A 835 and A 832.

by Caledonian MacBrayne : to Stornoway (Isle of Lewis) Monday/Saturday 1-4 daily (3 h 30 mn).

West Shore St. ☎ 2135 (summer only).

◆Edinburgh 215 – ◆Inverness 59.

Mercury (Mt. Charlotte Thistle), North Rd, IV26 2UD, ☎ 2314, – TV P. VISA
April-October – **M** (dinner only) 12.50 **st.** and a la carte 3.85 – **60 rm** 39.50/59.50 **t.** – SB 66.00/75.00 **st.**

✿ **Altnaharrie Inn** (Gunn Eriksen), IV26 2SS, SW : ½ m. via private ferry ☎ 085 483 (Dundonnell) 230, ≤ Loch Broom and Ullapool, « Idyllic setting on bank of Loch Broom », –
closed winter – **M** (booking essential) (restricted lunch, residents only)/dinner approx. 40.00 **st.** 4.50 – **8 rm** (dinner included) approx. 110.00 **st.**
Spec. A "soup" of langoustine and squat lobster with a scallop mousseline parcel, Layers of foie gras and asparagus on a bed of crisp potato cake, Assorted fish in a crisp pastry shell with two sauces.

Ceilidh Place, 14 West Argyle St., IV26 2TY, ℘ 2103, Fax 2886, « Tasteful decor » – rest. VISA
M (buffet lunch)/dinner 15.00 **st.** and a la carte – **15 rm** 33.00/80.00 **st.**

Harbour Lights, Garve Rd, IV26 2SX, ℘ 2222, ≤ Loch Broom, – VISA
M (bar lunch)/dinner 15.00 **t.** and a la carte 3.50 – **22 rm** 28.00/58.00 **t.** – SB (mid October-mid May) 72.00/80.00 **st.**

Ferry Boat Inn, Shore St., IV26 2UJ, ℘ 2366, ≤ – rest
11 rm.

UNST Shetland. (Shetland Islands) 401 R 1 – Shipping Services : see Shetland Islands.

UPHALL W. Lothian. (Lothian) 401 J 16 – ECD : Wednesday – 0506 Broxburn.

℘ 856404.

Edinburgh 13 – Glasgow 32.

Houstoun House, EH52 6JS, ℘ 853831, Fax 854220, « Gardens », park – . VISA
closed 26 to 27 December and 1 to 3 January – **M** *(closed Saturday lunch)* 15.00/27.00 **t.** 5.00 – **30 rm** 75.00/130.00 **t.** – SB (weekends only) 100.00/110.00 **st.**

VATERSAY Inverness. (Western Isles) 401 X 13 – Shipping Services : see Barra (Isle of).

WALKERBURN Peebles. (Borders) 401 402 K 17 – pop. 713 – 089 687.

Envir. : Traquair House★★, W : 4 m.

Edinburgh 32 – Galashiels 10 – Peebles 8.

Tweed Valley, Galashiels Rd, EH43 6AA, ℘ 636, Fax 639639, ≤, – . VISA
M 12.50/14.50 **t.** and a la carte 4.25 – **15 rm** 33.00/66.00 **t.** – SB (except New Year) 79.00/95.00 **st.**

WALLS Shetland. (Shetland Islands) 401 PQ 3 – see Shetland Islands (Mainland).

WEMYSS BAY Renfrew. (Strathclyde) 401 402 F 16 – ECD : Wednesday – 0475.

by Caledonian MacBrayne : to Rothesay (Isle of Bute) : frequent services daily (30 mn).

Hotels see : Largs S : 4½ m., ***Skelmorlie*** S : 1½ m.

WESTHILL Aberdeen. (Grampian) 401 N 12 – see Aberdeen.

WESTRAY (Isle of) Orkney. (Orkney Islands) 401 KL 6 – Shipping Services : see Orkney Islands (Mainland : Kirkwall).

WEST WEMYSS Fife. (Fife) – see Kirkcaldy.

WHALSAY (Isle of) Shetland. (Shetland Islands) 401 R 2 – Shipping Services : see Shetland Islands.

WHITEBRIDGE Inverness. (Highland) 401 G 12 – 045 63 Gorthleck.

Edinburgh 171 – Inverness 23 – Kyle of Lochalsh 67 – Oban 92.

Knockie Lodge, IV1 2UP, SW : 3½ m. by B 862 ℘ 276, ≤ Loch Nanlann and mountains, « Tastefully converted hunting lodge », , park – . VISA.
May-October – **M** (bar lunch residents only)/dinner 20.00 **t.** 4.50 – **10 rm** (dinner included) 75.00/170.00 **t.**

WHITENESS Shetland. (Shetland Islands) 401 Q 3 – see Shetland Islands (Mainland).

WHITING BAY Bute. (Strathclyde) 401 402 E 17 – see Arran (Isle of).

WHITHORN (Isle of) Wigtown. (Dumfries and Galloway) 401 402 G 19 **Scotland G** – pop. 989 – ECD : Wednesday – 098 85.

Envir. : Priory Museum (Early Christian Crosses★★) NW : 4 m. by A 750.

Edinburgh 152 – Ayr 72 – Dumfries 72 – Stranraer 34.

Queens Arms, 22 Main St., DG8 8LF, ℘ 369 – rest
9 rm.

Steam Packet, Harbour Row, DG8 8LL, ℘ 334, ≤, –
M 4.55/9.50 **t.** and a la carte 3.50 – **5 rm** 20.00/40.00 **t.**

WICK Caithness. (Highland) 401 K 8 **Scotland G** – pop. 7 770 – ECD : Wednesday – ☎ 0955.

Envir. : the Hill O'Many Stanes★, S by A 9 – Grey Cairns of Camster★, S by A 9 – Duncansby Head★ and the stacks of Duncansby★★, N : 17 m. by A 9.

Reiss ☎ 2726, N : 3 m.

✈ ☎ 2215, N : 1 m.

Whitechapel Rd off High St. ☎ 2596.

♦Edinburgh 282 – ♦Inverness 126.

Mercury (Mt. Charlotte Thistle), Riverside, KW1 4NL, ☎ 3344, Fax 5456 – TV ☎ P – 150. AE VISA
M (bar lunch)/dinner 12.50 **t.** and a la carte 3.95 – 6.50 – **48 rm** 48.00/66.00 **t.** – SB (weekends only) 72.00/102.00 **st.**

DATSUN, VAUXHALL Francis St. ☎ 4123 FORD Francis St. ☎ 2103

WIGTOWN Wigtown. (Dumfries and Galloway) 401 G 19 – pop. 1 040 – ECD : Wednesday – ✉ Newton Stewart – ☎ 098 84 (4 fig.) or 0988 (5 fig.).

Wigtown and Bladnoch ☎ 3354.

♦Edinburgh 137 – ♦Ayr 61 – ♦Dumfries 61 – Stranraer 26.

Corsemalzie House, DG8 9RL, SW : 6 ½ m. by A 714 on B 7005 ☎ 098 886 (Mochrum) 254, « Country house atmosphere », park – TV ☎ P. VISA
closed 20 January-7 March – **M** 10.00/17.75 **t.** and a la carte 3.30 – **15 rm** 35.50/53.00 **t.** – SB 72.00/84.00 **st.**

WORMIT Fife. (Fife) 401 L 14 – ECD : Wednesday – ✉ ☎ 0382 Newport-on-Tay.

♦Edinburgh 53 – ♦Dundee 6 – St. Andrews 12.

Sandford Hill, DD6 8RG, S : 2 m. at junction of A 914 and B 946 ☎ 541802, ≤, – TV ☎ P. AE VISA
closed 1 and 2 January – **M** 13.00/20.00 **t.** 4.00 – **15 rm** 42.00/66.00 **t.** – SB (weekends only) 72.00/78.00 **st.**

WYRE (Isle of) Orkney. (Orkney Islands) 401 L 6 – Shipping Services : see Orkney Islands (Mainland : Kirkwall).

YELL (Isle of) Shetland. (Shetland Islands) 401 Q 2 – Shipping Services : see Shetland Islands (Mainland).

Northern Ireland

Place with at least :

one hotel or restaurant ...... ● Londonderry
one pleasant hotel .... 🏨, ⌂, ✗ with rm
one quiet, secluded hotel .... 🐴
one restaurant with ..... ✿, ✿✿, ✿✿✿, M
See this town for establishments located in its vicinity .... BELFAST

Localité offrant au moins :

une ressource hôtelière .... ● Londonderry
un hôtel agréable .... 🏨, ⌂, ✗ with rm
un hôtel très tranquille, isolé .... 🐴
une bonne table à ...... ✿, ✿✿, ✿✿✿, M
Localité groupant dans le texte les ressources de ses environs ... BELFAST

La località possiede come minimo :

una risorsa alberghiera .... ● Londonderr
un albergo ameno .... 🏨, ⌂, ✗ with rn
un albergo molto tranquillo, isolato ..... 🐴
un'ottima tavola con .... ✿, ✿✿, ✿✿✿, M
La località raggruppa nel suo testo le risorse dei dintorni .... BELFAST

Ort mit mindestens :

einem Hotel oder Restaurant .. ● Londonderry
einem angenehmen Hotel .. 🏨, ⌂, ✗ with rn
einem sehr ruhigen und abgelegenen Hotel 🐴
einem Restaurant mit .... ✿, ✿✿, ✿✿✿, M
Ort mit Angaben über Hotels und Restaurants in seiner Umgebung .... BELFAST

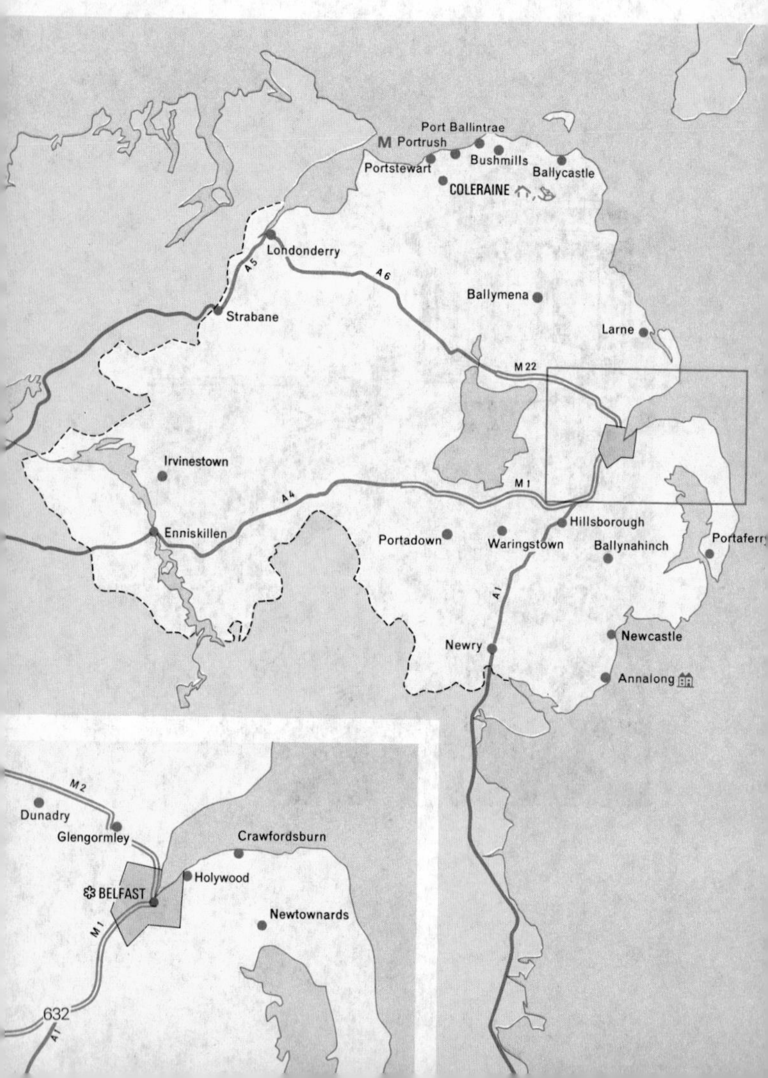

ANNALONG (Áth na Long) Down 405 O 5 – ☎ 039 67.

Belfast 37 – ◆Dundalk 36.

Glassdrumman Lodge ⛰, 85 Mill Rd, BT34 4RH, ☎ 68451, Fax 67041, ← Irish Sea and Mourne mountains, « Working farm », park – TV ☎ P. VISA.
M (communal dining) (bar lunch)/dinner 25.00 **t.** 5.00 – **8 rm** 45.00/75.00 **t.** – SB 85.00/110.00 **st.**

ANTRIM (Coast Road) (Aontroim) Antrim 405 O 3.

See : Road★★★ (A 2) from Larne to Portrush.

BALLYCASTLE (Baile an Chaistil) Antrim 405 N 2 – pop. 3 284 – ☎ 026 57.

See : Site★★. **Envir.** : Giant's Causeway★★★ (Chaussée des Géants) basalt formation (from the car-park *AC*, ½ h return on foot) NW : 12 m. – White Park Bay★★, NW : 8 ½ m. – Carrick-a-Rede (←★★ of Rathlin Island) NW : 5 ½ m.

18 ☎ 62536.

7 Mary St. ☎ 62024.

◆Belfast 60 – Ballymena 28 – Larne 40.

Hotels see : Portballintrae, W : 12 m.

BALLYMENA (An Baile Meánach) Antrim 405 N 3 – pop. 28 166 – ☎ 0266.

Envir. : Glen of Glenariff★★★ – Glenariff (or Waterfoot) site★, NE : 19 m.

18 128 Raceview Rd ☎ 861207, E : 2 m. on A 42.

Ardeevim, 80 Galgorm Rd ☎ 44111 – Town Hall, Bridge St. ☎ 41284.

◆Belfast 28 – ◆Dundalk 78 – Larne 21 – ◆Londonderry 51 – ◆Omagh 53.

Country House ⛰, 20 Doagh Rd ✉ Kells, BT42 3LZ, SE : 6 m. by A 36 on B 59 ☎ 891663, Fax 891477, – TV ☎ P – 200. AE VISA.
closed 25 and 26 December – **M** 7.95/15.00 **st.** and a la carte 3.50 – **38 rm** 49.50/125.00 **st.**

Adair Arms, 1-5 Ballymoney Rd, BT43 5BS, ☎ 653674, Fax 40436 – TV ☎ P – 250. AE VISA.
closed 25 December – **M** 9.00/12.95 **t.** 4.50 – **37 rm** 45.00/58.00 **st.** – SB (weekends only) 66.00/80.00 **st.**

Water Margin, 8-10 Cully Backey Rd, BT43 5DF, ☎ 652320, Chinese rest. – P.

Manley, State Cinema Arcade, Ballymoney Rd, BT43 5BY, ☎ 48967, Chinese (Canton, Peking) rest. – AE VISA
M 3.75/7.00 **t.** and a la carte.

LOTUS Pennybridge Ind Est, Larne Rd ☎ 652161
ROVER 1-3 Waveney Av. ☎ 653557
VW-AUDI 1-5 Railway St. ☎ 6546014
ATS Antrim Rd ☎ 652888

BALLYNAHINCH (Baile na hInse) Down 405 O 4 – pop. 3 721 – ☎ 0238.

9 20 Grove Rd ☎ 562365.

55 Windmill St. ☎ 561950.

◆Belfast 14 – Downpatrick 10.

Woodlands, 29 Spa Rd, BT24 8PT, SW : 1 ½ m. by A 24 on B 175 ☎ 562650, – P. VISA
closed Sunday, Monday and Tuesday – **M** (dinner only) (booking essential) 18.95 **st.** 3.75.

DAIHATSU-HYUNDAI Lisburn Rd ☎ 562597
FORD 41 Main St. ☎ 562519

BELFAST (Béal Feirste) Antrim 405 O 4 – pop. 329 958 – ☎ 0232.

See : City Hall★★ (1906) BZ – Queen's University★★ (1906) AZ **U** – Ulster Museum★ AZ **M** – Church House★ (1905) BZ **B** – Botanic Gardens (hot houses★) AZ – Bellevue Zoological Gardens (site★, ←★) *AC*, by A 6 AY.

Envir. : Stormont (Parliament House★ 1932, terrace : vista★★) E : 4 m. by Belmont Rd AZ – The Giant's Ring★ (prehistoric area) S : 5 m. by Malone Rd AZ – Lisburn (Castle gardens ←★) SW : 8 m. by A 1 AZ.

18 Balmoral, Lisburn Rd ☎ 381514 AZ – 18 Fortwilliam, Downview Av. ☎ 370770, N : 2 m. AY – 18 Shandon Park ☎ 793730, E : 3 m. by A55 AZ – 18 Knockbracken, Ballymaconaghy Rd ☎ 792108 Z – 18, 9 Malone, Upper Malone Rd ☎ 612695 AZ – 9 Ormeau, Ravenhill Rd ☎ 641069 AZ.

Belfast Airport : ☎ 08494 (Crumlin) 22888 , NW : 12 m. by M 2 Motorway Belfast City Airport : ☎ 457745 – **Terminal** : Coach service (Ulsterbus Ltd.) from Great Victoria Street Station (40 mn).

to Liverpool (Belfast Ferries) 1 daily (9 h) – to Isle of Man : Douglas (Isle of Man Steam Packet Co.) 2 weekly (4 h 45 mn) (summer only).

River House, 52 High St., BT1 2DS ☎ 246609 – City Hall ☎ 320202.

◆Dublin 103 – ◆Londonderry 70.

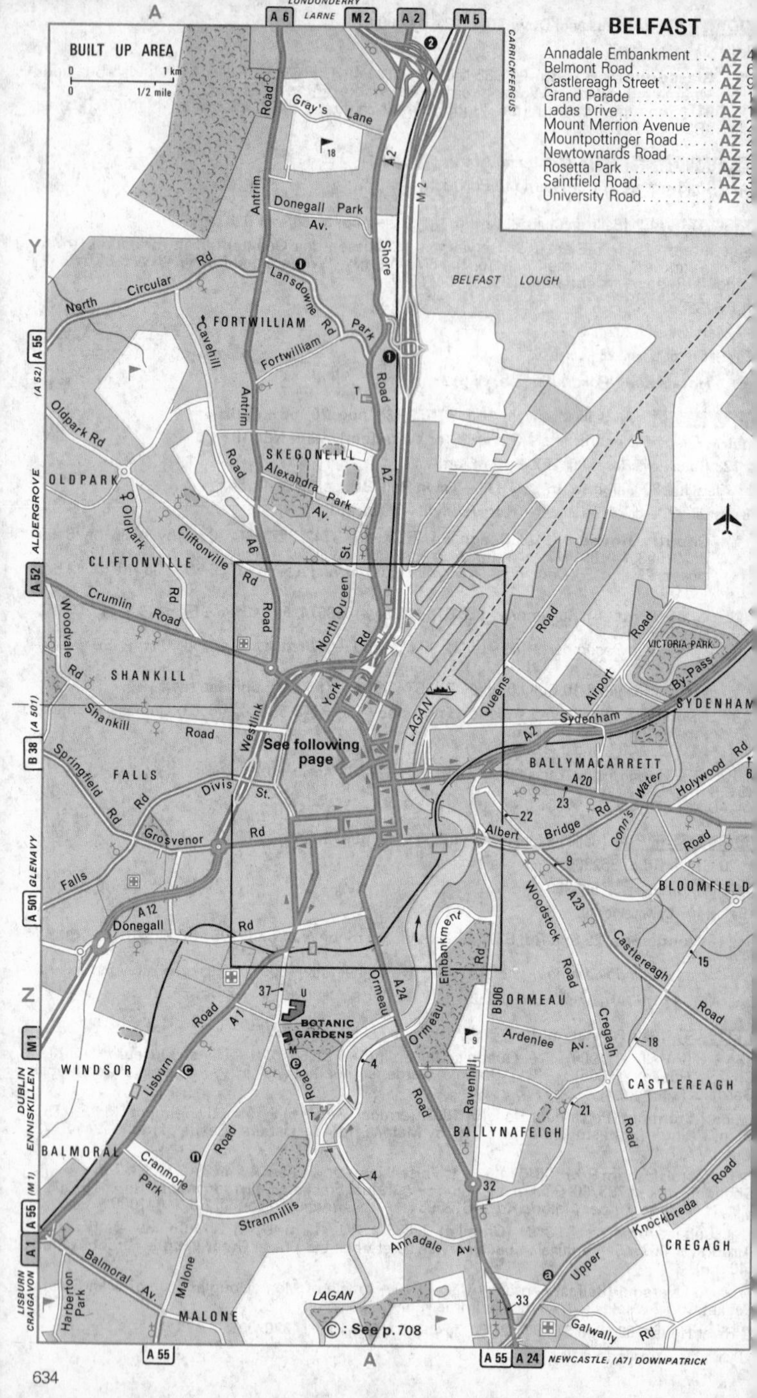

BELFAST
Annadale Embankment . . . AZ
Belmont Road . . . AZ
Castlereagh Street . . . AZ
Grand Parade . . . AZ
Ladas Drive . . . AZ
Mount Merrion Avenue . . . AZ
Mountpottinger Road . . . AZ
Newtownards Road . . . AZ
Rosetta Park . . . AZ
Saintfield Road . . . AZ
University Road . . . AZ
BUILT UP AREA
0 1 km
0 1/2 mile
LONDONDERRY
LARNE
A 6
M 2
A 2
M 5
CARRICKFERGUS
Gray's Lane
Antrim Road
Donegall Park Av.
Shore Road
A2
M 2
BELFAST LOUGH
North Circular Rd
Lansdowne Rd
Park
FORTWILLIAM
Cavehill
Fortwilliam
Antrim Road
A 55
(A 52)
ALDERGROVE
A 52
Oldpark Rd
OLDPARK
SKEGONEILL
Alexandra Park Av.
Oldpark
Cliftonville Rd
CLIFTONVILLE
A6
North Queen St.
Crumlin Road
Woodvale Rd
SHANKILL
Rd
Road
VICTORIA PARK
Airport Road
By-Pass
SYDENHAM
Sydenham
Queens
York
Rd
LAGAN
Westlink
See following page
(A 501)
Shankill Road
B 38
Springfield Rd
FALLS
Divis St.
Rd
Grosvenor Rd
A2
BALLYMACARRETT
A20
Holywood Rd
Conn's Water
Albert Bridge Rd
Road
BLOOMFIELD
GLENAVY
A 501
Falls
A 12
Donegall Rd
Embankment Rd
Woodstock Road
A23
Castlereagh Road
B 506
ORMEAU
Ormeau Road
A24
BOTANIC GARDENS
A1
Lisburn Road
M1
DUBLIN
ENNISKILLEN
WINDSOR
Ardenlee Av.
Cregagh Road
CASTLEREAGH
Ravenhill
BALLYNAFEIGH
BALMORAL
Cranmore Park
Road
Stranmillis
Road
Annadale Av.
Knockbreda Road
CREGAGH
Upper
(M 1)
A 55
A 1
LISBURN
CRAIGAVON
Balmoral Av.
Harberton Park
Malone
MALONE
LAGAN
Galwally Rd
©: See p.708
A 55
A 55
A 24
NEWCASTLE, (A7) DOWNPATRICK

BELFAST

CENTRE

Street	Grid	No.
Castlecourt Shopping Centre	BYZ	
Castle Place	BZ	
Donegal Place	BZ	
Royal Avenue	BYZ	
Albert Bridge Road	BZ	2
Albert Square	BY	3
Ann Street	BZ	5
Bradbury Place	BZ	7
Bridge Street	BZ	8
Clifton Street	BY	10
Corporation Square	BY	12
Donegall Quay	BYZ	13
Donegall Square	BZ	14
High Street	BYZ	16
Howard Street	BZ	17
Mountpottinger Road	BZ	22
Newtownards Road	BZ	23
Queen Elizabeth Bridge	BZ	25
Queen's Quay Road	BY	26
Queen's Bridge	BZ	27
Queen's Square	BY	29
Rosemary Street	BZ	30
Station Street	BY	35
University Road	BZ	37
Waring Street	BY	38
Wellington Place	BZ	39

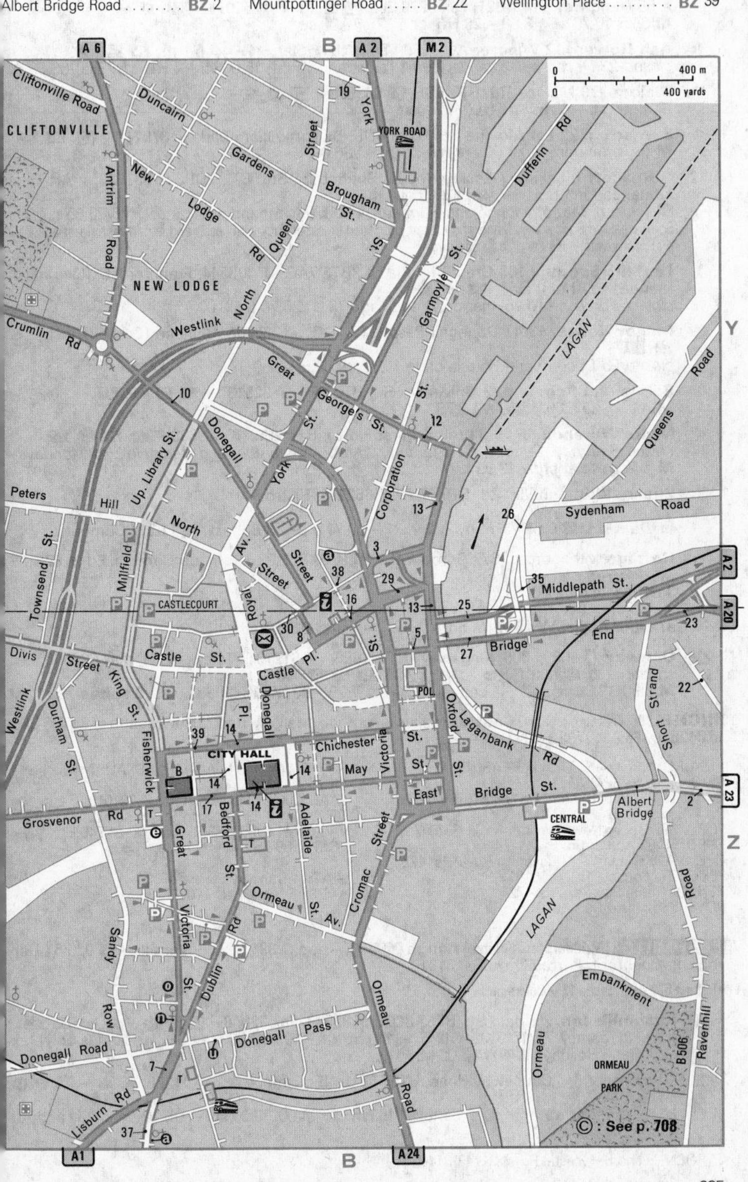

Europa, Great Victoria St., BT2 7AP, ☎ 327000, Telex 74491, Fax 327800, ← – |‡| ⇤ rm TV ☎ ♿ – 🏛 1 100
195 rm, 3 suites. BZ

Stormont, 587 Upper Newtownards Rd, BT4 3LP, E : 4 ½ m. by A 2 on A 20 ☎ 658621, Telex 748198, Fax 480240 – |‡| TV ☎ P – 🏛 250. AE VISA. ✻
M 6.50/15.50 **st.** and a la carte 🍷 4.00 – ☕ 7.50 – **67 rm** 74.00/96.00 **st.** – SB (weekends only) 90.50 **st.** on A 20 AZ

Drumkeen, Upper Galwally, by Upper Knockbreda Rd, BT8 4TL, SE : 3 m. by A 24 and A 55 (Ring Rd) ☎ 491321, Fax 692949 – TV ☎ P – 🏛 500. VISA. ✻ AZ
M 6.75/10.75 **st.** 🍷 3.50 – **28 rm** ☕ 57.75/70.00 **st.**

Ash Rowan, 12 Windsor Av., BT9 6EE, ☎ 661758, – ⇤ TV P. VISA. ✻ AZ
closed 23 December-2 January – **M** (by arrangement) 15.00 **st.** – **4 rm** ☕ 28.00/66.00 **st.**

Malone, 79 Malone Rd, BT9 6SH, ☎ 669565 – TV P. ✻ AZ
M 12.50 **st.** – **8 rm** ☕ 25.00/40.00 **st.**

Somerton, 22 Lansdowne Rd, BT15 4DB, by Fortwilliam Park ☎ 370717 – TV. VISA
M (by arrangement) 7.00 – **8 rm** ☕ 16.00/36.00. AY

XX ✿ **Roscoff** (Rankin), 7 Lesley House, Shaftsbury Sq., BT2 7DB, ☎ 331532, « Art Deco influenced interior » – ⇤. AE VISA BZ
M *(closed Saturday lunch and Sunday)* 14.50 **t.** (lunch) and a la carte 17.70/23.85 **t.** 🍷 3.50
Spec. Seafood boudin with fennel and lobster jus, Sliced breast of duck with cassis and lemon zest, Roast banana in puff pastry with vanilla and Jamaican rum.

X **La Belle Epoque,** 103 Great Victoria St., BT2 7AG, ☎ 323244, French rest., (Live music Monday to Thursday) – VISA BZ
closed Sunday – **M** (dinner only) a la carte 13.00/26.70 **t.** 🍷 3.00.

X **Manor House,** 43-47 Donegall Pass, BT7 1DQ, ☎ 238755, Chinese (Canton) rest. – VISA BZ
closed 25 December – **M** a la carte 10.00/19.00 **t.** 🍷 3.50.

X **Saints and Scholars,** 3 University St., BT7 1FY, ☎ 325137 – AE VISA BZ
M a la carte 6.65/12.55 **t.** 🍷 3.75.

X **Nicks Warehouse,** 35-39 Hill St. (1st Floor), BT1 2LB, ☎ 439690 – ▤. VISA
closed Saturday, Sunday, 8 to 12 July, 25 to 27 December and Bank Holiday Mondays – **M** a la carte approx. 12.95 **t.** BY

X Strand, 12 Stranmillis Rd, BT9 5AA, ☎ 682266, Bistro – AZ

at Dundonald E : 5 ½ m. by A 2 – BY – on A 20 – ✉ Belfast – ☎ 0247 Comber :

Cottage without rest., 377 Comber Rd, BT16 0XB, SE : 1 ¾ m. on Comber Rd ☎ 878189, – ⇤ P
3 rm ☕ 14.00/27.00 **st.**

at Dunmurry SW : 5 ½ m. on A 1 – AZ – ✉ ☎ 0232 Belfast :

Conway (T.H.F.), 300 Kingsway, BT17 9ES, ☎ 612101, Telex 74281, Fax 626546, , squash – |‡| ▤ rest TV ☎ P – 🏛 400. AE VISA
M 8.50/13.00 **st.** and a la carte 🍷 3.75 – ☕ 7.25 – **80 rm** 75.00/93.00 **st.**, **2 suites** 155.00 **st.**

MICHELIN Distribution Centre, Mallusk Park, 40 Mallusk Road, Newtonabbey, BT36 8PS, ☎ **842616, Fax 342732 by N7** AZ

ALFA-ROMEO, DAIHATSU, FERRARI 50 Gt. Georges St. ☎ 232111
CITROEN 357 Albertbridge Rd ☎ 457575 457766
FIAT Boucher Rd ☎ 247770
FORD 397 Upper Newtownards Rd ☎ 654687
FORD 58-82 Antrim Rd ☎ 744744
OPEL-VAUXHALL 17-29 Ravenhill Rd ☎ 451422
PEUGEOT Boucher Rd ☎ 661811
RENAULT Boucher Rd ☎ 381721
ROVER Saintfield Rd ☎ 649774
ROVER, DAIMLER-JAGUAR, RENAULT Boucher Rd ☎ 381721
SAAB 250-252 Donegall Rd ☎ 321019
TOYOTA 39-49 Adelaide St. ☎ 328225
VAUXHALL-OPEL 83-87 York Rd ☎ 746960
VOLVO 59-75 Ladas Drive ☎ 705666

ATS 4 Duncrue St. ☎ 749531
ATS 37 Boucher rd. ☎ 663623

BUSHMILLS **(Muileann na Buaise)** Antrim 405 M 2 – pop. 1 381 – ✉ Bushmills – ☎ 026 57 Dervock. Bushfoot, Portballintrae ☎ 31317.

◆Belfast 57 – Ballycastle 12 – Coleraine 10.

Bushmills Inn, 25 Main St., BT57 8QA, ☎ 32339, Fax 32048 – TV ☎ P – 🏛 60. VISA
M a la carte 7.75/15.90 **t.** 🍷 4.25 – **11 rm** ☕ 38.00/58.00 **t.** – SB (weekends only) (except Bank Holidays) 64.00/82.00 **st.**

Causeway ⛰, Causeway Head, BT57 8SU, NE : 2 m. by A 2 ☎ 31226, ←, – TV ☎ P. VISA. ✻
M 6.80/15.00 **st.** and a la carte – **16 rm** ☕ 24.00/39.00 **st.** – SB (except July and August) 55.00/60.00 **st.**

CITROEN Inland Ballycastle Rd ☎ 31748/31452

CASTLEROCK (Carraig Ceasail) Londonderry – see Coleraine.

COLERAINE (Cúil Raithin) Londonderry 405 L 2 – pop. 15 967 – ☎ 0265.

Envir. : Giant's Causeway★★★ (Chaussée des Géants) basalt formation (from the car-park *AC*, ½ h return on foot) NE : 9 m. – Downhill Castle (Mussenden Temple★ 18C : ≤★★★ *AC*) NW : 5 m. – Portrush (site★, ≤★) N : 6 m. – Dunluce Castle (site★, ≤★) NE : 8 m. – W : Benevenagh Mountain★.

18, 18, 9 Royal Portrush, Dunluce Rd, Portrush ☎ 822311 – 9 Brown Trout ☎ 209 (Agivey) 868209.

Swimming Pool, Main St., Castlerock ☎ 848258 – Council Offices, 41 Portstewart Rd ☎ 52181.

Belfast 53 – Ballymena 25 – ♦Londonderry 31 – ♦Omagh 65.

Blackheath House, 112 Killeague Rd, Blackhill, BT51 4HH, S : 8 m. by A 29 on Macosquin rd ☎ 868433, – ⓟ. VISA.
closed Monday and Christmas – **M Macduffs** (booking essential) (dinner only) 20.00 **t.** and a la carte 11.20/17.00 **t.** 3.50 – **5 rm** 25.00/55.00 **t.**

Greenhill House, 24 Greenhill Rd, Aghadowey, BT51 4EU, S : 9 m. by A 29 on B 66 ☎ 868241, – ⓟ. VISA.
March-October – **M** 10.00 – **7 rm** 20.00/33.00 – SB 52.00 **st.**

Camus House without rest., 27 Curragh Rd, SE : 3¾ m. on A 54 ☎ 42982, park – TV ⓟ
3 rm 15.00/30.00 **st.**

at Castlerock NW : 6 m. by A 2 on B 119 – ✉ ☎ 0265 Castlerock :

Maritima without rest., 43 Main St., BT51 4RA, ☎ 848388, ≤, – TV ⓟ.
3 rm 15.00/26.00.

VAUXHALL-OPEL Hanover Pl. ☎ 42386 — ATS Loguestown Ind Est., Bushmills Rd ☎ 42329

CRAWFORDSBURN (Sruth Chráfard) Down 405 O 4 – pop. 140 – ☎ 0247 Helen's Bay.

18 Carnalea, Station Rd ☎ 0247 (Bangor) 465004 – 18, 18 Clandeboye, Conlig ☎ 0247 (Bangor) 271767 – 18 Broadway ☎ 0247 (Bangor) 270922.

♦Belfast 10 – Bangor 3.

Old Inn, 15 Main St., BT19 1JH, ☎ 853255, Fax 852775, – TV ☎ ⓟ
32 rm.

DUNADRY (Dún Eadrath) Antrim 405 N 3 – ☎ 084 94 Templepatrick.

Envir. : Antrim (round tower★ 10C) NW : 5 m. – Shane's Castle★ (16C ruins) *AC*, NW : 5½ m. (access by miniature railway).

♦Belfast 15 – Larne 18 – ♦Londonderry 56.

Dunadry Inn, 2 Islandreagh Drive, BT41 2HA, ☎ 32474, Telex 747245, Fax 33389, – TV ☎ ⓟ – 250. AE VISA.
closed 24 to 26 December – **M** 10.50/15.50 **st.** and a la carte 3.25 – **67 rm** 75.00/120.00 **st.**

DUNDONALD (Dún Dónaill) Antrim 405 O 4 – see Belfast.

DUNMURRY (Dún Muirígh) Antrim 405 N 4 – see Belfast.

ENNISKILLEN (Inis Ceithleann) Fermanagh 405 J 4 – pop. 10 429 – ☎ 0365.

See : Lough Erne★★★ (Upper and Lower) – On Lower Lough Erne, by boat *AC* : Devenish Island (site★★, monastic ruins : scenery★) and White Island★.

Envir. : Castle Coole★ 18C (site★) E : 1 m. – Florence Court (site★, park★) *AC*, SW : 8 m.

9 Castlecoole ☎ 25250.

Lakeland Visitors Centre, Shore Rd ☎ 23110 and 25050.

♦Belfast 87 – ♦Londonderry 59.

Killyhevlin, Dublin Rd, BT74 4AU, SE : 1¾ m. on A 4 ☎ 323481, Fax 324726, ≤, park – TV ☎ ⓟ – 500. AE VISA.
M (carving lunch) 7.70/17.00 **st.** and a la carte – **21 rm** 45.00/65.00 **st.**, **1 suite** 120.00/150.00 **st.** – SB (weekends only) 75.00/95.00 **st.**

ROVER Dublin Rd ☎ 323475 — VAUXHALL-OPEL Tempo Rd ☎ 324366

GLENGORMLEY (Gleann Ghormlaithe) Antrim 405 O 3 – ✉ Newtownabbey – ☎ 023 13 (4 and 5 fig.) or 0232 (6 fig.).

♦Belfast 6 – Larne 15.

XX **Sleepy Hollow,** 15 Kiln Rd, Ballyhenry, BT36 8SU, N : 2 m. by A 8(M) off B 56 ☎ 342042 – ⓟ. AE VISA
closed Sunday to Tuesday – **M** (dinner only) 19.75 **t.** 3.95.

RENAULT 612 Antrim Rd ☎ 843817 — VW-AUDI 45 Mallusk Rd ☎ 0232 (Belfast) 342111
ROVER 144 Antrim Rd ☎ 0232 (Belfast) 773606

HILLSBOROUGH (Cromghlinn) Down 405 N 4 – ⊛ 0846.

See : Government House★ (18C) – the Fort★ (17C).

Envir. : Legananny Dolmen ≤★, S : 16 m.

ℹ The Square ℘ 682477.

◆Belfast 13.

- **White Gables,** 14 Dromore Rd, BT26 6HU, SW : ½ m. on A 1 ℘ 682755, Telex 74806 Fax 689532 – TV ☎ P – 200. AE VISA
  M 9.50/10.50 **t.** and a la carte – **31 rm** 55.00/80.00 **t.**
- **Hillside,** 21 Main St., BT26 6AE, ℘ 682765 – AE VISA
  M *(closed Sunday dinner and 25 December)* (buffet lunch)/dinner a la carte 14.65/17.15 4.50.

TOYOTA 23 Lisburn Rd ℘ 682188

HOLYWOOD (Ard Mhic Nasca) Down 405 O 4 – pop. 9 462 – ⊛ 023 17.

Envir. : Craigavad : Ulster Folk and Transport Museum★ (Cultra Manor) *AC*, NE : 3 m.

◆Belfast 5 – Bangor 6.

- **Culloden,** 142 Bangor Rd, BT18 0EX, E : 1½ m. on A 2 ℘ 5223, Telex 74617, Fax 6777, park, squash – TV ☎ P – 500
  closed 24 and 25 December – **M** *(closed Saturday lunch)* 13.00 **t.** and a la carte 15.50 23.50 **t.** 4.00 – **84 rm** 102.00/130.00 **t.**, **7 suites** 160.00/250.00 **t.**
- **Tudor Guest Lodge** , 60 Demesne Rd, BT18 9EX, by High St. and Downshire R ℘ 5859, – rest TV P.
  M (by arrangement) – **5 rm** 33.00/43.00 **st.**

La guida cambia, cambiate la guida ogni anno.

IRVINESTOWN (Baile an Irbhinigh) Fermanagh 405 J 4 – pop. 1 827 – ⊛ 036 56.

◆Belfast 78 – ◆Dublin 132 – Donegal 27.

- **Mahon's,** Mill St., BT74 9XX, ℘ 21656, Fax 21945 – TV ☎ P – 400. VISA
  M 6.00/9.50 **t.** and a la carte 3.20 – **18 rm** 20.00/40.00 **t.** – SB (September-Apri (except Easter) 36.00/42.00 **st.**

LARNE (Latharna) Antrim 405 O 3 – pop. 18 224 – ⊛ 0574.

Exc. : Antrim Coast Road★★★ (A 2) from Larne to Portrush.

18 Cairndhu, 192 Coast Rd ℘ 83248, N : 4 m. – 9 Larne, 54 Ferris Bay Rd, Islandmagee ℘ 8222 to Stranraer (Sealink) frequent services daily (2 h 20 mn) – to Cairnryan (P & O Europea Ferries) 4-6 daily (2 h 15 mn).

ℹ Council Offices, Victoria Rd ℘ 72313 – Car Park, Murrayfield Shopping Centre, Broadwa ℘ 72313 (summer only) – Larne Harbour ℘ 70517.

◆Belfast 23 – Ballymena 20.

- **Derrin House** without rest., 2 Prince's Gdns, BT40 1RQ, off Glenarm Rd (A 2) ℘ 7326 P
  7 rm 12.50/25.00 **s.**

FORD 39 Glynn Rd ℘ 75411
ROVER 104-106 Curran Rd ℘ 72071
ATS Narrow Guage Rd ℘ 74491

LONDONDERRY (Doire) Londonderry 405 K 2-3 – pop. 62 697 – ⊛ 0504.

See : City Walls★★ (17C) – Guildhall★ (1908) – Memorial Hall★.

Envir. : Grianan of Aileach★ (Republic of Ireland) (stone fort) ★★★, NW : 5 m. – Dungive (priory : site★) SE : 18 m.

18 City of Derry, 49 Victoria Rd, Prehen ℘ 311610.

Eglinton Airport : ℘ 810784, E : 6 m.

ℹ Foyle St. ℘ 267284.

◆Belfast 70 – ◆Dublin 146.

- **Everglades,** Prehen Rd, BT47 2PA, S : 1½ m. by A 5 ℘ 46722, Telex 748005, Fax 49200 – TV ☎ P – 300. AE VISA
  closed 25 December – **M** *(closed Saturday lunch)* 8.50/12.50 **t.** and a la carte – 4.95 – **52 rm** 55.00/65.00 **t.**, **2 suites** 85.00/135.00 **t.**
- White Horse Inn, 68 Clooney Rd, BT47 3PA, NE : 6 ½ m. on A 2 (Coleraine rd) ℘ 0504 (Campsie) 860606, Fax 860371 – TV ☎ P – 500.
  44 rm.
- Waterfoot, 14 Clooney Rd, Caw Roundabout, BT47 1TB, NE : 3¾ m. at junction of A 39, A 5 and A 2 ℘ 45500, Fax 311006 – TV ☎ P
  33 rm.

FORD 173 Strand Rd ℘ 367613
PEUGEOT-TALBOT Campsie ℘ 860588
VAUXHALL-OPEL Maydown ℘ 860601
VW-AUDI 24 Buncrana Rd ℘ 265985

NEWCASTLE (An Caisleán Nua) Down 405 O 5 – pop. 6 246 – ☎ 039 67.

Envir. : Tollymore Forest Park★ *AC*, NW : 2 m. by B 180 – Dundrum (castle★ 13C ruins : top ≤★★, 70 steps) NE : 3 m. – Loughinisland (the 3 churches★ : 1000-1547-1636) NE : 8 m.

Exc. : SW : Mourne Mountains★★ (Slieve Donard★, Silent Valley★, Lough Shannagh★ : reservoir 1948).

18, 18 Royal County Down ☎ 23314.

The Newcastle Centre, Central Promenade ☎ 22222.

Belfast 30 – ♦Londonderry 101.

Burrendale H. and Country Club, Castlewellan Rd, BT33 0JY, N : 1 m. on A 50 ☎ 22599, Telex 747377, Fax 22328, – 150. AE VISA. **M** (bar lunch Monday to Saturday)/dinner 14.00 **t.** and a la carte – **51 rm** 42.00/90.00 **t.** – SB 80.00/90.00 **st.**

TOYOTA 23 Bryansford Village ☎ 22382

NEWRY (An tIúr) Down 405 M N 5 – pop. 19 026 – ☎ 0693.

Envir. : Slieve Gullion★★, Ring of Gullion : Ballitemple viewpoint★★, Bernish Rock viewpoint★★ – Cam Lough★, Killevy Churches (site★) SW : 5 m. – Derrymore House (site★) *AC*, NW : 2½ m. – Rostrevor (Fairy Glen★) SE : 8¾ m. – Carlingford Lough★, SE : 10 m.

18 Warrenpoint, Dromore Rd ☎ 069 37 (Warrenpoint) 72219, S : 5 m.

Arts Centre, Bank Parade ☎ 61244.

♦Belfast 39 – Armagh 20 – ♦Dundalk 13.

Mourne Country, 52 Belfast Rd, BT34 1TR, N : 1 m. on A 1 ☎ 67922, Fax 62659 – – 350 – **44 rm.**

PEUGEOT-TALBOT 18 Edward St. ☎ 62877/63393
RENAULT 49-53 Merchants Quay ☎ 63626
ATS Downshire Rd ☎ 63077

NEWTOWNARDS (Baile Nua na hArda) Down 405 O 4 – pop. 20 531 – ☎ 0247.

Envir. : Scrabo Tower (site★) SW : 1 m. – Mount Stewart Gardens★ *AC* – Temple of the Winds ≤★ *AC*, SE : 5½ m. – Grey Abbey★ (Cistercian ruins 12C) *AC*, SW : 7 m.

18 Kirkistown Castle, 142 Main Rd, Cloughey ☎ 024 77 (Portavogie) 71233, SE : 25 m. – 18 Scrabo, 233 Scrabo Rd ☎ 812355, W : 2 m.

2 Church St. ☎ 812215.

♦Belfast 10 – Bangor 5.

Strangford Arms, 92 Church St., BT23 4AL, ☎ 814141, Fax 818846 – – 40. AE VISA. *closed 1-2 April and 25 December* – **M** (bar lunch)/dinner 12.50 **t.** and a la carte 3.80 – 6.25 – **42 rm** 56.00/75.00 **t.** – SB (weekends only) 59.00/75.50 **st.**

FORD Regent St. ☎ 812626
VAUXHALL-OPEL Portaferry Rd ☎ 813376

OMAGH (An Ómaigh) Tyrone 405 K 4 – pop. 14 627 – ☎ 0662.

Envir. : Gortin Glen Forest Park★, Gortin Gap★ (on B 48) NE : 9 m. – Glenelly Valley★, NE : 17 m. by Plumbridge.

9 Dublin Rd ☎ 3160 – 9 Fintona ☎ 0662 (Fintona) 841480, S : 5½ m.

1 Market St., ☎ 47831/2.

♦Belfast 68 – ♦Dublin 112 – ♦Dundalk 64 – ♦Londonderry 34 – ♦Sligo 69.

Hotels see : Irvinestown SW : 13 m.

RENAULT Cookstown Rd ☎ 243451
VW-AUDI, VAUXHALL-OPEL 13 Dublin Rd ☎ 243116
ATS Derry Rd ☎ 3266

PORTADOWN (Port an Dúnáin) Armagh 405 M 4 – ☎ 0762.

Envir. : Ardress House★ 17C (site★, drawing-room plasterwork★★) *AC*, W : 6 m. – Rich Hill (site★, church- : scenery★) SW : 5 m.

♦Belfast 28 – ♦Dundalk 32 – ♦Londonderry 76.

Hotels see : Newry S : 22 m.

BMW Seago Rd ☎ 338833
FIAT Mahon Rd, Ind. Est. ☎ 332552
RENAULT Station House, Annaghmore ☎ 851257
TOYOTA Tandragee Rd ☎ 332980
VAUXHALL 128 Bridge St. ☎ 332238
ATS Church St. ☎ 355865

PORTAFERRY (Port an Pheire) Down 405 P 4 – pop. 2 148 – ☎ 024 77.

Envir. : Castle Ward 1765 (great hall★), SW : 4 m. – Portaferry : Strangford (site★, Audley's Castle : top ※★★, 44 steps) SW : 1½ m. – Saul (St. Patrick's Memorial Church : site★, ≤★) SW : 7½ m.

♦ Belfast 29 – Bangor 24.

Portaferry, 10 The Strand, BT22 1PE, ☎ 28231, ≤ – **5 rm.**

PORT BALLINTRAE (Port Bhaile an Trá) Antrim 405 M 2 – pop. 586 – ✉ ☎ 026 57 Bushmills.

Portballintrae, Bushmills ☎ 31317, N : 1 m.

Beach Rd ☎ 31672.

♦Belfast 68 – Coleraine 15.

Bayview, 2 Bayhead Rd, BT57 8RZ, ☎ 31453, Fax 32360, ←, ⇋, ▢ – TV ☎ P. VISA
M *(closed Sunday dinner)* 6.95/14.00 **st.** and a la carte 2.50 – **16 rm** 34.00/52.00 **t.** – SB 60.00 **st.**

PORTRUSH (Port Rois) Antrim 405 L 2 – pop. 5 114 – ☎ 0265.

18, 18, 9 Royal Portrush, Dunluce Rd, ☎ 822311.

Town Hall ☎ 823333.

♦Belfast 58 – Coleraine 4 – ♦Londonderry 35.

Magherabuoy House, 41 Magheraboy Rd, BT56 8NX, SW : 1 m. by A 29 ☎ 82350Fax 824687, ←, – TV ☎ P. AE VISA.
closed Christmas Day – **M** (bar lunch Monday to Friday)/dinner a la carte 12.55/20.60 3.75 – **38 rm** 50.00/65.00 **t.**

XX **Ramore,** The Harbour, BT56 8DQ, ☎ 824313, ← – P. VISA
closed Sunday, Monday, 2 weeks February, 25 December and 1 January – **M** (bookin essential) (dinner only) a la carte 15.20/21.30 **t.** 4.00.

ROVER 100 Coleraine Rd ☎ 823702 VOLVO 154 Coleraine Rd ☎ 824330

PORTSTEWART (Port Stíobhaird) Londonderry 405 L 2 – pop. 5 312 – ☎ 026 583.

18, 18 117 Strand Rd ☎ 2015, West boundary.

Town Hall, The Crescent ☎ 2286.

♦Belfast 67 – Coleraine 6.

Edgewater, 88 Strand Rd, BT55 7LZ, ☎ 2224, Fax 2224 (ext : 217), ←, ⇋ – TV ☎ P. AE VISA.
M 7.50/10.00 **t.** and a la carte – **31 rm** 40.00/75.00 **t.** – SB (except July and August) 66.00/85.00 **st.**

STRABANE (An Srath Bán) Tyrone 405 J 3 – pop. 10 340 – ☎ 0504.

18 Ballycolman ☎ 382271.

Abercoin Square ☎ 883735.

♦Belfast 87 – Donegal 34 – ♦Dundalk 98 – ♦Londonderry 14.

Fir Trees, Melmount Rd, BT82 9JT, S : 1¼ m. on A 5 ☎ 382382, Fax 885932 – TV ☎ P
26 rm.

FORD 132 Melmount Rd ☎ 066 26 (Sion Mills) 58275 ROVER 4 Derry Rd ☎ 882334

WARINGSTOWN (Baile an Bhairínigh) Armagh 405 N 4 – pop. 1 167 – ☎ 0762.

♦Belfast 26 – Craigavon 4.

XX **Grange,** Main St., BT66 7QH, ☎ 881989, – P
closed Saturday lunch, Sunday dinner, Monday, 10 days mid July and 26 December – **M** 15.60/23.90 **t.** and a la carte 2.95.

Channel Islands

Place with at least :

one hotel or restaurant .... ● Herm
one pleasant hotel .... 🏨, ⌂, ✕ with rm
one quiet, secluded hotel .... 🐎
one restaurant with ..... ✿, ✿✿, ✿✿✿, M
See this town for establishments
located in its vicinity .... GOREY

La località possiede come minimo :

una risorsa alberghiera .... ● Her
un albergo ameno .... 🏨, ⌂, ✕ with r
un albergo molto tranquillo, isolato .....
un'ottima tavola con .... ✿, ✿✿, ✿✿✿,
La località raggruppa nel suo testo
le risorse dei dintorni .... GORE

Localité offrant au moins :

une ressource hôtelière .... ● Herm
un hôtel agréable .... 🏨, ⌂, ✕ with rm
un hôtel très tranquille, isolé .... 🐎
une bonne table à ...... ✿, ✿✿, ✿✿✿, M
Localité groupant dans le texte
les ressources de ses environs ..... GOREY

Ort mit mindestens :

einem Hotel oder Restaurant .... ● Her.
einem angenehmen Hotel .. 🏨, ⌂, ✕ with r
einem sehr ruhigen und abgelegenen Hotel
einem Restaurant mit .... ✿, ✿✿, ✿✿✿,
Ort mit Angaben über Hotels und Restaurant
in seiner Umgebung .... GORE

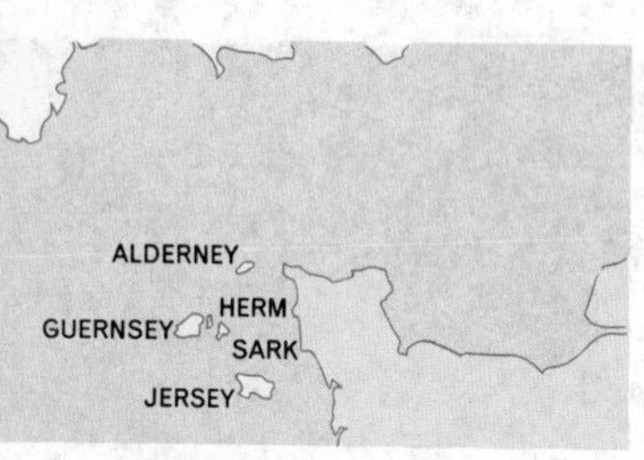

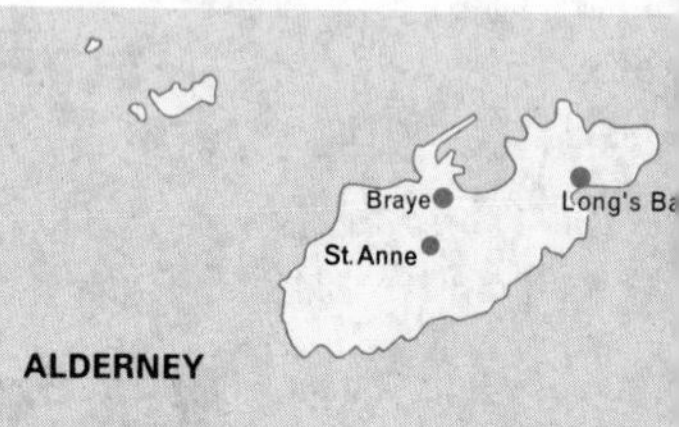

ALDERNEY 403 Q 33 and 230 ⑨ – pop. 2 068 – ECD : Wednesday – ☎ 0481.

See : Braye Bay★ – Mannez Garenne (≤★ from lighthouse) – Telegraph Bay★ – Vallée des Trois Vaux★ – Clonque Bay★.

✈ ☎ 822851 - Booking Office : Aurigny Air Services ☎ 822889, Air Ferries ☎ 822993.

⛴ To Torquay (Torbay Seaways) summer only.

⛴ Shipping connections with the Continent : to France (Saint-Malo) (via Guernsey, Sark and Jersey) (Condor : hydrofoil) (summer only) – to Jersey (St. Helier) (Condor : hydrofoil) weekly (summer only) – to Guernsey (St. Peter Port) (Condor: hydrofoil) (summer only) weekly.

States Office, St. Anne ☎ 2994.

St. Anne – ✉ St. Anne – ☎ 0481 Alderney.

Route des carrieres ☎ 2835, E : 1 m.

Inchalla , Le Val, ☎ 823220, ≤, – TV ☎ P. AE VISA.
closed 23 December-2 January – **M** *(closed Sunday dinner)* (dinner only and Sunday lunch)/dinner 13.75 and a la carte 2.75 – 4.90 – **11 rm** 27.50/55.00 – SB (except Christmas) 135.00/159.85.

Belle Vue, Butes Rd, ☎ 822844 – TV. AE VISA.
closed Christmas – **M** *(closed Sunday dinner)* 12.50 **s.** (lunch) and a la carte 3.50 – **29 rm** 27.25/37.25 **s.**

Nellie Gray's, Victoria St., ☎ 823333, – AE VISA
closed Monday to Saturday lunch October to March – **M** 7.50 **t.** (lunch) and a la carte 12.05/18.40 2.65.

Georgian House with rm, Victoria St., ☎ 822471 – TV. AE VISA.
M a la carte 12.00/24.00 2.50 – **4 rm** 25.00/50.00.

Braye – ✉ Braye – ☎ 0481 Alderney.

First and Last, ☎ 823162, ≤ harbour – AE VISA
closed Sunday dinner, Monday and November-April – **M** a la carte 7.50/18.00 **s.** 3.00.

Long's Bay – ✉ Long's Bay – ☎ 0481 Alderney

Essex Manor, ☎ 822537 – P.

To visit a town or region : use the Michelin Green Guides.

GUERNSEY 403 OP 33 and 230 ⑨ ⑩ – pop. 53 637 – ☎ 0481.

See : Site★ – Pezeries Point★★ – Icart Point★★ – Cobo Bay★★ – St Apollines Chapel★ – Vale Castle★ – Fort Doyle★ – La Gran'mère du Chimiquière★ – Moulin Huet Bay★ – Rocquaine Bay★ – St Martins Point★ – Jerbourg Point★.

✈ La Villiaze, Forest ☎ 37766.

⛴ to France (Saint-Malo) (Emeraude Ferries) summer only – to Poole (British Channel Island Ferries) summer : 2 daily, winter : 4-5 weekly – to Torquay (Torbay seaways) summer only.

⛴ Shipping connections with the Continent : to France (Saint-Malo) (Condor : hydrofoil) summer only – to France (Carteret and Cherbourg) (Service Maritime) summer only – to France via Jersey (Granville) (Emeraude Lines) summer only – to Jersey (St. Helier) (Condor : hydrofoil) 1-4 daily in summer – to Alderney (Condor : hydrofoil) summer only 1 weekly – to Herm by Herm Seaway, 7 daily (25 mn) – to Sark (Isle of Sark Shipping Co.) summer only Monday/Saturday 1-2 daily – to Weymouth (Condor : hydrofoil) 1-2 daily (summer only).

Crown Pier, St. Peter Port ☎ 23552 – The Airport, La Villiaze ☎ 37267.

L'Ancresse – ✉ Vale – ☎ 0481 Guernsey.

Royal Guernsey ☎ 47022.

Lynton Park , Hacse Lane, Clos du Valle, ☎ 45418, – TV ☎ P. VISA.
M *(closed Sunday dinner and Monday)* (dinner only and Sunday lunch)/dinner 10.25 and a la carte 3.25 – **15 rm** 35.50/59.00.

Catel – ✉ Catel – ☎ 0481 Guernsey.

Belvoir Farm, Rue de la Hougue, ☎ 56004, heated, – TV P.
May-September – **M** (by arrangement) – **14 rm** 39.00/58.00 **s.**

Fermain Bay – ✉ St. Peter Port – ☎ 0481 Guernsey.

La Favorita , Fermain Lane, ☎ 35666, Telex 94016631, Fax 35413, ≤, – rest TV ☎ P. VISA.
accommodation closed December-February – **M** *(closed 22 December-1 February)* 8.50/14.00 **s.** and a la carte 3.60 – **29 rm** 39.00/72.00 **s.** – SB 62.00/90.00 **s.**

Forest – ✉ Forest – ☎ 0481 Guernsey.

Tudor Lodge Deer Farm, Forest Rd, ☎ 37849, , park – TV ☎ P. VISA.
M (by arrangement) – **5 rm** 30.00/75.00.

Pembroke Bay – ✉ Vale – ☎ 0481 Guernsey.

St. Peter Port 5.

🏨 **Pembroke** ⛵, ✆ 47573 – TV ☎ P. AE VISA
closed February – **M** 9.50 and a la carte 🍷 2.50 – **11 rm** ☕ 26.00/52.00.

St. Martin – pop. 5 842 – ECD : Thursday – ✉ St. Martin – ☎ 0481 Guernsey.

St. Peter Port 2.

🏨 **Green Acres** ⛵, Les Hubits, ✆ 35711, Fax 35978, heated, – rest rest TV P. VISA.
M (bar lunch)/dinner 9.50 and a la carte 🍷 2.50 – **48 rm** ☕ 52.00/90.00.

🏨 **Saints Bay** ⛵, Icart, ✆ 38888, Fax 35558, heated, – TV ☎ P. AE VISA.
March-mid November – **M** 12.00/17.50 **s.** 🍷 3.20 – **24 rm** ☕ (dinner included) 22.00/70.00 **s.**

🏨 **Bella Luce,** La Fosse, Moulin Huet, ✆ 38764, heated, – TV ☎ P
closed 6 January-8 February – **M** (bar lunch Monday to Saturday)/dinner 25.00 and a la carte 11.40/20.60 🍷 4.25 – **31 rm** ☕ 38.00/73.00.

🏨 **Windmill,** Rue Poudreuse, ✆ 35383, heated, – rest TV ☎ P
April-October – **M** (bar lunch, residents only)/dinner 9.00 🍷 2.50 – **18 rm** ☕ 26.00/60.00.

🏨 **La Cloche** ⛵, Les Traudes, ✆ 35421, heated, – rest TV ☎ P.
29 March-1 November – **M** (bar lunch, residents only)/dinner 9.00 🍷 2.80 – **10 rm** ☕ 29.00/65.00.

🏨 Ambassador, Route De Sausmarez, ✆ 38356, Fax 39280, – TV P
20 rm.

🏨 **Wellesley** without rest., Route De Sausmarez, ✆ 38028, Fax 39501, – TV ☎ P.
April-October – **10 rm** ☕ 30.00/55.00.

ROVER, JAGUAR Ville au Roi ✆ 37661 — VOLVO St. Andrews Rd, Bailiffs Cross ✆ 37641

St. Peter in The Wood – ✉ St. Peters – ☎ 0481 Guernsey.

St. Peter Port 6.

✗ Taste of India, Sunset Cottage L'Eree, ✆ 64516 – P.

✗ **Cafe Du Moulin,** Due De Quanteraine, ✆ 65944 – VISA
closed Sunday dinner and Monday – **M** a la carte 15.00/23.90 **s.** 🍷 3.00.

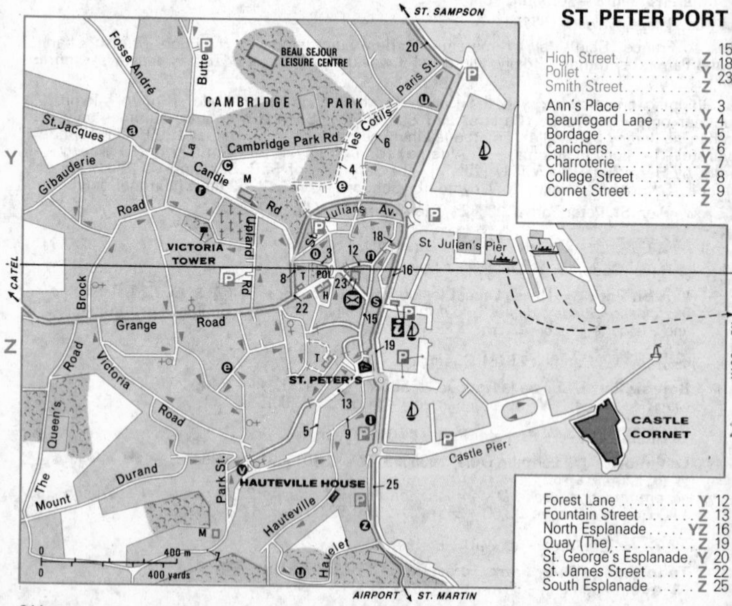

ST. PETER PORT

High Street Z 15
Pollet Y 18
Smith Street Z 23

Ann's Place Y 3
Beauregard Lane Y 4
Bordage Z 5
Canichers Z 6
Charroterie Y 7
College Street Z 8
Cornet Street Z 9

Forest Lane Y 12
Fountain Street Z 13
North Esplanade YZ 16
Quay (The) Z 19
St. George's Esplanade Y 20
St. James Street Z 22
South Esplanade Z 25

St. Peter Port – pop. 15 587 – ECD : Thursday – ✉ St. Peter Port – ☎ 0481 Guernsey.
See : Site★ – St. Peter's church★ Z – Hauteville House (Victor Hugo's house)★*AC* Z – Castle Cornet★*AC* Z. **Envir.** : Saumarez Park★ – The Little Chapel★.
Crown Pier ☎ 23552.

Plan opposite

St. Pierre Park, Rohais, ☎ 28282, Telex 4191662, Fax 712041, ≤, park, – ▯ TV ☎ & P – 220. VISA. by Grange Rd Z
M (see rest. **Victor Hugo** below) – **131 rm** 85.00/115.00, **3 suites** 195.00/220.00.

Duke of Richmond, Cambridge Park, ☎ 726221, Telex 4191462, Fax 728945, heated – rest TV ☎ – 60. AE VISA Y **c**
M 18.00/20.00 **s.** and a la carte 3.00 – **73 rm** 40.00/90.00 **s.**, **1 suite** 100.00/120.00 **s.** – SB (weekends only) 85.00/105.00 **s.**

Old Government House, St. Ann's Pl., ☎ 24921, Telex 4191144, Fax 24429, heated, – TV ☎ – 110. AE VISA Y **o**
April-October and Christmas-New Year – **M** 9.75/16.50 and a la carte 3.00 – **73 rm** 39.00/78.00.

De Havelet, Havelet, ☎ 722199, Fax 714057, – TV ☎ P. AE VISA. Z **u**
M 10.50 (dinner) and a la carte 13.50/27.00 3.15 – **30 rm** 44.50/84.00.

La Collinette, St. Jacques, ☎ 710331, Fax 713516, heated, – TV ☎ P. AE VISA. Y **a**
M 7.50/9.50 **s.** and a la carte 3.75 – **22 rm** 35.00/100.00 **s.**

Moore's Central, Le Pollet, ☎ 24452, Telex 4191342, Fax 714037 – TV ☎. AE VISA. Y **n**
M 8.50/10.75 and a la carte 3.50 – **48 rm** 33.00/66.00.

Midhurst House, Candie Rd, ☎ 724391, – TV. Y **r**
Mid March-mid October – **M** (dinner only) (residents only) 8.00 **s.** 1.70 – **7 rm** 30.00/50.00 **s.**

Abbey Court, Les Gravées, ☎ 720148, Fax 728829, – TV ☎ P. AE VISA.
16 March-10 November – **M** *(closed Sunday)* (bar lunch)/dinner 18.00 3.00 – **26 rm** (dinner included) 31.50/63.00. by Grange Rd Z

Kenwood House without rest., Allez St., ☎ 26146 – VISA. Z **e**
closed December and January – **8 rm** 26.00/40.00 **s.**

Spes Bona without rest., Les Vardes, Via Hauteville ☎ 725149, –
June-September – **7 rm** 34.00 **s.**

Marine without rest., Well Rd, ☎ 24978 Y **u**
11 rm 12.75/40.00 **s.**

XXXX **Victor Hugo** (at St. Pierre Park H.), Rohais, ☎ 28282, Telex 4191662, Fax 712041 – P. AE VISA by Grange Rd Z
closed Saturday lunch and Sunday dinner – **M** 14.00/30.00 and a la carte 3.50.

XXX **La Frégate** with rm, Les Cotils, ☎ 24624, Fax 20443, ≤ town and harbour, – TV ☎ P. AE VISA. Y **e**
M 10.50/16.00 **s.** and a la carte 3.50 – 7.00 – **13 rm** 48.00/95.00 **s.**

XXX **Louisiana,** South Esplanade, ☎ 713157, ≤ – . AE VISA Z **z**
closed Monday – **M** 8.75 **s.** (lunch) and a la carte approx. 14.00 4.00.

XX **Four Seasons,** Albert House, South Esplanade, ☎ 727444. VISA Z **i**
closed Sunday – **M** 9.00 **s.** (lunch) and a la carte 12.00/22.00 **s.** 3.00.

XX **The Absolute End,** Longstone, ☎ 723822, Seafood rest. – AE VISA
closed Sunday and January – **M** 9.00 (lunch) and a la carte 11.75/22.00 3.50.

XX **La Piazza,** Trinity Sq., ☎ 25085, Italian rest. – AE VISA Z **v**
closed Sunday and 24 December-24 January – **M** a la carte 10.20/17.40 2.90.

XX **Le Nautique,** Quay Steps, ☎ 21714, ≤ – AE VISA Z **s**
closed Sunday and first 2 weeks January – **M** a la carte 15.00/20.00 **s.** 3.75.

ORD Les Banques ☎ 24774
ONDA Doyle Rd ☎ 24025
RENAULT The Grange ☎ 26846
ROLLS-ROYCE, TOYOTA Trinity Sq. ☎ 24261

St. Saviour – pop. 2 432 – ✉ St. Saviour – ☎ 0481 Guernsey.
St. Peter Port 4.

L'Atlantique, Perelle Bay, ☎ 64056, Fax 63800, ≤, heated, – TV ☎ P. AE VISA.
closed January and February – **M** (bar lunch Monday to Saturday)/dinner 10.00 and a la carte 2.80 – **21 rm** 31.00/67.00 **s.**

Les Piques Farm, Route des Piques, ☎ 64515, « Part 15C farmhouse », – TV P. – **M** (dinner only) (residents only) 8.50 **s.** 2.75 – **25 rm** 28.00/56.00 **s.**

Vale – ✉ Vale – ☎ 0481 Guernsey.

Novotel, Les Dicqs, ☎ 48400, Telex 4191306, Fax 48706, ≤, heated, – rest TV ☎ & P – 200. AE VISA
M 12.00 **s.** and a la carte 3.20 – 6.00 – **99 rm** 60.00/70.00.

Vazon Bay – ⊠ Catel – ✪ 0481 Guernsey.

Les Embr ıns, Route de la Margion, ⊠ Catel, ℘ 64834, heated, – TV P
June-September – **M** (dinner only) (residents only) 12.50 2.25 – **16 rm** 21.00/42.00.

HERM ISLAND 403 P 33 and 230 ⑩ – pop. 37 – ✪ 0481 Guernsey.

to Guernsey by Herm Seaway, 6 daily (25 mn).

Administrative Office ℘ 22377.

Herm – ⊠ Herm – ✪ 0481 Guernsey.

White House, ℘ 22159, Fax 710066, ≤ Belle Greve Bay and Guernsey, , , park, – rest. VISA.
April-September – **M** 9.00/15.00 3.00 – **32 rm** 44.50/108.00.

JERSEY 403 OP 33 and 230 ⑪ – pop. 72 970 – ✪ 0534.

See : Site★★ – Chapels★ – German Occupation Museum★ – Jersey Zoo★ *AC* – Grosnez Point★ – St. Matthews Church Millbrook (glasswork★) – La Hougue Bie★ (Neolithic tomb) *AC* – St Catherines Bay (≤★ from lighthouse) – Noirmont Point★ – Millbrook St. Matthew's Church★.

States of Jersey Airport ℘ 46111, Telex 4192332.

Shipping connections with the Continent : to France (Saint-Malo) (Emeraude Ferries) – to Poole (British Channel Island Ferries) summer : 2 daily, winter : 4-5 weekly – to Weymouth (via Guernsey and Alderney) (Weymouth Maritime Services) weekly – to Torquay (Torbay Seaways) summer only.

Shipping connections with the continent : to France (Saint-Malo) (Condor : hydrofoil) (Vedettes Blanches) (Vedettes Armoricaines) summer only – to France (Granville) (Vedettes Armoricaines and Emeraude Lines) summer only - from Gorey to France (Carteret) (Service Maritime Carteret) summer only – from Gorey to France (Portbail) (Service Maritime Carteret) summer only – to Sark (Condor : hydrofoil) Monday/Saturday 1 daily – to Guernsey (St. Peter Port) (Condor : hydrofoil) 1-4 daily in summer (1 h) – to Alderney (Condor : hydrofoil) summer 4 weekly (1 h 30 mn) – to Weymouth (Condor : hydrofoil) 1-2 daily, summer only.

Weighbridge, St. Helier ℘ 78000/24779/31958.

Bonne Nuit Bay – ⊠ St. John – ✪ 0534 Jersey.

St. Helier 6.

Cheval Roc, ℘ 62865, Fax 62865, ≤ Bonne Nuit Bay, heated – TV ☎ P. VISA
May-late October – **M** 7.50/9.50 2.50 – **39 rm.**

Bouley Bay – ⊠ Trinity – ✪ 0534 Jersey.

St. Helier 5.

Water's Edge, JE3 5AS, ℘ 62777, Telex 4192521, Fax 63645, ≤ Bouley Bay, , heated, – TV ☎ P. AE VISA
April-October – **M** 12.50/16.00 and a la carte 3.50 – **47 rm** 50.00/115.00, **3 suites** 130.00/250.00.

Corbiere – ⊠ St. Brelade – ✪ 0534 Jersey.

St. Helier 8.

Sea Crest with rm, Petit Port, JE3 8HH, ℘ 46353, ≤, , – rest TV ☎ P. AE VISA
closed January and February – **M** *(closed Monday)* 10.00 (lunch) and a la carte 18.50/27.00 4.00 – **7 rm** 45.00/70.00.

Gorey – ⊠ St. Martin – ✪ 0534 Jersey.

See : Mont Orgueil Castle★ (≤★★) *AC* – Jersey Pottery★ *AC*.

St. Helier 4.

Old Court House, Gorey Village, JE3 9EX, ℘ 54444, Telex 4192032, Fax 53587, , heated, – TV ☎ & P. AE VISA.
March-October – **M** 6.00/10.50 **s.** and a la carte – **58 rm** 29.00/98.00 **s.**

Trafalgar Bay, Gorey Village, JE3 9ES, ℘ 56643, Fax 56922, heated, – TV P. VISA.
12 May-19 October – **M** (bar lunch)/dinner 8.00 – **27 rm** 25.00/50.00.

at Gorey Pier – ⊠ St. Martin – ✪ 0534 Jersey :

Dolphin, ℘ 53370, Group Telex 4192085, Fax 56660 – rest TV ☎. VISA.
M 9.25/30.00 **s.** and a la carte 2.75 – **16 rm** 25.00/82.00 **s.** – SB (November-March) 66.00/82.00 **s.**

Moorings, ℘ 53633, Group Telex 4192085, Fax 56660 – rest TV ☎. AE VISA.
M 9.50/40.00 **s.** and la carte 2.75 – **16 rm** 32.00/100.00 **s.** – SB (November-March) 77.00/93.00 **s.**

Grève De Lecq – ✉ St. Ouen – ☎ 0534 Jersey.

Hotel des Pierres, JE3 2DT, on B 65 ☎ 81858, Fax 85273 – TV P. VISA.
M (dinner only) 5.00 **s.** 2.75 – **14 rm** (dinner included) 28.00/60.00 **s.**

Grouville – ☎ 0534 Jersey.

18 Royal Jersey ☎ 54416.

Lavender Villa, Rue a Don, JE3 9DA, on A 3 ☎ 54937, – P.
March-mid November – **M** (dinner only) 9.00 2.00 – **21 rm** 20.00/70.00 **s.**

Mon Desir House, La Rue Des Prés, JE3 9DG, ☎ 54718, – TV P.
mid March-mid November – **13 rm** (dinner included) 21.00/56.00 **s.** – SB (except Summer) 36.00/43.00 **s.**

La Haule – ✉ St. Brelade – ☎ 0534 Jersey.

La Place, Route du Coin, by B 25 on B 43 ☎ 44261, Telex 4192522, Fax 45164, heated – TV ☎ P. AE VISA
closed January-March – **M** 10.00/20.00 and a la carte – **40 rm** 55.50/75.50.

Au Caprice, on A 1 ☎ 22083 – TV.
closed December and January – **M** 6.80 **s.** 2.50 – **14 rm** 11.00/22.00 **s.**

La Pulente – ✉ St. Brelade – ☎ 0534 Jersey.

St. Helier 7.

Atlantic, La Moye, JE3 8HE, ☎ 44101, Telex 4192405, Fax 44102, heated, – TV ☎ P – 60. AE VISA.
closed January-February – **M** 10.75/18.25 and a la carte – **49 rm** 70.00/170.00, **1 suite** 165.00/295.00.

Rozel Bay – ✉ St. Martin – ☎ 0534 Jersey.

St. Helier 6.

Chateau La Chaire, Rozel Valley, JE3 6AT, ☎ 63354, Fax 65137, – TV ☎ P. AE VISA
M 11.95 (lunch) and a la carte 19.50/24.50 4.00 – **13 rm** 52.00/105.00.

Le Couperon de Rozel, JE3 5BN, ☎ 65522, Fax 65332, heated – TV ☎ P. AE VISA.
Mid April-mid October – **M** 8.50/13.50 and a la carte – **32 rm** 40.00/80.00 **s.**

Granite Corner, Rozel Harbour, JE3 5BN, ☎ 63590, French rest. – AE VISA
closed Sunday and January – **M** (dinner only) a la carte 18.00/34.40.

St. Aubin – ✉ St. Aubin – ☎ 0534 Jersey.

St. Helier 4.

Panorama without rest., High St., JE3 8BR, ☎ 42429, Fax 45940, St. Aubin's Fort and Bay, – TV. AE VISA.
Late March-mid December – **17 rm** 20.00/54.00.

Bon Viveur, The Bulwarks, JE3 8AB, ☎ 41049, – TV. AE VISA.
mid March-October – **M** 4.95/7.25 and a la carte 2.25 – **19 rm** 13.50/20.50.

Tenby, Market Hill, ☎ 41099,
March-October – **M** 7.00 – **10 rm** 16.00/42.00.

Sabots d'or, High St., ☎ 43732
March-October – **M** (by arrangement) – **12 rm** 16.00/42.00.

Old Court House Inn with rm, St. Aubin's Harbour, ☎ 46433, Fax 45103 – TV ☎. VISA.
M a la carte 13.00/23.50 5.00 – **9 rm** 40.00/100.00, **1 suite** 100.00.

St. Brelade's Bay – pop. 8 566 – ✉ St. Brelade – ☎ 0534 Jersey.

See : Fishermans Chapel (frescoes★).

St. Helier 6.

L'Horizon, ☎ 43101, Telex 4192281, Fax 46269, St. Brelade's Bay, – rest TV ☎ P – 150. VISA.
M 10.50/19.50 and a la carte (see also rest. **Star Grill** below) – **100 rm** 60.00/170.00, **4 suites** 240.00/270.00.

St. Brelade's Bay, ☎ 46141, Telex 4192519, St.Brelade's Bay, heated, – rest TV ☎ P. AE VISA.
3 May-15 October – **M** 10.00/17.00 3.50 – **72 rm** 73.00/84.00 **s.**, **1 suite** 100.00 **s.**

Chateau Valeuse, Rue de la Valeuse, JE3 8EE, ☎ 46281, Fax 47110, heated, – TV ☎ P. VISA.
closed January and February – **M** 10.50 (lunch)/dinner a la carte 14.00/31.00 5.50 – **32 rm** 35.00/70.00.

XXX **Star Grill,** (at L'Horizon H.), ✆ 43101, Telex 4192281, Fax 46269, ≤ St. Brelade's Bay – P. VISA
M a la carte 16.75/30.00.

FORD Airport Rd ✆ 43222 — VW-AUDI Airport Rd ✆ 41131
NISSAN La Moye ✆ 45546

St. Clement – pop. 6 541 – ✉ St. Clement – ☎ 0534 Jersey.

Jersey recreation grounds ✆ 21938 – St. Helier 2.

Shakespeare, Samares, St. Clement's Coast Rd, JE2 6SD, ✆ 51915, Fax 56269 – ☎ P. AE VISA
closed 3 January-3 February – **M** (bar lunch Monday to Saturday)/dinner 13.50 and a carte 3.90 – **30 rm** 53.00/72.00.

St. Helier – pop. 29 941 – ECD : Thursday and Saturday – ✉ St. Helier – ☎ 0534 Jersey. **See :** Elizabeth Castle ※★ *AC* Z – Fort Regent ※★ *AC* Z.

Weighbridge ✆ 78000/24779/31958.

Plan opposite

Grand (De Vere), Esplanade, JE4 8WD, ✆ 22301, Telex 4192104, Fax 37815, ≤, rest ☎ P – 170. AE VISA. Y
M 11.50/16.50 and a la carte 3.00 – (see also rest. **Victoria's** below) – **110 rm** 65.00/145.00, **5 suites** 160.00/200.00 – SB 150.00/180.00 **s.**

De la Plage, Havre des Pas, JE2 4UQ, ✆ 23474, Telex 4192328, Fax 68642, ≤, – ☎ P. AE VISA. Z
28 March-26 October – **M** 9.50/12.50 and a la carte 3.00 – **78 rm** 44.00/135.00.

Pomme d'Or, Liberation Sq., JE2 3NR, ✆ 78644, Telex 4192309, Fax 37781 – rest ☎ – 180. AE VISA. Z
M 12.05/12.50 **s.** and a la carte 2.95 – **150 rm** 55.00/80.00 **s.** – SB (winter only) (weekends only) 79.00 **s.**

Apollo, 9 St. Saviour's Rd, JE2 4LA, ✆ 25441, Telex 4192086, Fax 22120, – ☎ P. AE VISA. Z
M 7.50/8.50 a la carte 4.50 – **85 rm** 42.00/92.00 – SB (weekends only) (November-March except Christmas) 70.00/76.00 **s.**

Beaufort, Green St., JE2 4UH, ✆ 32471, Telex 4192160, Fax 20371, – ☎ P. AE VISA. Z
M 9.50/15.00 and a la carte 2.50 – **54 rm** 64.50/121.00 – SB (weekends only) (September-March) 74.00 **s.**

Mountview, 46 New St. John's Rd, ✆ 78887, Fax 39763 – . VISA Y
mid March-October – **M** (bar lunch)/dinner 9.50 **s.** and a la carte 3.00 – **35 rm** 34.00/72.00 **s.**

Mornington, 60-68 Don Rd, JE2 4QD, ✆ 24452, Fax 34131 – rest ☎. AE VISA Z
closed January – **M** *(closed Sunday dinner)* (dinner only and Sunday lunch)/dinner 7.50 **s.** **31 rm** 35.00/60.00 **s.**

Sarum, 19-21 New St. John's Rd, JE2 3LD, ✆ 58163, Fax 68330 – . VISA.
23 March-16 November – **M** (residents only) (bar lunch) 2.40 – **49 rm** (dinner included) 41.50/77.00. Y

Uplands, St. John's Rd, JE2 3LE, ✆ 30151, Group Telex 4192371, Fax 68804, heated ☎ P. VISA. Y
M (residents only) (bar lunch)/dinner 6.00 **s.** – **43 rm** 27.00/54.00 **s.**

La Bonne Vie without rest., Roseville St., JE2 4PL, ✆ 35955 – . Z
closed 20 December-10 January – **10 rm** 19.50/39.00.

Almorah, 1 Almorah Cres., Lower Kings Cliff, JE2 3GU, ✆ 21648, Fax 68600, rest ☎ P. Y
16 rm (dinner included) 35.00/70.00 **s.** – SB 50.00/70.00 **s.**

Lion D'or, Harve Des Pas, JE2 4UQ, ✆ 30018 – VISA. Z
13 rm (dinner included) 12.00/24.00 **s.**

Lorraine, 8 Havre des Pas, JE2 4UQ, ✆ 74470, Fax 23462 – . AE VISA. Z
closed 5 November-10 January – **M** (by arrangement) 7.00 **s.** 1.90 – **10 rm** 15.25/37.50 **s.**

XXX **Victoria's,** (at Grand H.), Peirson Rd, JE4 8WD, ✆ 22301, Telex 4192104, Fax 37815 rest P. AE VISA Y
M 15.00 (lunch)/dinner a la carte 15.50/31.00 3.00.

XX **La Capannina,** 67 Halkett Pl., ✆ 34602, Italian rest. – AE VISA Z
closed Sunday – **M** (booking essential) a la carte 10.45/24.40 3.90.

XX **Princess Garden,** 37 La Motte St., JE2 4SY, ✆ 20147, Fax 24668, Chinese (Peking, szechuan) – . AE VISA Z
closed 25 and 26 December – **M** 8.00/25.00 and a la carte.

ROLLS-ROYCE, BENTLEY, LAND-ROVER 33-35 Lamotte St. ✆ 31341
CITROEN 10 Devonshire Pl. ✆ 24541
FORD Longueville ✆ 73777
PEUGEOT-TALBOT 17 Esplanade ✆ 33623
ROVER Havre des Pas ✆ 33233

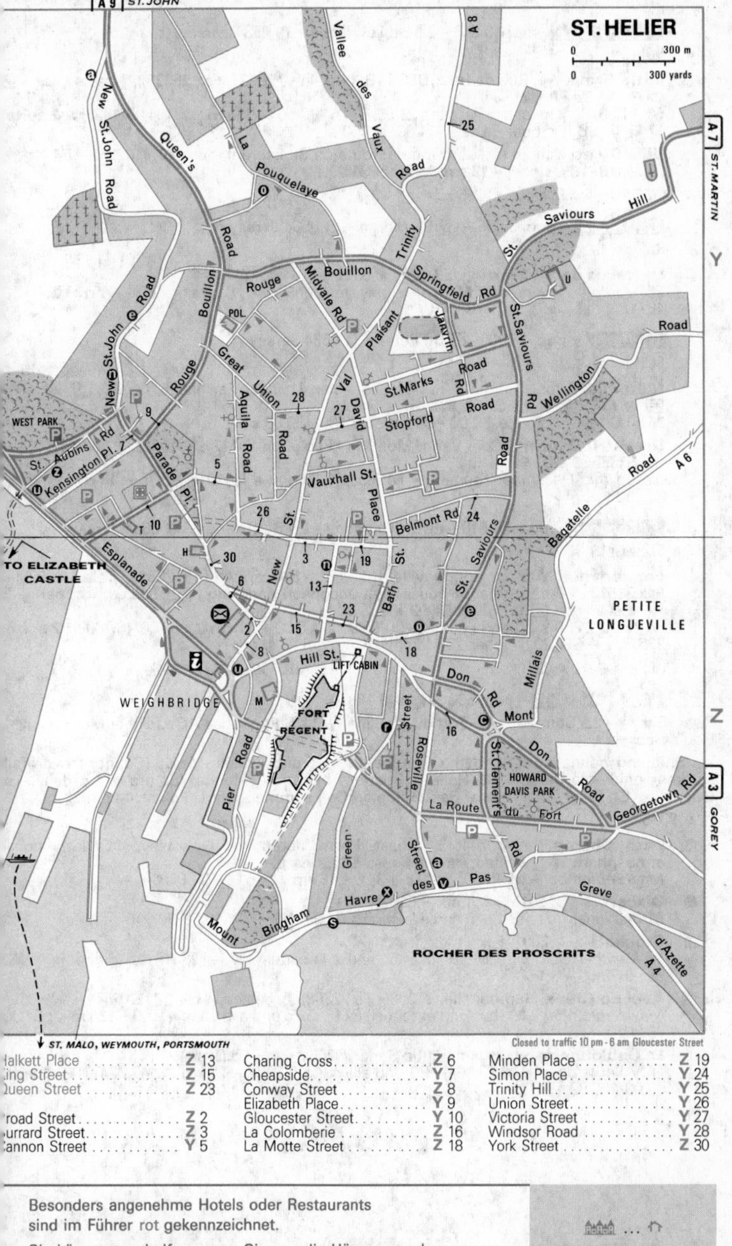

alkett Place . . . . Z 13	Charing Cross. . . . . Z 6	Minden Place . . . . Z 19
ing Street . . . . Z 15	Cheapside. . . . . Y 7	Simon Place. . . . . Y 24
ueen Street . . . . Z 23	Conway Street . . . . Z 8	Trinity Hill. . . . . Y 25
	Elizabeth Place. . . . . Y 9	Union Street. . . . . Y 26
road Street. . . . . Z 2	Gloucester Street . . . . Y 10	Victoria Street . . . . Y 27
urrard Street. . . . . Z 3	La Colomberie . . . . Z 16	Windsor Road . . . . Y 28
annon Street . . . . Y 5	La Motte Street . . . . Z 18	York Street . . . . Z 30

Besonders angenehme Hotels oder Restaurants sind im Führer rot gekennzeichnet.

Sie können uns helfen, wenn Sie uns die Häuser angeben, in denen Sie sich besonders wohl gefühlt haben.

Jährlich erscheint eine komplett überarbeitete Ausgabe aller Roten Michelin-Führer.

...

...

St. Lawrence – pop. 3 845 – ✉ St. Lawrence – ☎ 0534 Jersey.

St. Helier 3.

Little Grove ⅋, Rue de Haut, JE3 1JQ, by A 11 ☎ 25321, Fax 25325, heated, – TV ☎ P. AE VISA.
M 11.50 (lunch) and a la carte 21.55/30.25 7.50 – **11 rm** 104.00/142.50, **2 suite** 174.50 – SB (October-Easter) 111.00/143.00 **s.**

Villa D'Oro without rest., La Grande Route de St. Laurent, on A 10 ☎ 62262 – TV.
27 March-26 October – **12 rm** 30.00/34.00 **s.**

FIAT, MAZDA Belroyal Corner ☎ 22556

St. Martin – pop. 3 095 – ✉ St. Martin – ☎ 0534 Jersey.

St. Helier 4.

Le Relais de St. Martin, JE3 6EA, ☎ 53271, , – P.
28 March-4 November – **M** (dinner only, residents only) 8.50 **s.** 2.00 – **11 rm** 23.00 46.00.

St. Peter – pop. 3 713 – ✉ St. Peter – ☎ 0534 Jersey.

St. Helier 5.

Mermaid, Airport Rd, on B 36 ☎ 41255, Telex 4192249, Fax 45826, , , , ,
TV ☎ P – 80. AE VISA.
M 11.00 and a la carte 3.00 – **68 rm** 33.00/130.00 **s.**

Greenhill Country, Coin Varin, Mont de l'Ecole, on C 112 ☎ 81042, heated – TV ☎ P. AE VISA.
closed mid December-February – **M** 8.50/13.00 and a la carte 3.75 – **18 rm** 47.00 102.50 **s.**

St. Saviour – pop. 10 910 – ECD : Thursday – ✉ St. Saviour – ☎ 0534 Jersey.

St. Helier 1.

Longueville Manor, Longueville Rd, JE2 7SA, on A 3 ☎ 25501, Telex 4192306 Fax 31613, « Former manor house with Jacobean panelling », heated, , park – rest rest TV ☎ P. AE VISA
M 17.00/24.00 **s.** and a la carte 33.50/37.50 **s.** 6.00 – **31 rm** 82.00/167.00 **s.**, **2 suite** 236.00 **s.** – SB (20 October-25 March) 110.00/218.00 **s.**

PORCHE Five Oaks ☎ 69911 RENAULT Bagot Rd ☎ 36471

SARK 403 P 33 and 230 – pop. 560 – ☎ 048 183.

See : Site★★ – La Coupee★★★ – Port du Moulin★★ – La Seigneurie★ *AC* – Pilcher Monument★ Hog's Back★.

Shipping connections with the Continent : to France (Saint-Malo) (Condor : hydrofoil) summer only – to Jersey (St. Helier) (Condor : hydrofoil) Monday/Saturday 1-4 daily – to Guernsey (St. Peter Port) (Isle of Sark Shipping Co.) summer only 1-6 daily (40 mn).

☎ 2345.

Petit Champ ⅋, ☎ 2046, ≤ coast, Herm, Jetou and Guernsey, « Country house atmosphere », heated, – rest. AE VISA.
May-September – **M** 15.00/25.00 **s.** 3.00 – **16 rm** 25.00/52.00 **s.**

Dixcart ⅋, ☎ 2015, , park – VISA
M (bar lunch)/dinner 12.75 and a la carte 2.00 – **18 rm** 43.00/86.00.

Stocks ⅋, ☎ 2001, Fax 2130, , .
28 March-7 October – **M** 10.50/24.50 and a la carte 3.75 – **23 rm** (dinner included) 29.00/78.00 – SB 60.00/80.00 **s.**

Aval du Creux, Harbour Hill, ☎ 2036, Fax 2368, heated, – TV. VISA
May-September – **M** (booking essential) 8.00/15.25 and a la carte 2.00 – **12 rm** 34.00 75.00.

La Sablonnerie ⅋ with rm, Little Sark, ☎ 2061, – AE VISA
May-September – **M** 13.00/15.80 and a la carte 2.50 – **21 rm** 42.00/90.00, **1 suite** 90.00/100.00.

Isle of Man

'lace with at least :

ne hotel or restaurant .... ● Douglas
ne pleasant hotel .... 🏨,⌂,✕ with rm
ne quiet, secluded hotel .... 🐎
ne restaurant with .... ✿, ✿✿, ✿✿✿, M

ocalité offrant au moins :

ne ressource hôtelière .... ● Douglas
n hôtel agréable .... 🏨,⌂,✕ with rm
n hôtel très tranquille, isolé .... 🐎
ne bonne table à .... ✿, ✿✿, ✿✿✿, M

a località possiede come minimo :

na risorsa alberghiera .... ● Douglas
n albergo ameno .... 🏨,⌂,✕ with rm
n albergo molto tranquillo, isolato .... 🐎
n'ottima tavola con .... ✿, ✿✿, ✿✿✿, M

)rt mit mindestens :

inem Hotel oder Restaurant .... ● Douglas
inem angenehmen Hotel ..... 🏨,⌂,✕ with rm
inem sehr ruhigen und abgelegenen Hotel . 🐎
inem Restaurant mit ...... ✿, ✿✿, ✿✿✿, M

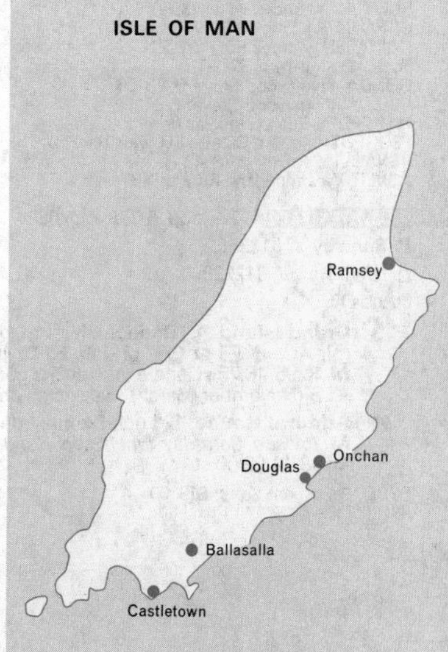

BALLASALLA 402 G 21 – ✆ 0624 Douglas.

Douglas 8.

- **Silverburn Lodge**, ✆ 822343 – P. VISA
  M *(closed Sunday dinner, Monday and October)* 12.00 **t.** (lunch) and a la carte **t.** 5.25.
- La Rosette, Main Rd, ✆ 822940.

CASTLETOWN 402 G 21 – pop. 3 141 – ECD : Thursday – ✆ 0624.

See : Rushen Castle★★ (13C) *AC* : Keep ★ – Port Erin (site★) W : 4½ m.

18 104 Ballyeriy Park ✆ 834422, E : 2 m – 18 Rowany, Port Erin ✆ 834108, W : 6 m.

Commissioner's Office, Parliament Sq. ✆ 823518.

Douglas 10.

- **Castletown Golf Links**, Fort Island, E : 2 m. ✆ 822201, Telex 627636, Fax 82463
  ≤ sea and golf links, , , 18 – TV ☎ P – 200. AE VISA
  M 17.00 **st.** (dinner) and a la carte 3.75 – **50 rm** 55.00/80.00 **st.**, **8 suites** 100.0
  160.00 **st.** – SB (except Christmas-New Year) 90.00/110.00 **st.**

ROVER Douglas Rd ✆ 822421

SKODA Alexandra Rd ✆ 823698

DOUGLAS 402 G 21 – pop. 19 944 – ECD : Thursday – ✆ 0624.

See : Manx Museum★★ – The Promenades★ – A 18 Road★★ From Douglas to Ramsey.

Envir. : Snaefell ★★★ (by electric railway from Laxey) *AC*, NE : 7 m. – Laxey (waterwheel★ Lady Isabella) NE : 6 m. – St. John's (Tynwald Hill) NW : 8 m. – Peel : Castle★ (ruins 13C-16(*AC*, NW : 11½ m.

18 Pulrose Park ✆ 75952, 1 m. from Douglas Pier – 18 Peel, Rheast Lane ✆ 062 484 (Peel) 222 W : 10 m.

Ronaldsway Airport, ✆ 0624 (Castletown) 823311, Telex 629243, SW : 7 m. – Termina Coach service from Lord St.

by Isle of Man Steam Packet Co : to Belfast : (summer only) (4 h 45 mn) – to Dublin (summer only) (4 h 45 mn) – to Fleetwood : (summer only) (3 h 20 mn) – to Heysham (3 h 45 mn to 4 h 30 mn) – to Liverpool : (summer only) (4 h) – to Stranraer : (summer only) (4 45 mn).

13 Victoria St. ✆ 74323 – Sefton Bureau, Harris Promenade ✆ 28627 – Sea Terminal ✆ 7432

- **Palace,** Central Promenade, ✆ 74521, Telex 627742, Fax 25535, ≤, , , – TV
  P – 250. AE VISA
  M 10.00/13.00 **st.** and a la carte 5.00 – 7.00 – **132 rm** 65.00/90.00 **st.**, **3 suite**
  120.00/200.00 **st.** – SB (weekends only) 90.00 **st.**
- **Sefton,** Harris Promenade, ✆ 626011, Telex 627519, Fax 676004, ≤, , – TV ☎
  AE VISA.
  M 7.00/13.50 **t.** – **79 rm** 45.00/56.50 **t.**, **1 suite** 95.00 **t.** – SB (except Easte Christmas and New Year) (weekends only) 60.00 **st.**

BMW 41-45 Bucks Rd ✆ 73380
CITROEN Kingswood Grove ✆ 24114
DAIHATSU Victoria Rd ✆ 22071
FORD Douglas ✆ 73211
HONDA Kingswood Grove ✆ 73196
MAZDA Kingswood Grove ✆ 24114
MERCEDES-BENZ Douglas Rd ✆ 822884
PEUGEOT-TALBOT, COLT, FIAT Peel Rd ✆ 24519
RENAULT Peel Rd ✆ 73342
ROVER Westmoreland Rd ✆ 23481

TOYOTA Westmoreland Rd ✆ 75556
VAUXHALL-OPEL The Milestone, Peel Rd ✆ 7378
VOLVO New Castletown Rd ✆ 74683
VW-AUDI 1 Main Rd ✆ 75885

ATS Geoff Duke Ltd, Mount Vernon, Peel F ✆ 22661
ATS Douglas Tyre and Battery Co., 5-7 South Qu ✆ 76532

RAMSEY 402 G 21 – pop. 5 778 – ✆ 0624.

18 Ramsey ✆ 813365.

Town Hall ✆ 812228.

Douglas 16.

- **Grand Island**, Bride Rd, N : 1 m. on A 10 ✆ 812455, Telex 629849, Fax 815291, ≤,
  , – TV ☎ P – 150. AE VISA.
  M 10.95/18.75 **st.** and a la carte 3.50 – **46 rm** 48.00/86.00 **t.**, **8 suites** 108.00/148.00
  – SB (November-March) (weekends only) 76.00 **st.**
- **Admiral House,** 12 Loch Promenade, ✆ 29551, Fax 75021, ≤ – TV ☎. VISA.
  M *(closed Saturday lunch and Sunday)* 10.00 **t.** (lunch) and a la carte 4.75 – **12 r**
  48.00/98.00 **st.**

FORD Parliament Sq. ✆ 813000

Republic of Ireland

Prices quoted in this section of the guide are in « Punts »

Dans cette partie du guide, les prix sont indiqués en monnaie irlandaise « Punts »

In questa parte della guida, i prezzi sono indicati in lire irlandesi « Punts »

In diesem Teil des Führers sind die Preise in irländischer Währung « Punts » angegeben

Ballyliffin
Rosapenna
DUNFANAGHY
Rathmullan
Letterkenny
Raphoe
Ballybofey
Ardara
N 15
Donegal
Rossnowlagh
N 16
SLIGO
N 59
Dromahair
Riverstown
Crossmolina
Ballina
Doogort
Castlebaldwin
ACHILL ISLAND
Newport
Boyle
Westport
T 40
Letterfrack
Cong
Clifden
Ballynahinch
N 4
Ballyconneely
Oughterard
Mullingar
Cashel Bay
M
Moycullen
N 84
Athlone
Furbogh
GALWAY
Spiddle
Barna
Ballinasloe
Banagher
Ballyvaughan
Birr
Lisdoonvarna
N 18
Emo
Ballinderry
Lahinch
Mountshannon
Mountrath
Feakle
Dromineer
Ennis
Ogonnelloe
Killaloe
N 7
Newmarket on Fergus
Bunratty
M
Castleconnell
Limerick
KILKENNY
Ballybunnion
Adare
M
N 21
N 24
Cashel
Thomastown
Tipperary
Templeglentan
Glen of Aherlow
Caher
Tralee
Carrick-on-Suir
Clonmel
Dingle
M
Kanturk
Ballymacarbry
Castletownrocne
WATERFORD
Caragh Lake
Banteer
Cappoquin
Glenbeigh
Killarney
M
Mallow
Ballyduff
Lismore
Dunmore East
N 22
Kenmare
Waterville
Tahilla
M
Macroom
Blarney
Youghal
N 25
Ardmore
Parknasilla
Garryvoe
Shanagarry M,
with rm
Ahakista M

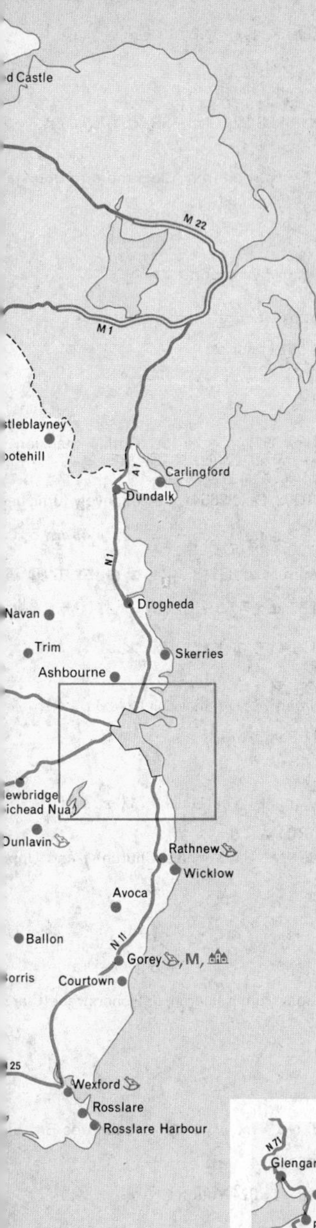

Place with at least :

one hotel or restaurant . . . . ● Navan
one pleasant hotel . . . . with rm
one quiet, secluded hotel . . . .
one restaurant with . . . . ✿, ✿✿, ✿✿✿, M
See this town for establishments
located in its vicinity . . . . SLIGO

Localité offrant au moins :

une ressource hôtelière . . . . ● Navan
un hôtel agréable . . . . with rm
un hôtel très tranquille, isolé . . . .
une bonne table à . . . . ✿, ✿✿, ✿✿✿, M
Localité groupant dans le texte
les ressources de ses environs . . . . SLIGO

La località possiede come minimo :

una risorsa alberghiera . . . . ● Navan
un albergo ameno . . . . with rm
un albergo molto tranquillo, isolato . . . .
un'ottima tavola con . . . . ✿, ✿✿, ✿✿✿, M
La località raggruppa nel suo testo
le risorse dei dintorni . . . . SLIGO

Ort mit mindestens :

einem Hotel oder Restaurant . . . . ● Navan
einem angenehmen Hotel . . . . with rm
einem sehr ruhigen und abgelegenen Hotel .
einem Restaurant mit . . . . . ✿, ✿✿, ✿✿✿, M
Ort mit Angaben über Hotels und Restaurants
in seiner Umgebung . . . . SLIGO

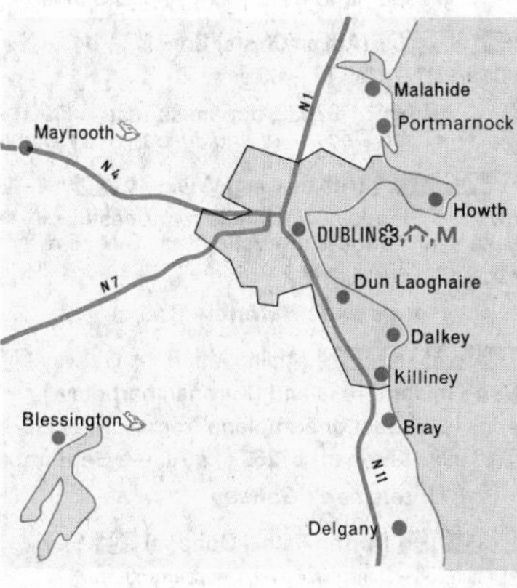

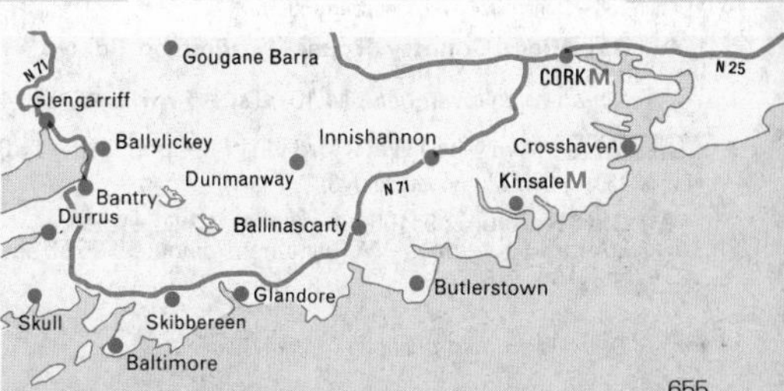

ABBEYLEIX (Mainistir Laoise) Laois 405 J 9 – pop. 1 402 – ECD : Wednesday – 0502 Portlaoise.

Envir. : Dunamase Rock (castle★★ 13C-16C ruins), site★★, ※★★, NE : 13½ m.

Portlaoise ✆ 31450.

♦Dublin 64 – Kilkenny 21 – ♦Limerick 65 – ♦Tullamore 30.

Hibernian House, Lower Main St., ✆ 31252 – VISA.
M 6.50/12.00 **st.** and a la carte 6.00 – **12 rm** 14.00/32.00 **st.** – SB 50.00/54.00 **st.**

ACHILL ISLAND (Acaill) Mayo 405 B 5/6.

See : Achill Sound★ – The Atlantic Drive★★★, SW : Coast road from Cloghmore to Dooega Keel : (the strand★) – Lough Keel★.

Achill, Keel ✆ 43202.

✆ Achill Sound 45384 (July and August).

Doogort (Dumha Goirt) – ✉ Achill Island – 098 Westport.

Gray's, ✆ 43244.
April-September – **M** 12.00 **t.** – **15 rm** 14.00/26.00 **t.**

ADARE (Áth Dara) Limerick 405 F 10 – pop. 785 – 061 Limerick.

See : ≤★ from the bridge of the River Maigue.

✆ 86255 (May-October).

♦Dublin 131 – ♦Killarney 59 – ♦Limerick 10.

Adare Manor, ✆ 86566, Telex 70733, Fax 86124, ≤, « 19C Gothic mansion extensive parkland », – 50. AE VISA.
M a la carte 19.50/28.00 **t.** 10.0 – **64 rm** 95.00/230.00 **st.**

Dunraven Arms, Main St., ✆ 396209, Telex 70202, Fax 396541, « Attractively furnishe antiques », – 150. AE VISA
closed Christmas Day – **M** 11.00/20.00 **t.** and a la carte 3.95 – 7.25 – **45 rm** 55.0 82.50 **t.**, **1 suite** 98.00 **t.** – SB (October-April) 96.00/112.00 **st.**

Woodlands House, SE : 2 m. by N 21 on Croom rd ✆ 86118. AE VIS
M (bar lunch Monday to Saturday)/dinner 14.95 **st.** 4.50 – **12 rm** 23.00/50.00 **st.** SB 67.00/70.00 **st.**

Abbey Villa without rest., Kildimo Rd, ✆ 396113. AE VISA.
6 rm 18.00/27.00 **st.**

Mustard Seed, Main St., ✆ 396451 – AE VISA
closed Sunday, Monday and 27 January-27 February – **M** (dinner only) 24.00 **t.** 4.75.

AHAKISTA (Áth an Chiste) Cork 405 D 13 – ✉ 027 Bantry.

♦Dublin 217 – ♦Cork 63 – ♦Killarney 59.

Shiro, ✆ 67030, Japanese rest. AE VISA
closed December and January – **M** (dinner only) (booking essential) 27.00 **st.** 8.50.

ANNAMOE (Áth na Long) Wicklow 405 N 8 – ✉ 0404 Wicklow.

Envir. : Glendalough (ancient monastic city★★ : site★★★, St. Kervin's Church★) and Upp Lake★ in Glendalough Valley★★★, SW : 5 m.

♦Dublin 29 – Wexford 72.

Hotels see : Rathnew E : 9 m.

ARAN ISLANDS (Árainn Mhór) ★★ Galway 405 CD 8.

See : Inishmore Island (Kilronan harbour★).

Access by boat or aeroplane from Galway city or by boat from Kilkieran, or Fisherstreet (Clare

✆ 099 (Kilronan) 61263 (12 June-2 September).

Hotels see : Galway.

ARDARA (Ard an Rátha) Donegal 405 G 3 – 075.

♦Dublin 188 – Donegal 24 – ♦Londonderry 58.

Bay View Country House, Portnoo Rd, N : ¾ m. ✆ 41145, ≤ Loughros Bay ar hills.
March-mid November – **M** 10.00 **st.** – **7 rm** 12.00/24.00 **st.**

ARDMORE (Aird Mhór) Waterford 405 I 12 – pop. 318 – 024 Youghal.

♦Dublin 139 – ♦Cork 34 – ♦Waterford 43.

Cliff House, ✆ 94106, ≤. AE VISA
26 April-September – **M** (bar lunch)/dinner 15.95 **st.** and a la carte 4.75 – **20 rm** 23.5 55.00 **st.**

There is no paid publicity in this Guide.

ASHBOURNE (Cill Dhéagláin) Meath 405 M 7 – ☎ 01 Dublin.

Dublin 13 – Drogheda 16.

Ashbourne House, ☎ 350167 – P
10 rm.

ATHLONE (Baile Átha Luain) Westmeath 405 I 7 – pop. 9 444 – ECD : Thursday – ☎ 0902.

Envir. : Clonmacnoise★★ (medieval ruins) SW : 8 m. – N : Lough Ree★.

Hodson Bay ☎ 92073.

17 Church St. ☎ 94630 (March-October).

Dublin 75 – ◆Galway 57 – ◆Limerick 75 – Roscommon 20 – ◆Tullamore 24.

Prince of Wales, Church St., ☎ 72626, Telex 53068, Fax 75658 – TV ☎ P – 300. AE VISA.
closed 25 and 26 December – **M** 11.90/16.95 **st.** and a la carte 5.95 – **42 rm** 37.00/62.00 **st.**

Shelmalier House, Retreat Rd, Cartrontroy, ☎ 72245 – P. VISA.
closed 24 December-6 January – **M** (by arrangement) 11.00 **st.** – **7 rm** 17.00/26.00 **st.**

FORD Dublin Rd ☎ 75426

AVOCA (Abhóca) Wicklow 405 N 9 – pop. 289 – ☎ 0402 Arklow.

See : Vale of Avoca★ from Arklow to Rathdrum on T 7.

Dublin 47 – ◆Waterford 72 – Wexford 55.

Woodenbridge Inn, Vale of Avoca, SW : 1 ½ m. ☎ 35146, – TV ☎ P
12 rm.

BALLINA (Béal an Átha) Mayo 405 E 5 – pop. 6 856 – ECD : Thursday – ☎ 096.

Envir. : Rosserk Abbey★ (Franciscan Friary 15C) N : 4 m. – Ballycastle (cliffs★) NW : 3 m. near Downpatrick Head★, NW : 18 m.

Mosgrove, Shanaghy ☎ 21050, E : 1 m. – 9 Belmullet ☎ 097 (Belmullet) 81093.

☎ 22422 (July-2 September).

Dublin 150 – ◆Galway 73 – Roscommon 64 – ◆Sligo 37.

Downhill, Sligo Rd, ☎ 21033, Telex 40796, Fax 21338, , , , , , squash – TV ☎ P. AE VISA.
closed 3 days at Christmas – **M** (buffet lunch)/dinner 15.90 **t.** and a la carte 5.00 – **52 rm** 35.00/75.00 **t.** – SB 90.00/100.00 **st.**

Mount Falcon Castle , Foxford Rd, S : 4 m. on N 57 ☎ 21172, Fax 21172, ←, « Country house atmosphere », , park, – P. AE VISA
closed February, March and Christmas – **M** (communal dining) (dinner only) 16.50 **t.** – **10 rm** 40.00/105.00 **t.**

NISSAN Lord Edward St. ☎ 21037

BALLINASCARTY (Béal na Scairte) Cork 405 F 12 – ✉ Clonakilty – ☎ 023 Bandon.

Envir. : Timoleague (Franciscan Abbey★ 16C) NW : 7 m.

Dublin 188 – ◆Cork 27.

Ardnavaha House , SE : 2 m. by L 63 ☎ 39135, Telex 75702, Fax 39316, ←, , heated, , , park, – ☎ P. AE VISA
M 9.50/20.00 **st.** and a la carte 6.50 – **36 rm** 46.00/120.00 **st.** – SB 80.00/110.00 **st.**

Árd na Gréine , NW : 1 ¾ m. by N 71 ☎ 39104, – P
M 12.00 **st.** – **6 rm** 18.00/28.00 **st.** – SB 48.00/52.00 **st.**

BALLINASLOE (Béal Átha na Sluaighe) Galway 405 H 8 – pop. 6 374 – ECD : Thursday – ☎ 0905.

☎ 42126 – 9 Mount Belleur ☎ 9259.

☎ 42131 (July and August).

Dublin 91 – ◆Galway 41 – ◆Limerick 66 – Roscommon 36 – ◆Tullamore 34.

Haydens, Dunlo St., ☎ 42347, Fax 42895, – TV ☎ P – 30. AE VISA.
closed 24 to 26 December – **M** 9.50/17.00 **st.** and a la carte 4.50 – 4.75 – **51 rm** 23.50/41.00 **st.** – SB 72.00/77.00 **st.**

FORD Kilmartins ☎ 42204
PEUGEOT Dunlo St. ☎ 42290
RENAULT Brackernagh ☎ 42420

BALLINDERRY (Baile an Doire) Tipperary 405 H 8 – ✉ ☎ 067 Nenagh.

Dublin 111 – ◆Galway 53 – ◆Limerick 41.

Gurthalougha House , W : 1 ¾ m. ☎ 22080, « ← Country house on banks of Lough Derg », , , park – P. AE VISA
(closed February and first 2 weeks March) (restricted service November-January) – **M** 21.00 **st.** 6.00 – **8 rm** 35.00/70.00 **st.** – SB 90.00/100.00 **st.**

BALLON **(Balana)** Carlow 405 L 9 – ☎ 0503 Carlow.

♦Dublin 55 – Kilkenny 26 – Wexford 33.

Ballykealey House ⛰, N : ½ m. on N 80 ☎ 59278, ←, ↖, park, ✂ – ☎ Ⓟ – 🏔 15 ▪ AE Ⓘ VISA. ✗
M 12.00/17.50 **t.** and a la carte 4.50 – **12 rm** ☕ 30.00/72.00 **st.** – SB (Octobe April) 65.00/75.00 **st.**

BALLYBOFEY **(Bealach Féich)** Donegal 405 I 3 – pop. 2 928 – ECD : Wednesday – ☎ 074 Letterkenny. 18 ☎ 31093.

♦Dublin 148 – ♦Londonderry 30 – ♦Sligo 58.

Kee's, Main St., Stranorlar, NE : ½ m. on N 15 ☎ 31018, Fax 31917 – TV ☎ Ⓟ. ▪ AE Ⓘ VISA
closed 25 and 26 December – **M** (dinner only and Sunday lunch)/dinner 16.00 and a la carte 3.50 – **27 rm** ☕ 27.50/55.00 **t.** – SB 57.00/68.50 **st.**

BALLYBUNNION **(Baile an Bhuinneánaigh)** Kerry 405 D 10 – ☎ 068.

♦Dublin 176 – ♦Limerick 56 – Tralee 26.

Marine, ☎ 27522, Fax 27666, ← – TV ☎ Ⓟ. ▪ AE Ⓘ VISA. ✗
Mid March-mid November – **M** (bar lunch Monday to Saturday)/dinner 19.50 and a la carte 4.25 – **13 rm** ☕ 32.50/45.00 **t.**

BALLYCONNEELY **(Baile Conaola)** Galway 405 B 7 – ✉ ☎ 095 Clifden.

18 Connemara, Aillebrack ☎ 23502.

♦Dublin 189 – ♦Galway 54.

Erriseask House ⛰, ☎ 23553, ← – ✗ rest ☎ Ⓟ. ▪ AE Ⓘ VISA. ✗
April-October – **M** (bar lunch)/dinner 17.00 **st.** and a la carte 5.00 – **11 rm** ☕ 29.0 46.00 **st.** – SB (weekends only) (April-October) 62.00/73.00 **st.**

BALLYDUFF **(An Baile Dubh)** Waterford 405 H 11 – ☎ 058 Dungarvan.

♦Dublin 139 – ♦Cork 32 – ♦Limerick 47 – ♦Waterford 69.

Blackwater Lodge ⛰, Upper Ballyduff, SW : 1 ½ m. ☎ 60235, ≘s, ↖ – Ⓟ. ▪ VISA
M (bar lunch Monday to Saturday)/dinner 15.00 **st.** and a la carte – **16 rm** ☕ 23.0 58.00 **st.**

BALLYHACK **(Baile Hac)** Wexford 405 L 11 – pop. 221 – ✉ New Ross – ☎ 051 Waterford.

♦Dublin 105 – ♦Waterford 8.5.

Neptune, Ballyhack Harbour, ☎ 89284, Seafood – ▪ AE Ⓘ VISA
Mid March-mid November – **M** (closed lunch Tuesday to Friday and Monday) a la car 14.00/19.80 **t.** 5.00.

BALLYLICKEY **(Béal Átha Leice)** Cork 405 D 12 – ✉ ☎ 027 Bantry.

♦Dublin 216 – ♦Cork 55 – ♦Killarney 45.

Ballylickey Manor House ⛰, ☎ 50071, Fax 50124, ←, heated, ↖, park – TV ☎ Ⓟ ▪ VISA. ✗
Mid March-early November – **M** *(closed Wednesday to non-residents)* (bar lunch)/dinner 22.50 **t.** 6.00 – **8 rm** ☕ 60.00/78.00, **3 suites** 110.00/130.00.

Sea View House ⛰, ☎ 50462, Fax 51555, ←, – ☎ ♿ Ⓟ. ▪ AE VISA
April-October – **M** (bar lunch Monday to Saturday)/dinner 19.25 **t.** and a la carte 5.50 **17 rm** ☕ -/70.00 **st.** – SB (except summer and Bank Holidays) 80.00/100.00 **st.**

BALLYLIFFIN **(Baile Lifín)** Donegal 405 J 2 – pop. 260 – ✉ Carndonagh – ☎ 077 Buncrana.

Envir. : Carndonagh (Donagh Cross★) SE : 6 m. – Lough Naminn★, S : 6 m.

18 Clonmany ☎ 76119.

♦Dublin 180 – Donegal 83 – ♦Londonderry 35.

Strand, ☎ 76107, Fax 76486, – TV ☎ Ⓟ. ▪ VISA. ✗
closed 24 to 26 December – **M** 8.00/16.00 **st.** and a la carte 3.75 – **19 rm** ☕ 25.0 45.00 **st.** – SB 73.00/78.50 **st.**

BALLYMACARBRY **(Baile Mhac Cairbre)** Waterford 405 I 11 – pop. 240 – ✉ ☎ 052 Clonmel.

♦Dublin 118 – ♦Cork 49 – Waterford 39.

Clonanay Farm ⛰, N : 1 m. by T 27 ☎ 36141, Fax 36141, ←, ↖, park – Ⓟ. ✗
Febraury-mid November – **M** 10.00 **st.** 3.20 – **9 rm** ☕ 15.00/30.00 **st.**

BALLYNAHINCH **(Baile na hInse)** Galway 405 C 7 – ✉ Recess – ☎ 095 Clifden.

See : Lake★.

♦Dublin 140 – ♦Galway 41 – Westport 49.

Ballynahinch Castle ⛰, Ballinafad, ☎ 31006, Fax 31085, ← Owenmore river and woods, ↖, park, ✂ – ☎ Ⓟ. ▪ AE Ⓘ VISA. ✗
M (bar lunch)/dinner 20.00 **st.** 6.00 – **28 rm** ☕ 57.50/95.00 **st.** – SB (October-March except Bank Holidays) 86.00/100.00 **st.**

BALLYVAUGHAN (Baile Uí Bheacháin) Clare 405 E 8 – ☎ 065 Ennis.

Envir. : SW : Coast road L 54 from Ailladie to Fanore : Burren District (Burren limestone terraces★★) – Corcomroe Abbey★ (or Abbey of St. Maria de Petra Fertilis : 12C Cistercian ruins) NE : 6 m.

◆Dublin 149 – Ennis 34 – ◆Galway 29.

Gregans Castle ⛰, SW : 3 ¼ m. on N 67 ℘ 77005, Fax 77111, ≤ countryside and Galway Bay, « Attractively furnished », – ☎ Ⓟ. VISA.
28 March-October – **M** (bar lunch)/dinner 22.50 **t.** and a la carte 7.00 – **15 rm** 60.00/80.00 **st.**, **1 suite** 140.00 **t.**

Hyland's, ℘ 77037, Fax 77131 – ☎ Ⓟ. AE VISA.
M (bar lunch)/dinner 19.00 **t.** 4.50 – **11 rm** 27.00/46.00 **t.** – SB 65.00/67.00 **st.**

BALTIMORE (Dún na Séad) Cork 405 D 13 – ☎ 028 Skibbereen.

◆Dublin 209 – ◆Cork 55 – ◆Killarney 72.

Chez Youen, ℘ 20136, Seafood rest. – AE VISA
closed mid January-mid March, October and November – **M** 11.00/19.50 **st.** and a la carte 5.50.

BANAGHER (Beannchar) Offaly 405 I 8 – pop. 1 378 – ☎ 0902.

See : ≤★ from the bridge of Shannon.

Envir. : Clonfert (St. Brendan's Cathedral : west door★ 12C, east windows★ 13C) NW : 4½ m. – Birr : Castle Demesne (arboretum★, gardens★, telescope of Lord Rosse) *AC*, SE : 8 m.

◆Dublin 83 – ◆Galway 54 – ◆Limerick 56 – ◆Tullamore 24.

Brosna Lodge, Main St., ℘ 51350, Fax 51521, – ☎ Ⓟ. AE VISA.
closed 1 February-14 March and 24-25 December – **M** (bar lunch Monday to Saturday) 15.95 **t.** and a la carte 4.50 – **14 rm** 23.00/40.00 **t.**

BANTEER (Bántír) Cork 405 F 11 – pop. 217 – ☎ 029.

◆Dublin 154 – ◆Cork 34 – ◆Killarney 29 – ◆Limerick 48.

Clonmeen Manor House ⛰, E : 2 m. on Mallow rd ℘ 56008, Fax 56260, , , park – ☎ Ⓟ. AE VISA.
closed 24 September-15 May – **M** (dinner only) 19.00 **t.** – **9 rm** 35.00/70.00 **t.**, **3 suites** 90.00/110.00 **t.**

Clonmeen Lodge ⛰, E : 2 m. on Mallow rd ℘ 56090, , park – Ⓟ. VISA.
closed March and October – **M** (by arrangement) 24.00 **t.** – **6 rm** 30.00/50.00 **st.** – SB (February-May) 70.00/75.00 **st.**

BANTRY (Beanntraí) Cork 405 D 12 – pop. 2 862 – ECD : Wednesday – ☎ 027.

See : Bantry Bay★★ – Bantry House (interior★★, ≤★) *AC*.

Envir. : Glengarrif (site★★★) NW : 8 m. – NE : Shehy Mountains★★.

Donemark ℘ 50579, on Glengariff rd.

℘ 50229 (26 June-2 September).

◆Dublin 218 – ◆Cork 57 – ◆Killarney 48.

Bantry House ⛰, ℘ 50047, ≤, « Early 18C stately home with formal gardens » – ☎ Ⓟ. AE VISA.
M *(closed Saturday, Sunday and November-April)* (dinner only) (residents only) 18.00 3.10 – **7 rm** 45.00/80.00, **1 suite** 100.00.

Dunavley ⛰ without rest., Seskin, NE : 1 m. by Vaughan's Pass rd ℘ 50290, ≤ – Ⓟ.
May-September – **5 rm** 18.00/31.00 **st.**

Larchwood House, Pearsons Bridge, NE : ¾ m. by N 71 ℘ 66181, ≤, – Ⓟ. VISA
closed sunday – **M** (dinner only) 16.00/25.00 **t.**

RENAULT Barrack St. ℘ 50092 VAUXHALL-OPEL Cork Rd ℘ 50023

BARNA (Bearna) Galway 405 E 8 – ☎ 091 Galway.

◆Dublin 135 – ◆Galway 3.

Ty Ar Mor, Sea Point, ℘ 92223, ≤, Seafood – Ⓟ. AE VISA
closed Tuesday and January-mid February – **M** 15.00/19.00 **st.** and a la carte 5.50.

BIRR (Biorra) Offaly 405 I 8 – pop. 3 679 – ☎ 0509.

Glenns ℘ 20082, N : 2 m.

℘ 20110 (15 May-8 October).

Athlone 28 – ◆Dublin 87 – Kilkenny 49 – ◆Limerick 49.

County Arms, Railway Rd, ℘ 20791, Fax 21234, , , squash – ☎ Ⓟ – 60. AE VISA.
M 9.00/14.50 **t.** and a la carte 5.00 – **18 rm** 25.00/55.00 **t.** – SB 66.00/78.00 **st.**

Inclusion in the Michelin Guide cannot be achieved by pulling strings or by offering favours.

BLARNEY (An Bhlarna) Cork 405 G 11 – pop. 1 980 – ✉ ☎ 021 Cork.

See : Castle★ (15C) (top ✻★, 112 steps) *AC*.

◆Dublin 167 – ◆Cork 6.

Blarney Park, ☎ 385281, Telex 75022, Fax 381506, ≘s, ⊡, ⚘, % – TV ☎ ♿ P – 🎪 200. VISA. ✻
M 9.00/15.00 **st.** and a la carte 5.00 – **76 rm** ⊐ 38.00/65.00 **st.** – SB (except Bank Ho days) 70.00/80.00 **st.**

BLESSINGTON (Baile Coimín) Wicklow 405 M 8 – pop. 988 – ☎ 045 Naas.

Envir. : Lackan ≤★, SE : 4½ m. – SE : Poulaphuca Lake★ (reservoir).

◆Dublin 20.

Tulfarris H. & Country Club ⚘, S : 6 m. by N 81 ☎ 64574, Fax 64423, ≤, « Pa Georgian country house overlooking Poulaphuca Lake », ≘s, ⊡, 9, ⚘, park, – TV ☎ ♿ P – 🎪 140. VISA
M 12.00/19.50 **st.** and a la carte 4.50 – **19 rm** ⊐ 67.50/115.00 **st.**, **2 suites** 95.0 115.00 **st.** – SB 98.00/118.00 **st.**

BORRIS (An Bhuiríos) Carlow 405 L 10 – ☎ 0503 Carlow.

9 Deerpark ☎ 73143.

◆Dublin 68 – Kilkenny 16 – ◆Waterford 30.

XX **Step House** with rm, ☎ 73401 – TV. VISA. ✻
closed Monday and February-20 March – **M** *(closed Sunday dinner and Monday)* (dinn only and Sunday lunch)/dinner 20.00 **st.** and a la carte 4.25 – **4 rm** ⊐ 25.00/40.00 **st.** SB (October-April) (Weekdays only) 70.00 **st.**

BOYLE (Mainistir na Buílle) Roscommon 405 H 6 – pop. 1 737 – ☎ 079.

See : Cistercian Abbey★ (12C).

Envir. : NE : Lough Key★.

9 Roscommon Rd ☎ 62594.

☎ 62145 (June-August).

◆Dublin 107 – Ballina 40 – ◆Galway 74 – Roscommon 26 – ◆Sligo 24.

Forest Park, Dublin Rd, E : ½ m. on N 4 ☎ 62229, ⚘ – TV ☎ P. VISA. ✻
closed 25 and 26 December – **M** 9.00/12.50 **st.** and a la carte 5.00 – **12 rm** ⊐ 30.0 50.00 **st.** – SB 60.00/70.00 **st.**

BRAY (Bré) Wicklow 405 N 8 – pop. 22 853 – ECD : Wednesday – ☎ 01 Dublin.

18 The old Conna, Ferndale Rd ☎ 826055 – 9 Ravenswell Rd ☎ 862484.

☎ 867128 (19 June-26 August).

◆Dublin 13 – Wicklow 20.

XX **Tree of Idleness,** Seafront, ☎ 863498, Greek-Cypriot rest. – VISA
closed Monday, first 2 weeks September and Christmas – **M** (dinner only) 19.25 **t.** and a carte 6.00.

BUNCLODY (Bun Clóidí) Wexford 405 M 10 – ☎ 054.

Clohamon House ⚘, Clohamon, SE : 1¾ m. by Carnew rd ☎ 77253, ≤, « Countr house atmosphere », ⚘, ⚘ – P. VISA. ✻
March-mid November – **M** (dinner only) (residents only) 18.00 **st.** – **4 rm** ⊐ 31.00/35.00.

BUNRATTY (Bun Raite) Clare 405 F 9 – ☎ 061 Limerick.

See : Castle (Great Hall★) *AC* – Folk Park★ *AC*.

◆Dublin 129 – Ennis 15 – ◆Limerick 8.

Fitzpatrick's Shannon Shamrock, ☎ 361177, Telex 72114, Fax 61252, ≘s, ⊡, ⚘ rest TV ☎ P – 🎪 200. VISA. ✻
M 10.50/17.00 **t.** and a la carte 5.00 – ⊐ 7.70 – **100 rm** 63.00/110.00 **t.**

Shannon View without rest., NW : 1 m. on N 18 ☎ 364056, ⚘ – rest P. ✻
April-October – **6 rm** ⊐ 15.00/30.00 **st.**

XX **MacCloskey's,** Bunratty House Mews, ☎ 364082, « Cellars of Georgian house » – P VISA
closed Sunday, Monday and 20 December-20 January – **M** (dinner only) 24.00 **t.** 5.00.

BUTLERSTOWN (Baile an Bhuitléaraigh) Bandon 405 F 13 – ✉ ☎ 023 Bandon.

◆Dublin 193 – ◆Cork 32.

X **Dunworley Cottage,** Dunworley, S : 2 m. ☎ 40314 – P. VISA
M *(closed lunch except Sunday and Bank Holidays)* 17.00 **t.** (dinner) and a la carte 3.50.

When looking for a quiet hotel
use the maps found in the introductory pages
or look for establishments with the sign ⚘ or ⚘

AHER (An Chathair) Tipperary 405 I 10 – pop. 2 120 – ECD : Thursday – ☎ 052.
ee : Castle★ (12C-15C) the most extensive medieval castle in Ireland.
Cahir Park, ℘ 41474, S : 1 m.
℘ 41453 (July and August).
ublin 112 – ♦Cork 49 – Kilkenny 41 – ♦Limerick 38 – ♦Waterford 39.

Kilcoran Lodge, SW : 4¾ m. on N 8 ℘ 41288, Fax 41994, ≤, , , – TV ☎ P – 50. AE VISA
M 9.00/15.00 **st.** and a la carte 5.50 – **23 rm** 35.00/60.00 **st.** – SB 80.00/90.00 **st.**

AHERDANIEL (Cathair Dónall) Kerry 405 B 12.
nvir. : Sheehan's Point ≤★★★, W : 5 m. – Staigue Fort★ (prehistoric stone fort : site★, ≤★)
C, NE : 5 m.
ublin 238 – ♦Killarney 48.

Hotels see : Waterville NW : 6 m.

APPOQUIN (Ceapach Choinn) Waterford 405 I 11 – pop. 950 – ✉ Lismore – ☎ 058 Dungar-
n.
Dublin 136 – ♦Cork 31 – ♦Waterford 40.

Richmond House , SE : ½ m. on N 72, ℘ 54278, , park – P. VISA.
February-October – **M** 10.00 **st.** – **9 rm** 21.00/36.00 **st.**

CARAGH LAKE (Loch Cárthaí) Kerry 405 C 11 – ☎ 066 Tralee.
ee : Lough Caragh★.
Dublin 212 – ♦Killarney 22 – Tralee 25.

Caragh Lodge , ℘ 69115, ≤, « Country house atmosphere », ≤, , , park, –
P. VISA.
April-mid October – **M** (bar lunch)/dinner 20.00 **t.** 5.00 – **9 rm** 42.50/75.00 **t.**

Ard-Na-Sidhe , ℘ 69105, ≤, « Country house atmosphere », , , park – ☎ P.
AE VISA.
closed October-May – **M** (dinner only) 22.50 **st.** 8.50 – **20 rm** 52.00/82.00 **st.**

"Short Breaks" (SB)
De nombreux hôtels proposent des conditions avantageuses
pour un séjour de deux nuits
comprenant la chambre, le dîner et le petit déjeuner.

CARLINGFORD (Cairlinn) Louth 405 N 5 – pop. 631 – ☎ 042.
Dublin 66 – ♦Dundalk 13.

McKevitt's Village, Market Sq., ℘ 73116, – TV ☎. AE VISA.
M 8.00/15.00 **st.** and a la carte 4.00 – **12 rm** 18.00/44.00 **st.** – SB 60.00/66.00 **st.**

CARRICK-ON-SUIR (Carraig na Siúire) Tipperary 405 J 10 – pop. 5 566 – ☎ 051 Waterford.
Garravone ℘ 40047.
Dublin 95 – ♦Cork 68 – ♦Limerick 62 – ♦Waterford 16.

Cedarfield House , Waterford Rd, E : 1 m. on N 24 ℘ 40164, – TV ☎ P. VISA.
closed 2 January-mid March – **M** *(closed Sunday dinner to non-residents)* (dinner only) 19.50 **st.** 5.25 – **6 rm** 27.50/70.00 **st.** – SB (except summer) 90.00/100.00 **st.**

ENAULT Carrigbeg ℘ 40202

CASHEL (Caiseal) Tipperary 405 I 10 – pop. 2 436 – ECD : Wednesday – ☎ 062.
ee : St. Patrick's Rock★★★ (or Rock of Cashel) : site and ecclesiastical ruins (12C-15C) (★★)
AC – Hore Abbey★ ruins (13C) – St. Dominick's Abbey★ ruins (13C).
nvir. : Holycross Abbey★★ (12C) *AC*, N : 9 m.
Town Hall ℘ 61333 (March-September).
Dublin 101 – ♦Cork 60 – Kilkenny 34 – ♦Limerick 36 – ♦Waterford 44.

Cashel Palace , Main St., ℘ 61411, Telex 70638, Fax 61521, « Former Archbishop's palace, gardens » – TV ☎ P – 25. AE VISA.
M (restricted lunch)/dinner 19.00 **t.** and a la carte **t.** 6.25 – 10.00 – **20 rm** 75.00/175.00 **t.** – SB 95.00/109.00 **st.**

Chez Hans, Rockside, ℘ 61177, « Converted 19C church » – P
closed Sunday, Monday and first 3 weeks January – **M** (dinner only) a la carte 21.55/28.25 **t.** 5.00.

ROTON, LADA Cahir Rd ℘ 61155

CASHEL BAY Galway 405 C 7 – ✆ 095 Clifden.

Envir. : SE : Kilkieran Peninsula★★.

♦Dublin 173 – Galway 41.

- **Cashel House** ⛰, ✆ 31001, Telex 50812, Fax 31077, ≤, « Country house atmosphe gardens », ⛰, park, ✗ – TV ☎ P. AE VISA
  closed 10 January-15 February and 15 November-20 December – **M** (bar lunch)/d ner 28.50 **t.** 6.75 – **32 rm** 44.00/128.00 **t.** – SB (February-April and November) 89.00
- Zetland ⛰, ✆ 31111, Fax 31117, ≤ Cashel Bay, « Country house, gardens », ⛰, rm ☎ P. AE VISA
  April-October – **19 rm** 55.00/110.00 **t.**

CASTLEBALDWIN **(Béal Átha na gCarraigíní)** Sligo 405 G 5 – ✉ Boyle (Roscommon) ✆ 071 Sligo.

♦Dublin 118 – Longford 42 – ♦Sligo 15.

- **Cromleach Lodge** ⛰, Ballindoon, SE : 3½ m. ✆ 65155, Fax 65455, ≤ Loch Arrow, – ☎ P. AE VISA.
  closed 22 to 30 December – **M** *(closed Sunday)* (dinner only) 21.95 **t.** 5.00 – **10 r** 20.00/96.00 **t.**

CASTLEBLAYNEY **(Baile na Lorgan)** Monaghan 405 L 5 – pop. 2 425 – ✆ 042.

✆ 40197.

♦Dublin 68 – ♦Belfast 58 – ♦Drogheda 39 – ♦Dundalk 17 – ♦Londonderry 80.

- **Glencarn,** Monaghan Rd, ✆ 46666, – TV ☎ P – 250. AE VISA.
  M 7.50/14.00 **st.** and a la carte 3.80 – **15 rm** 23.00/40.00 **st.** – SB (weekend only) 63.00/71.00 **st.**

__In alta stagione,__ e soprattutto nelle stazioni turistiche,
è prudente prenotare con un certo anticipo.
Avvertite immediatamente l'albergatore se non potete più
occupare la camera prenotata.
Se scrivete ad un albergo all'estero, allegate alla vostra
lettera un tagliando-risposta internazionale (disponibile presso gli uffici postali).

CASTLECONNELL **(Caisleán Uí Chonaill)** Limerick 405 G 9 – pop. 1 053 – ✆ 061 Limerick.

♦Dublin 111 – ♦Limerick 9.

- Castle Oaks House ⛰, ✆ 377666, Telex 70328, Fax 43073, ≤, ⛰, park – TV ☎ P 250
  11 rm.

CASTLETOWNROCHE **(Baile Chaisleáin an Róisligh)** Cork 405 G 11 – pop. 455 – ✆ 022 Mallo

♦Dublin 138 – ♦Cork 31 – ♦Killarney 50 – ♦Limerick 45 – ♦Waterford 68.

- **Blackwater Castle** ⛰, ✆ 26333, Fax 26210, ≤, « Renovated castle with distinctiv modern decor », ⛰, park, ✗ – TV ☎ P – 35. AE VISA.
  Mid March-mid November – **M** (bar lunch)/dinner 24.50 **t.** and a la carte 7.00 – **10 r** 65.00/165.00 **t.** – SB 120.00/140.00 **st.**

CAVAN **(An Cabhán)** Cavan 405 J 6 – pop. 3 240 – ✆ 049.

Drumelis ✆ 31283.

✆ 31942 (April-December).

♦Dublin 71 – Drogheda 58 – Enniskillen 40.

- **Kilmore,** Dublin Rd, E : 2 m. on N 3 ✆ 32288, Fax 32458 – TV ☎ ♿ P – 250. AE VISA.
  M 11.00/15.00 **st.** 4.20 – **39 rm** 25.00/45.00 **st.** – SB 56.00/70.00 **st.**

FIAT Dublin Rd ✆ 31188 FORD Farnham St. ✆ 31700

CHARLEVILLE **(RATHLUIRC) (An Ráth)** Cork 405 F 10 – pop. 2 874 – ECD : Thursday ✆ 063 Rathluirc.

Envir. : Kilmallock (Dominican Friary ruins 13C, SS. Peter and Paul church 14C : scenery★ ÜNE : 6 m. – Kilfinnane (site★) E : 11 m.

✆ 021 (Cork) 81257.

♦Dublin 138 – ♦Cork 38 – ♦Killarney 57 – ♦Limerick 24.

Hotel and restaurant see : **Mallow (Mala)** S : 15 m.

CLIFDEN **(An Clochán)** Galway 405 B 7 – pop. 796 – ECD : Thursday – ✆ 095.

Envir. : E : Connemara★★ : The Twelve Pins★ (mountains), Lough Inagh★ – Cleggan (site★★ NW : 6 m. – Streamstown Bay★, NW : 2 m.

✆ 21163 (June-August).

♦Dublin 181 – Ballina 77 – ♦Galway 49.

Rock Glen Country House ⑤, S : 1¼ m. by L 102 ✆ 21035, Fax 21737, ☞ – TV ☎ P. AE ① VISA. ✻
Mid March-October – **M** (bar lunch)/dinner 20.00 **t.** 5.00 – **29 rm** ☐ 45.00/105.00 **t.**

Abbeyglen Castle ⑤, Sky Rd, W : ½ m. ✆ 21201, Telex 50866, Fax 21797, ≤, ≘s, heated, ☞, ✂ – ⇔ rm TV ☎ P. AE ① VISA
closed 10 January-1 February – **M** (bar lunch)/dinner 21.00 **t.** and a la carte 7.00 – ☐ 7.00 – **38 rm** 60.00/65.00 **t.**, **2 suites** 90.00/130.00 **t.** – SB (except July-August and Bank Holidays) 88.00/98.00 **st.**

Ardagh ⑤, Ballyconneely rd, S : 1 ¾ m. on L 102 ✆ 21384, Fax 21314, ≤ Ardbear Bay, – TV ☎ P. AE ① VISA. ✻
Easter-October – **M** (bar lunch)/dinner 18.70 **st.** 4.75 – **21 rm** ☐ 39.05/60.50 **st.**

LONMEL (Cluain Meala) Tipperary 405 I 10 – pop. 12 407 – ECD : Thursday – 052.
ee : The Main Guard★ (1674).
nvir. : Ahenny (2 high crosses★) NE : 16 m. – S : Nire Valley★ (≤★★).
Lyreanearla, ✆ 21138.
✆ 22960 (July and August).
Dublin 108 – ◆Cork 59 – Kilkenny 31 – ◆Limerick 48 – ◆Waterford 29.

Hotel and restaurant see : **Cashel** N : 14 m.

UDI-VW, MAZDA, MERCEDES-BENZ, Upper ashtown ✆ 22199
OPEL Dungarvon Rd ✆ 22399
TOYOTA Cashel Rd ✆ 21652

CONG (Conga) Mayo 405 E 7 – pop. 213 – 092.
ee : Ashford Castle (site★).
nvir. : Ross Abbey★★, Franciscan Friary (tower ✻★, 80 steps) SE : 9 m.
Dublin 160 – Ballina 49 – ◆Galway 28.

Ashford Castle ⑤, ✆ 46003, Telex 53749, Fax 46260, ≤ Lough Corrib and countryside, « Part 13C and 18C converted castle », 9, ☞, park, ✂ – TV ☎ P – 50. AE ① VISA. ✻
M 18.00/29.00 **t.** and a la carte 29.00/45.00 **t.** 8.00 – (see also **Connaught Room** below) – ☐ 11.00 – **77 rm** 165.00/175.00 **st.**, **6 suites** 250.00/355.00 **st.** – SB (November-March) (except Christmas and New Year) 179.00 **st.**

XXX **Connaught Room,** (at Ashford Castle H.), ✆ 46003, Telex 53749, Fax 46260, ≤ Lough Corrib, ☞ – P. AE ① VISA
M (booking essential) 18.00/29.00 **t.** and a la carte 29.00/45.00 **t.** 8.00.

CORK (Corcaigh) Cork 405 G 12 – pop. 136 344 – 021.
ee : St. Patrick's Street★ YZ – St. Ann's Shandon Church★ (18C) (steeple ✻★ *AC*, 134 steps) A – University College★ (1845) X **U** – The Marina ≤★ X.
Monkstown ✆ 841225, S : 7 m. by L 66 X – 18 Little Island ✆ 353263 – 18 East Cork, Midleton ✆ 631687.
✆ 313131, Telex 32085, S : 4 m. by L 42 X – **Terminal :** Bus Station, Parnell Pl.
Shipping Connections with the continent : to France (Roscoff) (Brittany Ferries) – to France (Le Havre) (Irish Ferries) summer only.
Cork City, Tourist House, Grand Parade ✆ 273251 – Cork Airport ✆ 964347 (26 June-September).
Dublin 154.

Plan on next page

Fitzpatrick's Silver Springs, Tivoli, E : 2 ½ m. on N 8 ✆ 507533, Telex 76111, Fax 507641, 9, ☞, park, ✂, squash – rest TV ☎ P – 600 X **c**
103 rm, **3 suites.**

Jury's, Western Rd, by Washington St., ✆ 276622, Telex 76073, Fax 274477, heated, ☞, squash – TV ☎ & P – 600. AE ① VISA. ✻ Z **v**
closed 25 and 26 December – **M** 13.50/17.25 **t.** and a la carte 5.25 – ☐ 7.05 – **184 rm** 78.00/89.00 **t.**, **1 suite** 130.00/275.00 **t.**

Imperial, South Mall, ✆ 274040, Telex 75126, Fax 274040 (extn. 2507) – TV ☎ – 300. AE ① VISA. ✻ Z **n**
closed 1 week at Christmas – **M** 7.00/17.00 **t.** and a la carte 6.50 – **100 rm** ☐ 40.00/120.00 **t.**

Arbutus Lodge , Middle Glanmire Rd, Montenotte, ✆ 501237, Telex 75079, Fax 502893, ≤, ☞ – rest TV ☎ P. AE ① VISA. ✻ Y **a**
closed 24 to 29 December – **M** *(closed Sunday)* 15.25/19.25 **st.** and a la carte 6.25 – **20 rm** ☐ 30.00/98.00 **st.** – SB (weekends only) 90.00/120.00 **st.**

Country Club, Montenotte, ✆ 502922, Fax 502082, ☞ – TV ☎ P – 150 X **s**
36 rm.

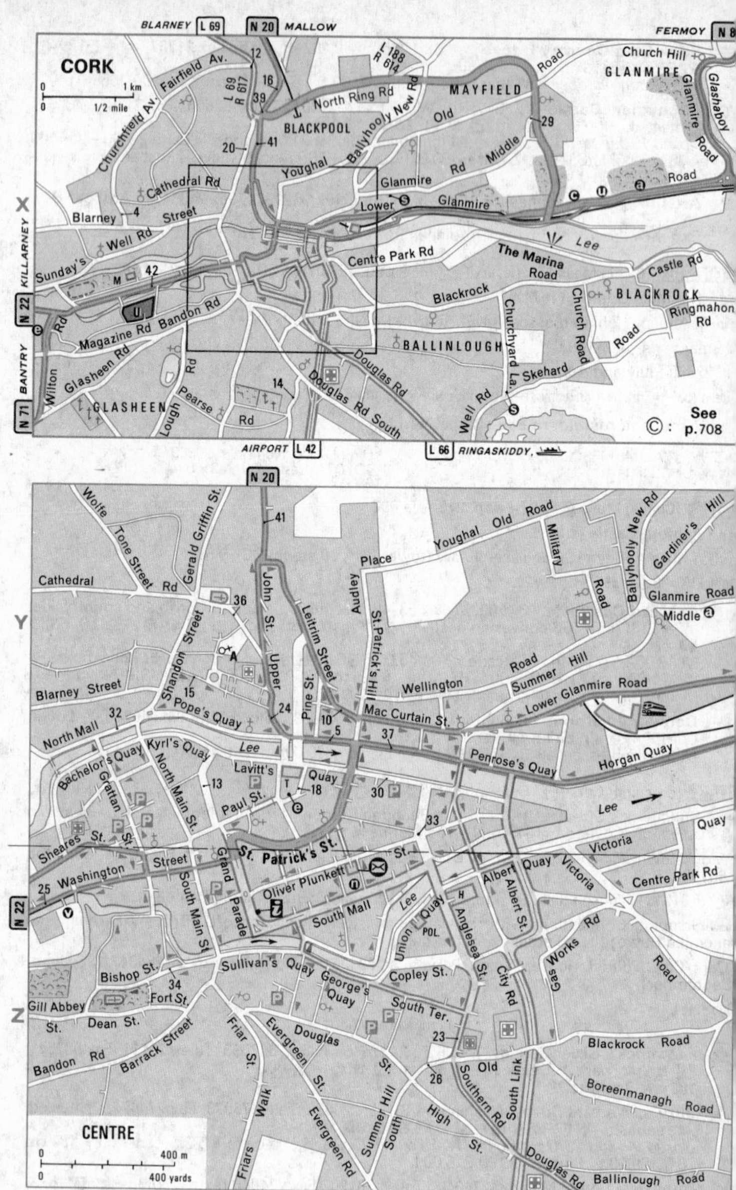

Oliver Plunkett Street . . . . Z
St. Patrick's Street . . . . YZ

Baker's Road . . . . X 4
Camden Place . . . . Y 5
Coburg Street . . . . Y 10
Commons Road . . . . X 12
Corn Market Street . . . . Y 13
Curragh Road . . . . X 14
Dominick Street . . . . Y 15
Dublin Street . . . . X 16
Emmet Place . . . . Y 18
Great William O'Brien Street X 20
Infirmary Road . . . . Z 23
John Redmond Street . . . . . . Y 24
Lancaster Quay . . . . Z 25
Langford Row . . . . Z 26
Lower Mayfield Road . . . . . . X 29
Merchant's Quay . . . . Y 3
Newsom's Quay . . . . Y 3
Parnell Place . . . . Y 3
Proby's Quay . . . . Z 3
Roman Street . . . . Y 3
St. Patrick's Quay . . . . Y 3
Thomas Davis Street . . . . . . X 3
Watercourse Road . . . . X 4
Western Road . . . . X 4

🏠 **Lotamore House** without rest., Tivoli, E : 3¼ m. on N 8 ✆ 822344, Fax 822219, park – TV ☎ P. VISA X a
20 rm 25.00/40.00 **st.**

🏠 **Victoria Lodge** without rest., Victoria Cross, ✆ 542233, Fax 542572 – TV ☎ P. VISA. X e
22 rm 23.00/36.00 **st.**

XX **Cliffords,** 18 Dyke Parade, ✆ 275333 – AE VISA
closed lunch Monday and Saturday, Sunday, 2 weeks August and 24-25 December – **M** 10.00/23.00 **t.** 7.00.

XX **Flemings** with rm, Silver Grange House, Tivoli, E : 2¾ on N 8 ✆ 821621 – TV ☎ P. AE VISA. X u
closed 3 days at Christmas – **M** 12.50/23.00 **st.** and a la carte 5.50 – **4 rm** 45.00/65.00 **st.** – SB (weekends only) 90.00.

XX **Lovett's,** Churchyard Lane, off Well Rd, Douglas, ✆ 294909 – P. AE VISA X s
closed Saturday lunch, Sunday and Bank Holidays – **M** 14.65/20.00 **t.** and a la carte 5.50.

X **Crawford Gallery Café,** Crawford Gallery, Emmet Pl., ✆ 274415 – VISA Y e
closed dinner Monday, Tuesday and Saturday, Sunday, 25 December-10 January and Bank Holidays – **M** (dinner booking essential) a la carte 10.20/14.00 **t.** 4.50.

at ***Glounthaune*** E : 7 m. on N 25 – X – ✉ 021 Cork :

🏠 **Ashbourne House,** ✆ 353319, Fax 354338, « Extensive gardens », heated, – TV ☎ P. AE VISA
M 7.95/16.00 **t.** 4.50 – **26 rm** 36.00/80.00 **t.** – SB 88.00/92.00 **st.**

AT 24 Watercourse Rd ✆ 503228
ORD Dennehys Cross ✆ 542846
OPEL 26 St. Patricks Quay ✆ 276657
RENAULT Bishop's Town Rd ✆ 544655

COURTOWN (Baile na Cúirte) Wexford 405 N 10 – pop. 337 – 055 Gorey.

Courtown Harbour ✆ 25166.

Dublin 62 – ◆Waterford 59 – Wexford 42.

🏠 **Courtown,** ✆ 25108, – ☎ P. AE VISA.
closed Easter-October – **M** 10.50/18.70 **st.** and a la carte – **21 rm** 22.55/55.00 **t.** – SB (weekends only) 61.00/67.50 **st.**

CROSSHAVEN (Bun an Tábhairne) Cork 405 H 12 – pop. 1 419 – ✉ 021 Cork.

Dublin 173 – ◆Cork 12.

🏠 **Whispering Pines,** ✆ 831843, Fax 831448, <, – ☎ P. AE VISA.
M (dinner only) 14.00 **st.** 5.00 – **20 rm** 18.00/34.00 **st.**

CROSSMOLINA (Grois Mhaoitíana) Mayo 405 E 5 – pop. 1 335 – ✉ 096 Ballina.

Dublin 157 – ◆Ballina 6.5.

🏠 **Enniscoe House**, Castlehill, S : 2 m. on L 140 ✆ 31112, Fax 31112, <, « Georgian country house, antiques », park – P. AE VISA.
April-mid October and January – **M** (dinner only) 18.00 **st.** 5.50 – **6 rm** 45.00/74.00 **st.**

DALKEY (Deilginis) Dublin 405 N 8 – 01 Dublin.

Dublin 11.

X **Guinea Pig,** 17-18 Railway Rd, ✆ 859055, Seafood – AE VISA
M (booking essential) (dinner only and Sunday lunch)/dinner 20.50 **t.** and a la carte **st.** 5.75.

DELGANY (Deilgne) Wicklow 405 N 8 – pop. 7 442 (inc. Greystones) – ✉ Bray – 01 Dublin.

✆ 404 (Wicklow) 874645.

◆Dublin 19.

🏠 **Glenview House**, Glen of the Downs, NW : 2 m. by L 164 on N 11 ✆ 873399, Fax 877511, <, park – TV ☎ P – 100. AE VISA.
closed 24 to 26 December – **M** 10.50/12.00 **t.** 4.95 – 6.00 – **24 rm** 41.00/62.00 **t.**

When travelling for business or pleasure in England, Wales, Scotland and Ireland:

- use the series of five maps (nos 401, 402, 403, 404 and 405) at a scale of 1:400 000
- they are the perfect complement to this Guide as towns underlined in red on the maps will be found in this Guide.

DINGLE (An Daingean) Kerry 405 B 11 – pop. 1 358 – ECD : Thursday – 066 Tralee.

See : Dingle Bay★.

Envir. : NE : Conair Pass ✳★ – Fahan : Belvedere (coast road) ≤★, SW : 7½ m. – Kilmaked (church★ 12C), Gallarus Oratory★ (8C), NW : 5 m.

ℹ ☎ 51188 (June-September).

♦Dublin 216 – ♦Killarney 51 – ♦Limerick 95.

- **Benners,** Main St., ☎ 51638, Telex 73937, Fax 51412 – TV ☎ P. VISA. **M** (bar lunch Monday to Saturday)/dinner 18.00 **t.** and a la carte 6.00 – **24** ... 43.00/72.00 **t.** – SB (weekends only) 81.00/101.00 **st.**
- **Skellig,** ☎ 51144, Fax 51501, ≤, – TV ☎ P. AE VISA. *March-November* – **M** (bar lunch Monday to Saturday)/dinner 19.50 **st.** – **70 rm** 40.0... 85.00 **st.**
- **Milltown House** without rest., W : ¾ m. ☎ 51372, ≤ – P. VISA. *April-October* – **7 rm** 20.00/28.00 **st.**
- **Alpine House** without rest., Mail Rd, ☎ 51250, – P. VISA. *March-November* – **14 rm** 26.00 **st.**
- XX **Beginish,** Green St., ☎ 51588, Seafood, – AE VISA. *Mid March-mid November* – **M** *(closed Monday and Sunday)* (dinner only) a la carte 16.4... 20.40 **t.** 5.50.
- X **Doyle's Seafood Bar** with rm, 4 John St., ☎ 51174, Fax 51816 – TV ☎. VISA. *Mid March-mid November* – **M** *(closed Sunday)* a la carte 14.00/19.00 **t.** 6.00 – **8 r...** 35.00/55.00 **st.**

DONEGAL (Dún na nGall) Donegal 405 H 4 – pop. 1 956 – ECD : Wednesday – 073.

See : Franciscan Priory (site★, ≤★).

18 Murvagh ☎ 073 (Ballintra) 34054.

ℹ ☎ 21148 (May-September).

♦Dublin 164 – ♦Londonderry 48 – ♦Sligo 40.

- **Ernan's House**, St. Ernans Island, SW : 2 ¼ m. by N 15 ☎ 21065, Fax 22098, Donegal Bay, park – TV ☎ P. VISA. *Easter-mid November* – **M** (dinner only) 22.50 **t.** 5.00 – **13 rm** 50.00/90.00 **t.**

FIAT Quay St. ☎ 21039

DROGHEDA (Droichead Átha) Louth 405 M 6 – pop. 23 247 – ECD : Wednesday – 041.

See : St. Lawrence's Gate★ (13C) – Hill of Slane (site★, ≤★) W : 8½ m.

Envir. : Mellifont Abbey★★ (Cistercian ruins 1142) NW : 4 ½ m. – Monasterboice (3 ta... crosses★★ 10C) NW : 5 ½ m. – Dowth Tumulus ✳★, W : 4 m. – Duleek (priory★ 12C ruin... SW : 5 m. – Newgrange Tumulus★ (prehistoric tomb) *AC*, SW : 7 m.

18 County Louth, Baltray ☎ 22327, E : 3 m.

ℹ ☎ 37070 (15 May-26 August).

♦Dublin 31 – ♦Dundalk 22 – ♦Tullamore 69.

Hotel and restaurant see : **Navan**: 19 m.

FORD North Rd ☎ 31106
NISSAN North Rd ☎ 38566
PEUGEOT Palace St. ☎ 37303

DROMAHAIR (Droim dhá Thiar) Leitrim 405 H 5 – 071 Sligo.

♦Dublin 146 – ♦Sligo 13.

- **Drumlease Glebe House**, E : 2 m. by Manorhamilton rd ☎ 64141, Fax 64490, « Country house atmosphere », heated, park – ☎ P. AE VISA. **M** (dinner only, residents only) 18.50 4.50 – **7 rm** 43.50/95.00 – SB (Octobe... March) (except Christmas-New Year) 85.00 **st.**

DROMINEER (Drom Inbhir) Tipperary 405 H 9 – ✉ 067 Nenagh.

♦Dublin 102 – ♦Galway 69 – ♦Limerick 32.

- **Sail Inn,** ☎ 24114, Fax 24288, ≤, – ☎ P. AE VISA. **M** 7.95/16.00 **st.** and a la carte 4.50 – **11 rm** 22.00/44.00 **st.**

UBLIN (Baile Átha Cliath) Dublin 405 N 7 – pop. 528 882 – ☎ 01.

ee : National Gallery★★★ BY – Castle (State apartments★★★ AC) BY – Christ Church Cathe-ral★★ (12C) BY – National Museum (Irish antiquities, Art and Industrial)★★ BY **M2** – Trinity ollege★ (Library★★) BY – National Museum (Zoological Collection)★ BY **M1** – Municipal Art allery★BX **M3** – O'Connell Street★ (and the General Post Office) BXY – St. Stephen's Green★ Z – St. Patrick's Cathedral (interior★) BZ – Phoenix Park (Zoological Gardens★) AY.

nvir. : St. Doolagh's Church★ (13C) (open Saturday and Sunday, afternoon only) NE : 7 m. yL 87 AY.

Edmondstown, Rathfarnham ☎ 932461, S : 3 m. by N 81 AZ – Elm Park, Nutley House, unnybrook ☎ 693438, S : 3 m. AZ – Lower Churchtown Rd, Milltown ☎ 977060, S : by T 43 Z – Royal Dublin, Bull Island ☎ 336346, E : by L 86 AY – Stackstown, Kellystown Rd ☎ 942338, SE: 7 m. AZ – Clontarf, Donnycarney House, Malahide Rd ☎ 311305, 2 m. AY – Rathfarnham, Newtown ☎ 931201, S : 6 m. AZ.

☎ 379900, Telex 31266, N : 5 ½ m. by N 1 AY – **Terminal** : Busaras (Central Bus Station) tore St.

to Holyhead (B & I Line) 2-4 daily (3 h 30 mn-4 h) – to the Isle of Man : Douglas (Isle of lan Steam Packet Co.) (summer only) (4 h 45 mn).

14 Upper O'Connell St. ☎ 747733 – Dublin Airport ☎ 376387 – Baggot St. ☎ 747733 February-27 October).

Belfast 103 – ♦Cork 154 – ♦Londonderry 146.

Plans on following pages

Conrad, Earlsfort Terr., ☎ 765555, Fax 765424, – rm rest – 300. AE VISA. BZ z
M 30.00/40.00 **t.** and a la carte 7.00 – 10.00 – **181 rm** 120.00/150.00 **t.**, **9 suites** 280.00/550.00 **t.**

Berkeley Court, Lansdowne Rd, Ballsbridge, ☎ 601711, Telex 30554, Fax 617238, – rest – 250. AE VISA. AZ c
M 14.50/19.00 **t.** and a la carte 5.00 – 7.50 – **200 rm** 115.00/145.00 **t.**, **9 suites** 225.00/1 200.00 **t.**

Westbury, Grafton St., ☎ 6791122, Telex 91091, Fax 6797078 – rest – 250. AE VISA. BY z
M 14.50/19.00 **t.** and a la carte 4.25 – 7.50 – **198 rm** 115.00/145.00 **t.**, **8 suites** 225.00/1 200.00 **t.**

Shelbourne (T.H.F.), 27 St. Stephen's Green, ☎ 766471, Telex 93653, Fax 616006 – – 400. AE VISA BZ s
M 18.00/22.00 **t.** and a la carte 5.50 – 9.50 – **162 rm** 105.00/185.00 **t.**, **5 suites** 210.00/525.00 **t.**

Gresham, O'Connell St., ☎ 746881, Telex 32473 – rest – 300 BY s
172 rm, **10 suites.**

Jurys, Pembroke Rd, Ballsbridge, ☎ 605000, Telex 93723, Fax 605540, heated – rm rest – 400. AE VISA. AZ c
M 15.50/19.50 **t.** and a la carte 5.75 – 7.75 – **294 rm** 93.00/104.00 **t.**, **4 suites** 300.00/500.00 **t.**

Annex : **Jury's (Towers),** Pembroke Rd, Ballsbridge, ☎ 605000, Telex 93723, Fax 605540 – rm . AE VISA.
M (see **Jurys H.** above) – 7.75 – **98 rm** 135.00/165.00 **t.**, **2 suites** 300.00/500.00 **t.**

Buswells, 25-26 Molesworth St., ☎ 764013, Telex 90622, Fax 762090 – – 100. AE VISA. BY u
M *(closed lunch Sunday and Bank Holidays and Saturday)* 10.50 **st.** (lunch) and a la carte dinner 4.50 – 6.50 – **67 rm** 49.00/78.00 **t.**

Stephens Hall without rest., 14-17 Lower Leeson St., ☎ 610585, Fax 610606 – . AE VISA. BZ o
M *(closed Saturday and Sunday)* (dinner only) (restricted menu) a la carte approx. 11.00 **st.** 4.75 – 6.00 – **37 rm** 80.00/120.00 **st.**, **34 suites** 120.00/160.00 **st.** – SB (weekends only) 140.00/200.00 **st.**

Mont Clare, Merrion Sq., ☎ 616799, Fax 615663 – – 150. AE VISA. BY v
M 11.50/15.00 **st.** and a la carte 4.60 – 7.00 – **74 rm** 72.00/150.00 **t.** – SB (weekends only and weekdays only July and August) 85.50 **st.**

Russell Court, 21-23 Harcourt St., ☎ 784991, Fax 784066 – – 100 BZ v
20 rm, **1 suite.**

Skylon, Upper Drumcondra Rd, N : 2 ½ m. on N 1 ☎ 379121, Group Telex 90790, Fax 372778 – – 40. AE VISA. AY e
M 6.00/10.00 **t.** and a la carte 3.50 – 5.00 – **92 rm** 48.00/68.00 **t.**

Tara Tower, Merrion Rd, SE : 4 m. on T 44 ☎ 694666, Fax 691027 – – 120. AE VISA. on T 44 AZ
M 6.00/10.00 **t.** and a la carte 3.50 – 5.00 – **82 rm** 48.00/68.00 **t.**

Blooms, Anglesea St., ☎ 715622, Telex 31688, Fax 715997 – – 30. AE VISA. BY e
M 9.50/17.00 **st.** and a la carte 9.50 – 10.00 – **86 rm** 70.00/110.00 **t.**

DUBLIN

Anne Street South .... BY 2
Dawson Street .... BY
Duke Street .... BY 27
Grafton Street .... BY
Henry Street .... BY
Irish Life Mall Centre .... BY
O'Connell Street .... BXY

Bath Avenue .... AZ 3
Belvidere Place .... BX 4
Benburb Street .... AY 5
Blessington Street .... BX 6
Botanic Road .... AY 7
Brunswick Street North .... BY 8
Bull Alley .... BY 9
Chancery Street .... BY 13
Charlotte Street .... BZ 15
College Street .... BY 19
Denmark Street .... BX 23
D'Olier Street .... BY 24
Donnybrook Road .... AZ 25
Eglinton Road .... AZ 29
Essex Quay .... BY 30
Fitzgibbon Street .... BX 31
Fitzwilliam Place .... BZ 32
Frederick Street North .... BX 33
Gardiner Place .... BX 35
George's Quay .... BY 36
Golden Lane .... BY 39
Harrington Street .... BZ 44
Infirmary Road .... AY 46
Kevin Street Upper .... BZ 47
Kildare Street .... BYZ 48
King Street South .... BY 49
Macken Street .... AZ 50
Marlborough Street .... BY 53
Merchants Quay .... BY 56
Montague Street .... BZ 59
Morehampton Road .... AZ 60
Mountjoy Street .... BX 6
Nicholas Street .... BY 6
Parnell Square East .... BX 6
Parnell Square North .... BX 6
Parnell Square West .... BX 6
Rathmines Road Uper .... AZ 7
Ringsend Road .... AZ 7
St. Alphonsus Rd .... AY 7
Sandford Road .... AZ 7
Shelbourne Road .... AZ 7
Stephen Street .... BY 8
Tara Street .... BY 8
Terenure Road East .... AZ 8
Victoria Quay .... AZ 9
Wellington Quay .... BY 9
Westland Row .... BY 9
Westmoreland Street .... BY 9
Wexford Street .... BZ 9
Winetavern Street .... BY 1
Wolfe Tone Quay .... AYZ 1
Wood Quay .... BY 1

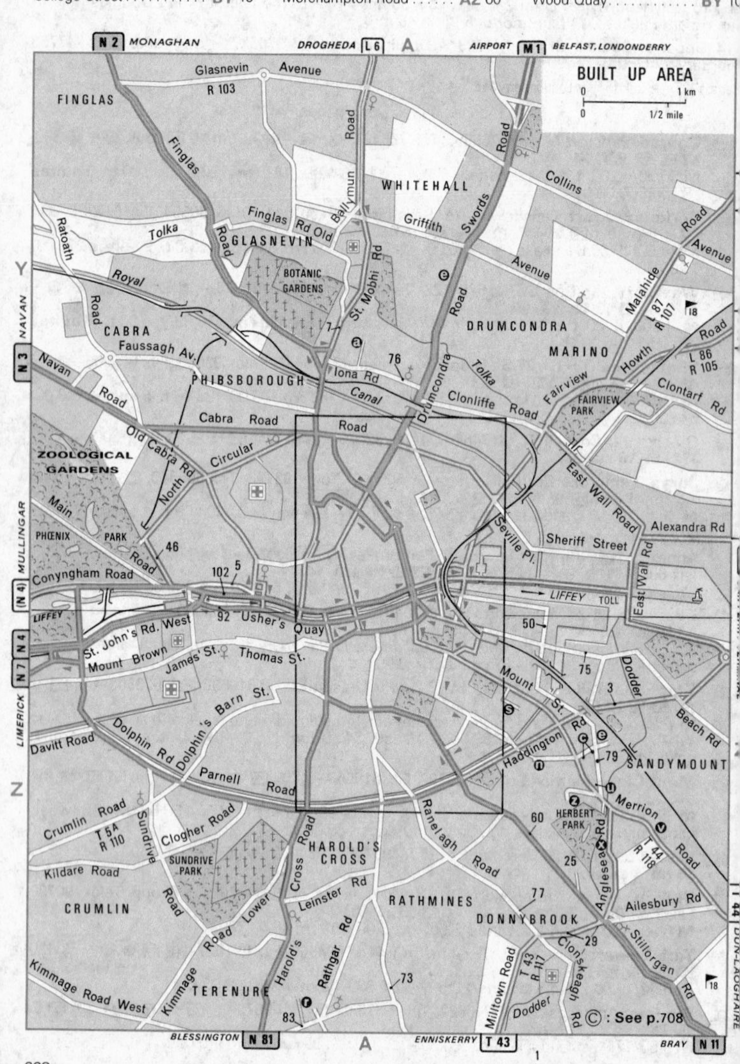

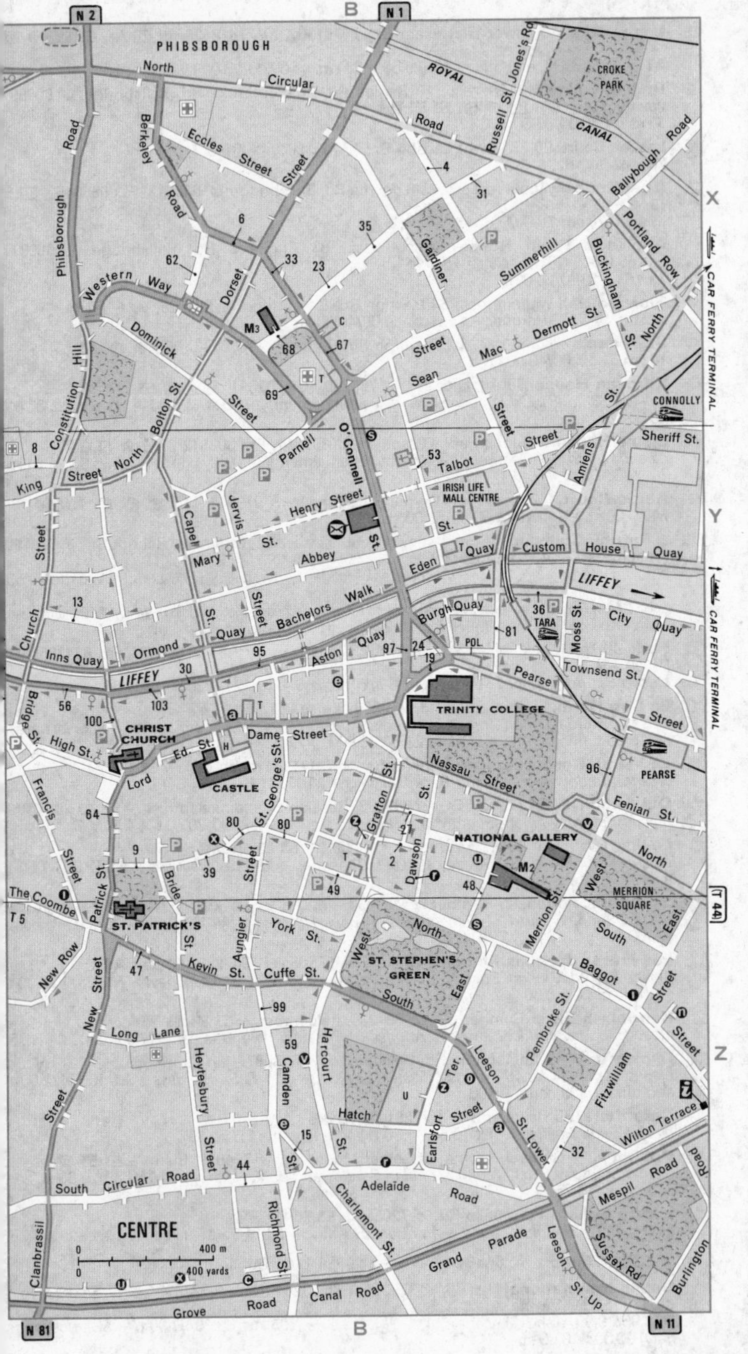
N 2
B
N 1
PHIBSBOROUGH
North Circular Road
ROYAL CANAL
CROKE PARK
Jones's Rd
Russell St
Ballybough Road
Portland Row
Phibsborough Road
Berkeley Road
Eccles Street
Dorset Street
Western Way
Dominick Street
Constitution Hill
Bolton St.
Gardiner Street
Summerhill
Buckingham St. North
Sean Mac Dermott St.
Parnell Street
O'Connell St.
Talbot Street
IRISH LIFE MALL CENTRE
Amiens St.
CONNOLLY
Sheriff St.
CAR FERRY TERMINAL
X
Y
Z
King Street North
Church Street
Capel St.
Jervis St.
Henry Street
Mary St.
Abbey St.
Eden Quay
Custom House Quay
LIFFEY
Bachelors Walk
Ormond Quay
Inns Quay
Burgh Quay
City Quay
TARA
Moss St.
Aston Quay
POL.
Pearse Street
Townsend St.
TRINITY COLLEGE
Bridge St.
High St.
CHRIST CHURCH
Dame Street
Lord Ed. St.
CASTLE
Gt. George's St.
Grafton St.
Dawson St.
Nassau Street
PEARSE
Fenian St.
NATIONAL GALLERY
M2
M3
Merrion St.
Merrion Square North
MERRION SQUARE
West
South
East
Francis Street
Patrick St.
Bride St.
The Coombe
ST. PATRICK'S
T 5
T 44
New Row
New Street
Aungier Street
York St.
Kevin St.
Cuffe St.
ST. STEPHEN'S GREEN
Baggot Street
Pembroke St.
Leeson St. Lower
Long Lane
Heytesbury Street
Camden St.
Harcourt St.
Hatch Street
Earlsfort Ter.
Fitzwilliam Street
Wilton Terrace
South Circular Road
Adelaide Road
Richmond St.
Charlemont St.
Mespil Road
Sussex Rd
Burlington Road
Grand Parade
Leeson St. Up.
CENTRE
0 400 m
0 400 yards
Clanbrassil Street
Grove Road
Canal Road
N 81
N 11

Longfield's, 10 Lower Fitzwilliam St., ✆ 761367, Fax 761542 – ▤ TV ☎. AE VISA ✻ BZ
M 12.00/20.00 **t.** and a la carte 5.50 – **28 rm** 69.00/98.00 **t.**

Raglan Lodge without rest., 10 Raglan Rd, off Pembroke Rd, Ballsbridge, ✆ 606697 Fax 606781, – TV ☎ P. AE VISA. ✻ AZ
7 rm 46.00/82.00 **st.**

Leeson Court, 26-27 Lower Leeson St., ✆ 763380 – ▤ TV ☎ BZ
20 rm.

Ariel House without rest., 52 Lansdowne Rd, Ballsbridge, ✆ 685512, Fax 685845 – TV ☎ P. AE VISA. ✻ AZ
6.50 **28 rm** 28.50/90.00 **t.**

Anglesea Town House without rest., 63 Anglesea Rd, Ballsbridge, ✆ 683877 Fax 683461 – TV ☎. AE VISA. ✻ AZ
7 rm 40.00/60.00.

Merrion Hall without rest., 54 Merrion Rd, Ballsbridge, ✆ 681426, – TV P. ✻
closed 14-31 December – **4 rm** 30.00/40.00 **st.** AZ

St. Aiden's without rest., 32 Brighton Rd, Rathgar, ✆ 906178 – TV ☎ P. VISA. ✻
10 rm 25.00/40.00 **st.** AZ

Kilronan House, 70 Adelaide Rd, ✆ 755266, Fax 782841 – TV ☎. VISA. ✻
closed 23 to 31 December – **M** (by arrangement) 20.00 **st.** 6.00 – **11 rm** 32.00/60.00 **st.** BZ

Egans House, 7-9 Iona Park, Glasnevin, ✆ 303611, Fax 303312 – TV ☎ P. VISA. ✻
closed 23 to 31 December – **M** (by arrangement) 14.00 **t.** 4.50 – 5.00 – **24 rm** 24.00/38.00 **t.** AY

Abrae Court, 9 Zion Rd, off Orwell Rd, Rathgar, ✆ 979944 – TV ☎ P. VISA. ✻
M 10.00 **st.** – **14 rm** 30.00/50.00 **st.** AZ

XXX ✿ **Patrick Guilbaud,** 46 St. James' Pl., St. James' St., off Lower Baggot St., ✆ 764192, French rest. – ▤. AE VISA BZ
closed Saturday lunch, Sunday and Bank Holidays – **M** 15.50/27.00 **t.** and a la carte 20.50/32.50 **t.**
Spec. Casserole of Dublin Bay prawns and lobster with aromatic butter, Black pudding, sweetbreads and crubeens with a pepper and red wine sauce, Fillet of new season lamb with homemade pasta (spring only).

XXX **Park,** 40 The Mews, Main St., Blackrock, SE : 4½ m. by T 44 ✆ 886177, Fax 834365 – AE VISA by T44 AZ
closed Saturday lunch, Sunday and Bank Holidays – **M** 12.00/26.50 **t.** 7.50.

XXX **Le Coq Hardi,** 35 Pembroke Rd, ✆ 689070 – P. AE VISA AZ
closed Saturday lunch, Sunday, 2 weeks August, 2 weeks Christmas and Bank Holidays – **M** 16.00 **t.** (lunch) and a la carte 23.50/30.50 **t.** 7.50.

XX **La Vie en Rose,** 6a Upper Stephen St., ✆ 781771, French rest. – AE VISA BY
closed Sunday, Monday and Bank Holidays – **M** 12.00/22.00 **t.**

XX **Old Dublin,** 90-91 Francis St., ✆ 542028, Russian-Scandinavian rest. – AE VISA
closed Saturday lunch, Sunday and Bank Holidays – **M** 11.00/20.50 **t.** 4.50. BY

XX **Locks,** 1 Windsor Terr., Portobello, ✆ 543391 – AE VISA BZ
closed Saturday lunch, Sunday, 1 week Christmas and Bank Holidays – **M** 12.95/17.50 **t.** and a la carte 5.15.

XX **Shannons,** Portobello Harbour, ✆ 782933 – P. AE VISA BZ
closed Sunday, 25 to 31 December and Bank Holidays – **M** 12.50/23.00 **t.** and a la carte 6.00.

XX **Les Frères Jacques,** 74 Dame St., ✆ 6794555, Fax 6794725 – AE VISA BY
closed Saturday lunch, Sunday, Christmas, New Year and Bank Holidays – **M** 13.00/20.00 **t.** and a la carte 6.50.

XX **Kapriol,** 45 Lower Camden St., ✆ 751235, Italian rest. – AE VISA BZ
closed Sunday and last 3 weeks August – **M** (dinner only) a la carte 17.00/28.00 **t.** 4.75.

XX **Osprey's,** 41-42 Shelbourne Rd, Ballsbridge, ✆ 608087 – AE VISA AZ
closed Saturday lunch, Sunday, Easter, Christmas and Bank Holidays – **M** 10.50/22.00 **t.** and dinner a la carte 5.00.

X **Cafe Klara,** 35 Dawson St., ✆ 778611 – VISA BY
closed Bank Holidays – **M** 10.50/14.50 **t.** and a la carte 6.50.

X **Dobbin's,** 15 Stephen's Lane off Lower Mount St., ✆ 764679, Bistro – AE VISA
closed Saturday lunch, Monday dinner, Sunday and Bank Holidays – **M** 24.50/29.90 **st.** and a la carte 5.75. AZ

X **Puerto Bella,** 1 Portobello Rd, ✆ 720851 – AE VISA BZ
closed Saturday lunch, Sunday and Bank Holidays – **M** 11.95/17.95 **t.** and a la carte 6.95.

at Dublin Airport N : 6½ m. by N 1 – AY – ✉ 01 Dublin :

Dublin International (T.H.F.), ✆ 379211, Telex 32849, Fax 425874 – rm TV ☎ & P – 120. AE VISA
M 8.95/13.95 **t.** and a la carte 4.95 – 6.50 – **195 rm** 68.00/91.00 **t.** – SB (weekends only) 90.00/110.00 **st.**

MICHELIN Distribution Centre, 4 Spilmak Pl., Bluebell Industrial Estate, Naas Rd, Dublin 12, ☏ 509096, Fax 504302 by N7 AZ

BMW, MITSUBISHI Ballygall Rd East ☏ 342577
BMW, TOYOTA Rathgar Av. ☏ 979456
CITROEN, PEUGEOT Buckingham St. ☏ 745821
DAIHATSU, TOYOTA ☏ 401393
FIAT, LANCIA 56 Howth Rd ☏ 332301
FIAT North Rd ☏ 342977
FIAT, LANCIA 84 Prussia St. ☏ 791722
FIAT Milltown Rd ☏ 698577
FORD Herberton Rd ☏ 754216
FORD 172-175 Parnell St. ☏ 747831
FORD Stillorgan Rd ☏ 886821
HONDA Clarince St., Dun Laoghaire ☏ 806467
HONDA, SUZUKI Harolds Cross Rd ☏ 975757
LAND-ROVER, MITSUBISHI Temple Rd ☏ 885085
MERCEDES-BENZ, TOYOTA 54 Glasnevin Hill ☏ 373771
NISSAN Howth Rd ☏ 314066
NISSAN Bluebell Av. ☏ 507887
NISSAN Merrion Rd ☏ 693911
OPEL, BMW Beach Rd ☏ 686011
OPEL 146 Cabra Rd ☏ 385222
OPEL Emmet Rd, Inchicore ☏ 534535
OPEL New Rd ☏ 592438
PEUGEOT, MAZDA Church Pl. ☏ 973999
PEUGEOT-TALBOT, CITROEN 23 Parkgate St. ☏ 710333
RENAULT 19 Conyngnam Rd ☏ 775677
RENAULT 27 Upper Drumcondra Rd ☏ 373706
ROVER, NISSAN 48-52 New St. ☏ 780033
ROVER Northbrook Rd ☏ 970811
ROVER, JAGUAR, NISSAN Richmond Rd ☏ 379162
SUZUKI 232 North Circular Rd, Grangegorman ☏ 300799
TOYOTA Kilbarrack Rd ☏ 322701
TOYOTA Smithfield Market ☏ 721222
VOLVO Townsend St. ☏ 779177
VW-AUDI, MAZDA, MERCEDES-BENZ 218-224 North Circular Rd ☏ 387211
VW-AUDI, MAZDA, MERCEDES-BENZ Ballybough Rd ☏ 723033

DUNDALK **(Dún Dealgan) Louth** 405 M 5 – **pop. 25 663 – ECD : Thursday – ☎ 042.**

18 Blackrock ☏ 21379, S : 3 m.

Market Sq. ☏ 35484.

♦**Dublin 53 – Drogheda 22.**

Ballymascanlon House (Best Western) ⛲, **N : 3½ m. by N 1 on R 173 ☏ 71124, Group Telex 43735, Fax 71598,** **, park, , squash –** **300.**
closed 24 to 26 December – **M** 10.50/16.50 **t.** and a la carte 5.50 – **36 rm** 37.00/65.00 **st.** – SB 83.00/87.00 **st.**

RENAULT Newry Rd ☏ 34603

DUNDERRY **Meath** 405 L 7 – **see Navan.**

DUNFANAGHY **(Dún Fionnachaidh) Donegal** 405 I 2 – **pop. 390 – ✉ ☎ 074 Letterkenny.**

Envir. : Doe Castle★ (16C ruins) (site★, ≤ ★) SE : 7½ m. – SW : Bloody Foreland Head★.

18 ☏ 36335.

♦**Dublin 172 – Donegal 54 –** ♦**Londonderry 43.**

Arnold's, **Main St., ☏ 36208, Fax 36352, ≤,** **–** **.**
Mid March-October – **M** (bar lunch Monday to Saturday)/dinner 15.50 **t.** and a la carte 4.00 – **34 rm** 26.00/55.00 **t.** – SB 68.00/75.00 **st.**

Carrig Rua, **Main St., ☏ 36133, Telex 80464, ≤ –** **.**
Easter-October – **M** (buffet lunch)/dinner 15.50 **t.** and a la carte 4.00 – **22 rm** 19.50/48.00 **t.** – SB 68.00/72.00 **st.**

at Port-na-Blagh **E : 1½ m. on T 72 – ✉ ☎ 074 Letterkenny :**

Port-na-Blagh, **☏ 36129, ≤ Sheephaven Bay and harbour,** **–** **.**
April-September – **M** 6.50/15.00 **st.** and a la carte 4.00 – **49 rm** 25.00/30.00 **st.** – SB (April-first week July and September) 64.00/73.60 **st.**

DUN LAOGHAIRE **(Dún Laoghaire) Dublin** 405 N 8 – **pop. 54 496 – ☎ 01 Dublin.**

See : Windsor Terrace ≤★ over Dublin Bay.

18 Eglinton Park ☏ 801055.

to Holyhead (Sealink) 2 daily (3 h 30 mn) – to Liverpool (Sealink) 1 daily (9 h).

St. Michaels Wharf ☏ 806984.

♦**Dublin 9.**

Plan on next page

Royal Marine, **Marine Rd, ☏ 801911, Telex 91277, Fax 801089, ≤,** **–** **rest** **– 500.** **n**
M 10.00/16.50 **t.** and a la carte 4.75 – 6.90 – **104 rm** 65.00/150.00 **t.** – SB (weekends only) 75.00/119.00 **st.**

XXX **na Mara, 1 Harbour Rd, ☏ 806767, Seafood.** **i**

XX **Digby's,** **5 Windsor Terr., ☏ 804600, ≤ –** **a**
closed Tuesday and Bank Holidays – **M** (dinner only and Sunday lunch) 18.50 **t.** and a la carte 4.80.

X **Trudi's,** **107 Lower George's St., ☏ 805318, Bistro –** **u**
closed Sunday and Monday – **M** (dinner only) a la carte 13.15/17.10 **t.** 4.00.

HONDA, OPEL Crofton Pl. ☏ 800341
MITSUBISHI, SUZUKI Glasthule Rd ☏ 802991
RENAULT Rochestown Av. ☏ 852555

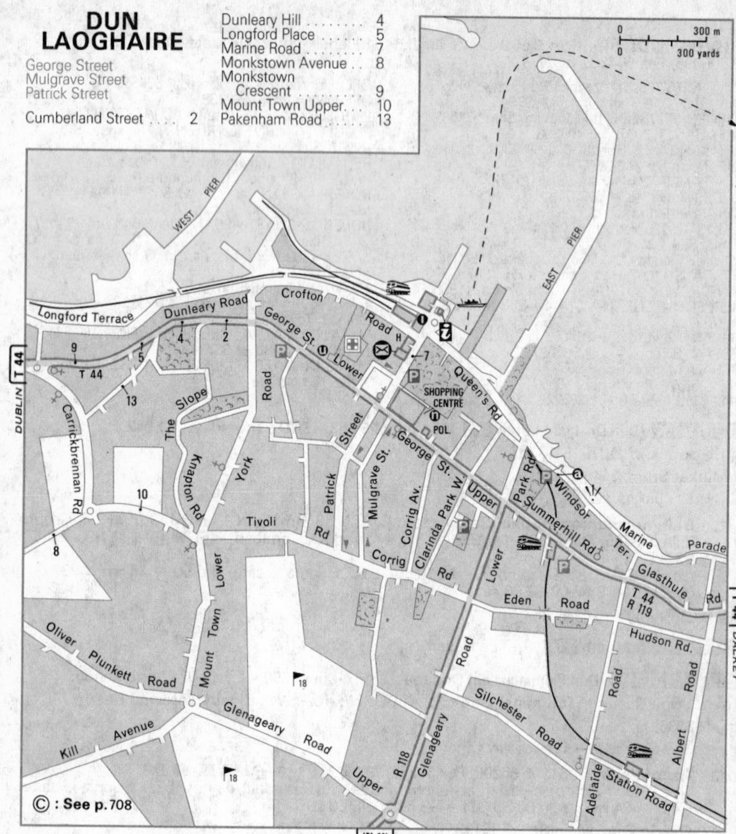

For maximum information from town plans: consult the conventional signs key.

DUNLAVIN **(Dún Luáin)** Wicklow 405 L 8 – pop. 583 – ☎ 045 Naas.

♦Dublin 31 – ♦Kilkenny 44 – Wexford 61.

Rathsallagh House 🐎, SW : 2 m. on Grangecon Rd ℘ 53112, Fax 53343, ≤, « Walled garden », ≘s, 🏊, park, 🎾 – ☎ Ⓟ – 🏊 25. 🆂 ⓓ VISA. ✕
closed 18 December-2 January – **M** *(closed Sunday dinner to non-residents)* (lunch by arrangement Monday to Saturday)/dinner 21.50 **t.** 🍷 6.00 – **12 rm** ☐ 80.00/100.00 **t.** – SB (weekdays only) 119.00/129.00 **st.**

DUNMANWAY **(Dún Manmhaí)** Cork 405 E 12 – ☎ 023 Bandon.

♦Dublin 191 – ♦Cork 37 – ♦Killarney 49.

Dun Mhuire, W : ½ m. by T 65 ℘ 45162, 🌳 – TV ☎ Ⓟ. 🆂 VISA. ✕
M (by arrangement) 15.00 **t.** 🍷 5.00 – **4 rm** ☐ 16.00/32.00 **t.**

DUNMORE EAST **(Dún Mór)** Waterford 405 L 11 – pop. 734 – ☎ 051 Waterford.

♦Dublin 108 – ♦Waterford 12.

Ship, Bayview, ℘ 83141 – 🆂 VISA
closed lunch and Sunday to Monday September-May – **M** a la carte 13.95/19.00 **t.** 🍷 4.95.

DURRUS **(Dúras)** Cork 405 D 13 – ☎ 027.

♦Dublin 210 – ♦Cork 56 – ♦Killarney 53.

Blairs Cove,, SW : 1 m. on L 56 ℘ 61127, « Converted barn », 🌳 – Ⓟ. 🆂 AE ⓓ VISA
Mid March-October – **M** *(closed Sunday dinner and Monday except July and August)* (booking essential) (dinner only and Sunday lunch)/dinner 22.00 **t.**

MO (Ioma) Laois 405 K 8 – pop. 200 – ✉ ☎ 0502 Portlaoise.

Dublin 49 – ◆Limerick 74 – ◆Tullamore 20.

New Montague (Best Western), E : 1 ¾ m. on N 7 ℘ 26154, Fax 26229, – TV ☎ ♿ P – 250
75 rm.

ENNIS (Inis) Clare 405 F 9 – pop. 6 223 – ECD : Thursday – ☎ 065.

See : Franciscan Friary★ (13C ruins).

Envir. : Tulla (site★, ancient church ✳★★) E : 10 m. – Killone Abbey (site★) S : 4 m. – Dysert O'Dea (site★) NW : 6 ½ m. – Kilmacduagh monastic ruins★ (site★) NE : 16 ½ m.

Drumbiggle Rd ℘ 24074.

Bank Pl. ℘ 28366.

Dublin 142 – ◆Galway 42 – ◆Limerick 22 – Roscommon 92 – ◆Tullamore 93.

Old Ground (T.H.F.), O'Connell St., ℘ 28127, Telex 70603, Fax 28112, – TV ☎ P – 200. AE VISA
M 9.00/17.00 **st.** and a la carte 4.50 – 8.00 – **59 rm** 58.00/120.00 **st.** – SB (weekends only) (except 15 December-8 January) 80.00/90.00 **st.**

Auburn Lodge, Galway Rd, N : 1 ½ m. on N 18 ℘ 21247, Telex 70177, , – TV ☎ P
45 rm.

FIAT Tulla Rd ℘ 22758
FORD Lifford ℘ 21035
FORD Limerick Gort Rd ℘ 061 (Limerick) 52244

ENNISKERRY (Áth an Sceire) Wicklow 405 N 8 – pop. 1 179 – ☎ 01 Dublin.

See : Site★ – Powerscourt Demesne (gardens★★★, Araucaria Walk★) *AC*.

Envir. : Powerscourt Waterfall★ *AC*, S : 4 m. – Lough Tay★★, SW by T 43, T 61 and L 161.

Dublin 17 – ◆Waterford 100.

Hotels and restaurants see : Dublin N : 17 m.

FAHAN (Fathain) Donegal 405 J 2 – ✉ Lifford – ☎ 077 Buncrana.

North West, Lisfannon, ℘ 61027.

Dublin 156 – ◆Londonderry 11 – ◆Sligo 95.

XX **St. John's,** ℘ 60289, « Lough-side setting » – P. AE VISA
closed Monday, 26 March and 25 December – **M** (dinner only) 14.50/20.00 **t.** 4.90.

FEAKLE (An Fhiacail) Clare 405 G 9 – pop. 188 – ☎ 0619.

Dublin 125 – ◆Galway 36 – ◆Limerick 25.

Smyth's Village, ℘ 24002, park, – P
May-September – **M** (booking essential) 6.50/10.00 3.50 – **12 rm** 16.00/30.00 – SB 54.00 **st.**

FURBOGH (Na Forbacha) Galway 405 E 8 – ☎ 091 Galway.

Dublin 42 – ◆Galway 7.

Connemara Coast, ℘ 92108, Group Telex 50905, Fax 92065, ←, heated – TV ☎ P – 600
83 rm, **1 suite.**

GALWAY (Gaillimh) Galway 405 E 8 – pop. 37 835 – ECD : Monday – ☎ 091.

See : Lynch's Castle★ (16C).

Envir. : NW : Lough Corrib★★★ – Claregalway (Franciscan Friary★ 13C) NE : 7 m. – Abbeyknockmoy (Cistercian Monastery★ 12C ruins) NE : 18 m. – Tuam (St. Mary's Cathedral : chancel arch★ 12C) NE : 20 m.

Galway, Salthill ℘ 23038, W : 3 m.

Carnmore Airport ℘ 55448, NE : 4 m.

to Aran Islands: Kilronan (Inishmore), Inishmaan and Inishere (C.I.E) 2 weekly.

Victoria Pl., Eyre Sq. ℘ 63081.

Dublin 135 – ◆Limerick 64 – ◆Sligo 90.

Great Southern, Eyre Sq., ℘ 64041, Telex 50164, Fax 66704, , – TV ☎ – 400. AE VISA.
closed 24 to 28 December – **M** (bar lunch)/dinner 18.00 **t.** and a la carte 4.50 – **117 rm** 61.00/175.00 **t.**

Ardilaun House, Taylor's Hill, ℘ 21433, Telex 50013, Fax 21546, – TV ☎ P – 50. AE VISA.
closed 22 to 30 December – **M** a la carte 14.50/22.50 **t.** 4.50 – **91 rm** 45.00/75.00 **t.**, **2 suites** 100.00/125.00 **t.** – SB (October-March) (weekends only) 90.00/110.00 **st.**

Galway Ryan, Dublin Rd, E : 1¼ m. on N 6 ✆ 53181, Telex 50149, Fax 53187, – |‡| TV ☎ P – 50. AE VISA.
M (dinner only) 14.00 **st.** and a la carte – 8.00 – **96 rm** 54.00/74.00 **st.**

Corrib Great Southern, Dublin Rd, E : 1¾ m. on N 6 ✆ 55281, Telex 50044, Fax 51390, – |‡| TV ☎ P – 100. AE VISA
M *(closed Saturday lunch)* 9.00/15.00 **t.** and a la carte 4.95 – 5.50 – **115 rm** 51.00/78.00 **t.**

Adare House without rest., 9 Father Griffin Pl., Lower Salthill, ✆ 62638, Fax 63963 – P
8 rm 16.00/29.00 **st.**

XX **Casey's Westwood,** Newcastle, NW : 1¾ m. on N 59 ✆ 21442 – P. AE VISA
M 8.50/16.50 **st.** and a la carte dinner 4.95.

at Salthill SW : 2 m. – ✉ Salthill – 091 Galway :

Rockbarton Park, 5-7 Rockbarton Park, ✆ 22018 – TV ☎ P. AE VISA.
M *(closed Sunday)/dinner* (bar lunch)/dinner a la carte approx. 11.00 **st.** 4.50 – 5.25 – **11 rm** 20.00/38.50 **st.**

GARRYVOE Cork 405 H 12 – ✉ Castlemartyr – 021 Cork.
♦Dublin 161 – ♦Cork 23 – Waterford 62.

Garryvoe, ✆ 646718, Fax 646824, ≤ – TV ☎ P. AE VISA.
closed Christmas Day – **M** 10.00/16.50 **st.** and a la carte 4.00 – **20 rm** 25.50/41.00 **st.**

CITROEN, PEUGEOT, SAAB Spanish Par. ✆ 62167

GLANDORE (Cuan Dor) Cork 405 E 13 – 028 Skibbereen.
♦Dublin 198 – ♦Cork 44 – ♦Killarney 75.

Marine, ✆ 33366, Fax 33600 – TV P – **16 rm.**

GLENBEIGH (Gleann Beithe) Kerry 405 C 11 – pop. 195 – 066 Tralee.
18 Dooks ✆ 68205.
♦Dublin 200 – ♦Killarney 21 – Tralee 24.

Towers, ✆ 68212, Fax 68260 – TV ☎ P. AE VISA
April-November – **M** (bar lunch Monday to Saturday)/dinner 19.00 **t.** and a la carte 5.00 – **34 rm** 35.00/60.00 **t.** – SB (April-October) 70.00 **st.**

GLENDALOUGH (Gleann da Loch) Wicklow 405 MN 8 – 0404.
See : Ancient monastic city★★ (site★★★, St. Kervin's Church★) and Upper Lake★ in Glendalough Valley★★★.
♦Dublin 34 – Wexford 71.

Hotels see : Rathnew E : 13 m.

GLENGARRIFF (An Gleann Garbh) Cork 405 D 12 – pop. 159 – 027.
See : Site★★★.
Envir. : S : Garinish Island (20 mn by boat *AC*) : Italian gardens★ – Martello Tower ✻★★ *AC.*
9 ✆ 63150, E : 1 m.
✆ 63084 (July and August).
♦Dublin 224 – ♦Cork 63 – ♦Killarney 37.

Hotels see : Ballylickey SE : 9 m.

GLEN OF AHERLOW (Gleann Eatharlaí) Tipperary 405 H 10 – ✉ 062 Tipperary.
See : Glen of Aherlow★ (statue of Christ the King★★).
♦Dublin 118 – Cahir 6 – Tipperary 9.

Glen, ✆ 56146, Fax 56152, – TV ☎ P. AE VISA
M 8.50/16.00 **st.** and a la carte 4.95 – **24 rm** 33.00/54.00 **st.** – SB 70.00/85.00 **st.**

GLOUNTHAUNE (An Gleanntan) Cork 405 G 12 – see Cork.

GOREY (Guaire) Wexford 405 N 9 – pop. 2 588 – ECD : Wednesday – 055.
✆ 21248 (July and August).
♦Dublin 58 – Waterford 55 – Wexford 38.

Marlfield House , Courtown Rd, E : 1 m. ✆ 21124, Telex 80757, Fax 21572, ≤, « Regency house and conservatory », , park – TV ☎ P. AE VISA.
closed December – **M** 16.50/27.00 **t.** 6.00 – **18 rm** 40.00/260.00 **t.**, **1 suite** 190.00/360.00 **t.**

PEUGEOT Courtown ✆ 27318

GOUGANE BARRA (Guagán Barra) Cork 405 D 12 – ✉ ☎ 026 Ballingeary.

See : Lake (site★).

Dublin 206 – ◆Cork 45.

Gougane Barra ⛰, ✆ 47069, ≤ lough and mountains, – ☎ ℗. VISA.
April-October – **M** 7.00/16.00 **st.** and a la carte 4.50 – **25 rm** 34.00/56.00 **st.**

HOWTH (Binn Éadair) Dublin 405 N 7 – ✉ ☎ 01 Dublin.

See : Howth Summit ≤★★ – Cliff Walk ≤★★ – Harbour★ – St Mary's Abbey★ (ruins 13C, 15C), site★ – Howth Gardens (rhododendrons★, site★, ≤★) AC.

Deer Park Hotel ✆ 322624.

Dublin 10.

Marine, Sutton Cross, NW : 1½ m. ✆ 322613, Fax 390442, ≤, – TV ☎ ℗ – 150. AE VISA.
M 15.00/22.00 **st.** and a la carte 5.00 – **27 rm** 48.00/80.00 **st.** – SB 96.00/100.00 **st.**

Howth Lodge (Best Western), ✆ 390288, Fax 322268, ≤ – TV ☎ ℗ – 90. AE VISA.
closed 24 to 28 December – **M** (bar lunch Monday to Saturday)/dinner 19.00 **t.** and a la carte 4.75 – 5.75 – **17 rm** 40.00/50.00 **t.**

King Sitric, Harbour Rd, East Pier, ✆ 325235, Fax 392442, Seafood – AE VISA
closed Sunday, 10 days Easter, 10 days Christmas and Bank Holidays – **M** (dinner only) 19.50 **t.** and a la carte 19.05/28.00 **t.** 5.75.

INNISHANNON (Inis Eonáin) Cork 405 G 12 – ☎ 021 Cork.

Dublin 169 – ◆Cork 15.

Innishannon House ⛰, S : ¾ m. on L 41 ✆ 775121, Fax 775609, – TV ☎ ℗. AE VISA
M 12.75/17.50 **t.** and a la carte 7.50 – **13 rm** 60.00/100.00 **st.** – SB 164.00/234.00 **st.**

KANTURK (Ceann Toirc) Cork 405 F 11 – pop. 1 976 – ECD : Wednesday – ☎ 029.

Fairy Hill ✆ 50534, SW : 1½ m.

Dublin 161 – ◆Cork 33 – ◆Killarney 31 – ◆Limerick 44.

Assolas Country House ⛰, E : 3¼ m. by L 38 and L 186 ✆ 50015, Fax 50795, ≤, « Part 17C and 18C country house, gardens, riverside setting », park, – ☎ ℗. AE VISA.
closed November-mid March – **M** (booking essential) (dinner only) 25.00 **st.** 5.00 – **9 rm** 63.00/126.00 **st.** – SB (weekends only) (except summer) 114.00/130.00 **st.**

KELLS (Ceanannas) Kilkenny 405 K 10 – pop. 2 623.

See : Augustinian Priory★★ (14C).

Envir. : Kilree's Church (site★, round tower★) S : 2 m.

◆Dublin 86 – Kilkenny 9 – ◆Waterford 23.

Hotels and restaurants see : Kilkenny N : 9 m.

MITSUBISHI, SUZUKI Bective St. ✆ 40681

KENMARE (Neidín) Kerry 405 D 12 – pop. 1 123 – ECD : Thursday – ☎ 064 Killarney.

Envir. : Kenmare River Valley★★, E : by L 62.

✆ 41291.

✆ 41233 (26 June-2 September).

◆Dublin 210 – ◆Cork 58 – ◆Killarney 20.

Park ⛰, ✆ 41200, Telex 73905, Fax 41402, ≤, « Antiques, paintings », park, – TV ☎ ♿ ℗. VISA.
April-mid November and Christmas-New Year – **M** 25.00/45.00 **t.** and a la carte 31.50/41.00 **t.** 8.50 – **44 rm** 110.00/226.00 **t.**, **6 suites** 270.00/340.00 **t.**

Hawthorn House without rest., Shelbourne St., ✆ 41035 – ℗.
closed Christmas and 2 weeks winter – **7 rm** 20.00/40.00 **t.**

Lime Tree, Shelbourne St., ✆ 41225, « Converted schoolhouse featuring local crafts » – ℗
16 March-6 October – **M** *(closed Sunday)* (dinner only) a la carte approx. 21.00 **st.** 4.80.

FORD Henry St. ✆ 41166 NISSAN, ROVER Shelbourne St. ✆ 41355

KILKENNY (Cill Chainnigh) Kilkenny 405 K 10 – pop. 9 466 – ECD : Thursday – ☎ 056.

See : St. Canice's Cathedral★★ (13C) – Grace's Castle (Courthouse)★ – Castle (park★, ≤★).

Envir. : Jerpoint Abbey★★ (ruins 12C-15C) SE : 12 m. – Callan (St. Mary's Church★ 13C-15C) SW : 13 m.

Glendine ✆ 22125, N : 1 m.

Shee Alms House ✆ 321755 (March-November).

◆Dublin 71 – ◆Cork 86 – ◆Killarney 115 – ◆Limerick 69 – ◆Tullamore 52 – ◆Waterford 29.

Kilkenny, College Rd, ☏ 62000, Fax 65984, – TV ☎ P – 250. AE VISA
M 9.50/16.75 **st.** and a la carte 4.50 – **60 rm** 34.00/95.00 **st.** – SB 85.00/92.50 **st.**

Newpark, Castlecomer Rd, N : ¾ m. on N 77 ☏ 22122, Fax 61111, – TV ☎ P – 300. AE VISA.
M *(restricted service January and February)* 9.50/14.50 **t.** and a la carte 4.95 – 6.75 – **60 rm** 33.00/59.00 **t.**

XX **Lacken House** with rm, Dublin Rd, ☏ 61085, Fax 62435, – TV ☎ P. AE VISA.
closed Sunday, Monday and 1 week Christmas – **M** (dinner only) 18.00 **t.** and a la carte 5.50 – **8 rm** 24.00/40.00 **t.**

at Knocktopher S : 13 m. on N 10 – ✉ ☏ 056 Kilkenny :

XX **Knocktopher Abbey,** ☏ 28618, Fax 28609, ←, – P. AE VISA
closed Sunday dinner and Monday – **M** (dinner only and Sunday lunch)/dinner 30.00 **t.** and a la carte.

NISSAN Patrick St. ☏ 21016 RENAULT Irishtown ☏ 21494

KILLALOE (Cill Dalua) Clare 405 G 9 – pop. 1 022 – ECD : Wednesday – ☏ 061.

See : Site★.

Envir. : N : Lough Derg Coast Road★★ (L 12) to Tuamgraney, Lough Derg★★★ (Holy Island site★★) – Nenagh : Butler Castle (keep★ 13C) NE : 9 m.

♦Dublin 109 – Ennis 32 – ♦Limerick 13 – ♦Tullamore 58.

Lakeside, ☏ 376122, Fax 376431, ←, – TV ☎ P – 130. AE VISA.
closed 24 to 26 December – **M** 8.50/15.00 **st.** and a la carte 4.75 – **32 rm** 28.00/52.00 **st.** – SB 65.00/71.00 **st.**

KILLARNEY (Cill Airne) Kerry 405 D 11 – pop. 7 693 – ECD : Thursday – ☏ 064.

Envir. : SW : Killarney District, Ring of Kerry : Lough Leane★★★, Muckross House (gardens★★★) – Muckross Abbey★ (ruins 13C), Tork Waterfall (Belvedere : ←★★, 251 steps), Lady's View Belvedere★★ – Gap of Dunloe★★.

18, 18 O'Mahoney's Point ☏ 31034, W : 3 m.

Farranfore Airport ☏ 066 (Farranfore) 64644/64259, N : 9½ m.

Town Hall ☏ 31633.

♦Dublin 189 – ♦Cork 54 – ♦Limerick 69 – ♦Waterford 112.

Europe, Fossa, W : 3 ½ m. on T 67 ☏ 31900, Telex 73913, Fax 32118, ← lake and mountains, park, – TV ☎ P – 500. AE VISA
April-October – **M** 18.50/22.50 **st.** and a la carte 8.50 – **170 rm** 75.00/102.00 **st.**, **40 suites** 130.00/350.00 **st.**

Dunloe Castle, Beaufort, W : 6 m. by T 67 ☏ 44111, Telex 73833, Fax 32118, ← Gap of Dunloe, countryside and mountains, park, – TV ☎ P – 500. AE VISA
May-September – **M** 18.50/22.50 **st.** and a la carte 8.50 – **140 rm** 52.00/92.00 **st.**

Great Southern, ☏ 31262, Telex 73998, Fax 31642, – TV ☎ P – 900. AE VISA.
closed January and February – **M** (bar lunch)/dinner a la carte 19.00/28.00 **t.** 5.00 – 7.00 – **178 rm** 65.00/110.00 **st.**, **2 suites** 150.00/175.00 **st.** – SB 96.00/130.00 **st.**

Aghadoe Heights, NW : 3 ½ m. by N 22 ☏ 31766, Telex 73942, Fax 31345, ← countryside, lake and mountains, – TV ☎ P – 90. AE VISA.
M 14.50/28.50 **st.** 5.50 – **58 rm** 80.00/120.00 **t.**, **3 suites** 160.00 **st.** – SB 150.00 **st.**

Cahernane, Muckross Rd, S : 1 m. on N 71 ☏ 31895, Fax 34340, ←, – ☎ P. AE VISA.
April-October and December – **M** (bar lunch)/dinner 24.00 **st.** and a la carte 6.00 – **50 rm** 60.00/95.00 **st.**

Castlerosse (Best Western), W : 2 m. on T 67 ☏ 31144, Telex 73910, Fax 31031, ←, – ☎ P. AE VISA.
Easter-October – **M** (bar lunch)/dinner 17.00 **t.** 6.00 – **67 rm** 41.00/80.00 **t.**

Royal, College St., ☏ 31853, Fax 34001 – TV ☎. VISA
M (dinner only and Sunday lunch May-September)/dinner 15.50 **st.** – **49 rm.**

Kathleens Country House, Tralee Rd, N : 2 m. on N 22 ☏ 32810, Fax 32340, ←, – rest TV ☎ P.
17 March-6 November – **M** 15.00 **st.** 6.00 – **10 rm** 40.00/50.00 **st.**

Castle Lodge without rest., Muckross Rd, ☏ 31545 – P. VISA.
17 rm 15.00/28.00 **st.**

Carriglea Farmhouse without rest., Muckross Rd, S : 1 ½ m. on N 71 ☏ 31116, ←, – P.
Easter-October – **9 rm** –/27.00 **t.**

X **Strawberry Tree,** 24 Plunkett St., ✆ 32688 – AE VISA
closed Sunday and Monday November-March, last 2 weeks January and last 2 weeks November – **M** (lunch by arrangement)/dinner a la carte approx. 20.90 **t.** 5.00.

X **Gaby's,** 17 High St., ✆ 32519, Seafood bistro – AE VISA
closed mid December-mid March – **M** *(closed Monday lunch and Sunday)* 16.00/25.00 **t.** and a la carte 5.00.

ROVER, NISSAN Muckross Rd ✆ 31237

KILLINEY **(Cill Iníon Leínín) Dublin** 405 N 8 – **01 Dublin.**

✆ 851983.

Dublin 8 – Bray 4.

Court, Killiney Bay, ✆ 851622, Telex 33244, Fax 852085, ←, – – 250. AE VISA
M 16.50 **t.** 4.50 – **86 rm** 54.10/85.50 **t.** – SB (weekends only) 76.00 **st.**

Fitzpatrick's Castle, ✆ 840700, Telex 30353, Fax 850207, , , , , , squash – – 400. AE VISA.
M 10.50/17.00 **t.** and a la carte 5.00 – 8.00 – **81 rm** 58.00/112.00 **t.**, **7 suites** 116.00/253.00 **t.**

KILLYBEGS **(Na Cealla Beaga) Donegal** 405 G 4 – pop. 1 570.

See : Fishing harbour★ – Carpet factory.

Envir. : NW : Glen Bay★★ – Glencolumbkille (site★★, folk village) NW : 14 m. – Portnoo (site★).

Dublin 181 – Londonderry 65 – Sligo 57.

KINSALE **(Cionn Eitigh) Cork** 405 G 12 – pop. 1 765 – ECD : Thursday – 021 Cork.

See : St. Multose's Church★ (12C).

Ringenane, Belgooly ✆ 772197.

✆ 772234 (26 June-2 September).

Dublin 178 – Cork 17.

Acton's (T.H.F.), Pier Rd, ✆ 772135, Telex 75443, Fax 772231, ←, , , – – 300. AE VISA
M (bar lunch)/dinner 18.00 **st.** and a la carte 4.75 – **57 rm** 44.00/84.00 **st.**

Blue Haven, 3 Pearce St., ✆ 772209, Fax 774268 – . AE VISA.
closed 24 and 25 December – **M** (see **Blue Haven** below) – **10 rm** 45.00/75.00 **st.** – SB 75.00/99.00 **st.**

Old Presbytery, Cork St., ✆ 772027, « Memorabilia » – .
M (by arrangement) 12.50 **st.** – **6 rm** 18.50/32.00 **st.**

XX **Skippers,** 23 Lower O'Connell St., ✆ 774043 – . AE VISA
closed Sunday and 2 weeks February – **M** (dinner only) 19.50 **t.** and a la carte 4.50.

XX **Vintage,** 50 Main St., ✆ 772502 – AE VISA
closed 15 January-15 March – **M** (dinner only) a la carte approx. 23.60 **t.** 6.00.

XX **Blue Haven** (at Blue Haven H.), 3 Pearse St., ✆ 772209, Fax 774268, Seafood – AE VISA
M (bar lunch)/dinner 19.50 **t.** and a la carte 15.00/27.50 **t.** 4.90.

XX Billy Mackesy's Bawnleigh House, N : 5½ m. on Old Cork Rd ✆ 771333 – .

X **Man Friday,** Scilly, SE : ½ m., ✆ 772260 – VISA
closed Sunday – **M** (dinner only) a la carte 17.40/23.45 **st.** 6.00.

X **Bernard's** with rm., 55 Main St. – VISA
M 15.75/20.00 **st.** 6.00 – **8 rm** 15.00/24.00 **st.**

KNOCKTOPHER **(Cnoc an Tóchair) Kilkenny** 405 K 10 – see Kilkenny.

LAHINCH **(An Leacht) Clare** 405 D 9 – pop. 473 – 065.

Envir. : Cliffs of Moher★★★ (O'Brien's Tower ★★ N : 1 h return on foot) NW : 5½ m.

18, 18 ✆ 81003.

Dublin 162 – Galway 49 – Limerick 41.

Aberdeen Arms, ✆ 81100, Telex 70132, Fax 81228, , – rest – 250
55 rm.

Atlantic House, Main St., ✆ 81049, Fax 81029 – . VISA
Easter-October – **M** (bar lunch)/dinner 17.50 **st.** and a la carte 6.95 – **14 rm** 24.50/44.50 **t.** – SB 72.30/75.50 **st.**

LEENANE **(An Líonán) Galway** 405 C 7.

See : ←★ on Killary Harbour★. **Exc. :** SE : Joyces Country : by road L 100 from Leenane to Clonbur : Lough Nafooey★ – ★ from the bridge on Lough Mask★★.

Dublin 173 – Ballina 56 – Galway 41.

Hotels see : Clifden SW : 19 m.

LETTERFRACK (**Leitir Fraic**) Galway 405 C 7 – ☎ 095 Clifden.

Envir. : Kylemore Abbey (site★★) and Kylemore Lake★, E : 4 m. – Renvyle (castle ≤★) NW 5 m. ♦Dublin 189 – Ballina 69 – ♦Galway 57.

- **Rosleague Manor** ⛰, W : 1 ½ m. on N 59 ☎ 41101, Fax 41168, ≤ Ballynakill harbour and Tully Mountain, « Country house atmosphere », park, ✕ – ✕ rest ☎ P. VISA
  Easter-October – **M** (bar lunch)/dinner 25.00 **t.** and a la carte 🍷 7.50 – **20 rm** ☕ 45.00/100.00 **t.** – SB (except summer) 90.00/120.00 **st.**

LETTERKENNY (**Leitir Ceanainn**) Donegal 405 I 3 – pop. 6 444 – ECD : Monday – ☎ 074.

See : St. Eunan's Cathedral ≤★.

Envir. : Grianan of Aileach★ (stone fort) ※★★★, NE : 18 m. – Gartan Lake★, NW : 8 ½ m.

18 Barnhill ☎ 21150, NE : 1 m. ℹ Derry Rd ☎ 21160.

♦Dublin 150 – ♦Londonderry 21 – ♦Sligo 72.

- **Gallagher's**, 100 Upper Main St., ☎ 22066, Fax 21016 – TV ☎ P. AE ⓓ VISA
  closed 3 days at Christmas – **M** 8.00 **st.** (lunch) and a la carte 🍷 3.75 – **27 rm** ☕ 22.00/52.00 **st.** – SB (weekends only) 50.00/52.00 **st.**

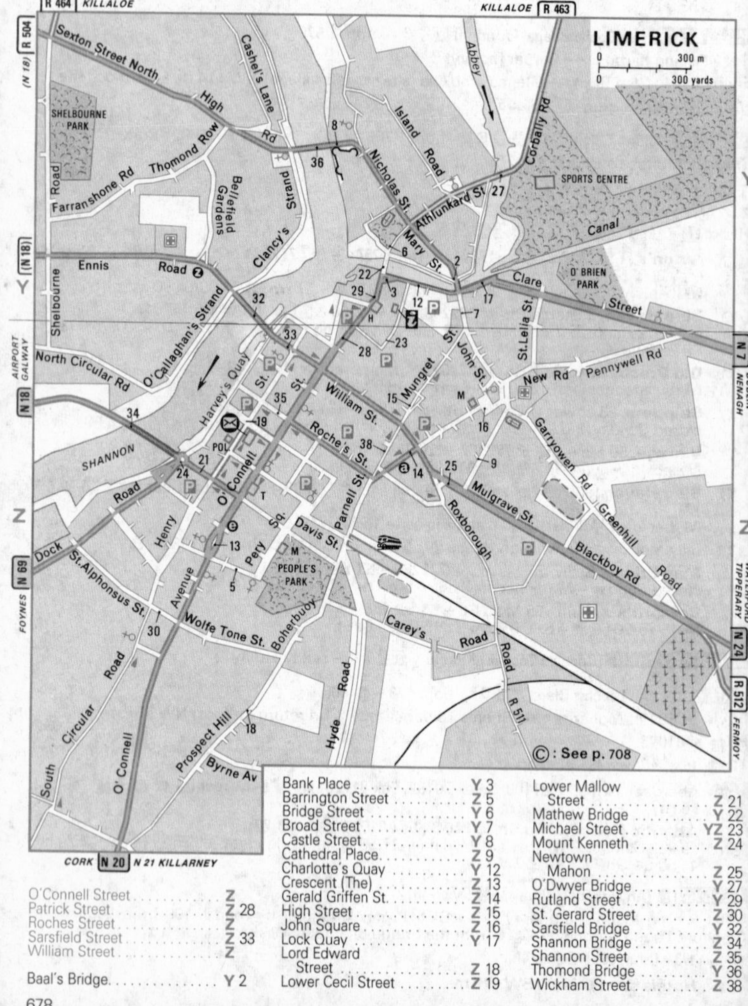

O'Connell Street	Z	
Patrick Street	Z	28
Roches Street	Z	
Sarsfield Street	Z	33
William Street	Z	
Baal's Bridge	Y	2
Bank Place	Y	3
Barrington Street	Z	5
Bridge Street	Y	6
Broad Street	Y	7
Castle Street	Y	8
Cathedral Place	Z	9
Charlotte's Quay	Y	12
Crescent (The)	Z	13
Gerald Griffen St.	Z	14
High Street	Z	15
John Square	Z	16
Lock Quay	Y	17
Lord Edward Street	Z	18
Lower Cecil Street	Z	19
Lower Mallow Street	Z	21
Mathew Bridge	Y	22
Michael Street	YZ	23
Mount Kenneth	Z	24
Newtown Mahon	Z	25
O'Dwyer Bridge	Y	27
Rutland Street	Y	29
St. Gerard Street	Z	30
Sarsfield Bridge	Y	32
Shannon Bridge	Z	34
Shannon Street	Z	35
Thomond Bridge	Y	36
Wickham Street	Z	38

LIMERICK (Luimneach) Limerick 405 G 9 – pop. 60 736 – ECD : Thursday – 061.

Envir. : Monasteranenagh Abbey★ (ruins 12C) S : 14 m. by N 20 Z.

Castleroy ☏ 335261 Z and N 27 – Ballyclough ☏ 44083.

Shannon Airport : ☏ 061 (Shannon) 61444, Telex 72016, W : 16 m. by N 18 Y – **Terminal** : Limerick Railway Station.

The Granary, Michael St. ☏ 317522.

◆Dublin 120 – ◆Cork 58.

Plan opposite

Jury's, Ennis Rd, ☏ 327777, Telex 70766, Fax 326400, – – 200. AE VISA. Y z
closed Christmas Day – **M** 12.00/13.50 **t.** and a la carte 4.50 – 7.25 – **94 rm** 56.50/72.00 **t.**, **1 suite** 125.00/150.00 **t.**.

Limerick Inn, Ennis Rd, NW : 4 m. on N 18 ☏ 51544, Telex 70621, Fax 326281, – rest – 500. AE VISA. on N 18 Y
closed 24 to 26 December – **M** 9.50/20.50 **st.** and a la carte 4.00 – 6.50 – **149 rm** 72.00/88.00 **t.**, **4 suites** 85.00 **t.** – SB 92.00/96.00 **st.**

Limerick Ryan, Ennis Rd, NW : 1¼ m. on N 18 ☏ 53922, Telex 70720, Fax 326333, – – 60. AE VISA. on N 18 Y
M (bar lunch Monday to Saturday)/dinner 13.50 a la carte 4.25 – 6.50 – **184 rm** 55.00/77.00 **t.** – SB (weekends only) 51.50/61.50 **st.**

Greenhills, Ennis Rd, NW : 2¼ m. on N 18 ☏ 53033, Telex 70246, Fax 53307, – – 350. AE VISA. on N 18 Y
closed 25 December – **M** 10.75/16.50 **st.** and a la carte 5.50 – **55 rm** 47.00/82.00 **st.** – SB 88.00/110.00 **st.**

Two Mile Inn, Ennis Rd, NW : 3½ m. on N 18 ☏ 53122, Telex 70157, Fax 53783, – – 40. on N 18 Y
125 rm.

De la Fontaine, 12 Upper Gerald Griffin St., ☏ 44461 – VISA Z a
closed lunch Monday and Saturday and Sunday – **M** 8.50/18.00 **t.** and a la carte 4.50.

Silver Plate, 74 O'Connell St., ☏ 316311 – AE VISA Z e
closed Sunday and Bank Holidays – **M** (dinner only) 18.00 **t.** and a la carte 4.00.

BMW, NISSAN Castle St. ☏ 43133
FORD Lansdowne ☏ 52244
MAZDA, VW-AUDI, MERCEDES-BENZ Dublin Rd ☏ 46000
OPEL Ennis Rd ☏ 53211
SUZUKI, VOLVO, MITSUBISHI Coonagh Cross ☏ 51577

LISDOONVARNA (Lios Dúin Bhearna) Clare 405 E 8 – pop. 607 – 065 Ennis.

Envir. : Cliffs of Moher★★★ (O' Brien's Tower ★★ N : 1 h return on foot) SW : 8 m.

☏ 74062 (June-September).

◆Dublin 167 – ◆Galway 39 – ◆Limerick 47.

Sheedy's Spa View, Sulphir Hill, ☏ 74026, – . AE VISA.
Mid March-October – **M** (bar lunch)/dinner 16.50 **t.** and a la carte 5.90 – **11 rm** 30.00/50.00 **t.**

LISMORE (Lios Mór) Waterford 405 I 11 – pop. 919 – ECD : Thursday – 058 Dungarvan.

See : Castle (site★).

Envir. : SE : Blackwater Valley★★ (from Lismore to the Mouth, by a scenic road along the right bank of the River Blackwater).

Ballyin ☏ 54026, N : 1 m.

◆Dublin 143 – ◆Cork 37 – ◆Killarney 74 – ◆Waterford 44.

Hotel see : Cappoquin E : 6 m.

FORD Dublin Rd ☏ 46421
NISSAN Drumlish ☏ 24104
RENAULT Athlone Rd ☏ 46615
TOYOTA Lismore ☏ 54147
TOYOTA Lanesboro ☏ 21159
TOYOTA Athlone Rd ☏ 45621
VW-AUDI Dublin Rd ☏ 46321

LOUGH GOWNA (Loch Gamhna) Cavan 405 J 6 – pop. 125 – 043 Longford.

◆Dublin 81 – ◆Tullamore 54.

Robin Hill, ☏ 83121, –
M (by arrangement) 11.00 **st.** – **6 rm** 11.00/22.00 **st.**

"Short Breaks" (SB)

Zahlreiche Hotels bieten Vorzugspreise bei einem Aufenthalt von zwei Nächten.
Diese Preise umfassen Zimmer, Abendessen und Frühstück.

MACROOM **(Maigh Chromtha)** Cork 405 F 12 – pop. 2 495 – ECD : Wednesday – 026.

Lackaduve 41072.

Dublin 186 – Cork 25 – Killarney 30.

Castle, Main St., 41074, Fax 41505 – AE VISA.
closed 3 days at Christmas – **M** 8.50/14.50 **st.** and a la carte 5.50 – **26 rm** 18.00/40.00 **st.** – SB 55.00/60.00 **st.**

MALAHIDE **(Mullach Íde)** Dublin 405 N 7 – pop. 9 158 – 01 Dublin.

Envir. : Swords (St. Columba's Church : towers★) W : 2½ m. – Lusk (church : round towers★) NW : 8 m.

Coast Rd 450248.

Dublin 9 – Drogheda 24.

Grand, 450633, Telex 31446, Fax 450987, ← – 600. AE VISA.
closed 24 to 26 December – **M** 9.50/17.00 **t.** and a la carte 5.00 – **99 rm** 40.00/77.00 **t.** **3 suites** 77.00/97.00 **t.**

Bon Appetit, 9 James's Terr., 450314, AE VISA
closed Saturday lunch, Sunday, 1 week Christmas and Bank Holidays – **M** 13.00/40.00 **st** and a la carte 5.00.

FORD Main St. 452044

MALLOW **(Mala)** Cork 405 F 11 – pop. 6 572 – ECD : Wednesday – 022.

Balleyellis 21145, SE : 1½ m. from Mallow Bridge.

Dublin 149 – Cork 21 – Killarney 40 – Limerick 41.

Longueville House, W : 3½ m. by N 72 47156, Fax 47459, ←, « Georgian mansion in extensive grounds », park – AE VISA.
closed 21 December-1 March – **M** (booking essential) 16.00/30.00 **t.** 7.45 – **16 rm** 50.00/140.00 **t.**

OPEL Buttevant 23338

MAYNOOTH **(Maigh Nuad)** Kildare 405 M 7 – pop. 3 388 – ECD : Wednesday – 01 Dublin.

Dublin 15.

Moyglare Manor, Moyglare, N : 2 m. 6286351, Fax 6285405, ←, « Georgian country house with antique furnishings », park – 25. AE VISA.
closed 3 days at Christmas – **M** *(closed Saturday lunch)* – **17 rm** 65.00/100.00 **st.**

MOUNTRATH **(Maighean Rátha)** Laois – 0502 Portlaoise.

Dublin 54 – Kilkenny 31 – Limerick 67.

Roundwood House, NW : 3 m. by Slieve Bloom rd 32120, ←, « Palladian country house », park – AE VISA.
M (by arrangement) 17.00 **st.** 4.50 – **6 rm** 32.00/52.00 **st.** – SB (weekdays only) 80.00 **st.**

MOUNTSHANNON **(Baile Uí Bheoláin)** Clare 405 G 9 – 0619.

Dublin 129 – Galway 45 – Limerick 30.

Mountshannon, Main St., 27162, –
11 rm.

MOYCULLEN **(Maigh Cuilinn)** Galway 405 E 7 – pop. 228 – Rosscahill – 091 Galway.

Dublin 139 – Galway 7.

Knockferry Lodge, Knockferry (on Lough Corrib), NE : 6½ m. 80122, Fax 80328, – AE VISA.
Mid May-September – **M** (booking essential) (bar lunch)/dinner 14.50 **st.** – **12 rm** 22.00/38.00 **st.**

Moycullen House, SW : 1 m. on Spiddle rd 85566, – AE VISA.
March-October – **M** (communal dining) 15.00 **st.** – **5 rm** 15.00/40.00 **st.**

Drimcong House, NW : 1 m. on N 59 85115, « 17C estate house », – AE VISA
closed Sunday, Monday and Christmas-March – **M** (booking essential)(dinner only) 16.50 **t.** and a la carte 21.50/27.50 **t.** 4.50.

MULLINGAR **(An Muileann gLearr)** Westmeath 405 JK 7 – pop. 7 854 – 044.

Envir. : N : Lough Derravaragah★ – Lough Owel★ – Multyfarman (Franciscan College park : Stations of the Cross★ – NE : Lough Lene★ – Fore (St. Feichin's Church and ruined priory 13C★) – S : Lough Ennell.

Belvedere 48366, S : 3 m.

Dublin Road 48650.

Dublin 49 – Drogheda 36.

FIAT, LANCIA Dublin Rd 48806 FORD Harbour St. 48403

AVAN (An Uaimh) Meath 405 L 7 – pop. 4 124 – ECD : Thursday – 046.

nvir. : Bective Abbey★ (12C ruins) S : 3 m.

Royal Tara, Bellinter Park 25244.

Dublin 30 – Drogheda 16 – ♦Dundalk 34.

Ardboyne (Best Western), Dublin Rd, SE : 1 m. on N 3 23119, Fax 22355, – – 350. AE VISA.
closed 24 and 25 December – **M** 11.50/17.50 **st.** and a la carte 4.50 – **26 rm** 40.50/95.00 **st.** – SB 83.50/103.50 **st.**

at Dunderry SW : 5½ m. by N 51 on L 23 – Navan – 046 Dunderry :

Dunderry Lodge, W : ¾ m., « Converted farm buildings » – . AE VISA
closed Saturday lunch, Sunday, Monday and January – **M** a la carte 21.85/29.00 **t.** 6.00.

PEL Dublin Rd 21212
EUGEOT-TALBOT Castlemartin 21949
RENAULT Cannon Row 21312
TOYOTA Kells Rd 21336

NEWBAWN (An Bábhún Nua) Wexford 405 L 10 – see New Ross.

NEWBRIDGE (An Droichead Nua) Kildare 405 L 8 – pop. 5 780 – ECD : Tuesday – 045 Naas.

nvir. : Kildare (St. Brigid's Cathedral★ 13C-19C and round tower★ 9C-10C) SW : 5 m. – Tully National Stud★, Japanese gardens★ *AC*) SW : 6 m. via Kildare – Old Kilcullen (site★, ★).

Curragh 045 (Curragh) 41238, S : 3 m. – Cill Dara, 045 (Kildare) 21433, Kildare Town, W : 5 m.

33835 (19 June-26 August).

Dublin 28 – Kilkenny 57 – ♦Tullamore 36.

Keadeen, Ballymany, SW : 1 m. on N 7 31666, Telex 60672, Fax 34402, – – 400. AE VISA
M 15.00/32.50 **t.** and a la carte 5.00 – **36 rm** 55.00/120.00 **t.**, **1 suite** 120.00/150.00 **t.**

ORD Moorefield 31725

NEWMARKET-ON-FERGUS (Cora Chaitlín) Clare 405 F 7 – pop. 1 348 – 061 Shannon.

♦Dublin 136 – Ennis 8 – ♦Limerick 15.

Dromoland Castle, NW : 1½ m. on N 18 71144, Telex 70654, Fax 363355, ←, « Converted castle », 18, , , park, – – 250. AE VISA.
M 18.00/44.00 **t.** and dinner a la carte – 10.50 – **67 rm** 175.00 **st.**, **6 suites** 250.00/355.00 **st.** – SB (October-May) 188.00/213.00 **st.**

Carrygerry House, NW : 8 m. by N 18 62339, Fax 62123, , park – . AE VISA.
closed 25 December – **M** (lunch by arrangement)/dinner 17.50 **t.** and a la carte 4.00 – **8 rm** 33.00/90.00 **t.** – SB (late October-April) 80.00/95.00 **st.**

NEWPORT (Baile Uí Fhiacháin) Mayo 405 D 6 – pop. 470 – 098.

See : St. Patrick's Church★, modern Irish-Romanesque style (site★).

Envir. : Burrishoole Abbey (site★) NW : 2 m.

♦Dublin 164 – Ballina 37 – ♦Galway 60.

Newport House , 41222, Telex 53740, Fax 41613, « Country house atmosphere, antiques », , , park – . AE VISA.
19 March-September – **M** (buffet lunch)/dinner 27.00 **st.** and a la carte 9.00 – **19 rm** 49.00/98.00 **st.**

NEW ROSS (Ross Mhic Thriúin) Wexford 405 L 10 – pop. 5 386 – ECD : Wednesday – 051.

Envir. : St. Mullins Monastery (site★) N : 9 m. – John F. Kennedy Memorial Park★ (1968) (arboretum, ←★) S : 7½ m. – SW : River Barrow Valley★.

9 Tinneranny 21433.

21857 (July and August).

♦Dublin 88 – Kilkenny 27 – ♦Waterford 15 – Wexford 23.

Old Rectory, Rosbercon, W : ½ m. by N 25 21719, – . VISA.
M 7.95/14.95 **st.** and a la carte 3.95 – **13 rm** 25.00/60.00 **st.**

at Newbawn E : 8 m. by N 25 off L 160 – 051 New Ross :

Cedar Lodge with rm, Carrigbyrne, N : 1½ m. on N 25 28386, Fax 28222, – . VISA.
closed January – **M** 12.50/19.00 **st.** and a la carte – **13 rm** 35.00/60.00 **st.** – SB 84.00 **st.**

FORD Waterford Rd 21403

Benutzen Sie für weite Fahrten in Europa die Michelin-Länderkarten :
970 Europa, 980 Griechenland, 984 Deutschland, 985 Skandinavien-Finnland, 986 Großbritannien-Irland, 987 Deutschland-Österreich-Benelux, 988 Italien, 989 Frankreich, 990 Spanien-Portugal, 991 Jugoslawien.

OGONNELLOE (Tuath Ó gConáile) Clare 405 G 9 – 0619 Scarriff.

♦Dublin 114 – Ennis 24 – ♦Limerick 20 – ♦Tullamore 63.

Lantern House, 23034 – P. AE VISA.
closed last 2 weeks January and November – **M** (by arrangement) 11.00 **t.** 4.75 – **6 r**
16.00/28.00 – SB 48.00 **st.**

OUGHTERARD (Uachtar Ard) Galway 405 E 7 – pop. 748 – 091 Galway.

See : The northern scenic road (cul-de-sac) ≤★★ on Lough Corrib★★★.

Envir. : Aughnanure Castle★ (16C) SE : 3 m. – Leckavrea Mountain★, NW : 13 m. – Gortmo (≤★★ S : on Kilkieran Bay, ≤★ NW : on the Twelve Pins) SW : 16 m.

18 Gurteeva 82131.

♦Dublin 149 – ♦Galway 17.

Connemara Gateway, SE : ¾ m. on N 59 82328, Telex 50905, Fax 82332, – rest P. AE VISA.
closed 7 to 31 January and 1 to 27 December – **M** 16.75 **st.** (dinner) and a la carte 5.00
62 rm 36.50/125.00 **st.** – SB 75.00/92.50 **st.**

Currarevagh House , NW : 4 m. 82313, ≤, « Country house atmosphere »,
, park, – rest P.
April-27 October – **M** (booking essential)(dinner only) 16.00 **t.** 4.25 – **15 rm** 35.0
70.00 **t.**

Sweeney's Oughterard House, W : ½ m. on N 59 82207, Fax 82161, –
P. AE VISA
closed 22 December-1 February – **M** (bar lunch)/dinner 19.00 **st.** and a la carte 5.00
20 rm 35.00/92.00 **st.**

Cnoc Na Curra without rest., Pier Rd, 82225, ≤, – P.
May-September – **4 rm** 15.00/30.00 **st.**

PARKNASILLA (Páirc na Saileach) Kerry 405 C 12 – 064 Killarney.

9 Parknasilla 45122.

♦Dublin 224 – ♦Cork 72 – ♦Killarney 34.

Great Southern , 45122, Telex 73899, Fax 45323, ≤ Kenmare river, bay an
mountains, 9, , park, – P – 50. AE VISA.
mid March-mid November, Christmas and New Year – **M** (bar lunch)/dinner 35.00 **t.** and
la carte 6.00 – 7.00 – **58 rm** 70.00/125.00 **t.**, **1 suite** 150.00/220.00 **t.**
SB (April, May and October) (weekends only) 100.00/125.00 **st.**

PORTLAOISE (Port Laoise) Laois 405 K 8 – pop. 4 049 – 0502.

18 Heath 46533, E : 4 m – 9 Rathdowney 46170 – 9 Abbey Leix 31450.

21178 (22 May-2 September).

♦ Dublin 54 – Kilkenny 31 – ♦Limerick 67.

Killeshin, Dublin Rd, E : 1 m. on N 7 21663, Telex 60036, Fax 21976 – P
300. AE VISA
M 10.00/18.00 **t.** and a la carte 5.50 – **44 rm** 30.00/55.00 **t.**

PORTMARNOCK (Port Mearnóg) Dublin 405 N 7 – 01 Dublin.

9, 9, 9 Portmarnock 323082, Fax 303738.

♦Dublin 5 – Drogheda 28.

Portmarnock H. & Country Club , 460611, Fax 462442, ≤, – P – 100
19 rm.

PORTNABLAHY (Port na Bláiche) Donegal 405 I 2 – see Dunfanaghy.

RAPHOE (Ráth Bloth) Donegal 405 J 3 – pop. 1 070 – 074.

Envir. : Beltany Stone Circle★ (site★) from the road 10 mn on foot, S : 2 m.

♦Dublin 139 – Donegal 29 – ♦Londonderry 20 – ♦Sligo 69.

Central, The Diamond, 45126 –
closed 24 December-1 January – **M** *(closed Sunday)* 8.00/10.50 **st.** and a la carte 3.50 –
10 rm 13.50/28.00 **st.**

RATH LUIRC (An Ráth) = Charleville.

RATHMULLAN (Ráth Maoláin) Donegal 405 J 2 – pop. 584 – 074 Letterkenny.

Envir. : Mulroy Bay★★, NW : 8 m. – Fanad Head ≤★, N : 20 m.

♦Dublin 165 – ♦Londonderry 36 – ♦Sligo 87.

Rathmullan House , N : ½ m. on R 247 58188, Fax 58200, ≤ Lough Swilly and hills,
« Early 19C country house, gardens », , park, – rest P. AE VISA.
Mid March-Christmas – **M** (bar lunch)/dinner 19.50 **t.** 5.00 – **18 rm** 32.50/80.00 **t.** –
SB 96.80/124.30 **st.**

ATHNEW (**Ráth Naoi**) Wicklow 405 N 8 – pop. 1 366 – ✉ ☎ 0404 Wicklow.

ublin 31 – ◆Waterford 82 – Wexford 65.

Tinakilly House 🐁, ☎ 69274, Fax 67806, <, « Victorian country house », 🌳, park, 🎾 – 📺 ☎ 🅿. VISA. ✻
M 18.70/27.50 **st.** 🍾 6.60 – **14 rm** ☐ 77.00/132.00 **st.** – SB (October-May except Christmas and New Year) 135.00/155.00 **st.**

Hunter's, Newrath Bridge, N : ¾ m. on L 29 ☎ 40106, « Converted 18C inn with garden » – ☎ 🅿. AE ① VISA. ✻
M 12.00/17.50 **t.** 🍾 5.00 – **18 rm** ☐ 30.00/60.00 **t.**

EDCASTLE (**Carraig Mhic Uidhilín**) Donegal 405 K 2 – ECD : Wednesday – ✉ ☎ 077 Moville.

ublin 160 – ◆Londonderry 14.

Redcastle Country 🐁, ☎ 82073, Fax 82214, <, Lš, ≘s, 🏊, 🏌9, 🎣, 🌳, park, 🎾 – 📺 ☎ 🅿 – 🏛 250. AE ① VISA. ✻
M 8.50/15.00 **t.** and a la carte 🍾 5.50 – **34 rm** ☐ 45.00/120.00 **st.**

IVERSTOWN (**Baile Idir dhá Abhainn**) Sligo 405 G 5 – pop. 262 – ☎ 071 Sligo.

Dublin 123 – ◆Sligo 13.

Coopershill 🐁, ☎ 65108, Fax 65466, <, 🌳, park – ⇆ rm 🅿. AE ① VISA. ✻
15 March-October – **M** (residents only) (dinner only) 17.50 **st.** 🍾 5.00 – **6 rm** ☐ 43.50/75.00 **st.** – SB (March-October) (except summer) 101.00 **st.**

ROSAPENNA (**Rosapenna**) Donegal 405 I 2 – ☎ 074 Letterkenny.

Golf Hotel ☎ 55301.

Dublin 216 – Donegal 52 – ◆Londonderry 47.

Rosapenna Golf (Best Western), Downings, ☎ 55301, Fax 55128, <, 🏌18, 🎾 – 📺 ☎ 🅿. AE ① VISA
23 March-26 October – **M** (bar lunch)/dinner 18.00 **t.** 🍾 4.50 – **40 rm** ☐ 33.00/60.00 **t.** – SB 80.00/90.00 **st.**

ROSSES POINT (**An Ros**) Sligo 405 G 5 – see Sligo.

ROSSLARE (**Ros Láir**) Wexford 405 M 11 – pop. 779 – ☎ 053.

Strand ☎ 32113.

Harbour ☎ 33232.

Dublin 104 – ◆Waterford 50 – Wexford 12.

Kelly's Strand, Strand Rd, ☎ 32114, Fax 32222, Lš, ≘s, 🏊 heated, 🏊, 🌳, 🎾, squash – 🛗 ▤ rest 📺 ☎ 🅿. VISA. ✻
March-9 December – **M** 10.50/19.50 **t.** 🍾 4.50 – **91 rm** ☐ 36.00/74.00 **t.**

Europe — Si le nom d'un hôtel figure en petits caractères, demandez à l'arrivée les conditions à l'hôtelier.

ROSSLARE HARBOUR (**Calafort Ros Láir**) Wexford 405 N 11 – pop. 777 – ☎ 053 Wexford.

⛴ Shipping connections with the Continent : to France (Cherbourg), (Le Havre) (Irish Ferries) – to Fishguard (Sealink) 1-3 daily (3 h 30 mn) – to Pembroke (B & I Line) 1 daily.

☎ 33232.

◆Dublin 105 – ◆Waterford 51 – Wexford 13.

Tuskar House, St. Martins Rd, ☎ 33363, <, 🌳 – 📺 ☎ 🅿. AE ① VISA. ✻
M 8.95/14.95 **t.** and a la carte 🍾 3.95 – **22 rm** ☐ 28.00/48.00 **t.** – SB 69.00/79.00 **st.**

Rosslare, ☎ 33110, Fax 33386, <, squash – 📺 ☎ 🅿
25 rm.

ROSSNOWLAGH (**Ros Neamhlach**) Donegal 405 H 4 – ☎ 072 Bundoran.

◆Dublin 157 – Donegal 9 – ◆Sligo 33.

Sand House 🐁, ☎ 51777, Fax 52100, < bay, beach and mountains, 🎣, 🎾 – ☎ 🅿. AE ① VISA. ✻
Easter-4 October – **M** 9.50/17.50 **t.** and a la carte 🍾 4.50 – **40 rm** ☐ 30.00/80.00 **t.** – SB (except Bank Holidays weekends) 75.00/95.00 **st.**

SALTHILL (**Bóthar na Trá**) Galway 405 E 8 – see Galway.

SCHULL (**An Scoil**) Cork 405 D 13 – pop. 502 – ☎ 028 Skibbereen.

Envir. : E : Roaringwater Bay★.

◆Dublin 226 – ◆Cork 65 – ◆Killarney 64.

Hotel see : **Skibbereen** NE : 11 m.

SHANAGARRY (An Seangharraí) Cork 405 H 12 – ✉ Midleton – ☎ 021 Cork.
◆Dublin 163 – ◆Cork 25 – ◆Waterford 64.

XX **Ballymaloe House** with rm, NW : 1 ¾ m. on L 35 ☎ 652531, Telex 75208, Fax 65202 ≤, « Country house atmosphere », heated, park, – ☎ ♿ P. AE VISA.
closed 23 to 26 December – **M** (buffet lunch)/dinner 28.00 **t.** 6.00 – 6.00 – **30 r** 53.00/88.00 **t.** – SB (except 15 March-October) 95.00/115.00 **st.**

SHANNON AIRPORT (Aerfort na Sionainne) Clare 405 F 9 – ☎ 061 Limerick.
18 ☎ Shannon 61020.
✈ ☎ 61444, Telex 26222 – **Terminal** : Limerick Railway Station ☎ 42433.
ℹ ☎ 61664.
◆Dublin 136 – Ennis 16 – ◆Limerick 15.

Hotels and restaurants see : Limerick

SKERRIES (Na Sairí) Dublin 405 N 7 – pop. 5 793 – ☎ 01 Dublin.
18 ☎ 491204.
◆Dublin 19 – Drogheda 15.

XX **Red Bank,** 7 Church St., ☎ 491005, Seafood – AE VISA
closed Sunday, Monday and 23 to 27 December – **M** (dinner only) 19.00 **t.** and a carte 17.50/24.00 **t.** 5.25.

SKIBBEREEN (An Sciobairín) Cork 405 E 13 – pop. 2 130 – ☎ 028.
9 ☎ 21227.
ℹ Town Hall ☎ 21766.
◆Dublin 205 – ◆Cork 51 – ◆Killarney 68.

XX **Mill House,** Rineen, E : 5 m. by L 60 on Union Hall rd ☎ 36299, – P. AE VISA
March-November – **M** (dinner only) (booking essential) 16.95 **t.** 4.50.

SKULL (An Scoil) = Schull.

SLIEVERUE (Sliabh Rua) Waterford – see Waterford.

SLIGO (Sligeach) Sligo 405 G 5 – pop. 17 232 – ☎ 071.
See : Sligo Abbey★ (13C ruins) – Court House★.
Envir. : E : Lough Gill★★★ (Innisfree★) Park's Castle (site★★), Lough Colgagh★★, Drumcliff (High Cross) ≤★ on Benbulbin Moutains, N : 4 m. – Glencar Lough★, NE : 6 m. – Carrowmore (Megalithic cemetery★) SW : 2 m.
18 Strandhill ☎ 68188, W : 8 m – 18 County Sligo, Rosses Point ☎ 77186.
ℹ Aras Reddan, Temple St. ☎ 61201.
◆Dublin 133 – ◆Belfast 126 – ◆Dundalk 106 – ◆Londonderry 86.

Sligo Park, Pearse Rd, S : 1 m. on N 4 ☎ 60291, Telex 40397, Fax 69556, , , , rm TV ☎ ♿ P – 500. AE VISA
M 9.50/17.50 **st.** and a la carte 4.40 – 5.50 – **87 rm** 50.00/75.00 **st.**, **3 suites** 80.00 **st.**

Ballincar House, Rosses Point Rd, NW : 2 ½ m. on R 291 ☎ 45361, Telex 91297 Fax 44198, ≤, , – TV ☎ P. AE VISA.
closed 23 December-21 January – **M** 8.50/17.50 **t.** and a la carte 5.00 – **26 rm** 40.00 75.00 **t.** – SB 90.00 **st.**

at Rosses Point NW : 5 m. on R 291 – ✉ ☎ 071 Sligo :

XX **Reveries,** ☎ 77371, ≤ Mount Knocknarae, Sligo Bay and Oyster Island – VISA
closed Sunday, Monday, 3 weeks November and 4 days at Christmas – **M** (dinner only) 22.95 **t.** 4.75.

FORD Bundoran Rd ☎ 42610
MAZDA Ballinode ☎ 42188
VW-AUDI Ballisodare ☎ 67291

SPIDDLE (An Spidéal) Galway 405 E 8 – ☎ 091 Galway.
◆Dublin 143 – ◆Galway 11.

Bridge House, Main St., ☎ 83118, – TV ☎ P. AE VISA.
closed 20 December-February – **M** 10.00/17.00 **st.** and a la carte 4.65 – **14 rm** 35.00/65.00 **st.** – SB (except July and August) 70.00/80.00 **st.**

Ardmour without rest., W : ½ m. on L 100 ☎ 83145, ≤, – rest P. VISA.
March-November – **8 rm** 18.00/26.00 **st.**

TAHILLA (Tathuile) Kerry 405 C 12 – ☎ 064 Killarney.
◆Dublin 222 – ◆Cork 70 – ◆Killarney 32.

Tahilla Cove , ☎ 45204, ≤, – P. AE VISA
April-September – **M** (bar lunch)/dinner 14.00 **st.** 4.50 – **9 rm** 25.00/50.00 **st.** – SB 70.00/75.00 **st.**

EMPLEGLENTAN (Teampall an Ghleanntáin) Limerick 405 E 10 – ☎ 069 Newcastle West.
ublin 154 – ♦Killarney 36 – ♦Limerick 33.

Devon Inn, ☎ 84122, Fax 84122 – TV ☎ P. VISA.
M 7.00/12.00 **t.** and a la carte 4.75 – **18 rm** 24.00/36.00 **t.** – SB 60.00/66.00 **st.**

HOMASTOWN (Baile Mhic Andáin) Kilkenny 405 K 10 – ☎ 056 Kilkenny.
ublin 77 – Kilkenny 11 – ♦Waterford 30 – Wexford 38.

Mount Juliet, NW : 1½ m. ☎ 24455, Telex 80355, Fax 24522, ←, « Victorian manor and private estate on banks of river Nore », park, – TV ☎ & P – 60. AE VISA.
M 15.00/30.00 and a la carte – **30 rm** 120.00/250.00 **st.**, **2 suites** 450.00/550.00 **st.**

IPPERARY (Tiobraid Árann) Tipperary 405 H 10 – pop. 4 984 – ECD : Wednesday – ☎ 062.
nvir. : S : Glen of Aherlow★ (statue of Christ the King ←★★).
Rathanny ☎ 51119, S : 1 m.
Dublin 113 – ♦Cork 57 – ♦Limerick 24 – ♦Waterford 53.

Ach-na-Sheen House, Waterford Rd, ☎ 51298 – P. VISA.
M 14.00 **st.** – **13 rm** 14.00/28.00 **st.**

RALEE (Trá Lí) Kerry 405 C 11 – pop. 16 495 – ECD : Wednesday – ☎ 066.
West Barrow ☎ 36379, W : 8 m.
Aras Siamsa, Godfrey Pl. ☎ 21288.
Dublin 185 – ♦Killarney 20 – ♦Limerick 64.

Ballygarry House, SE : 1½ m. on N 21 ☎ 23305, – TV ☎ P.
16 rm.

Brandon, Princes Quay, ☎ 23333, Group Telex 73130, Fax 25019, – TV ☎ P – 1000. AE VISA.
M 8.50/15.00 8.50 – **155 rm** 40.00/70.00 **st.**, **1 suite** 90.00 **st.**

AT Ashe St. ☎ 21124
ORD Edward St. ☎ 21555
TOYOTA Rithiss ☎ 21688
VW-AUDI The Market and Rock St. ☎ 21193

RIM (Baile Átha Troim) Meath 405 L 7 – pop. 2 144 – ECD : Thursday – ☎ 046.
☎ 31463, SW : 2½ m.
Dublin 28 – Drogheda 25 – ♦Dundalk 43.

Wellington Court, Summerhill Rd, ☎ 31516, Fax 36002, – TV ☎ P
20 rm.

TYRELLSPASS (Bealach an Tirialaigh) Westmeath 405 J 7 – pop. 307 – ☎ 044 Mullingar.
Dublin 51 – ♦Tullamore 13.

Village, ☎ 23171 – TV P. AE VISA.
closed 24 to 28 December – **M** *(closed Sunday dinner)* (bar lunch Monday to Saturday)/dinner 17.50 **t.** and a la carte 4.75 – **10 rm** 23.50/57.00 **t.**

VIRGINIA (Achadh an Iúir) Cavan 405 K 6 – pop. 657 – ☎ 049 Cavan.
Envir. : Kells : St. Columba's House★ (9C) – St. Columba's Church : old tower★ (1783) – Churchyard (high crosses★) SE : 11 m.
☎ 042 (Dundalk) 31283.
Dublin 52 – ♦Dundalk 39 – Roscommon 56 – ♦Tullamore 59.

Hotel see : Cavan NW : 20 m.

WATERFORD (Port Láirge) Waterford 405 K 11 – pop. 38 473 – ☎ 051.
See : Franciscan ruins of the French Church★ (13C-16C) (Grey Friars St.).
Newrath ☎ 76748.
41 The Quay ☎ 75788.
Dublin 96 – ♦Cork 73 – ♦Limerick 77.

Waterford Castle, The Island, Ballinakill, E : 2½ m. by R 684, Ballinakill Rd and private ferry ☎ 78203, Telex 80332, Fax 79316, ←, « 19C castle, river island setting », park, – TV ☎ P. AE VISA.
M 15.50/28.50 **t.** and a la carte 6.50 – 8.50 – **14 rm** 110.00/130.00 **t.**, **5 suites** 245.00/275.00 **t.** – SB 165.00/180.00 **st.**

Granville, Meagher Quay, ☎ 55111, Telex 80188, Fax 70307 – TV ☎ – 60. AE VISA.
closed 25 and 26 December – **M** 12.75/24.00 **st.** and a la carte 5.80 – **74 rm** 45.00/120.00 **st.** – SB (weekends only) 75.00 **st.**

Tower, The Mall, ☎ 75801, Telex 80699, Fax 70129 – TV ☎ – 300. AE VISA.
closed 24 and 27 December – **M** 9.95/17.00 **st.** and a la carte 4.75 – 6.50 – **84 rm** 36.00/150.00 **st.** – SB (weekends only) 65.00/68.00 **st.**

Foxmount Farm 🌿, off Passage East rd, SE : 4 ½ m. by R 684 and R 683 ✆ 74308, « Working farm », – Ⓟ.
17 March-October – **M** (by arrangement) 12.00 – **6 rm** 16.00/26.00 **st.**

Swiss Cottage, Newtown, S : ½ m. on R 684 ✆ 79580 – Ⓟ. VISA
closed Saturday lunch and Sunday – **M** 12.00/28.00 **t.** and a la carte 8.75.

at Slieverue NE : 2 ¼ m. by N 25 – ✉ 051 Waterford :

Diamond Hill, ✆ 32855, – Ⓟ. AE VISA.
closed 23 to 28 December – **M** (by arrangement) 14.00 4.50 – **10 rm** 18.00/32.00 s

OPEL Catherine St. ✆ 74988
TOYOTA William St. ✆ 74037

WATERVILLE (An Coireán) Kerry 405 B 12 – pop. 478 – 0667.

Envir. : Sheehan's Point ≤★★★, S : 6 m. – Remains of Carhan House (birthplace of Dani O'Connell) N : 11 m. – Ballinskelligs (Augustinian Monastery ≤★) W : 9 m.

18 Ring of Kerry ✆ 4102, W : 1 m.

◆Dublin 238 – ◆Killarney 48.

Waterville Lake 🌿, ✆ 4133, Telex 73806, Fax 4482, ≤ Lough Currane, Atlantic ar countryside, – 50
80 rm, **8 suites.**

Butler Arms, ✆ 4144, Fax 4520, – Ⓟ. VISA.
Mid April-mid October – **M** (dinner only) 20.00 **t.** 5.00 – **29 rm** 35.00/80.00 **t.**

White House without rest., ✆ 4233 – Ⓟ. AE VISA.
March-September – **8 rm** 12.00/24.00 **st.**

WESTPORT (Cathair na Mart) Mayo 405 D 6 – pop. 3 378 – ECD : Wednesday – 098 Nev port.

See : Westport House★ *AC.*

Envir. : Croagh Patrick Mountain★ (statue of St. Patrick ≤★, pilgrimage) SW : 6 m. – Roona Quay ≤★ on Clare Island, W : 15 m.

18 Carrowholly ✆ 25113.

The Mall ✆ 25711.

◆Dublin 163 – ◆Galway 50 – ◆Sligo 65.

Westport Ryan, Louisburgh Rd, W : ¾ m. on T 39 ✆ 25811, Telex 53757, Fax 26212, – Ⓟ. AE VISA.
closed January and February – **M** (bar lunch)/dinner 16.00 **st.** and a la carte 5.00 – 6.0 – **57 rm** 53.00/74.00 **st.** – SB (except July and August) (weekends only) 60.00/90.00 **st.**

Wilmaur withour rest., Rosbeg, W : 2 m. on T 39 ✆ 098 (Westport) 25784, ≤, – Ⓟ
3 rm 17.00/26.00 **st.**

Ardmore, The Quay, W : 1 ½ m. on T 39 ✆ 25994, ≤ – Ⓟ. AE VISA
closed Sunday, 1 week March and 2 weeks November – **M** (dinner only) 17.00 and a la carte 4.75.

WEXFORD (Loch Garman) Wexford 405 M 10 – pop. 11 417 – ECD : Thursday – 053.

Envir. : Johnstown Castle (the park-arboretum★) SW : 4 m.

18 Mulgannon ✆ 42238, SE : 1 m.

Crescent Quay ✆ 23111 (March-November).

◆Dublin 88 – Kilkenny 49 – ◆Waterford 38.

Ferrycarrig 🌿, Ferrycarrig Bridge, NW : 2 ¾ m. on N 11 ✆ 22999, Fax 80147, ≤, – Ⓟ. AE VISA
M 12.00/23.50 **st.** and a la carte 6.00 – **34 rm** 39.00/86.00 **st.**, **1 suite** 75.00/120.00 s – SB 90.00/114.00 **st.**

White's (Best Western), George's St., ✆ 22311, Telex 80630, Fax 45000 – Ⓟ 60. AE VISA.
closed 24 to 26 December – **M** 12.50/18.50 **st.** and a la carte 5.00 – **75 rm** 43.00 72.50 **st.**, **1 suite** – SB 66.00/80.00 **st.**

Talbot, Trinity St., ✆ 22566, Telex 80658, Fax 23377, squash – Ⓟ 400. AE VISA.
M 16.50/17.95 **t.** and a la carte 5.75 – 7.50 – **103 rm** 34.50/75.00 **t.** – SB 80.00/90.00 s

Newbay Country House 🌿, W : 4 m. by N 25 and Clonard rd ✆ 22779, ≤, park Ⓟ. AE VISA.
18 March-13 November – **M** (communal dining) (dinner only) (residents only) 20.00 st 6.00 – **6 rm** 30.00/48.00 **st.**

Clonard House 🌿, Clonard Great, SW : 2 ¼ m. by R 733 ✆ 23141, – Ⓟ.
M 12.00 **st.** – **9 rm** 17.00/28.00 **st.**

FORD Ferrybank ✆ 23329
MITSUBISHI, SUZUKI The Saythe ✆ 22998
OPEL Ferrybank ✆ 22107
PEUGEOT Drinagh ✆ 22377
TOYOTA Carriglawn, Newtown Rd ✆ 43788

WICKLOW (Cill Mhantáin) Wicklow 405 N 9 – pop. 5178 – ECD : Thursday – ☎ 0404.

Envir. : Ashford (Mount Usher or Walpole's Gardens★) *AC*, NW : 4 m.

Blainroe ☎ 68168, S : ½ m – 9 Dunbur Rd ☎ 67379.

Dublin 33 – ♦Waterford 84 – Wexford 67.

XX **Old Rectory** with rm, ☎ 67048, Fax 69181, – rest TV ☎ P. AE VISA.
April-mid October – **M** (booking essential) (dinner only) 21.50 **st.** and a la carte 6.00 –
5 rm 37.00/74.00 **st.** – SB 99.00/106.00 **st.**

FORD Whitegates ☎ 67331

YOUGHAL (Eochaill) Cork 405 I 12 – pop. 5 870 – ECD : Wednesday – ☎ 024.

See : St. Mary's Collegiate Church★ (13C).

Envir. : Ardmore (site★, round tower★ 10C, cathedral ruins★ 12C, ≤★) E : 5½ m.

Knockaverry ☎ 92787.

☎ 92390 (26 June-2 September).

Dublin 146 – ♦Cork 30 – ♦Waterford 47.

XX **Aherne's Seafood Bar,** 163 North Main St., ☎ 92424 – P. VISA
closed 5 days at Christmas – **M** (bar lunch Sunday)11.00 **st.** (lunch) and a la carte 18.20/
24.75 **st.**

ISUZU North Abbey ☎ 92019/92010

Motorway hotels

Hotels d'autoroute – Alberghi autostradali

Autobahn-Rasthäuser

Hotels included in the Guide on, or near the interchanges of motorway and A (M) class roads. See appropriate town for details.

Les hôtels ci-dessous, sélectionnés dans le guide, se trouvent sur le autoroutes ou les routes principales, à proximité des échangeurs. Pour tou détails, voir le nom de la ville.

I sottoindicati alberghi, selezionati nella guida, si trovano lungo l autostrade o lungo le strade principali, in prossimità degli svincoli. Per og dettaglio vedere la località interessata.

Die unten aufgeführten Hotels befinden sich an Autobahnen, Hauptver kehrsstraßen oder in der Nähe von Autobahnausfahrten. Nähere Einzelhe ten unter dem Ortstext.

Location	Town	Hotel
M 1		
Junction 5 – S : ½ m. on A 41	**Watford**	Hilton Nationa
Junction 6 – NE : 1 m. on A 405 (this hotel also under M 10)	**St. Albans**	Noke Thistle
Junction 8 – W : ½ m. on A 414	**Hemel Hempstead**	Post House
Junction 9 – NW : 1 m. on A 5	**Flamstead**	Hertfordshire Moat House
Junction 11 – E : ¾ m. on A 505	**Luton**	Chiltern
Junction 11 – on A 505	**Luton**	Crest
Junction 11 – E : ½ m. on A 505	**Luton**	Humberstone
Newport Pagnell Service Area 3	**Newport Pagnell**	Welcome Lodg
Junction 121 – S : ½ m.	**Toddington**	Granada Lodg
Junction 13 – SW : 1 ½ m. by A 507	**Aspley Guise**	Moore Place
Junction 14 – S : 1 m. by A 509 and A 5130	**Milton Keynes**	Broughton
Junction 14 – SW : 1 ½ m. by A 509	**Milton Keynes**	Wayfarer
Junction 14 – N : ¾ m. on A 509	**Newport Pagnell**	Coach House
Junction 15 – NE : 3 m. by A 508 on A 45	**Northampton**	Swallow
Junction 15 – N : 1 m. on A 508	**Northampton**	Midway Toby
Junction 15 – N : 2 ¼ m. by A 508 on B 526	**Northampton**	Queen Eleanor
Junction 16 – E : 1 ¼ m. on A 45	**Northampton**	Travel Inn
Junction 16 – NW : 1 ½ m. on A 45	**Weedon Bec**	Heyford Mano
Junction 18 – E : 1 m. on A 428	**Rugby (at Crick)**	Post House
Junction 20 – NW : ¾ m. by A 427 on A 426	**Lutterworth**	Denbigh Arms
Junction 21 – E : ½ m.	**Leicester (at Braunestone)**	Country Court
Junction 21/21A – NE : 2 ½ m. on A 46	**Leicester (at Braunstone)**	Post House
Junction 22 – W : ¼ m. on A 50	**Markfield**	Granada Lodge
Junction 24 – SW : 2 m. on A 453	**Castle Donington**	Donington Thistle
Junction 25 – W : ¼ m. on A 52	**Nottingham (at Sandiacre)**	Post House
Junction 25 – S : ½ m. on B 6002	**Nottingham (at Long Eaton)**	Novotel Nottingham
Junction 28 – on A 38	**South Normanton**	Swallow
Junction 28 – SW : 3 ½ m. by A 38 on Swanwick Rd	**Alfreton**	Granada
Junction 30 – NW : 1 ½ m. on A 616	**Renishaw**	Sitwell Arms
Junction 30 – E : 1 ¾ m. by A 616 on A 619	**Clowne**	Van Dyk

ocation	Town	Hotel
unction 31 – E : 1 m. on A 57	**Todwick**	Red Lion
unction 31 – W : ½ m. by A 57 on A 6067	**Aston**	Aston Hall
unction 39 – W : ¼ m. on A 636	**Wakefield**	Cedar Court
unction 40 – E : ¼ m. on A 638	**Wakefield**	Post House
Voolley Edge Service Area		Granada Lodge
1 (M)		
unction 1, A 638 – N : 2 ½ m. on A 1	**Wentbridge (at Barnsdale Bar)**	Travelodge
unction 3 – S : ½ m. on A 1001	**Hatfield**	Hazel Grove
unction 7 – W : ¼ m.	**Stevenage**	Novotel
1 (M) via A 66 (M) – E : 2 m. on A 66	**Darlington**	Blackwell Grange Moat House
1 (M) – E : ¼ m.	**Buckden**	Lion
1 (M) via A 167 – S : ¾ m. by A 167	**Darlington (at Coatham Mundeville)**	Hall Garth Country House
1 (M) via A 630 – SW : ¼ m. on A 630	**Doncaster**	Doncaster Moat House
1 (M) Junction with A 195 – E : ½ m. by A 1231	**Washington**	Post House
1 (M) Washington Service Area (Southbound Carriageway)	**Washington Service Area**	Granada Lodge
1 (M) via A 5135 – NW : ⅓ m. by A 5135	**Borehamwood**	Oaklands Toby
1 (M) Junction A 6 and M 25 (this hotel also under M 25)	**South Mimms**	Crest
1 (M) – N : 4 ½ m. at Junction with A 6065 (Southbound Carriageway)	**Newark-on-Trent (at North Muskham)**	Travelodge
1 (M) Junction with A 614	**Blyth (Notts.)**	Granada Lodge
1 – NE : ½ m. on A 605	**Peterborough (at Alwalton)**	Swallow
1 (Southbound Carriageway)	**Peterborough (at Alwalton)**	Travelodge
arthing Corner Service Area	**Farthing Corner**	Farthing Corner Lodge
M 2		
Junction 1 – W : 1 ½ m. on A 2	**Shorne**	Inn on the Lake
Junction 3 – N : ½ m. on A 229	**Rochester**	Bridgewood Manor
Junction 3 – N : 1 m. on A 229	**Rochester**	Crest
Junction 6 – S : 2 m.	**Faversham**	Throwley House
M 3		
Junction 3 – N : 1 m. on A 30	**Bagshot**	Cricketer's
Junction 6 – N : 1 m. at Black Dam roundabout	**Basingstoke**	Hilton Lodge
Junction 6 – SW : 1 ½ m. at junction A 30 and A 339	**Basingstoke**	Crest
Junction 7 – SW : 2 m. on A 30	**North Waltham**	Wheatsheaf
M 4		
Leigh Delamere Service Area		Granada Lodge
Heston Service Area (Westbound Carriageway)	**Heston (L.B. of Hounslow)**	Granada Lodge
Junction 4 – S : ½ m. on B 379	**Heathrow Airport**	Post House
Junction 4 – N : ¼ m. on B 379	**Heathrow Airport**	Holiday Inn
Junction 5 – NW : 1 m. by A 287 and 2 m. by A 30	**Basingstoke (at Rotherwick)**	Tylney Hall
Junction 5 – NW : ¼ m. on A 4	**Slough**	Holiday Inn
Junction 8 – NE : 1 m. on Airport rd	**Stanted Airport**	Harlequin
Junction 8-9 – SE : 3 m. by A 308 (M) and A 308	**Windsor**	Oakley Court
Junction 9 A – NE : 1 m. by A 423 (M) on Shoppenhangers Rd	**Maidenhead**	Fredericks
Junction 9 A – NE : ½ m. by A 423 (M) off Shoppenhangers Rd	**Maidenhead**	Crest

Location	Town	Hotel
Junction 10 – SE : 2 ½ m. by A 329 (M)	**Wokingham**	St. Anne's Manor
Junction 11 – N : ½ m. on A 33	**Reading**	Post House
Junction 11 – N : 1 m. on A 33	**Reading**	Travelodge
Junction 13 – South at Junction with A 34 (Northbound Carriageway)	**Newbury**	Stakis Newbur
Junction 15 – SW : 1 m. by A 345 on B 4005	**Swindon (at Chiseldon)**	Chiseldon House
Junction 15 – N : 2 m. by A 419 on A 4259	**Swindon**	Post House
Junction 16 – SW : 2 m. by A 4005	**Swindon (at Salthrop)**	Salthrop Hous
Junction 17 – NW : 1 m. by A 429	**Malmesbury (at Stanton St. Quinton)**	Stanton Mano
between junctions 18 and 17 (Eastbound Carriageway)	**Leigh Delamere Service Area**	Granada Lodg
Junction 19 – SW : 2 ½ m. by M 32 on A 4174 (this hotel also under M 32)	**Bristol (at Hambrook)**	Crest
Junction 21	**Aust Services**	Rank Motorlodge
Junction 24 – S : ½ m. on A 48	**Newport (Gwent)**	Celtic Manor
Junction 24 – E : ¼ m. on A 48	**Newport (Gwent) (at Langstone)**	Country Court
Junction 24 – E : 1 ½ m. on A 48	**Newport (Gwent) (at Langstone)**	New Inn
Junction 24 – S : ¼ m. on A 48	**Newport (Gwent)**	Hilton National
Junction 26 – S : ½ m. by Malpas Rd	**Newport (Gwent)**	Newport Lodge
Junction 29 – SW : 2 m. by A 48	**Cardiff**	Travelodge
Junction 34 – N : 1 ¾ m. by A 4119 (Groes Faen road)	**Miskin**	Miskin Manor
Junction 35 – N : 1 m. by A 473 off Felindre Rd	**Pencoed**	Travelodge
Junction 36	**Sarn Park Service Area**	Travelodge
Junction 38 (A 48 m) – NW : 1 m. on A 48	**Port Talbot**	Twelve Knights
Junction 45 – S : 2 ¼ m. by A 4067 off A 48	**Swansea Enterprise Park**	Hilton National
Junction 47 – S : 1 m. on A 483	**Swansea**	Fforest
M 5		
Junction 1 – W : 1 m. by A 41	**Birmingham (at West Bromwich)**	West Bromwich Moat House
Junction 2 – W : ¾ m. on A 4123	**Birmingham (Oldbury)**	Travelodge
between Junctions 3 and 4	**Birmingham (at Frankley)**	Granada Lodge
Junction 4 – S : 1 m. on A 38	**Bromsgrove**	County Court
Junction 5 – SW : ½ m. on A 38	**Droitwich**	Travelodge
Junction 11 – E : 1 m. on A 40	**Cheltenham**	Golden Valley Thistle
Junction 13 – SE : 1 ¾ m. on A 419	**Stroud**	Stonehouse Court
Junction 16 – S : 2 ½ m. by A 38	**Bristol (at Patchway)**	Stakis Leisure Lodge
Sedgemoor Service Area (Northbound Carriageway)	**Sedgemoor**	Travelodge
Junction 22 – N : 1 m. on A 38	**Brent Knoll**	Battleborough Grange
Junction 25 – by approach road	**Taunton**	Crest
Junction 25 – W : ½ m. by A 358	**Taunton**	Travel Inn
between junction 25 and 26 Southbound	**Taunton Service Area**	Road Chef Lodge
Junction 27	**Sampford Peverell Service Area**	Travelodge
Junction 29 – N : 1 ½ m. by Moor Lane	**Exeter (at Pinhoe)**	Gipsy Hill
Junction 30 – Exeter Service Area	**Exeter**	Granada Lodge
Junction 31 – S : 2 ½ m. at junction of A 379 and B 3182	**Exeter**	Countiswell Lodge

Location	Town	Hotel
M 6		
Junction 2 – NE : ¼ m. on B 4065	**Coventry (at Ansty)**	Ansty Hall
Junction 2 – SW : ½ m. on A 4600	**Coventry (at Walsgrave-on-Sowe)**	Crest
Junction 2 – SW : ¾ m. by A 4600	**Coventry (at Walsgrave-on-Sowe**	Campanile
Junction 3 – SE : 1 m. on A 444	**Coventry (at Longford)**	Novotel
Junction 5 – N : 3 ⅓ m. by A 452 on B 4148	**Sutton Coldfield**	New Hall
Junction 7 – N : ¼ m. on A 34	**Birmingham (at Great Barr)**	Post House
Junction 7 – NW : 2 ½ m. on A 34	**Walsall**	Crest
Junction 10 – on A 454	**Walsall**	Friendly Lodge
Junction 10 – SW : 2 ½ m. by A 454 and A 462 off Willenhall Street	**Darlaston**	Petite
between junctions 10 A and 11	**Hilton Park Service Area**	Rank Motor Lodge
Junction 11 – NE : 1 ⅓ m. by A 40	**Cheltenham (at Staverton)**	White House
Junction 12 – E : 2 m. on A 5	**Cannock**	Roman Way
Junction 12 – E : 2 ¼ m. on A 5	**Cannock**	Travel Inn
Junction 13 – N : 1 m. on A 449	**Stafford**	Garth
Junction 14 – SE : ½ m. on A 5013	**Stafford**	Tillington Hall
Junction 15 – N : ¼ m. on A 519	**Newcastle-under-Lyme**	Post House
Junction 15 – N : ¾ m. on A 519	**Newcastle-under-Lyme**	Clayton Lodge
Junction 15 – NE : 1 ½ m. on A 34	**Stoke on Trent**	White House
Junction 17 – E : ½ m. on A 534	**Sandbach**	Chimney House
Junction 19 – NE : 2 ½ m. on A 556 (this hotel also under M 56)	**Knutsford (at Bucklow Hill)**	Swan
Junction 19 – N : on A 556	**Knutsford**	Travelodge
Junction 21	**Warrington**	Garden Court Holiday Inn
Junction 23 – N : ½ m. on A 49	**Haydock**	Post House
Junction 23 – NW : ½ m. by A 49 on A 599	**Haydock**	Haydock Thistle
Junction 23 – W : 2 m. on A 580	**Haydock**	Travelodge
Junction 28 – W : ¼ m. on B 5256	**Leyland**	Penguin
Junction 29 – SE : ¼ m. by A 6	**Preston (at Bamber Bridge)**	Novotel
Junction 31 – W : ¼ m. on A 59	**Preston (at Samlesbury)**	Tickled Trout
Junction 31 – E : 1 ¼ m. on A 59	**Preston (at Samlesbury)**	Swallow Trafalgar
Junction 34 – SW : ¼ m. on A 683	**Lancaster**	Post House
Junction 40 – on A 592	**Penrith**	North Lakes Gateway
Junction 40 – W : ½ m. on A 66	**Penrith**	Travelodge
Junction 44 – N : ¼ m. on A 7	**Carlisle (at Kingstown)**	Crest
Southwaite Service Area		Granada Lodge
M 8		
Junction 3 – SE : 2 ½ m. by A 899	**Livingston**	Hilton National
Junction 11 – E : 1 ¾ m. by M 898 and on A 726	**Erskine**	Crest
Junction 27 – N : ¼ m. on A 741	**Renfrew**	Glynhill
Junction 27 – S : ½ m. on A 741	**Paisley**	Rockfield
M 9		
Junction 6 – NW : ¼ m. on A 905	**Falkirk (at Grangemouth)**	Grange Manor
Junction 9 – at junction of M 9 and M 80	**Stirling**	Granada Lodge
M 10		
Junction 1 – SW : 1 m. on A 405 (this hotel also under M 1)	**St. Albans**	Noke Thistle
M 11		
Junction 7 – NW : 1 m on A 414	**Harlow**	Harlow Moathouse

Location	Town	Hotel
Junction 10 – SE : 1 ½ m. by A 505	**Cambridge (at Duxford)**	Duxford Lodg
Junction 10 – SE : 1 ½ m. by A 505	**Cambridge (at Duxford)**	Duxford Lodg
Junction 14 with A 604 – NW : 1 ¾ m. on A 604	**Cambridge (at Bar Hill)**	Cambridgeshi Moat Hous
M 20		
Junction 2 A – SE : 1 m. on A 20	**Wrotham Heath**	Post House
Junction 3 – SE : 3 ½ m. on A 20	**Brands Hatch**	Brands Hatch Thistle
Junction 3 – SE : 3 ½ m. on A 20	**Brands Hatch**	Brands Hatch Place
Junction 9 – SE : 1 ½ m. on A 28	**Ashford**	Post House
Junction 9 – S : ½ m. on A 28	**Ashford**	Ashford Internationa
M 23		
Junction 9 – in Gatwick Airport	**Gatwick**	Gatwick Hilto Internationa
Junction 9 – W : 1 m. on A 23	**Gatwick**	Gatwick Pent
Junction 9 – W : 1 m. on A 23	**Gatwick**	Post House
M 25		
Junction 3 – SE : 3 ½ m. on A 20	**Brands Hatch**	Brands Hatch Thistle
Junction 3 – SE : 3 ½ m. on A 20	**Brands Hatch**	Brands Hatch Place
Junction 8 – S : ½ m. on A 217	**Reigate**	Bridge House
Junction 10 – N : ¼ m. by A 3 and A 245	**Cobham**	Hilton Nationa
Junction 10 – NE : 1 ½ m. by A 3 on A 245	**Cobham**	Cedar House
Junction 10 – NE : 4 m. by A 3 and A 245	**Cobham**	Woodlands Park
Junction 13 – S : 1 m. by A 30 on A 308	**Egham**	Runnymede
Junction 21 A – N : ½ m. on A 405	**St. Albans**	Noke Thistle
Junction 26 – S : 4 m. on B 1393 and A 121	**Epping**	Post House
Junction 26 – At Exit Roundabout	**Waltham Abbey**	Swallow
Junction 28 – NE : ¾ m. on A 1023	**Brentwood**	Brentwood Moat House
Junction 28 – NE : ¼ m. on A 1023	**Brentwood**	Post House
Junction 29 – E : 3 ½ m.	**East Horndon**	Travelodge
Junction A 6 and A 1 (M) (this hotel also under A 1 (M))	**South Mimms**	Crest
M 26		
Junction 2 A – SE : ¼ m. on A 20	**Wrotham Heath**	Post House
M 27		
Junction 1 – on A 337 at Junction of A 31 and A 336	**Cadnam**	Bartley Lodge
Junction 12 – N : at junction of A 3 and A 27	**Portsmouth & Southsea (at Cosham)**	Holiday Inn
Junction 12 – E : 1 m. on A 27 at junction with A 2030	**Portsmouth & Southsea (at Farlington)**	Hilton National
M 32		
Junction 1 – W : ½ m. on A 4174 (this hotel also under M 4)	**Bristol (at Hambrook)**	Crest
M 40		
Junction 2 – E : 1 ¾ m. by A 355 on A 40	**Beaconsfield**	Bellhouse
Junction 4 – on Crest Road	**High Wycombe**	Crest
Junction 7 – W : 2 m. by A 329	**Oxford (at Great Milton)**	Le Manoir aux Quat Saisons

ocation	Town	Hotel
M 42		
unction 1 – N : 1 m. on A 38	**Bromsgrove**	County Court
unction 2 – N : 1 ¼ m. on A 441	**Hopwood**	Westmead
unction 4 – S : 3 m. by A 34	**Hockley Heath**	with rm, Nuthurst Grange
unction 4 – NW : 1 m. on A 34	**Solihull (at Shirley)**	Regency
unction 5 – NW : 1 ¾ m. by A 41 and B 4025	**Solihull**	George
unction 5 – NW : 1 ¾ m. by A 41 on B 4025	**Solihull**	St. Johns Swallow
unction 6 – NW : 1 m.	**Birmingham (at National Exhibition Centre)**	Birmingham Metropole
unction 6 – W : ½ m. on A 45	**Birmingham (at National Exhibition Centre)**	Arden
unction 10 – E : ⅓ m. on A 5	**Dordon**	Hall End Hall
unction 10	**Tamworth Service Area**	Granada Lodge
M 45		
unction 1 – NW : 1 m. on A 45	**Dunchurch**	Travelodge
unction 1 – E: 1 ¼ m. on A 45	**Dunchurch**	Dun Cow
M 50		
unction 1 – S: ½ m. on A 38	**Tewkesbury**	Tewkesbury Hall
M 53		
: Junction 5 and A 41	**Eastham**	Travelodge
M 54		
unction 5 – SW: ½ m.	**Telford**	Telford Moat House
M 55		
unction 1 – N : ¾ m.	**Preston (at Broughton)**	Broughton Park
M 56		
unction 5 – on Airport Approach Road	**Manchester (at Airport)**	Hilton National
unction 5 – on Airport Approach Road	**Manchester (at Airport)**	Excelsior
unction 6 – N: ¼ m. on A 538	**Altrincham (at Halebarns)**	Four Seasons
unction 6 – S: 2 m. on A 538	**Wilmslow**	Valley Lodge
unction 7/8 – SW: 2 m. on A 556 (this hotel also under M 6)	**Knutsford (at Bucklow Hill)**	Swan
unction 11 – N: ¼ m. on A 56	**Daresbury**	Lord Daresbury
unction 12 – SE: ½ m. by A 557	**Runcorn**	Crest
M 57		
unction 2 – E: ½ m.	**Kirkby**	Cherry Tree
M 61		
unction 5 – NE: 1 m. on A 58	**Bolton**	Crest
M 62		
unction 7 – S: 1 ¼ m. by A 569	**Widnes**	Hillcrest
unction 13 – W: ¼ m. on A 572	**Manchester (at Worsley)**	Novotel Manchester West
unction 18-19	**Birch Service Area**	Granada Lodge
unction 24 – SE: 1 ½ m. on A 629	**Huddersfield**	Pennine Hilton
unction 25 – N: ½ m. on A 644	**Brighouse**	Forte
M 65		
unction 10 : E at Junction of A 671 and A 679	**Burnley**	Travelodge

Location	Town	Hotel
M 69		
Junction with M 1 – NE : 2 ½ m. on A 46	**Leicester (at Braunstone)**	Post House
Junction 1 – NW : 1 m. by A 447	**Hinckley**	Sketchley Grange
Junction 1 – SE : ¼ m. on A 5	**Hinckley**	Hinckley Islan
M 74		
between Junctions 6 and 5 (Northbound Carriageway)	**Hamilton Service Area**	Roadchef Lodg
M 80		
Junction 9 – at junction of M 9 and M 80	**Stirling**	Granada Lodg
M 90		
Junction 6 – at junction with A 977	**Kinross**	Granada Lodg
M 600		
Junction 1 – E : ¼ m.	**Bradford**	Novotel Bradford

Major hotel groups

Abbreviations used in the Guide and central reservation telephone numbers

Principales chaines hôtelières

Abréviations utilisées dans nos textes et centraux téléphoniques de réservation

Principali catene alberghiere

Abbreviazoni utilizzate nei nostri testi e centrali telefoniche di prenotazione

Die wichtigsten Hotelketten

Im Führer benutzte Abkürzungen der Hotelketten und ihre Zentrale für telefonische Reservierung

BERNI AND CHEF & BREWER HOTELS .... *(No central reservations – Contact Hotels direct)*	BCB	
BEST WESTERN HOTELS	BEST WESTERN	081 (London) 541 0033 041 (Glasgow) 221 7077 061 (Manchester) 832 9452
DE VERE HOTELS PLC	DE VERE	0925 (Warrington) 65050
HILTON HOTELS	HILTON	071 (London) 734 6000
HOLIDAY INNS INTERNATIONAL	HOLIDAY INN	071 (London) 722 7755
INTER-CONTINENTAL HOTELS LTD	INTER-CON	081 (London) 847 2277 or calls from outside London 0345 581444
LANSBURY HOTELS	LANSBURY	0582 (Luton) 400158
MOUNT CHARLOTTE THISTLE HOTELS PLC .	MT. CHARLOTTE THISTLE	071 (London) 937 8033
QUEENS MOAT HOUSES PLC	Q.M.H.	0800 289330
RANK HOTELS LTD	RANK	081 (London) 569 7120
STAKIS HOTELS	STAKIS	0800 833775
SWALLOW HOTELS LTD	SWALLOW	091 (Tyneside) 529 4666
TRUSTHOUSE FORTE (U.K.) LTD	T.H.F.	081 (London) 567 3444

Traffic signs
A few important signs
Signalisation routière
Quelques signaux routiers importants
Segnaletica stradale
Alcuni segnali importanti
Verkehrszeichen
Die wichtigsten Straßenverkehrszeichen

Please note: The maximum speed limits in Great Britain are 70 mp (112 km/h) on motorways and dual carriageways and 60 mph (96 km/h on all other roads, except where a lower speed limit is indicated.

N.B. N'oubliez pas qu'il existe des limitations de vitesse en Grande Bretagne : 70 mph (112 km/h) sur routes à chaussée séparée et autoroutes 60 mph (96 km/h) sur autres routes, sauf indication d'une vitesse inférieure

N.B. In Gran Bretagna esistono dei limiti di velocità : 70 mph (112 km/h sulle strade a doppia carreggiata e sulle autostrade, 60 mph (96 km/h) sull altre strade, salvo che sia indicata una velocità inferiore.

Zur Beachtung : in Großbritannien gelten folgende Geschwindigkeitsbe grenzungen : 70 mph (112 km/h) auf Autobahnen und Straßen mi getrennten Fahrbahnen, 60 mph (96 km/h) auf allen anderen Straßen wenn keine niedrigere Geschwindigkeit angezeigt ist.

Warning signs – Signaux d'avertissements
Segnali di avvertimento – Warnzeichen

T Junction
Jonction avec autre route
Confluenza con altra strada
Straßeneinmündung

Roundabout
Sens giratoire
Senso rotatorio
Kreisverkehr

Dual carriageway ends
Fin de chaussée à deux voies
Fine di doppia carreggiata
Ende der zweispurigen Fahrbahn

Change to opposite carriageway
Déviation sur chaussée opposée
Deviazione sulla carreggiata opposta
Überleitung auf Gegenfahrbahn

Distance to give way sign ahead
Cédez le passage à 50 iards
Dare la precedenza a 50 iarde
Vorfahrt gewähren in 50 yards Entfernung

Right-hand lane closed
Voie de droite barrée
Corsia di destra sbarrata
Rechte Fahrbahn gesperrt

Quayside or river bank
Débouché sur un quai ou une berg
Banchina o argine senza sponda
Ufer

Two-way traffic crosses one-way roa
Voie à deux sens croisant voie à sens unique
Strada a due sensi che incrocia un strada a senso unico
Straße mit Gegenverkehr kreuzt Einbahnstraße

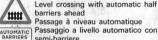

Level crossing with automatic half barriers ahead
Passage à niveau automatique
Passaggio a livello automatico con semi-barriere
Bahnübergang mit automatischen Halbschranken

Height limit
Hauteur limitée (en pieds et pouce
Altezza limitata (piedi e pollici)
Maximale Höhe (in Fuß und Zoll)

Ralentir maintenant
Rallentare subito
Geschwindigkeit verringern

Opening or swing bridge
Pont mobile
Ponte mobile
Bewegliche Brücke

Signs giving orders
Signaux de prescriptions absolues
Segnali di prescrizione (di divieto o d'obbligo)
Gebots- und Verbotszeichen

National speed limit applies
Fin de limitation de vitesse
Fine di limitazione di velocità
Ende der Geschwindigkeitsbeschränkung

School crossing patrol
Sortie d'école
Uscita di scolari
Achtung Schule

No stopping (« clearway »)
Arrêt interdit
Fermata vietata
Halteverbot

All vehicles prohibited (plate gives details)
Circulation interdite à tous véhicules (plaque donnant détails)
Divieto di transito a tutti i veicoli (la placca sottostante fornisce dei dettagli)
Verkehrsverbot für Fahrzeuge aller Art (näherer Hinweis auf Zusatzschild)

Give priority to vehicles from opposite direction
Priorité aux véhicules venant de face
Dare la precedenza ai veicoli che provengono dal senso opposto
Gegenverkehr hat Vorrang

Voie à stationnement réglementé
Sosta regolamentata
Fahrbahn mit zeitlich begrenzter Parkerlaubnis

Width limit
Largeur limitée (en pieds et pouces)
Larghezza limitata (piedi e pollici)
Breite begrenzt (in Fuß und Zoll)

Plate below sign at end of restriction
Fin d'interdiction
Fine del divieto posta sotto il segnale
Ende einer Beschränkung

Information signs – Signaux de simple indication
Segnali di indicazione – Hinweiszeichen

One-way street
Rue à sens unique
Via a senso unico
Einbahnstraße

No through road
Voie sans issue
Strada senza uscita
Sackgasse

Accès à une chaussée à deux voies
Accesso ad una carreggiata a due corsie
Zufahrt zu einer zweispurigen Fahrbahn

Ring road
Voie de contournement
Strada di circonvallazione
Ringstraße

Warning signs on rural motorways
Signaux d'avertissement sur autoroutes
Segnali di avvertimento su autostrade
Warnzeichen auf Autobahnen

Maximum advised speed
Vitesse maximum conseillée
Velocità massima consigliata
Empfohlene Höchstgeschwindigkeit

1 Lane closed
1 voie barrée
1 Corsia sbarrata
1 Fahrstreifen gesperrt

Count-down markers at exit from motorway (or primary route if green-backed)
Balises situées sur autoroute ou route principale (fond vert) et annonçant une sortie
Segnali su autostrada o strade principali (fondo verde) annuncianti un'uscita
Hinweise auf Abfahrten an Autobahnen und Hauptverkehrsstraßen (grüner Grund)

End of restriction
Route libre
Strada libera
Straße frei

Direction to service area, with fuel, parking, cafetaria and restaurant facilities
Indication d'aire de service avec carburant, parc à voitures, cafeteria et restaurant

Indicazione di area di servizio con carburante, parcheggio, bar e ristorante
Hinweis auf Tankstelle, Parkplatz, Cafeteria und Restaurant

Warning signs on urban motorways
Signaux d'avertissement sur autoroutes urbaines
Segnali di avvertimento su autostrade urbane
Warnzeichen auf Stadtautobahnen

_1_

_2_

_3_

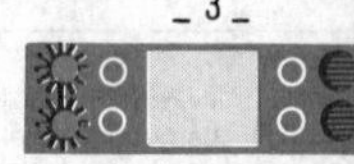

The insets show (flashing amber lights) (1) advised maximum speed, (2) lane to be used ; (3) (flashin red lights), you must stop.

L'ensemble de ces panneaux indique : (1) la vitesse maximale conseillée, (2) la voie à utiliser (signau lumineux jaunes) ; (3) l'arrêt obligatoire (signaux lumineux rouges).

L'insieme di questi segnali indica : (1) la velocità massima consigliata, (2) la corsia da imboccare (segna luminosi gialli) ; (3) la fermata obbligatoria (segnali luminosi rossi).

Diese Schilder (mit blinkenden Ampeln) weisen hin auf : (1) die empfohlene Höchstgeschwindigkeit (2) die zu befahrende Fahrbahn (gelbes Licht) und (3) Halt (rotes Licht).

In town – En ville
In città – in der Stadt

SIGNALISATION SHOWN ON OR ALONG KERBS
SIGNALISATION MATÉRIALISÉE SUR OU AU LONG DES TROTTOIRS
SEGNALI TRACCIATI SOPRA O LUNGO I MARCIAPIEDI
ZEICHEN AUF ODER AN GEHWEGEN

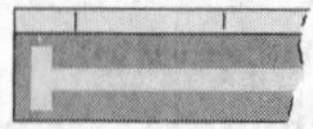

No waiting during every working day
Stationnement interdit tous les jours ouvrables
Sosta vietata nel giorni feriali con indicazioni complementari
Parkverbot an Werktagen

OTHER ROAD SIGNS
AUTRES PANNEAUX
ALTRI CARTELLI INDICATORI
ZUSÄTZLICHE VERKEHRSZEICHEN

Stationnement interdit de 8 h 30 à 18 h 30 du lundi au samedi
Sosta vietata da lunedì a sabato dalle 8,30 alle 18,30
Parkverbot Montag bis Samstag von 8.30 bis 18.30 Uhr

No loading or unloading during every working day
Livraisons interdites tous les jours ouvrables
Carico e scarico vietato nei giorni feriali con indicazioni complementari
Be- und Entladen verboten an allen Werktagen

Livraisons interdites de 8 h 30 à 18 h 30 du lundi au samedi
Carico e scarico vietato da lunedì a sabato dalle 8.30 alle 18.30
Be- und Entladen verboten von Montag bis Samstag von 8.30 bis 18.30 Uhr

---

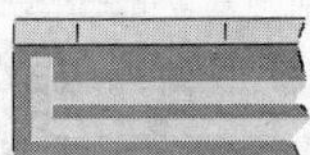

No waiting during every working day and additional times as indicated
Stationnement interdit tous les jours ouvrables plus autres périodes indiquées sur panneaux
Divieto di sosta tutti i giorni feriali e negli altri periodi indicati sul cartello
Parkverbot an Werktagen und zu den auf Zusatzschildern angegebenen Zeiten

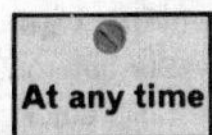

Stationnement interdit en permanence
Divieto permanente di sosta
Parkverbot zu jeder Zeit

No loading or unloading during every working day and additional times as indicated
Livraisons interdites tous les jours ouvrables plus autres périodes indiquées sur panneaux
Divieto di carico e scarico tutti i giorni feriali e negli altri periodi indicati sul cartello
Be- und Entladen verboten an Werktagen und zu den auf Zusatzschildern angegebenen Zeiten

No loading at any time

Livraisons interdites en permanence
Divieto permanente di carico e scarico
Be- und Entladeverbot zu jeder Zeit

No waiting during any other periods
Stationnement interdit à toute autre période
Sosta vietata in determinate ore
Parkverbot zu bestimmten Zeiten

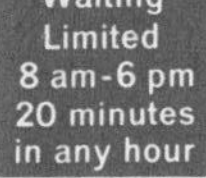

Stationnement limité à 20 mn de 8 h à 18 h
Sosta limitata a 20 mn dalle 8 alle 18
Höchstparkdauer 20 Min. in der Zeit von 8.00 bis 18.00 Uhr

No loading or unloading during any other periods
Livraisons interdites à toute autre période
Divieto di carico e scarico in determinate ore
Be- und Entladeverbot zu bestimmten Zeiten

No loading
Mon-Fri
8.00-9.30 am
4.30-6.30 pm

Livraisons interdites du lundi au vendredi de 8 h à 9 h 30 et de 16 h 30 à 18 h 30
Carico e scarico vietato da lunedì a venerdì dalle 8 alle 9,30 e dalle 16,30 alle 18,30
Be- und Entladeverbot Montag bis Freitag von 8.00 bis 9.30 und von 16.30 bis 18.30 Uhr

***Remember :** speed limit in Great Britain 70 mph and in Eire 60 mph.*

Direction signs on the road network
Panneaux de direction sur le réseau routier
Cartelli direzionali sulla rete stradale
Richtungsschilder auf den Straßen

401 Michelin maps
402 Cartes Micheli
403 Carte Michelir
404 Michelin-Karte

Motorways and A (M) class roads
Sur autoroutes et routes classées A (M)
Sulle autostrade e strade classificate A (M)
Auf Autobahnen M (und Schnellstraßen) A (M)

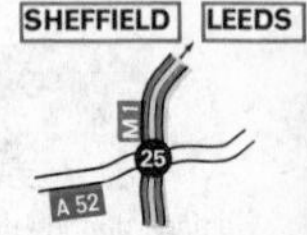

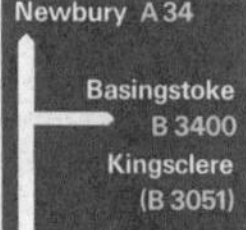

Primary routes
Apart from motorways, « Primary routes » provide the major road network linking towns of local and national traffic importance.

Sur grands itinéraires routiers « Primary routes »
En complément du système autoroutier, les grands itinéraires constituent un réseau de routes recommandées reliant les villes selon leur importance dans le trafic national.

Sui principali itinerari stradall (Primary routes)
I principali itinerari, unitamente alle autostrade, costituiscono una rete di strade consigliate che collegano le città secondo la loro importanza nel traffico nazionale

Auf empfohlenen Fernverkehrsstraßen (Primary routes)
Diese bilden ein überregionales Straßennetz, das verkehrswichtige Orte verbindet; sie ergänzen das Autobahnnetz

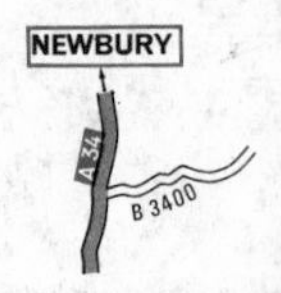

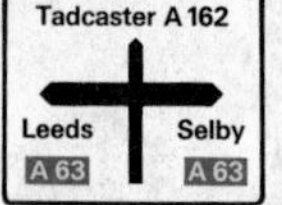

Other A class roads
Sur autres routes classées A
Sulle altre strade classificate A
Auf andere Straßen der Kategorie A

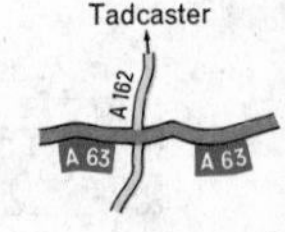

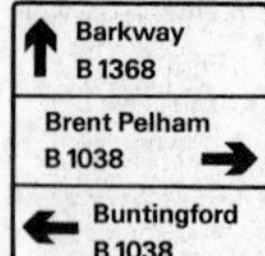

B class roads
Sur routes classées B
Sulle strade classificate B
Auf Straßen der Kategorie B

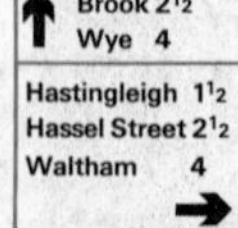

Unclassified roads – Local direction sign
Sur routes non classées – Signalisation locale
Sulle strade non classificate – Segnaletica locale
Auf nicht klassifizierten Straßen – Örtliche Richtungsschilder

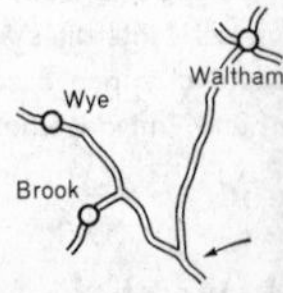

Addresses of shipping companies and their principal agents

Adresses des compagnies de navigation et de leurs principales agences

Indirizzi delle compagnie di navigazione e delle loro principali agenzie

Adressen der Schiffahrtsgesellschaften und ihrer wichtigsten Agenturen

BELFAST FERRIES

47 Donegal Quay, Belfast, BTI 3ED, ✆ (0232) 326800, 320364, Telex 74268 BELFER, Fax 331239.

Agent : North Brocklebank Dock, Bootle, Merseyside, L20 1DB, ✆ (051) 922 6234, Telex 627167 BELCAR, Fax 9441540.

B & I LINE

16 Westmoreland St., Dublin 2, Eire, ✆ (01) 6797977, Telex 30912, Fax 778146.

Agent : 150 New Bond St., London, W1Y 0AQ, ✆ (071) 734 4681.

BRITISH RAIL see SEALINK and HOVERSPEED

BRITISH CHANNEL ISLAND FERRIES

Fairfield House, Kingston Cres., Portsmouth, PO2 8AA, ✆ (0705) 666900.

Agents : P.O. Box 315, Poole, Dorset, BH15 4DB, ✆ (0202) 681155, Telex 418125.
New North Quay, St. Helier, Jersey, Channel Islands, ✆ (0534) 38300.
White Rock, St. Peter Port, Guernsey, Channel Islands, ✆ (0481) 711111.

BRITTANY FERRIES

BAI Brittany Ferries, Gare Maritime Roscoff, Port du Bloscon 29211, France, ✆ 98 61 22 11, Telex 940360.

Agents : Millbay Docks, Plymouth, PL1 3EW, Devon, ✆ (0752) 221321, Telex 45380.
The Brittany Centre, Wharf Rd, Portsmouth, PO2 8RU, Hampshire, ✆ (0705) 827701, Telex 86878.
Gare Maritime, F-35400 St-Malo, France, ✆ 99 82 41 41, Telex 740426.
Tourist House, 42 Grand Parade, Cork, Eire, ✆ (021) 277801, Telex 75088.
Modesto Pineiro & Co., 27 Paseo de Pereda, Santander, Spain, ✆ (042) 214500, Telex 35913.

CALEDONIAN MACBRAYNE LTD.

Ferry Terminal, Gourock, PA19 1QP, Renfrewshire, Scotland, ✆ (0475) 34531, Telex 779318, Fax 37607.

CONDOR LTD.

P.O. Box 10 Commodore House, Bulwer Av., St. Sampsons, Guernsey, Channel Islands, ✆ (0481) 48771, Telex 4191289, Fax 45049.

Agents : Commodore Travel Ltd., 28 Conway St., St. Helier, Jersey, Channel Islands, ✆ (0534) 71263, Telex 419 2079, Fax 58194.
Condor Ltd., Morvan Fils, 2 Place du Poids du Roi, F-35402 St. Malo, France, ✆ 99 56 42 29, Telex 950486, Fax 99402366.
Condor Passenger Dept., New Jetty, White Rock, St. Peter Port, Guernsey, Channel Islands, ✆ (0481) 26121, Telex 4191417, Fax 712555.
Weymouth Quay, Dorset DT4 8DX, ✆ (0305) 761551, Telex 418219, Fax 760776.

CORAS IOMPAIR EIREANN

Ceant Station, Galway, Eire, ✆ (091) 63555.

CUNARD LINE LTD.

South Western House, Canute Rd, Southampton, Hampshire, SO9 1ZA, ✆ (0703) 634166, Telex 477577.

Agents : 30a Pall Mall, London SW1Y 5LS, ✆ (071) 491 3930, Telex 295483.

555 Fifth Av., New York, NY 10017, USA, ✆ (212) 880 7500, Telex 220436.

Compagnie Générale de Croisières, 22 Rue Royale, F-75008 Paris, France, ✆ 42 60 36 63, Telex 215755 F.

EMERAUDE LINES

Gare Maritime du Naye, F-35400, St. Malo, France, ✆ 99 40 48 40, Telex 950271, Fax 99 81 28 73.

Agents : Channel Islands Handling Ltd., Elisabeth Harbour, St. Helier, Jersey, Channel Islands ✆ (0534) 58034, Telex 4192052, Fax 66363.

Emeraude Lines, New Jetty, White Rock, St. Peter Port, Guernsey, ✆ (0481) 711414, Telex 4191571 EMFERY G.

FRED OLSEN LINES KDS

Fergeterminaten, P.O. Box 82, N 4601 Kristiansand, Norway, ✆ (042) 70501, Telex 21969, Fax 24907.

Agents : Fred Olsen Lines, Tyne Commission Quay, Albert Edward Dock, North Shields NE29 6EA, ✆ (091) 257 9682, Telex 53329, Fax 257 9702.

Fred Olsen Lines, PO Box 1159 Centrum, N-0107, Oslo 1, Norway, ✆ (02) 67 80 00, Telex 77538.

Fred Olsen Lines, Postboks 30, DK-9850, Hirtshals, Denmark, ✆ (98) 94 19 66, Telex 67752, Fax 94 50 92.

HERM SEAWAY

Guernseybus Ltd., Picquet House, St. Peter Port, Guernsey, Channel Islands, ✆ (0481) 24677

HOVERSPEED

Maybrook House, Queens Gardens, Dover, Kent CT17 9UQ, ✆ (0304) 240241, Telex 96323

Agents : International Hoverport, Boulogne, France, ✆ 21 30 27 26, Telex 110008.
International Hoverport, Calais, France, ✆ 21 96 65 70, Telex 810856.

HOVERTRAVEL LTD.

Quay Road, Ryde, Isle of Wight, P033 2HB, ✆ (0983) 811333, Telex 86513, Fax 812859

Agent : Clarence Pier, Southsea, Portsmouth, P05 3AD, Hampshire, ✆ (0705) 829988.

IRISH FERRIES

2-4 Merrion Row, Dublin 2, Eire, ✆ (01) 610511, Telex 30355 IFD, Fax (01) 610743.

Agent : Transport et Voyages, 40 Rue Kleber, F-92307, Levallois-Perret, France, ✆ 47 59 44 21, Telex 613491 FERYVOY, Fax 47 59 45 23.

ISLE OF MAN STEAM PACKET CO. LTD.

P.O. Box 5, Imperial Buildings, Douglas, Isle of Man, ✆ (0624) 661661, Telex 629414, Fax 661065.

Agents : W.E. Williames (N.I.) Ltd., Northern Rd, Belfast, BT3 9AL, Northern Ireland ✆ (0232) 351009, Telex 747166.

Sea Terminal, Heysham, Lancashire, LA3 2XF, ✆ (0524) 53802.

Sealink British Ferries, Ferry Terminal, Stranraer, Wigtownshire DG9 8EJ, ✆ (0776) 2262, Telex 778125.

Dublin Maritime, Maritime House, North Wall, Dublin, ✆ (01) 741231, Telex 33425, Fax 725714

ISLE OF SARK SHIPPING CO. LTD.

White Rock, St. Peter Port, Guernsey, Channel Islands, ✆ (0481) 24059, Telex 419 1549, Fax 712081.

ISLES OF SCILLY STEAMSHIP CO. LTD.

Quay St., Penzance, TR18 4BD, Cornwall, ✆ (0736) 62009/64013.

Agent : Hugh Town, St. Mary's, Isles of Scilly, TR21 OLJ, ✆ 0720 (Scillonia) 22357/8.

UNDY CO.

undy, Bristol Channel, via Bideford, Devon, EX39 2LY, ✆ 0271 (Woolacombe) 870870.

IERSEYSIDE PASSENGER TRANSPORT EXECUTIVE

lersey Ferries, Victoria Pl., Seacombe, Wallasey, Merseyside, L44 6QY, ✆ (051) 236 7676.

IORTH SEA FERRIES LTD.

loordzee Veerdiensten, Beneluxhaven, Europoort, P.O. Box 1123, 3180 AC Rozenburg Z.H., letherlands, ✆ (01819) 55500, Telex 29571, Fax 55215.

.gents : King George Dock, Hedon Rd, Hull, HU9 5QA, Humberside, ✆ (0482) 795141, elex 592349, Fax 712170.

eopold II Dam (Havendam) B8380, Zeebrugge, Belgium, ✆ (050) 543430, Telex 81469, ax 546835.

IORTH SEA FERRIES LTD.

ostboks 4004, N-5023 Bergen-Dreggen, Norway, ✆ (05) 322780, Telex 40425 NLINE, ax 326766.

.gent : Tyne Commission Quay, North Shields, NE29 6EA, ✆ (091) 296 1313, Telex 537275 ILINE, Fax 296 1540.

LAU-LINE (UK) LTD.

heerness, Kent, ME12 1SN, ✆ (0795) 666666, Telex 965605.

.gents : Olau-Line Terminal, Buitenhaven, P.O. Box 231, Vlissingen, Netherlands, ✆ (01184) 88000, Telex 37817.

RKNEY ISLANDS SHIPPING CO. LTD.

Ayre Road, Kirkwall, Orkney Islands, Scotland, ✆ (0856) 2044.

RWELL & HARWICH NAVIGATION CO. LTD.

he Quay, Harwich, Essex, ✆ (0255) 502004.

& O EUROPEAN FERRIES

hannel House, Channel View Rd, Dover, CT17 9TJ, ✆ (0304) 203388, Telex 96200, ax 223223.

.gents : Peninsula House, Wharf Rd, Portsmouth, Hants., PO2 8TA, ✆ (0705) 772000.

uropean House, The Docks, Felixstowe, Suffolk, IP11 8TB, ✆ (0394) 604802.

airnryan, Stranraer, Wigtownshire, Scotland, ✆ (058 12) 276 and 277.

arne Harbour, Larne, Co. Antrim, Northern Ireland, BT40 1AQ, ✆ (0574) 74321, Telex 74528.

egie Voor Martiem Transport, Natienkaai 5, B-8400 Ostend, Belgium, ✆ (059) 70 76 01.

ar Ferry Terminal, Doverlaan 7, B-8380 Zeebrugge, Belgium, ✆ (050) 54.50.50, Telex 81306.

erminal Car Ferry, 62226 Calais Cedex, France, ✆ 21 97 21 21, Telex 120878.

iare Maritime, Quai Chanzy BP 309, F-62204, Boulogne, France, ✆ 21 31 78 00, Telex 130187.

Place de la Madeleine, F-75008 Paris, France, ✆ 42 66 40 17, Telex 210679.

iare Maritime, 50101 Cherbourg, France, ✆ 33 44 20 13, Telex 170765.

uai de Southampton, 76600 Le Havre, France, ✆ 35 21 36 50, Telex 190757.

& O SCOTTISH FERRIES : ORKNEY & SHETLAND SERVICES

.O. Box 5, P & O Ferries Terminal, Jamieson's Quay, Aberdeen, AB9 8DL, Scotland, ✆ (0224) 58911, Telex 73344.

.gents : Terminal Building, Scrabster, Caithness, KW14 7UJ, Scotland, ✆ (0847) 62052.

lolmsgarth Terminal, Lerwick, Shetland Islands, ZE1 0PW, Scotland, ✆ (0595) 5252, elex 75294.

erminal Building, Stromness, Orkney Islands, KW16 3AA, Scotland, ✆ (0856) 850655, elex 75221.

ED FUNNEL SERVICES

2 Bugle St., Southampton, S09 4LJ, Hampshire, ✆ (0703) 330333.

.gents : Foutain Pier, West Cowes, Isle of Wight, ✆ (0983) 292101 (car ferry) and 292704 lydrofoil).

HE SALLY LINE LTD.

.rgyle Centre, York St., Ramsgate, Kent, CT11 9DS, ✆ (0843) 595522, Telex 96389.

.gents : 81 Piccadilly, London W1 9HF, ✆ (081) 858 1127, Telex 291860, Fax (071) 491 7256.

ally Line, Dunkerque Port-Ouest, F-59279 Loon Plage, France, ✆ 28.21.43.44, Telex 130078.

SCANDINAVIAN SEAWAYS

DFDS Travel Centre, 15 Hanover St., London, W1R 9HG, ✆ (071) 491 7256, Telex 2825 Fax 493 4668.

Agents : Sankt Annae Plads 30, DK-1295 Copenhagen K, Denmark, ✆ (33) 15 63 0(Telex 19435.

DFDS Travelbureaü (Scandinavian Seaways), Axelborg Vesterbrogade 4a, DK-1620 Copenh gen, Denmark, ✆ (33) 15 63 41, Telex 22983, Fax 936330.

Scandinavian Seaways, Tyne Commission Quay, North Shields, NE29 6EE, Tyne and Wea ✆ (091) 296 0101, Telex 53201, Fax 296 0127.

Scandinavian Seaways, Karl Johansgate 1, Oslo 1, Norway, ✆ (02) 429350, Telex 7812 Fax 412752.

Scandinavian Seaways, Skandiahamnen, P.O. Box 8895, S-40272 Gothenburg, Swede ✆ (031) 65 06 00, Telex 21724, Fax 543925.

Scandinavian Seaways, Jessenstrasse 4, 2000 Hamburg 1, West Germany, ✆ (040) 389037 Telex 02161759, Fax 389 03120.

SEALINK U.K. LTD.

Sealink UK Ltd., 163/203 Eversholt St., London, NW1 1BG, ✆ (071) 387 1234, Telex 26929 SELINK G.

SNCF, 88 Rue Saint-Lazare, F.75436 Paris Cedex 09, France, ✆ 15 38 52 29.

Agents : *For services from all English and Welsh ports contact :*

Sealink UK Ltd., Charter House, Park St., Ashford, Kent, TN24 8EX, ✆ (0233) 64703 Telex 965954, Fax 642024.

For Isle of Wight services contact :

Sealink UK Ltd., Isle of Wight Ferry Services, P.O. Box 59, Portsmouth, Hampshire, PO1 2X ✆ (0705) 827744, Telex 86440.

For services between Scotland and Northern Ireland contact :

Sealink (Scotland and Northern Ireland) Ltd., 4-6 South Strand St., Stranraer, Dumfries an Galloway, DG9 7JW, ✆ (0776) 3515, Telex 777578.

Other European Agents : GT Link A/S V, Farimagsgade 3, DK-1606 Copenhagen V., Denmar ✆ (33) 14 70 00, Telex 19800 VIKING DK, Fax (33) 14 65 11.

Armement Naval SNCF, Gare Maritime BP 27, F-62201 Boulogne-sur-Mer, Franc ✆ 21 30 25 11, Telex 110908.

Agence Maritime Teller, Gare Maritime, F-50100 Cherbourg, France, ✆ 33 20 43 3 Telex 170559.

Armement Naval SNCF, Gare Maritime BP 85, F-76203 Dieppe, France, ✆ 35 84 22 6 Telex 770924.

SMZ, Post Box 2, 3150 AA, Hook of Holland, Netherlands, ✆ (1747) 3944, Telex 31272.

SERVICE MARITIME CARTERET-JERSEY

BP 15, F-50270 Barneville-Carteret, France, ✆ 33 53 87 21, Telex 170477, Fax 33 04 54 6

Agents : CNTM Ltd., Gorey, Jersey, Channel Islands, ✆ (0534) 53737.

Gare Maritime, F-50580 Port Bail, France, ✆ 33 04 86 71, Telex 170477.

SHETLAND ISLANDS COUNCIL

Grantfield, Lerwick, Shetland, ZE1 ONT, ✆ (0595) 2024, Telex 75218.

SMYRIL LINE

P.O. Box 370, Jonas Broncksgøta 25, FR-110 Thorshavn, Faroe Islands, ✆ (009) 298 1590 Telex 81296, Fax 15707.

Agents : P & O Scottish Ferries, Orkney & Shetland Services, P.O. Box 5, P & O Ferry Termina Aberdeen, AB9 8DL, Scotland, ✆ (0224) 572615, Telex 73344, Fax 574411.

Norreena Ferdaskristofar, Smyril Line Iceland, Langavegur 3, 101 Reykjavik, Icelan ✆ (91) 62 63 62, Telex 3122, Fax (91) 29450.

Smyril Line (Norge) Postboks 4128, Dreggen, N-5023, Bergen Noway ✆ (05) 32097 Telex 42109, Fax 960272.

THOMAS & BEWS FERRIES

Ferry Office, John O'Groats, Caithness, Scotland, ✆ (095 581) 353 (summer).

Windieknap, Brough, Thurso, Caithness, Scotland, ✆ (084 785) 619 (winter).

TORBAY SEAWAYS

Beacon Quay, Torquay, Devon, ✆ (0803) 214397, Telex 42500, Fax 296462.

TRUCKLINE FERRIES POOLE LTD.

New Harbour Rd, Poole, Dorset, BH15 4AJ, ✆ (0202) 666466, Telex 418125.

EDETTES ARMORICAINES

are Maritime de la Bourse, B.P. 180, F-35049 St-Malo, France, ✆ 99 40 17 70, Telex 950196 AVIPAX.

gents : Vedettes Armoricaines, Albert Pier, St. Helier, Jersey, ✆ 20361, Telex 4192131 AVIEX.

outins Travel Bureau, Library Pl., St. Helier, Jersey, ✆ 21532/3/4, Telex 4192149.

2 rue Georges-Clémenceau, B.P. 304, F-50403 Granville, France, ✆ 33 50 77 45, elex 170449 F.

VESTERN FERRIES (ARGYLL) LTD.

6 Woodside Crescent, Glasgow, Scotland, G3 7UT, ✆ (041) 332 9766, Telex 77203 LYDE-BUILT.

DISTANCES

All distances in this edition are quoted in miles. The distance is given fror each town to other nearby towns and to the capital of each region a grouped in the guide. Towns appearing in the charts are preceded by diamond ♦ in text.

To avoid excessive repetition some distances have only been quoted onc – you may therefore have to look under both town headings.

The distances in miles quoted are not necessarily the shortest but hav been based on the roads which afford the best driving conditions and ar therefore the most practical.

DISTANCES EN MILES

Pour chaque région traitée, vous trouverez au texte de chacune des localité sa distance par rapport à la capitale et aux villes environnantes. Lorsqu ces villes sont celles des tableaux, leur nom est précédé d'un losang noir ♦.

La distance d'une localité à une autre n'est pas toujours répétée au deux villes intéressées : voyez au texte de l'une ou de l'autre.

Ces distances ne sont pas nécessairement comptées par la route la plu courte mais par la plus pratique, c'est-à-dire celle offrant les meilleure conditions de roulage.

Dublin - Sligo: 133 Miles

	Belfast	Cork	Dublin	Dundalk	Galway	Killarney	Limerick	Londonderry	Omagh	Sligo	Tullamore
Cork	250										
Dublin	103	154									
Dundalk	50	200	53								
Galway	196	122	135	153							
Killarney	273	54	189	223	133						
Limerick	204	58	120	154	64	69					
Londonderry	70	281	146	98	176	300	231				
Omagh	68	247	112	64	148	266	197	34			
Sligo	126	200	133	106	90	216	147	86	69		
Tullamore	132	118	60	82	82	141	72	163	129	95	
Waterfor	197	73	96	147	141	112	77	242	208	176	81

DISTANZE IN MIGLIA

Per ciascuna delle regioni trattate, troverete nel testo di ogni località la su distanza dalla capitale e dalle città circostanti. Quando queste città sor comprese nelle tabelle, il loro nome è preceduto da una losanga ♦.

Le distanza da una località all'altra non è sempre ripetuta nelle due citt interessate : vedere nel testo dell'una o dell'atra.

Le distanze non sono necessariamente calcolate seguendo il percorso pi breve, ma vengono stabilite secondo l'itinerario più pratico, che offre cic le migliori condizioni di viaggio.

ENTFERNUNGSANGABEN IN MEILEN

Die Entfernungen der einzelnen Orte zur Landeshauptstadt und zu de nächstgrößeren Städten in der Umgebung sind im allgemeinen Ortstex angegeben. Die Namen der Städte in der Umgebung, die auf der Tabell zu finden sind, sind durch eine Raute ♦ gekennzeichnet.

Die Entfernung zweier Städte voneinander können Sie aus den Angabe im Ortstext der einen oder der anderen Stadt ersehen.

Die Entfernungsangaben gelten nicht immer für den kürzesten, sonder für den günstigsten Weg.

Distances between major towns

Distances entre principales villes

Distanze tra le principali città

Entfernungen zwischen den grösseren Städten

	Aberdeen	Ayr	Birmingham	Blackpool	Brighton	Bristol	Cambridge	Cardiff	Carlisle	Coventry	Dover	Dumfries	Dundee	Edinburgh	Glasgow	Inverness	Ipswich	Kingston upon Hull	Leeds	Leicester	Liverpool	London	Manchester	Middlesbrough	Newcastle	Norwich	Nottingham	Oban	Oxford	Plymouth	Portsmouth	Sheffield	Southampton	Stoke on Trent	Swansea
Ayr	196																																		
Birmingham	442	293																																	
Blackpool	336	187	130																																
Brighton	616	467	180	304																															
Bristol	526	377	91	214	157																														
Cambridge	500	351	110	221	117	166																													
Cardiff	545	396	110	233	191	46	200																												
Carlisle	242	93	201	95	375	285	259	304																											
Coventry	461	311	18	148	158	96	88	124	219																										
Dover	637	488	201	325	84	199	120	233	396	179																									
Dumfries	221	59	234	128	408	318	292	337	34	252	429																								
Dundee	67	129	375	269	549	459	433	478	175	394	570	154																							
Edinburgh	130	81	301	195	475	385	335	404	101	319	459	80	63																						
Glasgow	150	35	300	194	474	384	358	403	100	318	495	79	83	46																					
Inverness	107	207	468	362	642	552	526	571	268	487	663	247	134	156	172																				
Ipswich	553	404	163	274	123	203	54	237	312	141	126	345	486	388	411	579																			
Kingston upon Hull	397	247	139	144	250	230	137	249	155	141	262	188	330	231	254	423	190																		
Leeds	366	216	119	88	262	210	147	229	124	121	272	157	299	200	223	392	200	61																	
Leicester	470	320	43	157	165	121	74	149	228	24	186	261	403	293	327	496	127	96	101																
Liverpool	368	219	103	56	277	187	208	173	127	121	298	160	301	227	226	394	261	131	75	130															
London	558	409	122	246	53	121	55	155	317	100	76	350	491	417	416	584	76	183	204	107	219														
Manchester	363	214	86	51	260	170	163	189	122	105	281	155	296	222	221	389	216	99	43	91	35	202													
Middlesbrough	331	182	177	123	319	267	200	286	90	178	325	123	264	146	189	357	253	89	66	159	141	246	109												
Newcastle	235	150	206	150	349	297	230	316	59	208	354	91	168	105	157	261	283	126	95	188	170	276	139	41											
Norwich	527	377	161	248	170	225	61	259	285	149	173	318	460	361	384	553	43	148	174	117	235	109	190	227	256										
Nottingham	432	282	50	143	193	149	88	166	190	52	214	223	365	266	289	458	141	94	74	26	130	135	72	132	161	120									
Oban	180	127	400	294	574	484	458	503	200	419	595	179	116	123	93	118	511	355	324	428	326	516	321	289	258	485	390								
Oxford	509	360	63	197	105	73	100	107	268	54	146	301	442	368	367	535	138	187	167	70	170	59	153	224	254	160	98	467							
Plymouth	641	492	206	329	222	124	287	161	400	211	320	433	574	500	499	667	324	345	325	236	302	242	285	382	412	346	264	599	194						
Portsmouth	604	455	148	292	48	100	133	143	363	139	142	396	537	463	462	630	157	255	267	171	265	78	248	325	354	192	199	562	85	182					
Sheffield	418	268	89	105	232	180	122	199	176	91	253	209	351	240	275	444	175	68	36	71	80	174	41	105	135	149	44	376	137	295	237				
Southampton	583	434	127	271	61	79	128	122	342	118	152	375	516	442	441	609	166	251	263	166	244	87	227	320	350	188	194	541	64	161	21	233			
Stoke on Trent	397	248	46	85	220	130	133	149	156	65	241	189	330	256	255	423	186	132	95	59	58	162	41	161	190	177	50	355	113	245	208	53	187		
Swansea	542	392	136	229	227	82	236	40	300	149	269	333	475	400	399	568	273	275	255	184	187	191	215	312	342	295	192	500	143	197	179	225	158	175	
Wick	233	333	594	488	768	678	652	697	394	613	789	373	260	282	298	126	705	549	518	622	520	710	515	483	387	679	584	244	661	793	756	570	735	549	694

Example Esempio

Exemple Beispiel

Edinburgh* - *Southampton

442 Miles

MAJOR ROADS AND PRINCIPAL SHIPPING ROUTES	
Motorway	
Road number	A 4. T 35. N 2
Mileage	20

PRINCIPALES ROUTES ET LIAISONS MARITIMES	
Autoroute	
Nº de route	A 4. T 35. N 2
Distance en miles	20

PRINCIPALI STRADE E ITINERARI MARITTIMI	
Autostrada	
Numero di strada	A 4. T 35. N 2
Distanza in miglia	20

HAUPTVERKEHRSSTRASSEN UND SCHIFFSVERBINDUNGEN	
Autobahn	
Straßennummer	A 4. T 35. N 2
Entfernung in Meilen	20

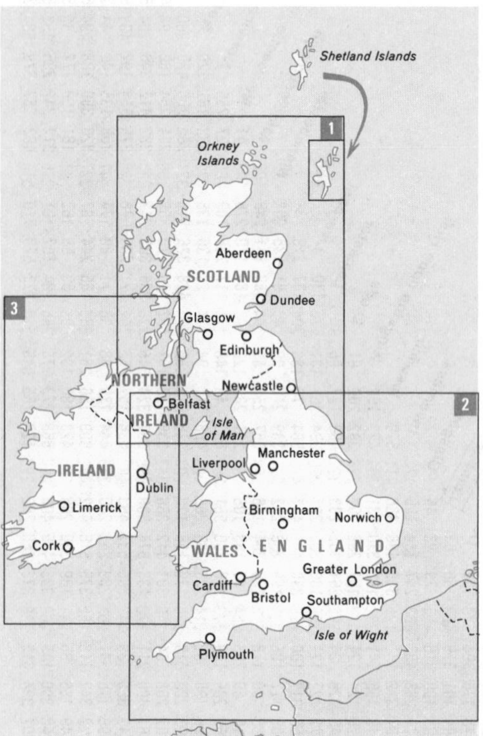

GREAT BRITAIN : the maps and town plans in the Great Britain Section of this Guide are based upon the Ordnance Survey of Great Britain with the permission of the Controller of Her Majesty's Stationery Office, Crown Copyright reserved.

NORTHERN IRELAND : the maps and town plans in the Northern Ireland Section of this Guide are based upon the Ordnance Survey of Northern Ireland with the sanction of the Controller of H.M. Stationery Office, Permit number 359.

REPUBLIC OF IRELAND : the maps and town plans in the Republic of Ireland Section of this Guide are based upon the Ordnance Survey of Ireland by permission of the Government of the Republic, Permit number 5320.

SHETLAND ISLANDS
Unst
Yell
Whalsay
Mainland
Scalloway
Lerwick
Kirkwall
Aberdeen
ORKNEY ISLANDS
Westray
Sanday
Rousay
Stronsay
Mainland
Stromness
Kirkwall
Hoy
Scalloway
Durness
Thurso
Tongue
Wick
Brora
Ullapool
Loch Shin
Garve
Inverness
Nairn
Elgin
Banff
Fraserburgh
Keith
Kyle of Lochalsh
Loch Ness
Spey
ABERDEEN
Lerwick
Mallaig
Invergarry
Kingussie
Braemar
Dee
Stonehaven
Fort William
SCOTLAND
Craignure
Oban
Crianlarich
Loch Tay
Perth
DUNDEE
Arbroath
Lochearnhead
St. Andrews
Tarbet
Stirling
Firth of Forth
Kirkcaldy
Lochgilphead
Greenock
Falkirk
Dunfermline
NORTH SEA
GLASGOW
EDINBURGH
Rothesay
Largs
Motherwell
Berwick upon Tweed
Ardrossan
Peebles
Galashiels
Brodick
Kilmarnock
Arran
Ayr
Abington
Campbeltown
Hawick
Alnwick
Bergen
Stavanger
Kristiansand
Oslo
Göteborg
Hirtshals
Esbjerg
New Galloway
Dumfries
Tynemouth
NEWCASTLE-UPON-TYNE
Cairnryan
Stranraer
Carlisle
Sunderland
Durham
Penrith
Hartlepool
Workington
Whitehaven
Keswick
Darlington
Middlesbrough
Isle of Man
Kendal
Scarborough
ENGLAND
Douglas
Barrow-in-Furness
Swale
Wharfe
Heysham
Lancaster
Harrogate
York

NORTHERN IRELAND
Larne
Stranraer
Carlisle
Sunderland
Durham
Lough Neagh
Bangor
BELFAST
Ballygawley
Strangford Lough
Armagh
Banbridge
Newcastle
Monaghan
Isle of Man
Douglas
Workington
Whitehaven
Penrith
Keswick
Darlington
Kendal
ENG
Barrow-in-Furness
Heysham
Lancaster
Harrogate
Wharfe
Dundalk/
Dun Dealgan
IRISH
SEA
Kells
Drogheda/
Droichead Átha
Boyne
DUBLIN/
BAILE ÁTHA CLIATH
BLACKPOOL
Preston
Blackburn
Bradford
Burnley
Halifax
Southport
Bolton
Oldham
Wigan
LIVERPOOL
MANCHESTER
Birkenhead
Stockport
Naas
Dún Laoghaire
Bray
Holyhead/
Caergybi
Colwyn Bay/
Bae Colwyn
Bangor
Caernarfon
Mold/
Yr Wyddgrug
Warrington
Chester
Macclesfield
Wicklow
Wrexham/
Wrecsam
Matlock
STOKE-ON-TRENT
Carlow
Arklow
Dolgellau
Shrewsbury
Enniscorthy
Welshpool/
Y Trallwng
Wolverhampton
Walsall
Dudley
Wexford
Aberystwyth
BIRMINGHAM
Rosslare
Llangurig
Ludlow
Severn
Warwick
ST GEORGE'S CHANNEL
Llandrindod Wells
Worcester
Stratford-upon-Avon
Wye
WALES
Fishguard/
Abergwaun
Carmarthen/
Caerfyrddin
Hereford
Brecon/
Aberhonddu
Ross
Cheltenham
Milford Haven/
Aberdaugleddau
Merthyr Tydfil
Gloucester
le Havre
Cherbourg
Pembroke Dock/
Doc Penfro
Newport/
Casnewydd
Swindon
Swansea/
Abertawe
CARDIFF/
CAERDYDD
Bristol Channel
BRISTOL
Bath
Ilfracombe
Minehead
Wells
Barnstaple
Bridgwater
Salisbury
Taunton
Yeovil
Avon
Bude
EXETER
Honiton
Dorchester
BOURNEMOUTH
Exmouth
Weymouth
Newquay
Bodmin
Torquay
Torbay
PLYMOUTH
Truro
Penzance
Falmouth
ENGLISH
Rosslare
Isles of Scilly
Santander
Roscoff
Alderney
Guernsey
Cherbourg
Sark
St.Peter-Port
Jersey
St.Hélier
St-Malo

NORTH SEA

Hartlepool
Middlesbrough
Scarborough
York
KINGSTON UPON HULL
Immingham
Rotterdam
Zeebrugge
Wakefield
Scunthorpe
Doncaster
Great Grimsby
Rotherham
SHEFFIELD
Lincoln
Skegness
Boston
NOTTINGHAM
Cromer
King's Lynn
NORWICH
Great Yarmouth
Lowestoft
Wisbech
LEICESTER
Stamford
Peterborough
Coventry
Rugby
Ely
Bury St.Edmunds
Northampton
CAMBRIDGE
Bedford
Ipswich
Zeebrugge
Felixstowe
Göteborg
Esbjerg
Hoek van Holland
Hamburg
Harwich
Colchester
Stevenage
Luton
Aylesbury
Harlow
Chelmsford
OXFORD
GREATER LONDON
Tilbury
Southend-on-Sea
NEDERLAND
Vlissingen
Reading
Windsor
Newbury
Basingstoke
Sheerness
Margate
Ramsgate
Canterbury
Deal
Zeebrugge
OOSTENDE
BRUGG
Guildford
Crawley
Maidstone
Royal-Tunbridge Wells
Dover
Folkestone
Dunkerque
BELGIË
BELGIQU
Winchester
SOUTHAMPTON
Calais
Gravelines
Chichester
BRIGHTON
Hastings
Worthing
Eastbourne
Newhaven
Boulogne
St-Omer
LILLE
PORTSMOUTH
Newport
Isle of Wight
St-Malo
Arras
Cambrai
Abbeville
CHANNEL
Dieppe
AMIENS
St-Quentin
Somme
Rosslare
FRANCE
Beauvais
Compiègne
Soissons
LE HAVRE
ROUEN
Senlis
Lisieux
CAEN
SEINE

3

ATLANTIC OCEAN
NORTH CHANNEL
NORTHERN IRELAND
IRELAND
CELTIC SEA
ST GEORGE'S CHANNEL
Colonsay
Port Askaig
Jura
Islay
Port Ellen
Londonderry
Coleraine
Waterfoot
Letterkenny
Strabane
Ballymena
Larne
Donegal
Omagh
Lough Neagh
Ballygawley
BELFAST
Strangford Lough
Enniskillen
Sligo/
Sligeach
L. Allen
Armagh
Banbridge
Newcastle
Ballina
Monaghan
Boyle
Cavan
Castlebar
Westport
Dundalk/
Dun Dealgan
L. Mask
Longford
Kells
Roscommon
Drogheda/
Droichead Átha
Boyne
Clifden
L. Corrib
L. Ree
Mullingar
Athlone
DUBLIN/
BAILE ÁTHA CLIATH
Galway/
Gaillimh
Ballinasloe
Tullamore
Lisdoonvarna
Naas
Dún Laoghaire
Bray
River Shannon
Roscrea
Ennis/
Inis
Wicklow
Kilkee
Carlow
Thurles
Suir
Arklow
LIMERICK/
LUIMNEACH
Kilkenny/
Cill Chainnigh
Cashel/
Caiseal
Enniscorthy
Barrow
Tralee
Caher
Dingle
Carrick on Suir
Wexford
Killarney/
Cill Airne
Fermoy
Waterford/
Port Lairge
Rosslare
R. Blackwater
Lismore
CORK/
CORCAIGH
Youghal
Cobh
Glengarriff
Bantry
Roscoff
le Havre
Cherbourg
Milford H
Aberdaugled
Fishg
Aberg

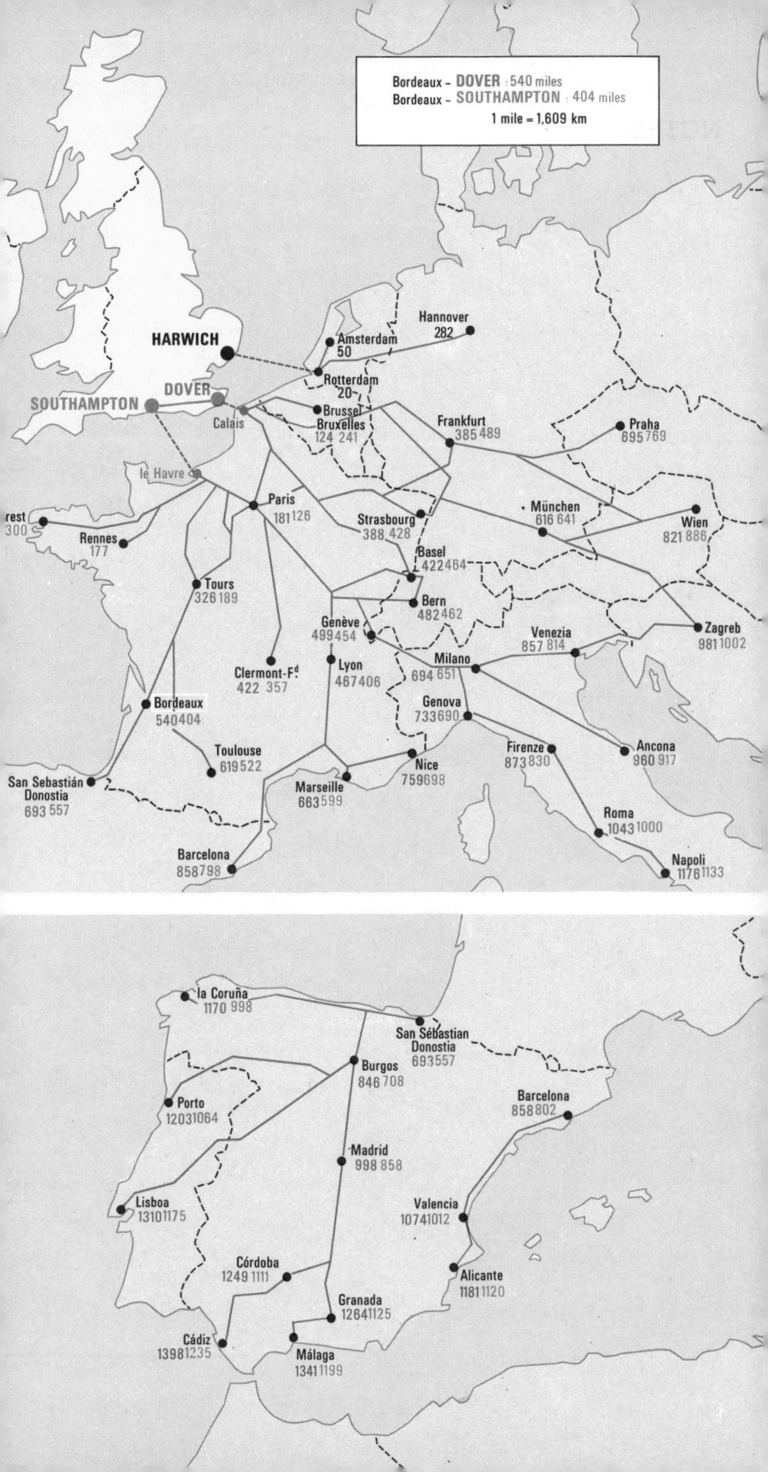

Bordeaux – DOVER : 540 miles
Bordeaux – SOUTHAMPTON : 404 miles
1 mile = 1,609 km
HARWICH
SOUTHAMPTON
DOVER
Calais
le Havre
Hannover 282
Amsterdam 50
Rotterdam 20
Brussel Bruxelles 124 241
Frankfurt 385 489
Praha 695 769
Brest 300
Rennes 177
Paris 181 126
Strasbourg 388 428
München 616 641
Wien 821 886
Basel 422 464
Tours 326 189
Bern 482 462
Genève 499 454
Lyon 467 406
Clermont-Fd 422 357
Venezia 857 814
Zagreb 981 1002
Milano 694 651
Genova 733 690
Bordeaux 540 404
Toulouse 619 522
Firenze 873 830
Ancona 960 917
Nice 759 698
Marseille 663 599
San Sebastián Donostia 693 557
Roma 1043 1000
Barcelona 858 798
Napoli 1176 1133
la Coruña 1170 998
San Sébastian Donostia 693 557
Burgos 846 708
Porto 1203 1064
Barcelona 858 802
Madrid 998 858
Lisboa 1310 1175
Valencia 1074 1012
Córdoba 1249 1111
Alicante 1181 1120
Granada 1264 1125
Cádiz 1398 1235
Málaga 1341 1199

NOTES

MANUFACTURE FRANÇAISE DES PNEUMATIQUES MICHELIN
Société en commandite par actions au capital de 875 000 000 de francs
Place des Carmes-Déchaux - 63 Clermont-Ferrand (France)
R.C.S. Clermont-Fd B 855 200 507

Dépôt légal 2-91 - ISBN 2.06.006.519-4

Printed in France - 12-90-57 - Impression : MAURY Imprimeur S.A. Malesherbes n° 32059

MAIN ROAD MAP

1/1 000 000

MICHELIN
Motoring Atlas
Great Britain
and Ireland
1/300000 - 1 in : 4.75 miles
maps • Index • Town plans